INSTRUCTOR'S GUIDE TO ACCOMPANY

AUTOMOTIVE TECHNOLOGY

A SYSTEMS APPROACH

THIRD EDITION

■

JACK ERJAVEC
RENE GREEN

Delmar
Thomson Learning™

Africa • Australia • Canada • Denmark • Japan • Mexico • New Zealand • Philippines
Puerto Rico • Singapore • Spain • United Kingdom • United States

Notice to Reader

Publisher does not warrant or guarantee any of the products described herein or perform any independent analysis in connection with any of the product information contained herein. Publisher does not assume, and expressly disclaims, any obligation to obtain and include information other than that provided to it by the manufacturer.

The reader is expressly warned to consider and adopt all safety precautions that might be indicated by the activities herein and to avoid all potential hazards. By following the instructions contained herein, the reader willingly assumes all risks in connection with such instructions.

The publisher makes no representation or warranties of any kind, including but not limited to, the warranties of fitness for particular purpose or merchantability, nor are any such representations implied with respect to the material set forth herein, and the publisher takes no responsibility with respect to such material. The publisher shall not be liable for any special, consequential, or exemplary damages resulting, in whole or part, from the readers' use of, or reliance upon, this material.

Delmar Staff
Publisher: Alar Elken
Acquisitions Editor: Vernon R. Anthony
Developmental Editor: Catherine Wein
Editorial Assistant: Bridget Morrison
Executive Marketing Manager: Maura Theriault
Channel Manager: Mona Caron
Marketing Coordinator: Kasey Young
Executive Production Manager: Mary Ellen Black
Production Coordinator: Karen Smith
Project Editor: Barbara L. Diaz
Art & Design Coordinator: Cheri Plasse
Technology Project Manager: Tom Smith

Online Services

Delmar Online
To access a wide variety of Delmar products and services on the World Wide Web, point your browser to:
http://www.Delmar.com
or email: info@delmar.com

COPYRIGHT © 2000
By Delmar Publishers
a division of International Thomson Publishing Inc.

Printed in the United States of America

For more information, contact:

Delmar Publishers
3 Columbia Circle, Box 15015
Albany, New York 12212-5015

International Thomson Publishing Europe
Berkshire House 168-173
High Holborn
London, WC1 V 7AA
England

Thomas Nelson Australia
102 Dodds Street
South Melbourne, 3205
Victoria, Australia

Nelson Canada
1120 Birchmount Road
Scarborough, Ontario
Canada M1K 5G4

International Thomson Editores
Campos Eliseos 385, Piso 7
Col Polanco
11560 Mexico D F Mexico

International Thomson Publishing GmbH
Königswinterer Strasse 418
53227 Bonn
Germany

International Thomson Publishing Asia
221 Henderson Road
#05 - 10 Henderson Building
Singapore 0315

International Thomson Publishing - Japan
Hirakawacho Kyowa Building, 3F
2-2-1 Hirakawacho
Chiyoda-ku, Tokyo 102
Japan

2 3 4 5 6 7 8 9 10 XXX 02 01 00
Library of Congress Cataloging-in-Publication Data
ISBN 0-7668-0700-2

95-42891
CIP

CONTENTS

PREFACE

Automotive Technology: A Systems Approach was developed as a complete learning package that gives the instructor the tools needed to train students to be professional automotive technicians. The main text gives you comprehensive, state-of-the-art coverage—including the latest technical developments in the automotive industry, in both the vehicles and in the diagnostics and repair of those vehicles—in a logical but flexible chapter arrangement. Organized around the eight ASE areas, both text and *Tech Manual* constantly revisit professionalism and certification.

This Instructor's Guide will help coordinate teaching activities from lecture to shop assignments to testing and ASE preparation. The guide is broken down into five parts:

Curriculum Guide. This portion of the *Instructor's Guide* gives all the information you need to gain the most value from your use of *Automotive Technology*. Several features will help coordinate all the elements of the teaching package:

Chapter Overview and Chapter Objectives will give a brief orientation to the contents and purpose of each chapter.

Instructional Outline with Teaching Hints gives a thorough outline of each chapter's contents. The instructor will find suggested assignments from the text and *Tech Manual*, plus hints for improving student comprehension and for teaching difficult areas.

Tech Manual Correlation lists the salient points that will be covered by the Job Sheets.

Shop Hints will give suggestions for making your labs run smoothly.

Answers sections provide the responses to all of the test areas in the package: Chapter Review Questions; ASE Prep Tests; Tech Manual Case Studies; Tech Manual Review Questions; and Tech Manual ASE Prep Tests.

Transparency Masters in a perforated section consist of selected artwork from the textbook.

Crossover Guide. This unique resource will help "make the switch" from your current text to *Automotive Technology* without the toil of locating coverage of the topics you want to teach. The Crossover Guide gives you a topic-by-topic index to the coverage in three of the best-selling texts in this field, and then compares it to the coverage in *Automotive Technology*.

ASE and NATEF Task Correlation Chart. This reference will help you locate the textbook and *Tech Manual* pages that are relevant to teaching the NATEF and ASE Tasks listed.

PowerPoint™ Presentation on CD-ROM. This electronic resource includes the Instructional Outline with Teaching Hints in a PowerPoint Presentation accompanied by over 700 full-color illustrations from the textbook.

THE AUTOMOTIVE INDUSTRY

CHAPTER OVERVIEW

This chapter takes a close look at the automotive industry today and the changes that are occurring in the industry. It is important to service vehicles today largely because of the technology used in those vehicles. Only a properly trained technician can perform the necessary service in the current automotive industry. A detailed description is given of what it takes to be a professional technician, and descriptions of career opportunities, job classifications, and ASE certification are also provided.

CHAPTER OBJECTIVES

- Describe the reasons why today's automotive industry is considered a global industry.
- Explain how computer technology has changed the way vehicles are built and serviced.
- Explain why the need for qualified automotive technicians is increasing.
- Describe the major types of businesses that employ automotive technicians.
- List some of the many job opportunities available to people with a background in automotive technology.
- Describe what it takes to be a good technician.
- Explain the role ASE now plays within the automotive service industry.
- Describe the requirements for ASE certification as an automotive technician and a master auto technician.

INSTRUCTIONAL OUTLINE WITH TEACHING HINTS

    I. The Technology Boom—**Assignment: Read pages 1–8.**
      A. On-Board Diagnostics
      B. I/M (Inspection/Maintenance)
        Hint: Hold a discussion on the idea of personal transportation, how it will change in the future, and how that will affect our lifestyles.
      C. The Need for Quality Service
        1. Diagnostic Skills
      D. The Need for On-Going Service
        1. Preventive maintenance (PM)—See Transparency Master #1
        2. Warranties
        3. Increased vehicle age (longevity)

4. Residual value
5. Emissions and fuel economy requirements
   Hint: Hold a discussion on the idea that complex older cars need repairs and that qualified technicians will be needed to repair them.

   E. Career Opportunities
1. Dealerships
2. Independent service shops
3. Franchise repair shops
4. Store-associated shops
5. Fleet service and maintenance
   Hint: Hold a discussion on career opportunities in all areas of service and repair.

II. Job Classifications—**Assignment: Read pages 8–10.**
   A. Service Technician
   B. Shop Foreman
   C. Service Advisor
   D. Service Manager
   E. Parts Counterperson
   F. Parts Manager
   Hint: Hold a discussion on the various automotive shop positions and how each one relates to the technician.

III. Related Career Opportunities—**Assignment: Read page 10.**
   A. Parts Distribution
   B. Marketing and Sales
   C. Other Opportunities
   Hint: Hold a discussion on job classifications and their importance to the automotive industry.

IV. Working as an Automotive Technician—**Assignment: Read pages 10–12.**
   A. Compensation
1. Hourly
2. Flatrate

   B. Employer-Employee Relationships
   C. Employer Obligations
1. Instruction and supervision
2. Clean and safe place to work
3. Wages
4. Fringe benefits
5. Opportunity and fair treatment

   D. Employee Obligations
1. Regular attendance
2. Following directions
3. Responsibility
4. Productivity
5. Loyalty
6. "Getting along"
7. Customer relations
   Hint: Hold a discussion on the importance of employee-employer relationships and how they affect the technician.

V. Training for a Career in Automotive Service—**Assignment: Read page 12.**
   A. Schools

       B. Secondary
       C. Post-Secondary
       D. Vocational Schools
       E. Technical and Community Colleges
       F. Manufacturer—School Programs
       G. Life-Long Learning
    VI. ASE Certification—**Assignment: Read pages 12–13.**
       A. Certification Areas for Automotive Technicians
          1. Engine repair
          2. Automatic transmission/transaxles
          3. Manual transmissions and drive axles
          4. Suspension and steering
          5. Brakes
          6. Electrical systems
          7. Heating and air conditioning
          8. Engine performance
       B. Requirements for Certification
          1. Two years work experience or one year work and one year in an approved program
          2. Basic technical knowledge
          3. Repair knowledge and skill
          4. Testing and diagnostic knowledge and skill
   VII. Service Technician Society—**Assignment: Read page 13.**
       A. SAE-Based Information
       B. Students Can Enroll
       Hint: Schedule a field trip to a dealership, independent shop, and fleet facility.

ANSWERS TO REVIEW QUESTIONS

1. The use of electronics allows for quick response times to changes. Electronic devices are also inexpensive and lightweight and, because they have no moving parts, they are very reliable.

2. To be a successful and professional automotive technician, you must get along with others, respect others, deal honestly with your place of employment and customers, study to make your yourself better, and keep up-to-date with the latest technology.

3. (1) Dealerships. They provide repair and maintenance work for vehicles under warranty by the manufacturer. The technical support, the special diagnostic equipment provided by the manufacturer, and the opportunity for on-going training are usually excellent at a dealership. The disadvantage would be the limiting effect on the scope of your servicing expertise that comes from being tied into only one or two particular model lines. (2) Independent Service Shops. They service all types of vehicles, sometimes specializing in imports or certain domestic lines. This type of shop may present constant diagnostic and servicing challenges and lead to a well-rounded technical background. However, it may also lack the sophisticated diagnostic equipment and available training a large dealership can offer. (3) Store-Associated Shops. They offer certain specialized services such as brake, exhaust system repair, and wheel and tire work. An advantage would be the chance to specialize in a certain service area and know the parts the store offers. This would detract from developing a well-rounded background, however, and you would be bound to install and service only those parts the store stocked. (4) Specialty Service Shops. They specialize in repair areas

such as engine rebuilding, transmission/transaxle overhauling, and brake, exhaust, cooling, emissions, and electrical work. Service technicians can become very good in their area of vehicle repair but they can also limit themselves. (5) Fleet Service and Maintenance. They provide vehicle service and preventive maintenance to a fleet of company vehicles. This provides a technician with the opportunity to become familiar with a wide range of vehicles and to service the same vehicles over a period of time. This familiarity and repetitiveness could also be considered a disadvantage.

4. The employer is obligated to provide instruction and supervision, a clean and safe workplace, pay on designated paydays, promotion opportunity, fair treatment, and notification of any fringe benefits. An employee's obligations include regular attendance, following directions, responsibility, productivity, a positive attitude, and loyalty to the employer's best interests.

5. The National Institute for Automotive Service Excellence actively promotes professionalism within the industry. Its certification program for automotive technicians and master auto technicians helps guarantee a high level of quality service. The ASE certification process involves both written tests and credit for on-the-job experience. Testing is available in eight separate areas of auto technology. Certification in engine machining, heavy-duty truck servicing, auto body painting, and collision repair is also offered.

6. b	**11.** b
7. c	**12.** b
8. d	**13.** a
9. d	**14.** c
10. d	**15.** b

ANSWERS TO TECH MANUAL QUESTIONS

1. Hydraulics, electronics, pneumatics, mechanical
2. Leads to success and self-confidence and to customer confidence
3. PM is performing services on a scheduled basis to prevent problems, not repair them.
4. OBD is concerned with emissions. CAFE is concerned with fuel economy.
5. Some specialty shops are franchised shops.
6. Diagnose, act professionally, be honest, receive updated training
7. Each service operation has a standard time that is allotted for completion of the operation. A technician may be paid an hourly wage based on the time allotted for a particular job.
8. Diagnosis, system knowledge, experience
9. Technician, parts counter person, service advisor, equipment sales or service, instructor
10. Answers will vary.

WORKING SAFELY

CHAPTER OVERVIEW

This chapter discusses shop safety in detail. The topics range from clothing and eye protection to handling tools, vehicle handling in the shop, and handling hazardous waste. The instructor might want to refer to parts of Chapter 2 for review when discussing safety issues in later chapters.

CHAPTER OBJECTIVES

- Understand the importance of safety and accident prevention in an automotive shop.
- Explain the basic principles of personal safety, including protective eye wear, clothing, gloves, shoes, and hearing protection.
- Explain the procedures and precautions for safely using tools and equipment.
- Explain the precautions that need to be followed to safely raise a vehicle on a lift.
- Explain what should be done to maintain a safe working area in a shop, including running the engines of vehicles in the shop and venting the exhaust gases.
- Describe the purpose of the laws concerning hazardous wastes and materials, including the right-to-know laws.
- Describe your rights, as an employee and/or student, to have a safe place to work.

INSTRUCTION OUTLINE WITH TEACHING HINTS

I. Personal Safety—**Assignment: Read pages 16–19.**
   A. Eye Protection
   B. Eye flushing
   C. Clothing
   D. Hair and Jewelry
   E. Shoes
   F. Gloves
   G. Ear Protection
   H. Respiratory Protection
   I. Lifting and Carrying
   J. Professional Behavior
   Hint: Have a discussion on the importance of wearing protective clothing. Find out whether there are any employee objections to various protective garments.

II. Tool and Equipment Safety—**Assignment: Read pages 19–24.**
   A. Hand Tool Safety
   B. Power Tool Safety
   C. Electrical Tool Safety
   D. Compressed Air Equipment or Pneumatic Tool Safety
   E. Lift Safety
   F. Jack and Jack Stand Safety
   G. Chain Hoists and Crane Safety—See Transparency Master #2
   H. Cleaning Equipment Safety
      1. Chemical cleaning
      2. Thermal cleaning
      3. Abrasive cleaning
   I. Vehicle Operation
      Hint: After the lecture, conduct a shop tour; point out equipment, safety devices, and warning signs.

III. Work Area Safety—**Assignment: Read pages 24–26.**
   A. Flammables
   B. Volatile Liquids
   C. Fire Extinguishers (PASS)—See Transparency Master #3
      1. **P**ull the pin from the handle of the extinguisher.
      2. **A**im the extinguisher's nozzle at the base of the fire.
      3. **S**queeze the handle.
      4. **S**weep the entire width of the fire with the contents of the extinguisher.
         Hint: After the lecture, go to the shop and find all the fire extinguishers and identify the types of fires that they are approved for.

IV. Manufacturer's Warnings and Government Regulations—**Assignment: Read pages 26–29.**
   A. Chemical Hazards
   B. Hazardous Wastes
   C. Physical Hazards
   D. Ergonomic Hazards

V. OSHA
   A. Right-To-Know Law
      1. MSDS—Material Safety Data Sheets—See Transparency Master #4
      2. WHMIS—Workplace Hazardous Materials Information System (Canada)
         Hint: Begin a discussion on hazmats and the right-to-know laws.

VI. Guidelines for Handling Shop Wastes—**Assignment: Read pages 29–30.**
   A. Oil
   B. Oil Filters
   C. Batteries
   D. Metal Residue from Machining
   E. Refrigerants
   F. Solvents
   G. Containers
   H. Other Solids
   I. Liquid Recycling
   J. Shop Towels/Rags
   K. Hiring a Hauler
   L. Waste Storage
      Hint: Visit an automotive shop or tour your working area and demonstrate how to clean it up and where to store hazmats.

VII. Asbestos—**Assignment: Read pages 30–31.**
   Hint: Hold a discussion on the hazardous nature of asbestos and the safety measures required to work around it.

ANSWERS TO REVIEW QUESTIONS

1. Waste is considered hazardous if it is on the EPA list of materials known to be harmful or has one or more of the following characteristics: ignitability, corrosivity, reactivity, or EP toxicity.
2. Up-to-date numbers for a doctor, hospital, and fire and police departments should be clearly posted next to the telephone.
3. Whenever working with or near risks such as dust, vapors, metal shaving, and liquids.
4. By smothering it, with an extinguisher that gives a blanketing, flame-interrupting effect, covering the whole flaming liquid surface
5. In the Code of Federal Regulations

6. d	11. b	16. d
7. a	12. d	17. c
8. c	13. d	18. b
9. a	14. c	19. d
10. d	15. d	20. d

TECH MANUAL ANSWERS

1. **a.** wear eye protection
   b. no horseplay
   c. wear proper clothing
   d. use tools and equipment properly
   e. proper care of long hair
   f. there are many other shop safety items that will be covered by the instructor
2. The tires should be blocked, the car should be in park or neutral with the parking brake set, there should be an exhaust vent system hooked to the vehicle.
3. **a.** solvents
   b. paints
   c. gas
   d. lubricants
   e. fluids
   f. cleaners
4. **a.** recycle
   b. have material picked up by a licensed disposal company
5. Material name, compounds found in material, safety precautions, degree of danger of material, disposal procedures, health precautions, procedures to follow if there is contact with the skin or if it is swallowed.
6. b
7. c
8. False
9. False
10. False

AUTOMOTIVE SYSTEMS

CHAPTER OVERVIEW

This chapter discusses significant features of design evolution. The latest, most progressive changes are emphasized. The basic automobile systems that will be covered in later chapters are introduced.

CHAPTER OBJECTIVES

- Explain the major events that have influenced the development of the automobile during the last 35 years.
- Explain the difference between unitized and body-over-frame vehicles.
- Describe the manufacturing process used in a modern automated automobile assembly plant.
- List the basic systems that make up an automobile and name their major components and functions.
- Explain the importance of preventive maintenance, and list at least six examples of typical preventive maintenance.

INSTRUCTIONAL OUTLINE WITH TEACHING HINTS

I. Modern Power Plants—**Assignment: Read page 35.**
   Hint: Hold a discussion on the comparison of large older engines and today's engines as it pertains to CAFE, emissions, and performance.
II. Design Evolution—**Assignment: Read pages 35–36.**
   A. Unitized Construction or Unibody
   B. Body-Over-Frame Construction—See Transparency Master #5
III. Body Shapes—**Assignment: Read pages 36–39.**
   A. Sedan
   B. Convertibles
   C. Liftback or Hatchback
   D. Station Wagon
   E. Pickups
   F. Vans
   G. Sport Utility Vehicles (SUVs)
   H. Aerodynamics

    1. Vehicle form

    2. Air drag reduction

    3. Air dams

    4. Spoilers

    5. Wings

    Hint: Hold a discussion on Unitized vs. Frame construction and how aero-dynamics plays an important role in CAFE.

IV. The Electronic Revolution—**Assignment: Read page 39.**

  A. Computers

  B. Engines

  C. Miller-Stroke

  D. Stirling Engine

  E. Hydrogen Fuel Cell

  F. Hybrid

  G. Solar and/or Battery

  Hint: Hold a discussion on the advantages and disadvantages of gasoline engines and why alternative power plants are being explored.

V. The Basic Engine—**Assignment: Read pages 39–41.**

  A. Cylinder Block—See Transparency Master #6

  B. Cylinder Head

    1. Combustion chamber

    2. Ports

  C. Piston

  D. Connecting Rods and Crankshaft

  E. Valve Train

  F. Manifolds

    1. Intake manifold

    2. Exhaust manifold

    Hint: Display a disassembled engine, then present the individual parts.

VI. Engine Systems—**Assignment: Read pages 41–46.**

  A. Lubrication System

    1. Oil pan

    2. Oil sump

  B. Cooling System

    1. Water pump

    2. Water jackets

    3. Radiator

    4. Pressure cap

    5. Thermostat

  C. Fuel and Air System

    1. Stores the fuel for later use

    2. Collects and cleans the outside air

    3. Delivers fuel

    4. Regulates the fuel/air ratio

  D. Emission Control System

    1. Hydrocarbons (HC)

    2. Carbon monoxide (CO)

    3. Oxides of nitrogen (NO_X)

    4. Positive crankcase ventilation (PVC)

    5. Evaporative emission control

    6. Exhaust gas re-circulation (EGR)

7. Catalytic converter
8. Air injection

E. Exhaust System
   1. Exhaust manifold and gasket
   2. Exhaust pipe, seal, and connector pipe
   3. Intermediate pipes
   4. Catalytic converter(s)
   5. Muffler
   6. Resonator
   7. Tailpipe
   8. Heat shields
   9. Clamps, gaskets, and hangers

F. Electrical and Electronic Systems
   1. Ignition system
      a. Crankshaft position sensor
      b. Distributor
      c. Spark plug
   2. Starting and charging systems—See Transparency Masters #7 and #8
      a. Solenoid
      b. Starter motor
   3. AC generator.

G. Electronic Engine Controls
   1. Input sensors
   2. Microprocessor
   3. Output devices
      Hint: Have the students identify some of these components on a car.

VII. Drivetrain—**Assignment: Read pages 46–50.**
   A. Clutch
   B. Manual Transmission
   C. Automatic Transmission
   D. Driveline
   E. Differential
   F. Driving Axles
   G. Transaxle
   H. Four-Wheel-Drive System

VIII. Running Gear—**Assignment: Read pages 50–52.**
   A. Suspension System
      1. Springs
      2. Torsion bars
      3. Shock absorbers
   B. Steering System
      1. Rack-and-pinion
      2. Recirculating ball
      3. Steering gears
   C. Brakes
      1. Master cylinder
      2. Disk brakes
      3. Drum brakes
      4. Brake booster
      5. Antilock brake system (ABS)
   D. Wheels and Tires

IX. Preventive Maintenance—**Assignment: Read pages 52–61.**
    A. Typical PM Services
        1. Engine oil
        2. Cooling system
        3. Drive belts and battery
        4. Transmission fluid
        5. Power-steering fluid
        6. Brake fluid
        7. Windshield washer fluid
        8. Windshield wipers
        9. Tires
    B. Additional PM Checks (See pages 60–61).
       Hint: Discuss the PM schedule in Figure 3–40.

ANSWERS TO REVIEW QUESTIONS

1. They're tested for the number of miles they can be driven on a gallon of gas.
2. A unibody has no separate frame and all major parts are welded together.
3. The burning that takes place inside the engine and creates heat energy
4. The alternator or generator, voltage regulator, indicator light, and the necessary wiring
5. Check the engine oil level, check the windshield washer fluid level, and look for low or underinflated tires.

6. c	**11.** c	**16.** c
7. c	**12.** d	**17.** d
8. a	**13.** a	**18.** a
9. d	**14.** b	**19.** c
10. c	**15.** b	**20.** b

TECH MANUAL
The following procedures are included in Chapter 3 of the *Tech Manual*.

    1. Basic preventive maintenance checks.

TECH MANUAL ANSWERS

1. EPA, NTSA, many others to be covered by the instructor
2. In the owner's manual or on the decal or placard glued to the doorjamb
3. An air/fuel mixture is ignited in a sealed cylinder. There is a drastic increase in pressure in the cylinder due to the combustion of the air/fuel mixture. This pressure pushes down on the cylinder's piston. The pressure or force moving the piston down is used to power the vehicle.
4. The suspension system helps the driver maintain control of the vehicle while it is traveling on a bumpy road.
5. Preventive maintenance is the proper care of a vehicle to prevent premature component failure.
6. Corporate Average Fuel Economy
7. c
8. c
9. False
10. False

SHOP TOOLS

CHAPTER

4

CHAPTER OVERVIEW

This chapter will present some of the more commonly used hand and power tools, with which every technician must be familiar. Since units of measurement play such an important part in tool selection and in diagnosing automotive problems, this chapter begins with a presentation of measuring systems. Prior to the discussion on tools, there is a discussion on another topic that relates very much to measuring systems—fasteners.

CHAPTER OBJECTIVES

- List the basic units of measure for length, volume, and mass in the two measuring systems.
- Describe the different types of fasteners used in the automotive industry.
- List the various mechanical measuring tools used in the automotive shop.
- Describe the proper procedure for measuring with a micrometer.
- List some of the common hand tools used in auto repair.
- Describe the use of common pneumatic, electrical, and hydraulic power tools found in an automotive service department.
- Describe the different sources for service information that are available to technicians.

INSTRUCTIONAL OUTLINE WITH TEACHING HINTS

I. Measuring Systems—**Assignment: Read pages 64–65.**
   A. Linear Measurements
   B. Square Measurements
   C. Volume Measurements
   D. Weight Measurements
   E. Temperature Measurements
   F. Pressure Measurements
   G. Torque Measurements
      Hint: Review conversions, but emphasize using the metric system without converting it.
II. Fasteners—**Assignment: Read pages 65–68**—See Transparency Master #9.
   A. Bolts
   B. Cap Screws
   C. Studs

    D. Nuts

    E. Setscrews

    F. Bolt Identification—See Transparency Master #10

       1. Bolt diameter

       2. Bolt shank

       3. Thread pitch

       4. Grade marks

    G. Tightening Bolts

    H. Washers

       Hint: Discuss various fasteners and how the grade strengths make a difference in torque and holding power (compare a 3/8″ coarse grade 2 bolt to a 3/8″ coarse grade 8 bolt).

III. Measuring Tools—**Assignment: Read pages 68–77.**

    A. Machinists Rule

    B. Vernier Caliper

    C. Dial Caliper

    D. Micrometers—See Transparency Master #11

    E. Reading a Metric Micrometer

       1. Each number on the sleeve of the micrometer represents 5.0 millimeters (mm).

       2. Each of the ten equal spaces between each number, with index lines alternating above and below the horizontal line, represents 0.5 mm.

       3. The beveled edge of the thimble is divided into 50 equal divisions, with every fifth line numbered: 0, 5, 10, . . . 45.

       4. As with the inch-graduated micrometer, the three separate readings are added together to obtain the total reading.

    F. Using an Outside Micrometer

    G. Reading an Inside Micrometer

    H. Reading a Depth Micrometer

    I. Telescoping Gauge

    J. Small Hole Gauge

    K. Feeler Gauge

    L. Screw Pitch Gauge

    M. Dial Indicator

    N. Torque Indicating Wrench

       1. Beam type

       2. "Click" type

       3. Dial indicator type

       Hint: Discuss Photo Sequence 2 and Figures 4–14A to 4–15.

IV. Hand Tools—**Assignment: Read pages 77–89.**

    A. Wrenches

       1. Open-end

       2. Box-end

       3. Combination

       4. Socket

       5. Allen

    B. Screwdrivers

       1. Standard

       2. Phillips

       3. Pozidriv®

4. Torx®
5. Clutch driver
6. Scrulox®
C. Pliers
1. Combination
2. Adjustable
3. Needle nose
4. Locking
5. Diagonal cutting
6. Snap or lock ring
7. Retaining ring
D. Hammers
E. Taps and Dies
F. Chisels and Punches
G. Removers
1. Extractors
H. Hacksaws
I. Files
J. Tubing Tools
K. Gear and Bearing Pullers
V. Power Tools—**Assignment: Read pages 89–91.**
A. Impact Wrench
B. Air Ratchet
C. Air Drill
D. Air Chisel or Hammer
E. Blowgun
F. Bench Grinder
G. Trouble Light
H. Presses
VI. Service Manuals—**Assignment: Read pages 91–93.**
A. Auto Manufacturer's Manuals
B. Aftermarket Supplier's Guides and Catalogs
C. General and Specialty Repair Manuals
D. Flat-Rate Manuals
E. Computer-Based Information
F. Hotline Services

ANSWERS TO REVIEW QUESTIONS

1. It should be checked weekly, and whenever it unexpectedly drops.
2. Measuring valve lift, journal concentricity, flywheel or brake rotor runout, gear backlash, and crankshaft end play
3. The width of the jaw opening from face to face measured in either metric or SAE. This size is actually slightly larger than its nominal size so that the wrench fits around a nut or bolt head of equal size.
4. Grinding wheel, wire wheel brush, buffing wheel
5. Updates are published as service bulletins and provided to dealers and repair facilities on a regular basis.
6. c
7. c
8. d

9. c	**13.** d	**17.** b
10. b	**14.** a	**18.** d
11. c	**15.** a	**19.** d
12. d	**16.** c	**20.** a

TECH MANUAL

The following procedures are included in **Chapter 4 of the** *Tech Manual.*

1. Cutting with a chisel.
2. Using a punch to remove a rivet.
3. Repairing and/or replacing damaged threads.
4. Proper use of a stationary grinder.
5. Proper use of a hydraulic floor jack.
6. Proper use of a vehicle hoist.
7. Proper use of a service manual.

SHOP HINTS

- Discuss the power tools provided in the shop and the safety rules for each tool.
- Demonstrate as many tools in Chapter 4 as practical.
- Have students sort and identify bolts and other fasteners by grade, thread pitch, and type.
- Demonstrate and review shop manual usage.

TECH MANUAL ANSWERS

Review Questions

1. A better grip on the head of a bolt or nut is possible with a box-end wrench.
2. Hands can be cut by the sharp edges of a mushroomed chisel. The mushroomed edges of a chisel can break off and go into your eyes when the chisel is struck with a hammer.
3. Hand tools
4. The exact procedure for a particular vehicle may be different than that used for other vehicles. Failure to follow the correct procedure can lead to frustration, wasted time, and poor repairs.
5. Although this situation should be avoided, if necessary the block should be placed between the saddle of the lift and the lifting point on the vehicle.
6. b
7. b
8. c
9. d
10. Dial indicator
11. False
12. 6-point
13. Check the service manual.
14. A tap is used for cutting internal threads and a die is used for cutting external threads.
15. Combination, water pump, needle nose, channel lock, slip joint, vise grip

DIAGNOSTIC EQUIPMENT

CHAPTER 5

CHAPTER OVERVIEW

This chapter covers the most common diagnostic tools used on yesterday's and today's vehicles. Technicians need to know how to conduct tests with the latest testers, as well as knowing how to conduct tests with the most basic of testers.

CHAPTER OBJECTIVES

- Explain the basic principles of electricity.
- Diagnose electrical problems by logic and symptom description.
- Perform troubleshooting procedures using meters, test lights, and jumper wires.
- Explain the proper use of a logic probe.
- Describe what is displayed on an oscilloscope.
- Explain the proper use of a Digital Storage Oscilloscope.
- Explain basic infrared analyzer operation.
- Describe the major test capabilities of an engine analyzer.
- Name the diagnostic tools and equipment commonly used in vehicle repair work.
- Describe the basic applications and operation of these tools.

INSTRUCTIONAL OUTLINE WITH TEACHING HINTS

I. Electrical Fundamentals—**Assignment: Read pages 96–98.**
   A. Flow of Electricity
      1. Atom
         a. Nucleus
            (1) Protons
            (2) Neutrons
            (3) Electrons
   B. Energy sources
      1. Chemical
      2. Magnetic
      Hint: Cover the fundamentals of electricity only briefly, then review them later in conjunction with Chapter 14.
II. Measuring Electricity—**Assignment: Read pages 98–100**—See Transparency Master #12.
   A. Electrical Flow (Current)

    B. Resistance
    C. Electrical Pressure
    D. Ohm's Law
    E. Power
    F. Circuits
    G. Basic Electrical Diagnosis
       1. Open
       2. Short
       3. High resistance

III. Electrical Test Equipment—**Assignment: Read pages 100–103.**
    A. Circuit Tester
       1. Test light
       2. Continuity tester
    B. Voltmeter
    C. Ammeter
    D. Ohmmeter
    E. Volt/Ampere Tester
    F. Logic Probes

IV. DMM Usage—**Assignment: Read pages 103–106.**
    A. Multimeter
       1. DVOM
       2. DMM
       3. RMS
       4. Average responding
       5. RFI
       6. Duty cycle
       7. Pulse width
       8. Frequency

V. Ignition System Test Equipment—**Assignment: Read pages 106–109.**
    A. Tachometer
    B. Tach-Dwellmeter
    C. Timing Light
       1. BTDC
       2. ATDC
    D. Magnetic Timing Probe—See Transparency Master #13
    E. Electronic Ignition Tester
       1. Shorted module test
       2. Cranking current test
       3. Key on/engine off current test
       4. Idle current test
       5. Cruise current test
       6. Cranking primary voltage test
       7 Idle primary voltage test
       8. Cruise primary voltage test

VI. Lab Scopes—**Assignment: Read pages 109–113.**
    A. Dual-Trace Oscilloscopes
       1. Glitches
       2. Analog
       3. Digital
    B. Wave Forms

VII. Engine Diagnostic Tools—**Assignment: Read pages 113–120.**
   A. Compression Testers
   B. Cylinder Leakage Tester
   C. Cylinder Power Balance Test
   D. Vacuum Gauge
   E. Vacuum Pump
   F. Vacuum Leak Detector
   G. Cooling System Pressure Tester
   H. Coolant Hydrometer
   I. Oil Pressure Gauge
   J. Belt Tension Gauge
   K. Stethoscope

VIII. Fuel System Test Equipment—**Assignment: Read pages 120–122.**
   A. Pressure Gauge
   B. Injector Balance Tester
   C. Injector Circuit Test Light
   D. Fuel Injector Cleaners
      Hint: Briefly cover fuel system test equipment, then review the topic later in conjunction with Chapter 24.

IX. Exhaust Analyzers—**Assignment: Read pages 122–123.**
   A. Two Gas
   B. Four Gas
   C. Five Gas

X. Scan Tools—**Assignment: Read pages 123–124.**
   A. Scanners
   B. Breakout Boxes
   C. OBD-II

XI. Engine Analyzers—**Assignment: Read pages 124–125.**
   A. All in One
      1. Compression gauge
      2. Emission analyzer
      3. Pressure analyzer
      4. Voltmeter
      5. Vacuum gauge
      6. Ohmmeter
      7. Vacuum pump
      8. Ammeter
      9. Tachometer
      10. Oscilloscope
      11. Timing light/probe
      12. Computer scan tool
   B. Tests Performed by Engine Analyzers
      1. Cranking voltage
      2. Relative compression
      3. Charging voltage
      4. Primary circuit voltage
      5. Secondary circuit kilovoltage
      6. Cylinder power balance
      7. Engine vacuum

XII. Hydraulic System Testers—**Assignment: Read pages 125–127.**
   A. Pressure Gauges

ANSWERS TO REVIEW QUESTIONS

1. The battery (chemical reaction) and the alternator-generator (magnetism or induction)
2. They identify shorted and open circuits. There are several types of testers: Low-voltage testers troubleshoot 6- to 12-volt circuits, high-voltage circuit testers diagnose primary and secondary ignition circuits, self-powered circuit testers (continuity testers) have a small internal battery.
3. The push-in gauge, which is simple to use yet tends to be inaccurate if not held tightly in the spark plug hole, and the screw-in gauge, which is leakproof if properly installed.
4. The vacuum gauge, which measures the difference in pressure between the intake manifold and the outside atmosphere.
5. It is the process of producing electricity through magnetism, achieved by moving a wire (a conductor) through an already existing magnetic field (such as a permanent magnet), producing current flow (electricity).

6. c	**10.** b	**14.** b	**18.** b
7. c	**11.** d	**15.** d	**19.** a
8. b	**12.** d	**16.** b	**20.** c
9. c	**13.** a	**17.** b	

TECH MANUAL
The following procedures are included in Chapter 5 of the *Tech Manual.*

1. Basic use of a test light.
2. Understanding DMM controls.
3. Basic use of a DMM.
4. Using a vacuum gauge.
5. Using an exhaust analyzer.

SHOP HINTS

- Demonstrate DMM voltage, amps, and ohm tests on various car circuits.
- Demonstrate how to observe ignition timing with a timing light and how timing affects engine operation.
- Demonstrate how to connect and adjust a labscope.
- Demonstrate on a two or four gas exhaust analyzer how the gases change if a cylinder is disabled.
- Discuss details of how to hook up an engine analyzer to a vehicle.

TECH MANUAL ANSWERS

1. When electrons are able to flow along a path between two points, an electrical circuit is formed. An electrical circuit is considered complete when there is a path that connects the positive and negative terminals of the electrical power source.
2. Voltage is the electrical pressure that causes the movement of electricity, whereas current is the movement of electricity.

3. c	**6.** False	**9.** b
4. a	**7.** a	**10.** c
5. True	**8.** False	

AUTOMOTIVE ENGINES

CHAPTER 6

CHAPTER OVERVIEW

This chapter introduces the internal combustion engine. It discusses the variety of designs in popular usage today. It also offers a general introduction to engine diagnosis and testing.

CHAPTER OBJECTIVES

- Describe the various ways in which engines can be classified.
- Explain what takes place during each stroke of the four-stroke cycle.
- Outline the advantages and disadvantages of the in-line and V-type engine designs.
- Define important engine measurements and performance characteristics, including bore and stroke, displacement, compression ratio, engine efficiency, torque, and horsepower.
- Explain how to evaluate the condition of an engine.
- List and describe nine abnormal engine noises.
- Outline the basics of diesel, rotary, stratified and Miller-cycle engine operation.

INSTRUCTIONAL OUTLINE WITH TEACHING HINTS

   I. Engine Construction—**Assignment: Read pages 133–134**—See Transparency Master #14.

  II. Engine Classifications—**Assignment: Read page 134.**
- A. Operational Cycles
  - 1. Four-stroke cycle
  - 2. Two-stroke cycle
- B. Number of Cylinders
- C. Cylinder Arrangement
- D. Valve Train Type
  - 1. OHC
  - 2. OHV
  - 3. DOHC
- E. Ignition Type
- F. Cooling System Type
- G. Fuel Type

III. Four-Stroke Gasoline Engines—**Assignment: Read pages 134–136.**
- A. Intake Stroke

B. Compression Stroke

C. Power Stroke

D. Exhaust Stroke

IV. Two-Stroke Gasoline Engines—**Assignment: Read page 137.**

V. Characteristics of Four-Stroke Engine Design—**Assignment: Read pages 137–140.**

  A. In-Line Engines

  B. V-Type Engines

  C. Slant Cylinder Engines

  D. Opposed Cylinder Engines

  E. Valve and Camshaft Placement Configurations

    1. Overhead valve

    2. Overhead cam

  F. Valve Arrangement

  G. Valve and Camshaft Operation—See Transparency Master #15

  H. Engine Location

    1. Front engine longitudinal

    2. Front engine transverse

    3. Mid-engine transverse

    Hint: Discuss engine design and how it will change in the future.

VI. Gasoline Engine Systems—**Assignment: Read pages 140–141.**

  A. Air/Fuel Systems

  B. Ignition Systems

  C. Lubrication System

  D. Cooling System

  E. Exhaust System

  F. Emission Control System

VII. Engine Measurement and Performance—**Assignment: Read pages 141–144.**

  A. Bore and Stroke

  B. Displacement

  C. Compression Ratio

  D. Engine Efficiency

  E. Torque and Horsepower

    Hint: Discuss displacement, compression, and torque with students.

VIII. Engine Identification—**Assignment: Read pages 144–145.**

IX. Engine Diagnostics—**Assignment: Read pages 145–146.**

  A. Engine Temperature Tests

  B. Oil Pressure Testing

X. Evaluating the Engine's Condition—**Assignment: Read pages 146–148.**

  A. Noise Diagnosis

    1. Using a stethoscope

    2. Common noises

      a. Ring noise

      b. Piston slap

      c. Piston pin knock

      d. Ridge noise

      e. Rod-bearing noise

      f. Main or thrust bearing noise

      g. Tappet noise

      h. Abnormal combustion noises

      Hint: Try to describe the various noises and the speed with which they happen (crankshaft or camshaft speed).

XI. Other Engine Designs—**Assignment: Read pages 148–152.**
  A. Diesel Engine
  B. Rotary Engine
  C. Stratified Charge Engine
  D. Miller-Cycle Engine
  E. Electric Motors
  F. Hybrid Vehicles
  Hint: Discuss the diesel, rotary, stratified charge, Miller-cycle engines, and electric motors and hybrids in class. Try to arrange a visit from a dealership that has an EV.

ANSWERS TO REVIEW QUESTIONS

1. The chamber is the space between the top of the piston and the cylinder head in which the gasoline and air mixture is burned. The air/fuel mixture enters through an intake valve, the piston compresses it, it ignites and then is removed from the cylinder through an exhaust valve.

2. The intake stroke, the compression stroke, the power stroke, and the exhaust stroke. A stroke is the full travel of the piston either up or down in the cylinder bore, and all four strokes take place to complete the combustion cycle.

3. It should also increase, in order to avoid abnormal combustion. Gasoline with a low octane rating may explode rather than burn. The higher the rating, the less likely it is to explode or lead to preignition.

4. The cylinder power balance test, which is performed more quickly and easier using an engine analyzer, can determine if a cylinder or bank of cylinders is producing its share of engine power. Ideally, all the cylinders should be doing the same amount of work.

5. It is a light regular clicking sound that is the result of excessive clearance in the valve train. This noise is more noticeable when the engine is idling.

6. b	**11.** d	**16.** c
7. a	**12.** c	**17.** c
8. c	**13.** a	**18.** a
9. a	**14.** c	**19.** b
10. a	**15.** b	**20.** a

TECH MANUAL
The following procedures are included in Chapter 6 of the *Tech Manual.*

1. Performing a cylinder compression test.
2. Performing a cylinder leakage test.
3. Measuring engine oil pressure.

SHOP HINTS

■ Demonstrate power balance testing, then evaluate the engine's condition.
■ Have the students identify their family vehicles as to engine type, valve train, location, and cylinder arrangement.

TECH MANUAL ANSWERS

Review Questions

1. An engine's compression ratio expresses the decrease in the volume of the cylinder as the piston moves from BDC to TDC. The pressure of the mixture changes proportionally with the change in volume.
2. An engine's displacement is the total volume of all of the engine's cylinders.
3. A VIN gives the year, make, model, country of origin, engine size, and serial number of the vehicle.
4. Ring noise
5. Ridge noise
6. Loose crankshaft thrust bearing
7. b
8. c
9. The computer makes adjustments to the fuel and ignition systems of the vehicle to match the temperature at which it is operating. Therefore, if the computer senses that the engine is hot, it will make adjustments to maintain the present temperature or to cool it down, even when the engine may need to become hotter. The end result may be poor driveability and fuel economy.
10. Look for air leaking from the carburetor, tailpipe, or crankcase and for air bubbles in the radiator.
11. Loss of performance, excessive engine noise, and poor starting
12. Low oil level, oil dilution, worn oil pump, and worn main bearings
13. Carbon buildup on the piston and combustion chamber may cause an increase in compression ratio; therefore, the compression pressure readings may seem normal in spite of the fact that the cylinder is not properly sealed.
14. Remove the air cleaner
15. Usually 6 or 7 revolutions

ENGINE DISASSEMBLY

CHAPTER 7

CHAPTER OVERVIEW

This chapter instructs students in engine removal and disassembly of the cylinder head and cylinder block. It further discusses, in depth, the identification and cleaning of engine parts and crack repair.

CHAPTER OBJECTIVES

- Prepare an engine for removal.
- Explain what is involved in lifting an engine.
- Describe how to disassemble and inspect an engine.
- Name the three basic cleaning processes.
- Identify the different types of cleaning equipment.
- Describe the common ways to repair cylinder head cracks.

INSTRUCTIONAL OUTLINE WITH TEACHING HINTS

I. Preparing the Engine for Removal—**Assignment: Read page 156.**
II. Lifting an Engine—**Assignment: Read pages 156–157**—See Transparency Master #16.
   Hint: Remind students to use a manufacturer's service manual for specific procedures.
III. Engine Disassembly and Inspection—**Assignment: Read pages 157–162.**
   A. Cylinder Head Removal
   B. Cylinder Head Disassembly—See Transparency Master #17
   C. Cylinder Block Disassembly—See Transparency Master #18
IV. Cleaning Engine Parts—**Assignment: Read pages 162–167.**
   A. Types of Soil Contaminants
      1. Water-soluble soils
      2. Organic soils
         a. Petroleum byproducts
         b. Combustion byproducts
         c. Coatings
      3. Rust
      4. Scale

   B. Cleaning with Chemicals
      1. Parts washers
      2. Soak tanks
      3. Hot spray tanks
   C. Thermal Cleaning
   D. Abrasive Cleaners
      1. Abrasive blaster
      2. Parts tumbler
      3. Vibratory cleaning
      4. Cleaning by hand
   E. Alternative Cleaning Methods
      1. Ultrasonic cleaning
      2. Citrus chemicals
      3. Salt bath
         Hint: Be sure students understand the importance of reading the labels on cleaning solvents or chemicals before mixing or using them. Show students different types of abrasives.
V. Crack Repair—**Assignment: Read pages 167–168.**
   A. Crack Detection Methods
   B. Furnace Welding Crack Repairs
   C. Repairing Aluminum Heads
      1. Cracks in the aluminum between the valve seat rings
      2. Cracks coming from the coolant passages
      3. Cracks across the main oil gallery
      4. Detonation damage
      5. Meltdown damage
      6. Coolant-related metal erosion
         Hint: Arrange a field trip to a local machine shop.

ANSWERS TO REVIEW QUESTIONS

1. The electronic and fuel injection components should be covered with plastic bags during steam or other cleaning procedures in order to avoid direct contact with steam, water, or other cleaning agents. EPA regulations should always be followed when steam cleaning.
2. Protective gloves and goggles are necessary.
3. The convection oven, which uses indirect heat to bake parts clean, and the pyrolytic oven (also called an open- or direct-flame oven), which aims a flame directly on the parts to sear off the contaminants.
4. Furnace welding, in which the entire casting is preheated, thus eliminating the problem of stress cracks forming during the cooling-off period.
5. TIG welding is the preferred repair technique.

6. c	11. c	16. d
7. c	12. d	17. c
8. a	13. c	18. d
9. a	14. a	19. a
10. b	15. b	20. c

TECH MANUAL
The following procedures are included in Chapter 7 of the *Tech Manual.*

1. Preparing engine for removal.
2. Removing and disassembling the cylinder head.
3. Removing cylinder ring ridge.

SHOP HINTS

- Disassemble a cylinder block in the shop.
- Display samples of soil contaminants for students to view.
- Demonstrate chemical, abrasive, or some other cleaning method.
- Use and review all MSDSs for the shop chemical cleaning agents.

TECH MANUAL ANSWERS

Review Questions

1. negative
2. File away the excess metal on the tip before pushing the valve out of the guide.
3. label both sides of each connection to aid reassembly.
4. To prevent head warpage and to ensure a good seal
5. Reverse the procedure for tightening the bolts.
6. a
7. 1 1/2 times the bolt diameter
8. b
9. Chemical, thermal, by hand with soap and water, abrasives, vibration, ultrasonic, and salt baths
10. with your fingernail

SHORT BLOCKS

CHAPTER 8

CHAPTER OVERVIEW

This chapter discusses the engine's cylinder block, crankshaft, crankshaft bearings, connecting rods, pistons and rings, oil gallery, core plugs, flywheel, and harmonic balancer, focusing attention on the design and function of these essential parts of gasoline engines.

CHAPTER OBJECTIVES

- List the parts that make up a short block and briefly describe their operation.
- Describe the major service and rebuilding procedures performed on cylinder blocks.
- Explain crankshaft construction, inspection, and rebuilding procedures.
- Explain the function of engine bearings, flywheels, and harmonic balancers.
- Explain the common service and assembly techniques used in connecting rod and piston servicing.
- Explain the purpose and design of the different types of piston rings.
- Describe the procedure for installing pistons in their cylinder bores.

INSTRUCTIONAL OUTLINE WITH TEACHING HINTS

I. Cylinder Block—**Assignment: Read pages 171–172.**
   A. Lubricating and Cooling
   B. Core Plugs
   C. Cylinder Sleeves
II. Cylinder Block Reconditioning—**Assignment: Read pages 172–178.**
   A. Deck Flatness
   B. Cylinder Walls
   C. Cylinder Bore Inspection
      1. Taper
      2. Out of roundness
   D. Cylinder Bore Surface Finish
      1. Cylinder deglazing
      2. Cylinder boring
      3. Cylinder honing—See Transparency Master #19
   E. Installing Core Plugs
      1. Disc- or dished-type

2. Cup-type
3. Expansion-type
   Hint: Be sure students are familiar with all three core plug installation methods.

III. Crankshaft—**Assignment: Read pages 178–180**—See Transparency Master #20.
   A. Vibration Damper
   B. Flywheel
   C. Balance Shafts
   Hint: Discuss the differences among the various crankshaft configurations.

IV. Crankshaft Inspection and Rebuilding—**Assignment: Read pages 180–185.**
   A. Checking Crankshaft Saddle Alignment
   B. Checking Crankshaft Straightness
   C. Checking Crankshaft Clearance and End Play
   D. Flywheel Inspection
   E. Crankshaft Bearings
   F. Bearing Spread
   G. Bearing Crush
   H. Bearing Locating Devices
   I. Oil Grooves
   J. Oil Holes
   K. Oil Clearance
   L. Bearing Failure and Inspection
   Hint: Show students different types of distressed bearings. Use the service manual to find crankshaft specifications.

V. Installing Main Bearings and Crankshaft—**Assignment: Read pages 185–190.**
   A. Plastigage
   B. Crankshaft End Play—See Transparency Master #21
   C. Connecting Rod
   Hint: Demonstrate plastigage techniques and crankshaft end play measurements.

VI. Pistons and Piston Rings—**Assignment: Read pages 190–193.**
   A. Pistons
      1. Head or dome
      2. Ring lands
      3. Piston pin
   B. Piston Rings
      1. Compression rings
      2. Oil control rings

VII. Installing Pistons and Connecting Rods—**Assignment: Read page 194.**

ANSWERS TO REVIEW QUESTIONS

1. They insert a machined sleeve after the block has been machined so if the cylinder is somehow damaged, the sleeve can be removed and replaced rather easily.
2. It's the top of the engine block where the cylinder head mounts.
3. It occurs at the top of the ring travel area.
4. The resizable insert bearing, which can be machined to any desired size up to and including standard size.
5. They form the seal between the piston and the cylinder walls by using combustion pressure to force the ring against the bottom edge of the ring groove.

6. b	11. d	16. b
7. d	12. a	17. c
8. a	13. b	18. b
9. b	14. d	19. c
10. c	15. c	20. c

TECH MANUAL
The following procedures are included in Chapter 8 of the *Tech Manual*.

1. Measuring cylinder bore.
2. Measuring crankshaft journals.
3. Checking crankshaft endplay.
4. Installing pistons and connecting rods.

SHOP HINTS

- Measure deck warpage.
- Demonstrate deglazing and honing.
- Demonstrate a crankshaft inspection.
- Demonstrate how to use plastigage on the main and rod bearings.

TECH MANUAL ANSWERS

Review Questions

1. **a.** crank
   b. main bearing
   c. rod bearing
2. Two
3. Ring expander
4. Micrometer
5. Dial gauge
6. Before teardown is complete
7. They should be covered with protective boots.
8. False
9. Criss-cross pattern with lines intersecting at 50-degree angles
10. The grooves should cross at 50° angles, 300–500 rpm.
11. Micrometer
12. At least 8
13. c
14. Warped block, misaligned crankcase housing bores
15. Use a micrometer and measure the journal diameter vertically and horizontally at both ends. Then compare measurements. If the vertical measurement is different than the horizontal, the journal is out-of-round. If there is a difference between the ends, the journal has taper.

CYLINDER HEADS AND VALVES

CHAPTER 9

CHAPTER OVERVIEW

This chapter concentrates attention on the various types of combustion chambers and intake and exhaust valves. The discussion continues on to reconditioning aluminum cylinder heads, resurfacing cylinder heads, grinding valves, valve guide reconditioning, and reconditioning valve seats.

CHAPTER OBJECTIVES

■ Describe the purpose of an engine's cylinder head, valves, and related valve parts.
■ Describe the types of combustion chamber shapes found on modern engines.
■ Explain the procedures involved in reconditioning cylinder heads, valve guides, valve seats, and valve faces.
■ Explain the steps in cylinder head and valve reassembly.

INSTRUCTIONAL OUTLINE WITH TEACHING HINTS

    I. Cylinder Head—**Assignment: Read page 198.**
    II. Combustion Chamber—**Assignment: Read pages 198–200.**
        A. Wedge Chamber—See Transparency Master #22
        B. Hemispherical Chamber
        C. Swirl Chamber
        D. Chamber-in-Piston
        E. Fast-Burn Combustion Chamber
          Hint: Discuss and compare for students the different combustion chamber designs.
    III. Intake and Exhaust Valves—**Assignment: Read pages 200–202.**
        A. Poppet Design
        B. Valve Face
        C. Margin
        D. Valve Guides
        E. Valve Springs, Retainers, and Seals—See Transparency Master #23
        F. Valve Rotators
        G. Multivalve Engines

Hint: Discuss the reasons why multivalve engines have gained in popularity over the years.

IV. Aluminum Cylinder Heads—**Assignment: Read pages 203–204.**
   A. Reconditioning Aluminum Cylinder Heads

V. Resurfacing Cylinder Heads—**Assignment: Read pages 204–207.**
   A. Surface Finish
   B. Belt Surfacers
   C. Milling Machines
   D. Broaching Machines
   E. Surface Grinders
   F. Stock Removal Guidelines
      1. Combustion chamber volumes
         a. Compression ratio
         b. Piston/valve interference and misalignment
            Hint: Remind students of the reasons why and the methods how cylinder heads are resurfaced.

VI. Grinding Valves—**Assignment: Read pages 207–208.**

VII. Valve Guide Reconditioning—**Assignment: Read pages 208–212**—See Transparency Master #24.
   A. Knurling
   B. Reaming and Oversized Valves
   C. Thin-Walled Guide Liners
   D. Valve Guide Replacement
      1. Integral guides
      2. Insert guides
         Hint: Compare reaming and oversized valves with thin-walled and steel guide replacements.

VIII. Reconditioning Valve Seats—**Assignment: Read pages 212–215.**
   A. Installing Valve Seat Inserts
   B. Reconditioning Integral Seats
   C. Grinding Valve Seats
   D. Cutting Valve Seats
   E. Machining Valve Seats
      Hint: Review for students the procedure for insert valve seat removal and replacement.

IX. Valve Stem Seals—**Assignment: Read pages 215–218.**
   A. Installing Positive Valve Seals
   B. Installing Umbrella-Type Valve Seats
   C. Installing O-Rings
      Hint: Discuss the advantages of positive seals over the other types.
   D. Valve Spring
      1. Freestanding height test
      2. Spring squareness test
      3. Open/close spring pressure test
   E. Valve Spring Retainers and Keepers
      1. Valve rotators
         Hint: Review Photo Sequence 8 beginning on page 220.

X. Assembling the Cylinder Head—**Assignment: Read pages 218–222.**

ANSWERS TO REVIEW QUESTIONS

1. Valve float
2. The area between the valve face and the head of the valve that allows for some machining of the valve face, which is sometimes necessary to restore its finish, and allows the valve an extra capacity to hold heat.
3. It is usually the result of overheating due to low coolant, uneven coolant circulation within the head, a too-lean fuel mixture, or incorrect ignition timing.
4. It is equal to one-millionth (0.000001) of an inch, and is the unit of measurement used when checking cylinder head surface finish.
5. Because it restores only a portion of the worn valve guide's original surface. As the raised ridges are worn, wear accelerates and clearances become excessive long before they would have if the entire ID of the guide had been restored.

6. c	11. a	16. c
7. c	12. c	17. b
8. c	13. c	18. d
9. d	14. a	19. d
10. d	15. d	20. a

TECH MANUAL

The following procedures are included in Chapter 9 of the *Tech Manual.*

1. Inspecting cylinder head for wear.
2. Inspecting and testing valve springs for squareness, pressure, and free height comparison.
3. Inspecting valve spring retainers, locks, and valve lock grooves.
4. Replacing valve stem seals, in vehicle.
5. Reconditioning valve faces.

SHOP HINTS

■ Check the head surface for warpage with a straight edge and feeler gauge.
■ Pass around a valve with a too-narrow margin.
■ Demonstrate how to check for valve spring tensions.
■ Check for cam bore warpage on an OHC head.

TECH MANUAL ANSWERS

Review Questions

1. a. inadequate lubrication
   b. valve geometry problems
   c. wrong value stem-to-guide clearance
2. Exhaust valves require more clearance.
3. To allow for heat expansion (exhaust valves run hotter)
4. Inadequate lubrication
5. Small hole gauge or telescoping gauge, and micrometer

6. Stem-to-guide clearance is the difference between the smallest diameter of the stem and the largest diameter of the guide.
7. A valve seat runout gauge (also called a concentricity gauge) is used.
8. The valve seat should be replaced by either machining a counter bore to install an insert seat, or grinding, cutting or machining an integral seat.
9. The face should be ground first.
10. 0.010 inch can be removed from the valve tip before it must be replaced.

CAMSHAFTS AND VALVE TRAINS

CHAPTER OVERVIEW

This chapter explains how the parts of the camshaft and valve train work together to open and close the intake and exhaust valves of the engine. There is also a focus on installing the camshaft, the cylinder head and valve train, and the timing components.

CHAPTER OBJECTIVES

- Describe the purpose, operation, and location of the camshaft.
- Identify the parts of the valve train and the purpose of each.
- Inspect the camshaft, valve train, and timing components.
- Describe the four types of camshaft drives.
- Explain the factors involved in camshaft/crankshaft timing.
- Explain how to adjust valve lash.

INSTRUCTIONAL OUTLINE WITH TEACHING HINTS

I. Camshaft—**Assignment: Read pages 225–232.**
   A. Camshaft Bearings
   B. Valve Lifters
      1. Operation of hydraulic lifters
   C. Pushrods
   D. Pushrod Guide Plates
   E. Rocker Arms—See Transparency Master #25
   F. Timing Mechanisms
      1. Gear drive
      2. Chain drive
      3. Belt drive
      4. Timing belt and chain tensioners
      5. Timing marks
      6. Auxiliary shafts
   G. Variable Valve Timing
      Hint: Discuss valve timing operations, mechanisms and the advantages of a variable timing system.

II. Camshaft and Valve Train Inspection—**Assignment: Read pages 232–236.**
    A. Camshaft—See Transparency Master #26
    B. Valve Lifters
    C. Pushrods
    D. Rocker Arms
       Hint: Describe in class the two methods of measuring cam lobes for wear. Also, compare lifter wear patterns and their causes.
    E. Timing Components
       1. Timing gear backlash
       2. Timing belt
       3. Camshaft/crankshaft timing

III. Installing the Camshaft—**Assignment: Read pages 236–237.**
    A. Camshaft End Play

IV. Installing the Cylinder Head and Valve Train—**Assignment: Read pages 237–242**—See Transparency Master #27.
    A. Adjusting Valves
    B. Valve Lash
       Hint: Review for students proper installation of the cylinder head, valve train, timing components, and valve adjustments.

V. Installing the Timing Components—**Assignment: Read page 242.**
    Hint: Review Photo Sequence 9 on pages 240–241.

ANSWERS TO REVIEW QUESTIONS

1. It is mounted in or on the cylinder head, eliminating the need for pushrods.
2. Pushrod guide plates are used to hold the pushrods in alignment with the rocker arms.
3. The dial indicator test, which is conducted with the camshaft in the engine, and the outside micrometer test, for which the camshaft must be removed from the engine.
4. The normal wear of the valve lifters that is the result of two solid surfaces (camshaft lobe and lifter face) that are in rubbing contact.
5. By rotating them with the valve closed.

6. b	11. d	16. b
7. c	12. c	17. b
8. c	13. c	18. b
9. a	14. d	19. b
10. a	15. a	20. d

TECH MANUAL

The following procedures are included in Chapter 10 of the *Tech Manual.*

1. Installing camshaft bearings.
2. Inspecting and replacing camshaft drives.
3. Testing for worn cam lobes.
4. Inspecting and reconditioning valve lifters, pushrods, and rocker arms.

SHOP HINTS

- Demonstrate both methods of measuring a camshaft for lobe wear.
- Demonstrate valve lifter testing and inspection.
- Demonstrate timing component inspection and the proper installation procedures for the components.
- Demonstrate proper camshaft installation and checking for end play.
- Demonstrate valve adjustments on OHV (hydraulic and mechanical), and OHC (rocker and shims).

TECH MANUAL ANSWERS

Review Questions

1. Overhead cam engines sometimes have split bearings.
2. True, but only on cast-iron heads, never aluminum
3. When the mandrel is flush with the face of the block
4. **a.** dial indicator
   b. outside micrometer
5. Outside micrometer
6. A cup-shaped adaptor that fits on the pushrod
7. **a.** Outside micrometer
   b. Telescoping gauge
8. **a.** Adjusting nut or valve tip end of rocker arm
   b. Adjustment of disc or shim between the cam lobe surface and follower
   c. Screw threaded into follower
   d. Adjustable tappets
9. With a dial indicator and holding fixture
10. c

LUBRICATING AND COOLING SYSTEMS

CHAPTER 11

CHAPTER OVERVIEW

This chapter describes the components of typical lubricating and cooling systems and how each functions. Also included are oil types, oil pump inspection, service, and installation as well as the liquid cooling system and its service.

CHAPTER OBJECTIVES

- Name and describe the components of a typical lubricating system.
- Inspect, service, and install an oil pump.
- Describe the purpose of a crankcase ventilation system.
- Explain oil service and viscosity ratings.
- List and describe the major components of the cooling system.
- Describe the operation of the cooling system.
- Describe the function of the water pump, radiator, radiator cap, and thermostat in the cooling system.
- Test and service the cooling system.

INSTRUCTIONAL OUTLINE WITH TEACHING HINTS

    I. Lubrication—**Assignment: Read pages 246–248.**
      A. Oil Types
      B. Oil Consumption
    II. Lubricating Systems—**Assignment: Read pages 249–253.**
      A. Oil Pumps
      B. Oil Pump Pickup
      C. Oil Pan or Sump
      D. Pressure Relief Valve
      E. Oil Filter
      F. Engine Oil Passages or Galleries
      G. Engine Bearings
      H. Oil Pressure Indicator
      I. Oil Seals and Gaskets
      J. Dipstick
      K. Oil Cooler

    III. Oil Pump
        A. Types of Oil Pumps
           1. Rotor type—See Transparency Master #28
           2. Gear type
        B. Pressure Regulation
        C. Measuring Oil pressure
        D. Oil Pressure Indicators
        E. Oil Filters
        Hint: Show students different types of oil pumps. Disassemble and examine the various parts.
    IV. Oil Pump Inspection and Service—**Assignment: Read pages 253–257.**
    V. Installing the Oil Pump—**Assignment: Read pages 257–258.**
    Hint: Remind students that the manufacturer's service manual should be consulted for oil pump disassembly and installation instructions.
    VI. Cooling Systems—**Assignment: Read pages 258–269.**
        A. Liquid Cooled System
           1. Coolant
              a. Expansion or recovery tank
           2. Water pump
           3. Radiator
           4. Radiator pressure caps
           5. Water outlet
           6. Hoses—See Transparency Master #29
           7. Thermostat
           8. Belt drives
           9. Fans and fan clutches—See Transparency Master #30
           10. Water jackets
           11. Temperature indicator
           12. Heater system
           13. Oil cooler
        B. Air-Cooled System—**Assignment: Read page 269.**
        Hint: Be sure students understand the functioning of the closed-cooling system.
    VII. Cooling System Servicing—**Assignment: Read pages 269–275.**
        A. Testing the Cooling System for Leaks
        B. Repairing Radiators
        C. Testing the Radiator Pressure Cap
        D. Testing the Thermostat
        E. Checking and Replacing Hoses
        F. Water Pump Service
        G. Checking Fans and Fan Clutches
        H. Checking Belts
        I. Flushing Cooling Systems
        J. Refilling and Bleeding
        Hint: Demonstrate the testing of a thermostat. Explain the difference between the two types of thermostats.

ANSWERS TO REVIEW QUESTIONS

1. Increasing the difference between the temperature of the coolant and the outside air flowing through it
2. Faulty head gasket
3. Squeeze upper hose while revving the engine.
4. Off the camshaft or crankshaft
5. Pressure regulating valve

6. d	11. c	16. c
7. b	12. c	17. c
8. a	13. b	18. c
9. b	14. b	19. b
10. c	15. c	20. c

TECH MANUAL

The following procedures are included in Chapter 11 of the *Tech Manual.*

1. Servicing and installing oil pump and oil pan.
2. Inspecting, replacing, and adjusting drive belts and pulleys.
3. Cleaning, inspecting, testing, and replacing electric cooling fans and cooling system-related temperature sensors.
4. Testing cooling system.

SHOP HINTS

- Examine and discuss an oil pump pressure valve.
- Examine an oil pressure system, pointing out the location of sending units, oil lines, and gauges.
- Completely inspect several types of oil pumps according to manufacturer's recommendations.
- Examine the various types of radiator core constructions.
- Pressure test the cooling system for leaks.

TECH MANUAL ANSWERS

Review Questions

1. **a.** cold engine
   b. stuck pressure regulating valve
   c. high-viscosity oil
2. **a.** leaking head gasket
   b. crack in head, manifold, or block
3. **a.** insufficient coolant
   b. radiator pressure cap not releasing
   c. blocked hose

4. Replace the pump if the clearance between any gear tooth and the housing exceeds 0.005 inch.
5. a baffle plate assembly
6. The system is pressurized manually and checked for loss of pressure.
7. relieve system pressure
8. There is air trapped in the cooling system.
9. **a.** camshaft
   b. extension shaft from the distributor
10. **a.** They may interface with reinstalling the oil pan.
    b. The oil pickup may end up above the surface of the oil.
11. False
12. False
13. c
14. c
15. c

INTAKE AND EXHAUST SYSTEMS

CHAPTER 12

CHAPTER OVERVIEW

This chapter covers all the recent advances in intake and exhaust systems. Among these are thermostatic air cleaners, catalytic converters, turbochargers, and superchargers. There is some attention given to inspection and replacement of various components.

CHAPTER OBJECTIVES

- Explain the operation of the components in an air induction system, including ductwork, air cleaner/filters, and intake manifolds.
- Describe how the engine creates vacuum and how vacuum is used to operate and control many automotive devices.
- Inspect and troubleshoot vacuum and air induction systems.
- Explain the operation of exhaust system components, including exhaust manifold, gaskets, exhaust pipe and seal, catalytic converter, muffler, resonator, tailpipe, and clamps, brackets, and hangers.
- Properly perform an exhaust system inspection, and service and replace exhaust system components.
- Explain the purpose and operation of a turbocharger.
- Inspect a turbocharger, and describe some common turbocharger problems.
- Explain supercharger operation, and identify common supercharger problems.

INSTRUCTIONAL OUTLINE WITH TEACHING HINTS

I. Air Induction System—**Assignment: Read pages 279–288.**
  A. Air Intake Ductwork—See Transparency Master #31
    1. Air cleaner/filter
      a. Air filter design
      b. Air filter service
      c. Thermostatic air cleaners
    2. Intake manifold
      a. Servicing an intake manifold
        Hint: Demonstrate intake manifold design, describing open and closed intake, exhaust crossover, EGR system, and electric heater system.

B. Vacuum Systems
   1. Vacuum basics
   2. Vacuum controls
   3. Vacuum schematic
   4. Diagnosis and troubleshooting
   5. Vacuum test equipment
      Hint: Discuss the vacuum schematics in Figure 12–13. Make sure students understand how a vacuum system operates.

II. Exhaust System Components—**Assignment: Read pages 288–294.**
   A. Exhaust Manifold
   B. Exhaust Pipe and Seal
   C. Catalytic Converters
   D. Mufflers
   E. Resonator
   F. Tail Pipe
   G. Heat Shields
   H. Clamps, Brackets, and Hangers
      Hint: Discuss and compare for students the different types of catalytic converters.

III. Exhaust System Service—**Assignment: Read pages 294–296.**
   A. Exhaust System Inspection
   B. Exhaust Restriction Test
   C. Exhaust Manifold and Exhaust Pipe Servicing
   D. Replacing Exhaust System Components
      1. Replacing leaking gaskets and seals

IV. Turbochargers and Superchargers—**Assignment: Read pages 296–302.**
   A. Turbocharger Operation—See Transparency Master #32
      1. Turbocharger system
      2. Waste gate valve
      3. Intercooler
      4. Lubricating system
      5. Spark-retard system
      6. Computer-controlled systems
   B. Turbocharger Inspection
   C. Waste Gate Service
   D. Common Turbocharger Problems
      1. Turbo-lag
      2. Replacing turbocharger
   E. Turbo Start-Up and Shutdown
      Hint: Discuss the importance of proper turbocharger startup and shutdown.
   F. Superchargers
      1. Supercharger operation
      2. Supercharger designs
         a. Roots
         b. G-Lader
      3. Supercharger problems

ANSWERS TO REVIEW QUESTIONS

1. Soapy water
2. Improved fuel evaporation; cleaner burning; lower emissions
3. Distribute air or air/fuel mixture; make mixture uniform quality; vaporize
4. Checking a catalytic converter's output with a four-gas infrared analyzer, measuring the temperature of the inlet and outlet of the converter, and measuring the backpressure of the exhaust.
5. Two

6. d	11. d	16. a
7. c	12. c	17. b
8. b	13. c	18. c
9. b	14. d	19. a
10. c	15. d	20. d

TECH MANUAL

The following procedure is included in Chapter 12 of the *Tech Manual*.

1. Inspecting exhaust system.

SHOP HINTS

- Examine these manifold designs: open and closed intake, exhaust crossover, and EGR system.
- Measure the vacuum on a live vehicle. Explain the different readings at idle and accelerating.
- Test an exhaust system for backpressure. Explain why excessive backpressure is not desired.
- Hook up a four-gas analyzer and explain the measurements and how they relate to the intake, vacuum, and exhaust systems.
- Discuss turbocharger operation and service.
- Discuss supercharger operation and service.

TECH MANUAL ANSWERS

Review Questions

1. lower
2. a. Waste gate valve stuck closed
   b. Computer control problem
3. With engine running at idle, listen for hissing or rumbling.
4. True
5. There will be a general lack of air to the engine, which results in poor driveability and fuel economy.
6. False. (Both are signs of overheating.)
7. c
8. True

9. No. Normal 16 to 21 inches of mercury.
Cause may be a blocked exhaust.
10. Silence air intake noise, heat and cool the air as required, provide the air needed by the engine to operate, filter the air to protect the engine from wear, monitor airflow temperature, volume, and/or density for efficient combustion, operate with the PCV system, and provide air for some air injection systems.

ENGINE SEALING AND REASSEMBLY

CHAPTER 13

CHAPTER OVERVIEW

This important chapter describes the various hardware used to seal today's engines. A great deal of attention is given to subjects such as fasteners, gaskets, sealants, and adhesives.

CHAPTER OBJECTIVES

- Explain the purpose of the various gaskets used to seal an engine.
- Identify the major gasket types and their uses.
- Explain general gasket installation procedures.
- Describe the methods used to seal the timing cover and rear main bearing.
- Reassemble an engine including core plugs, bearings, crankshaft, camshaft, pistons, connecting rods, timing components, cylinder head, valve train components, oil pump, oil pan, and timing covers.
- Explain the ways to prelubricate a rebuilt engine.
- Reinstall an engine and observe the correct starting and break-in procedures.

INSTRUCTIONAL OUTLINE WITH TEACHING HINTS

    I. Torque Principles—**Assignment: Read pages 305–308**—See Transparency Master #33.
       A. Elasticity
       B. TTY
       C. Thread Repair
         Hint: Remind students of the importance of knowing torque specifications for standard bolts and nuts. Refer to Table 13–1 on page 306 of text for this discussion.
    II. Gaskets—**Assignment: Read pages 308–312.**
       A. Gasket Materials
       B. General Gasket Installation Procedures
       C. Cylinder Head Gaskets
         1. Bimetal engine requirements
       D. Manifold Gaskets
       E. Valve Cover Gaskets
       F. Oil Pan Gaskets—See Transparency Master #34

Hint: Be sure students understand the procedure of impression testing to check head gasket seals.

III. Adhesives, Sealants, and Other Chemical Sealing Materials—**Assignment: Read pages 312–315.**
   A. Adhesives
   B. Sealants
      1. General-purpose sealants
      2. Flexible sealants
      3. Silicone formed-in-place sealants
      4. Anaerobic formed-in-place sealants
      5. Antiseize compounds
      Hint: Discuss the importance of oxygen sensor safe RTV and antiseize.

IV. Oil Seals—**Assignment: Read pages 315–318.**
   A. Timing Cover Oil Seals—See Transparency Master #35
   B. Rear Main Bearing Seals
   C. Other Seals
      Hint: Discuss oil seal "burning" and the importance of lubricating the seal lip.

V. Engine Reassembly—**Assignment: Read pages 318–320.**
   A. Install Timing Cover
   B. Install the Vibration Damper
   C. Install the Valve Cover
   D. Pre-Lubrication Check
   E. Install Oil Pan
   F. Install Intake Manifold
   G. Install the Thermostat and Water Outlet Housing
   H. Install the Fuel Pump
   I. Paint the Engine
   J. Spin Test the Engine
   K. Install Exhaust Manifold
   L. Install Flywheel or Flex Plate
   M. Install Clutch Parts
   N. Install Torque Converter
   O. Install Motor Mounts

VI. Installing the Engine—**Assignment: Read page 320.**
   A. Starting Procedure.
      1. Break-in procedure
      Hint: Remind students that the manufacturer's service manual should be consulted for engine reassembly.

ANSWERS TO REVIEW QUESTIONS

1. Clamping pressure will be at least 25% less.
2. Won't return to original length
3. Cylinder head, exhaust manifold, some intake gaskets
4. On threads of bolts that go into fluid
5. Gap-filling ability

6. d	**11.** b	**16.** d
7. c	**12.** d	**17.** c
8. d	**13.** c	**18.** a
9. c	**14.** d	**19.** b
10. c	**15.** b	**20.** d

TECH MANUAL

The following procedures are included in Chapter 13 of the *Tech Manual*.

1. Applying RTV silicone sealant.
2. Adjusting valves on an OHC engine.

SHOP HINTS

- Examine various metric and UNS bolts. Identify the size of the bolt head, and the diameter, length, and thread pitch of each bolt.
- Demonstrate impression testing.
- Demonstrate RTV, antiseize, Loctite, and other gasket sealers.
- Demonstrate engine pre-lubrication processes.

TECH MANUAL ANSWERS

Review Questions

1. Hard gaskets are made of steel, stainless steel, copper, or a combination of metals with a compound sandwiched between the metals. A soft gasket is made of cork, rubber, a combination of cork and rubber, or rubber-coated steel, paper, or other compressible materials.
2. Aerobic
3. In the absence of air or free oxygen
4. A TTY bolt is tightened just barely into a yield condition. This stretches the bolt to its near maximum amount without distorting it, providing for maximum clamping ability.
5. Once the engine is bolted to its motor mounts.
6. With a torque wrench, to manufacturer's torque specifications
7. Wipe plug seats, check gasket, adjust gap, install plugs/finger tighten, tighten to manufacturer's specs with torque wrench.
8. The radiator and the water pump
9. True
10. d

SECTION 2

Answers to ASE Prep Test

1. a	6. a	11. c	16. c
2. c	7. c	12. b	17. a
3. a	8. b	13. b	18. c
4. c	9. c	14. c	19. c
5. a	10. a	15. b	20. b

BASICS OF ELECTRICAL SYSTEMS

CHAPTER 14

CHAPTER OVERVIEW

This quite technical chapter forms a foundation for the electrical systems covered in the following chapters. The first five pages of Chapter 5 can be reviewed in conjunction with this chapter.

CHAPTER OBJECTIVES

- Define the terms normally used to describe electricity.
- Use Ohm's Law to determine voltage, current, and resistance.
- List the basic types of electrical circuits.
- Describe the differences between a series and a parallel circuit.
- Name the various electrical components and their uses in electrical circuits.
- Describe the different kinds of automotive wiring.
- Read automotive electrical diagrams.
- Describe how each of the major types of electrical test equipment is connected and operated.
- Perform troubleshooting procedures using meters, testlights, and jumper wires.
- Explain the principles of magnetism and electromagnetism.

INSTRUCTIONAL OUTLINE WITH TEACHING HINTS

I. Basics of Electricity—**Assignment: Read pages 325–327.**
   A. Flow of Electricity—See Transparency Master #36
II. Electrical Terms—**Assignment: Read pages 327–330.**
   A. Circuit Terminology
      1. Open circuit
      2. Closed circuit
      3. Continuity
   B. Ohm's Law
   C. Power
III. Conductors and Insulators—**Assignment: Read pages 330–348.**
   A. Circuits
      1. Series circuits
         a. Voltage drops

2. Parallel circuits
3. Series-parallel circuits
B. Grounding the Load—See Transparency Master #37
C. Circuit Components
    1. Resistors
    2. Fixed value resistors
    3. Tapped or stepped resistors
    4. Variable resistors
    5. Circuit protective devices
        a. Fuse
        b. Fuse links
        c. Maxi-fuses
        d. Circuit breakers
        e. Voltage limiter
    6. Switches
    7. Relays
    8. Solenoids
    9. Capacitors (condensers)
   10. Wiring
   11. Printed circuits
   12. Electrical wiring diagrams—See Transparency Master #38
   13. Electrical problems
        Hint: Discuss electrical and electronics systems and how to read automotive wiring diagrams.

IV. Electrical Test Meters—**Assignment: Read pages 348–358.**
A. Test Meter Use
    1. Voltmeters
    2. Ammeters
    3. Ohmmeters
    4. Volt-ohmmeter
    5. Testlights
    6. Jumper wires
    7. Variable resistors
B. Troubleshooting Circuits
    1. Testing basic electrical components
        a. Protection devices
        b. Switches
        c. Relays
        d. Stepped resistors
        e. Variable resistors
        f. Connector and wire repairs
        Hint: Discuss electrical components, their functions and how they can be tested. Review Photo Sequence 11 on pages 362–363 for wire soldering.

V. Electromagnetism Basics—**Assignment: Read pages 358–364.**
A. Fundamentals of Magnetism
    1. Poles
    2. Flux field
    3. Flux density
    4. Coils
B. Magnetic Circuits and Reluctance
C. Induced Voltage
   Hint: Discuss the role that magnetism plays in charging and starting systems.

ANSWERS TO REVIEW QUESTIONS

1. Ohm's Law, which expresses the mathematical relationship between current, voltage, and power
2. Equal to the sum of all the individual resistors
3. An electrical schematic
4. In series, parallel
5. Trimmers or tuners
6. Sensors, actuators, microcomputer, and related wiring
7. Current decreases
8. Voltage is pressure, current is flow
9. Rosin core solder
10. A single pole, single throw or simply an on-off switch for a simple circuit
11. b
12. c
13. c
14. c
15. d
16. d
17. 2
18. a
19. b
20. b

TECH MANUAL
The following procedures are included in Chapter 14 of the *Tech Manual.*

1. Checking continuity in a circuit with a test light.
2. Checking applied voltages with a voltmeter.
3. Checking voltage drop across connectors.
4. Inspecting and checking fuses, fusible links, and circuit breakers.

SHOP HINTS

- Demonstrate how to perform a voltage drop test.
- Examine several electrical components and explain how each works.
- Demonstrate the features of a typical DMM and show how and when to use each one.
- Demonstrate proper wire repair and terminal replacement, including soldering techniques.

TECH MANUAL ANSWERS

Review Questions

1. False
2. Voltage causes electrical flow, whereas current is electrical flow.
3. d
4. Because they operate at very low amperages and will not damage electronic components.
5. True
6. False
7. c
8. c
9. Zero
10. True

BASICS OF ELECTRONICS

CHAPTER 15

CHAPTER OVERVIEW

This chapter looks at the design and components of the on-board computers and basic electronics systems. There is considerable attention given to system components and testing.

CHAPTER OBJECTIVES

- Describe how semiconductors, diodes, and transistors work.
- Explain the principles of operation for common electronic circuits.
- Explain the principle of multiplexing.
- Describe the basic function of the central processing unit (CPU).
- List and describe the functions of the various sensors used by computers.
- Describe the principle of analog and digital signals.
- Explain the principle of computer communications.
- Summarize the function of a binary code.
- Name the various memory systems used in automotive microprocessors.
- List and describe the operation of output actuators.
- Identify the proper procedure to safeguard electronic systems.
- Describe the basic electronic logic circuits.
- Explain how to use an oscilloscope for diagnosing electronic systems.

INSTRUCTIONAL OUTLINE WITH TEACHING HINTS

    I. Semiconductors—**Assignment: Read pages 366–370.**
       A. N-Type Semiconductors—See Transparency Master #39
       B. P-Type Semiconductors—See Transparency Master #40
       C. Hole Flow
       D. Semiconductor Uses
       E. Diodes and Transistors
       F. Diodes
          1. PN junction
          2. Forward bias
          3. Reverse bias
          4. Zener diodes
          5. LEDs

6. Clamping diodes
7. Photo diodes
G. Transistors
1. PNP
2. NPN
3. Emitter
4. Base
5. Collector
H. Semiconductor Circuits
II. Integrated Circuits—**Assignment: Read page 370.**
III. Operation of Microprocessors—**Assignment: Read pages 371–383.**
A. Sensors
1. Feedback
2. Vref
3. NTC
4. PTC
5. Wheatstone bridges
a. Piezoresistive
6. Voltage generating devices
7. Magnetic pulse generators
8. Pick-up coil
9. Hall-effect switches
B. Communication Signals
1. Analog
2. Digital
a. Bit
b. Byte
3. A/D converter
C. Logic Gates (FET)
1. NOT gates
2. AND gates
3. OR gates
4. NAND and NOR gates
5. Exclusive-OR (XOR) gate
6. Gate combinations
a. Decoder circuits
b. Multiplexer
c. Demultiplexer
d. RS and clocked RS flip-flop circuits
e. Registers
f. Accumulators
D. Memories—See Transparency Master #41
1. ROM
2. PROM
3. EPROM
4. RAM
5. KAM
6. NVRAM
E. Actuators
1. Output driver

2. LCD
3. VFD
F. Power Supply
IV. Multiplexing—**Assignment: Read pages 383–384.**
V. Protecting Electronic Systems—**Assignment: Read pages 384–385.**
VI. Testing Electronic Circuits and Systems—**Assignment: Read pages 385–386.**
A. RMS
B. Frequency
C. Hertz

ANSWERS TO REVIEW QUESTIONS

1. ROM, RAM, PROM
2. Microprocessor or computer
3. Analog
4. Square wave
5. Feedback
6. PROM
7. Inputs, processor, outputs
8. Diode
9. The length of time something is kept on
10. Information in ROM cannot be erased. In RAM, information is erased when the engine is stopped.

11. d	16. d
12. c	17. d
13. c	18. c
14. b	19. b
15. c	20. d

TECH MANUAL

The following procedures are included in Chapter 15 of the *Tech Manual.*

1. Checking continuity across electronic components and circuits with an ohmmeter.
2. Using a DSO on sensors and switches.

TECH MANUAL ANSWERS

Review Questions

1. False
2. True
3. ROM—Read Only Memory
   PROM—Programmable ROM
   RAM—Random Access Memory
   KAL—Keep Alive Memory
4. rosin core

5. c
6. a
7. Clamping diode or capacitor
8. False
9. Reference voltage
10. True

BATTERIES: THEORY AND SERVICE

CHAPTER 16

CHAPTER OVERVIEW

This chapter looks at the different battery types. It covers cleaning, servicing, and the charging processes.

CHAPTER OBJECTIVES

- Explain the purpose of a battery.
- Describe the basic parts of an automotive battery.
- Compare conventional and maintenance-free batteries.
- Explain the chemical reaction that occurs to produce current in a battery.
- Describe the differences, advantages, and disadvantages of the different types of batteries.
- Describe the different types of battery terminals used.
- Describe the different types of ratings used with batteries.
- Explain the effects of temperature on battery output.
- Demonstrate all safety precautions and rules associated with servicing batteries.
- Perform a visual inspection of a battery.
- Test a conventional battery's specific gravity.
- Perform open circuit tests.
- Test the capacity of a battery.
- Correctly slow- and fast-charge a battery.
- Jump-start a vehicle by using a booster battery and jumper cables.
- Remove, clean, and reinstall a battery properly.

INSTRUCTIONAL OUTLINE WITH TEACHING HINTS

I. Conventional Design Battery—**Assignment: Read pages 392–395**—See Transparency Master #42.
   A. Elements and Cells
   B. Electrolyte and Specific Gravity
   C. Discharging and Charging
   D. Casing Design
   E. Battery Cables

F. Battery Hold-Downs
G. Heat Shields
II. Low-Maintenance and Maintenance-Free Batteries—**Assignment: Read pages 395–396.**
A. Gasing
B. Advantages
C. Disadvantages
III. Hybrid Batteries—**Assignment: Read pages 396–397.**
A. Radial
IV. Recombination Batteries—**Assignment: Read page 397.**
V. Battery Voltage and Capacity—**Assignment: Read pages 397–398.**
VI. Battery Rating Methods—**Assignment: Read page 398.**
A. Reserve Capacity
B. Ampere-Hour Rating
C. Cold Cranking
VII. Battery Size Selection—**Assignment: Read pages 398–399.**
VIII. Factors Affecting Battery Life—**Assignment: Read pages 399–400.**
A. Improper Electrolyte Levels
B. Corrosion
C. Overcharging
D. Undercharge/Sulfation
E. Poor Mounting
F. Cycling
IX. Safety Procedures—**Assignment: Read pages 400–401.**
X. Routine Inspections—**Assignment: Read page 401.**
XI. Routine Cleaning—**Assignment: Read pages 401–405.**
XII. Battery Testing—**Assignment: Read pages 405–409.**
A. Specific Gravity Tests
B. Temperature Correction—See Transparency Master #43
1. Interpreting results
C. Built-In Hydrometers
D. Open Circuit Voltage Test
E. Battery Leakage Test
F. Battery Drain Test
G. Capacity Test
1. Interpreting results
XIII. Battery Charging—**Assignment: Read page 409.**
A. Trickle Chargers
XIV. Jump-Starting—**Assignment: Read pages 409–410**—See Transparency Master #44.

ANSWERS TO REVIEW QUESTIONS

1. An electrical current that drains the battery when the ignition is off; often these drains are necessary to keep a computer's memory or to keep a clock or radio set.
2. Cell size, type of electrolyte, and type of plates
3. The red lead of the voltmeter is placed on the positive terminal of the battery and the black or negative lead is placed on the battery case. The negative lead is moved all around the case and the reading on the meter observed.
4. Conventional, low-maintenance

5. Electrolyte, gasing
6. hybrid
7. Charging and discharging which causes a heating of the chemicals
8. Improper electrolyte levels, corrosion, overcharging, undercharge/sulfation, poor mounting, and cycling
9. 12.6 volts
10. Specific gravity is the weight of a given volume of any liquid divided by the weight of an equal volume of water.

11. d	16. c
12. c	17. a
13. c	18. d
14. c	19. c
15. a	20. a

TECH MANUAL

The following procedures are included in Chapter 16 of the *Tech Manual.*

1. Removing, cleaning, and replacing a battery.
2. Inspecting a battery.
3. Testing a battery's state of charge.
4. Testing a battery's capacity.
5. Charging a maintenance-free battery.

SHOP HINTS

- Demonstrate a visual inspection of a battery.
- Demonstrate a hydrometer test for specific gravity in a maintenance type battery.
- Demonstrate an open circuit voltage test.
- Demonstrate a capacity (load) test with a VAT.
- Demonstrate proper slow and fast charging of a battery.
- Demonstrate proper jump-start procedures with battery cables and a booster battery (or between vehicles).

TECH MANUAL ANSWERS

Review Questions

1. A parasitic load is a load that draws current from the battery when the engine is off.
2. Open-circuit battery voltage is the amount of voltage present across the battery terminals when the engine is off and there is no load on the battery.
3. c
4. True
5. False
6. Explode
7. Negative

8. Baking soda and water
9. Load
10. The battery capacity test measures the battery's ability to provide a specific amount of current for a specific amount of time.

STARTING SYSTEMS

CHAPTER 17

CHAPTER OVERVIEW

This chapter introduces the starting system and covers its service and repair.

CHAPTER OBJECTIVES

- Explain the purpose of the starting system.
- List the components of the starting system, starter circuit, and control circuit.
- Explain the different types of magnetic switches and starter drive mechanisms.
- Explain how a starter motor operates.
- Describe the operation of the different types of starter motors.
- Perform basic tests to determine the problem areas in a starting system.
- Perform and accurately interpret the results of a current draw test.
- Disassemble, clean, inspect, repair, and reassemble a starter motor.

INSTRUCTIONAL OUTLINE WITH TEACHING HINTS

I. Starting System—Design and Components—**Assignment: Read pages 414–422.**
   A. Starter Circuit
      1. Battery and cables
      2. Magnetic switches
         a. Solenoids
            (1) Pull in winding
            (2) Hold in winding
            (3) Pinion gear
      3. Starter relays
   B. Starter Motor—See Transparency Master #45
      1. Starter housing or frame
      2. Field coils
      3. Pole shoes
      4. Brushes
      5. Armature
      6. Commutator
      7. Operating principles—See Transparency Master #46

    C. Drive Mechanisms
        1. Positive engagement movable pole shoe drive
        2. Solenoid-actuated gear reduction drive
    D. Permanent Magnet Starting Motor—See Transparency Master #47
  II. Starter Drives—**Assignment: Read pages 422–423.**
    A. Overrunning Clutches
 III. Control Circuit—**Assignment: Read pages 423–424.**
    A. Starting Safety Switch
 IV. Starting System Testing—**Assignment: Read pages 424–427.**
    A. Preliminary Checks
    B. Safety Precautions
    C. Troubleshooting Procedures
    D. Battery Load Test
    E. Cranking Voltage Test
        1. Test conclusions
    F. Cranking Current Test
        1. Test conclusions
    G. Insulated Circuit Resistance Test
        1. Test conclusions
    H. Starter Relay By-pass Test
        1. Test conclusions
    I. Ground Circuit Resistance Test
        1. Test conclusions
    J. Voltage Drop Test of the Control Circuit
        1. Test conclusions
    K. Test Starter Drive Components
        1. Test conclusions
  V. Removing the Starter Motor—**Assignment: Read pages 427–435.**
    A. Free Speed (no-load) Test
    B. Starter Motor Disassembly
    C. Starter Motor Component Tests
        1. Field coil tests
        2. Armature tests
        3. Brush inspection
        4. Overrunning clutch inspection
        5. Starter motor reassembly

ANSWERS TO REVIEW QUESTIONS

1. A starter draws a large amount of current, which can drain a battery, and will draw more if other components (cables and connectors included) cause a voltage drop in the circuit.

2. b	**7.** a	**12.** c	**17.** a
3. a	**8.** b	**13.** d	**18.** Commutator
4. c	**9.** a	**14.** a	**19.** c
5. b	**10.** c	**15.** b	**20.** c
6. a	**11.** d	**16.** c	

TECH MANUAL
The following procedures are included in Chapter 17 of the *Tech Manual.*

1. Removing, inspecting, and replacing a starter motor.
2. Testing cranking voltage.
3. Testing cranking current.
4. Testing the resistance of the starting control circuit.

SHOP HINTS

- Demonstrate the basic tests for determining problem areas in a starting system.
- Demonstrate and accurately interpret the results of a current draw test.
- Demonstrate and accurately interpret the results of voltage drop tests on the insulated and ground circuits.
- Demonstrate starter bench tests and interpret the results.
- Disassemble, clean, inspect, repair, and reassemble a starter motor.

TECH MANUAL ANSWERS

Review Questions

1. True
2. c
3. False
4. True
5. c
6. d
7. b
8. **a.** Starter motor
   b. Starter relay
   c. Starter solenoid
   d. Starter drive
   There are several other components that may be listed
9. A typical starter motor is grounded through its mounting on the engine and/or transmission.
10. This switch allows the starter motor to be used only when the vehicle shift lever is in neutral or park.

CHAPTER 18

CHARGING SYSTEMS

CHAPTER OVERVIEW

This chapter looks at the design and components of the charging system. There is considerable attention given to testing the systems and there is a focus on alternating current charging systems.

CHAPTER OBJECTIVES

- Explain the purpose of the charging system.
- Identify the major components of the charging system.
- Explain the purpose of the major parts of an AC generator.
- Explain half- and full-wave rectification and how they relate to AC generator operation.
- Identify the different types of AC voltage regulators.
- Describe the two types of stator windings.
- Perform charging system inspection and testing procedures using electrical test equipment.

INSTRUCTIONAL OUTLINE WITH TEACHING HINTS

   I. Induced Voltage—**Assignment: Read page 439.**
  II. Alternating Current Charging Systems—**Assignment: Read pages 439–451.**
     A. AC Generator Construction
       1. Rotor
       2. Slip ring and brushes—See Transparency Master #48
       3. Stator
       4. End frame assembly
       5. Cooling fans
     B. Alternator Operation
       1. DC rectification—See Transparency Master #49
         a. Half wave
         b. Full wave
       2. Voltage regulation
         a. Sensing voltage
       3. Field circuits

C. Electronic Regulators
　　1. Integrated circuit voltage regulator
　　2. Fail-safe circuits
　　3. Computer regulation
D. Older Voltage Regulator Designs—See Transparency Master #50
E. Indicators
　　1. Indicator light
　　2. Voltmeter
　　3. Ammeter
F. Voltmeter
G. Ammeter
　　Hint: Discuss the advantages of AC generators over DC generators.
III. Preliminary Checks—**Assignment: Read pages 451–457.**
A. Safety Precautions
B. Inspection
C. General Test Procedures
　　1. Voltage output test
　　2. Current output test
　　3. Regulator by-pass test
　　4. Oscilloscope checks
　　5. Circuit and ground resistance
IV. AC Generator Service—**Assignment: Read pages 457–460.**
Hint: Follow service manual procedures for disassembling, inspecting, testing, and rebuilding AC generators.

ANSWERS TO REVIEW QUESTIONS

1. b
2. Rotor
3. Fail safe
4. Changes AC produced in the stator to rectified DC
5. Controls the amount of current to the rotor, which changes the strength of its magnetic field
6. a
7. The output will be reduced by about 1/3.

8. a	**13.** c	**17.** c
9. b	**14.** d	**18.** c
10. d	**15.** b	**19.** a
11. a	**16.** a	**20.** c
12. d		

TECH MANUAL
The following procedures are included in Chapter 18 of the *Tech Manual.*

1. Visually inspecting the charging system.
2. Adjusting drive belt.
3. Removing and replacing an AC generator.
4. Testing the charging system.
5. Disassembling and assembling an AC generator.
6. Testing components of an AC generator.

SHOP HINTS

- Perform charging system inspection and testing procedures using electrical test equipment.
- Disassemble an early-model AC generator and test all of the individual components.
- Disassemble a late-model AC generator and compare its components with the previous model.
- Demonstrate how a loose fan belt can affect AC generator output.

TECH MANUAL ANSWERS

Review Questions

1. With an ohmmeter
2. Electronic components
3. Shorts and opens
4. Disconnect, negative cable
5. Decreases output
6. True
7. c
8. b
9. True
10. Shorts and Opens

LIGHTING SYSTEMS

CHAPTER OVERVIEW

This chapter employs schematic diagrams to aid the student in understanding the circuits of this electrical system. Such knowledge is important in order to maintain the safety and convenience the lighting system provides in automobiles.

CHAPTER OBJECTIVES

- Explain the operating principles of the various lighting systems.
- Describe the different types of headlights and how they are controlled.
- Understand the functions of turn, stop, and hazard warning lights.
- Know how backup lights operate.
- Replace headlights and other burned-out bulbs.
- Explain how to aim headlights.
- Explain the purpose of auxiliary automotive lighting.
- Describe the operation and construction of the various automotive lamps.
- Diagnose lighting problems.

INSTRUCTIONAL OUTLINE WITH TEACHING HINTS

    I. Lamps—**Assignment: Read page 463**—See Transparency Master #51.
   II. Headlights—**Assignment: Read pages 463–476.**
      A. Sealed-Beam Headlights
      B. Halogen Headlights
      C. Composite Headlights
      D. HID Headlights
      E. Headlight Switches
      F. Dimmer Switches
         1. Flash-to-pass
         2. Automatic headlight dimmer
      G. Headlight Circuits—See Transparency Master #52
      H. Daytime Running Lights
      I. Concealed Headlights
      J. Automatic Light Systems
         1. Photocell sensor

        K. Headlight Replacement

        L. Headlight Adjustment

          Hint: Discuss automotive headlight systems and headlight adjustments in accordance with state laws.

   III. Interior Light Assemblies—**Assignment: Read pages 476–478.**

        A. Engine Compartment Light

        B. Glove Box Light

        C. Luggage Compartment Light

        D. Trunk Lid Light

        E. Vanity Lights

        F. Courtesy Lights

        G. Illuminated Entry System

   IV. Rear Exterior Light Assemblies—**Assignment: Read pages 478–487.**

        A. Turn, Stop, and Hazard Warning Light Systems

        B. Flashers

        C. Stop Light Switch

        D. Back-Up Lights

          Hint: Discuss lighting system components and functions.

   V. Light Bulbs—**Assignment: Read pages 487–489.**

        A. Other Bulbs

        B. Auxiliary Lights

        C. Driving and Passing Lights

        D. Fog Lights

   VI. Lighting Maintenance—**Assignment: Read pages 488–489.**

    Hint: Have students identify the various lighting systems found on their family vehicles.

ANSWERS TO REVIEW QUESTIONS

  1. The pull-out design, push-button design, and turn-signal-mounted rotary switch

  2. When the brake is used, when the turn signal is activated, when the hazards are used, or when the parking lights or headlights are on.

  3. Puts out a whiter light that improves visibility, and the lamps last longer and stay brighter

  4. Sealed beam

  5. Dielectric grease

  6. b

  7. d

  8. d

  9. a

10. a

11. Dimmer switch

12. a

13. a

14. c

15. a

16. b

17. c

18. c

19. To allow the bulb to be on some of the time and to allow for some illumination in the dark

20. HID

TECH MANUAL
The following procedures are included in Chapter 19 of the *Tech Manual.*

1. Checking a headlight switch.
2. Headlight aiming.
3. Adjusting or replacing a stop-light switch.

SHOP HINTS

- Demonstrate headlight adjustments required by state and/or federal laws.
- Have students remove all the bulbs on a shop car and catalog them.
- Demonstrate how to troubleshoot a lighting system using an electrical schematic.

TECH MANUAL ANSWERS

Review Questions

1. Turn signals, headlight flashers, headlight low/high beam control, windshield wipers and washer, horn
2. High-intensity discharge bulbs, sealed beams, halogen bulbs, composite bulbs
3. vibration
4. dim instrument lights, turn on interior light
5. c
6. c
7. True
8. Six total, one for each filament plus a common ground at each side
9. Two
10. b

ELECTRICAL INSTRUMENTS AND ACCESSORIES

CHAPTER 20

CHAPTER OVERVIEW

This chapter introduces the various gauges, warning devices, and comfort controls likely to be in an instrument cluster. Schematic diagrams are employed to aid students in understanding these electrical instruments and a broad range of accessories.

CHAPTER OBJECTIVES

- Know the purpose of the various designs of gauges and how they function.
- Describe the operation of the various gauges used in an instrument cluster.
- Describe the two types of instrument panel displays.
- Know the basic operation of electric windshield wiper and washer systems.
- Explain the operation of power door locks, power windows, and power seats.
- Determine how well the defroster system performs.
- Understand how cruise or speed control operates and the differences of various systems.
- Consider the use and value of engine cooling fans.

INSTRUCTIONAL OUTLINE WITH TEACHING HINTS

     I. Body Control Modules—**Assignment: Read pages 492–494.**
        A. Trouble codes
        B. Entering diagnostics
     II. Instrument Panels—**Assignment: Read pages 494–495**—See Transparency Master #53.
        A. Light-Emitting Diode
        B. Liquid Crystal Display
        C. Vacuum Florescent
     III. Instrument Gauges—**Assignment: Read pages 495–498.**
        A. IVR (Instrument Voltage Regulator)
        B. Magnetic Gauges
        C. Thermal or Bimetallic Gauge
            Hint: Discuss electrical/electronic instruments and gauges and how accuracy has improved.
     IV. Basic Information Gauges—**Assignment: Read pages 498–501.**
        A. Speedometer—See Transparency Master #54

  B. Odometer
  C. Other Gauges
   1. Oil pressure gauge
   2. Coolant temperature gauge
   3. Fuel level gauge—See Transparency Master #55
   4. Tachometer
   5. Charging gauges
 V. Indicators and Warning Devices—**Assignment: Read pages 501–505.**
  A. Air Bag Readiness Light
  B. Air Suspension Light
  C. Fasten Belts Indicator
  D. High-Beam Light
  E. Left and Right Turn Indicators
  F. Antilock Light
  G. Retractable Headlight
  H. Oil Temperature Warning Light
  I. Charge Indicator Light
  J. Oil Pressure Indicator Light
  K. Stop Light Warning Light
  L. Lamp-Out Warning Light
  M. Brake Warning Light
  N. Brake Fluid Level Warning Light
  O. Low Fuel Warning Light
  P. Check Engine Warning Light
  Q. Door Lock Indicator Light
  R. Door Ajar Warning Light
  S. Rear (or Front) Defrost Indicator Light
  T. Drive Indicator Light
  U. Sound Warning Devices
   Hint: Discuss various gauges, accessories, and warning devices.
  V. Diagnosis and Testing
   1. Fuses
   2. Indicator bulbs
   3. Detector switches (indicator systems)
   4. Sender units (gauge systems)
   5. IVR (gauge systems)
   6. Gauges (gauge systems)
  W. Driver Information Centers
  X. Steering Wheel Touch Controls
  Y. Head-up Display (HUD)
   Hint: Discuss typical warning indicators using Figure 20–19, page 503.
 VI. Electrical Accessories—**Assignment: Read pages 505–527.**
  A. Windshield Wiper/Washer Systems
   1. Permanent magnet motor circuits
   2. Electromagnetic field motor circuits
    a. Three-speed motors
   3. Intermittent wiper systems
   4. Windshield washers
   5. Windshield wiper linkage and blades
   6. Liftgate wiper/washer system

B. Wiper System Service
C. Washer System Service
   Hint: Discuss the "park" feature of wiper systems and how they work.
D. Power Door Lock Systems
E. Power Trunk Release
F. Power Windows
   1. Circuit operation (see pages 513–515).
G. Power Seats
   1. Power lumbar supports
   2. Heated seats
   3. Memory seats
   4. Adaptive seating
   5. Massaging seats
   6. Adjustable pedals
H. Power Mirror System
I. Rear- and Front-Window Defrosters and Heated Mirror System
J. Heated Windshields
K. Night Vision
L. Moon (Sun) Roof System
M. Horns/Clocks/Cigarette (Cigar) Lighter System
   1. Horn
   2. Clocks
   3. Cigarette lighter
N. Cruise (Speed) Control System
O. Electrical and Vacuum Circuits
P. Electronic Cruise Control Components
   1. Cruise control system service (see pages 526–527)

ANSWERS TO REVIEW QUESTIONS

1. Ammeter
2. Tachometer
3. Light-Emitting Diode (LED)
   Liquid Crystal Display (LCD)
   Vacuum Fluorescent
4. Vehicle Speed Sensor (VSS)
5. Potentiometer

6. a	11. a	16. d
7. a	12. c	17. d
8. c	13. c	18. d
9. d	14. c	19. a
10. a	15. c	20. d

TECH MANUAL
The following procedures are included in Chapter 20 of the *Tech Manual.*

1. Removing and replacing a temperature sensor.
2. Testing and repairing a rear-window defogger grid.
3. Performing a speed or cruise control simulated road test.

SHOP HINTS

■ Demonstrate as many of the above systems as possible on a shop car.
■ Have students use the shop manual or ETM for circuit information.

TECH MANUAL ANSWERS

Review Questions

1. False. Check another window first.
2. **a.** Cruise control switch, transducer, servo unit, two brake-activated switches
   b. vehicle speed transducer
   c. servo unit
   d. brake switch
3. d
4. **a.** magnetic gauges
   b. thermal gauges
5. True
6. The transducer senses vehicle speed and controls a vacuum source that operates the throttle servo.
7. The fuel gauge will always read full.
8. **a.** binding in wiper mechanical linkages
   b. faulty harness connections
   c. faulty motor assembly
9. **a.** non-resume
   b. resume
   c. electronic
10. insulated directional

SECTION 3

Answers to ASE Prep Test

1. d	6. d	11. c	16. b
2. c	7. d	12. b	17. a
3. d	8. d	13. b	18. b
4. a	9. a	14. a	19. a
5. d	10. b	15. b	20. c

IGNITION SYSTEMS

CHAPTER 21

CHAPTER OVERVIEW

This chapter explains the basic principles of ignition systems and describes their components and how they function. It compares several types of ignition systems and indicates the advantages of recent innovations.

CHAPTER OBJECTIVES

- Describe the three major functions of an ignition system.
- Name the operating conditions of an engine that affect ignition timing.
- Name the two major electrical circuits used in ignition systems and their common components.
- Describe the operation of ignition coils, spark plugs, and ignition cables.
- Explain how high voltage is induced in the coil secondary winding.
- Explain the basic operation of a computer-controlled ignition system.
- Explain how the fuel injection system may rely on components of the ignition system.
- Describe the various types of spark timing systems, including electronic switching systems and their related engine position sensors.
- Describe the operation of distributor-based ignition systems.
- Describe the operation of distributorless ignition systems.

INSTRUCTIONAL OUTLINE WITH TEACHING HINTS

   I. Ignition Timing—**Assignment: Read pages 534–535.**
      A. BTDC
      B. ATDC
      C. Engine RPM
      D. Engine Load
      E. Firing Order—See Transparency Master #56
        Hint: Discuss ignition system operation.
  II. Basic Circuitry—**Assignment: Read pages 535–539.**
      A. Primary Circuit Operation
      B. Secondary Circuit Operation
 III. Ignition Components—**Assignment: Read pages 539–542.**

    A. Ignition Coils—See Transparency Master #57
      1. Secondary voltage
    B. Spark Plugs
      1. Size
      2. Reach
      3. Heat range
      4. Spark plug air gap
    C. Ignition Cables
      Hint: Discuss ignition components and their functions.
  IV. Spark Timing Systems—**Assignment: Read pages 542–544.**
    A. Breaker Point Ignition
      1. Contact points
      2. Breaker plate
    B. Solid State Ignition—See Transparency Master #58
      1. Control module
    C. Computer-Controlled Ignition
      Hint: Discuss and compare different types of ignition systems.
  V. Electronic Switching Systems—**Assignment: Read pages 544–549.**
    A. Engine Position Sensors
    B. Magnetic Pulse Generator
    C. Metal Detection Sensors
    D. Hall-Effect Sensor
    E. Photoelectric Sensor
      Hint: Discuss various types of sensors.
    F. Timing Advance
      1. Centrifugal advance
      2. Vacuum advance
      3. Distributor
        Hint: Discuss the need for differences in ignition timing at different engine rpm and load.
  VI. Distributor Ignition System Operation—**Assignment: Read pages 549–554.**
    A. DI Systems with External Ignition Module
    B. DI Systems with Module on the Distributor
    C. DI Systems with Internal Ignition Module
    D. Computer-Controlled DI Systems
      1. Chrysler's dual pickup system
      2. Distributors with optical-type pickups
      3. GM's HEI with EST
      4. Honda's DI system with EST
      5. Ford's TFI-IV system
 VII. Electronic Ignition System Operation—**Assignment: Read pages 555–564.**
    A. Advantages
    B. EI System Operation

ANSWERS TO REVIEW QUESTIONS

  1. The pickup unit provides a magnetic field and the rotating timing disc provides the needed movement through the magnetic field to induce voltage. As the disc teeth approach the pickup coil, they repel the magnetic field, forcing it to concentrate around the pickup coil. Once the tooth passes by the pickup coil, the magnetic field is free to expand or unconcentrate until the next tooth on the disc approaches. Approaching teeth concentrate the magnetic lines of force, while passing teeth allow them to expand. This pulsation of the magnetic field causes the lines of magnetic force to cut across the winding in the pickup coil, inducing a small amount of AC voltage.

2. Dwell is the period of time in which current is flowing through the primary winding of a coil. The longer current is allowed to flow through the winding, the more saturated the coil will be. When a coil is fully saturated, it can provide a maximum amount of voltage.

3. Engine speed and engine load

4. Systems with a coil for every two spark plugs use the waste spark method of spark distribution. Each end of the coil's secondary winding is attached to a spark plug. When the magnetic field in the coil collapses, voltage is sent to both spark plugs. One plug will fire in the normal direction (positive center electrode to the negative side electrode) and the other plug fires from the side to the center electrode.

5. A magnetic pulse generator consists of a timing disc and a pickup coil. The timing disc may be mounted on the distributor shaft, at the rear of the crankshaft, or on the crankshaft damper. The pickup coil consists of a length of wire wound around a weak magnet.

6. c	11. b	16. c
7. d	12. b	17. d
8. c	13. c	18. b
9. c	14. a	19. c
10. b	15. b	20. c

SHOP HINTS

- Discuss and compare breaker point, solid state, and computer-controlled ignition systems.
- Demonstrate a metal detection sensor, Hall-effect sensor, and a photoelectric sensor.
- Demonstrate timing advance on an early HEI ignition system with vacuum and centrifugal advance and compare this to a later computer-controlled system.
- Demonstrate setting the timing on an early HEI system and on a later computer-controlled system.

CHAPTER 21/22 TECH MANUAL

Answers to Review Questions

1. A rich air/fuel mixture, low ignition coil output, and low engine compression
2. In the primary ignition circuit
3. The duration and voltage of the spark
4. Disconnect the computer controls so that base timing can be observed.
5. The engine will have a constant misfire.
6. False
7. b
8. c
9. b
10. a

IGNITION SYSTEM SERVICE

CHAPTER OVERVIEW

This chapter describes ignition system inspection and testing techniques. Included is how to use an oscilloscope to monitor various phases of ignition system performance. The testing procedures described can be demonstrated in the shop.

CHAPTER OBJECTIVES

- Perform a no-start diagnosis and determine the cause of the condition.
- Determine the cause of an engine misfire.
- Perform a visual inspection of ignition system components, primary wiring, and secondary wiring to locate obvious trouble areas.
- Describe what an oscilloscope is, its scales and operating modes, and how it is used in ignition system troubleshooting.
- Test the components of the primary and secondary ignition circuits.
- Test individual ignition components using test equipment such as a voltmeter, ohmmeter, and test light.
- Service and install spark plugs.
- Describe the effects of incorrect ignition timing.
- Check and set (when possible) ignition timing.
- Diagnose engine misfiring on EI-equipped engines.

INSTRUCTIONAL OUTLINE WITH TEACHING HINTS

 I. Combustion—**Assignment: Read pages 567–568.**
    A. Detonation
 II. General Ignition System Diagnosis—**Assignment: Read pages 568–569.**
 III. Visual Inspection of Ignition Systems—**Assignment: Read pages 569–573.**
    A. Primary Circuit
    B. Ground Circuits
    C. Electromagnetic Interference
    D. Timing Advance Mechanisms
    E. Sensors
    F. Breaker Points
    G. Control Modules

H. Secondary Circuit

I. Distributor Cap and Rotor—See Transparency Master #59

IV. No-Start Diagnosis—**Assignment: Read pages 573–575.**

A. No-Start Diagnosis of EI Systems

V. General Testing—**Assignment: Read pages 575–577.**

A. Diagnosing with an Engine Analyzer

B. Cylinder Performance Test

C. Ignition Performance Tests

D. Battery, Starting, and Charging System Tests

E. Emission Level Analysis

VI. Testing with a Scope—**Assignment: Read pages 577–584.**

A. Scales—See Transparency Master #60

B. Pattern Phases

C. Pattern Display Modes

1. Raster

2. Superimposed

D. Understanding Single Cylinder Patterns

1. Firing line

2. Spark line

3. Intermediate section

4. Dwell section

E. Coil Output Test

F. Spark Duration Testing

G. Spark Plug Firing Voltage

1. Under load

Hint: Discuss firing line diagnosis and troubleshooting spark plugs.

H. Coil Condition

I. Primary Circuit Checks

J. Stress Testing Components

1. Cold testing

2. Heat testing

3. Moisture testing

VII. Effects of Improper Timing—**Assignment: Read pages 584–585.**

VIII. Setting Ignition Timing—**Assignment: Read pages 585–587.**

A. Base Timing

B. Crank/Cam Sensors

C. Checking Mechanical Advance Units

IX. DI and EI Systems—**Assignment: Read pages 587–588.**

A. DI Systems

B. EI Systems

X. Primary Circuit Components—**Assignment: Read pages 588–594.**

A. Testing with a Soldering Gun

B. Using a DMM

C. Ignition Switch

D. Primary Resistor

E. Ignition Coil Resistance

F. Pickup Coil

G. Hall-Effect Sensors

H. Using a Logic Probe

I. Using a Lab Scope

J. Using Special Equipment

ANSWERS TO REVIEW QUESTIONS

1. Cold testing, heat testing, and moisture testing; cold testing and heat testing involve directing cold or heat onto components and watching for signs of malfunction on a tester or scope. Likewise, moisture testing involves lightly spraying components and watching for malfunctions.

2. Base timing is normally checked and adjusted at idle speed or low engine speeds when the mechanical advance system will not be in operation. In order to disable the vacuum advance unit, the vacuum hose to the advance unit is simply removed and plugged. On engines with computer-controlled ignition timing, the computer must be disconnected from the distributor. Disconnecting a connector as described in the service manual typically does this.

3. The three types of pattern display modes used on an oscilloscope are the display or parade pattern, the raster pattern, and the superimposed pattern. The parade pattern allows for easy comparison of the voltage peaks from one cylinder to another. The raster pattern allows for a quick comparison of the timing of events in the ignition circuit. The superimposed pattern allows for the identification of a cylinder whose pattern is different than that of the other cylinders.

4. A rich air/fuel mixture or an ignition fault causes cold fouling. Gasoline or oil on the plug causes wet fouling. The plug is wet with gasoline if it is not firing. If the plug is wet with oil, a problem with the valve guides or piston rings is normally indicated.

5. Most Hall-effect sensors can be tested by connecting a 12-volt battery across the plus (+) and minus (–) voltage terminals of the Hall layer, and a voltmeter across the minus (–) and signal voltage terminals. With the voltmeter hooked up, insert a steel feeler gauge or knife blade between the Hall layer and the magnet. If the sensor is good, the voltmeter should read within 0.5 volt of battery voltage when the feeler gauge or knife blade is inserted and touching the magnet. When the feeler gauge or blade is removed, the voltage should read less than 0.5 volt.

   A Hall-effect switch is also easily checked with a logic probe. If the switch has three wires, probe the outer two wires with the ignition on. The red light should come on when one of the wires is probed and the green light should come on when the other wire is probed. If the red light does not turn on at either wire, check the power feed circuit to the sensor. If the green light does not come on, check the sensor's ground circuit. Back probe the center wire and crank the engine. All three lights should flash as the engine is cranked. The red light will come on when the sensor's output is above 10 volts. As this signal drops below 4 volts, the green light should come on. The yellow light will flash each time the voltage changes from high to low. If the logic probe's lights do not respond in this way, check the wiring at the sensor. If the wiring is okay, replace the sensor.

   A Hall-effect sensor can also be tested with a lab scope. Digital waves should be seen on the scope. All pulses should be identical in spacing, shape, and amplitude.

6. b	**11.** d	**16.** c
7. c	**12.** c	**17.** a
8. b	**13.** c	**18.** c
9. b	**14.** c	**19.** b
10. c	**15.** c	**20.** a

TECH MANUAL
The following procedures are included in Chapter 21/22 of the *Tech Manual.*

1. Setting ignition timing.
2. Testing individual components.
3. Scope testing an ignition system.
4. Visually inspecting an EI system.
5. Testing an ignition coil.

SHOP HINTS

- Demonstrate how to conduct a complete visual inspection of an ignition system.
- Discuss open circuit precautions.
- Perform *Installing and Timing the Distributor* on pages 865–866.
- Perform Procedures on page 872.
- Demonstrate the advantages of individual component testing in ignition systems.
- Discuss *Using Service Manuals* on page 856.
- Discuss Table 22–1.

FUEL SYSTEMS

CHAPTER OVERVIEW

This chapter focuses on the fuel transport system. It offers a knowledge of petroleum-based fuels, alternative fuels, and electrical power sources, as well as mechanical and electrical fuel pump operation and circuitry.

CHAPTER OBJECTIVES

- Describe the four performance characteristics of gasoline.
- Describe the various types of gasoline and additives.
- Describe the different alternative fuels, including diesel.
- Define the fuel delivery system components and their functions, including the fuel tank, fuel lines, filters, and pump.
- Describe the different fuel filter designs and mountings.
- Explain the operation of a mechanical fuel pump.
- Describe the operation of an electric fuel pump, including the operation of the relief valve and check valve.
- Describe the purpose of the inertia switch in a fuel pump circuit.
- Explain the purpose of the oil pressure switch that is connected in parallel with some fuel pump relays.

INSTRUCTIONAL OUTLINE WITH TEACHING HINTS

   I. Gasoline—**Assignment: Read page 611**—See Transparency Master #61.
  II. Fuel Performance—**Assignment: Read pages 611–613.**
     A. Antiknock Quality
       1. MON
       2. RON
     B. Lean Fuel Mixture
     C. Ignition Timing Overlap
     D. Compression Ratio
     E. Valve Timing
     F. Turbocharging
     G. Coolant Temperature
     H. Cylinder to Cylinder Distribution

I. Excessive Carbon Deposits
J. Air Inlet Temperature
K. Combustion Chamber Shape
L. Octane Number
M. Volatility
    1. Cold starting and warm-up
    2. Temperature
    3. Altitude
    4. Carburetor icing protection
    5. Crankcase oil dilution
    6. Driveability
N. Sulfur Content
O. Deposit Control
    Hint: Discuss gasoline and how its composition has been influenced over the years by environmental and performance issues.

III. Basic Fuel Additives—**Assignment: Read pages 613–614.**
A. Anti-Icing or Deicer
B. Metal Deactivators and Rust Inhibitors
C. Gum or Oxidation Inhibitors
D. Detergents
E. Ethanol
F. Methanol
    1. MTBE

IV. Alternative Fuels—**Assignment: Read pages 614–618.**
A. Diesel Fuel
B. LP-Gas
C. Compressed Natural Gas
D. Electric Vehicles
E. Hybrid Electric Vehicles
F. Fuel Cells—See Transparency Master #62
    Hint: Discuss the viability of alternative fuels, electric vehicles, and how the market will drive the issue.

V. Fuel Delivery System—**Assignment: Read pages 618–629.**
A. Fuel Tanks
B. Fuel Lines and Fittings
C. Fuel Filters
D. Mechanical Fuel Pumps
E. Electric Fuel Pumps—See Transparency Master #63
F. Electric Fuel Pump Circuits
    1. Oil pressure switch
    2. ASD relay
    3. Circuit opening relay
        Hint: Discuss and compare various types of fuel and fuel delivery systems.

ANSWERS TO REVIEW QUESTIONS

1. Cetane rating
2. Compressed natural gas (CNG) and liquefied natural gas (LNG)
3. Fuel tanks, fuel lines, fuel filters, and fuel pumps
4. In-tank, in-carburetor, in-line, out-of-pump
5. Diaphragm, plunger, bellows, and impeller or rotary

6. When the carburetor float bowl has the proper level of fuel, the float movement closes the inlet needle and seat. This needle and seat action causes pressure to build up in the fuel line, filter, and fuel pump diaphragm chamber. This increase in fuel pressure forces the diaphragm upward against the spring tension, and the pin on the lower end of the pull rod is moved upward away from the rocker arm. Under this condition, the rocker arm continues to move up and down, but the rocker arm no longer moves the pull rod. This diaphragm and pull rod action limits the fuel pump pressure. The pull rod seal prevents crankcase oil from entering the diaphragm area of the pump.

7. Fuel moves from the discharge port through the inside of the pump's motor and out the check valve and outlet connection, which is connected via the fuel line to the fuel filter and underhood fuel system components. A pressure relief valve near the check valve opens if the fuel supply line is restricted and pump pressure becomes very high. When the relief valve opens, fuel is returned through this valve to the pump inlet. This action protects fuel system components from high fuel pressure. Each time the engine is shut off, the check valve prevents fuel from draining out of the underhood fuel system components into the fuel tank.

8. a	**13.** a	**18.** a
9. a	**14.** c	**19.** a
10. c	**15.** c	**20.** c
11. b	**16.** c	
12. d	**17.** d	

TECH MANUAL
The following procedures are included in Chapter 23 of the *Tech Manual.*

1. Testing fuel pump pressure.
2. Removing and replacing a fuel filter.

SHOP HINTS

- Demonstrate fuel pump pressures on a fuel injection and carburetor type vehicle and discuss the differences.
- Arrange for an electric vehicle demonstration either at a dealership or in your shop.
- Demonstrate how the fuel pump relay operates on a fuel injected car.

CHAPTER 23/24 TECH MANUAL

Answers to Review Questions

1. True
2. b
3. Lean, rich
4. Incorrect fuel pump pressure or low fuel volume delivered
5. b
6. a
7. A rollover check valve prevents fuel leaks from the fuel tank vent and feed lines in the event of a vehicle rollover.
8. Load increases, pressure increases
9. c
10. c

FUEL SYSTEM DIAGNOSIS AND SERVICE

CHAPTER
24

CHAPTER OVERVIEW

This chapter focuses on the fuel transport system in terms of diagnosis and repair. Inspecting, testing, and replacing fuel tanks, lines, filters, and pumps will be covered, as well as diagnosing fuel delivery problems.

CHAPTER OBJECTIVES

- Conduct a visual inspection of a fuel system.
- Test alcohol content in the fuel.
- Relieve fuel system pressure.
- Inspect and service fuel tanks.
- Remove, inspect, service, and replace electric fuel pumps and gauge sending units.
- Inspect and service fuel lines and tubing.
- Remove and replace fuel filters.
- Conduct a pressure and volume output test on a mechanical and an electric fuel pump.
- Service and test mechanical fuel pumps.
- Service and test electric fuel pumps.

INSTRUCTIONAL OUTLINE WITH TEACHING HINTS

    I. Alcohol-in-Fuel Test—**Assignment: Read pages 632–633**—See Transparency Master #64.

    II. Fuel System Pressure Relief—**Assignment: Read pages 633–634.**

    III. Fuel Tanks—**Assignment: Read pages 634–636.**
        A. Fuel Tank Draining
        B. Fuel Tank Service—See Transparency Master #65

    IV. Fuel Lines—**Assignment: Read pages 636–640.**
        A. Fittings
            1. Compression flare
            2. Double flare

    V. Fuel Filters—**Assignment: Read pages 640–641.**
        A. Servicing Filters

    VI. Fuel Pumps—**Assignment: Read pages 641–649.**

A. Mechanical Fuel Pumps
  1. Pressure tests
  2. Volume or capacity tests
  3. Replacement
B. Electrical Fuel Pumps
  1. Troubleshooting
     a. Pressure tests
  2. No-start diagnosis
  3. Replacement—See Transparency Master #66
  4. Removal and replacement
  5. Fuel tank removal
  6. Fuel pump inlet filter

ANSWERS TO REVIEW QUESTIONS

1. volume
2. engine speed
3. d
4. Class B
5. Battery
6. To control the rate of vapor flow from the fuel tank to the vapor storage tank
7. Lean, rich

8. c	13. c	18. c
9. c	14. c	19. c
10. b	15. b	20. a
11. a	16. d	
12. a	17. c	

TECH MANUAL
The following procedures are included in Chapter 24 of the *Tech Manual.*

1. Relieving fuel system pressure.
2. Testing fuel pump pressure on an EFI engine.

SHOP HINTS

- Demonstrate how a defective oil pressure switch will affect engine operation on fuel injected cars.
- Demonstrate removal and replacement of various fuel filters.
- Demonstrate electric fuel pump pressure troubleshooting procedures.
- Demonstrate the proper way to handle gasoline removal and filling when removing fuel lines, pumps, and tanks.

CARBURETORS

CHAPTER 25

CHAPTER OVERVIEW

This chapter covers the basic functioning of today's feedback carburetors and their many parts in great detail. Basic computer controls are also discussed.

CHAPTER OBJECTIVES

- Describe the basic principles of carburetion.
- Explain the purpose and operation of the different carburetor circuits.
- Describe the various auxiliary carburetor controls.
- Describe the different types of carburetors.
- Define open loop and closed loop in relation to computer-controlled carburetor systems.
- Explain the term duty cycle as it relates to an oxygen feedback solenoid.
- Describe the operation of the idle speed control motor on a computer-controlled carburetor system.

INSTRUCTIONAL OUTLINE WITH TEACHING HINTS

   I. Basic Carburetor Design—**Assignment: Read pages 652–654**—See Transparency Master #67.
      A. Carburetion—See Transparency Master #68
         1. Metering
            a. Stoichiometric ratio
               (1) Lean
               (2) Rich
         2. Atomization
   II. Basic Carburetor Circuits—**Assignment: Read page 654.**
      A. Float
      B. Idle
      C. Main Metering
      D. Power
      E. Accelerator Pump
      F. Choke

III. Carburetor Systems—**Assignment: Read pages 654–655.**
   A. Choke Qualifier
   B. Dashpot
   C. Hot-Idle Compensator (HIC) Valve
   D. Vacuum Break
   E. Choke Unloader
   F. Throttle Position Solenoid
IV. Types of Carburetors—**Assignment: Read pages 655–656.**
   A. Carburetor Barrels
     1. Two
     2. Four
       a. Single stage
       b. Primary stage
       c. Secondary stage
   B. Variable Venturi Carburetor
    Hint: Discuss why the carburetor has so many different circuits and how manifold vacuum (load) and/or temperature affects each one.
V. Feedback Carburetor Systems—**Assignment: Read pages 656–659**—See Transparency Master #69.
   A. Open Loop
   B. Closed Loop
   C. Mixture Control Solenoids
   D. Duty Cycle
   E. Idle System Air/Fuel Ratio Control
   F. Air Control Solenoid Systems
    Hint: Discuss and compare various carburetor types.
VI. Electronic Idle Speed Control—**Assignment: Read pages 659–661.**
   A. Throttle Kicker and Idle Stop Solenoid
   B. Vacuum-Operated Throttle Kicker
   C. Temperature Compensated Pump
   D. Variable Voltage Choke Relay

ANSWERS TO REVIEW QUESTIONS

1. Venturi
2. Metering, atomization, and vaporization
3. Venturi vacuum is created by the airflow through the venturi. This vacuum increases in relation to engine speed. Remember that an increase in vacuum is a decrease in pressure. Manifold vacuum is created as the downward piston movement on the intake strokes attempts to pull air past the restriction of the throttle. Manifold vacuum is highest with the throttle closed at idle and on deceleration. When the throttle is opened, manifold vacuum decreases. This vacuum is lowest at wide-open throttle.
4. Totally closed
5. The dashpot is used during rapid deceleration to retard the closing of the throttle. This allows a smooth transition from the main metering system to the idle system and prevents stalling due to the overly rich air/fuel mixture. It also controls the level of HC in the exhaust during deceleration.
6. A throttle position solenoid is used to control the position of the throttle plate. It can have several functions, depending on its application. When the basic function is to prevent dieseling, the solenoid is called a throttle stop solenoid or an idle stop solenoid.

When the engine is started, the solenoid is energized and touches the throttle plates open slightly to the curb idle position. When the ignition switch is turned off, the solenoid allows the throttle plate to close completely, and shuts off the air/fuel supply to prevent dieseling or run-on. The throttle position solenoid is also used to increase the curb idle speed to compensate for extra loads on the engine. When this is its primary function, the solenoid might also be called an idle speed-up solenoid or a throttle kicker. This feature is most often used on cars with air conditioners.

7. TP sensor, MAP, CTS, and air conditioning, power steering, and transmission switches
8. When the PCM ignores the signals from the oxygen sensor and does not regulate the ratio of fuel to air, the carburetor is functioning in a conventional manner and is said to be operating in open loop. The carburetor operates in open loop until the oxygen sensor reaches a certain temperature. The carburetor also goes into open loop when a richer than normal air/fuel mixture is required, such as during warm-up and heavy throttle application.
9. Before the computer will go into closed loop, the oxygen sensor's and engine's temperature must reach a minimum point. Whenever the computer is in closed loop, the oxygen sensor is constantly monitoring the oxygen in the exhaust, and the PCM is constantly making adjustments to the air/fuel mixture based on the fluctuations in the sensor's voltage output.
10. The throttle kicker maintains engine idle speed when the engine accessory load is increased, such as during A/C compressor clutch operation. This kicker also maintains idle speed during warm-up, after the fast idle cam has dropped away from the fast idle screw.
11. Oxygen sensor
12. a
13. c
14. a
15. c
16. b
17. a
18. c
19. b
20. c

TECH MANUAL

The following procedure is included in Chapter 25 of the *Tech Manual.*

1. Visually inspecting a carburetor.

SHOP HINTS

- Demonstrate the low pressure effect of moving air; show that a low pressure air flow will draw a liquid out of a small diameter hose. For example, place a small diameter, clear plastic hose in a bucket of water. (Some food coloring will make this demonstration more effective.) Direct the air stream from a spray nozzle over the end of the tubing. (Holding the air nozzle close to and parallel with the tubing will help). Water from the bucket will be drawn up and out of the tubing. Wear goggles and direct the spray away from personnel.
- Discuss when it is necessary to prime the fuel system and how this should be done.
- Demonstrate the proper shop procedure for laying out and keeping track of small parts that have been removed.

- Demonstrate the proper procedure for cleaning small parts such as carburetor parts that have been removed from the vehicle.
- Demonstrate poor or no idle by pulling the mixture control solenoid fuse.

CHAPTER 25/26 TECH MANUAL

Answers to Review Questions

1. Back it out
2. 4- or 5-gas exhaust analyzer
3. Throttle position and vacuum
4. a. choke not opening completely
   b. engine and/or carburetor flooded
   c. leaking float bowl
   d. fuel percolation
5. Check service manual.
6. Check service manual.
7. On the emissions decal under the hood
8. For dump valves with two vacuum fittings, disconnect and plug the hoses; for dump valves with a single fitting, disconnect the line at the valve and plug it. Connect a slave hose from the dump valve vacuum fitting to the intake manifold vacuum fitting; correct idle mixture limiter if it is not set to maximum rich position; check, and if needed, reset the engine's curb idle speed; with the transmission in neutral, run the engine at approximately 2500 rpm for 15 seconds before each mixture check; with the engine at normal operating temperature, place the transmission into the position specified by the service manual.
9. The feedback system tries to maintain a stoichiometric mixture during all operational phases of the engine.
10. Idle the engine at normal operating speed; place the fast-idle lever on the specified step of the fast-idle cam; disconnect the EGR if necessary, be sure the high cam speed positioner lever is disengaged.

CARBURETOR DIAGNOSIS AND SERVICE

CHAPTER 26

CHAPTER OVERVIEW

This chapter describes how to diagnose and repair various carburetor problems. Also covered is how to replace, test, and adjust older and late-model carburetors. Special attention is given to electronic control diagnosis as well as service procedures.

CHAPTER OBJECTIVES

- Recognize carburetor-related performance problems.
- Remove and replace carburetors.
- Explain how various carburetor adjustments are made.
- Diagnose carburetor feedback problems
- Adjust idle speed and mixture on carburetors with those provisions.
- Perform a fast idle speed check.
- Perform a computer-controlled carburetor system performance test.
- Diagnose the results of a computer-controlled carburetor system performance test.
- Test and service mixture control solenoids.

INSTRUCTIONAL OUTLINE WITH TEACHING HINTS

I. Carburetor Diagnosis—**Assignment: Read pages 664–668.**
   A. O$_2$ Levels
   B. Engine Idle Speed Check—See Transparency Master #70
   C. Fast Idle Speed Check
   D. Idle Mixture Adjustment
      1. Idle Adjustment Using Propane Enrichment Method
   E. Choke Adjustments
   F. Choke Pull-Down Adjustments
   G. Checking the Accelerator Pump
   H. Throttle Position Sensors
II. Electronic Control Diagnostics—**Assignment: Read pages 668–673.**
   A. Visual Inspections
      1. Air filter
      2. PCV
      3. EVAP

        4. Battery
        5. Vacuum systems
        6. Sensors and actuators
    B. General Motors' CCC System—See Transparency Master #71
        1. Dwell stays below 10 degrees
        2. Dwell stays above 50 degrees
        3. Dwell is fixed between 10 and 50 degrees
        4. MC solenoid service
        5. Mixture control solenoid adjustments
    C. Ford Electronic Feedback Systems
    D. Chrysler Feedback Systems
  III. Carburetor Service—**Assignment: Read pages 673–674.**

ANSWERS TO REVIEW QUESTIONS

1. At idle speeds, the O_2 level should be between 1 and 4%. If the oxygen level is greater than that, a lean mixture or ignition problem is evident. If the readings are below 1%, the mixture is too rich.

2. The O_2 sensor will read a lean mixture and the PCM will respond by enriching the mixture. Also, if there is an intake manifold vacuum leak, the PCM senses the increase in manifold pressure caused by the vacuum leak. Under this condition, the PCM supplies more fuel and the idle speed increases.

3. The service procedures given by the manufacturer must be followed. These will contain the proper way to keep the system in open loop. When the system is kept in open loop, the computer is not controlling the idle speed. Often a connector must be disconnected at the carburetor to prevent the system from going into closed loop.

4. A choke can cause an overly lean mixture if it is stuck open and the engine is cold and cranking. If the choke is stuck closed, there will be a restriction of airflow, both during cranking and while the engine is running. If the choke is stuck closed and the engine is started while it is cold, there will be little affect on engine operation. However, if the choke is stuck closed while the engine is warm, the engine will run excessively rich.

5. The TP sensor must work properly and be adjusted correctly. An improperly adjusted TP sensor can cause idle problems, incorrect air/fuel mixtures, and possibly delay or prevent the PCM's switching to closed loop from open loop.

6. An O_2 sensor can be checked with a scan tool, voltmeter, or lab scope to make sure it is working correctly. This should be done whether or not a DTC suggested a problem with the O_2 sensor. Remember, the sensor can be lazy or biased and still not trigger a DTC in the computer's memory. The preferred way to check an O_2 sensor is with a lab scope. A dual trace will allow you to observe the switching of the O_2 while watching the activity of the PCM in response to the O_2 sensor's signals.

7. A contaminated oxygen sensor may provide a continually high voltage reading because the oxygen in the exhaust stream does not contact the sensor.

8. a

9. When engine vacuum is low, a heavy load is indicated and the engine requires a richer mixture. When the vacuum is high, the engine needs a leaner mixture.

10. b

11. a

12. c

13. The duty cycle of the MC solenoid can be measured with a dwell meter or a DMM with a duty cycle feature. Duty cycle is the same measurement as dwell except it is stated in percentages of on-time. Duty cycle readings can be converted to dwell degree readings.
14. The duty cycle will be decreased.
15. c
16. b
17. c
18. b
19. c
20. a

TECH MANUAL
The following procedure is included in Chapter 26 of the *Tech Manual*.

1. Checking the operation of an MC solenoid.

SHOP HINTS

- Demonstrate how to remove and replace carburetors.
- Demonstrate how various carburetor adjustments are made.
- Demonstrate how to test and diagnose carburetor feedback problems.
- Demonstrate how to test and diagnose a computer-controlled carburetor system performance test.
- Demonstrate how to test and service mixture control solenoids.

ELECTRONIC FUEL INJECTION

CHAPTER OVERVIEW

This chapter describes the advantages of fuel injection over carburetion. It discusses the various types of fuel injection systems in use today and how they are designed and operate.

CHAPTER OBJECTIVES

- Explain the differences in point of injection in throttle body or port injection systems.
- Describe the difference between a sequential fuel injection (SFI) system and a multiport fuel injection (MFI) system.
- Explain the design and function of major EFI components.
- Explain the design and function of CIS-E components.
- Describe the inputs used by the computer to control the idle air control and idle air control by-pass air motors.
- Describe how the computer supplies the correct air/fuel ratio on a throttle body injection (TBI) system.
- Explain how the clear flood mode operates on a TBI system.
- Explain why manifold vacuum is connected to the pressure regulator in an MFI system.
- Describe the operation of the pressure regulator in a returnless EFI system.
- Describe the operation of the central injector and poppet nozzles in a central port injection (CPI) system.

INSTRUCTIONAL OUTLINE WITH TEACHING HINTS

I. Types of Fuel Injection—**Assignment: Read page 678**—See Transparency Master #72.
   A. EFI
      1. TBI
      2. CPI and CMFI
      3. PFI
      4. GDI
      5. CIS-E
II. Continuous Injection Systems—**Assignment: Read pages 678–680.**
   A. Basic Operation
      1. Fuel delivery system
      2. Fuel injectors

III. Basic EFI—**Assignment: Read pages 680–683.**
   A. Powertrain Control Module
   B. Fuel Injectors
   C. Idle Speed Control
IV. Throttle Body Fuel Injection—**Assignment: Read pages 683–685.**
   A. TBI Advantages
   B. Injectors
   C. Throttle Body Internal Design and Operation
   D. Injector Internal Design and Electrical Connections
      1. Pulse width
   E. Air/Fuel Ratio Enrichment
V. Port Fuel Injection—**Assignment: Read pages 685–691.**
   A. Port Firing Control
   B. Port Fuel Injection System Design
      1. Cold start injector—See Transparency Master #73
      2. Pressure regulators
   C. Sequential Fuel Injection Systems
   D. Typical Sequential Fuel Injection Systems
      1. Returnless fuel system pressure regulators
      2. Typical import sequential fuel injection system
VI. Central Multi-Port Fuel Injection (CMFI)—**Assignment: Read pages 691–693.**
   A. Pressure Regulator
   B. Injector Design and Operation
   C. Poppet Nozzles
VII. Gasoline Direct-Injection Systems—**Assignment: Read pages 693–694.**
   Hint: Pass around various injectors and discuss the advantages and disadvantages of each type of fuel injection system.
VIII. Input Sensors—**Assignment: Read pages 694–696.**
   A. Airflow Sensors
      1. Volume airflow sensor
      2. Karman vortex
   B. Air Temperature Sensor
   C. Mass Airflow Sensor
   D. Manifold Absolute Pressure Sensor
IX. Other EFI System Sensors—**Assignment: Read pages 696–697.**
   A. Coolant Temperature
   B. Throttle Position
   C. Engine Speed
   D. Cranking Enrichment
   E. Altitude Compensation
   F. Coasting Shutoff
   G. Additional Input Information Sensors
      1. Detonation
      2. Crankshaft position
      3. Camshaft position
      4. Air charge temperature
      5. Air conditioner operation
      6. Gearshift lever position
      7. Battery voltage
      8. Vehicle speed
      9. Oxygen in exhaust gases
     10. EGR valve position

ANSWERS TO REVIEW QUESTIONS

1. In a throttle body injection system, fuel is delivered to a central point. In the port injection system, there is one injector at each cylinder. Central multi-port is a mixture of both throttle-body and port injection.

2. SFI systems control each injector individually so that it is opened just before the intake valve opens. This means that the mixture is never static in the intake manifold and that adjustments to the mixture can be made almost instantaneously between the firing of one injector and the next. Sequential firing is the most accurate and desirable method of regulating port injection.

3. In a speed density EFI system, the computer uses the MAP or MAF and engine rpm inputs to calculate the amount of air entering the engine. The computer then calculates the required amount of fuel to go with the air entering the engine. The TP sensor's signal is used by the PCM to note the current operating condition.

4. The engine coolant temperature sensor signals the PCM when the engine needs cold enrichment, as it does during warm-up. This adds to the base pulse, but decreases to zero as the engine warms up.

5. The air/fuel ratio on an EFI engine is most often controlled by the PCM's control of injector pulse width.

6. The MAP sensor measures changes in the intake manifold pressure that result from changes in engine load and speed. The pressure measured by the MAP sensor is the difference between barometric pressure and manifold pressure. At closed throttle, the engine produces a low MAP value. A wide-open throttle produces a high value. This high value is produced when the pressure inside the manifold is the same as the pressure outside the manifold, and 100% of the outside air is being measured. This MAP output is the opposite of what is measured on a vacuum gauge. The use of this sensor also allows the control computer to adjust automatically for different altitudes.

7. A central multi-port injection system has one central injector and a poppet nozzle in each intake port. The central injector is operated by the PCM, and the poppet nozzles are operated by fuel pressure. This system is actually a combination of TBI and PFI systems.

8. higher
9. fuel vaporization
10. richer
11. pulse width
12. MAP or MAF and engine speed
13. fuel vaporization
14. richer
15. lower
16. b
17. d
18. b
19. a
20. b

TECH MANUAL
The following procedure is included in Chapter 27 of the *Tech Manual.*

1. Visually inspecting an EFI system.

SHOP HINTS

- Demonstrate what happens when one injector on a TBI system is disconnected.
- Demonstrate the effects of a manifold vacuum leak at the pressure regulator in an MFI system.
- Demonstrate the spray patterns of a good and bad fuel injector using water.

CHAPTER 27/28 TECH MANUAL

Answers to Review Questions

1. Speed density and mass airflow
2. 1. Check fuel system for leaks.
   2. Check the state of charge of the battery.
   3. Check all wiring and connectors.
   4. Check coolant level.
   5. Check ignition system.
   6. Check air cleaner and filter.
   7. Check fuel system pressure.
   8. Check fuel lines for restrictions.
   9. Check vacuum lines for leaks and restrictions.
3. Faulty MAP sensor, poor seal to manifold, faulty fuel pressure regulator
4. Between the fuel filter and the throttle body
5. To isolate a clogged or electrically defective injector
6. a
7. Rough idle, stalling, or slow acceleration
8. False
9. b
10. c

FUEL INJECTION SYSTEM DIAGNOSIS AND SERVICE

CHAPTER 28

CHAPTER OVERVIEW

This chapter describes the testing, diagnosis, and repair of fuel injection systems and TBI, MFI, and SFI injector testing and service.

CHAPTER OBJECTIVES

- Perform a preliminary diagnostic procedure on a fuel injection system.
- Remove, clean, inspect, and install throttle body assemblies.
- Explain the results of incorrect fuel pressure in a TBI, MFI, or SFI system.
- Perform an injector balance test and determine the injector condition.
- Clean injectors on an MFI or SFI system.
- Perform an injector sound, ohmmeter, noid light, and scope test.
- Perform an injector flow test and determine injector condition.
- Perform an injector leakage test.
- Remove and replace the fuel rail, injectors, and pressure regulator.
- Diagnose causes of improper idle speed on vehicles with fuel injection.

INSTRUCTIONAL OUTLINE WITH TEACHING HINTS

    I. Preliminary Checks—**Assignment: Read pages 700–702**—See Transparency Master #74.
- A. Battery
- B. Charging System
- C. Fuses and Fusible Links
- D. Wiring
- E. Vacuum Lines
- F. PCV
- G. Emission Control Systems
- H. Coolant/Antifreeze
- I. Secondary Ignition
- J. Base Timing
- K. Engine Condition
- L. Gasoline Quality
- M. EFI System Component Checks

1. Adequate air supply
2. Adequate fuel pressure
3. Injector firing signal

II. Service Precautions—**Assignment: Read page 702.**

III. Basic EFI System Checks—**Assignment: Read pages 702–720.**
   A. Oxygen Sensor Diagnosis
      1. Block integrator
      2. Block learn
   B. Air Induction System Checks
   C. Air Flow Sensors
   D. Throttle Body
      1. Throttle body inspection
      2. Throttle body removal and cleaning
   E. Fuel System Checks
      1. Fuel delivery
   F. Injector Checks
      1. Checking voltage signals—See Transparency Master #75
      2. Injector balance test
      3. Injector sound test
      4. Injector flow testing—See Transparency Master #76
      5. Oscilloscope checks
         a. Peak and hold injector
         b. Pulse modulated injector
   G. Injector Service
      1. Injector cleaning
   H. Fuel Rail, Injector, and Regulator Service
      1. Injector replacement
      2. Fuel rail, injector, and pressure regulator removal
      3. Cold start injector removal and testing
   I. Idle Speed Checks
      1. Idle contact switch test
      2. Scan tester diagnosis
      3. IAC by-pass air motor and valve diagnosis
      4. IAC by-pass air motor removal and cleaning
      5. IAC BPA motor diagnosis and installation
      6. Diagnosis of fast idle thermo valve
      7. Diagnosis of starting air valve

IV. CIS Checks and Tests—**Assignment: Read pages 720–721.**

ANSWERS TO REVIEW QUESTIONS

1. In any electronic throttle body or port injection system, three things must occur for the system to operate: an adequate air supply must be supplied for the air/fuel mixture, a pressurized fuel supply must be delivered to properly operating injectors, and the injectors must receive a trigger signal from the control computer, which must first receive an rpm signal from the ignition.

2. Trouble codes only indicate the particular circuit in which a problem has been detected. They do not pinpoint individual components. So if a code indicates a defective lambda or oxygen sensor, the problem could be the sensor itself, the wiring to it, or its con-

nector. Trouble codes are not a signal to replace components. They signal that a more thorough diagnosis is needed in that area.

3. An O_2 sensor can be checked with a voltmeter. Connect it between the O_2 sensor wire and ground. The sensor's voltage should be cycling from low voltage to high voltage. The signal from most O_2 sensors varies between 0 and 1 volt. If the voltage is continually high, the air/fuel ratio may be rich or the sensor may be contaminated. When the O_2 sensor voltage is continually low, the air/fuel ratio may be lean, the sensor may be defective, or the wire between the sensor and the computer may have a high-resistance problem. If the O_2 sensor voltage signal remains in a mid-range position, the computer may be in open loop or the sensor may be defective.

4. Block Integrator represents a short-term correction to the amount of fuel delivered during closed loop. Block Learn makes long-term corrections. Injector pulse width is adjusted according to both Block Integrator and Block Learn. Block Integrator and Block Learn are also known as short-term fuel trim and long-term fuel trim, or adaptive memory and additive fuel factor.

5. If the block integrator, or block learn, numbers are considerably below 128, the PCM is continually decreasing fuel, which indicates that the O_2 sensor voltage must be always high, or rich.

6. d

7. Each type of throttle body assembly is designed to allow a certain amount of air to pass through it at a particular amount of throttle opening. If anything accumulates on the throttle plates or in the throttle bore, the amount of air that can pass through is reduced. This will cause a driveability problem.

8. a

9. An ohmmeter can be used to test the electrical soundness of an injector. Connect the ohmmeter across the injector terminals after the wires to the injector have been disconnected. If the meter reading is infinite, the injector winding is open. If the meter shows more resistance than the specifications call for, there is high resistance in the winding. A reading that is lower than the specifications indicates that the winding is shorted. If the injector is even a little bit out of specifications, it must be replaced.

10. The pulse width is the time in milliseconds that the injector is energized. The duty cycle is the percentage of on-time to total cycle time.

11. To make sure the injectors are firing at the correct time, use a dual trace scope and monitor the ignition reference signal and a fuel injector signal at the same time. The two signals should have some sort of rhythm between them. For example, there can be one injector firing for every four ignition reference signals. This rhythm is dependent upon several things, however, it doesn't matter what the rhythm is; it only matters that the rhythm is constant. If the injector's waveform is fine but the rhythm varies, the ignition reference sensor circuit is faulty and is not allowing the injector to fire at the correct time. If the ignition signal is lost because of a faulty sensor, the injection system will also shut down. If the injector circuit and the ignition reference circuit shut down at the same time, the cause of the problem is probably the ignition reference sensor. If the injector circuits shuts off before the ignition circuit, the problem is the injector circuit or the PCM.

12. a
13. c
14. b
15. c
16. d

17. c
18. c
19. c
20. b

TECH MANUAL

The following procedures are included in Chapter 28 of the *Tech Manual.*

1. Checking the operation of the fuel injectors on an engine.
2. Conducting an injector balance test.

SHOP HINTS

- Demonstrate how to hook up a scan tool and what the readings mean on a problem-free vehicle.
- Demonstrate how to bleed-down and remove TBI and MFI injectors for inspection, cleaning, and testing.
- Show the activity of a fuel injector and oxygen sensor on a lab scope.
- Demonstrate idle speed checks using the various meters and scan tools.

EMISSION CONTROL SYSTEMS

CHAPTER 29

CHAPTER OVERVIEW

This chapter discusses the latest in emission control theory, components, and operation. Also included are: pollutants, history of emission legislation, and development of emission control devices.

CHAPTER OBJECTIVES

- Explain why hydrocarbon (HC) emissions are released from an engine's exhaust.
- Explain how carbon monoxide (CO) emissions are formed in the combustion chamber.
- Describe oxygen (O_2) emissions in relation to air/fuel ratio.
- Describe how carbon dioxide (CO_2) is formed in the combustion chamber.
- Describe how oxides of nitrogen (NO_x) are formed in the combustion chamber.
- Describe the operation of an evaporative control system during the canister purge and nonpurge modes.
- Explain the purpose of the positive crankcase ventilation system.
- Describe the operation of the detonation sensor and electronic spark control module.
- Describe the operation of an exhaust gas recirculation valve.
- Explain the design and operation of a positive and negative backpressure EGR valve.
- Explain the operation of a digital EGR valve.
- Explain the operation of a linear EGR valve.
- Define the purpose of a catalytic converter.
- Describe the operation of a secondary air injection system.

INSTRUCTIONAL OUTLINE WITH TEACHING HINTS

I. Legislative History—**Assignment: Read pages 724–727**—See Transparency Master #77.
  A. Periodic Motor Vehicle Inspection
  B. Development of Emission Control Devices
    1. AIR
    2. Evaporative control
    3. Pre-combustion control
    4. Post-combustion control

5. Pollutants
   a. Hydrocarbons
   b. Carbon monoxide
   c. Oxides of nitrogen
   d. Oxygen
C. Emission Testing
   Hint: Explain how and why California's emission standards were always higher than those for cars in the other 49 states.

II. Evaporative Emission Control Systems—**Assignment: Read pages 727–729.**
   A. Charcoal (Carbon) Canister
   B. Canister Purge Valve
      Hint: Pass around an EVAP canister that has been cut in half and point out the various components and how they work.

III. Pre-combustion Systems—**Assignment: Read pages 729–738.**
   A. Engine Design Changes
      1. Pistons
      2. Combustion chamber designs
      3. Lower compression
      4. Decreased friction
      5. Intake manifold designs
      6. Improved cooling systems
   B. PCV Systems
   C. PCV Valve
      1. Fixed orifice tube PCV system
         Hint: Pass around a PCV valve and explain the procedure for checking it on the car.
   D. Spark Control System
   E. EGR Systems
      1. EGR valve
      2. Valve controls—See Transparency Master #78
         a. Thermal vacuum switch
         b. Ported vacuum switch
         c. Venturi vacuum amplifier
         d. EGR delay timer control
         e. WOT
         f. Backpressure transducer
      3. Types of EGR valves
         a. Positive backpressure
         b. Negative backpressure
         c. Digital
         d. Linear
            Hint: Pass around positive and negative type EGR valves and have the students try to test them with a vacuum pump. Explain why this is not a conclusive test.
      4. Electronic EGR controls
         a. Twin solenoid EGR system
         b. EGR vacuum regulator (EVR)
         c. EGR system with pressure feedback sensor (PFE)
         d. EGR system with pressure transducer (EPT)

F. Intake Heat Control Systems
   1. Computer-controlled mixture heater systems
   2. Port fuel injection

IV. Post-Combustion Systems—**Assignment: Read pages 739–743.**
   A. Catalytic Converters
   B. Air Injection Systems
      1. Pump type
         a. Air control valve
         b. Air by-pass or diverter valve
      2. Pulse type
      3. Electronic secondary air system
         a. AIRB valve
         b. AIRD valve
      4. By-pass mode
      5. Upstream mode
      6. Downstream mode

ANSWERS TO REVIEW QUESTIONS

1. A small PCV valve opening is all that is needed to move the blowby gases out of the crankcase at idle speed because the engine is not under heavy load and the amount of blowby gas is minimal.

2. ESC (Electronic Spark Control) is used because it was discovered that the proper timing of the ignition spark helped to reduce exhaust emissions and develop more power output. Incorrect timing affects the combustion process. Incomplete combustion results in HC emissions. High CO emissions can also result from incorrect ignition timing. Advanced timing can also increase the production of NO_x. When timing is too far advanced, combustion temperatures rise. For every one degree of overadvance, the temperature increases by 125 degrees. Spark control on today's engines is handled by the PCM. Through input signals from various sensors, the PCM adjusts ignition timing for optimal performance with minimal emissions levels. Many engines with EFI have a knock sensor, or sensors. When the engine detonates, a vibration occurs in the engine. The piezoelectric sensing element changes this vibration to an analog voltage, and this signal is sent to the knock sensor module. The knock sensor module changes the AC voltage signal to a digital voltage signal and sends this signal to the PCM. When the PCM receives this signal, it reduces the spark advance to prevent detonation.

3. A digital EGR valve contains up to three electric solenoids that are operated directly by the PCM. Each solenoid contains a movable plunger with a tapered tip that seats in an orifice. When any solenoid is energized, the plunger is lifted and exhaust gas is allowed to recirculate through the orifice into the intake manifold. The solenoids and orifices are different sizes. The PCM can operate one, two, or three solenoids to supply the amount of exhaust recirculation required to provide optimum control of NO_x emissions.

4. An air control valve (or air-switching valve) routes the air from the pump either to the exhaust manifold or to the catalytic converter. During engine warm-up, the valve directs the air into the exhaust manifold. Once the engine is warm, the extra air in the manifold would affect EGR operation, so the air control valve directs the air to the converter, where it aids the converter in oxidizing emissions. A thermal vacuum switch controls the vacuum to the air control valve. When the coolant is cold, it signals the valve to

direct air to the exhaust manifold. Then, when the engine warms to normal operating temperature, the thermal vacuum switch signals the air control valve to reroute the air to the converter.

5. HC, CO, NO_x
6. Blowby gases
7. Knock sensor module
8. Closed
9. Exhaust gases
10. Fuel storage or delivery
11. Catalyst
12. c
13. d
14. b
15. b
16. c
17. a
18. c
19. It relieves the crankcase from unwanted pressure and prevents the formation of oil sludge.
20. b

TECH MANUAL

The following procedures are included in Chapter 29 of the *Tech Manual.*

1. Conducting a visual inspection of the emission control devices and their vacuum hoses and electrical wires.
2. Checking the emission levels from the tailpipe of a vehicle.

SHOP HINTS

- Demonstrate oxygen (O_2) emissions in relation to air/fuel ratio using a five-gas analyzer and propane enrichment.
- Demonstrate how oxides of nitrogen (NO_x) are formed in the combustion chamber using a five-gas analyzer, disconnecting the EGR valve, and loading the engine.
- Demonstrate the operation of an evaporative control system by disconnecting the purge line and using an exhaust analyzer for HC at the port.
- Demonstrate how to check the positive crankcase ventilation system.
- Demonstrate the operation of an exhaust gas recirculation valve on a car, using a vacuum pump while the engine is running with a slight load.

CHAPTER 29/30 TECH MANUAL

Answers to Review Questions

1. False
2. Change the engine's oil.
3. EGR valve stuck open; PVS is failing to open; dirt is on the valve seat, not allowing the valve to close; and loose mounting bolts
4. Disconnect the throttle air bypass valve solenoid.
5. The valve is stuck open.
6. c
7. a
8. c
9. The discharge hose to the exhaust tubes
10. EGR
11. When it is noisy or seized.

EMISSION CONTROL DIAGNOSIS AND SERVICE

CHAPTER 30

CHAPTER OVERVIEW

This chapter describes the testing, diagnosis, and repair of emission control components and systems.

CHAPTER OBJECTIVES

- Describe oxygen (O_2) emissions in relation to air/fuel ratio.
- Describe how carbon dioxide (CO_2) is formed in the combustion chamber.
- Describe how oxides of nitrogen (NO_x) are formed in the combustion chamber.
- Describe the inspection and replacement of PCV system parts.
- Diagnose spark control systems.
- Diagnose engine performance problems caused by improper EGR operation.
- Diagnose and service the various types of EGR valves.
- Diagnose EGR vacuum regulator (EVR) solenoids.
- Diagnose and service the various intake heat control systems.
- Check the efficiency of a catalytic converter.
- Diagnose and service secondary air injection systems.
- Diagnose and service evaporative (EVAP) systems.

INSTRUCTIONAL OUTLINE WITH TEACHING HINTS

I. Emissions Testing—**Assignment: Read pages 746–751**—See Transparency Master #79 and 80.
   A. Excessive HC Emissions May Be Caused By:
      1. Ignition system misfiring
      2. Improper ignition timing
      3. Excessively lean or rich air/fuel ratio
      4. Low cylinder compression
      5. Defective valves, guides, or lifters
      6. Defective rings, pistons, or cylinders
      7. Vacuum leaks
   B. Excessive CO Emissions May Be Caused By:
      1. Rich air/fuel mixtures
      2. Dirty air filter

       3. Faulty injectors

       4. Higher than normal fuel pressures

       5. Defective system input sensor

  C. Excessive HC and CO Emissions May Be Caused By:

       1. Plugged PCV system

       2. Excessively rich air/fuel ratio

       3. Stuck open heat riser valve

       4. AIR pump inoperative or disconnected

       5. Engine oil diluted with gasoline

  D. Lower-than-Normal O_2 Emissions May Be Caused By:

       1. Rich air/fuel mixtures

       2. Dirty air filter

       3. Faulty injectors

       4. Higher than normal fuel pressures

       5. Defective system input sensor

       6. Restricted PCV system

       7. Charcoal canister purging at idle and low speeds

  E. Lower-than-Normal CO_2 Emissions May Be Caused By:

       1. Leaking exhaust system

       2. Rich air/fuel mixture

  F. Higher-than-Normal O_2 Emissions May Be Caused By:

       1. An engine misfire

       2. Lean air/fuel mixtures

       3. Vacuum leaks

       4. Lower than specified fuel pressures

       5. Defective fuel injectors

       6. Defective system input sensor

  G. Higher-than-Normal NO_x Emissions May Be Caused By:

       1. An overheated engine

       2. Lean air/fuel mixtures

       3. Vacuum leaks

       4. Over-advanced ignition timing

       5. Defective EGR system

  H. I/M240 Test

  I. Other I/M Testing

II. PVC System Diagnosis and Service—**Assignment: Read pages 751–752.**

  A. Functional Checks of PCV System

III. EGR System Diagnosis and Service—**Assignment: Read pages 753–757.**

  A. Rough Idle

  B. No-Start, Surging, or Stalling

  C. Detonation

  D. Excessive NO_x Emissions

  E. Poor Fuel Economy.

  F. EGR System Troubleshooting—See Transparency Master #80

  G. EGR Valves and Systems Testing

       1. Diagnosis of negative backpressure EGR valve

       2. Diagnosis of positive backpressure EGR valve

       3. Digital EGR valve diagnosis

       4. Linear EGR valve diagnosis

  H. Checking EGR Efficiency

I. Electronic EGR Controls
   1. EVR tests
   2. Exhaust gas temperature sensor diagnosis
      Hint: Explain to the students the various controls that relate directly to the EGR system.
IV. Spark Control Systems—**Assignment: Read pages 757–759.**
   A. Diagnosis of Knock Sensor and Knock Sensor Module
   B. Thermal Vacuum Valve (TVV) Diagnosis
V. Intake Heat Control Diagnosis and Service—**Assignment: Read page 759.**
VI. Catalytic Converter Diagnosis—**Assignment: Read pages 759–761.**
VII. AIR Injection System Diagnosis and Service—**Assignment: Read pages 761–763.**
   A. Check Valve Testing
   B. Pulsed Secondary AIR Injection System Diagnosis
   C. Secondary AIR Injection System Service and Diagnosis
      1. Electric air pumps
   D. AIR System Component Diagnosis
   E. System Efficiency Test
VIII. Evaporative Emission Control System Diagnosis and Service—**Assignment: Read pages 763–765.**
   A. EVAP System Component Diagnosis

ANSWERS TO REVIEW QUESTIONS

1. d
2. With too little EGR flow, the engine can overheat, detonate, and emit excessive amounts of NO_x. A reduction in flow can be caused by an electronic fault, vacuum leaks, sticking valves, obstructions, and loss of vacuum.
3. A saturated charcoal filter can cause symptoms that can be mistaken for fuel system problems. Rough idle, flooding, and other conditions can indicate a canister problem.
4. If the PCV valve is stuck in the open position, excessive air flow through the valve causes a lean air-fuel ratio and possible rough idle operation or engine stalling.
5. To test a negative backpressure EGR valve, make sure the engine is at normal operating temperature and the ignition switch off. Then disconnect the vacuum hose from the EGR valve and connect a hand vacuum pump to the vacuum fitting on the valve. Supply 18 inches of vacuum to the EGR valve. The EGR valve should open and hold the vacuum for 20 seconds. If the valve doesn't open or can't hold the vacuum, it must be replaced. If the valve had okay results in the first test, continue by applying 18 inches of vacuum to the valve and start the engine. The vacuum should drop to zero, and the valve should close. If the valve doesn't react this way, replace it. Testing a positive backpressure EGR valve requires the same basic tests as a negative-type but should have the opposite results. If the valve fails any part of the test, it should be replaced.
6. c
7. Like most EGR valves, a port valve is opened by vacuum; however, a port-type valve is opened by the vacuum that is present above the throttle plates.
8. Higher-than-normal HC emissions may be caused by ignition system misfiring; improper ignition timing; an excessively lean or rich air/fuel ratio; low cylinder compression; defective valves, guides, or lifters; defective rings, pistons, or cylinders; and/or vacuum leaks.

9. Carbon monoxide (CO) is formed in the engine when there is not enough oxygen to combine with the carbon during combustion. CO is a by-product of combustion. If combustion doesn't take place, CO will be low. When the engine receives enough oxygen in the mixture, carbon dioxide (CO_2) is formed. Therefore, as the mixture becomes rich, the chances of CO being formed increases. CO is found in the exhaust principally, but can also be in the crankcase.

10. Increase

11. a	16. d
12. a	17. b
13. a	18. c
14. c	19. c
15. c	20. c

TECH MANUAL
The following procedures are included in Chapter 30 of the *Tech Manual.*

1. Checking the operation of the PCV system.
2. Checking the operation of the EGR valve.

SHOP HINTS

- Demonstrate how to diagnose spark control systems.
- Demonstrate engine performance problems caused by improper EGR operation (using a vacuum pump or screwdriver, hold the EGR valve open at idle).
- Demonstrate service procedures for the various types of EGR valves.
- Demonstrate EGR vacuum regulator (EVR) solenoid diagnosis.
- Demonstrate how to diagnose and service the various intake heat control systems.
- Check the efficiency of a catalytic converter using a pyrometer, followed by a pre-cat test.
- Demonstrate how to diagnose and service secondary air injection systems.
- Demonstrate how to diagnose and service evaporative (EVAP) systems.

ON-BOARD DIAGNOSTIC SYSTEMS

CHAPTER OVERVIEW

This technical chapter discusses the theory, components, and operation of on-board diagnostic systems and OBD II. An understanding of these systems is essential to becoming a diagnostic technician or *diagnostician*.

CHAPTER OBJECTIVES

- Understand how a typical computerized engine control system operates.
- Explain the operation of various input and output sensors.
- Explain what is meant by open loop and closed loop.
- Explain the reasons for OBD II.
- Describe the primary provisions of OBD II.
- Explain the requirements to illuminate the malfunction indicator light in an On-Board Diagnostics II system.
- Briefly describe the monitored systems in an OBD II system.
- Describe the main hardware differences between an OBD II system and other systems.
- Describe an OBD II warm-up cycle.
- Explain trip and drive cycle in an OBD II system.
- Describe how engine misfire is detected in an OBD II system.
- Describe the differences between an A misfire and a B misfire.
- Describe the purpose of having two oxygen sensors in an exhaust system.
- Briefly describe what the comprehensive component monitor looks at.

INSTRUCTIONAL OUTLINE WITH TEACHING HINTS

   I. System Functions—**Assignment: Read page 768.**
     A. Air/Fuel Ratio
     B. Emission Control Devices
     C. Engine Efficiency at Cold Start
     D. Ignition Timing
     E. Control Loop Operation
   II. System Components—**Assignment: Read pages 768–771**—See Transparency Master #81.
     A. Sensors

     B. Computer (PCM)
     C. Actuators
     D. Adaptive Strategy

III. Primary Sensors—**Assignment: Read pages 771–775.**
     A. Air-Conditioning (A/C) Demand Sensor
     B. Brake Switch
     C. Barometric Pressure (BARO) Sensor
     D. Engine Coolant Temperature (ECT) Sensor
     E. Engine Position Sensor
     F. EGR Diagnostic Switch
     G. EGR Valve Position Sensor
     H. Engine Speed Sensor
     I. Feedback Pressure EGR Sensor
     J. Heated Windshield Module
     K. High Gear Switch
     L. Intake Air Temperature (IAT) Sensor
     M. Knock Sensor (KS)
     N. Manifold Absolute Pressure (MAP)
     O. Mass Airflow Sensor (MAS)
     P. Neutral Drive/Neutral Gear Switch (NDS)
     Q. Oxygen Sensors (O_2S)
     R. Power Steering Switch (PS)
     S. System Battery Voltage
     T. Throttle Position Sensor (TP)
     U. Vacuum Sensor
     V. Vehicle Speed Sensor
       Hint: Pass around various sensors and discuss their operation. Hook up a voltmeter to the knock sensor and tap it with a small ballpeen hammer, explaining the resulting voltage and what it does to the system.

IV. Computer Outputs and Actuators—**Assignment: Read pages 775–776.**
     A. Air Management Solenoid
     B. Evaporative Emission (EVAP) Canister Purge Valve
     C. EGR Flow Solenoids
     D. Fuel Injectors
     E. Idle Speed Controls
     F. Ignition Module
     G. Mixture Control (MC) Solenoids
     H. Motors and Lights
     I. Other Solenoids
       Hint: Pass around various actuators and discuss their operation.

V. System Operation—**Assignment: Read pages 776–778.**
     A. Diagnostics
        1. PCM
        2. MIL
     B. Closed Loop Mode
     C. Open Loop Mode
     D. Fail Safe or Limp-In Mode
     E. Spark Control Systems
     F. Fuel Control Systems
     G. Emission Control System

H. Control of Non-Engine Functions
I. Computer Logic
VI. OBD II Standards—**Assignment: Read pages 778–779.**
   A. Data Link Connector (DLC)
      1. Standard location
   B. Diagnostic Trouble Codes (DTCs)
   C. Standard Communication Protocol
   D. Common Scan Tools
   E. Common Diagnostic Test Modes
   F. VIN Information Automatically Transferred to Scan Tools
   G. Stored Trouble Codes Cleared by Scan Tools
   H. Record Operating Conditions (Snapshots) That Existed when Faults Occurred
   I. Store Codes
   J. Standard Glossary
   K. OBD II Introduction and Implementation
      Hint: Discuss the advantages of OBD II and how the system developed.
VII. Monitoring Capabilities—**Assignment: Read pages 779–785.**
   A. Catalyst Efficiency Monitor
   B. Misfire Monitor
      1. Type A misfires
      2. Type B misfires
   C. Fuel System Monitoring
   D. Heated Oxygen Sensor Monitor
   E. EGR System Monitoring
   F. Evaporative (EVAP) Emission System Monitor
   G. Secondary Air Injection (AIR) System Monitor
   H. Comprehensive Monitor
VIII. OBD II Diagnostics—**Assignment: Read pages 785–791.**
   A. System Readiness Mode
   B. ODB II Trip
   C. Drive Cycle
   D. Test Connector—See Transparency Master #82
   E. Malfunction Indicator Lamp Operation
   F. Data Links
   G. Test Modes
   H. Snapshots
IX. ODB II Terms—**Assignment: Read pages 791–792.**

ANSWERS TO REVIEW QUESTIONS

1. While in closed loop, the PCM reacts to feedback information. While in open loop, the PCM operates by predetermined parameters.
2. By comparing information from the look-up tables, system strategy, and system sensors, the PCM makes informed decisions.
3. OBD II standards define a warm-up cycle as a period of vehicle operation, after the engine had been turned off, in which the coolant rises by at least 40°C and reaches at least 160°C.
4. The OBD II trip consists of an engine start following an engine off period, with enough vehicle travel to allow the following monitoring sequences to complete their tests: misfire, fuel system, and comprehensive system components, EGR (this test requires a series

of idle speed operations, acceleration, and deceleration to satisfy the conditions needed for completion) and HO$_2$S (this test requires a steady speed for about 20 seconds at speeds between 20 and 45 mph after warm-up to be complete). An OBD II drive cycle consists of an engine start and vehicle operation that brings the vehicle into closed loop and includes whatever specific operating conditions are necessary either to initiate and complete a specific monitoring sequence or to verify a symptom or verify a repair. A minimum drive cycle is from engine start-up and vehicle operation until after the PCM enters closed loop. To complete a drive cycle, all five trip monitors must be completed, followed by the catalyst monitor. The catalyst monitor must be completed after the other five monitors are completed in a trip. A steady throttle opening between 40 to 60 mph (64 to 96 kph) for 80 seconds is required to complete the catalyst efficiency monitor.

5. Cylinder misfire monitoring requires measuring the contribution of each cylinder to engine power.

6. OBD II vehicles use a minimum of two oxygen sensors. One of these is used for feedback to the PCM for fuel control and the other gives an indication of the efficiency of the converter.

7. Monitors included in OBD II are: Catalyst efficiency, engine misfire, fuel system, heated exhaust gas oxygen sensor, EGR, EVAP, secondary air injection, and comprehensive component monitors. Fuel system monitoring checks short-term fuel trim and long-term fuel trim while the PCM is operating in closed loop. Heated Oxygen Sensor Monitor checks lean to rich and rich to lean time responses. The EGR monitors use several different strategies to determine if the system is operating properly. OBD II monitors the evaporative system's ability of the fuel tank to hold pressure and of the purge system to vent the gas fumes from the charcoal canister. The AIR system operation can be verified by turning the AIR system on to inject air upstream of the oxygen sensor while monitoring its signal. The comprehensive monitor looks at any electronic input that could affect emissions.

8. 2% to 3%, 1,000-rpm

9. EVAP

10. AIR, active, passive

11. Short-term fuel trim, long-term fuel trim

12. a		17. c	
13. d		18. b	
14. c		19. c	
15. c		20. c	
16. b			

TECH MANUAL
The following procedure is included in Chapter 31 of the *Tech Manual.*

1. Visually inspecting the components and circuits of an OBD II system.

SHOP HINTS

- Demonstrate on a live vehicle (with a timing light and scan tool) what is meant by open loop and closed loop.
- Demonstrate (using a live vehicle and scan tool) the OBD II warm-up cycle.

■ Describe how engine misfire is detected in an OBD II system.
■ Demonstrate (using a live vehicle and scan tool) the OBD II trip cycle.

CHAPTER 31/32 TECH MANUAL

Answers to Review Questions

1. With computerized engine controls, emission levels, fuel consumption, driveability, and durability are carefully balanced to achieve maximum results with minimum waste. Some of the things engine control systems are designed to do are: air/fuel ratios are held as closely to 14.7 to 1 as possible, allowing maximum catalytic converter efficiency and minimizing fuel consumption; emission control devices, such as EGR valve, carbon canister, and air pump, are operated at predetermined times to increase efficiency; the engine is operated as efficiently as possible when it is cold and is warmed up rapidly, reducing unburned hydrocarbon emissions and engine wear due to raw gas washing oil from the piston rings and getting into the crankcase to form sludge and varnish; ignition timing is advanced as much as possible under all conditions; timing and air/fuel ratios are precisely controlled under all operating conditions; and control loop operation enables the engine to make rapid changes to match changes in engine temperature, load, and speed.

2. Monitors included in OBD II are:
   a. Catalyst efficiency monitor
   b. Engine misfire monitor
   c. Fuel system monitor
   d. Heated exhaust gas oxygen sensor monitor
   e. Exhaust gas recirculation monitor
   f. Evaporative system monitor
   g. Secondary air injection monitor
   h. Comprehensive component monitor

3. OBD II systems have a downstream heated oxygen (HO_2S) sensor mounted downstream from the catalytic converter. The conventional HO_2S sensor is mounted in the exhaust manifold. The downstream HO_2S monitors the efficiency of the conventional or upstream HO_2S.

4. c
5. b
6. True
7. b
8. d
9. A scan tool can retrieve DTCs, monitor serial data, and give a snapshot of the conditions that were present when a DTC was set. Some scan tools can also be used to activate an output.

10. TSBs are especially helpful in diagnostics because they identify common faults or problems in the system that the manufacturer has discovered since the vehicle was built. Often these problems are difficult to isolate and correct without a TSB.

SECTION 4

Answers to ASE Prep Test

1. b	**6.** c	**11.** a	**16.** b
2. a	**7.** d	**12.** a	**17.** a
3. b	**8.** a	**13.** b	**18.** b
4. c	**9.** a	**14.** c	**19.** b
5. a	**10.** d	**15.** a	**20.** b

ON-BOARD DIAGNOSTIC SYSTEM DIAGNOSIS AND SERVICE

CHAPTER 32

CHAPTER OVERVIEW

This chapter covers diagnostic and service procedures of the OBD II system in depth. Included is the extensive use of scan tools for gathering and interpreting OBD II system information.

CHAPTER OBJECTIVES

- Perform flash code diagnosis on various vehicles.
- Obtain fault codes with an analog voltmeter.
- Perform a scan tester diagnosis on various vehicles.
- Conduct preliminary checks on an OBD II system.
- Use a symptom chart to set up a strategic approach to troubleshooting a problem.
- Define the terms associated with OBD II diagnostics.
- Identify the cause of an illuminated MIL.
- Explain the basic format of OBD II DTCs.
- Monitor the activity of OBD II system components.
- Explain how to diagnose intermittent problems.
- Diagnose computer voltage supply and ground wires.
- Test and diagnose switch-type input sensors.
- Test and diagnose variable resistance-type input sensors.
- Test and diagnose generating-type input sensors.
- Test and diagnose output devices (actuators).

INSTRUCTIONAL OUTLINE WITH TEACHING HINTS

    I. Electronic Service Precautions—**Assignment: Read pages 795–796.**
      A. Electrostatic Discharge
   II. Basic Diagnosis of Electronic Engine Control Systems—**Assignment: Read pages 796–798.**
      A. Logical Diagnosis
      B. Isolating Computerized Engine Control Problems
        1. Visual checks
        2. Ohmmeter checks

3. Voltmeter checks
4. Lab scope checks

C. Service Bulletin Information
   Hint: Review *Examples 1, 2, 3,* and *4* on pages 797–798.

III. Self-Diagnosis—**Assignment: Read pages 798–801**—See Transparency Master #83.

A. Visual Inspection
B. Unlocking Trouble Codes—See Transparency Master #84
C. Using a Scan Tool
   1. Snapshot testing

IV. Retrieving Trouble Codes—**Assignment: Read pages 801–806.**

A. General Motors' Vehicles
B. Ford Motor Company Vehicles
   1. Key on, engine off (KOEO) test
   2. Key on, engine running (KOER) test
   3. Continuous self-test
   4. Erasing fault codes
C. Chrysler Corporation Vehicles
D. Toyota Vehicles
E. Nissan Vehicles

V. OBD II System Diagnosis and Service—**Assignment: Read pages 806–808.**

VI. OBD II Diagnostics—**Assignment: Read pages 808–817.**

A. Visual Inspection
B. Scan Tool Diagnosis
C. OBD II Terminology
   1. Drive cycle
   2. Monitoring sequence
   3. Enable criteria
   4. Diagnostic test
   5. Pending situation
   6. Serial data
   7. Similar conditions
   8. Trip
   9. Two trip monitors
   10. Warm-up cycle
D. Malfunction Indicator Lamp
   1. MIL history codes
E. Freeze Frame
   1. Air/fuel ratio
   2. Air flow rate
   3. Fuel trim
   4. Engine speed
   5. Engine load
   6. Engine coolant temperature
   7. Vehicle speed
   8. TP angle
   9. MAP/BARO
   10. Injector base pulse width
   11. Loop status
F. Diagnostic Trouble Codes

ANSWERS TO REVIEW QUESTIONS

1. Scan tools can be used to check for DTCs, monitor the activity of inputs and outputs, and take snapshots that capture the sensor voltage readings into the tester's memory when a problem occurs.

2. **Visual Checks**—This means looking for obvious problems. Any part that is burned, broken, cracked, corroded, or has any other visible problem must be replaced before continuing the diagnosis. **Ohmmeter Checks**—Most sensors and output devices can be checked with an ohmmeter. **Voltmeter Checks**—Many sensors, output devices, and their wiring can be diagnosed by checking the voltage to them, and in some cases, from them. Even some oxygen sensors can be checked in this manner. **Lab Scope Checks**—The activity of sensors and actuators can be monitored with a lab scope. By watching their activity, you are doing more than testing them. Often problems elsewhere in the system will cause a device to behave abnormally. These situations are identified by the

trace on a scope and by the technician's understanding of a scope and the device being monitored.

3. When handling any electronic part, especially those that are static sensitive, follow the guidelines below to reduce the possibility of electrostatic build-up on your body and the inadvertent discharge to the electronic part. If you are not sure if a part is sensitive to static, treat it as if it is.

   a. Always touch a known good ground before handling the part. This should be repeated while handling the part and more frequently after sliding across a seat, sitting down from a standing position, or walking a distance.

   b. Avoid touching the electrical terminals of the part, unless you are instructed to do so in the written service procedures. It is good practice to keep your fingers off all electrical terminals because the oil from your skin can cause corrosion.

   c. When you are using a voltmeter, always connect the negative meter lead first.

   d. Do not remove a part from its protective package until it is time to install the part.

   e. Before removing the part from its package, ground yourself and the package to a known good ground on the vehicle.

4. When diagnosing engine control system problems, service bulletin information is absolutely essential. If a technician does not have service bulletin information, many hours of diagnostic time may be wasted. This information is available from different suppliers of CD-ROM and paper TSBs. Some difficult problems are only quickly discovered by using a TSB or by having much experience with similar problems and their causes.

5. 0, 1

6. All PCMs cannot operate properly unless they have good ground connections and the correct voltage at the required terminals. Computer ground wires usually extend from the computer to a ground connection on the engine or battery. The voltage drop across the ground wires should be 30 millivolts or less. Not only should the computer ground be checked, but so should the ground (and positive) connection at the battery. Ideally there should be a zero volt reading across any wire unless it is a resistance wire that is designed to drop voltage; even then, check the drop against specifications to see if it is dropping too much. A good ground is especially critical for all reference voltage sensors. A bad ground will cause the reference voltage (normally 5 volts) to be higher than normal. If the reference voltage to a sensor is too high, the output signal from the sensor to the computer will also be too high. Poor grounds can also allow EMI or noise to be present on the reference voltage signal. This noise causes small changes in the voltage going to the sensor; therefore, the output signal from the sensor will also have these voltage changes. The computer will try to respond to these small rapid changes, which can cause a driveability problem.

7. Low

8. a

9. d

10. c

11. c

12. c

13. a

14. b

15. c

16. b

17. a

18. c

19. a

20. b

TECH MANUAL

The following procedures are included in Chapter 32 of the *Tech Manual.*

1. Conducting a diagnostic check on an engine equipped with OBD II.
2. Monitoring the adaptive fuel strategy on an OBD II-equipped engine.
3. Testing an ECT sensor.
4. Checking the operation of a TP sensor.
5. Testing an O_2 sensor.
6. Testing a MAP sensor.

SHOP HINTS

- Demonstrate how disabled sensors will affect the system.
- Induce sensor problems and have the students follow the service manual's troubleshooting guides to test and diagnose the problems.
- Induce an intermittent connection problem on various sensors and demonstrate if OBD II will "capture" the fault.
- Demonstrate test and diagnostic procedures using the scanner, DVOM, and lab scope.

CLUTCHES

CHAPTER 33

CHAPTER OVERVIEW

This chapter describes in detail the design and operation of each part of a clutch. Considerable attention is given to clutch diagnosis and service.

CHAPTER OBJECTIVES

- Describe the various clutch components and their functions.
- Name and explain the advantages of the different types of pressure plate assemblies.
- Name the different types of clutch linkages.
- List the safety precautions that should be followed during clutch servicing.
- Explain how to perform basic clutch maintenance.
- Name the six most common problems that occur with clutches.
- Explain the basics of servicing a clutch assembly.

INSTRUCTIONAL OUTLINE WITH TEACHING HINTS

I. Operation—**Assignment: Read pages 843–850**—See Transparency Master #86.
   A. Flywheel
   B. Clutch Disc
   C. Pilot Bushing
   D. Pressure Plate Assembly
      1. Coil spring pressure plate assembly—See Transparency Master #87
      2. Diaphragm spring pressure plate assembly
   E. Clutch Release Bearing
      1. Rotating release bearing
   F. Clutch Fork
   G. Clutch Linkage
      1. Shaft and lever linkage
      2. Cable linkage
      3. Self-adjusting clutch
      4. Hydraulic clutch linkage
         Hint: Discuss typical clutch systems and components using Figures 33–1 through 33–22.

II. Clutch Service Safety Precautions—**Assignment: Read pages 850–851.**
III. Clutch Maintenance—**Assignment: Read pages 851–852.**
   A. Clutch Linkage Adjustment
   B. External Clutch Linkage Lubrication
IV. Clutch Problem Diagnosis—**Assignment: Read pages 852–854.**
   A. Slippage
   B. Drag and Binding
   C. Chatter
   D. Pedal Pulsation
   E. Vibration
   F. Noises
V. Clutch Service—**Assignment: Read pages 854–857.**
   A. Removing the Clutch—See Transparency Master #88

ANSWERS TO REVIEW QUESTIONS

1. Molded friction facing and woven friction facing
2. Some vehicles use semicentrifugal pressure plates because these plates increase their clamping pressure with an increase of rotational speed; therefore the clutch disc becomes more firmly implanted between the flywheel and plate as engine speed increases.
3. Belleville spring
4. Hydraulic, cable, shaft and lever
5. Tape measure or ruler
6. b
7. c
8. depressed
9. a
10. d
11. a
12. c
13. c
14. c
15. c
16. a
17. a
18. c
19. c
20. c

TECH MANUAL
The following procedures are included in Chapter 33 of the *Tech Manual.*

1. Troubleshooting clutch assembly.
2. Inspecting and adjusting clutch linkage.
3. Inspecting a clutch assembly.

SHOP HINTS

- Demonstrate how to adjust a cable or mechanical linkage clutch.
- Demonstrate how to remove and reinstall the clutch, T.O. bearing, pressure plate, and pilot bearing using an alignment tool, pilot bearing remover, and torque wrench.
- Demonstrate the proper way to handle older clutch materials containing asbestos.

TECH MANUAL ANSWERS

Review Questions

1. Shaft and lever, cable, hydraulic
2. Yes
3. a
4. To prevent clutch cover distortion
5. Oil-soaked or worn disc facing, warped pressure plate, weak diaphragm, release bearing contracting and applying pressure to the release levers
6. c
7. Clutch disc dust may contain asbestos, which should be removed only with a special, approved vacuum collection system or an approved liquid cleaning system.
8. To check clutch pedal free travel, use a tape measure or ruler. Place the tape measure or ruler beside the clutch pedal and the end against the floor. Note the reading, and then depress the clutch pedal to take up the free travel. The difference in readings is the clutch pedal free travel.
9. c
10. Worn clutch bearing, weak pressure plate springs, pilot bearing/bushing is loose in the crankshaft

MANUAL TRANSMISSIONS AND TRANSAXLES

CHAPTER OVERVIEW

Understanding the major parts of manual transmission/transaxles is key to being able to diagnose these units. The complexity of these parts and units is emphasized in this general discussion.

CHAPTER OBJECTIVES

- Explain the design characteristics of the gears used in manual transmissions and transaxles.
- Explain the fundamentals of torque multiplication and overdrive.
- Describe the purpose, design, and operation of synchronizer assemblies.
- Describe the purpose, design, and operation of internal and remote gearshift linkages.
- Explain the operation and power flows produced in typical manual transmissions and transaxles.

INSTRUCTIONAL OUTLINE WITH TEACHING HINTS

    I. Transmission versus Transaxle—**Assignment: Read page 861**—See Transparency Master #89.

        A. Transmission Designs

    II. Gears—**Assignment: Read pages 861–863.**

        A. Gear Design

            1. Gear pitch

            2. Spur gears

            3. Helical gears

            4. Idler gears—See Transparency Master #90

    III. Basic Gear Theory—**Assignment: Read pages 863–866.**

        A. Torque

        B. Gear Ratios

        C. Transmission Gear Sets

        D. Reverse Gear Ratios

        Hint: Have a removed transmission available and demonstrate gear ratios via the input and output shafts while shifting through the various gears.

    IV. Transmission/Transaxle Design—**Assignment: Read pages 866–868.**
      A. Transmission Features
      B. Transaxle Features
    V. Synchronizers—**Assignment: Read pages 868–870.**
      A. Synchronizer Design
      B. Operation
        Hint: Discuss gears, gear design, and how the synchronizers function.
    VI. Gearshift Mechanisms—**Assignment: Read pages 870–872**—See Transparency Master #91.
      A. Gearshift Linkages
        1. Internal
        2. External
    VII. Transmission Power Flow—**Assignment: Read pages 872–874.**
      A. Neutral
      B. First Gear
      C. Second Gear
      D. Third Gear
      E. Fourth Gear
      F. Reverse
    VIII. Five-Speed Overdrive—**Assignment: Read page 874.**
    IX. Transaxle Power Flows—**Assignment: Read pages 874–876.**
      A. Neutral
      B. First Gear
      C. Second Gear
      D. Third Gear
      E. Fourth Gear
      F. Reverse
    X. Final Drive Gears and Overall Ratios—**Assignment: Read page 876.**
    XI. Electrical Systems—**Assignment: Read pages 876–878.**
      A. Reverse Lamp Switch
      B. High Gear Switch
      C. Vehicle Speed Sensor
      D. Upshift Lamp Circuit
      E. Shift Blocking

ANSWERS TO REVIEW QUESTIONS

1. Location of drive wheels, front or rear
2. The amount of torque increase from a driving gear to a driven gear is directly proportional to speed decrease.
3. Torque is calculated by multiplying the applied force by its distance from the centerline of its rotation. When a smaller gear drives a larger gear, the torque will increase by the same ratio as the size of the two gears. Likewise, the speed of the gear will be decreased by that same ratio.
4. The ring and pinion gearset in a differential is what all vehicles use to provide an additional gear reduction above and beyond that which the transmission or transaxle gearing can produce.
5. Each shift rail/shift fork is used to control the movement of a synchronizer, and each synchronizer is capable of engaging and locking two speed gears to the main shaft.

6. d
7. b
8. c
9. a
10. a
11. a
12. a
13. c
14. b
15. driven, driving
16. b
17. d
18. a
19. d
20. a

TECH MANUAL

The following procedures are included in Chapter 34 of the *Tech Manual.*

1. Checking fluid level in a transmission.
2. Checking fluid level in a transaxle.
3. Inspecting and adjusting shift linkage.

SHOP HINTS

- Discuss and demonstrate precision measuring techniques such as determining runout or measuring parts to see if they fall within specifications.
- Have the students install and remove bearings using a bearing press.
- Discuss the importance of replacing sets of gears rather than a single gear to prevent a new part from failing prematurely.
- Emphasize neat and orderly work areas and using the technical literature to ensure parts are reassembled correctly.

CHAPTER 34/35 TECH MANUAL

Answers to Review Questions

1. The engine mounts on FWD cars are important to the operation of the clutch and transaxle. Any engine movement may change the effective length of the shift and clutch control cables and therefore may affect the engagement of the clutch and/or gears. A clutch may slip due to clutch linkage changes as the engine pivots on its mounts. To check the condition of the transaxle mounts, pull up and push down on the transaxle case while watching the mount. If the mount's rubber separates from the metal plate or if the case moves up but not down, replace the mount. If there is movement between the metal plate and its attaching point on the frame, tighten the attaching bolts to an appropriate torque.

2. a. Transmission not aligned
   b. Bad bearings
   c. Low oil level
   d. Broken gears
   e. Excess end play
   f. Bad clutch
3. a. Clutch not releasing
   b. Stuck interlock
   c. Misadjusted linkage
   d. Bad synchronizer
   e. Low lube level
4. Using a pry bar and feeler gauge set, using a pry bar and dial indicator
5. d
6. c
7. No
8. a
9. a
10. Retained in the transaxle or transmission case so that it is in mesh with a gear on the output shaft

MANUAL TRANSMISSION/ TRANSAXLE SERVICE

CHAPTER 35

CHAPTER OVERVIEW

This chapter helps develop an understanding of the importance of transmission/transaxle lubrication. It focuses on maintenance, cleaning and inspection guidelines, and typical disassembly and assembly procedures.

CHAPTER OBJECTIVES

- Perform a visual inspection of transmission/transaxle components for signs of damage or wear.
- Check transmission oil level correctly, detect signs of contaminated oil, and change oil as needed.
- Describe the steps taken to remove and install transmissions/transaxles, including the equipment and safety precautions used.
- Identify common transmission problems and their probable causes and solutions.
- Describe the basic steps and precautions taken during transmission/transaxle disassembly, cleaning, inspection, and reassembly procedures.

INSTRUCTIONAL OUTLINE WITH TEACHING HINTS

I. Lubricant Check—**Assignment: Read pages 881–884**—See Transparency Master #92.
   A. Lubricant Leaks
      1. Excessive lubricant in unit
      2. Wrong fluid
      3. Loose/broken/damaged input shaft bearing retainer O-ring and/or lip seal
      4. Loose/missing case bolts
      5. Case cracked/porosity problem
      6. Leaking shift lever seal
      7. Gaskets/seals are damaged/missing
      8. Loose drain plug
   B. Fluid Changes
   C. In-Vehicle Service
   D. Rear Oil Seal and Bushing Replacement

      E. Linkage Adjustment

      F. Backup Light Switch Service

      G. Speedometer Drive Gear Service

II. Diagnosing Problems—**Assignment: Read pages 884–889.**

      A. Visual Inspection

      B. Transmission Noise

      C. Rough, Growling Noise

      D. Clicking or Knocking Noise

      E. Gear Clash

      F. Hard Shifting

      G. Jumping out of Gear

      H. Locked in Gear

         1. Shift linkage

           Hint: Discuss various types of problems with manual transmissions and transaxles.

III. Transmission/Transaxle Removal—**Assignment: Read pages 889–890**—See Transparency Master #93.

      Hint: Review the shop manual removal and disassembly procedures with the students before removing the transmission/transaxle.

IV. Cleaning and Inspection—**Assignment: Read pages 890–895.**

      A. Aluminum Case Repair

      Hint: Discuss cleaning and inspections, then review procedures on pages 891 and 894.

V. Disassembly and Reassembly of the Differential Cases—**Assignment: Read page 895.**

      A. Shim Selection

VI. Reassembly/Reinstallation of Transmission/Transaxle—**Assignment: Read pages 895–898.**

VII. Installing the Transmission/Transaxle—**Assignment: Read page 898.**

ANSWERS TO REVIEW QUESTIONS

1. Extensive internal wear or damage
2. Check for lubricant leaks at all gaskets and seals, transmission mount inspection, clutch and gearshift linkage checks, drive axle check, and CV joint inspection. Check the cage body for signs of porosity that show up as leakage.
3. Improperly aligned engines, improperly torqued mounting bolts, damaged or missing rubber mounts, cracked brackets, loose objects in engine compartment
4. A gear puller
5. It should always be placed on the tight bearing race.
6. d
7. b
8. Input shaft bearings
9. d
10. c
11. b
12. a
13. c
14. b
15. d
16. a
17. c
18. b
19. c
20. a

TECH MANUAL

The following procedures are included in Chapter 35 of the *Tech Manual.*

1. Road testing a vehicle for transmission problems.
2. Tracing a transmission's power flow.

SHOP HINTS

- Discuss and demonstrate precision measuring techniques such as determining runout or measuring parts to see if they fall within specifications.
- Have the students install and remove bearings using a bearing press.
- Discuss the importance of replacing sets of gears rather than a single gear to prevent a new part from failing prematurely.
- Emphasize neat and orderly work areas and using the technical literature to ensure that parts are reassembled correctly.

DRIVE AXLES AND DIFFERENTIALS

CHAPTER 36

CHAPTER OVERVIEW

This chapter develops an understanding of drive axles and differentials using figures to identify the many parts of these complex units. Also included is drive axle and differential diagnosis and service.

CHAPTER OBJECTIVES

- Name and describe the components of a front-wheel-drive axle.
- Describe the operation of a front-wheel-drive axle.
- Diagnose problems in CV joints.
- Perform preventive maintenance on CV joints.
- Explain the difference between CV joints and universal joints.
- Name and describe the components of a rear-wheel-drive axle.
- Describe the operation of a rear-wheel-drive axle.
- Explain the function and operation of a differential and drive axles.
- Describe the various differential designs including complete, integral carrier, removable carrier, and limited slip.
- Describe the three common types of driving axles.
- Explain the function of the main driving gears, drive pinion gear, and ring gear.
- Describe the operation of hunting, nonhunting, and partial nonhunting gears.
- Describe the different types of axle shafts and axle shaft bearings.

INSTRUCTIONAL OUTLINE WITH TEACHING HINTS

I. Front-Wheel-Drive (FWD) Axles—**Assignment: Read page 901.**
II. Types of CV Joints—**Assignment: Read pages 901–904.**
   A. Inboard and Outboard Joints—See Transparency Master #94
   B. Fixed and Plunge Joints
   C. Ball-Type Joints
      1. Fixed ball CV joints
      2. Plunging ball-type joints
   D. Tripod CV Joints
      1. Tripod plunging joints—See Transparency Master #95
      2. Fixed tripod joint

III. Front-Wheel-Drive Applications—**Assignment: Read pages 904–905.**
IV. CV Joints—**Assignment: Read pages 905–907.**
    A. Diagnosis and Inspection
       Hint: Review text pages 905–906.
       1. Obtaining CV repair parts
V. CV Joint Servicing—**Assignment: Read pages 907–910.**
    A. CV Shaft and Rubber Boot Care Tips
       Hint: Discuss Photo Sequence 37 on pages 908–910
VI. Rear-Wheel Drive Shafts—**Assignment: Read pages 910–911.**
    A. Slip Yoke
    B. Drive Shaft and Yokes
       Hint: Discuss constant velocity (CV) joints and universal (U) joints.
VII. Operation of U-Joints—**Assignment: Read pages 911–913.**
    A. Speed Variations
    B. Phasing of Universal Joints
    C. Canceling Angles
VIII. Types of U-Joints—**Assignment: Read page 913.**
    A. Single Universal Joints
    B. Double-Cardan Universal Joints
IX. Diagnosis of Drive Shaft and U-Joint Problems—**Assignment: Read pages 913–915.**
X. Differentials and Drive Axles—**Assignment: Read pages 915–922.**
    A. Differential Components
       1. Hunting gearset
       2. Nonhunting gearset
       3. Partial nonhunting gearset
       4. Hypoid gear
    B. Rear Axle Housing and Casing—See Transparency Master #96
       1. Integral housing
    C. Differential Operation
XI. Limited Slip Differentials—**Assignment: Read pages 922–925.**
    A. Clutch Packs
    B. Brake Cones
XII. Axle Shafts—**Assignment: Read pages 925–927.**
    A. Semifloating Axle Shafts
    B. Three-Quarter Floating Axle
    C. Full-Floating Axle Shafts
    D. Independently Suspended Axles
    E. Axle Shaft Bearings
       1. Radial loading
       2. Thrust loading
       Hint: Discuss axle shafts, bearings, and service using the shop manuals for various types of axle systems.
XIII. Servicing the Final Drive Assembly—**Assignment: Read pages 927–930.**
    A. Pinion Gear Depth
    B. Backlash
XIV. Diagnosing Differential Noises—**Assignment: Read pages 930–933.**

ANSWERS TO REVIEW QUESTIONS

1. By position, by function, or by design
2. Removable carrier axle housing
3. Dead axle
4. Three-quarter floating axle
5. A leak or noise

6. d	11. c	16. a
7. d	12. d	17. a
8. a	13. c	18. c
9. b	14. c	19. b
10. a	15. b	20. d

TECH MANUAL

The following procedures are included in Chapter 36 of the *Tech Manual*.

1. Inspecting and diagnosing a drive axle.
2. Servicing CV joints.
3. Checking U-joints.
4. Road checking differential noise.
5. Measuring ring gear runout and backlash.

SHOP HINTS

- Discuss methods of isolating drive axles and differential gear noises.
- Make sure students know how to install oil seals and dust seals.
- Discuss ball bearing inspection and evaluation techniques.
- Demonstrate how to set up a differential for pinion gear depth, backlash, and gear patterns.

TECH MANUAL ANSWERS

Review Questions

1. Inspect the joint and replace the boot and grease.
2. Wiped clean with rags; the solvent can damage the needle bearings and contaminate the lubricant.
3. Measuring driveshaft angles
4. Out-of-balance vibration
5. Nonhunting and partial nonhunting
6. Press them off; never burn them loose with a torch.
7. Inside the axle housing
8. By installing shims
9. b
10. c

SECTION 5

Answers to ASE Prep test

1. c	6. b	11. c	16. a
2. a	7. c	12. c	17. d
3. c	8. c	13. b	18. b
4. d	9. d	14. c	19. a
5. b	10. c	15. d	20. d

AUTOMATIC TRANSMISSIONS AND TRANSAXLES

CHAPTER 37

CHAPTER OVERVIEW

This chapter discusses automatic transmission and transaxle theory, components, and operation.

CHAPTER OBJECTIVES

- Explain the basic design and operation of standard and lockup torque converters.
- Describe the design and operation of a simple planetary gearset and Simpson geartrain.
- Name the major types of planetary gear controls used on automatic transmissions and explain their basic operating principles.
- Describe the construction and operation of common Simpson geartrain-based transmissions and transaxles.
- Describe the construction and operation of common Ravigneaux geartrain-based transmissions.
- Describe the construction and operation of Ford AXOD and General Motors' 4T60 (THM 440-T4) transaxles that use planetary gearsets in tandem.
- Describe the construction and operation of automatic transmissions that use helical gears in constant mesh.
- Describe the construction and operation of CVTs.
- Describe the design and operation of the hydraulic controls and valves used in modem transmissions and transaxles.
- Explain the role of the following components of the transmission control system: pressure regulator valve, throttle valve, governor assembly, manual valve, shift valves, and kickdown valve.
- Identify the various pressures in the transmission, state their purpose, and tell how they influence the operation of the transmission.
- Explain the advantages of using electronic controls for transmission shifting.
- Briefly describe what determines the shift characteristics of each selector lever position.
- Identify the input and output devices in a typical electronic control system and briefly describe the function of each.

INSTRUCTIONAL OUTLINE WITH TEACHING HINTS

    I. Torque Converter—**Assignment: Read pages 938–940**—See Transparency Master #97.
        A. Design
        B. Components
            1. Impeller
            2. Stator
            3. Turbine
        C. Basic Operation
        D. Types of Oil Flow
            1. Rotary
            2. Vortex
        E. Overrunning Clutch
        Hint: Have available a cut-away torque converter for students to see.

   II. Lockup Torque Converter—**Assignment: Read pages 941–942.**
        A. Lockup Piston Clutch (PLC)
        B. Forced Disengagement

  III. Planetary Gears—**Assignment: Read pages 942–944.**
        A. Sun Gear
        B. Planetary Pinion Gears
        C. Annulus
        D. Planetary Carrier
        E. How Planetary Gears Work
            1. Maximum forward reduction
            2. Minimum forward reduction
            3. Maximum overdrive
            4. Slow overdrive
            5. Slow reverse
            6. Fast reverse
            7. Direct drive
            8. Neutral operation
        Hint: Pass around a planetary gear set and discuss it with the students.

  IV. Compound Planetary Gear Sets—**Assignment: Read pages 944–950**—See Transparency Master #98.
        A. Simpson Geartrain
        B. Ravigneaux Geartrain
        C. Planetary Gearsets in Tandem
        D. Honda's Non-Planetary Based Transmission
        E. Continuously Variable Transmissions (CVT)

   V. Planetary Gear Controls—**Assignment: Read pages 951–952.**
        A. Transmission Bands
        B. Transmission Servos
            1. Simple servo—See Transparency Master #99
            2. Compound servos

  VI. Transmission Clutches—**Assignment: Read pages 952–954.**
        A. Overrunning Clutches
        B. Multiple-Disc Clutches
        C. Planetary Control Terminology

    VII. Bearings, Bushings, and Thrust Washers—**Assignment: Read pages 954–957.**
   VIII. Snaprings—**Assignment: Read page 957.**
    IX. Gaskets and Seals—**Assignment: Read pages 957–960.**
       A. Gaskets
       B. Seals
          1. O-rings
          2. Lip seals
          3. Square-cut seal
       C. Metal Sealing Rings
          1. Butt-end
          2. Hook-end
       D. Teflon Seals
       Hint: Pass around various seals and explain their functions.
     X. Final Drives and Differentials—**Assignment: Read page 960.**
       A. Final Drive Assemblies
    XI. Hydraulic System—**Assignment: Read pages 960–962.**
       A. Hydraulic Principles
   XII. Pumps—**Assignment: Read page 962.**
  XIII. Valve Body—**Assignment: Read pages 962–963.**
  XIV. Valves—**Assignment: Read pages 963–964.**
       A. Check Ball Valve
       B. Poppet Valve
       C. Spool Valve
       Hint: Discuss hydraulic systems and valves as you pass around a valve body.
    XV. Pressure Regulator Valve—**Assignment: Read pages 964–967.**
       A. Increasing Pressure
       B. Vacuum Modulator Operation
       C. Throttle Pressure
       D. Relay Valve
       E. Shift Valve
          1. Governor
       F. Manual Valve
   XVI. Governor Assembly—**Assignment: Read page 967.**
  XVII. Shift Feel—**Assignment: Read pages 967–968.**
       A. Accumulators
 XVIII. Hydraulic Circuits—**Assignment: Read pages 968–973.**
       Hint: Review the pressure information on pages 968–973.
   XIX. Electronic Controls—**Assignment: Read pages 973–978.**
       A. Torque Converter Lockup
       B. Electronically Controlled Shifting
       C. Adaptive Controls
       D. Manual Shifting
          1. BMW's Steptronic
          2. Chrysler AutoStick
          3. Honda's Sequential SportShift
          4. Tiptronic
    XX. Chrysler Systems—**Assignment: Read pages 978–979.**
   XXI. Ford Motor Company Systems—**Assignment: Read page 979.**
  XXII. General Motors' Systems—**Assignment: Read pages 979–980.**

ANSWERS TO REVIEW QUESTIONS

1. Rotary oil flow is the oil flow around the circumference of the torque converter caused by the rotation of the torque converter on its axis. Vortex oil flow is the oil flow occurring from the impeller to the turbine and back to the impeller.
2. The overrunning clutch
3. Both gears turn in the same direction
4. Single wrap and double wrap
5. It transmits engine torque as in the torque converter, controls valve body operation, and operates planetary controls such as in multiple-disc clutches, band and servo mechanisms. (There are many other purposes.)

6. e	11. a	16. b
7. c	12. a	17. a
8. a	13. a	18. b
9. c	14. b	19. c
10. b	15. c	20. c

TECH MANUAL
The following procedures are included in Chapter 37 of the *Tech Manual.*

1. Visually inspecting an automatic transmission.
2. Road testing to check the operation of a lockup torque converter.
3. Road testing to check the operation of an automatic transmission.

SHOP HINTS

Many students will be working in general repair shops and will be handling components like automobile transmissions as one unit. All technicians, however, can expect at some time to repair leaky or broken hydraulic fittings, seals, and gaskets.

- Demonstrate how to reseal a "leaky" transmission using the pump seal, o-ring, gasket, tail shaft seal, and pan gasket on a removed transmission.
- Demonstrate how to properly install cooling lines.
- Demonstrate how to measure the pump for reuse.

CHAPTER 37/38 TECH MANUAL

Answers to Review Questions

1. 5 seconds
2. True
3. To eliminate other parts
4. c
5. Ravigneaux, Simpson, tandem
6. d
7. c
8. Servos and clutches
9. It links the throttle valve of the transmission with the throttle plate of the engine's throttle body assembly. The motion of the throttle plate is transferred to the throttle valve.
10. Oil pump, governor, and throttle circuits

AUTOMATIC TRANSMISSION/ TRANSAXLE SERVICE

CHAPTER 38

CHAPTER OVERVIEW

This chapter offers a general overview of diagnosis and servicing of transmissions and transaxles.

CHAPTER OBJECTIVES

- Diagnose unusual fluid usage, level, and condition problems.
- Replace automatic transmission fluid and filters.
- List possible causes of oil leaks.
- Describe how to perform a road test analysis accurately.
- Explain how to check the gear selector and throttle valve linkages.
- Explain how to test electrical/electronic components.
- Explain why proper power train mount alignment is important
- Perform lockup converter system tests.
- Inspect, test, flush, and replace cooler, lines, and fittings.
- Describe the procedure for adjusting a band.
- Explain when and how oil pressure tests are performed.
- Explain the basics of computer and solenoid valve tests.

INSTRUCTIONAL OUTLINE WITH TEACHING HINTS

I. Automatic Transmission Fluid—**Assignment: Read pages 988–989**—See Transparency Master #100.
   A. Miscibility
   B. Recommended Applications
      1. Friction modifiers
      2. Dextron III
      3. Mercon
II. Diagnostics—**Assignment: Read pages 989–992.**
   A. Fluid Check
      1. Aeration
   B. Fluid Changes
III. Fluid Leaks—**Assignment: Read pages 992–994.**

A. Oil Pan
B. Torque Converter
C. Extension Housing
D. Speedometer Drive
E. Electrical Connections
F. Checking Transaxle Mounts
IV. Road Testing the Vehicle—**Assignment: Read pages 994–996.**
A. Noises
B. Common Problems
C. Vacuum Modulator
V. Linkages—**Assignment: Read pages 996–997.**
A. Gear Selector Linkage
B. Throttle Valve Linkages
C. Kickdown Switch Adjustment
VI. Electrical Controls—**Assignment: Read pages 997–999.**
A. Testing Switches
B. Speed Sensors
C. Electronic Defaults
D. Band Adjustment—See Transparency Master #101
VII. Pressure Tests—**Assignment: Read pages 999–1002.**
A. Valve Body
B. Governor
C. Servo Assemblies
D. Parking Pawl
VIII. Torque Converters—**Assignment: Read pages 1002–1009.**
A. Lockup Converter Testing
B. Transmission Cooler and Lines
IX. Rebuilding a Transmission—**Assignment: Read page 1009.**
Hint: Review the service manual for specific transmission rebuilding procedures.

ANSWERS TO REVIEW QUESTIONS

1. External fluid leaks
2. Milky ATF indicates that engine coolant is leaking into the transmission cooler in the radiator outlet tank.
3. ATF and transmission filter need to be changed.
4. Neutral safety switch
5. A ruptured diaphragm in the vacuum modulator

6. d	11. b	16. c
7. a	12. b	17. a
8. d	13. c	18. d
9. c	14. d	19. a
10. c	15. a	20. a

TECH MANUAL

The following procedures are included in Chapter 38 of the *Tech Manual.*

1. Conducting a stall test.
2. Pressure testing an automatic transmission.
3. Servicing a valve body.
4. Overhauling a multiple-disc clutch assembly.
5. Using a lab scope on sensors and switches.

SHOP HINTS

Many students will be working in general repair shops and will be handling components like automobile transmissions as one unit. All technicians, however, can expect at some time to repair leaky or broken hydraulic fittings.

- Have your students assemble fittings, hoses, and tubing, depending on what is available, so they can learn how to make proper cuts and flanges and how to select the proper hardware.
- In conjunction with the above exercise, you can have each student's project start and end with a certain fitting, so that in the end they can all be connected together and put under fluid pressure. (This might give the students a sense of teamwork and show how important the individual's contribution is to the group; it may also show how just one component can make an entire system fail.)
- Take the students through changing the filter in an automatic transmission. Stress work area cleanliness and proper gasket installation.
- Make sure the students can restore the automatic transmission fluid to its proper level.
- Demonstrate the procedure for protecting components and open lines from contamination while the system is open.

FOUR- AND ALL-WHEEL DRIVE

CHAPTER OVERVIEW

This chapter presents a general explanation of the design and servicing of four- and all-wheel-drive systems. These systems are very popular and therefore the need for service and repair is increasing.

CHAPTER OBJECTIVES

- Identify the advantages of four- and all-wheel drive.
- Name the major components of a conventional four-wheel-drive system.
- Name the components of a transfer case.
- State the differences between the transfer, open, and limited slip differentials.
- State the major purpose of locking/unlocking hubs.
- Name the five shift lever positions on a typical 4WD vehicle.
- Understand the difference between four- and all-wheel drive.
- Know the purpose of a viscous clutch in all-wheel drive.

INSTRUCTIONAL OUTLINE WITH TEACHING HINTS

    I. 4WD versus AWD—**Assignment: Read page 1013.**
        A. Transfer Case
        B. Locking Hubs
        C. Interaxle Differential
        D. Viscous Clutch
        Hint: Discuss the popularity of 4/AWD systems, their advantages and disadvantages, and service problems that might be associated with them.
   II. Four-Wheel-Drive Systems—**Assignment: Read pages 1013–1014.**
  III. Transfer Case—**Assignment: Read pages 1014–1015.**
        A. Driveline Windup
        B. Interaxle Differentials—See Transparency Master #102
  IV. Locking/Unlocking Hubs—**Assignment: Read pages 1015–1018.**
        A. Axle Disconnects
   V. Operational Modes—**Assignment: Read pages 1018–1019**—See Transparency Master #103.

    VI. 4WD Passenger Cars—**Assignment: Read pages 1019–1020.**
        A. Limited Slip and Open Differentials
   VII. Servicing 4WD Vehicles—**Assignment: Read pages 1020–1021.**
        A. Servicing the Transfer Case
  VIII. All-Wheel-Drive Systems—**Assignment: Read pages 1021–1026.**
        A. Viscous Clutch
        B. Center Differential AWD
          Hint: Discuss components of and differences between four-wheel-drive and all-wheel-drive systems. Review Photo Sequences 43 and 44 on pages 1022–1025.

ANSWERS TO REVIEW QUESTIONS

1. Improved traction and handling ability
2. Transfer case, front drive shaft, front drive axle
3. It is used to drive the axle with low tractive effort, taking the place of the interaxle differential.
4. To dissipate driveline windup by allowing the front and rear axles to run at different speeds
5. Power cannot be applied to the wheels in reverse.
6. c
7. Shear or cut through
8. a
9. The action of the fluid limits the amount of slip between the axles or shafts. Plates attached to each of the shafts rotate through the fluid. A limited amount of slippage is allowed. AWD systems use this type of assembly in place of a center differential or transfer case because it is compact and self-regulating.

10. b		16. d	
11. c		17. b	
12. d		18. c	
13. d		19. b	
14. c		20. a	
15. d			

TECH MANUAL
The following procedures are included in Chapter 39 of the *Tech Manual.*

1. Inspecting and replenishing the lubricant in a transfer case.
2. Road checking a transfer case.
3. Replacing an output shaft seal and bushing.

SHOP HINTS

- Examine and discuss CV joints and U-joints.
- Discuss the advantages and disadvantages of limited slip differentials in 4/AWD systems.
- Examine and discuss locking/unlocking hubs.

TECH MANUAL ANSWERS

Review Questions

1. Four-wheel drive
2. True
3. True
4. False
5. Front-engine, rear-wheel-drive
6. The limited slip differential can be used to dissipate driveline windup. Also, this system provides greater traction than one with an open differential.
7. b
8. The viscous clutch transfers torque to the axle with more traction. It also dissipates driveline windup.
9. c
10. d

SECTION 6

Answers to ASE Prep Test

1. b	6. c	11. a	16. a
2. c	7. b	12. c	17. a
3. b	8. a	13. c	18. d
4. b	9. d	14. b	19. c
5. c	10. c	15. a	20. b

TIRES AND WHEELS

CHAPTER 40

CHAPTER OVERVIEW

This chapter explains the value of quality care of tires and wheels. Also included is an in-depth look at these common automotive components.

CHAPTER OBJECTIVES

- Describe basic wheel and hub design.
- Recognize the basic parts of a tubeless tire.
- Explain the differences between the three types of tire construction in use today.
- Explain the tire ratings and designations in use today.
- Describe why certain factors affect tire performance, including inflation pressure, tire rotation, and tread wear.
- Remove and install a wheel and tire assembly.
- Dismount and remount a tire.
- Repair a damaged tire.
- Describe the differences between static balance and dynamic balance.
- Balance wheels both on and off a vehicle.
- Describe the three popular types of wheel hub bearings.

INSTRUCTIONAL OUTLINE WITH TEACHING HINTS

I. Wheels—**Assignment: Read pages 1031–1032.**
   A. Lug Nuts
   B. Valve Stem
   C. Drop Center
   D. Offset
II. Tires—**Assignment: Read pages 1032–1038.**
   A. Tube and Tubeless Tires
      1. Plies
      2. Bead
      3. Tread
      4. Sipes
      5. Sidewalls

  B. Types of Tire Construction
  C. Bias Ply
  D. Belted Bias Ply
  E. Radial Ply
  F. Specialty Tires
  G. Tread Designs
  H. Spare Tires
   1. High-pressure mini
   2. Space-saver
   3. Lightweight skin
  I. High-Performance (Speed-Rated) Tires
  J. Tire Ratings and Destinations
   1. Tire profile
   2. Series
  K. Tire Placard
   Hint: Discuss various types of tires and their ratings.
  L. Tire Care
   1. Inflation pressure
   2. Tire rotation—See Transparency Master #104
   3. Tread wear
    Hint: Discuss the importance of maintaining proper tire inflation pressures and their effect on handling and safety.
III. Tire Repair—**Assignment: Read pages 1038–1041.**
  A. Plug Repair
  B. Cold Patch Repair
  C. Hot Patch Repair
  D. Installation of Tire/Wheel Assembly on Vehicle—See Transparency Master #105
IV. Tire/Wheel Runout—**Assignment: Read page 1041.**
 V. Tire/Wheel Assembly Service—**Assignment: Read pages 1014–1043.**
  A. Tire/Wheel Balance
   1. Static balance
   2. Dynamic balance
VI. Wheel Bearings—**Assignment: Read pages 1043–1045.**
  A. Front Wheel Hubs
  B. Rear Hubs
  C. Wheel Bearing Grease Specification
  D. Bearing Troubleshooting

ANSWERS TO REVIEW QUESTIONS

1. Wheels are made of either stamped or pressed steel discs riveted or welded together. They are also available in the form of aluminum or magnesium rims that are die-cast or forged.
2. Dynamic wheel balance—the equal distribution of weight on each side of the center-line. Static wheel balance—the equal distribution of weight around the wheel.
3. Drop center
4. To repair a puncture, a plug that is slightly larger than the size of the puncture is inserted into the hole from the inside of the tire with an insertion tool. Before doing this,

insert the plug into the eye of the tool and coat the hole, plug, and tool with vulcanizing fluid. While holding and stretching the long end of the plug, insert it into the hole. The plug must extend above both the tread and inner liner surface. If the plug pops through, throw it away and insert a new plug. Once the plug is in place, remove the tool and trim off the plug 1/32-inch above the inner surface. Be careful not to pull on the plug while cutting it.

5. Static
6. A properly inflated tire gives the best tire life, riding comfort, handling stability, and fuel economy for normal driving conditions. Too little air pressure can result in tire squeal, hard steering, excessive tire heat, abnormal tire wear, and increased fuel consumption by as much as 10%.

7. d	12. d	17. c
8. a	13. b	18. d
9. c	14. b	19. c
10. a	15. b	20. d
11. d	16. b	

TECH MANUAL
The following procedures are included in Chapter 40 of the *Tech Manual.*

1. Inspecting tires for inflation and wear.
2. Removing and installing front wheel bearings on a RWD vehicle.
3. Balancing a tire and wheel assembly.

SHOP HINTS

- Compare samples of several types of tire construction.
- Discuss tire/wheel runout.
- Discuss the importance of maintaining wheel offset when changing to sport wheels.
- Discuss the ratings in terms of performance and wear.
- Demonstrate how to properly rotate tires and torque the lug nuts.
- Discuss the limitations on spare tires.

TECH MANUAL ANSWERS

Review Questions

1. Provide traction
2. Directional, nondirectional, symmetrical
3. Head-type plug, cold patch, hot patch
4. Axle bearings are on an axle that drives the wheels; wheel bearings are on axles that do not drive.
5. Record the part number of the old bearing.
6. Ball or tapered-roller
7. Dial indicator
8. c
9. a
10. b

SUSPENSION SYSTEMS

CHAPTER 41

CHAPTER OVERVIEW

This chapter looks closely at torsion bar suspension, live-axle rear suspension, independent suspension, electronically controlled suspension, and other types. There are details of the various parts and some servicing discussions.

CHAPTER OBJECTIVES

- Name the different types of springs and how they operate.
- Name the advantages of ball joint suspensions.
- Explain the important differences between sprung and unsprung weight with regard to suspension control devices.
- Identify the functions of shock absorbers and struts, and describe their basic construction.
- Identify the components of a MacPherson strut system and describe their functions.
- Identify the functions of bushings and stabilizers.
- Perform a general front suspension inspection.
- Check chassis height measurements to specifications.
- Identify the three basic types of rear suspensions and know their effects on traction and tire wear.
- Identify the various types of springs, their functions, and locations in the rear axle housing.
- Describe the advantages and operation of the three basic electronically controlled suspension systems: level control, adaptive, and active.
- Explain the function of electronic suspension components including air compressors, sensors, control modules, air shocks, electronic shock absorbers, and electronic struts.
- Explain the basic towing, lifting, jacking, and service precautions that must be followed when servicing air springs and other electronic suspension components.

INSTRUCTIONAL OUTLINE WITH TEACHING HINTS

I. Suspension System Components—**Assignment: Read pages 1050–1056.**
   A. Springs
      1. Spring Rate
      2. Jounce
      3. Rebound

4. Sprung weight

5. Unsprung weight

6. Coil springs

   a. Linear rate

   b. Variable rate

   c. Servicing coil springs

7. Leaf springs

   a. Multiple leaf springs

   b. Mono-leaf springs

   c. Fiber composite leaf springs

8. Air Springs

B. Torsion Bar Suspension System

C. Shock Absorbers

   1. Shock-assist

   2. Gas-charged

   3. Air shock systems

   4. Shock absorber ratio

   5. Electronically controlled shock absorbers

II. MacPherson Strut Suspension Components—**Assignment: Read pages 1056–1059**—See Transparency Master #106.

A. Struts

B. Lower Suspension Components

C. Springs

III. Independent Front Suspension—**Assignment: Read pages 1059–1063.**

A. Short-Long Arm and Double-Wishbone Suspensions

B. Control Arms

C. Ball Joints

D. Coil Springs

E. Other Front-System Components

   1. Bushings

   2. Stabilizers

IV. General Front-Suspension Inspection—**Assignment: Read page 1063–1064.**

A. Chassis Height Specifications

V. Front-Suspension Component Servicing—**Assignment: Read pages 1064–1070.**

A. Coil Springs

B. Removing a Spring

C. Torsion Bars

D. Ball Joints—See Transparency Master #107

   1. Radial check

   2. Axial check

   3. Wear indicators

E. Control Arm Bushings

F. Strut Rod Bushings

G. Sway Bar Bushings

H. Shock Absorbers

   Hint: Review Photo Sequence 46 on page 1065 and Photo Sequence 47 on page 1068.

I. MacPherson Strut Suspension

   Hint: Review Photo Sequence 48 on page 1071.

VI. Rear-Suspension Systems—**Assignment: Read page 1070.**
  A. Live Axle
  B. Semi-Independent
  C. Independent
VII. Live-Axle Rear-Suspension Systems—**Assignment: Read pages 1070–1072.**
  A. Leaf Spring Live-Axle System
  B. Coil Spring Live-Axle System
  C. Live-Axle Suspension System Servicing
VIII. Semi-Independent Suspension—**Assignment: Read page 1073.**
  A. Semi-Independent Suspension System Servicing
IX. Independent Suspension—**Assignment: Read pages 1073–1075.**
  A. Servicing Independent Suspension Systems
    1. Rear coil spring
    2. Rear control arms
X. Electronically Controlled Suspensions—**Assignment: Read pages 1073–1075—** See Transparency Master #108.
  A. Adaptive Suspensions
  B. System Components
    1. Compressor
    2. Sensors
    3. Electronic shock absorbers
    4. Electronic struts
    5. Computer control module
    6. Electronic leveling control
     Hint: Discuss electronically controlled suspensions and their advantages over conventional systems.
XI. Servicing Electronic Suspension Components—**Assignment: Read pages 1079–1080.**
  A. Vehicle Alignment
XII. Active Suspensions—**Assignment: Read pages 1080–1081.**

ANSWERS TO REVIEW QUESTIONS

1. The stabilizer bar transfers a similar movement from one wheel to the wheel on the other side of the vehicle through twisting or torsional movement. This tends to keep the car level.
2. Sprung weight consists of all the vehicle's weight supported by the suspension system. Unsprung weight consists of components not supported by the springs.
3. The principle of the air spring involves increasing air pressure inside an air bag by a piston-like mount that resists jounce.
4. The conventional shock absorber works on the principle of fluid displacement. The extension cycle controls motions of the vehicle body sprung weight. The compression cycle controls the same motions of the unsprung weight. This motion energy is converted to heat energy and is dissipated into the atmosphere.
5. Independent front-wheel suspension allows each front wheel to react independently to input from the road surface, braking, torque, and vehicle body motion without affecting each other.
6. b
7. d

8. c	**13.** a	**18.** a
9. d	**14.** b	**19.** a
10. b	**15.** a	**20.** c
11. c	**16.** d	
12. b	**17.** a	

TECH MANUAL
The following procedures are included in Chapter 41 of the *Tech Manual.*

1. Inspect suspension components.
2. Replace a strut assembly
3. Replace a cartridge in a strut.
4. Remove and install a control arm bushing.

SHOP HINTS

- Display and discuss several types of shock absorbers, including worn ones.
- Examine and discuss the components of a front strut.
- Perform a general front-suspension inspection using guidelines and the service manual.
- Replace ball joints on a vehicle.

TECH MANUAL ANSWERS

Review Questions

1. Coil, leaf, torsion bar
2. c
3. a
4. c
5. To the left
6. The shock absorber contains oil that contacts and lubricates the inner wall of the strut body.
7. Ball joints
8. Precise wheel alignment settings or angles
9. Difficult steering and handling, braking not smooth, excessive bouncing after stops
10. c

STEERING SYSTEMS

CHAPTER 42

CHAPTER OVERVIEW

This chapter discusses manual, power, and four-wheel steering systems theory, operation, and components in depth.

CHAPTER OBJECTIVES

- Describe the similarities and differences between parallelogram, worm and roller, and rack and pinion steering linkage systems.
- Identify the typical manual steering system components and their functions.
- Name the five basic types of steering linkage systems.
- Identify the components in a parallelogram steering linkage arrangement and describe the function of each.
- Identify the components in a manual rack and pinion steering arrangement and describe the function of each.
- Describe the function and operation of a manual steering gearbox and the steering column.
- Explain the various manual steering service procedures.
- Describe the service to the various power-steering designs.
- Perform general power-steering system checks.
- Describe the common four-wheel steering systems.

INSTRUCTIONAL OUTLINE WITH TEACHING HINTS

    I. Manual Steering Systems—**Assignment: Read pages 1085–1091.**
       A. Steering Linkage
       B. Parallelogram Steering Linkage
          1. Pitman arm
          2. Idler arm
          3. Links
          4. Tie-Rods
       C. Rack and Pinion Steering Linkage
          1. Rack
          2. Pinion

      3. Yoke adjustment

      4. Tie-rods

   D. Manual Steering Gear

      1. Worm and roller

   E. Steering Wheel and Column

   F. Steering Damper

     Hint: Pass around various components and discuss front-, rear-, and four-wheel steering systems.

II. Power Steering—**Assignment: Read pages 1091–1096**—See Transparency Master #109.

   A. External Piston Linkage System

   B. Integral Piston System

   C. Power-Assisted Rack and Pinion System

   D. Components

      1. Power-steering pump

      2. Flow control and pressure relief valves

      3. Power-steering gearbox

      4. Power-assisted rack and pinion steering

      5. Power-steering hoses

        Hint: Discuss steering system subsystems and components.

III. Electronically Controlled Power-Steering Systems—**Assignment: Read pages 1096–1098.**

   A. Electric/Electronic Rack and Pinion System

IV. Steering System Diagnosis—**Assignment: Read pages 1098–1101.**

   A. Excessive Steering Wheel Play

   B. Feedback

   C. Hard Steering

   D. Nibble

   E. Pulling or Drifting

   F. Shimmy

   G. Sticking Steering or Poor Return

   H. Wandering

V. Visual Inspection—**Assignment: Read pages 1101–1108**—See Transparency Master #110.

   A. Pitman Arm

   B. Idler Arm

   C. Center Link

   D. Tie-Rod Assembly

   E. Steering Damper

   F. Dry Park Check

   G. Pressure Check

   H. Turning Effort

   I. Tie-Rod Articulation Effort

   J. Worm and Roller Steering

   K. Rack and Pinion Steering

   L. Steering Gear Adjustments

   M. Steering Columns

   N. Power-Steering Servicing

VI. Four-Wheel Steering Systems—**Assignment: Read pages 1108–1112.**

   A. Mechanical 4WS

B. Hydraulic 4WS

C. Electro/Hydraulic 4WS

ANSWERS TO REVIEW QUESTIONS

1. Parallelogram and worm and roller: the pitman arm connects the linkage to the steering column and transmits motion from the steering gear to the linkage, causing the linkage to turn the wheels in the appropriate direction. Rack and pinion: the steering input received from the pinion gear that is attached to the steering column. The gear moves a toothed rack that is attached to the tie-rods. The rack pushes and pulls the tie-rods to change the wheel's direction.

2. Pump, steering gear box

3. It is the most common conventional power-steering system and consists of a power-steering pump and reservoir, power-steering pressure and return box, and steering gear. The power cylinder and control valves are in the same housing as the steering gear.

4. Number of input turns per output turn of the steering gearbox

5. Cornering capability, steering response, straight-line stability, lane-changing stability, low-speed maneuverability

6. c	11. a	16. b
7. c	12. d	17. d
8. b	13. b	18. c
9. c	14. a	19. a
10. c	15. d	20. b

TECH MANUAL

The following procedures are given in Chapter 42 of the *Tech Manual.*

1. Diagnose, remove, and replace an idler arm.

2. Remove and replace an outer tie-rod end on a parallelogram steering linkage.

3. Flush a power-steering system.

4. Test the pressure of a power-steering pump.

5. Inspect a rack and pinion steering gear.

SHOP HINTS

- Display and discuss several types of steering components, including worn ones.
- Examine and discuss the components of a worm and roller steering system.
- Examine and discuss the components of a rack and pinion steering system.
- Demonstrate the dry park check method for checking steering systems.

TECH MANUAL ANSWERS

Review Questions

1. Rack and pinion, worm and roller, recirculating ball

2. Dry park

3. Pull scale
4. True
5. (a) Always wear safety glasses when repairing an air bag system or when handling an air bag module. (b) To prevent accidental deployment and possible injury, the backup power supply for the air bag must be depleted before replacing an air bag and before servicing, replacing, adjusting, or striking components close to the air bag sensors. (c) To deplete backup power supply, disconnect the ground cable of the battery and wait at least one minute (some manufacturers recommend a longer waiting period). (d) Refer to the appropriate service manual to identify the location of the air bag sensors. (e) Never probe the connectors on the air bag module because doing so can cause accidental deployment. (f) Carry a live air bag module with the air bag and trim cover pointed away from your body. (g) Never set a live air bag module down with the trim cover face down. (h) If a vehicle with an air bag was involved in an accident, inspect its sensor mounting bracket and wiring harness for damage. Replace any damaged parts. (i) After deployment of an air bag, the bag and the surrounding surfaces may contain sodium hydroxide, which is a skin irritant. Wash your hands with soap and water after working around the bag.
6. c
7. b
8. d
9. a
10. c

WHEEL ALIGNMENT

CHAPTER OVERVIEW

This chapter discusses the theory and importance of proper two- and four-wheel alignment procedures. Alignment equipment and tools are also covered.

CHAPTER OBJECTIVES

- Explain the benefits of accurate wheel alignment.
- Explain the importance of correct wheel alignment angles.
- Describe the different functions of camber and caster with regard to the vehicle's suspension.
- Identify the purposes of steering axis inclination.
- Explain why toe is the most critical tire wear factor of all the alignment angles.
- Identify the purposes of turning radius or toe-out.
- Explain the condition known as tracking.
- Perform a prealignment inspection.
- Describe the various types of equipment that can be used to align the wheels of a vehicle.
- Describe how alignment angles can be changed on a vehicle.
- Understand the importance of rear-wheel alignment.
- Know the difference between two-wheel and four-wheel alignment procedures.

INSTRUCTIONAL OUTLINE WITH TEACHING HINTS

I. Alignment Geometry—**Assignment: Read pages 1116–1120.**
   A. Caster
   B. Camber
   C. Toe
   D. Thrust Line Alignment—See Transparency Master #111
   E. Steering Axis Inclination (SAI)—See Transparency Master #112
   F. Turning Radius
   G. Tracking
   H. Load Distribution.
      Hint: Review Table 43–1 on page 1116 for misalignment effects.
II. Pre-Alignment Inspection—**Assignment: Read page 1120.**

    A. Road Test
    B. Tire Wear/Runout
    C. Wheel Bearings
    D. Weight Distribution
    E. Ride Height
    F. Steering Wheel Play
    G. Jounce Test
    H. Inspection
  III. Wheel Alignment Equipment—**Assignment: Read pages 1120–1122.**
    A. Turning Radius Gauges
    B. Caster-Camber Gauge
    C. Optical Toe Gauge
    D. Trammel Bar Gauge
    E. Miscellaneous Tools
      Hint: Demonstrate and pass around various gauges and tools.
  IV. Alignment Machines—**Assignment: Read pages 1122–1124.**
    A. Alignment Rack
    B. Two-Wheel
    C. Four-Wheel
  V. Adjusting Wheel Alignment—**Assignment: Read pages 1124–1129.**
    A. Caster/Camber Adjustment
    B. Eccentrics and Shims
    C. Slotted Frame
    D. Rotating Ball Joint and Washers
    E. MacPherson Suspension Adjustment
    F. Rear Wheel Camber Adjustments
    G. Toe Adjustment—See Transparency Master #113
      1. Rear toe
      2. Thrust line
  VI. Four-Wheel-Drive Vehicle Alignment—**Assignment: Read pages 1129.**

ANSWERS TO REVIEW QUESTIONS

1. Positive camber is the angle represented by the tilt of either the front or rear wheels outward from the vertical as viewed from the front of the car.
2. With excessive negative camber, the inside edges of the tires will be worn.
3. Negative caster can cause wandering, unintentional weaving, and instability at high speeds.
4. Toe is the distance comparison between the leading edge and trailing edge of the front tires. If the edge distance is less, then there is toe-in. If it is greater, then there is toe-out.
5. The difference of rear toe from the geometric centerline of the vehicle is called the thrust angle. The vehicle tends to travel in the direction of the thrust line, rather than straight ahead.
6. The tires will drag as the vehicle moves, causing excessive tire wear.
7. The bottom of a tire and wheel assembly must be moved inwardly to add more positive camber.
8. The design of the steering linkage allows for toe-out on turns.
9. a
10. Wheel runout, front and rear camber, front and rear caster, and front and rear toe; the thrust angle created by the rear wheels can then be determined.

11. A caster-camber bubble gauge is used with the turning radius plate to check caster and camber. The gauge is normally attached to the wheel hub with a magnet. Make sure the vehicle is on a level surface and then jounce the front bumper several times to stabilize the suspension. Now look at the bubble gauges to read camber and compare your reading with the specifications. Do both front wheels. Apply the brakes and hold the brake pedal down with a brake pedal lock. Turn one front tire 20 degrees out and adjust the bubble gauge to read zero. Now turn the wheel 20 degrees in and take the reading off the bubble gauge. This is the caster reading for that wheel. Compare it to specifications. Now measure caster on the other front tire. If any reading is outside the specifications, the angles need to be adjusted.

12. Correct tracking refers to a situation with all suspension and wheels in their correct location and condition and aligned so that the rear wheels follow directly behind the front wheels while moving in a straight line. For this to occur, all wheels must be parallel with one another and axle and spindle lines must be at 90-degree angles to the vehicle centerline. Simply stated, all four wheels should form a perfect rectangle.

13. The following are guidelines for a pre-alignment inspection:

   ■ Begin with a road test. While driving the car, check to see that the steering wheel is straight. Feel for vibration in the steering wheel as well as in the floor or seats. Notice any pulling or abnormal handling problems, such as hard steering, tire squeal while cornering, or mechanical pops or clunks.

   ■ Carefully inspect the tire wear patterns and mismatched tire sizes or types. Check the tires' inflation and correct if necessary. Also, look for the results of collision damage and towing damage.

   ■ Check the tires and wheels for radial runout.

   ■ Check the wheel bearings.

   ■ Remove heavy items from the trunk and passenger compartment. If these items are normally carried in the vehicle, such as toolboxes, leave them in.

   ■ Check the vehicle's ride height. Every vehicle is designed to ride at a specific curb height. Curb height specifications and the specific measuring points are given in service manuals. Proper alignment is impossible if the ride height is incorrect.

   ■ Check the play of the steering wheel.

   ■ Jounce the vehicle to check the condition of the shock absorbers.

   ■ With the vehicle raised, inspect all steering components such as control arm bushings, upper strut mounts, pitman arm, idler arm, center link, tie-rod ends, ball joints, and shock absorbers. Check the CV joints (if equipped) for looseness, popping sounds, binding, and broken boots. Damaged components must be repaired before adjusting alignment angles.

14. a
15. a
16. c
17. c
18. d
19. d
20. b

TECH MANUAL
The following procedures are given in Chapter 43 of the *Tech Manual.*

1. Measure front and rear wheel alignment angles.
2. Center a steering wheel.

SHOP HINTS

■ Demonstrate how to do a pre-alignment inspection.
■ Demonstrate how to "read" tire wear in terms of alignment problems.
■ Demonstrate how to adjust camber and caster.
■ Demonstrate how to adjust front wheel toe-in.
■ Demonstrate how to adjust camber, caster, and toe on rear wheels.

TECH MANUAL ANSWERS

Review Questions

1. Greater safety, longer tire life, reduced fuel consumption
2. Toe adjustments
3. On the tie-rod ends
4. By installing an aftermarket caster adjustment kit
5. True
6. c
7. c
8. c
9. a
10. Equal camber means each wheel is tilted outward or inward the same amount.

SECTION 7

Answers to ASE Prep Test

1. c	6. c	11. b	16. d
2. c	7. a	12. c	17. c
3. b	8. c	13. a	18. c
4. b	9. c	14. d	19. c
5. d	10. b	15. b	20. b

BRAKE SYSTEMS

CHAPTER 44

CHAPTER OVERVIEW

This chapter explains at length the principles of friction and the components and operation of hydraulic brake systems, including power brakes and antilock brakes. There is a general discussion of diagnosis, testing, and servicing.

CHAPTER OBJECTIVES

- Explain the basic principles of braking, including kinetic and static friction, friction materials, application pressure, and heat dissipation.
- Describe the components of a hydraulic brake system and their operation, including brake lines and hoses, master cylinders, system control valves, and safety switches.
- Perform both manual and pressure bleeding of the hydraulic system.
- Briefly describe the operation of drum and disc brakes.
- Inspect and service hydraulic system components.
- Describe the operation and components of both vacuum-assist and hydraulic-assist braking units.

INSTRUCTIONAL OUTLINE WITH TEACHING HINTS

I. Friction—**Assignment: Read pages 1133–1135**—See Transparency Master #114.
   A. Kinetic Friction
   B. Static Friction
   C. Factors Governing Braking
      1. Pressure
      2. Coefficient of friction
      3. Frictional contact surface
      4. Heat dissipation
   D. Brake Lining Friction Materials
      1. Fully metallic
      2. Semimetallic
      3. Nonasbestos
II. Principles of Hydraulic Brake Systems—**Assignment: Read pages 1135–1137.**
   A. Dual Braking Systems

1. Front/rear split system
2. Diagonally-split system

III. Hydraulic Brake System Components—**Assignment: Read pages 1137–1138.**
   A. Brake Fluid
   B. Brake Pedal
   C. Master Cylinders

IV. Master Cylinder Operation—**Assignment: Read pages 1138–1141.**
   A. Master Cylinder Components
      1. Reservoirs
      2. Pistons
      3. Cups
      4. Ports
      5. Residual check valve
         Hint: Pass around various master cylinder components and discuss their functions.

V. Hydraulic Tubes and Hoses—**Assignment: Read pages 1141–1142**—See Transparency Master #115.
   A. Brake Line Tubing
   B. Fittings
   C. Brake Line Hoses

VI. Hydraulic System Safety Switches and Valves—**Assignment: Read pages 1142–1145.**
   A. Pressure Differential (Warning Light) Switches
   B. Metering and Proportioning Valves
      1. Metering valves
      2. Proportioning valves
         a. Height sensing proportional valve
      3. Combination valves—See Transparency Master #116
      4. Three-function valves
      5. Two-function valves
   C. Stop Light Switch

VII. Drum and Disc Brake Assemblies—**Assignment: Read pages 1145–1146.**
   A. Drum Brakes
   B. Disc Brakes
      1. Rotor
      2. Caliper
         Hint: Briefly cover drum and disc brake assemblies and review in conjunction with Chapters 45 and 46.

VIII. Hydraulic System Service—**Assignment: Read pages 1146–1151.**
   A. Brake Fluid Inspection
   B. System Flushing
   C. Brake Line Inspection
   D. Brake Pedal Inspection
      1. Pedal reserve
   E. Master Cylinder Rebuilding
   F. Hydraulic System Bleeding
      1. Manual bleeding
      2. Pressure bleeding
   G. Power Brakes
   H. Vacuum-Assist Power Brakes

      I. Operation
         1. Servicing vacuum-assist booster units
         2. Pressure check
         3. Pedal travel
         4. Vacuum reading
         5. Release problems
         6. Hard pedal
         7. Grabbing brakes
         8. Check of internal binding
    IX. Pushrod Adjustment—**Assignment: Read page 1151.**
      A. Gauge Method
      B. Air Method
    X. Hydraulic-Assist Power Booster—**Assignment: Read pages 1151–1153.**
      A. Operation
      B. Basic Operational Test
      C. Accumulator Test
      D. Noise Troubleshooting
        Hint: Discuss types and operations of master cylinders.

ANSWERS TO REVIEW QUESTIONS

  1. Air in the hydraulic system compresses as pressure increases, reducing the force that can be transmitted by the fluid.

  2. Each piston applies hydraulic pressure to two wheels; so if one circuit fails, the other can still stop the car.

  3. Vacuum booster, which uses engine manifold vacuum to increase the force applied to the brake pedal and hydraulic pressure developed by the power steering pump and also increases the pressure exerted on the pistons of the master cylinder.

  4. A pressure differential valve responds to a loss of pressure in one of the hydraulic circuits. Its action turns on the brake warning lamp.

  5. Combines metering and proportioning valves with pressure differential valve, balances braking characteristics of disc and drum brakes, and operates warning light switch

6. a	**11.** b	**16.** c
7. c	**12.** b	**17.** a
8. a	**13.** a	**18.** d
9. b	**14.** b	**19.** d
10. d	**15.** b	**20.** d

TECH MANUAL

The following procedures are included in Chapter 44 of the *Tech Manual.*

  1. Bench bleed a master cylinder.

  2. Pressure bleed a brake system.

  3. Perform power vacuum brake test.

SHOP HINTS

- Display and discuss fully metallic, semimetallic, and nonasbestos brake lining friction materials.
- Display and discuss hydraulic tubes and hoses.
- Examine and discuss drum and disc brake assemblies.
- Demonstrate methods of pushrod adjustment.

TECH MANUAL ANSWERS

Review Questions

1. Replenishing or compensating port
2. False
3. Damage
4. To convert mechanical force into hydraulic pressure
5. ¼-inch
6. To allow braking if one wheel or one circuit leaks
7. Brake discs that exhibit a lack of parallelism, brake discs that have excessive lateral runout, brake drums that are out-of-round
8. Compressible
9. Vacuum assist, hydraulic assist
10. d

DRUM BRAKES

CHAPTER 45

CHAPTER OVERVIEW

This chapter is devoted to drum brake operation design and components. It emphasizes road testing brakes, drum brake inspection, drum refinishing, wheel cylinder inspection and servicing, and parking brakes.

CHAPTER OBJECTIVES

- Explain how drum brakes operate.
- Identify the major components of a typical drum brake and describe their functions.
- Explain the difference between duo-servo and nonservo drum brakes.
- Perform a cleaning and inspection of a drum brake assembly.
- Recognize conditions that adversely affect the performance of drums, shoes, linings, and related hardware.
- Reassemble a drum brake after servicing.
- Explain how typical drum parking brakes operate.
- Adjust a typical drum parking brake.

INSTRUCTIONAL OUTLINE WITH TEACHING HINTS

    I. Drum Brake Operation—**Assignment: Read page 1156**—See Transparency Master #117.

    II. Drum Brake Components—**Assignment: Read pages 1157–1158.**

    A. Wheel Cylinders

    B. Brake Shoes and Linings

      1. Primary shoe

      2. Secondary shoe

    C. Mechanical Components

      1. Shoe return springs

      2. Shoe hold-downs

      3. Shoe anchors

    D. Drums

      Hint: Discuss components of rear-wheel drum brakes using Figure 45–1 on page 1156.

III. Drum Brake Designs—**Assignment: Read pages 1158–1162.**
    A. Duo-Servo Drum Brakes
    B. Automatically Adjusted Servo Brakes
       1. Basic cable
       2. Cable with overtravel spring
       3. Lever with override
       4. Lever and pawl
    C. Nonservo Drum Brakes
    D. Automatically Adjusted Nonservo Brakes
       1. Automatic cam adjusters
       2. Ratchet automatic adjuster
    E. Inspection and Service
       1. Brake noise
IV. Road Testing Brakes—**Assignment: Read pages 1162–1164.**
V. Drum Brake Inspection—**Assignment: Read pages 1164–1169.**
    A. Shoe and Lining Removal
    B. Drum Inspection
       1. Scored drum surface
       2. Bell-mouthed drum
       3. Concave drum
       4. Convex drum
       5. Hard spots on the drum
       6. Threaded drum surface
       7. Heat checks
       8. Cracked drum
       9. Out-of-round drums
    C. Drum Measurements
    D. Drum Refinishing
    E. Cleaning Newly Refaced Drums
       Hint: Discuss various drum conditions that require attention.
VI. Brake Shoes and Linings—**Assignment: Read pages 1170–1171.**
    A. Brake Relining
    B. Sizing New Linings
    C. Lining Adjustment—See Transparency Master #118
    D. Drum Shoe and Brake Installation
VII. Wheel Cylinder Inspection and Servicing—**Assignment: Read pages 1171–1172.**
    A. Inspecting and Cleaning Wheel Cylinders
    B. Replacing Wheel Cylinders
VIII. Drum Parking Brakes—**Assignment: Read pages 1172–1173.**
    A. Types of Parking Brake Systems
IX. Integral Parking Brakes—**Assignment: Read pages 1173–1175**—See Transparency Master #119.
    A. Adjusting and Replacing Parking Brakes
       1. Testing

ANSWERS TO REVIEW QUESTIONS

1. Riveting and bonding
2. The anchor pin acts as a brake shoe stop and creates a wedging action between the shoe and the drum. This, combined with applied brake force, creates a self-multiplied brake force.

3. Scored drum surface, bell-mouthed drum, concave drum, convex drum, hard spots on drum, threaded drum surface, heat checks, cracked drum, out-of-round drum
4. Prevent fluid leakage or air from getting into system
5. When the parking brake pedal is applied, the cables and the equalizer pull on the levers of the rear brakes. The rear brake levers with parking brake struts move the shoes against the brake drums. The shoes are held in position until the parking brake pedal is released.

6. c	**11.** b	**16.** c
7. b	**12.** a	**17.** a
8. a	**13.** c	**18.** b
9. d	**14.** a	**19.** b
10. d	**15.** d	**20.** c

TECH MANUAL

The following procedures are included in Chapter 45 of the *Tech Manual.*

1. Inspect and service duo-servo drum brakes.
2. Inspect and service nonservo drum brakes.
3. Adjust parking brake linkage (cable).

SHOP HINTS

- Discuss the precautions for road testing brakes.
- Have students complete a pre-brake job inspection checklist as they perform a routine brake inspection.
- Demonstrate how to measure drum diameter and discuss the limits as indicated in the shop manual or on drum markings.
- Demonstrate the differences between primary and secondary shoes and where each goes on the backing plate.

TECH MANUAL ANSWERS

Review Questions

1. False
2. Brake drum micrometer
3. a
4. True
5. 0.090 inch or 0.030 inch less than the discard diameter
6. Duo-servo brakes have a double-piston wheel cylinder that activates the primary and secondary brake shoes. The self-energizing force is transferred from one shoe to the other with the wheel rotating in either direction.
7. Large domestic vehicles
8. They are used on smaller cars to reduce the chance of rear brake lockup.
9. c
10. Improperly adjusted parking brake, grease or fluid on linings, improper size or type of fittings

DISC BRAKES

CHAPTER OVERVIEW

This chapter is devoted to disc brake design and function. It emphasizes inspection and servicing of disc brake components.

CHAPTER OBJECTIVES

- List the advantages of disc brakes.
- List disc brake components and describe their functions.
- Explain the difference between the three types of calipers commonly used on disc brakes.
- Describe the two types of parking brake systems used with disc brakes.
- Describe the causes of common disc brake problems.
- Explain what precautions should be taken when servicing disc brake systems.
- Describe the general procedure involved in replacing disc brake pads.
- List and describe five typical disc brake rotor problems.

INSTRUCTIONAL OUTLINE WITH TEACHING HINTS

I. Disc Brake Components and Their Functions—**Assignment: Read pages 1178–1182.**
   A. Hub and Rotor Assembly—See Transparency Master #120
      1. Splash shield
   B. Caliper Assembly
      1. Piston
      2. Dust boot
   C. Fixed Caliper Disc Brakes—See Transparency Master #121
   D. Floating Caliper Disc Brakes—See Transparency Master #122
   E. Sliding Caliper Disc Brakes
   F. Brake Pad Assembly
      1. Audible sensors
   G. Rear Disc/Drum (Auxiliary Drum) Parking Brake
   H. Rear Disc Parking Brakes
   Hint: Discuss disc brake components and their functions.

II. Disc Brake Diagnosis—**Assignment: Read pages 1182–1184.**
   A. Warning Lights
   B. Pulsating Pedal
   C. Spongy Pedal
   D. Hard Pedal
   E. Dragging Brakes
   F. Grabbing Brakes
   G. Noise
   H. Pulling
III. Service Precautions—**Assignment: Read pages 1184–1185.**
IV. General Caliper Inspecting and Servicing—**Assignment: Read pages 1185–1192.**
   A. Caliper Removal
   B. Brake Pad Removal
   C. Caliper Disassembly
   D. Loaded Calipers
   E. Caliper Reassembly
      1. Anti-squeal shim
   F. Brake Pad Installation
      1. Fixed caliper brake pads
      2. Sliding caliper brake pads
      3. Floating caliper brake pads
         Hint: Pass around a caliper assembly and identify the various components and their functions.
V. Rotor Inspecting and Servicing—**Assignment: Read pages 1192–1194.**
   A. Lateral Runout
   B. Lack of Parallelism
   C. Scoring
   D. Bluing or Heat Checking
   E. Rusty Rotor
   F. Rotor Service

ANSWERS TO REVIEW QUESTIONS

1. Disc brakes are resistant to heat fade and water fade, perform more straight-line stops, and automatically adjust as pads wear.
2. Hub and rotor assembly, caliper assembly, brake pad assembly
3. Fixed, floating, sliding
4. Rear disc/drum or auxiliary drum parking brake
5. One, two, or four cylinder bores and pistons
6. d
7. The pads just move slightly away from the rotor after the brakes have been released.
8. Ventilated, solid
9. c
10. a
11. d
12. a
13. b
14. The bore can be wiped down with denatured alcohol or clean brake fluid. If the rust, corrosion, pitting, or scratches are more than slight, the caliper should be replaced.

15. c
16. c
17. a
18. b
19. a
20. b

TECH MANUAL

The following procedures are included in Chapter 46 of the *Tech Manual.*

1. Inspect and measure brake pads and motors.
2. Replace brake pads.

SHOP HINTS

- Examine and discuss disc brake components and their functions.
- Review service precautions for all disc brakes before performing servicing techniques.
- Demonstrate how to replace brake pads.
- Demonstrate how to check rotors for thickness and parallelism.

TECH MANUAL ANSWERS

Review Questions

1. False
2. Set the dial indicator on the rotor's surface and rotate the rotor.
3. Thickness
4. Caliper piston seal
5. A floating caliper uses a single piston that forces the inboard pad against the rotor. The reaction force against the caliper slides the caliper and forces the caliper inward. This pulls the outboard pad against the rotor.
6. Worn disc brake pads, air in the system
7. Failure of the power brake booster or a failed vacuum line
8. c
9. a
10. Sticking caliper in a floating caliper system; stuck piston in a fixed caliper

ANTILOCK BRAKE SYSTEMS

CHAPTER 47

CHAPTER OVERVIEW

This chapter explains the different antilock braking systems. Also covered will be components, service, diagnosis, and repair of these systems, as well as traction control.

CHAPTER OBJECTIVES

- Explain how antilock brake systems work to bring a vehicle to a controlled stop.
- Describe the differences between an integrated and a nonintegrated ABS.
- Briefly describe the major components of a two-wheel antilock brake system.
- Briefly describe the major components of a four-wheel antilock brake system.
- Describe the operation of the major components of an antilock brake system.
- Describe the operation of the major components of automatic traction and stability control systems.
- Explain the best procedure for finding ABS faults.
- List the precautions that should be followed whenever working on an ABS.

INSTRUCTIONAL OUTLINE WITH TEACHING HINTS

    I. Antilock Brakes—**Assignment: Read pages 1197–1199**—See Transparency Master #123.
       A. Pressure Modulation—See Transparency Master #124
       B. Pedal Feel
    II. ABS Components—**Assignment: Read pages 1199–1202.**
       A. Hydraulic Components
          1. Accumulator
          2. Antilock hydraulic control valve assembly
          3. Booster pump
          4. Booster/master cylinder assembly
          5. Fluid accumulators
          6. Hydraulic control unit
          7. Main valve
          8. Modulator unit
          9. Solenoid valve

         10. Valve block assembly
         11. Wheel circuit valves
     B. Electrical/Electronic Components
         1. ABS control module
         2. Brake pedal sensor
         3. Data link connector (DLC)
         4. Diagnostic trouble code (DTC)
         5. Indicator lights
         6. Lateral acceleration sensor
         7. Pressure switch
         8. Pressure differential switch
         9. Relay
         10. Toothed ring
         11. Wheel speed sensor
            Hint: Pass around various ABS electrical and nonelectrical components and discuss their functions.

III. Types of Antilock Brake Systems—**Assignment: Read pages 1202–1204.**
     A. Integral
     B. Non-Integral
     C. Two-Wheel System
         1. 1 channel
         2. 2 channel
     D. Full (Four Wheel) Systems
         1. 3 channel
         2. 4 channel

IV. ABS Operation—**Assignment: Read pages 1204–1212.**
     A. Two-Wheel Systems (Non-Integral)
     B. Four-Wheel Systems (Non-Integral)
         1. Modulator assembly—See Transparency Master #125
         2. Self-diagnosis
     C. Four-Wheel Systems (Integral)
     D. General Motors' Electromagnetic Antilock Brake Systems—See Transparency master #126
     E. Other Brake System Controls

  V. Automatic Traction Control—**Assignment: Read pages 1212–1213.**
 VI. Automatic Stability Control—**Assignment: Read pages 1213–1214.**
VII. Antilock Brake System Service—**Assignment: Read pages 1214–1216.**
     A. Safety Precautions
     B. Relieving Accumulator Pressure

VIII. Diagnosis and Testing—**Assignment: Read pages 1216–1221.**
     A. Pre-Diagnostic Inspection
     B. Visual Inspection
         Hint: Review procedure on page 1216.
     C. Test Drive
     D. Self-Diagnosis
     E. Testers and Scanning Tools
     F. Testing Components with ABS Scan Tools
         Hint: Review procedure on pages 1218–1219.
     G. Testing Components with a Lab Scope
     H. Component Replacement
         1. Wheel speed sensor service
         2. Brake system bleeding

ANSWERS TO REVIEW QUESTIONS

1. Integral vs. non-integral, level of control (number of channels), and which axles are controlled
2. Automatic traction control (ATC) is a system that applies the brakes when a drive wheel attempts to spin and lose traction. Automatic stability systems correct oversteer and understeer by applying one wheel brake.
3. Sends individual wheel speed information to the ABS control unit
4. In non-integrated systems, the hydraulic control unit is separate from the master cylinder and the booster.
5. (1) Pre-test checks or inspections, (2) on-board control module testing, (3) warning light symptom troubleshooting, (4) individual trouble code or component troubleshooting
6. ABS units turn the brake fluid pressure to an individual wheel on and off. The wheel brake units are pulsed.
7. Normal ABS braking causes a slight pulsation of the brake pedal.
8. It modulates the fluid pressure to a wheel brake unit when it is needed. It interrupts the steady flow of pressurized fluid to the brake units.
9. The Delco ABS VI uses small motors with electric brakes to modulate the fluid pressure rather than a hydraulic unit. Pressures in ABS VI are much lower than those found in other antilock brake systems.
10. Understeer is a condition in which the vehicle is slow to respond to steering changes. Oversteer occurs when the rear wheels try to swing around or fishtail.

11. c		16. b	
12. c		17. c	
13. d		18. c	
14. b		19. a	
15. a		20. c	

TECH MANUAL
The following procedures are included in Chapter 47 of the *Tech Manual.*

1. Perform ABS tests with a scan tool.
2. Monitor the operation of the ABS solenoids with a lab scope.
3. Test a wheel-speed sensor and adjust its gap.

SHOP HINTS

- Point out the major components of a two-wheel antilock brake system.
- Point out the major components of a four-wheel antilock brake system.
- Describe the operation of the major components of automatic traction and stability control systems.
- Demonstrate how to find ABS faults using scanners and lab scopes.
- Demonstrate the precautions that should be followed whenever working on an ABS.

TECH MANUAL ANSWERS

Review Questions

1. DOT3
2. False
3. True
4. a
5. c
6. d
7. c
8. True
9. False
10. 3-channel—rear axle plus individual front wheel brakes

SECTION 8

Answers to ASE Prep Test

1. a	6. a	11. b	16. d
2. c	7. b	12. a	17. b
3. c	8. c	13. c	18. a
4. a	9. c	14. a	19. b
5. b	10. d	15. a	20. b

HEATING AND AIR CONDITIONING

CHAPTER OVERVIEW

This chapter discusses heating, venting, and air conditioning theory, components, and operation. The new non-CFC refrigerants are stressed as well as interchange concerns.

CHAPTER OBJECTIVES

- Identify the purpose of a ventilation system.
- Identify the common parts of a heating system.
- Compare the vacuum and mechanical controls of a heating system.
- Describe how an automotive air conditioning system operates.
- Explain why R-134a is the current refrigerant of choice.
- Locate, identify, and describe the function of the various air conditioning components.
- Describe the operation of the three types of air conditioning control systems.

INSTRUCTIONAL OUTLINE WITH TEACHING HINTS

    I. Ventilation System—**Assignment: Read pages 1225–1226**—See Transparency Master #127.
    II. Automotive Heating Systems—**Assignment: Read pages 1226–1229.**
       A. Heater Core
       B. Heater Control Valve
       C. Blower Motor
          1. Blend door
       D. Heater and Defroster Duct Hoses
    III. Theory of Automotive Air Conditioning—**Assignment: Read page 1229.**
       A. Heat Flow
       B. Heat Absorption
       C. Pressure and Boiling Points
    IV. Refrigerants in Air Conditioning Systems—**Assignment: Read pages 1229–1230.**
       A. Clean Air Act
       B. R-12
       C. R-134a
       D. A/C Technician and the Law

E. Basic Operation of an Air Conditioning System—See Transparency Master #128

V. The Air Conditioning System and Its Components—**Assignment: Read pages 1230–1237.**
   A. The Compressor
      1. Piston compressor
      2. Rotary vane compressor
      3. Scroll-type compressor
   B. Refrigerant Oils
      1. Mineral
      2. PAG
      3. Ester
   C. Compressor Clutches
   D. Condenser—See Transparency Master #129
   E. Receiver/Dryer
      1. Accumulator
   F. Thermostatic Expansion Valve/Orifice Tube
   G. Evaporator
   H. Refrigerant Lines
   I. Sight Glass
   J. Blower Motor/Fan
   Hint: Pass around various A/C components and discuss their functions.

VI. Air Conditioning Systems and Controls—**Assignment: Read pages 1237–1240.**
   A. Evaporator Pressure Control System
   B. Cycling Clutch System
      1. Cycling clutch system with thermostatic expansion valve
      2. Cycling clutch system with orifice tube (CCOT)
   C. Compressor Controls
      1. Ambient temperature switch
      2. Thermostatic switch
      3. Pressure cycling switch
      4. Low-pressure cutoff or discharge pressure switch
      5. High-pressure cutout switch
      6. High-pressure relief valve
      7. Compressor control valve
      8. Electronic cycling clutch switch (ECCS)

VII. Temperature Control Systems—**Assignment: Read pages 1240–1244.**
   A. Manual/Semiautomatic Temperature Controls
   B. Automatic Temperature Control
   C. Case/Duct Systems

ANSWERS TO REVIEW QUESTIONS

1. Latent (or hidden) heat
2. Stationary coil clutch
3. Because R-134a is a hydrofluorocarbon (HFC), it causes less damage to the ozone layer when released to the atmosphere. It also works well and safely.
4. The refrigerant flow to the evaporator must be controlled to obtain maximum cooling while ensuring complete evaporation of the liquid refrigerant within the evaporator. This is accomplished by a thermostatic switch, expansion valve, or a fixed orifice tube.

5. Objects can be in one of three forms: solid, liquid, or gas. When objects change from one state to another, large amounts of heat can be transferred. For example, when water temperature goes below 32°F, water changes from a liquid to a solid (ice). If the temperature of water is raised to 212°F, the liquid turns into a gas (steam). But an interesting thing occurs when water, or any matter, changes from a solid to a liquid and then from a liquid to a gas. Additional heat is necessary to change the state of the substance, even though this heat does not register on a thermometer. For example, ice at 32°F requires heat to change into water, which will also be at 32°F. Additional heat raises the temperature of the water until it reaches the boiling point of 212°F. More heat is required to change water into steam. But if the temperature of the steam was measured, it would also be 212°F. The amount of heat necessary to change the state of a substance is called latent heat—or hidden heat—because it cannot be measured with a thermometer. This hidden heat is the basic principle behind all air conditioning systems.

6. Refrigerant leaves the compressor as a high-pressure, high-temperature vapor. By removing heat via the condenser, the vapor becomes a high-pressure, high-temperature liquid.

7. The process of heat loss from air to the evaporator core surface causes humidity in the air to condense on the evaporator.

8. d

9. a

10. d

11. c

12. c

13. c

14. b

15. d

16. d

17. There should be an underhood decal noting that the system requires the use of R-134a. Plus R-134a systems are required to be fitted with quick-disconnect fittings through the system. These also have hoses specially made for R-134a.

18. d

19. c

20. a

TECH MANUAL
The following procedures are included in Chapter 48 of the *Tech Manual.*

1. Identifying the type of air conditioning system in a vehicle.
2. Identifying the components in an air conditioning system.
3. Conducting a visual inspection of an air conditioning system.

SHOP HINTS

- Review the functions of the primary components of a heating system.
- Review the functions of the primary components of an air conditioning system.
- Demonstrate how to hook up A/C gauges and check the line pressures for an R-12 and R-134a system.

CHAPTER 48/49 TECH MANUAL

Answers to Review Questions

1. The A/C system must be discharged at the compressor.
2. True
3. The heater core, the heater control valve, the blower motor and fan, and the heater and defroster duct hoses
4. On the heater core housing assembly
5. Suction and discharge
6. d
7. c
8. c
9. b
10. a

HEATING AND AIR CONDITIONING SERVICE

CHAPTER 49

CHAPTER OVERVIEW

This chapter discusses the handling procedures for automotive refrigerants, retrofitting A/C systems, and A/C troubleshooting and service procedures.

CHAPTER OBJECTIVES

- Understand the special handling procedures for automotive refrigerants.
- Explain the concerns and precautions regarding retrofitting an A/C system.
- Describe how to connect a manifold gauge set to a system.
- Describe methods used to check refrigerant leaks.
- Use approved methods and equipment to discharge, reclaim/recycle, evacuate, and recharge an automotive air conditioning system.
- Perform a performance test on an A/C system.
- Interpret pressure readings as an aid to diagnose A/C problems.

INSTRUCTIONAL OUTLINE WITH TEACHING HINTS

    I. Maintenance Precautions—**Assignment: Read pages 1247–1248.**
   II. Refrigerant Safety Precautions—**Assignment: Read pages 1248–1249.**
  III. Guidelines for Converting (Retrofitting) R-12 Systems to R-134a—**Assignment: Read pages 1249–1250.**
      A. Refrigerants
  IV. Air Conditioner Testing and Servicing Equipment—**Assignment: Read pages 1250–1254.**
      A. Manifold Gauge Set
      B. Purity Test
      C. Service Valves—See Transparency Master #130
         1. Stem service valve—See Transparency Master #131
         2. Schrader service valve—See Transparency Master #132
      D. Leak Testing a System
         1. Visual inspection
         2. Electronic leak detector
         3. Fluorescent leak tracer
         4. Fluid leak detector

V. Service Procedures—**Assignment: Read pages 1254–1259.**
   A. Certification
   B. Refrigerant Recovery
   C. System Flushing
   D. Compressor Oil Level Checks
   E. Evacuating and Charging the System
      1. Thermistor vacuum gauge
      2. Charging cylinder
   F. Performance Testing
VI. Diagnostic and Troubleshooting Procedures—**Assignment: Read page 1259.**
VII. Electrical System Inspection—**Assignment: Read pages 1259–1260**—See Transparency Master #133.
VIII. Heating System Service—**Assignment: Read page 1260.**
   A. Basic Heater Inspection and Checks
      Hint: Discuss and compare for students the stacked core reheat and the blend air reheat duct systems.

ANSWERS TO REVIEW QUESTIONS

1. a
2. When you are not sure of the refrigerant used in a system or if you suspect a mixing of refrigerants has occurred, you should run a purity test and/or use a refrigerant identifier. Equipment is available to do both of these checks. Knowing what refrigerant is in the system, or what condition it is in, will help you determine what steps you need to take to properly service the system.
3. c
4. b
5. Vacuum is any pressure less than atmospheric pressure. Total vacuum is best defined as the total absence of air.

6. DMM	11. c	16. c
7. d	12. a	17. b
8. c	13. c	18. b
9. b	14. b	19. c
10. d	15. b	20. c

TECH MANUAL

The following procedures are included in Chapter 49 of the *Tech Manual.*

1. Conduct a system performance test.
2. Inspect, test, and service a compressor clutch.
3. Identify and recover refrigerant.
4. Recycle refrigerant.
5. Label and store refrigerant.
6. Test recycled refrigerant for noncondensable gases.

SHOP HINTS

- Discuss the special handling procedures for automotive refrigerants.
- Explain the concerns and precautions regarding retrofitting an A/C system.
- Demonstrate how to connect a manifold gauge set to a system.
- Demonstrate methods used to check refrigerant leaks.

OTHER COMFORT, SAFETY, AND SECURITY EQUIPMENT

CHAPTER 50

CHAPTER OVERVIEW

This chapter surveys safety and security equipment. Among these are safety glass, restraint systems, air bags, and antitheft devices. Other electronic equipment mentioned are audio systems, power antennae, and cellular phones.

CHAPTER OBJECTIVES

- Identify and describe devices that contribute to automotive safety.
- Explain the difference between active and passive restraint systems.
- Identify the major parts of passive belt systems.
- Know how to service and repair passive belt systems.
- Describe the function and operation of air bags.
- Safely disarm and inspect an air bag assembly.
- Describe the operation of keyless entry systems.
- Identify the various security disabling devices.
- Understand the operation of the various security alarms.
- Identify the components of typical radio and audio systems.

INSTRUCTIONAL OUTLINE WITH TEACHING HINTS

I. Restraint Systems—**Assignment: Read pages 1264–1268.**
   A. Seat Belts—See Transparency Master #134
   B. Servicing Seat Belts
      1. Webbing inspection
      2. Buckle inspection
      3. Retractor inspection
      4. Drive track assembly and anchor inspection
      5. Seat belt tensioners
   C. Rear Seat Restraint System
   D. Child Seat
   E. Warning Light and Sound Systems
II. Air Bags—**Assignment: Read pages 1268–1272**—See Transparency Master #135.
   A. Electrical System Components

　　　　1. Sensors
　　　　2. Diagnostic monitor assembly
　　　　3. Wiring harness
　　　　4. Clock spring
　　　　5. SIR or air bag readiness light
　　　B. Air Bag Module
　　　C. Passenger-Side and Side Air Bags
　III. Servicing the Air Bag System—**Assignment: Read pages 1272–1274.**
　　　A. Air Bag Safety and Service Warnings—See Transparency Master #136
　　　B. Service Guidelines
　　　　Hint: Review elements of the air bag system and their functions.
　　　　Hint: Be sure students understand the trouble code index and how to read the scan tool.
　IV. Security and Antitheft Devices—**Assignment: Read pages 1274–1277.**
　　　A. Locks
　　　B. Keyless Entry System
　　　C. Disabling Devices
　　　D. Pass-Key Systems
　　　E. Alarm Systems
　　　F. Vehicle Tracking Systems
　　V. Other Electronic Equipment—**Assignment: Read pages 1277–1280.**
　　　A. Navigation Systems
　　　B. Sound Systems
　　　C. Speaker and Sound Quality
　　　D. Cellular Phones

ANSWERS TO REVIEW QUESTIONS

1. An amplifier increases the volume of a sound without distorting it. Amplifiers are typically rated by the maximum power (watts) they can put out. In order to take advantage of the power output, speakers must be chosen that match the output. This ensures clean sound output. Using a good and powerful amplifier with poor speakers will not provide quality sound. Likewise, using a poor-quality amplifier with great speakers will also not provide clean sound.

2. A speaker emits sound by the vibration of its diaphragm. The vibration is set up by electrical pulses it receives from the radio, cassette player, or CD player. A permanent magnet and coil of wire change these electrical pulses into motion. This motion causes the speaker's diaphragm to vibrate. The vibration sends out pressure waves that we hear as sound.

3. The inflater module

4. a	**9.** d	**14.** d	**19.** c
5. b	**10.** c	**15.** a	**20.** d
6. c	**11.** c	**16.** b	
7. c	**12.** a	**17.** c	
8. a	**13.** c	**18.** c	

TECH MANUAL
The following procedures are included in Chapter 50 of the *Tech Manual.*

1. Inspecting seat belts.
2. Working safely around air bags.
3. Identifying the source of static on a radio.

CHAPTER 50 TECH MANUAL

Answers to Review Questions

1. Systems that operate automatically without an action by the driver or passenger
2. Webbing, buckle, retractor, anchors
3. Disconnect the positive battery cable and wait one minute.
4. With the horn pad facing up and the aluminum or metallic housing facing down
5. No
6. No
7. c
8. False
9. a
10. a

SECTION 9

Answers to ASE Prep Test

1. b	6. c	11. b	16. a
2. c	7. b	12. b	17. d
3. a	8. c	13. d	18. d
4. b	9. d	14. d	19. b
5. b	10. a	15. c	20. c

TRANSPARENCY MASTER CONTENTS

USING THE MAINTENANCE SCHEDULE

GM wants to help keep these vehicles in good working condition. Because of all the different ways people use their GM vehicles, maintenance needs vary. More frequent checks and replacement than you'll find in the schedules in this section may be needed. Read this section, and keep in mind the customer's driving habits.

The proper fluids and lubricants to use are listed in Part D. Use the proper fluids and lubricants whenever servicing these vehicles.

The schedules are for vehicles that:
- carry passengers and cargo within recommended limits. Refer to "Vehicle Certification Label" in this section.
- are driven on reasonable road surfaces within legal driving limits.
- are driven off-road in the recommended manner. Refer to the Owner's Manual.
- use the recommended unleaded fuel.

SELECTING THE RIGHT SCHEDULE

Schedule I Definition
Follow Maintenance Schedule I if any one of these are true:
- Most trips are less than 5 to 10 miles (8 to 16 km). This is particularly important when outside temperatures are below freezing.
- Most trips include extensive idling (such as frequent driving in stop and go traffic).
- The vehicle is operated in dusty areas or off-road frequently.
- Trailer towing or using a carrier on top of the vehicle frequently.

Schedule I should also be followed if the vehicle is used for delivery service, police, taxi, or other commercial applications.

Schedule II Definition
Follow Schedule II ONLY if none of the conditions from Schedule I are true.

Schedule I Intervals
Every 3,000 Miles (4,800 km) or 3 Months
Engine Oil and Filter Change
Chassis Lubrication
Drive Axle Service
At 6,000 Miles (9,600 km)
Tire Rotation

Every 15,000 Miles (24,000 km)
Air Filter Inspection,
if driving in dusty conditions
Front Wheel Bearing Repack (two-wheel drive only) (or at each brake relining, whichever occurs first).
Every 30,000 Miles (48,000 km)
Air Filter Replacement
Fuel Filter Replacement
Every 50,000 Miles (80,000 km)
Automatic Transmission Service (severe conditions only).
Every 60,000 Miles (96,000 km)
Engine Accessory Drive Belt Inspection
Engine Timing Check
Fuel Tank, Cap and Lines Inspection
Every 100,000 Miles (160,000 km)
Spark Plug Replacement
Spark Plug Wire Inspection
Positive Crankcase Ventilation (PCV) Valve Inspection
Every 150,000 Miles (240,000 km)
Cooling System Service (or every 60 months, whichever occurs first)

Schedule II Intervals
Every 7,500 Miles (12,000 km)
Engine Oil and Filter Change (or every 12 months, whichever occurs first)
Chassis Lubrication (or every 12 months, whichever occurs first)
Drive Axle Service
Tire Rotation
Every 30,000 Miles (48,000 km)
Fuel Filter Replacement
Air Filter Replacement
Front Wheel Bearing Repack (two-wheel drive only) (or at each brake relining, whichever occurs first)
Every 50,000 Miles (80,000 km)
Automatic Transmission Service (severe conditions only)
Every 60,000 Miles (96,000 km)
Engine Accessory Drive Belt Inspection
Fuel Tank, Cap and Lines Inspection
Engine Timing Check
Every 100,000 Miles (160,000 km)
Spark Plug Wire Inspection
Spark Plug Replacement
Positive Crankcase Ventilation (PCV) Valve Inspection
Every 150,000 Miles (240,000 km)
Cooling System Service (or every 60 months, whichever occurs first)

Transparency 1

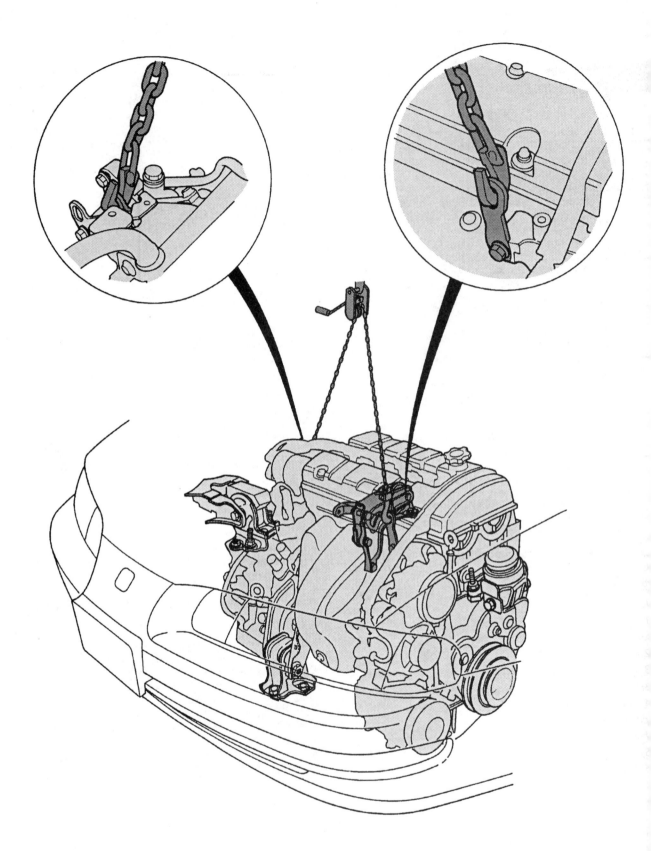

Transparency 2

Automotive Technology: A Systems Approach, 3E

TABLE 2–1 GUIDE TO EXTINGUISHER SELECTION

	Class of Fire	Typical Fuel Involved	Type of Extinguisher
Class **A** Fires (green)	**For Ordinary Combustibles** Put out a class A fire by lowering its temperature or by coating the burning combustibles.	Wood Paper Cloth Rubber Plastics Rubbish Upholstery	Water*[1] Foam* Multipurpose dry chemical[4]
Class **B** Fires (red)	**For Flammable Liquids** Put out a class B fire by smothering it. Use an extinguisher that gives a blanketing, flame-interrupting effect; cover whole flaming liquid surface.	Gasoline Oil Grease Paint Lighter fluid	Foam* Carbon dioxide[5] Halogenated agent[6] Standard dry chemical[2] Purple K dry chemical[3] Multipurpose dry chemical[4]
Class **C** Fires (blue)	**For Electrical Equipment** Put out a class C fire by shutting off power as quickly as possible and by always using a nonconducting extinguishing agent to prevent electric shock.	Motors Appliances Wiring Fuse boxes Switchboards	Carbon dioxide[5] Halogenated agent[6] Standard dry chemical[2] Purple K dry chemical[3] Multipurpose dry chemical[4]
Class **D** Fires (yellow)	**For Combustible Metals** Put out a class D fire of metal chips, turnings, or shavings by smothering or coating with a specially designed extinguishing agent.	Aluminum Magnesium Potassium Sodium Titanium Zirconium	Dry powder extinguishers and agents only

*Cartridge-operated water, foam, and soda-acid types of extinguishers are no longer manufactured. These extinguishers should be removed from service when they become due for their next hydrostatic pressure test.

Notes:

1) Freezes in low temperatures unless treated with antifreeze solution, usually weighs over 20 pounds (9 kg), and is heavier than any other extinguisher mentioned.

2) Also called ordinary or regular dry chemical. (sodium bicarbonate)

3) Has the greatest initial fire-stopping power of the extinguishers mentioned for class B fires. Be sure to clean residue immediately after using the extinguisher so sprayed surfaces will not be damaged. (potassium bicarbonate)

4) The only extinguishers that fight A, B, and C classes of fires. However, they should not be used on fires in liquefied fat or oil of appreciable depth. Be sure to clean residue immediately after using the extinguisher so sprayed surfaces will not be damaged. (ammonium phosphates)

5) Use with caution in unventilated, confined spaces.

6) May cause injury to the operator if the extinguishing agent (a gas) or the gases produced when the agent is applied to a fire is inhaled.

Transparency 3

PRODUCT NAME CLEAN-R-CARB (AEROSOL) #-MSDS05079
PRODUCT- 5079,5079T,5081,5081T

(Page 1 of 2)

1. INGREDIENTS	CAS #	ACGIH TLV	OSHA PEL	OTHER LIMITS	%
Acetone	67-64-1	750 ppm	750 ppm		2-5
Xylene	1330-20-7	100 ppm	100 ppm		68-75
2-Butoxy Ethanol	111-76-2	25 ppm	25 ppm	(skin)	3-5
Methanol	67-56-1	200 ppm	200 ppm		3-5
Detergent	-	NA	NA		0-1
Propane	74-98-6	NA	1000 ppm		10-20
Isobutane	75-28-5	NA	NA	1000ppm	10-20

2. PHYSICAL DATA : (without propellent)

Specific Gravity : 0.865   Vapor Pressure : ND
                                  % Volatile   : > 99
Boiling Point   : 176 F initial   Evaporation Rate : Moderately fast
Freezing Point : ND   Vapor Density : ND
Appearance and Odor: pH: NA
      A clear colorless liquid, aromatic odor

Solubility   :   Partially soluble in water.

3. FIRE AND EXPLOSION DATA

Flashpoint : -40 F Method : TCC
Flammable Limits   : propellent   LEL:1.8   UEL:9.5
Extinguishing Media : CO2, dry chemical, foam
Unusual Hazards   : Aerosol cans may explode when heated above 120 F.

4. REACTIVITY AND STABILITY

Stability   : Stable
Hazardous decomposition products
                   : CO2, carbon monoxide (thermal)

Materials to avoid : Strong oxidizing agents and sources of ignition.

5. PROTECTION INFORMATION

Ventilation :   Use mechanical means to insure vapor conc. is
                       below TLV.

Respiratory :   Use self-contained breathing apparatus above TLV.

      Gloves : Solvent resistant   Eye & Face : Safety glasses
Other Protective Equipment: Not normally required for aerosol product usage.

Transparency 4

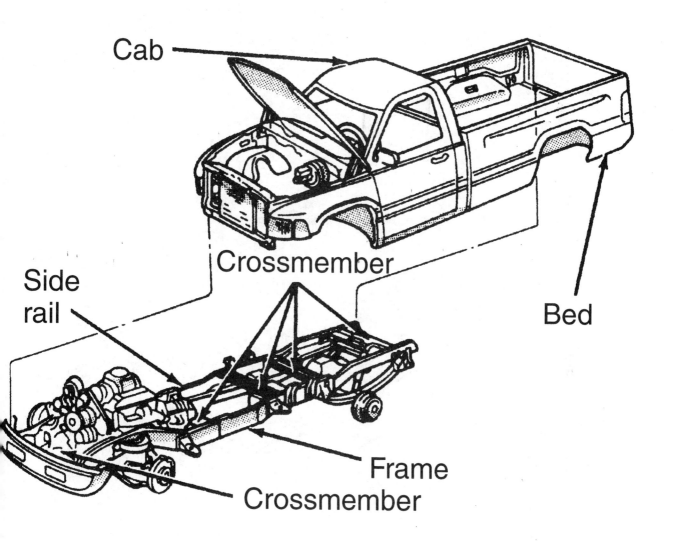

Cab

Crossmember

Bed

Side
rail

Frame
Crossmember

Transparency 5

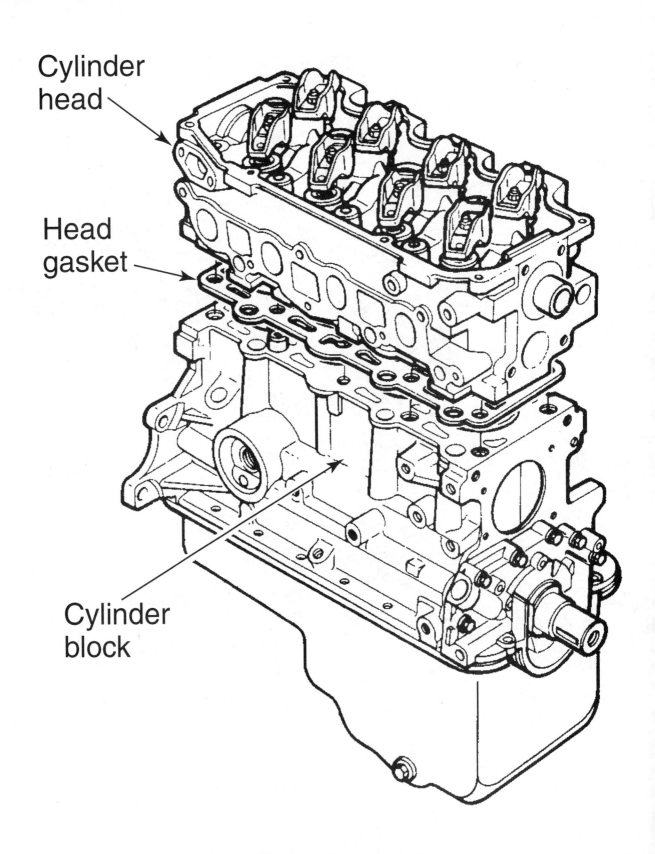

Cylinder
head

Head
gasket

Cylinder
block

Transparency 6

Automotive Technology: A Systems Approach, 3E

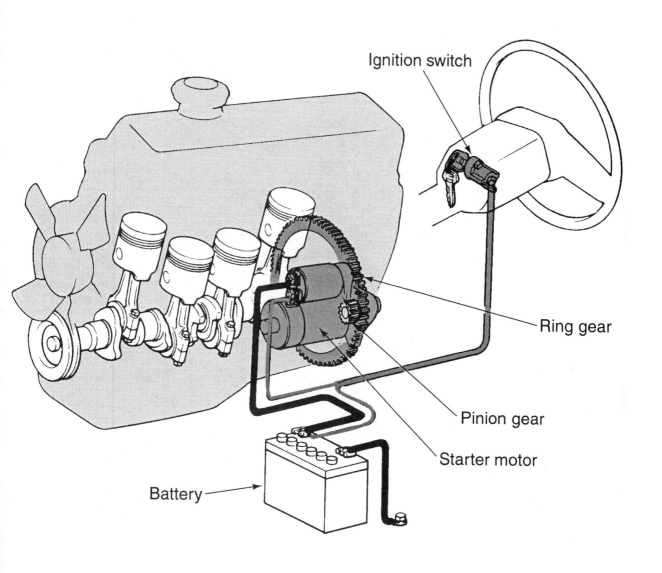

Ignition switch

Ring gear

Pinion gear

Starter motor

Battery

Transparency 7

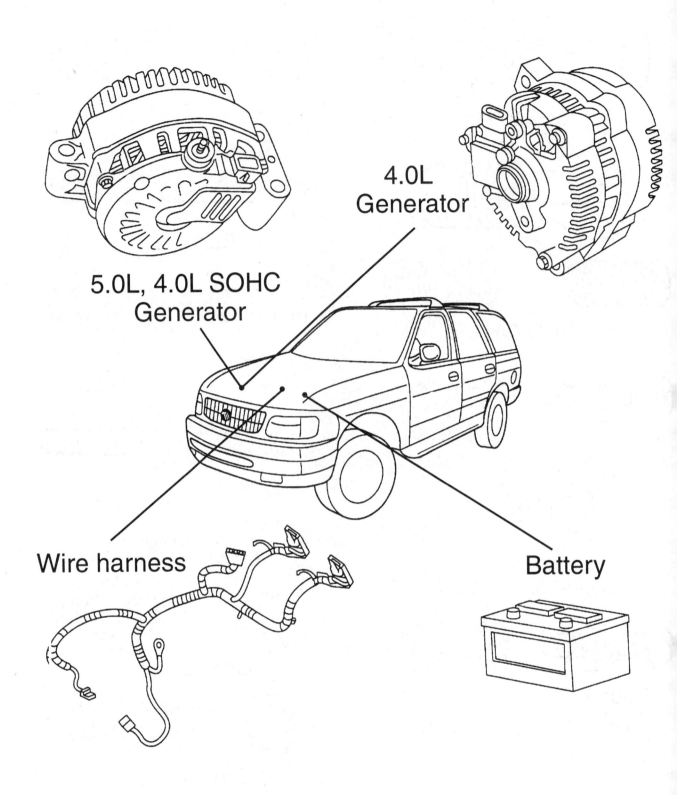

4.0L
Generator

5.0L, 4.0L SOHC
Generator

Wire harness

Battery

Transparency 8

Automotive Technology: A Systems Approach, 3E

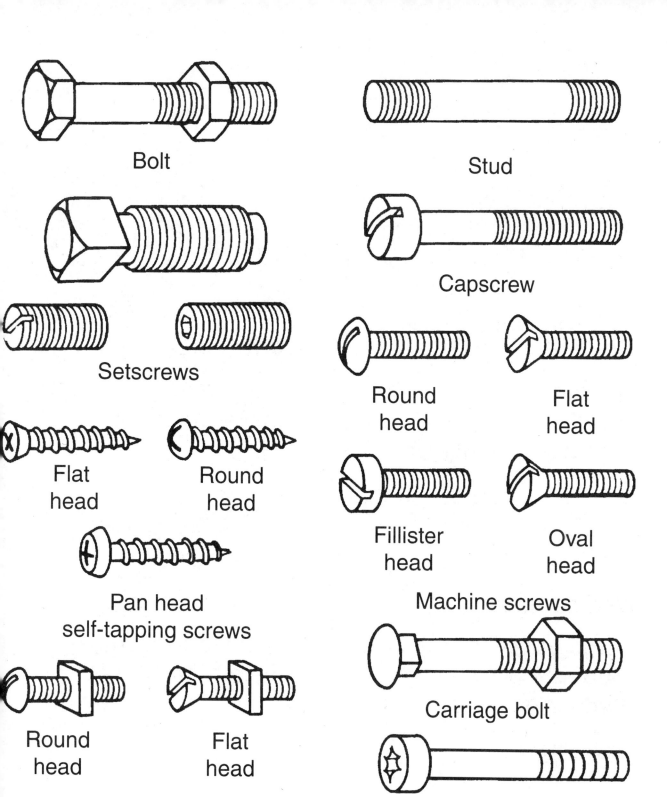

Bolt

Stud

Setscrews

Capscrew

Flat head

Round head

Round head

Flat head

Pan head self-tapping screws

Fillister head

Oval head

Machine screws

Round head

Flat head

Carriage bolt

Torx head bolt

Transparency 9

Grade 2   Grade 5   Grade 7   Grade 8

Customary (inch) bolts—identification marks correspond to bolt strength—increasing numbers represent increasing strength.

Metric bolts—identification class numbers correspond to bolt strength—increasing numbers represent increasing strength.

Transparency 10

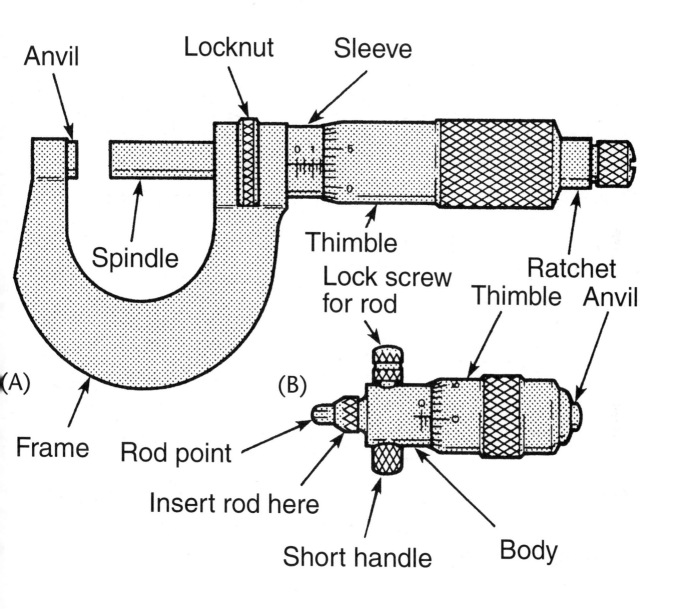

Anvil

Locknut

Sleeve

Spindle

Thimble

Lock screw
for rod

Ratchet

Thimble

Anvil

(A)

(B)

Frame

Rod point

Insert rod here

Short handle

Body

Transparency 11

PREFIX	SYMBOL	RELATION TO BASIC UNIT
Mega	M	1,000,000
Kilo	K	1,000
Milli	m	0.001 or $\dfrac{1}{1000}$
Micro	μ	$.000001$ or $\dfrac{1}{1000000}$
Nano	n	.000000001
Pico	p	.000000000001

Transparency 12

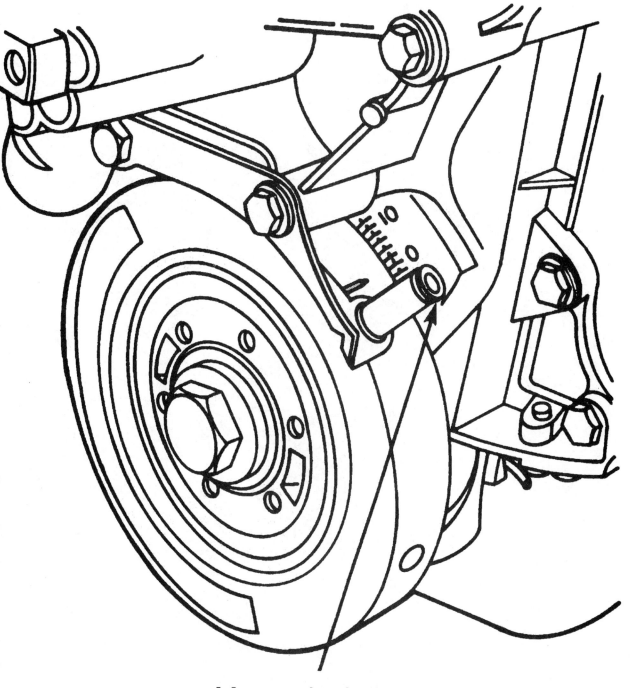

Magnetic timing
probe receptacle

Transparency 13

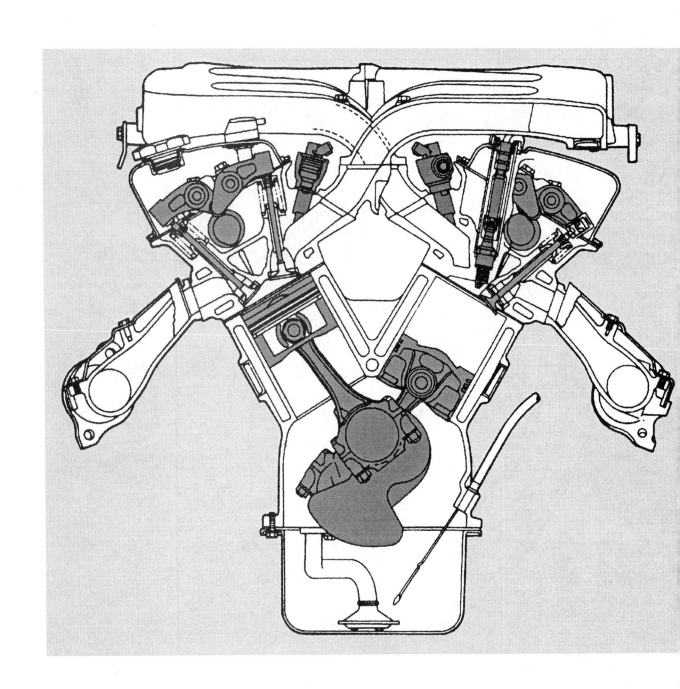

Transparency 14

Automotive Technology: A Systems Approach, 3E

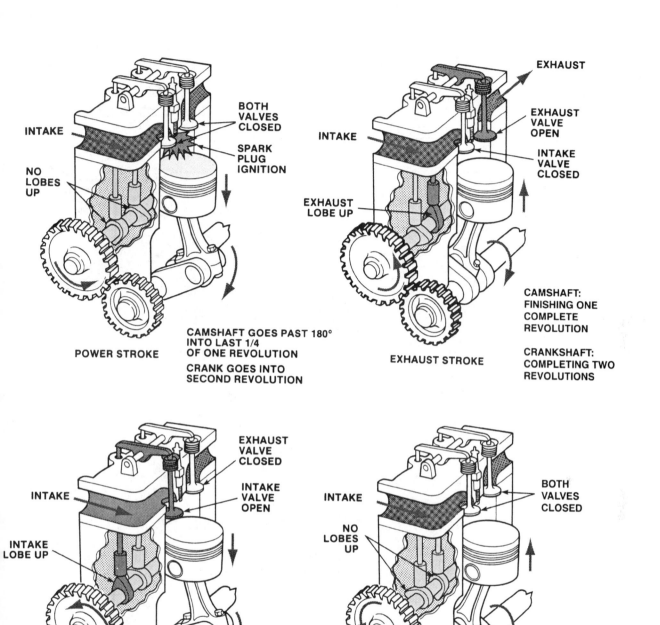

POWER STROKE

INTAKE

NO LOBES UP

BOTH VALVES CLOSED

SPARK PLUG IGNITION

CAMSHAFT GOES PAST 180° INTO LAST 1/4 OF ONE REVOLUTION

CRANK GOES INTO SECOND REVOLUTION

EXHAUST STROKE

INTAKE

EXHAUST LOBE UP

EXHAUST

EXHAUST VALVE OPEN

INTAKE VALVE CLOSED

CAMSHAFT: FINISHING ONE COMPLETE REVOLUTION

CRANKSHAFT: COMPLETING TWO REVOLUTIONS

INTAKE STROKE

INTAKE

INTAKE LOBE UP

GEAR RATIO:1   2

EXHAUST VALVE CLOSED

INTAKE VALVE OPEN

CRANK PULLS PISTON DOWN

COMPRESSION STROKE

INTAKE

NO LOBES UP

BOTH VALVES CLOSED

CAMSHAFT 1/4 REVOLUTION CRANKSHAFT 1/2 REVOLUTION

Transparency 15

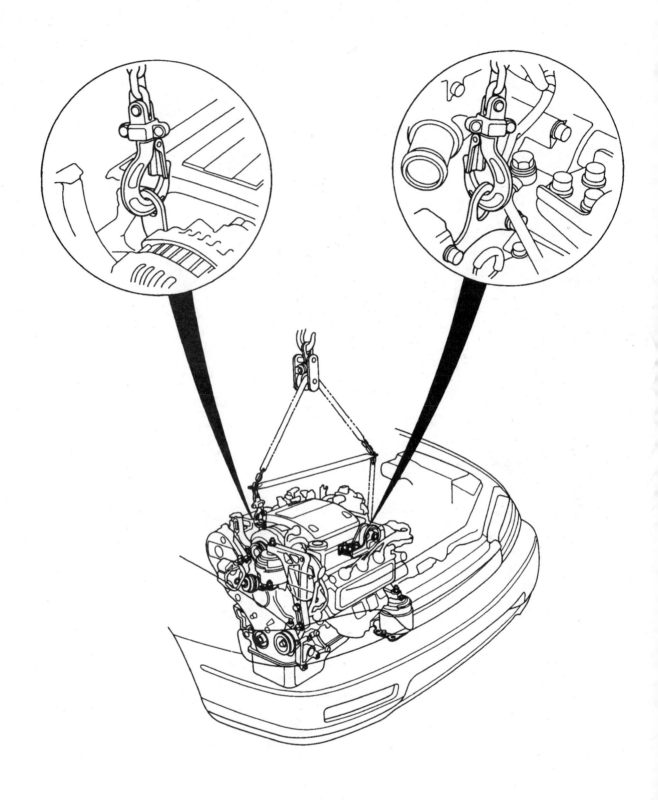

Transparency 16

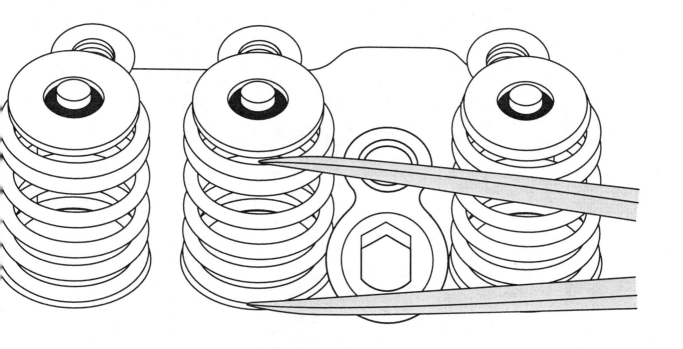

Transparency 17

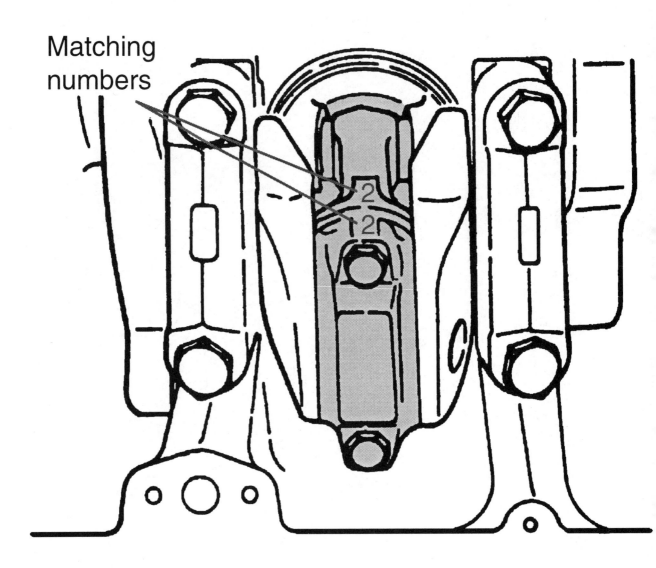

Matching numbers

2

2

Transparency 18

Automotive Technology: A Systems Approach, 3E

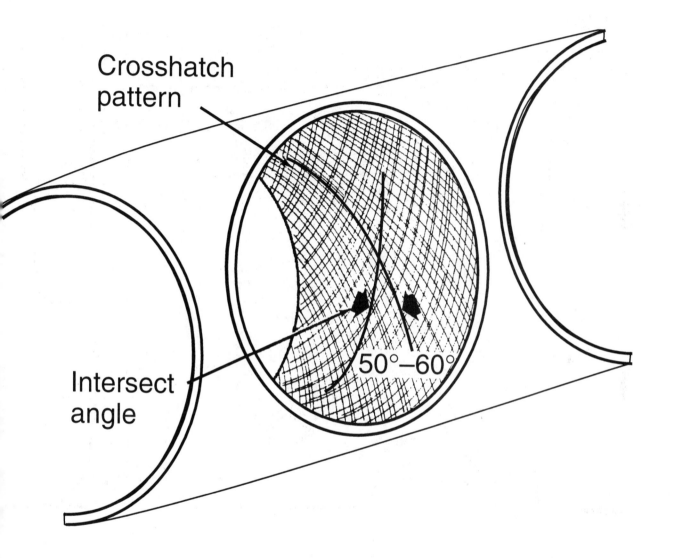

Crosshatch pattern

Intersect angle

50°–60°

Transparency 19

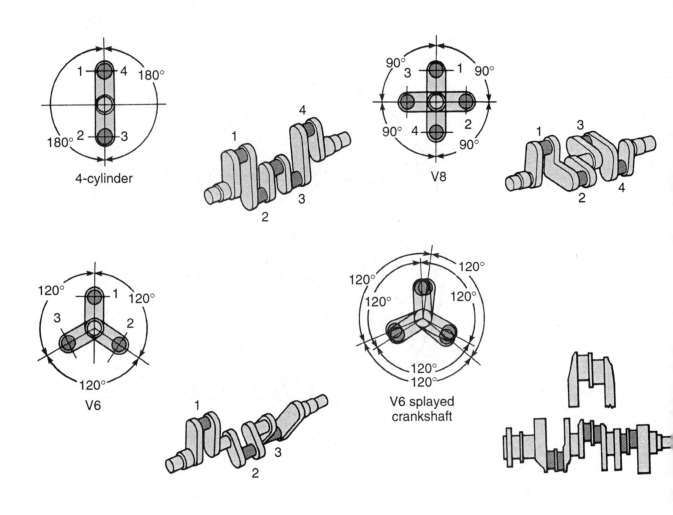

4-cylinder

V8

V6

V6 splayed crankshaft

Transparency 20

Automotive Technology: A Systems Approach, 3E

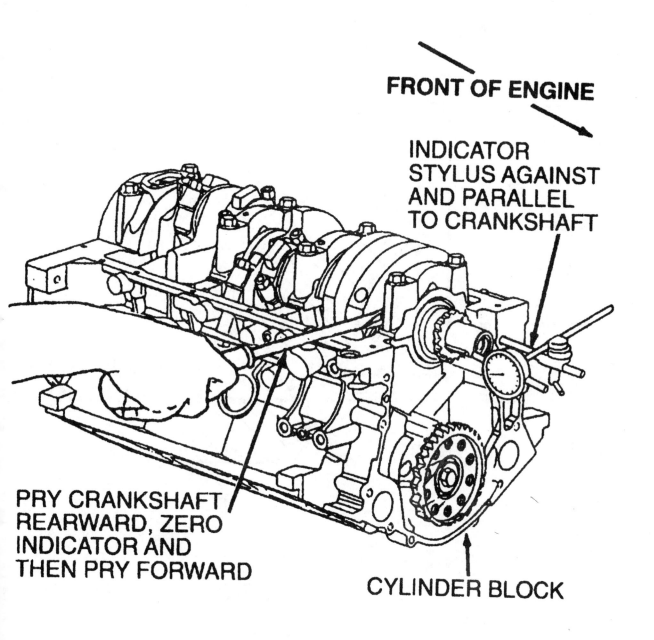

FRONT OF ENGINE

INDICATOR
STYLUS AGAINST
AND PARALLEL
TO CRANKSHAFT

PRY CRANKSHAFT
REARWARD, ZERO
INDICATOR AND
THEN PRY FORWARD

CYLINDER BLOCK

Transparency 21

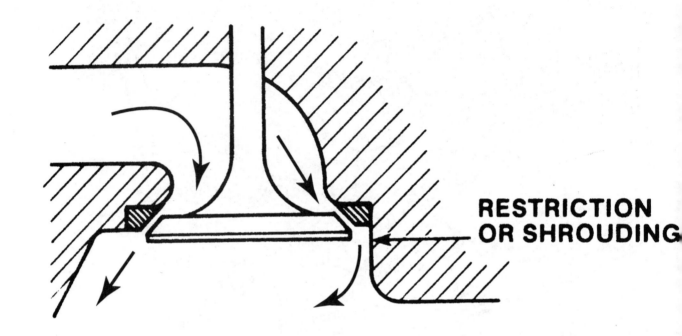

**RESTRICTION
OR SHROUDING**

Transparency 22

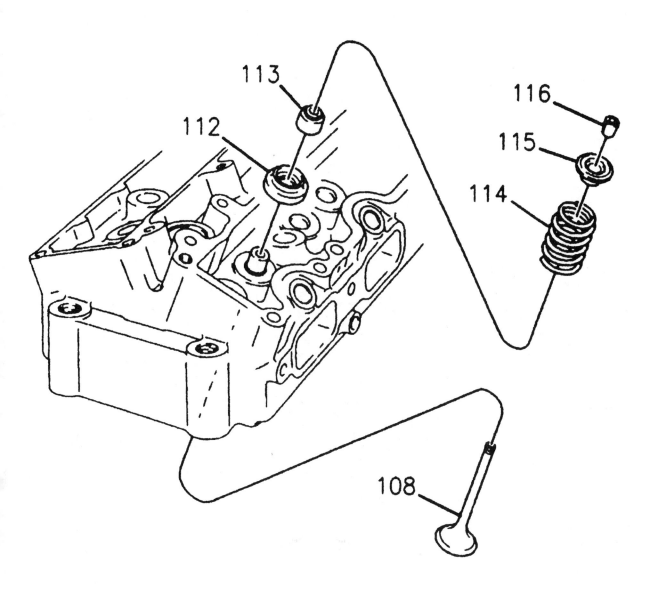

108   VALVE (INTAKE SHOWN)

112   ROTATOR ASSEMBLY

113   SEAL, VALVE STEM

114   SPRING

115   RETAINER

116   KEYS

Transparency 23

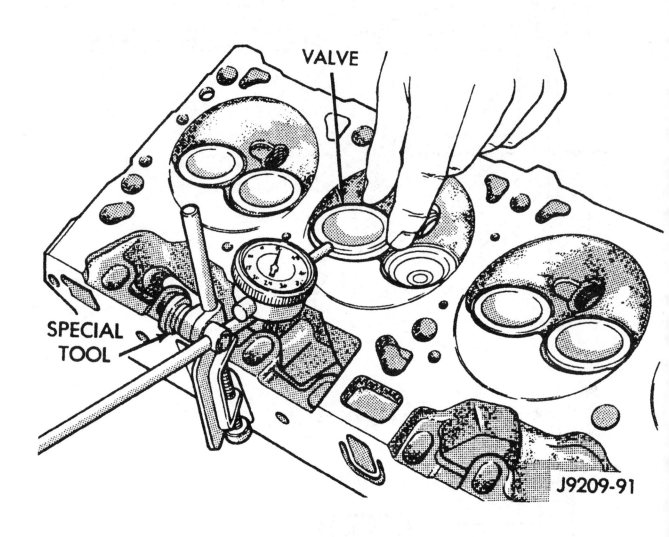

VALVE

SPECIAL
TOOL

J9209-91

Transparency 24

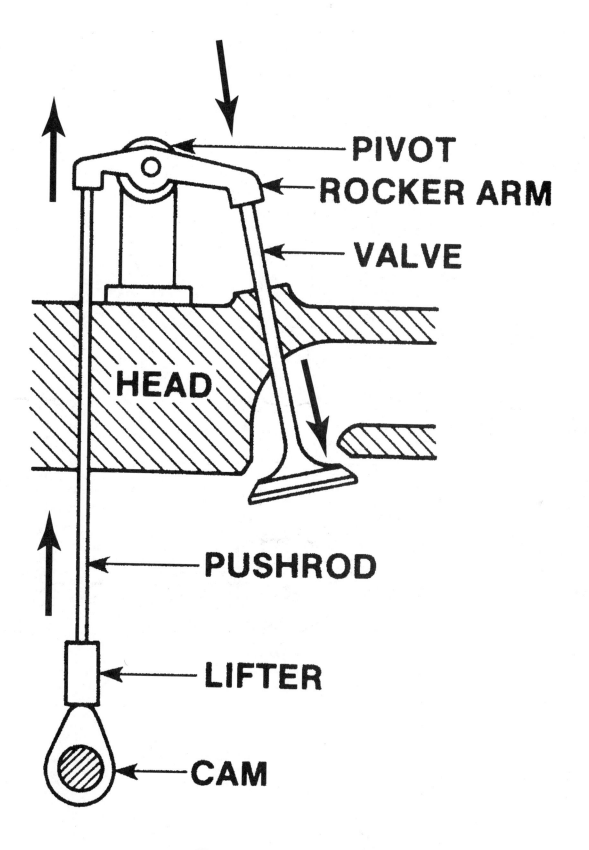

PIVOT

ROCKER ARM

VALVE

HEAD

PUSHROD

LIFTER

CAM

Transparency 25

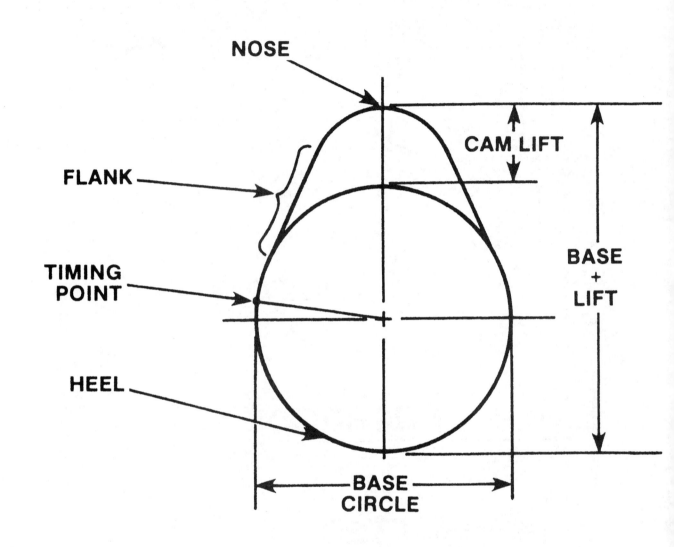

NOSE

CAM LIFT

FLANK

TIMING
POINT

BASE
+
LIFT

HEEL

BASE
CIRCLE

Transparency 26

Automotive Technology: A Systems Approach, 3E

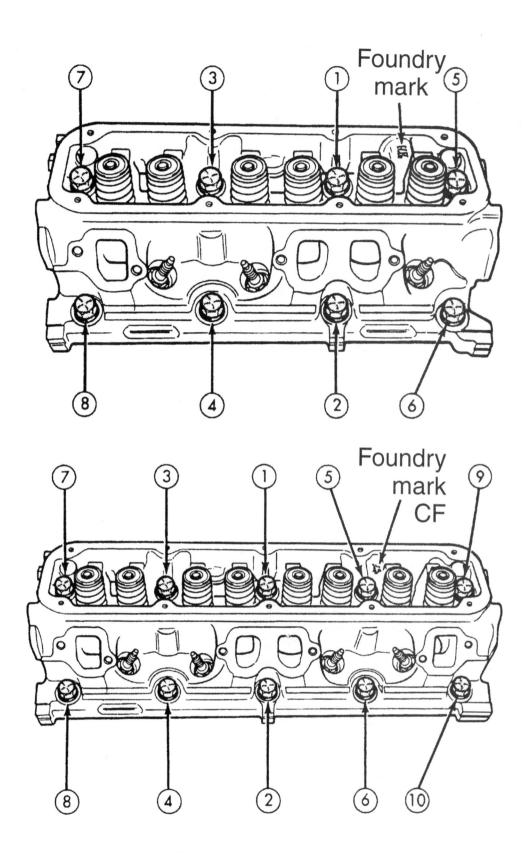

Foundry mark

Foundry mark CF

Transparency 27

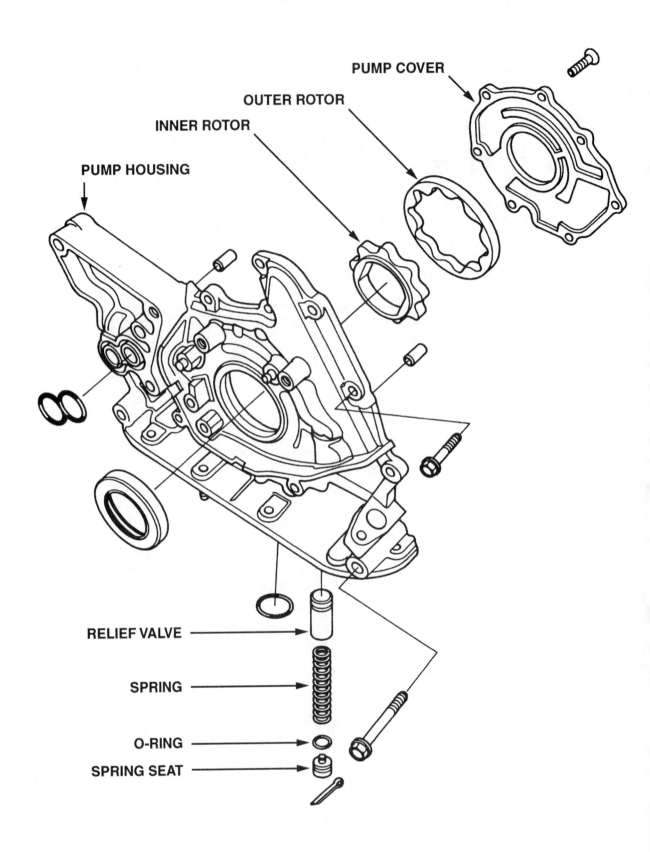

PUMP COVER

OUTER ROTOR

INNER ROTOR

PUMP HOUSING

RELIEF VALVE

SPRING

O-RING

SPRING SEAT

Transparency 28

Automotive Technology: A Systems Approach, 3E

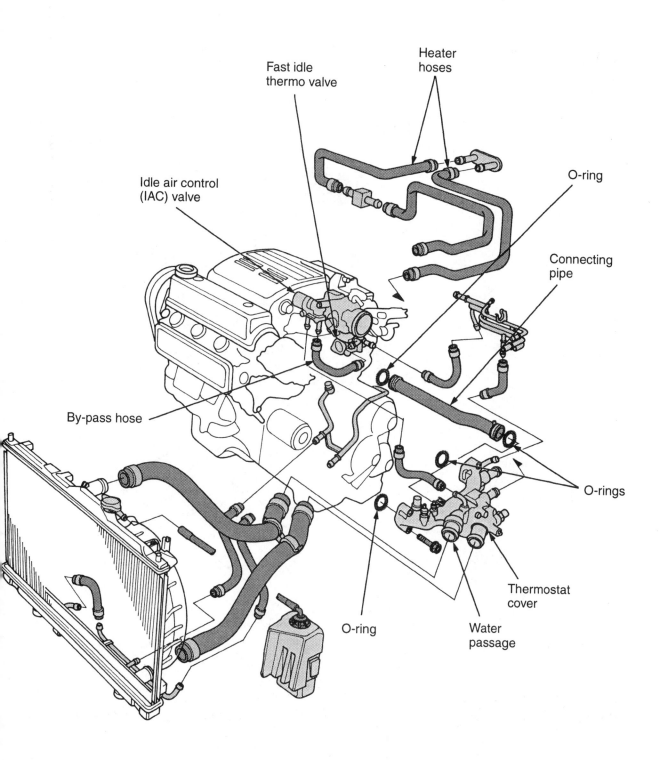

Fast idle
thermo valve

Heater
hoses

O-ring

Idle air control
(IAC) valve

Connecting
pipe

By-pass hose

O-rings

Thermostat
cover

O-ring

Water
passage

Transparency 29

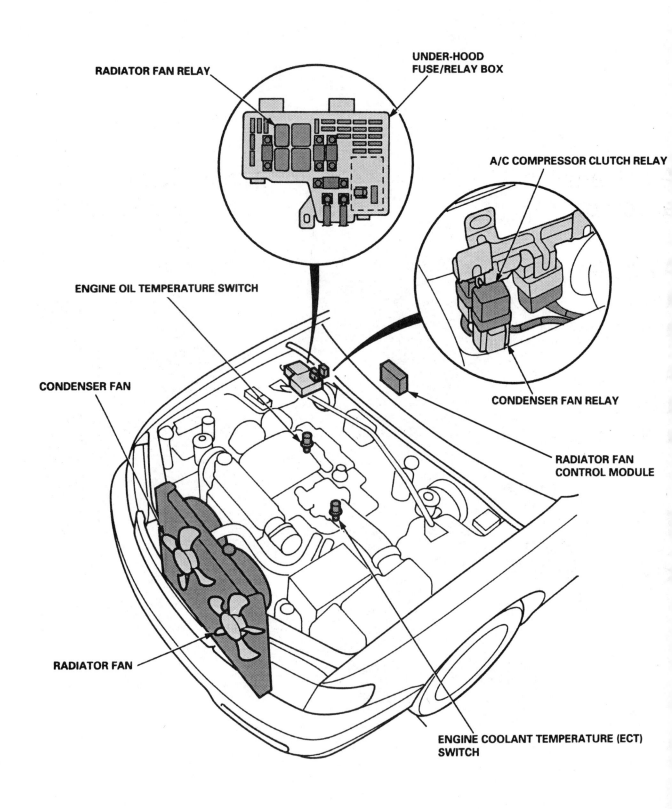

RADIATOR FAN RELAY

UNDER-HOOD
FUSE/RELAY BOX

A/C COMPRESSOR CLUTCH RELAY

ENGINE OIL TEMPERATURE SWITCH

CONDENSER FAN

CONDENSER FAN RELAY

RADIATOR FAN
CONTROL MODULE

RADIATOR FAN

ENGINE COOLANT TEMPERATURE (ECT)
SWITCH

Transparency 30

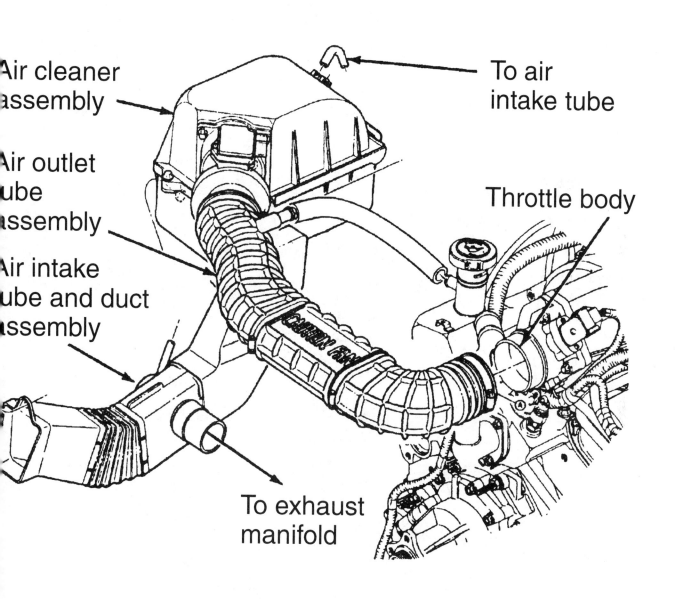

Air cleaner assembly

Air outlet tube assembly

Air intake tube and duct assembly

To air intake tube

Throttle body

To exhaust manifold

Transparency 31

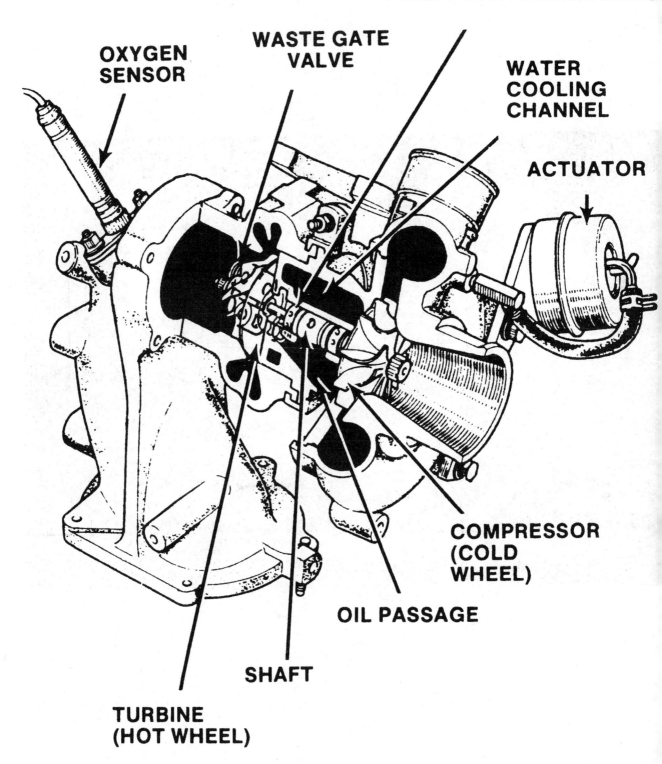

OXYGEN SENSOR

WASTE GATE VALVE

FULL-FLOATING BEARING

WATER COOLING CHANNEL

ACTUATOR

COMPRESSOR (COLD WHEEL)

OIL PASSAGE

SHAFT

TURBINE (HOT WHEEL)

Transparency 32

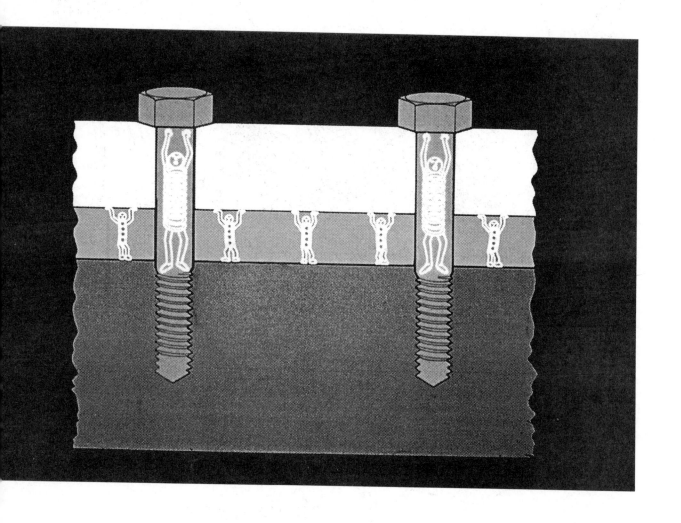

Transparency 33

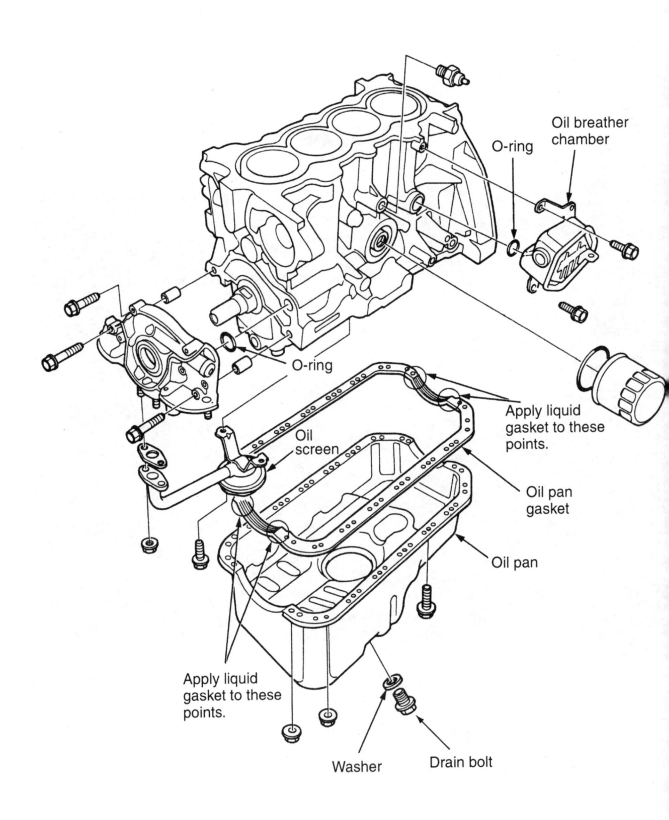

O-ring

Oil breather
chamber

O-ring

Apply liquid
gasket to these
points.

Oil
screen

Oil pan
gasket

Oil pan

Apply liquid
gasket to these
points.

Washer

Drain bolt

Transparency 34

Automotive Technology: A Systems Approach, 3E

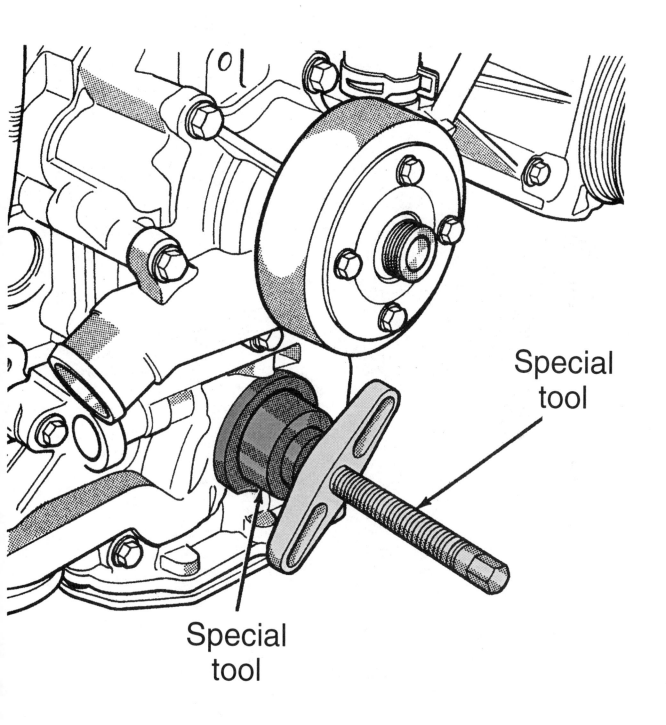

Special
tool

Special
tool

Transparency 35

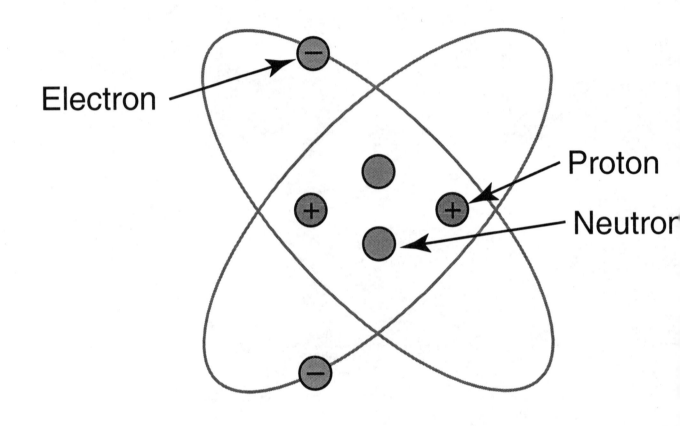

Electron

Proton

Neutron

Transparency 36

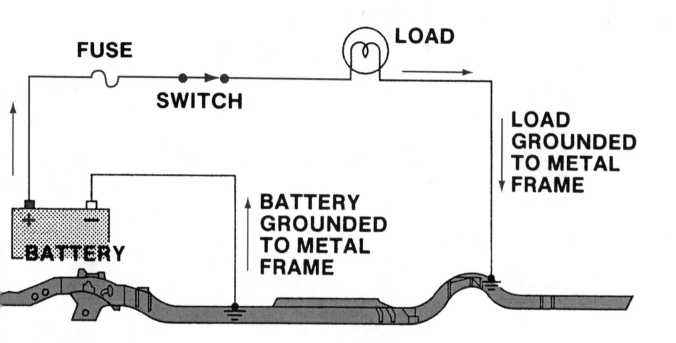

FUSE

SWITCH

LOAD

LOAD GROUNDED TO METAL FRAME

BATTERY

BATTERY GROUNDED TO METAL FRAME

Transparency 37

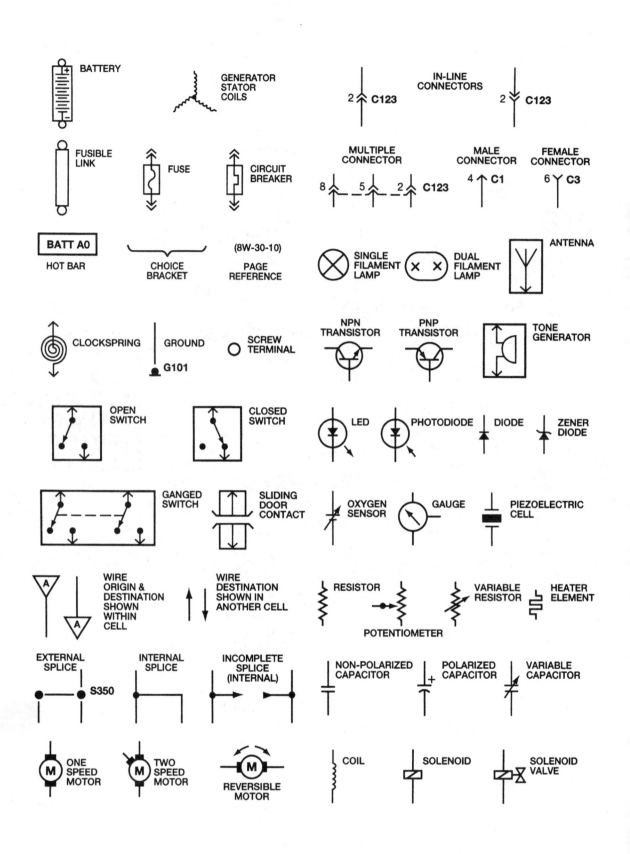

Transparency 38

Automotive Technology: A Systems Approach, 3E

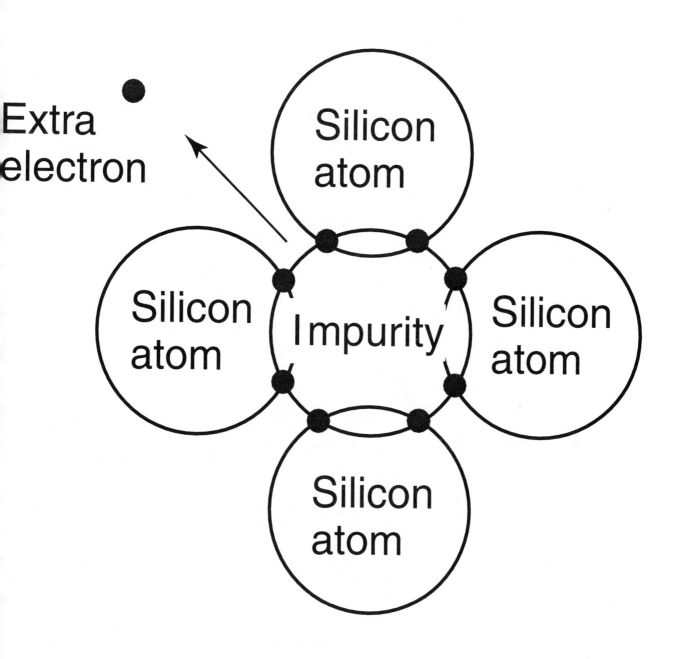

Extra electron

Silicon atom

Silicon atom

Impurity

Silicon atom

Silicon atom

Transparency 39

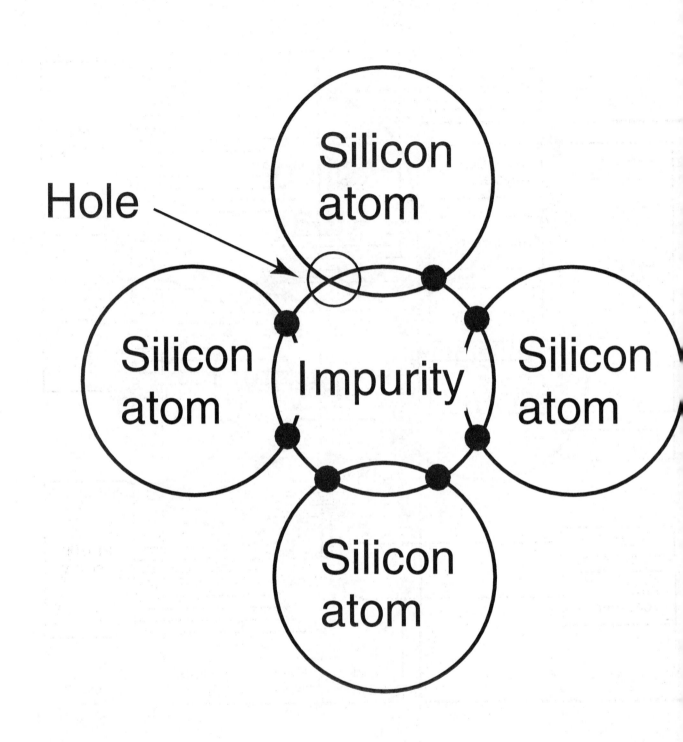

Automotive Technology: A Systems Approach, 3E

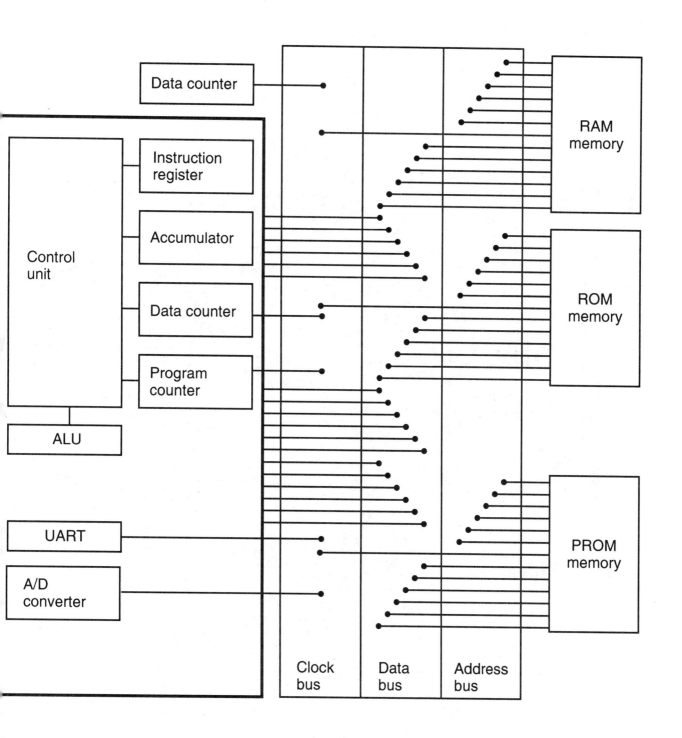

Transparency 41

Battery

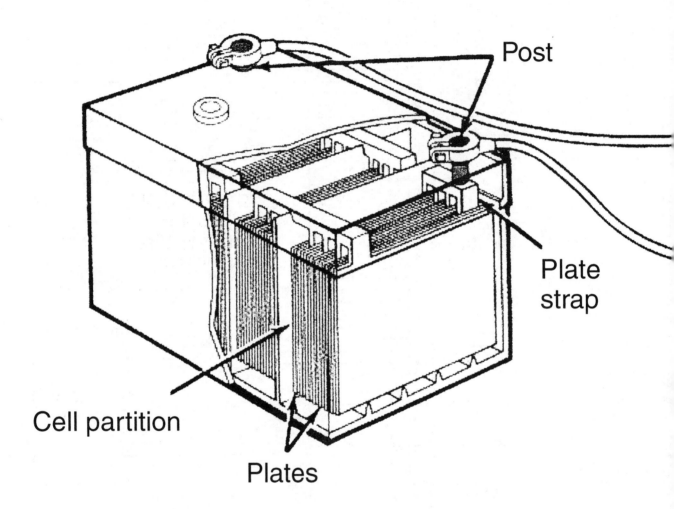

Post

Plate strap

Cell partition

Plates

Transparency 42

Automotive Technology: A Systems Approach, 3E

ELECTROLYTE TEMPERATURE (F)		SPECIFIC GRAVITY CORRECTION
120°		+.016
110°		+.012
100°		+.008
90°		+.004
80°		0
70°		−.004
60°		−.008
50°		−.012
40°		−.016
30°		−.020
20°		−.024
10°		−.028
0°		−.032
−10°		−.036
−20°		−.040

CHANGE HYDROMETER READING BY AMOUNT SHOWN ON THIS SIDE.

Transparency 43

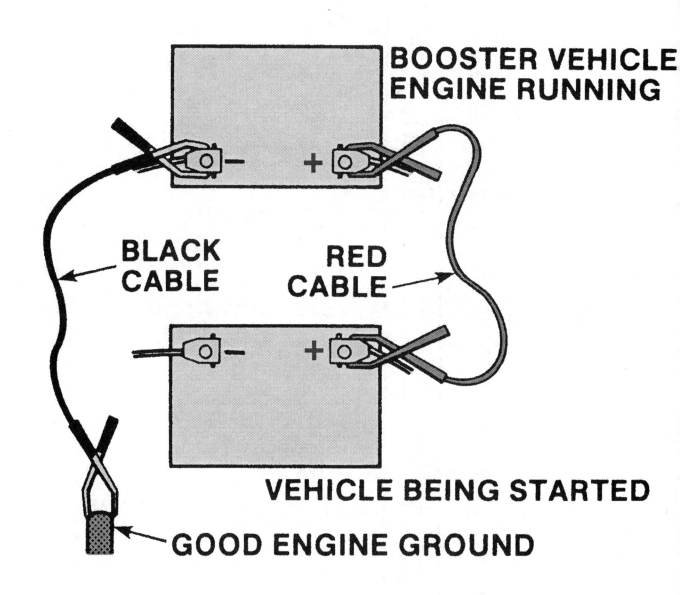

BOOSTER VEHICLE
ENGINE RUNNING

BLACK
CABLE

RED
CABLE

VEHICLE BEING STARTED

GOOD ENGINE GROUND

Transparency 44

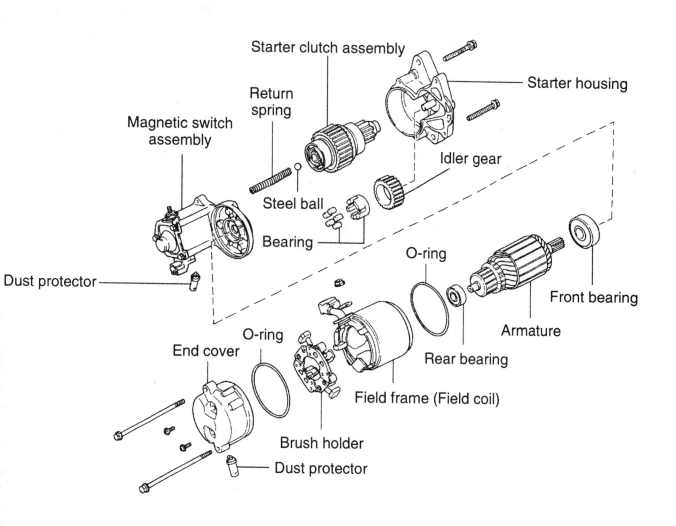

Starter clutch assembly

Starter housing

Return spring

Magnetic switch assembly

Idler gear

Steel ball

Bearing

O-ring

Dust protector

Front bearing

Armature

O-ring

Rear bearing

End cover

Field frame (Field coil)

Brush holder

Dust protector

Transparency 45

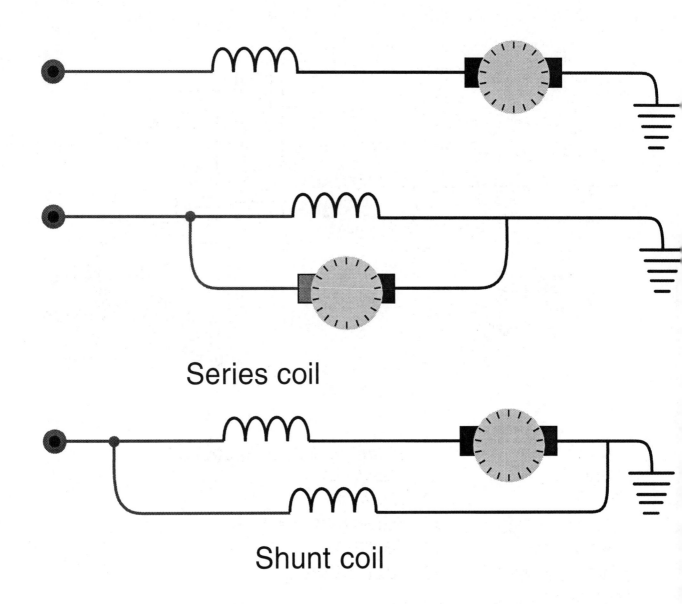

Series coil

Shunt coil

Transparency 46

Automotive Technology: A Systems Approach, 3E

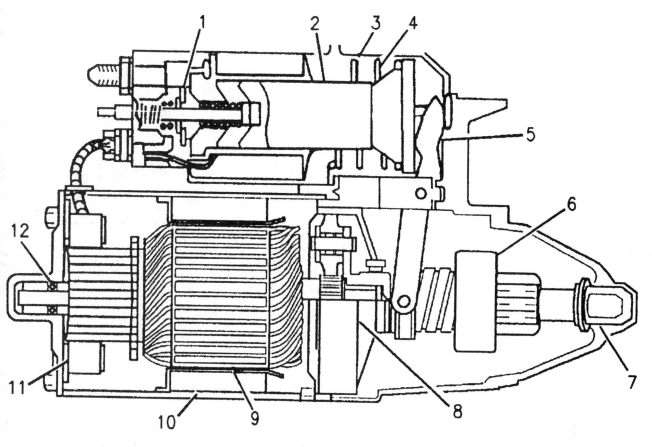

1	CONTACT DISC	8 PLANETARY GEAR REDUCTION
2	PLUNGER	ASSEMBLY
3	SOLENOID	9 ARMATURE
4	RETURN SPRING	10 PERMANENT MAGNETS
5	SHIFT LEVER	11 BRUSH
6	DRIVE ASSEMBLY	12 BALL BEARINGS
7	ROLLER BEARING	

Transparency 47

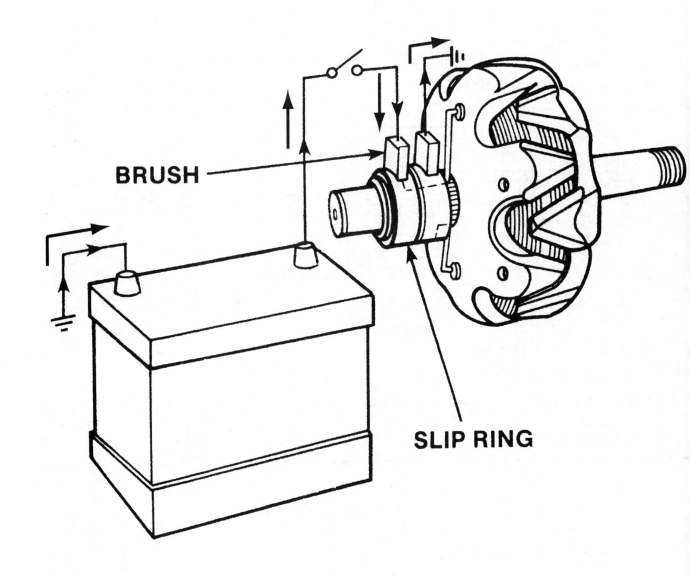

BRUSH

SLIP RING

Transparency 48

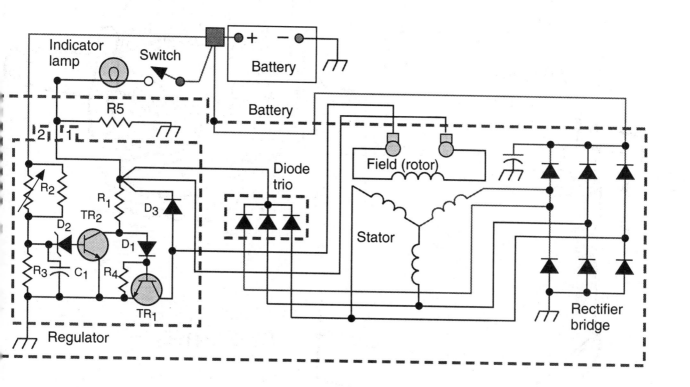

Transparency 49

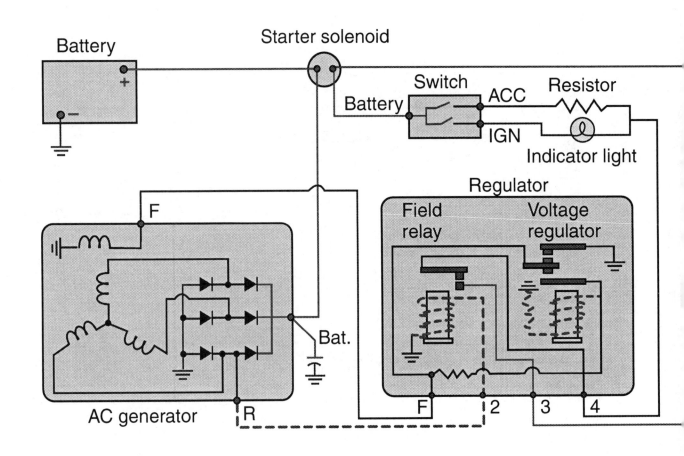

Battery

Starter solenoid

Switch

Battery

ACC

IGN

Resistor

Indicator light

Regulator

Field relay

Voltage regulator

F

AC generator

Bat.

R

F

2

3

4

Transparency 50

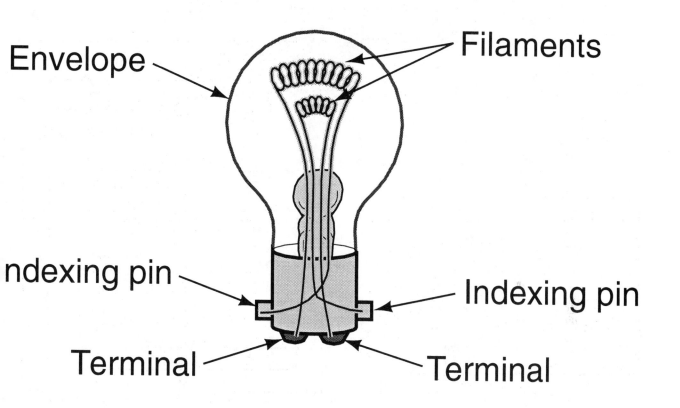

Envelope

Filaments

Indexing pin

Indexing pin

Terminal

Terminal

Transparency 51

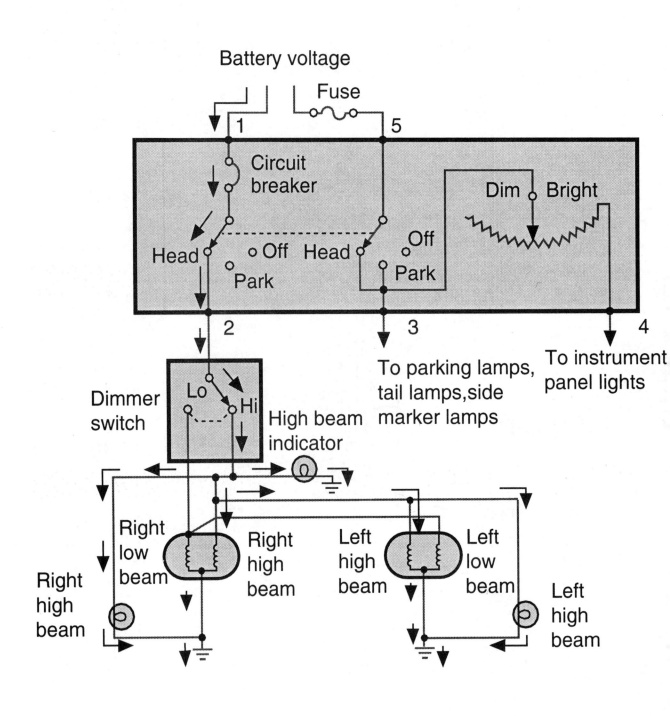

Battery voltage

Fuse

1 5

Circuit breaker

Dim Bright

Head Off Head Off
Park Park

2 3 4

Dimmer switch

Lo Hi

High beam indicator

To parking lamps, tail lamps, side marker lamps

To instrument panel lights

Right low beam

Right high beam

Left high beam

Left low beam

Right high beam

Left high beam

Transparency 52

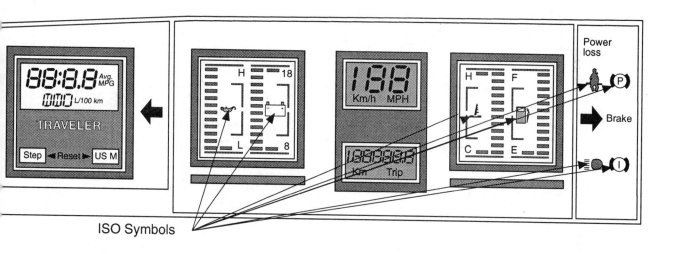

ISO Symbols

Transparency 53

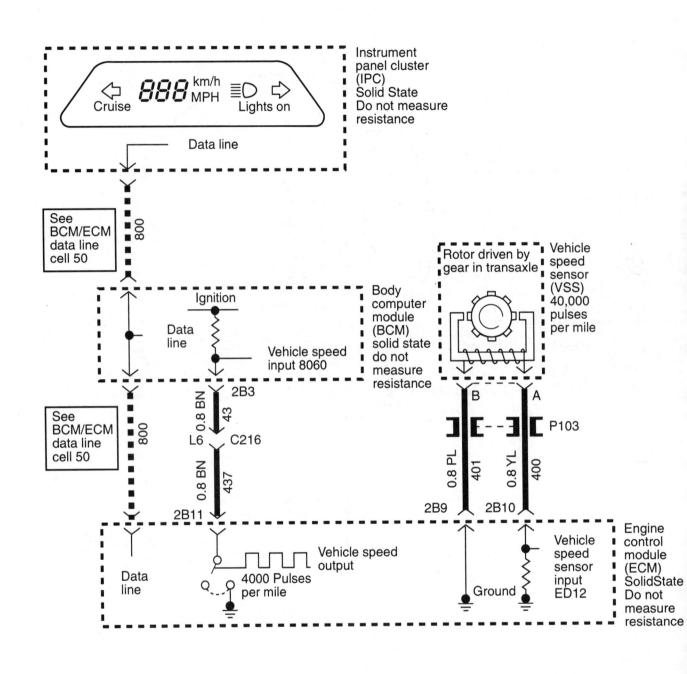

Transparency 54

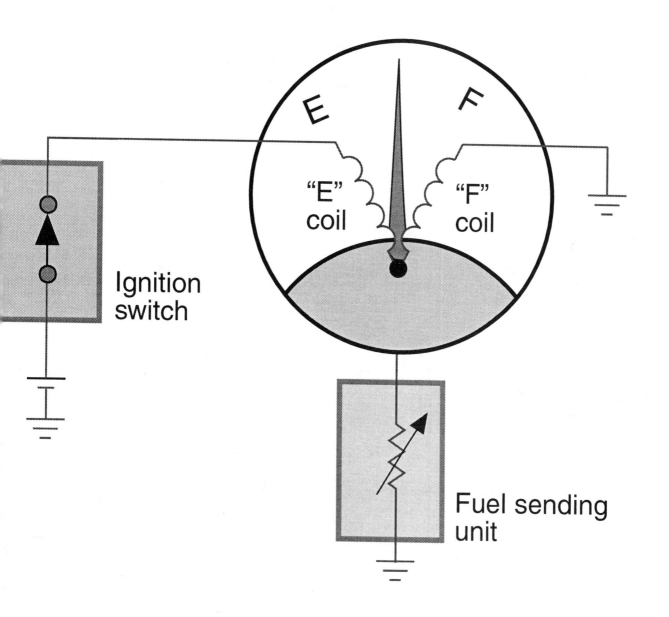

E F

"E" coil   "F" coil

Ignition switch

Fuel sending unit

Transparency 55

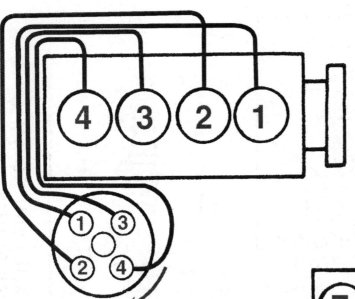

**FIRING ORDER:
1-3-4-2**

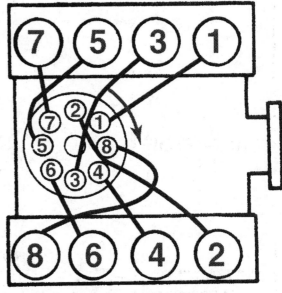

**FIRING ORDER:
1-8-4-3-6-5-7-2**

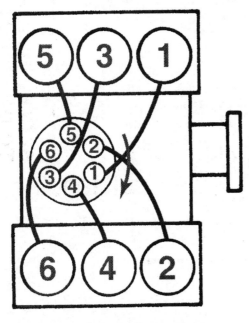

**FIRING ORDER:
1-4-3-6-5-2**

Transparency 56

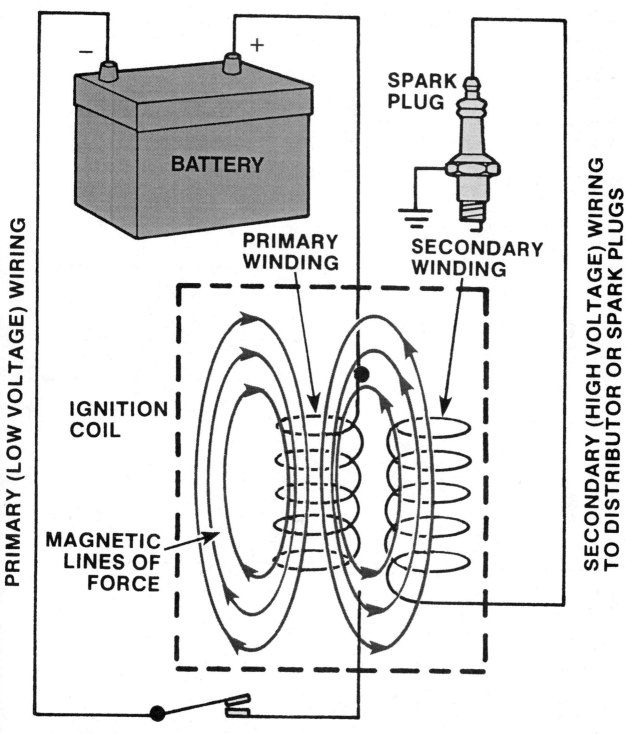

PRIMARY (LOW VOLTAGE) WIRING

SECONDARY (HIGH VOLTAGE) WIRING TO DISTRIBUTOR OR SPARK PLUGS

BATTERY

SPARK PLUG

PRIMARY WINDING

SECONDARY WINDING

IGNITION COIL

MAGNETIC LINES OF FORCE

SWITCH (TRANSISTOR OR BREAKER POINTS)

Transparency 57

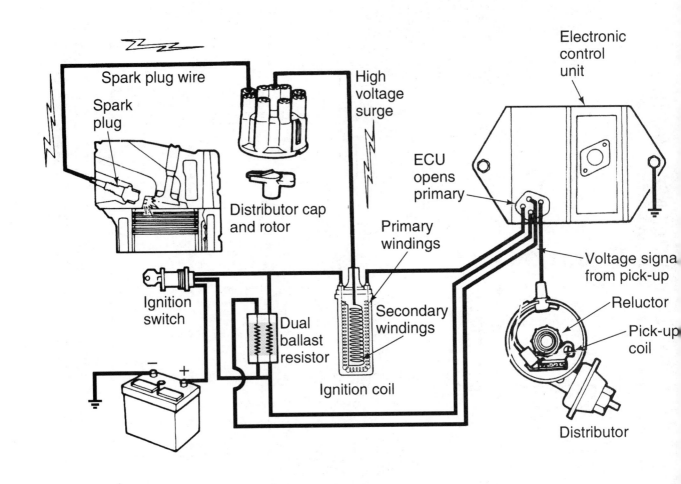

Spark plug wire

Spark plug

Distributor cap and rotor

High voltage surge

Electronic control unit

ECU opens primary

Primary windings

Ignition switch

Dual ballast resistor

Secondary windings

Ignition coil

Voltage signal from pick-up

Reluctor

Pick-up coil

Distributor

Transparency 58

Automotive Technology: A Systems Approach, 3E

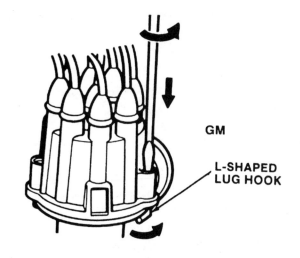

GM

L-SHAPED
LUG HOOK

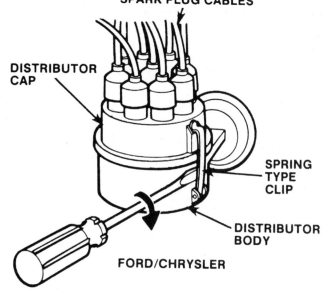

SPARK PLUG CABLES

DISTRIBUTOR
CAP

SPRING
TYPE
CLIP

DISTRIBUTOR
BODY

FORD/CHRYSLER

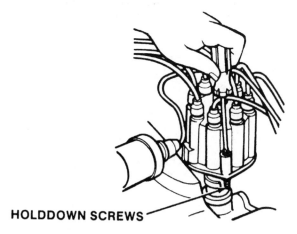

HOLDDOWN SCREWS

Transparency 59

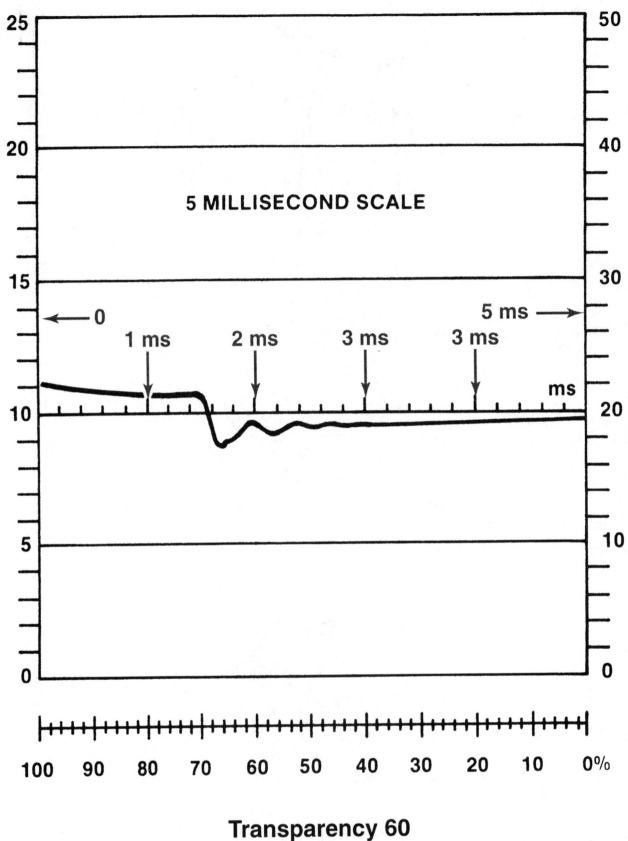

5 MILLISECOND SCALE

0

1 ms

2 ms

3 ms

3 ms

5 ms →

ms

25   50
20   40
15   30
10   20
5   10
0   0

100   90   80   70   60   50   40   30   20   10   0%

Transparency 60

Automotive Technology: A Systems Approach, 3E

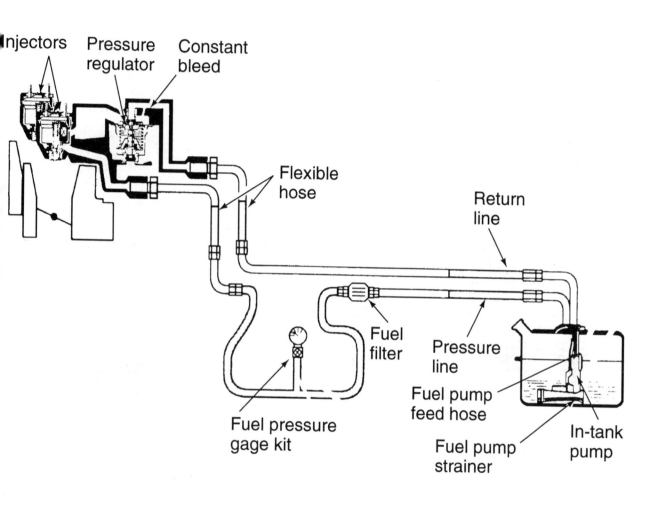

Injectors Pressure   Constant
           regulator   bleed

Flexible
hose

Return
line

Fuel
filter

Pressure
line

Fuel pump
feed hose

Fuel pressure
gage kit

Fuel pump
strainer

In-tank
pump

Transparency 61

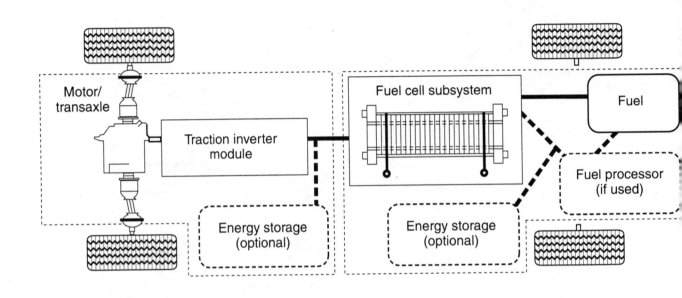

Transparency 62

Automotive Technology: A Systems Approach, 3E

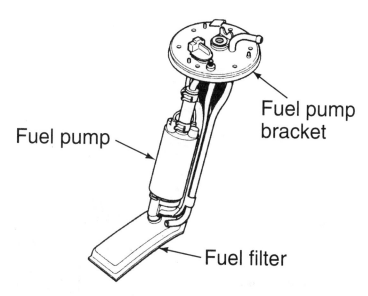

Fuel pump bracket

Fuel pump

Fuel filter

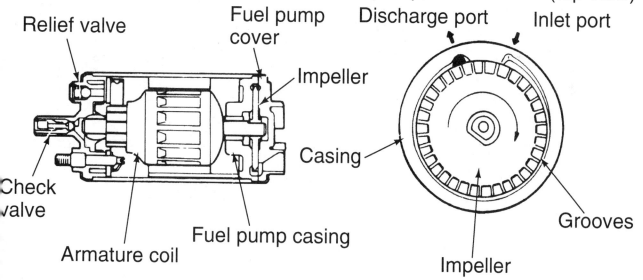

Fuel pump cross section (side view)

Relief valve

Fuel pump cover

Impeller

Check valve

Armature coil

Fuel pump casing

Fuel pump cross section (top view)

Discharge port

Inlet port

Casing

Grooves

Impeller

Transparency 63

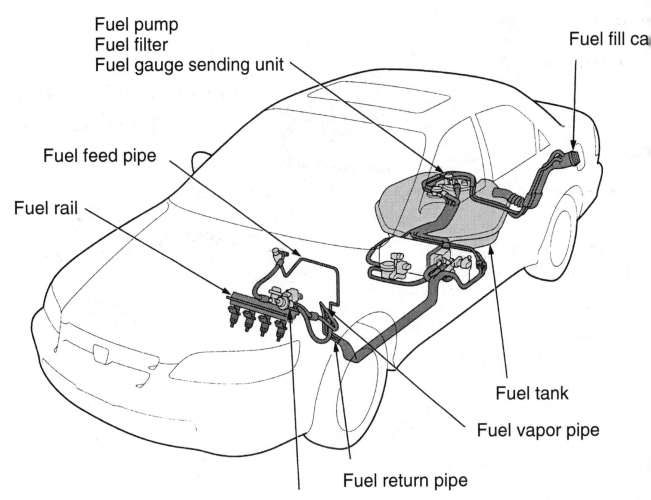

Fuel pump
Fuel filter
Fuel gauge sending unit

Fuel fill ca

Fuel feed pipe

Fuel rail

Fuel tank

Fuel vapor pipe

Fuel return pipe

Fuel pressure regulator

Transparency 64

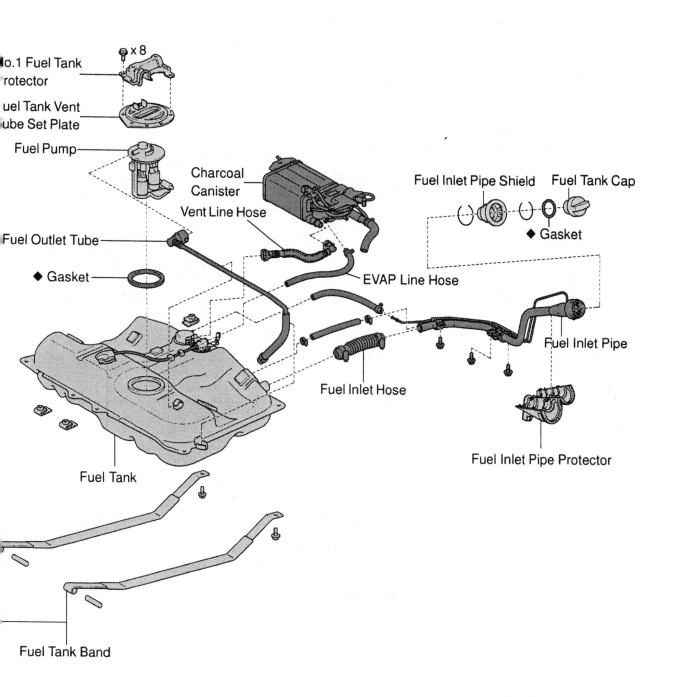

No.1 Fuel Tank Protector

Fuel Tank Vent Tube Set Plate

Fuel Pump

Charcoal Canister

Vent Line Hose

Fuel Inlet Pipe Shield

Fuel Tank Cap

Fuel Outlet Tube

◆ Gasket

◆ Gasket

EVAP Line Hose

Fuel Inlet Pipe

Fuel Inlet Hose

Fuel Tank

Fuel Inlet Pipe Protector

Fuel Tank Band

x 8

Transparency 65

Retaining bolts

Fuel
pump

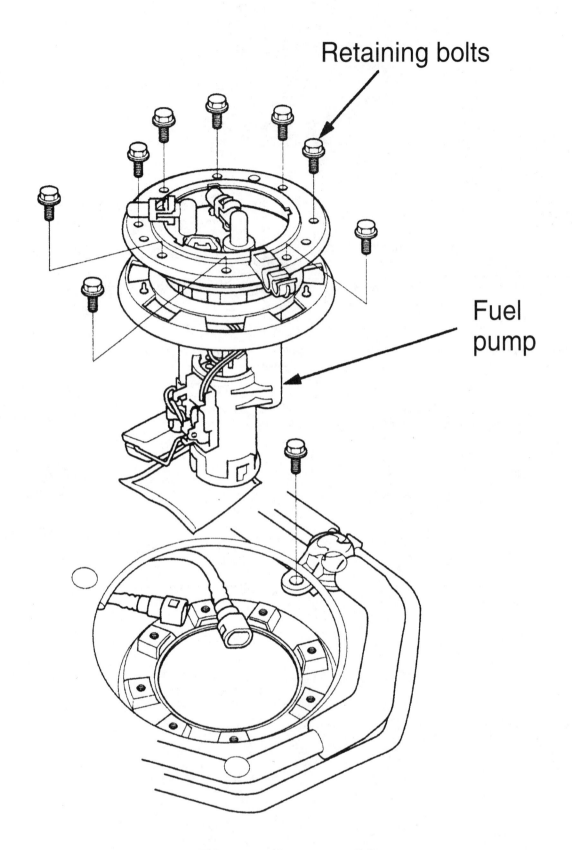

Transparency 66

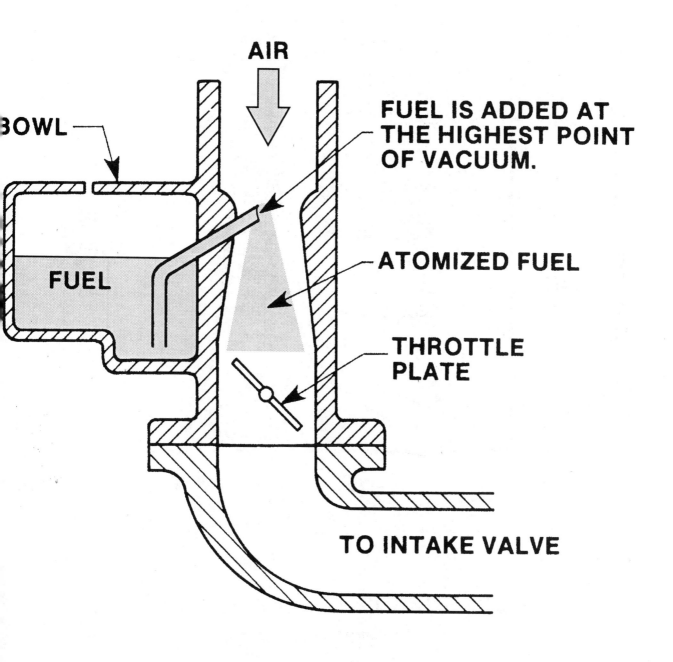

AIR

FUEL IS ADDED AT
THE HIGHEST POINT
OF VACUUM.

ATOMIZED FUEL

THROTTLE
PLATE

BOWL

FUEL

TO INTAKE VALVE

Transparency 67

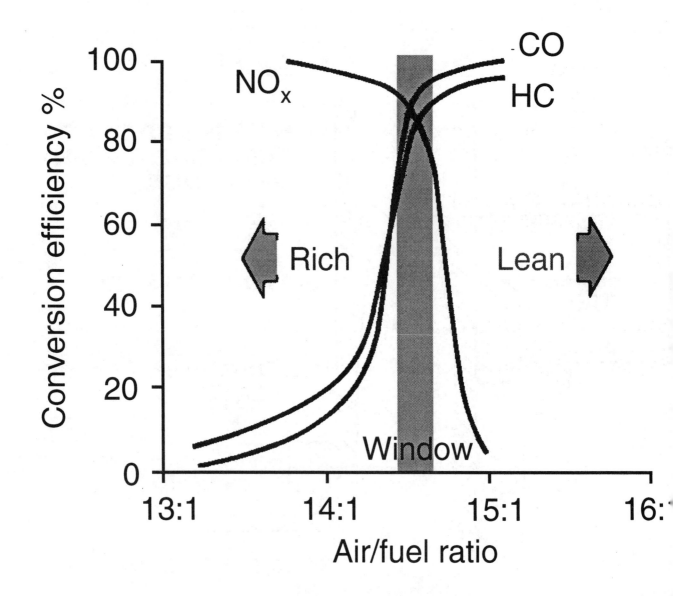

Characteristic Conversion Efficiencies
Three-Way Catalyst

Transparency 68

**LEAN MIXTURE
O$_2$ IN EXHAUST
GAS**

**CARBURETOR CONTROL
LEANS MIXTURE**

**LOW SENSOR
VOLTAGE**

**ELECTRONIC CONTROL
ENERGIZES
CARBURETOR SOLENOID**

**ELECTRONIC CONTROL
DE-ENERGIZES
CARBURETOR SOLENOID**

**HIGH SENSOR
VOLTAGE**

**CARBURETOR CONTROL
ENRICHES MIXTURE**

**LESS O$_2$ IN
EXHAUST GAS**

Transparency 69

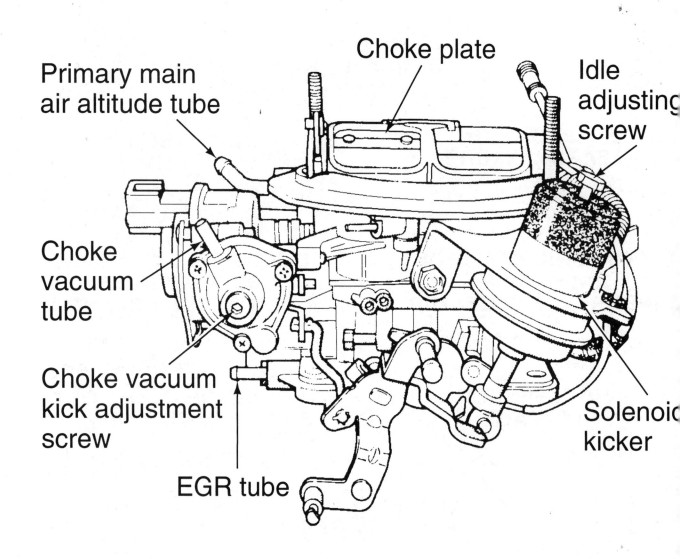

Primary main
air altitude tube

Choke plate

Idle
adjusting
screw

Choke
vacuum
tube

Choke vacuum
kick adjustment
screw

EGR tube

Solenoid
kicker

Transparency 70

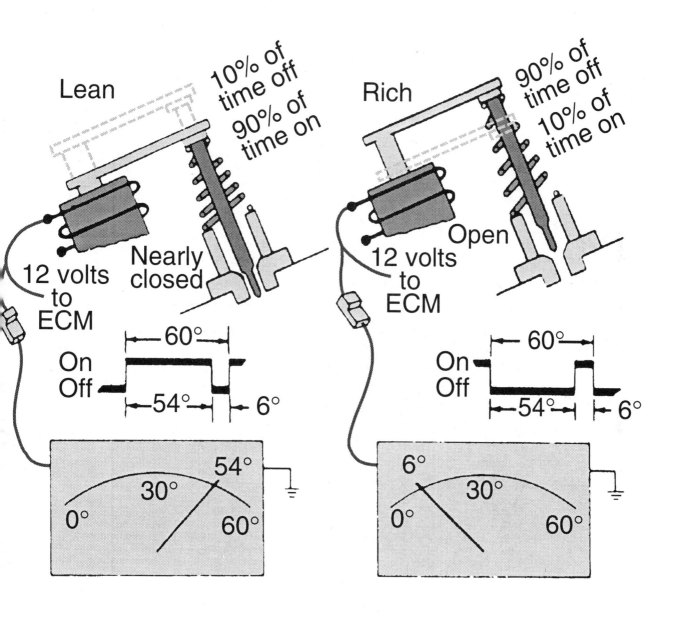

Lean

10% of time off

90% of time on

Nearly closed

12 volts to ECM

On
Off

|←— 60° —→|

|←— 54° —→| |← 6°

54°
30°
0°   60°

Rich

90% of time off

10% of time on

Open

12 volts to ECM

On
Off

|←— 60° —→|

|←— 54° —→| |← 6°

6°
30°
0°   60°

Transparency 71

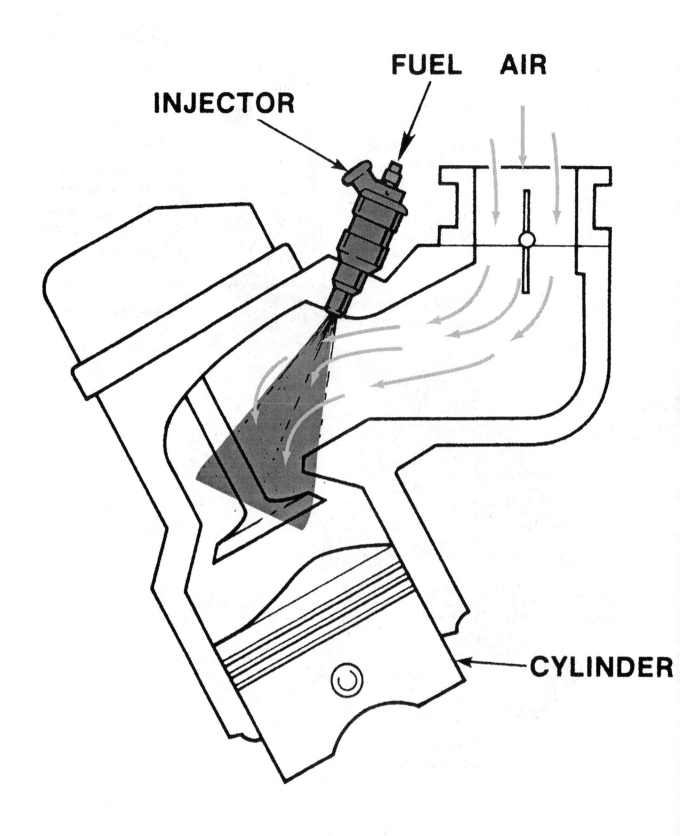

FUEL AIR

INJECTOR

FUEL

CYLINDER

Transparency 72

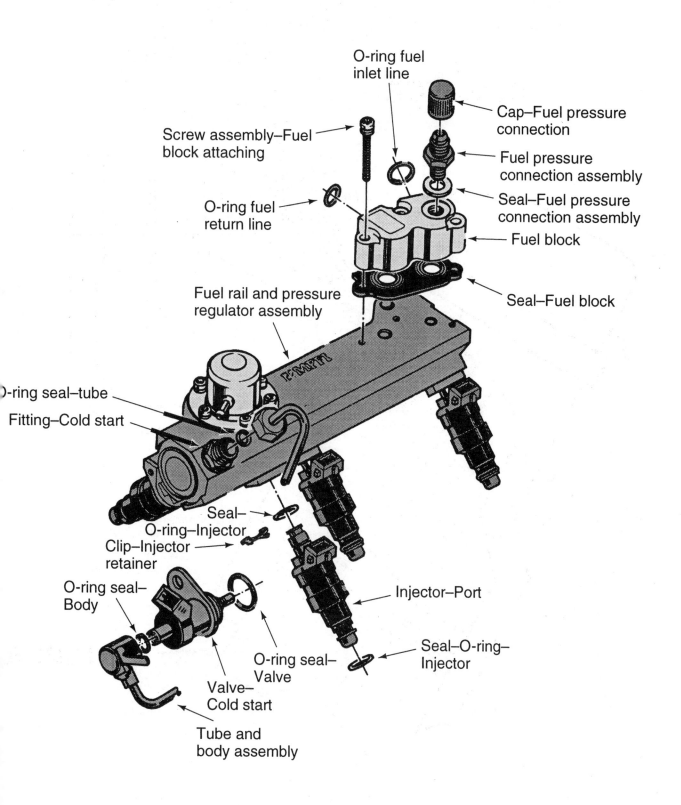

O-ring fuel
inlet line

Cap–Fuel pressure
connection

Screw assembly–Fuel
block attaching

Fuel pressure
connection assembly

O-ring fuel
return line

Seal–Fuel pressure
connection assembly

Fuel block

Fuel rail and pressure
regulator assembly

Seal–Fuel block

O-ring seal–tube

Fitting–Cold start

Seal–
O-ring–Injector

Clip–Injector
retainer

Injector–Port

O-ring seal–
Body

Seal–O-ring–
Injector

O-ring seal–
Valve

Valve–
Cold start

Tube and
body assembly

Transparency 73

Automotive Technology: A Systems Approach, 3E

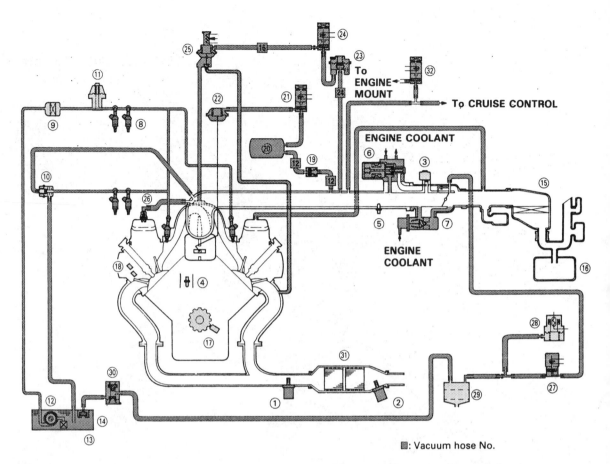

■: Vacuum hose No.

1. PRIMARY HEATED OXYGEN SENSOR (HO2S) (SENSOR 1)
2. SECONDARY HEATED OXYGEN SENSOR (HO2S) (SENSOR 2)
3. MANIFOLD ABSOLUTE PRESSURE (MAP) SENSOR
4. ENGINE COOLANT TEMPERATURE (ECT) SENSOR
5. INTAKE AIR TEMPERATURE (IAT) SENSOR
6. IDLE AIR CONTROL (IAC) VALVE
7. FAST IDLE THERMO VALVE
8. FUEL INJECTOR
9. FUEL FILTER
10. FUEL PRESSURE REGULATOR
11. FUEL PULSATION DAMPER
12. FUEL PUMP (FP)
13. FUEL TANK
14. FUEL TANK EVAPORATIVE EMISSION (EVAP) VALVE
15. AIR CLEANER
16. RESONATOR
17. CRANK POSITION (CKP) SENSOR
18. TOP DEAD CENTER/CYLINDER POSITION (TDC/CYP) SENSOR

19. INTAKE AIR BYPASS (IAB) CHECK VALVE
20. INTAKE AIR BYPASS (IAB) VACUUM TANK
21. INTAKE AIR BYPASS (IAB) CONTROL SOLENOID VALVE
22. INTAKE AIR BYPASS (IAB) CONTROL DIAPHRAGM
23. EXHAUST GAS RECIRCULATION (EGR) VACUUM CONTROL VALVE
24. EXHAUST GAS RECIRCULATION (EGR) CONTROL SOLENOID VALVE
25. EXHAUST GAS RECIRCULATION (EGR) VALVE
26. POSITIVE CRANKCASE VENTILATION (PCV) VALVE
27. EVAPORATIVE EMISSION (EVAP) PURGE CONTROL SOLENOID VALVE
28. EVAPORATIVE EMISSION (EVAP) PURGE FLOW SWITCH
29. EVAPORATIVE EMISSION (EVAP) CONTROL CANISTER
30. EVAPORATIVE EMISSION (EVAP) TWO WAY VALVE
31. THREE WAY CATALYTIC CONVERTER (TWC)
32. ENGINE MOUNT CONTROL SOLENOID VALVE

Transparency 74

Automotive Technology: A Systems Approach, 3E

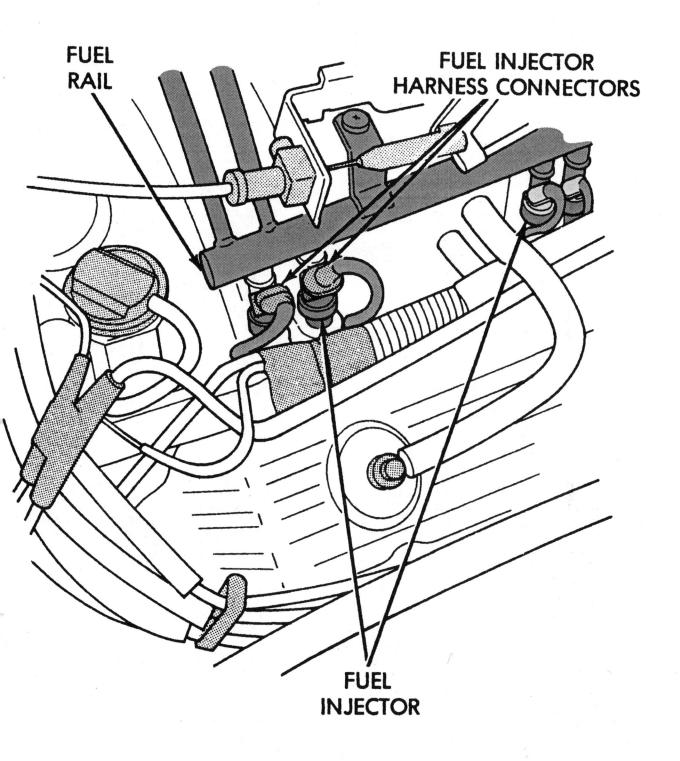

FUEL
RAIL

FUEL INJECTOR
HARNESS CONNECTORS

FUEL
INJECTOR

Transparency 75

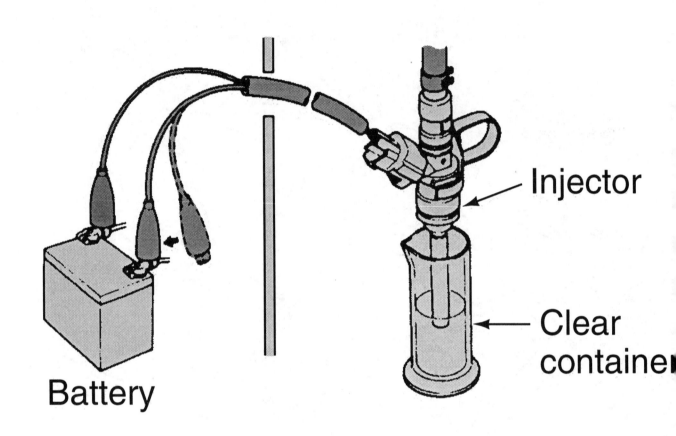

Injector

Clear
container

Battery

Transparency 76

	HC	CO	NO$_x$
1990 – U.S.	0.41	3.4	1.0
1994 – U.S.	0.25*	3.4	0.4
1993 – Calif.	0.25	3.4	0.40
1994 – TLEV	0.125	3.4	0.40
1997 – LEV	0.075	3.4	0.20
2000 – ULEV	0.040	1.7	0.20

*non-methane HC

Transparency 77

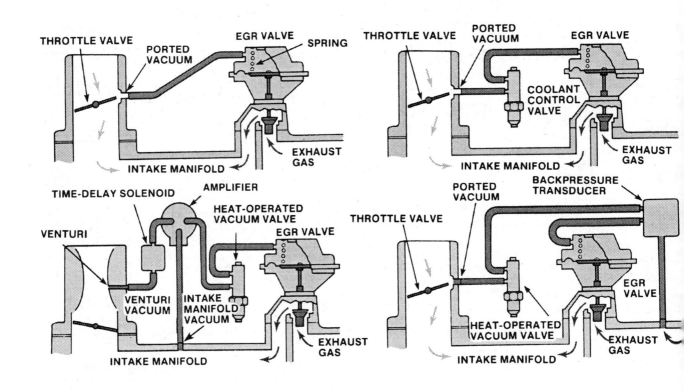

THROTTLE VALVE
PORTED VACUUM
EGR VALVE
SPRING
INTAKE MANIFOLD
EXHAUST GAS

THROTTLE VALVE
PORTED VACUUM
EGR VALVE
COOLANT CONTROL VALVE
INTAKE MANIFOLD
EXHAUST GAS

TIME-DELAY SOLENOID
AMPLIFIER
HEAT-OPERATED VACUUM VALVE
EGR VALVE
VENTURI
VENTURI VACUUM
INTAKE MANIFOLD VACUUM
INTAKE MANIFOLD
EXHAUST GAS

BACKPRESSURE TRANSDUCER
PORTED VACUUM
THROTTLE VALVE
EGR VALVE
HEAT-OPERATED VACUUM VALVE
INTAKE MANIFOLD
EXHAUST GAS

Transparency 78

Automotive Technology: A Systems Approach, 3E

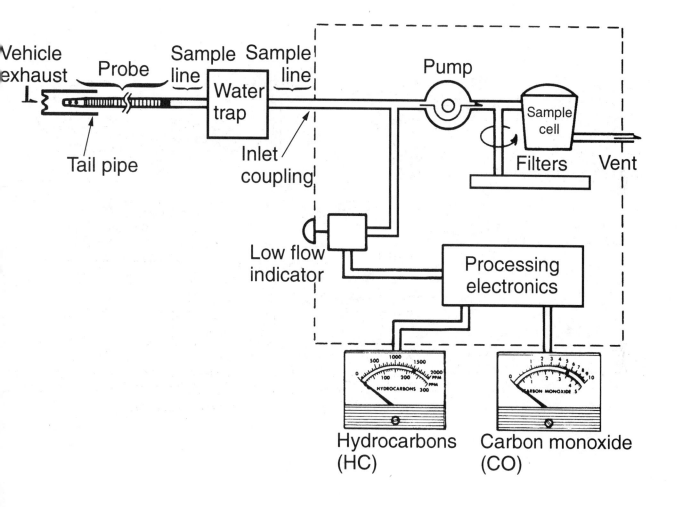

Vehicle exhaust

Probe

Sample line

Sample line

Water trap

Pump

Sample cell

Tail pipe

Inlet coupling

Filters

Vent

Low flow indicator

Processing electronics

Hydrocarbons (HC)

Carbon monoxide (CO)

Transparency 79

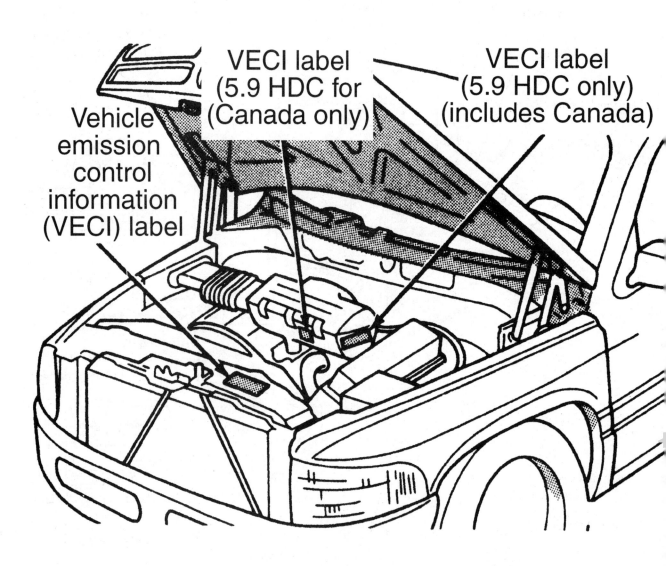

VECI label
(5.9 HDC for
(Canada only)

VECI label
(5.9 HDC only)
(includes Canada)

Vehicle
emission
control
information
(VECI) label

Transparency 80

Automotive Technology: A Systems Approach, 3E

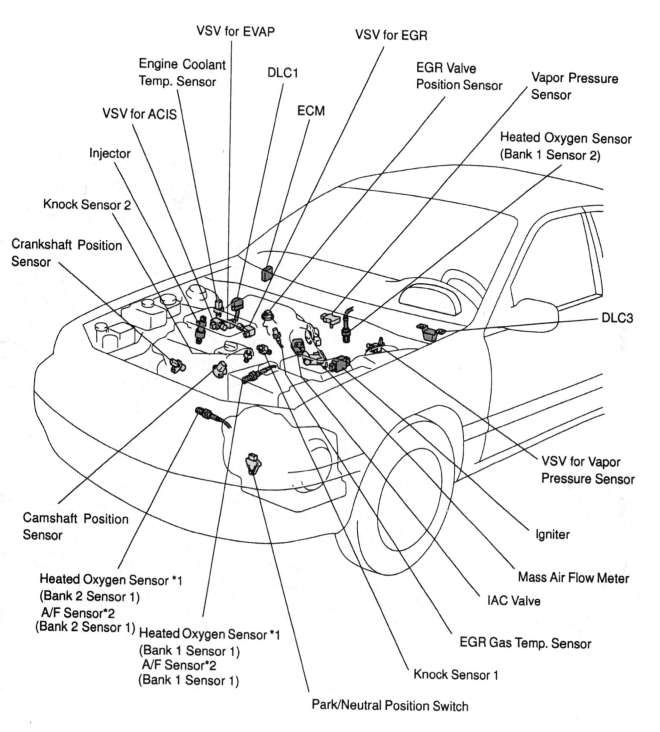

VSV for EVAP

VSV for EGR

Engine Coolant
Temp. Sensor

DLC1

EGR Valve
Position Sensor

Vapor Pressure
Sensor

VSV for ACIS

ECM

Injector

Heated Oxygen Sensor
(Bank 1 Sensor 2)

Knock Sensor 2

Crankshaft Position
Sensor

DLC3

VSV for Vapor
Pressure Sensor

Igniter

Camshaft Position
Sensor

Mass Air Flow Meter

Heated Oxygen Sensor *1
(Bank 2 Sensor 1)
A/F Sensor*2
(Bank 2 Sensor 1)

IAC Valve

Heated Oxygen Sensor *1
(Bank 1 Sensor 1)
A/F Sensor*2
(Bank 1 Sensor 1)

EGR Gas Temp. Sensor

Knock Sensor 1

Park/Neutral Position Switch

*1 : Except California Specification vehicles
*2 : Only for California Specification vehicles

Transparency 81

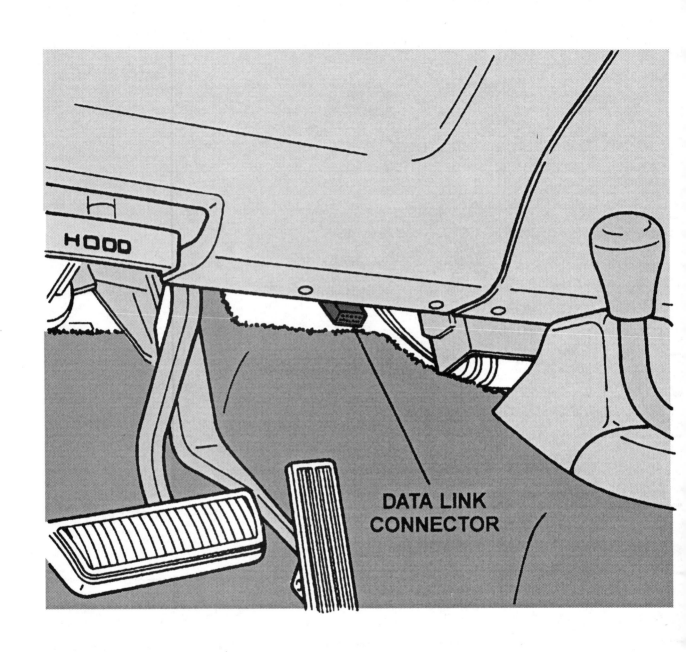

HOOD

DATA LINK
CONNECTOR

Transparency 82

Automotive Technology: A Systems Approach, 3E

SENSOR TROUBLE CODES

Sensor	Trouble Codes		
	GM	Ford	Chrysler
Oxygen (EGO)	13,44, 45,55	43,91, 92,93	21,51,52
Throttle Position (TPS)	21,22	23,53, 63,73	24
Engine Vacuum (MAP)	31,33,34	22,72	13,14
Barometric Pressure (BARO)	32	—	37
Coolant (ECT)	14,15	21,51,61	17,22
Knock	42,43	25	17 (some only)
Vehicle Speed (VSS)	24	—	15
Air Temperature (MAT, VAT, ACT)	23,25	24,54,64	23
Airflow (VAF, MAF)	33,34, 44,45	26,56, 66,76	—
EGR Valve (EGR, EVP)	—	31,32,33, 34,83,84	31

Transparency 83

Diagnostic Trouble Code (DTC) 13

Heated oxygen sensor (HO$_2$S) circuit
(open/grounded circuit)

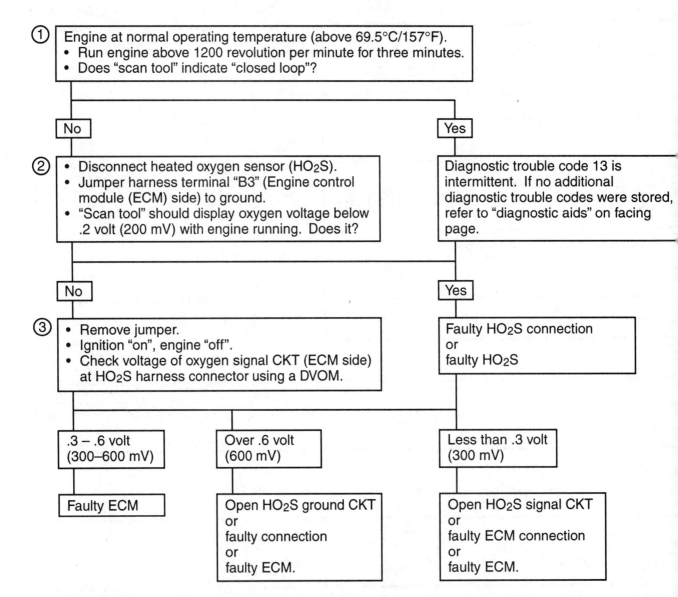

① Engine at normal operating temperature (above 69.5°C/157°F).
  • Run engine above 1200 revolution per minute for three minutes.
  • Does "scan tool" indicate "closed loop"?

No

Yes

② • Disconnect heated oxygen sensor (HO$_2$S).
  • Jumper harness terminal "B3" (Engine control module (ECM) side) to ground.
  • "Scan tool" should display oxygen voltage below .2 volt (200 mV) with engine running. Does it?

Diagnostic trouble code 13 is intermittent. If no additional diagnostic trouble codes were stored, refer to "diagnostic aids" on facing page.

No

Yes

③ • Remove jumper.
  • Ignition "on", engine "off".
  • Check voltage of oxygen signal CKT (ECM side) at HO$_2$S harness connector using a DVOM.

Faulty HO$_2$S connection
or
faulty HO$_2$S

.3 – .6 volt
(300–600 mV)

Over .6 volt
(600 mV)

Less than .3 volt
(300 mV)

Faulty ECM

Open HO$_2$S ground CKT
or
faulty connection
or
faulty ECM.

Open HO$_2$S signal CKT
or
faulty ECM connection
or
faulty ECM.

Clear diangostic trouble codes and confirm "closed loop" operation and normal "check ingine" malfunction indicator lamp operation.

Transparency 84

CHARGED TEMPERATURE SENSOR TEMPERATURE VS. VOLTAGE CURVE

Temperature	Voltage
−20°F	4.81 V
0°F	4.70 V
20°F	4.47 V
40°F	4.11 V
60°F	3.67 V
80°F	3.08 V
100°F	2.51 V
120°F	1.97 V
140°F	1.52 V
160°F	1.15 V
180°F	0.86 V
200°F	0.65 V
220°F	0.48 V
240°F	0.35 V
260°F	0.28 V

Transparency 85

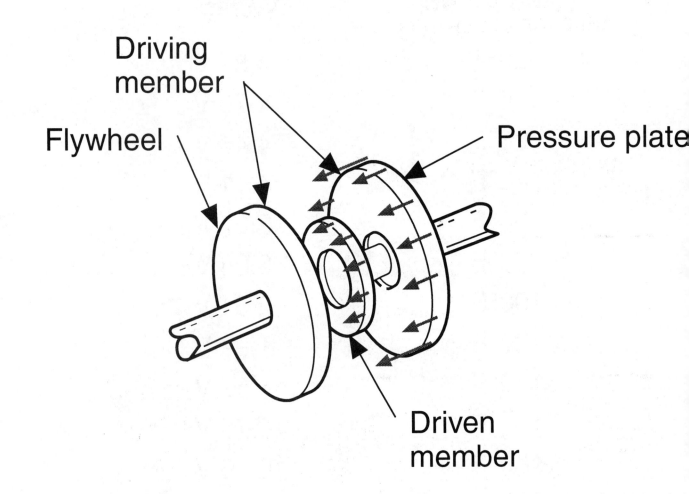

Driving
member

Flywheel

Pressure plate

Driven
member

Transparency 86

Automotive Technology: A Systems Approach, 3E

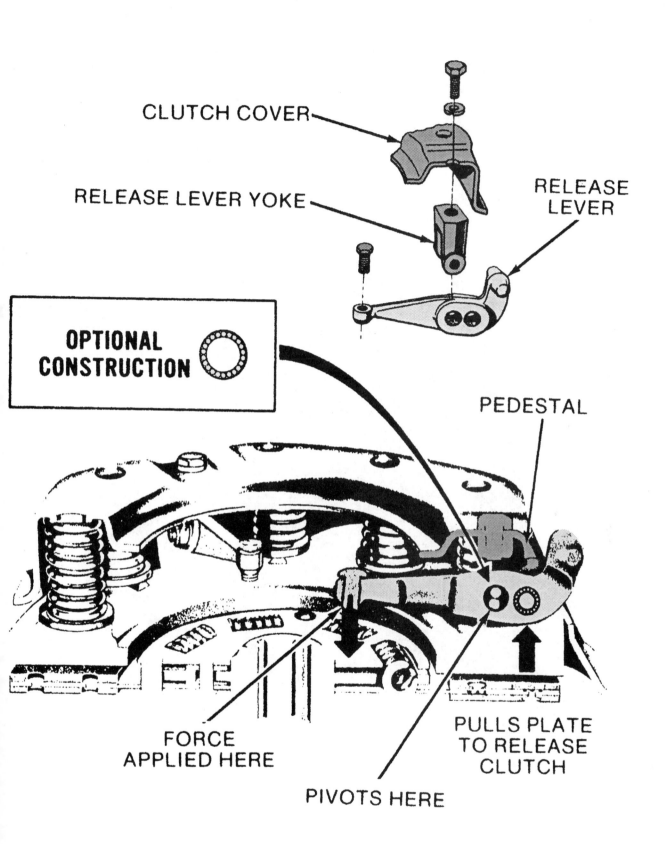

CLUTCH COVER

RELEASE LEVER YOKE

RELEASE LEVER

OPTIONAL CONSTRUCTION

PEDESTAL

FORCE APPLIED HERE

PULLS PLATE TO RELEASE CLUTCH

PIVOTS HERE

Transparency 87

Automotive Technology: A Systems Approach, 3E

Standard (new): 0.05 mm (0.002 in) max.
Service limit: 0.15 mm (0.006 in) max.

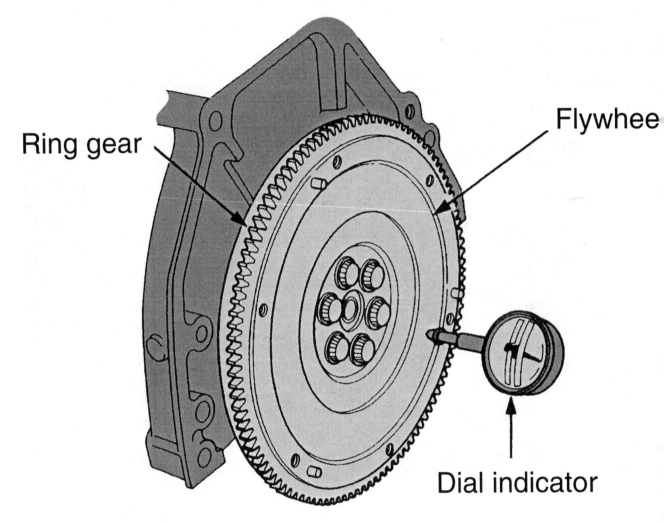

Ring gear

Flywhee

Dial indicator

Transparency 88

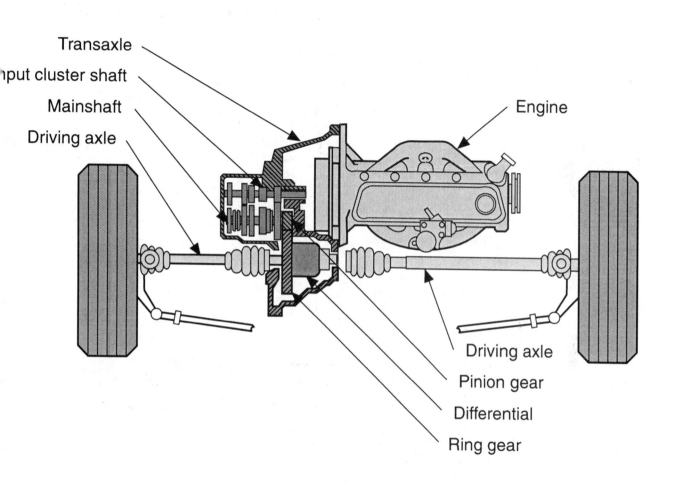

Transaxle

Input cluster shaft

Mainshaft

Driving axle

Engine

Driving axle

Pinion gear

Differential

Ring gear

Transparency 89

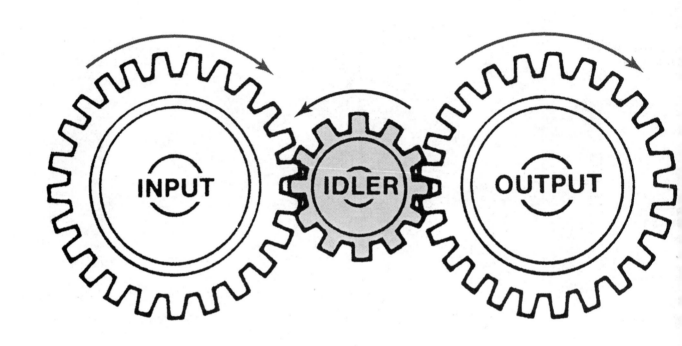

Transparency 90

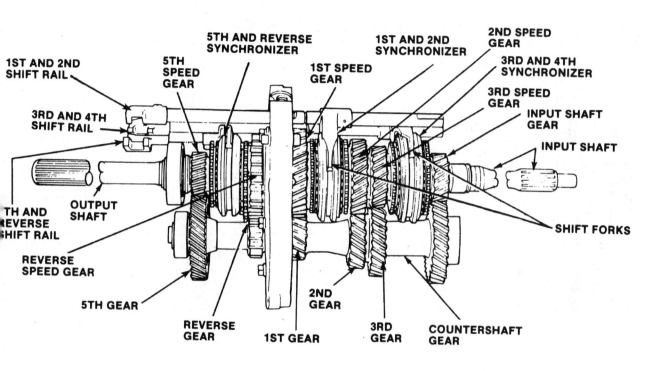

1ST AND 2ND
SHIFT RAIL

3RD AND 4TH
SHIFT RAIL

TH AND
REVERSE
SHIFT RAIL

OUTPUT
SHAFT

REVERSE
SPEED GEAR

5TH GEAR

REVERSE
GEAR

1ST GEAR

2ND
GEAR

3RD
GEAR

COUNTERSHAFT
GEAR

5TH
SPEED
GEAR

5TH AND REVERSE
SYNCHRONIZER

1ST SPEED
GEAR

1ST AND 2ND
SYNCHRONIZER

2ND SPEED
GEAR

3RD AND 4TH
SYNCHRONIZER

3RD SPEED
GEAR

INPUT SHAFT
GEAR

INPUT SHAFT

SHIFT FORKS

Transparency 91

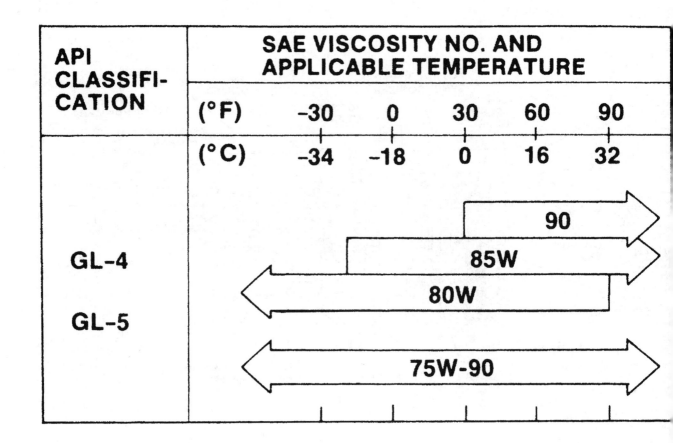

API CLASSIFI-CATION	SAE VISCOSITY NO. AND APPLICABLE TEMPERATURE				
	(°F)	−30	0	30	60	90
	(°C)	−34	−18	0	16	32
GL–4 GL–5	90 / 85W / 80W / 75W–90				

Transparency 92

Automotive Technology: A Systems Approach, 3E

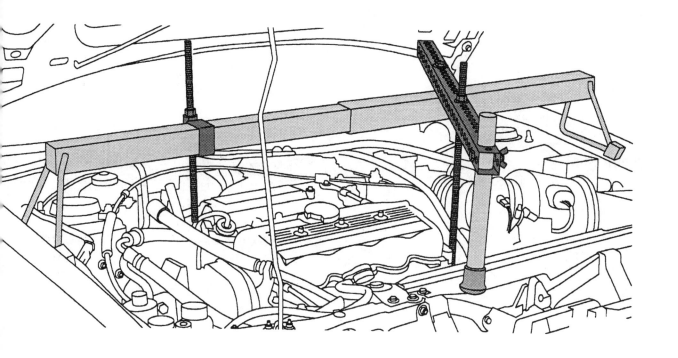

Transparency 93

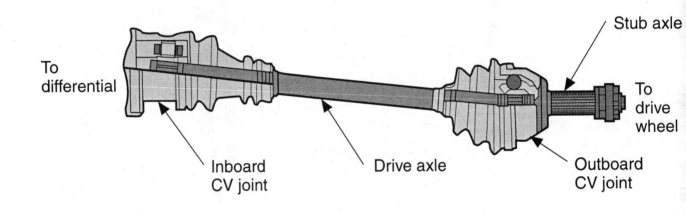

To
differential

Stub axle

To
drive
wheel

Inboard
CV joint

Drive axle

Outboard
CV joint

Transparency 94

Automotive Technology: A Systems Approach, 3E

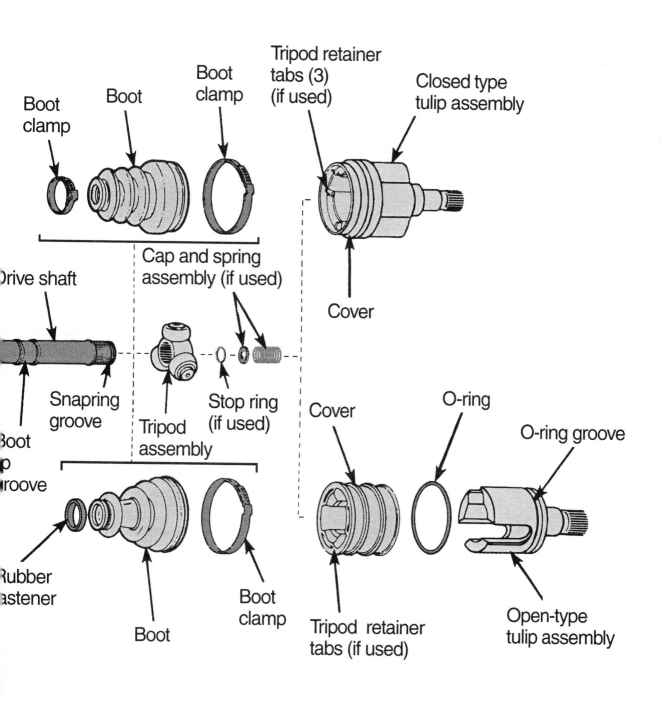

Boot
clamp

Boot

Boot
clamp

Tripod retainer
tabs (3)
(if used)

Closed type
tulip assembly

Cap and spring
assembly (if used)

Drive shaft

Cover

Snapring
groove

Stop ring
(if used)

Tripod
assembly

Cover

O-ring

O-ring groove

Boot
p
roove

Rubber
astener

Boot

Boot
clamp

Tripod retainer
tabs (if used)

Open-type
tulip assembly

Boot

Transparency 95

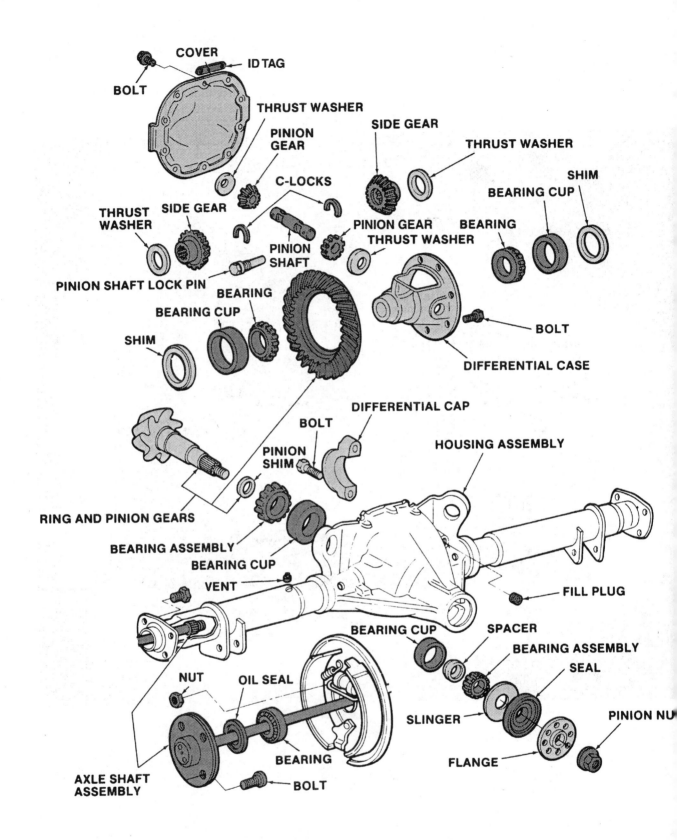

Transparency 96

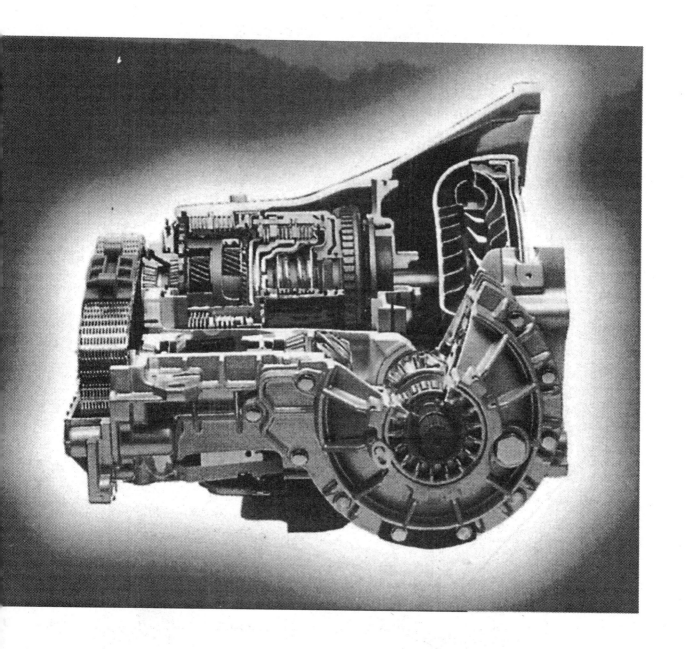

Transparency 97

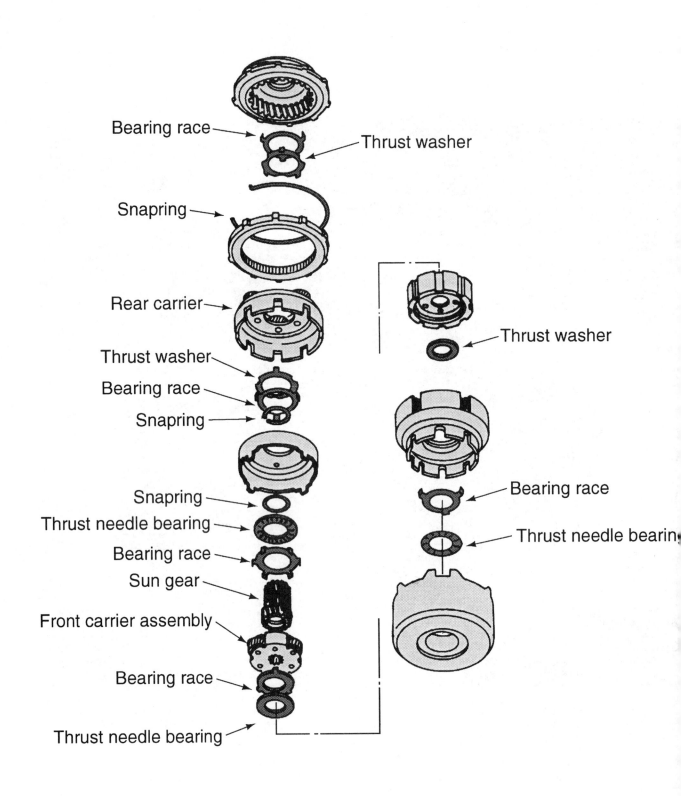

Bearing race

Thrust washer

Snapring

Rear carrier

Thrust washer

Bearing race

Snapring

Snapring

Thrust needle bearing

Bearing race

Sun gear

Front carrier assembly

Bearing race

Thrust needle bearing

Thrust washer

Bearing race

Thrust needle bearin

Transparency 98

Automotive Technology: A Systems Approach, 3E

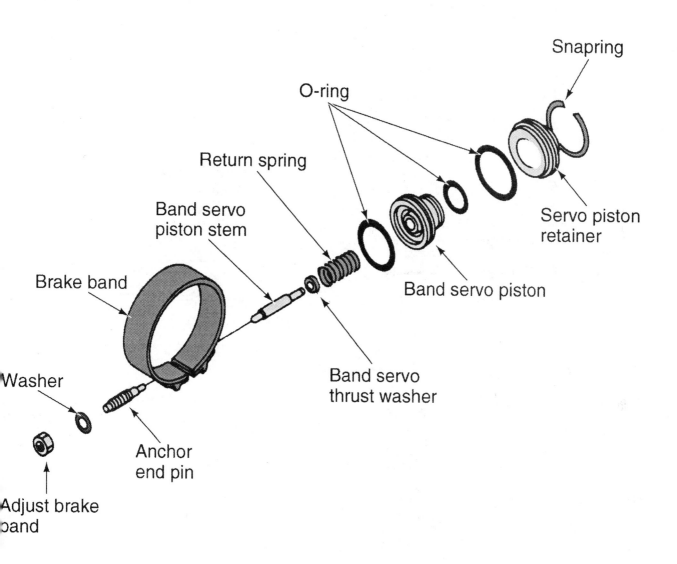

Snapring

O-ring

Return spring

Band servo
piston stem

Brake band

Washer

Adjust brake
band

Anchor
end pin

Band servo
thrust washer

Band servo piston

Servo piston
retainer

Transparency 99

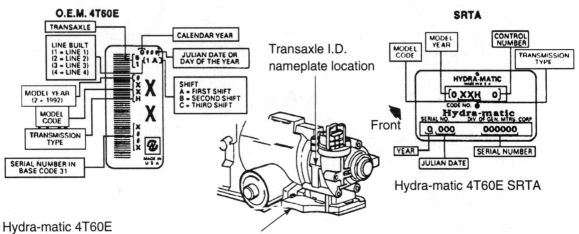

O.E.M. 4T60E

TRANSAXLE

LINE BUILT
(1 = LINE 1)
(2 = LINE 2)
(3 = LINE 3)
(4 = LINE 4)

MODEL YEAR
(2 - 1992)

MODEL
CODE

TRANSMISSION
TYPE

SERIAL NUMBER IN
BASE CODE 31

CALENDAR YEAR

JULIAN DATE OR
DAY OF THE YEAR

SHIFT
A = FIRST SHIFT
B = SECOND SHIFT
C = THIRD SHIFT

MADE IN
U.S.A.

Transaxle I.D.
nameplate location

Front

SRTA

MODEL
CODE

MODEL
YEAR

CONTROL
NUMBER

TRANSMISSION
TYPE

HYDRA-MATIC

CODE NO.

Hydra-matic
DIV OF GEN. MTRS. CORP.

SERIAL NO.

YEAR

JULIAN DATE

SERIAL NUMBER

Hydra-matic 4T60E SRTA

Hydra-matic 4T60E
Transaxle vehicle identification number is stamped into the horizontal cast rib on right rear of the transaxle housing

Transparency 100

Automotive Technology: A Systems Approach, 3E

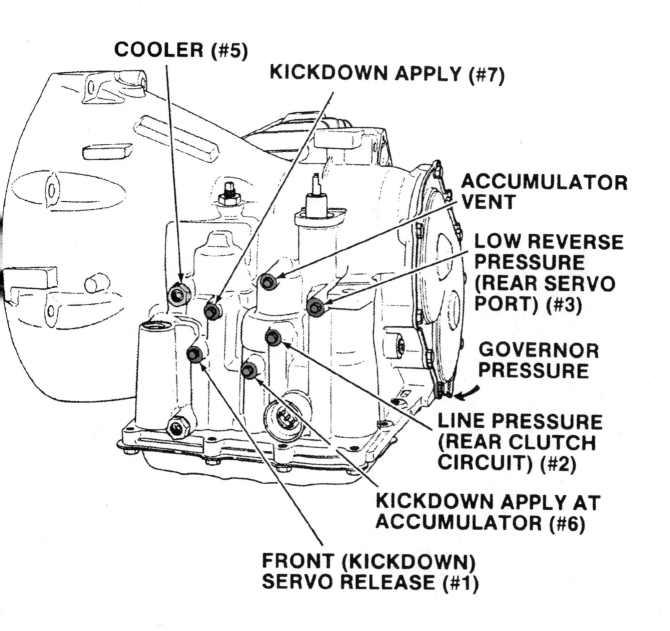

COOLER (#5)

KICKDOWN APPLY (#7)

ACCUMULATOR VENT

LOW REVERSE PRESSURE (REAR SERVO PORT) (#3)

GOVERNOR PRESSURE

LINE PRESSURE (REAR CLUTCH CIRCUIT) (#2)

KICKDOWN APPLY AT ACCUMULATOR (#6)

FRONT (KICKDOWN) SERVO RELEASE (#1)

Transparency 101

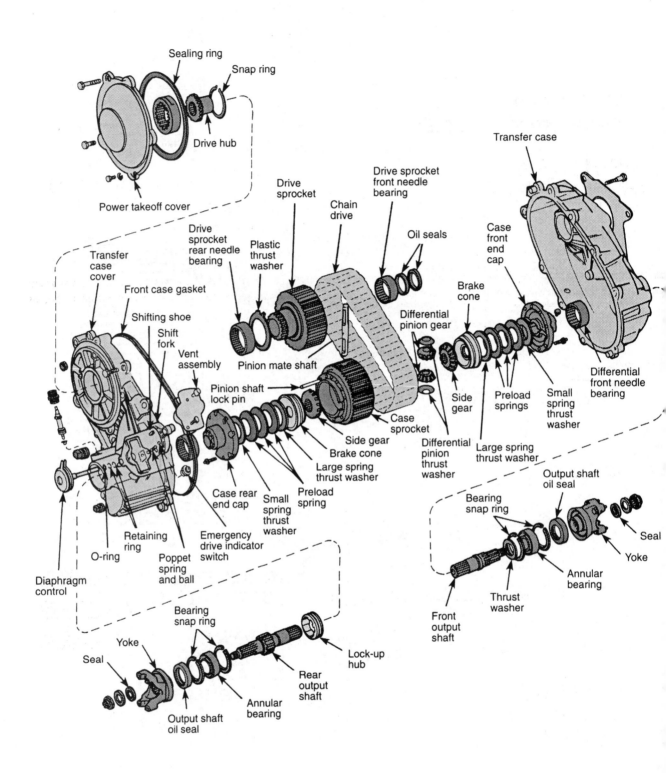

Sealing ring

Snap ring

Drive hub

Power takeoff cover

Transfer case

Drive sprocket
front needle
bearing

Drive
sprocket

Chain
drive

Oil seals

Case
front
end
cap

Drive
sprocket
rear needle
bearing

Plastic
thrust
washer

Brake
cone

Transfer
case
cover

Front case gasket

Differential
pinion gear

Differential
front needle
bearing

Shifting shoe

Shift
fork

Pinion mate shaft

Small
spring
thrust
washer

Vent
assembly

Pinion shaft
lock pin

Side
gear

Preload
springs

Large spring
thrust washer

Case
sprocket

Side gear

Brake cone

Differential
pinion
thrust
washer

Output shaft
oil seal

Large spring
thrust washer

Bearing
snap ring

Seal

Large spring
thrust washer

Case rear
end cap

Small
spring
thrust
washer

Preload
spring

Annular
bearing

Yoke

Retaining
ring

Emergency
drive indicator
switch

O-ring

Poppet
spring
and ball

Front
output
shaft

Thrust
washer

Diaphragm
control

Bearing
snap ring

Yoke

Lock-up
hub

Seal

Rear
output
shaft

Output shaft
oil seal

Annular
bearing

Transparency 102

Automotive Technology: A Systems Approach, 3E

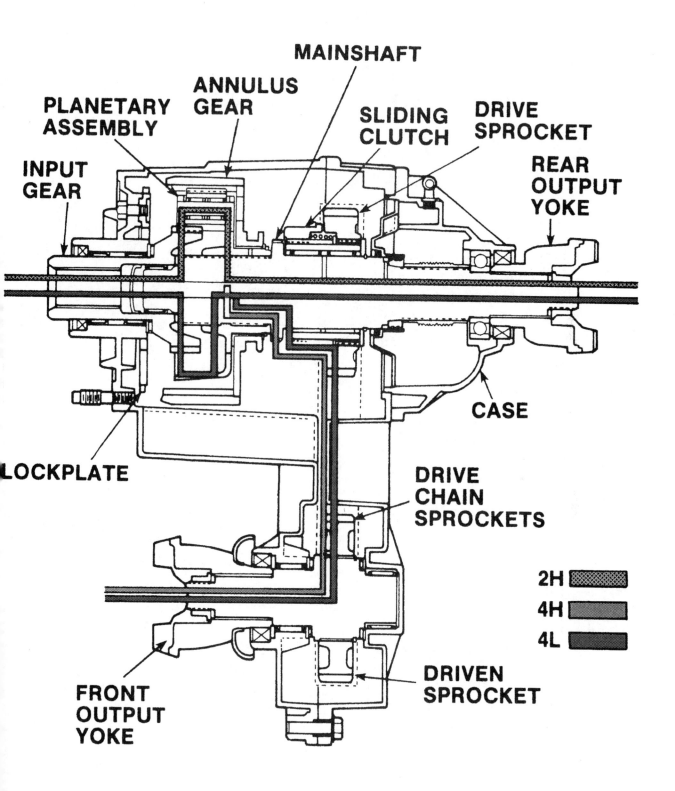

PLANETARY ASSEMBLY

ANNULUS GEAR

MAINSHAFT

SLIDING CLUTCH

DRIVE SPROCKET

REAR OUTPUT YOKE

INPUT GEAR

CASE

LOCKPLATE

DRIVE CHAIN SPROCKETS

2H
4H
4L

DRIVEN SPROCKET

FRONT OUTPUT YOKE

Transparency 103

Radial tires

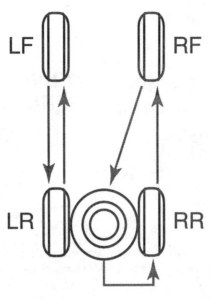

5 Wheel rotation

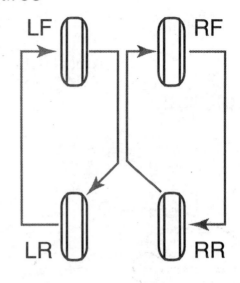

4 Wheel rotation

Bias-belted tires

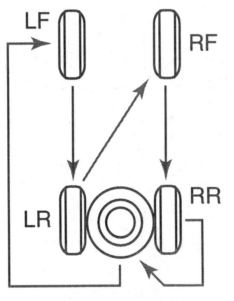

5 Wheel rotation

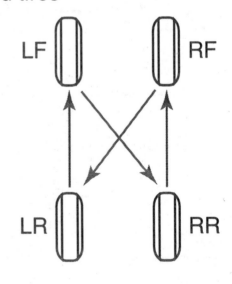

4 Wheel rotation

Transparency 104

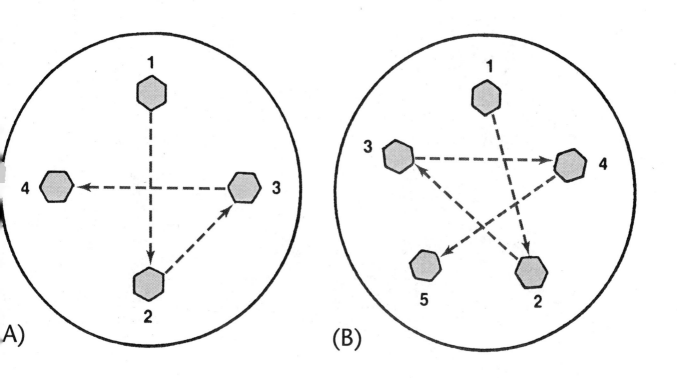

(A)

(B)

Transparency 105

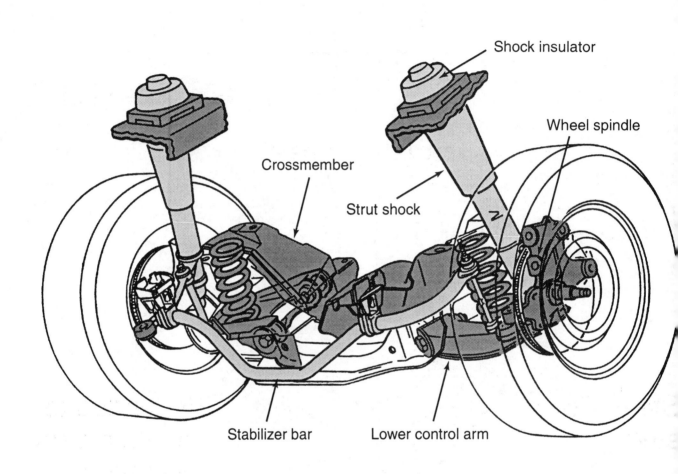

Shock insulator

Wheel spindle

Crossmember

Strut shock

Stabilizer bar

Lower control arm

Transparency 106

Automotive Technology: A Systems Approach, 3E

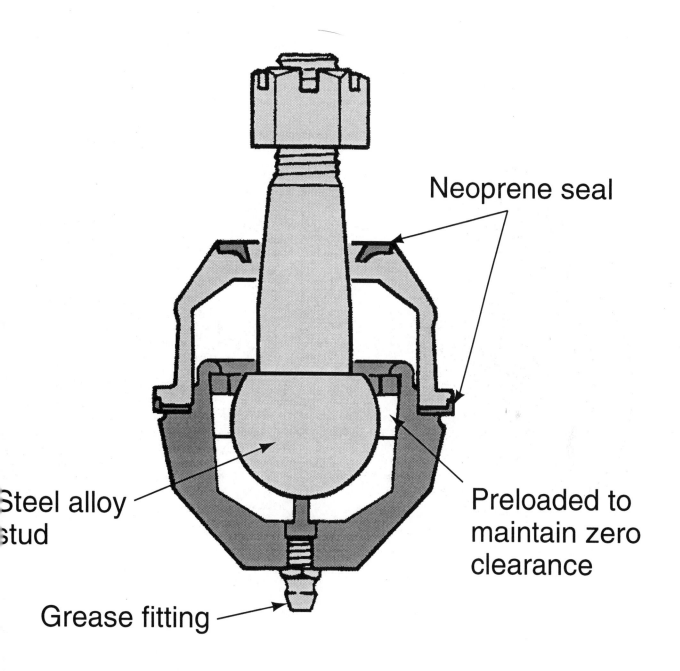

Neoprene seal

Steel alloy stud

Grease fitting

Preloaded to maintain zero clearance

Transparency 107

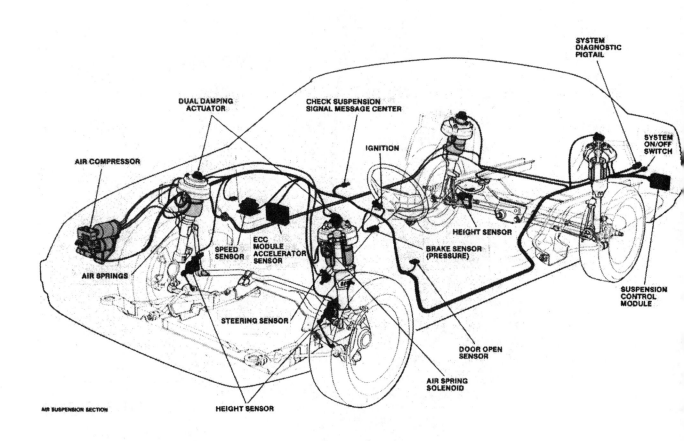

DUAL DAMPING
ACTUATOR

CHECK SUSPENSION
SIGNAL MESSAGE CENTER

SYSTEM
DIAGNOSTIC
PIGTAIL

IGNITION

SYSTEM
ON/OFF
SWITCH

AIR COMPRESSOR

SPEED
SENSOR

ECC
MODULE
ACCELERATOR
SENSOR

HEIGHT SENSOR

AIR SPRINGS

BRAKE SENSOR
(PRESSURE)

SUSPENSION
CONTROL
MODULE

STEERING SENSOR

DOOR OPEN
SENSOR

AIR SPRING
SOLENOID

AIR SUSPENSION SECTION

HEIGHT SENSOR

Transparency 108

Copyright © 2000 by Delma
a division of Thomson Learning

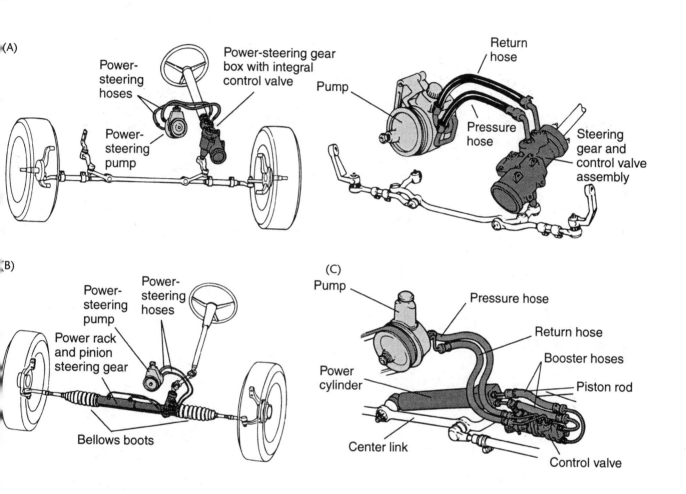

(A)

Power-steering hoses

Power-steering gear box with integral control valve

Power-steering pump

Return hose

Pump

Pressure hose

Steering gear and control valve assembly

(B)

Power-steering pump

Power-steering hoses

Power rack and pinion steering gear

Bellows boots

(C)

Pump

Pressure hose

Return hose

Booster hoses

Piston rod

Power cylinder

Center link

Control valve

Transparency 109

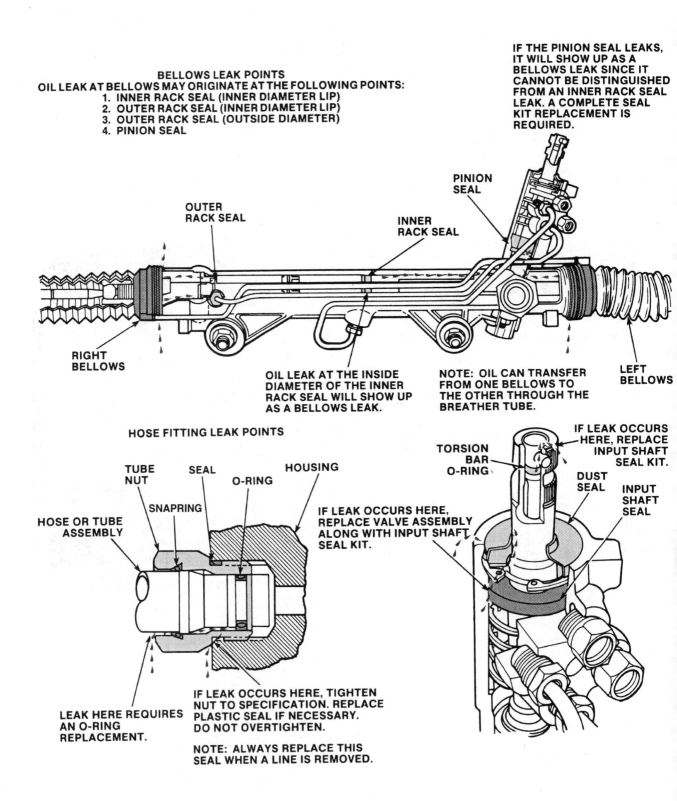

BELLOWS LEAK POINTS
OIL LEAK AT BELLOWS MAY ORIGINATE AT THE FOLLOWING POINTS:
1. INNER RACK SEAL (INNER DIAMETER LIP)
2. OUTER RACK SEAL (INNER DIAMETER LIP)
3. OUTER RACK SEAL (OUTSIDE DIAMETER)
4. PINION SEAL

IF THE PINION SEAL LEAKS, IT WILL SHOW UP AS A BELLOWS LEAK SINCE IT CANNOT BE DISTINGUISHED FROM AN INNER RACK SEAL LEAK. A COMPLETE SEAL KIT REPLACEMENT IS REQUIRED.

OUTER RACK SEAL

INNER RACK SEAL

PINION SEAL

RIGHT BELLOWS

OIL LEAK AT THE INSIDE DIAMETER OF THE INNER RACK SEAL WILL SHOW UP AS A BELLOWS LEAK.

NOTE: OIL CAN TRANSFER FROM ONE BELLOWS TO THE OTHER THROUGH THE BREATHER TUBE.

LEFT BELLOWS

HOSE FITTING LEAK POINTS

TUBE NUT   SEAL   HOUSING
SNAPRING   O-RING

HOSE OR TUBE ASSEMBLY

IF LEAK OCCURS HERE, REPLACE VALVE ASSEMBLY ALONG WITH INPUT SHAFT SEAL KIT.

TORSION BAR O-RING

IF LEAK OCCURS HERE, REPLACE INPUT SHAFT SEAL KIT.

DUST SEAL

INPUT SHAFT SEAL

LEAK HERE REQUIRES AN O-RING REPLACEMENT.

IF LEAK OCCURS HERE, TIGHTEN NUT TO SPECIFICATION. REPLACE PLASTIC SEAL IF NECESSARY. DO NOT OVERTIGHTEN.

NOTE: ALWAYS REPLACE THIS SEAL WHEN A LINE IS REMOVED.

Transparency 110

Automotive Technology: A Systems Approach, 3E

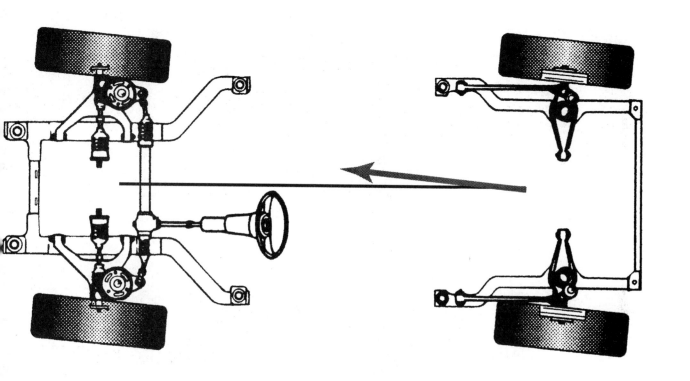

Transparency 111

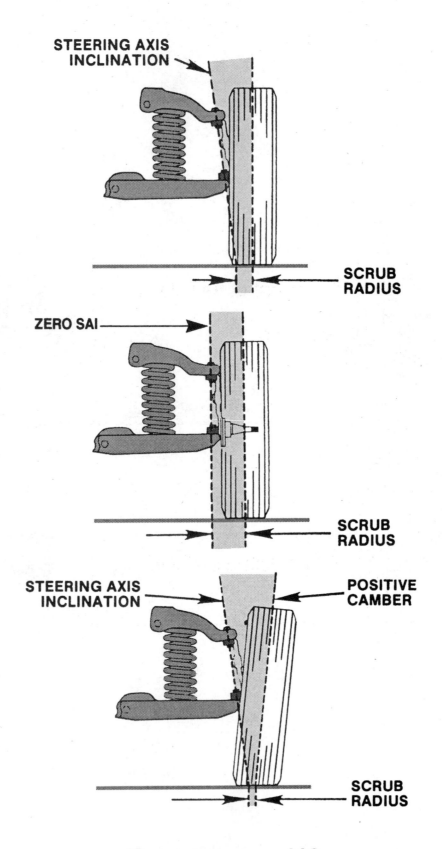

STEERING AXIS
INCLINATION

SCRUB
RADIUS

ZERO SAI

SCRUB
RADIUS

STEERING AXIS
INCLINATION

POSITIVE
CAMBER

SCRUB
RADIUS

Transparency 112

Automotive Technology: A Systems Approach, 3E

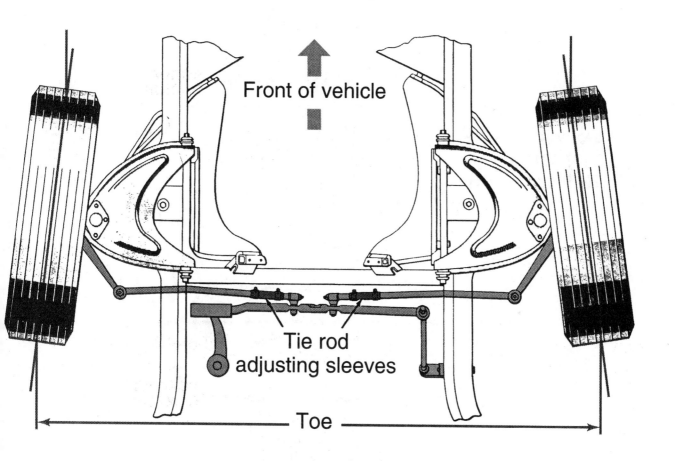

Front of vehicle

Tie rod
adjusting sleeves

Toe

Transparency 113

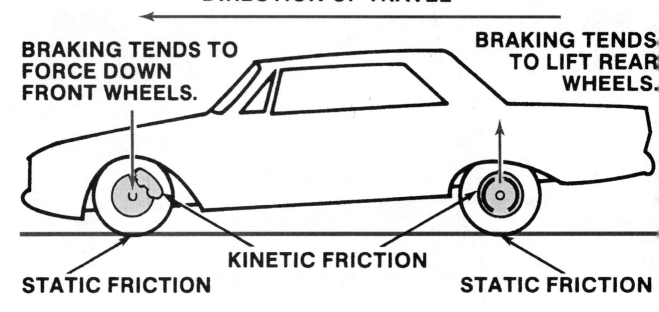

DIRECTION OF TRAVEL

BRAKING TENDS TO FORCE DOWN FRONT WHEELS.

BRAKING TENDS TO LIFT REAR WHEELS.

STATIC FRICTION

KINETIC FRICTION

STATIC FRICTION

Transparency 114

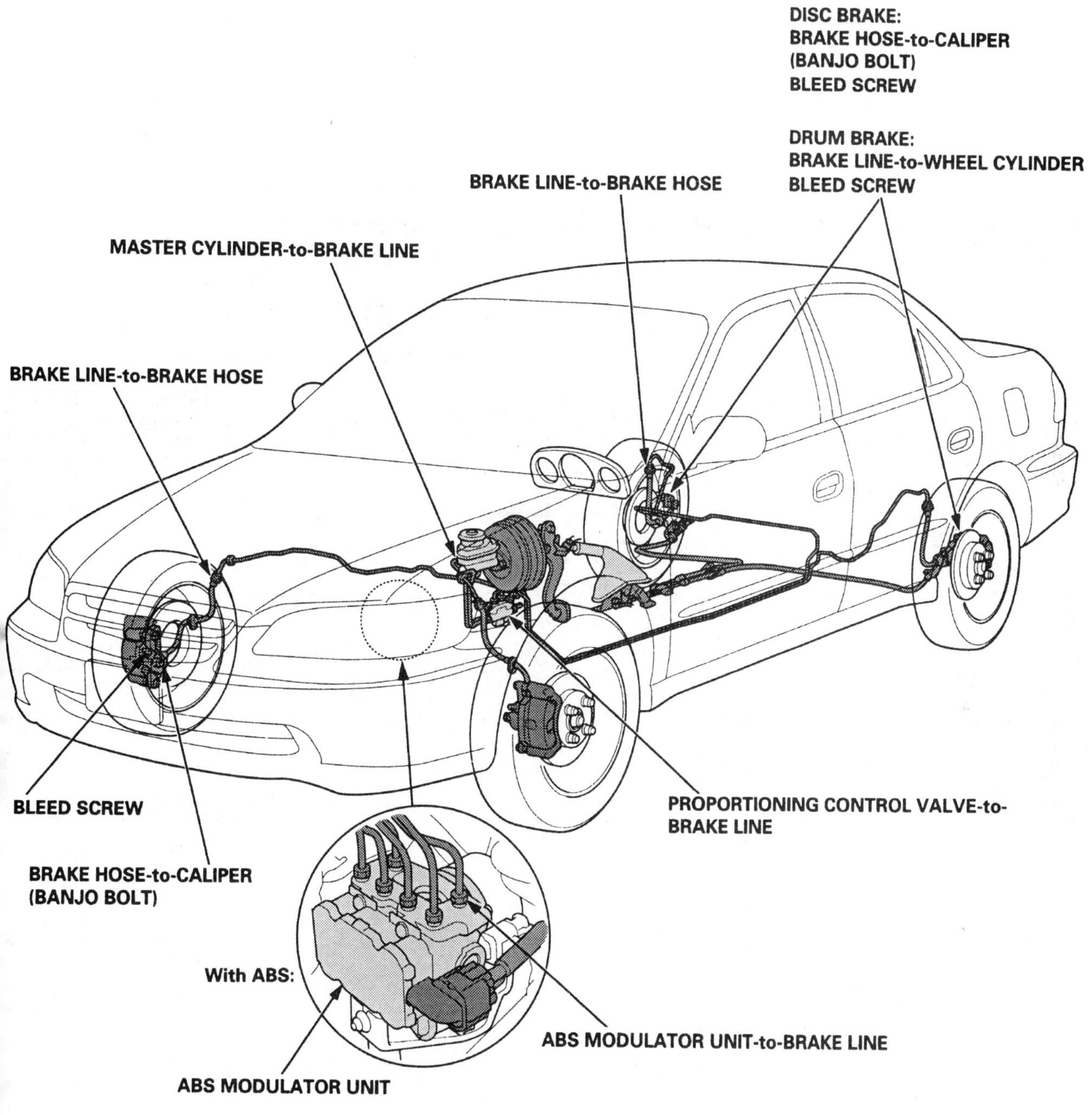

DISC BRAKE:
BRAKE HOSE-to-CALIPER
(BANJO BOLT)
BLEED SCREW

DRUM BRAKE:
BRAKE LINE-to-WHEEL CYLINDER
BLEED SCREW

BRAKE LINE-to-BRAKE HOSE

MASTER CYLINDER-to-BRAKE LINE

BRAKE LINE-to-BRAKE HOSE

BLEED SCREW

BRAKE HOSE-to-CALIPER
(BANJO BOLT)

With ABS:

ABS MODULATOR UNIT

PROPORTIONING CONTROL VALVE-to-
BRAKE LINE

ABS MODULATOR UNIT-to-BRAKE LINE

Transparency 115

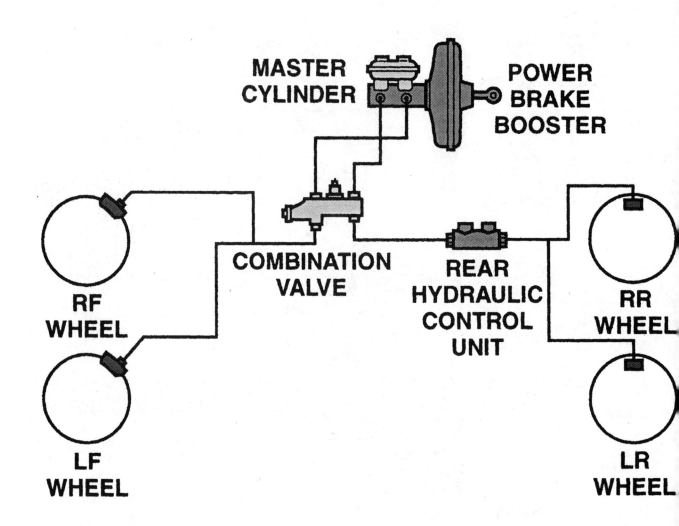

MASTER
CYLINDER

POWER
BRAKE
BOOSTER

RF
WHEEL

LF
WHEEL

COMBINATION
VALVE

REAR
HYDRAULIC
CONTROL
UNIT

RR
WHEEL

LR
WHEEL

Transparency 116

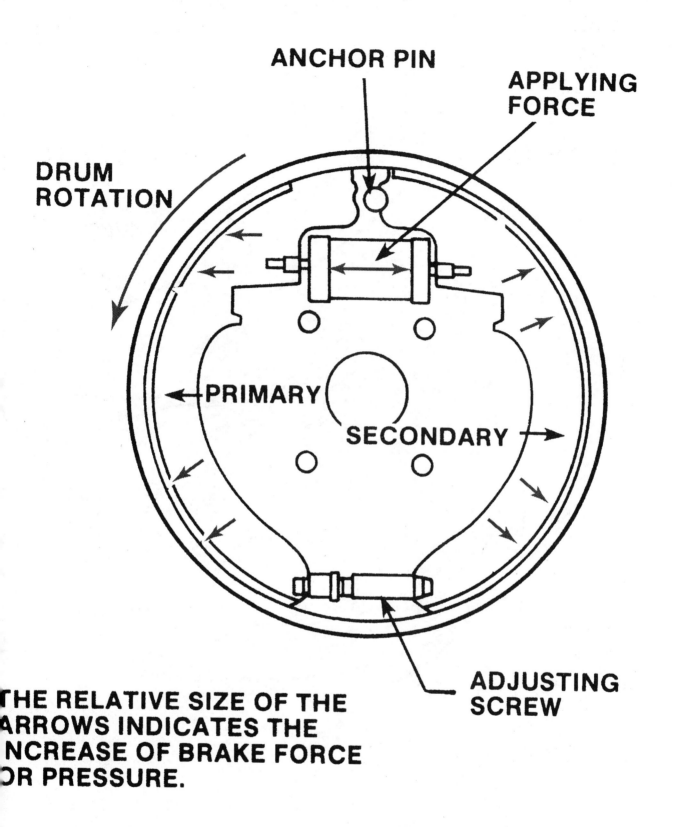

ANCHOR PIN

APPLYING FORCE

DRUM ROTATION

PRIMARY

SECONDARY

ADJUSTING SCREW

THE RELATIVE SIZE OF THE ARROWS INDICATES THE INCREASE OF BRAKE FORCE OR PRESSURE.

Transparency 117

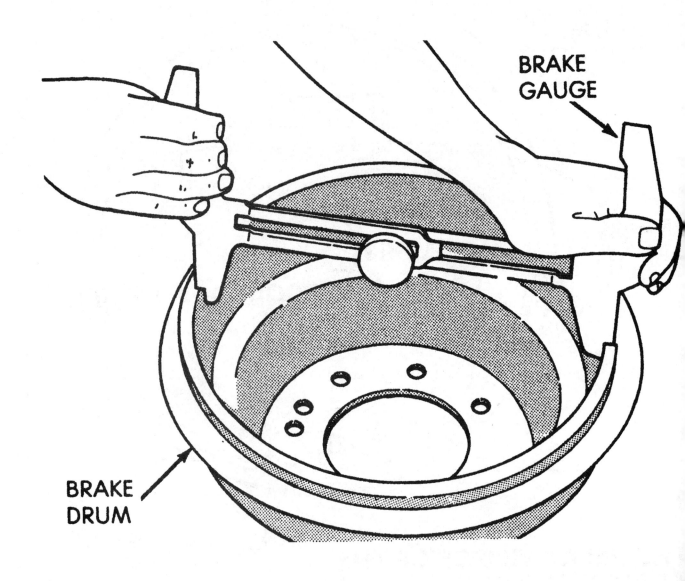

BRAKE
GAUGE

BRAKE
DRUM

Transparency 118

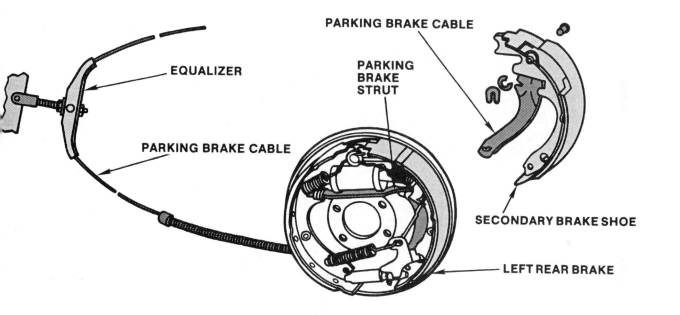

EQUALIZER

PARKING BRAKE CABLE

PARKING BRAKE CABLE

PARKING BRAKE STRUT

SECONDARY BRAKE SHOE

LEFT REAR BRAKE

Transparency 119

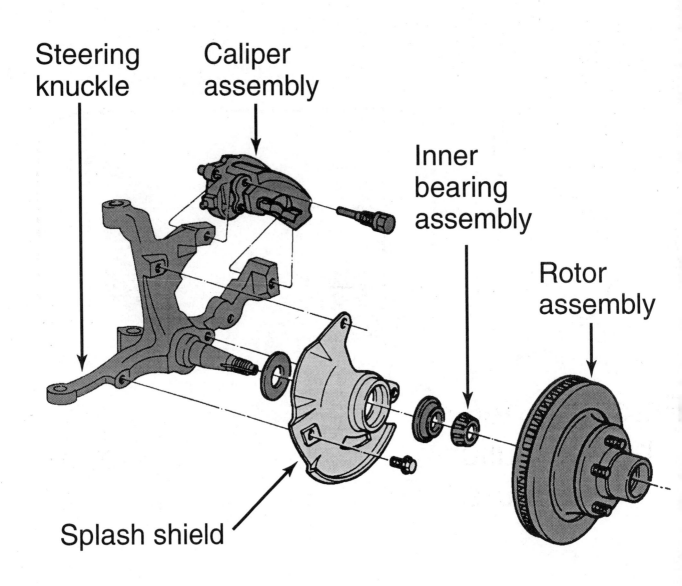

Steering knuckle

Caliper assembly

Inner bearing assembly

Rotor assembly

Splash shield

Transparency 120

Automotive Technology: A Systems Approach, 3E

Fixed caliper

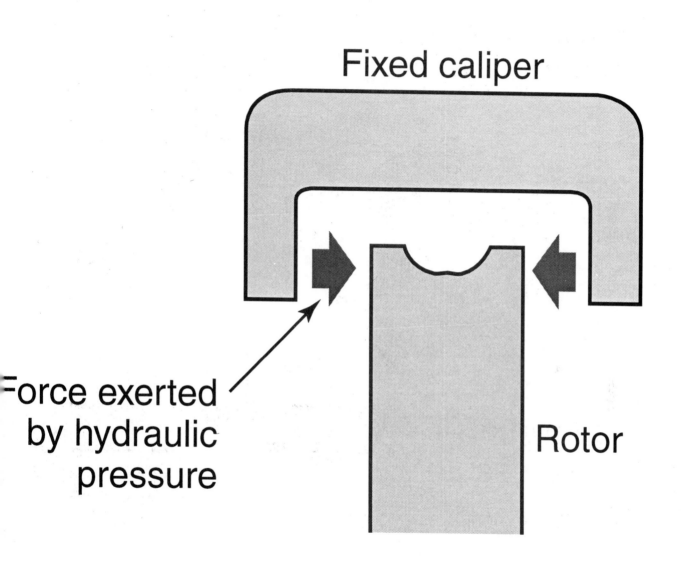

Force exerted
by hydraulic
pressure

Rotor

Transparency 121

Moving caliper

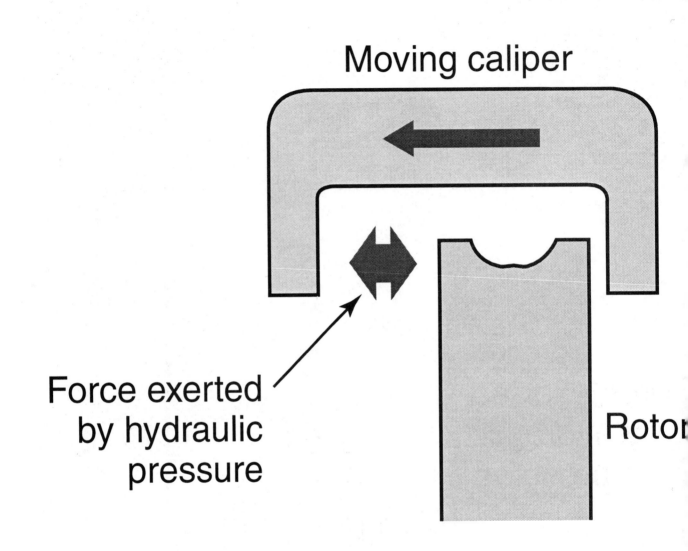

Force exerted by hydraulic pressure

Rotor

Transparency 122

Automotive Technology: A Systems Approach, 3E

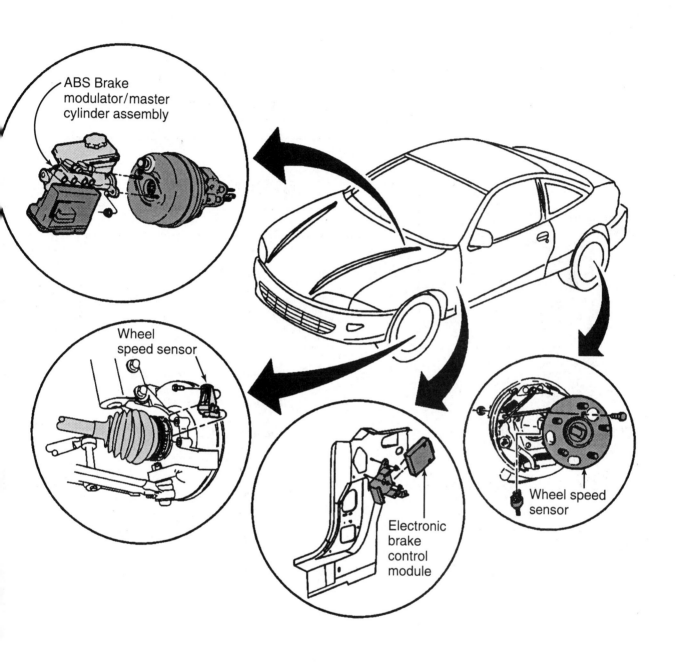

ABS Brake modulator/master cylinder assembly

Wheel speed sensor

Electronic brake control module

Wheel speed sensor

Transparency 123

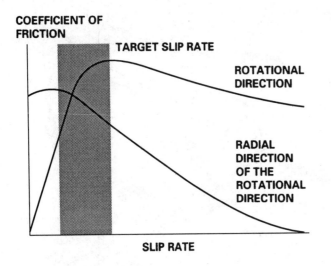

COEFFICIENT OF FRICTION

TARGET SLIP RATE

ROTATIONAL DIRECTION

RADIAL DIRECTION OF THE ROTATIONAL DIRECTION

SLIP RATE

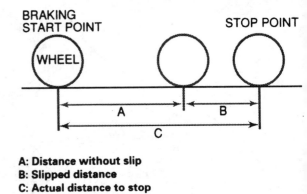

BRAKING START POINT

STOP POINT

WHEEL

A

B

C

A: Distance without slip
B: Slipped distance
C: Actual distance to stop

$$\text{SLIP RATE} = \frac{B}{C} = \frac{\text{VEHICLE SPEED} - \text{WHEEL SPEED}}{\text{VEHICLE SPEED}}$$

Transparency 124

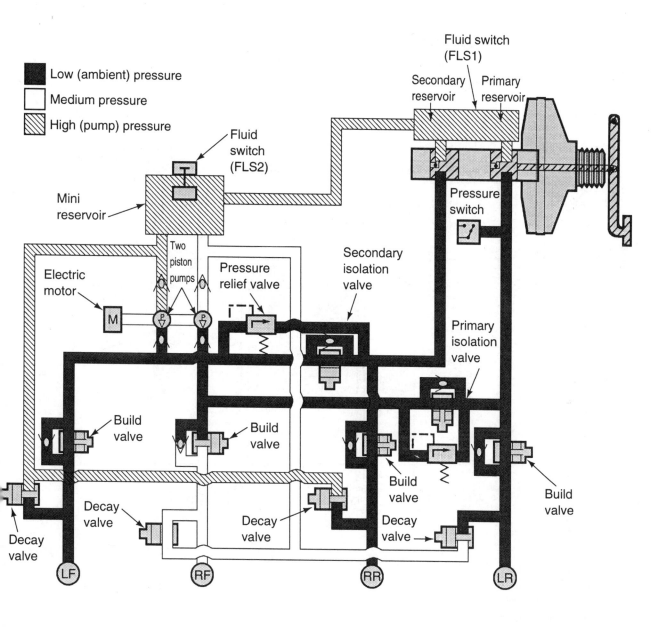

Low (ambient) pressure

Medium pressure

High (pump) pressure

Fluid switch
(FLS1)

Secondary
reservoir

Primary
reservoir

Fluid
switch
(FLS2)

Mini
reservoir

Pressure
switch

Electric
motor

Two
piston
pumps

Pressure
relief valve

Secondary
isolation
valve

Primary
isolation
valve

M

Build
valve

Build
valve

Build
valve

Build
valve

Decay
valve

Decay
valve

Decay
valve

Decay
valve

Decay
valve

LF

RF

RR

LR

Transparency 125

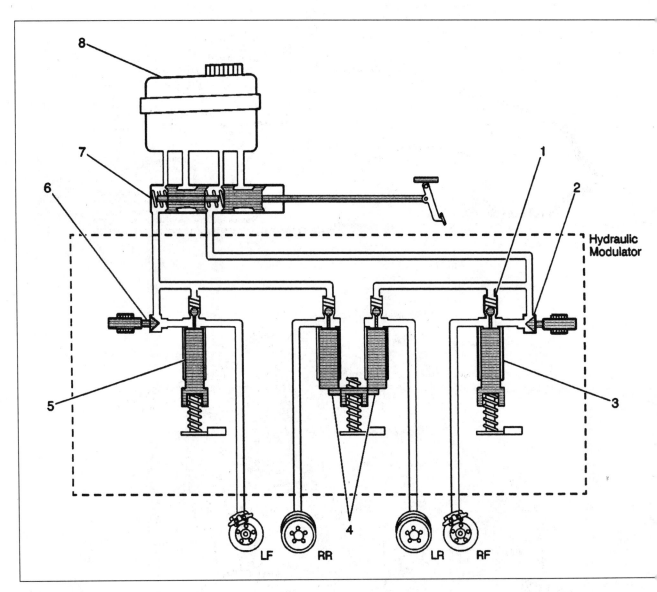

Legend

(1) Check Valve
(2) Right Front Solenoid Valve
(3) Right Front Modulation Piston
(4) Rear Modulation Pistons

(5) Left Front Modulation Piston
(6) Left Front Solenoid Valve
(7) Master Cylinder
(8) Master Cylinder Reservoir

Transparency 126

Automotive Technology: A Systems Approach, 3E

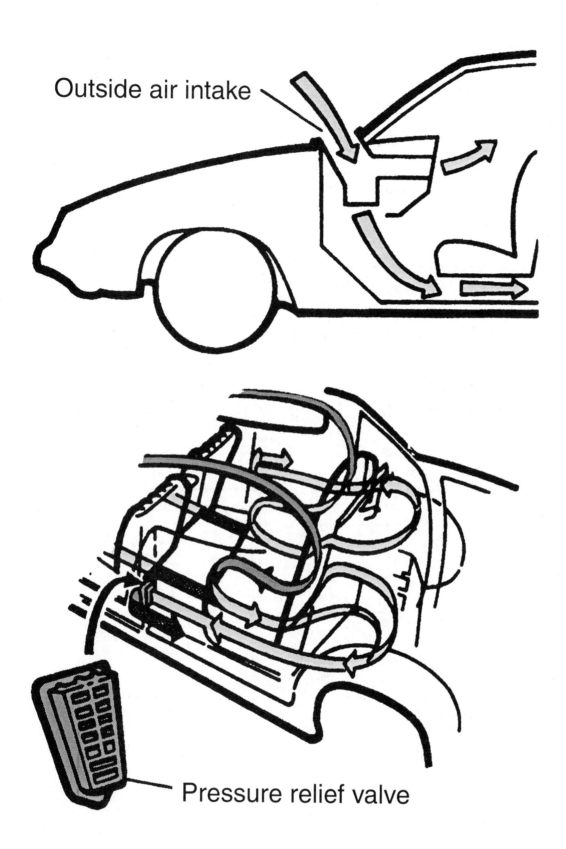

Outside air intake

Pressure relief valve

Transparency 127

STANDARD TEMPERATURE/ PRESSURE CHART FOR R-134a

°F	PSI	°F	PSI	°F	PSI	°F	PSI	°F	PSI
65	69	77	86	89	107	101	131	113	158
66	70	78	88	90	109	102	133	114	160
67	71	79	90	91	111	103	135	115	163
68	73	80	91	92	113	104	137	116	165
69	74	81	93	93	115	105	139	117	168
70	76	82	95	94	117	106	142	118	171
71	77	83	96	95	118	107	144	119	173
72	79	84	98	96	120	108	146	120	176
73	80	85	100	97	122	109	149		
74	82	86	102	98	125	110	151		
75	83	87	103	99	127	111	153		
76	85	88	105	100	129	112	156		

METRIC TEMPERATURE/ PRESSURE CHART FOR R-134a

°C	kPa	°C	kPa	°C	kPa
18	476	29	676	40	945
19	483	30	703	41	979
20	503	31	724	42	1007
21	524	32	752	43	1027
22	545	33	765	44	1055
23	552	34	793	45	1089
24	572	35	814	46	1124
25	593	36	841	47	1158
26	621	37	876	48	1179
27	642	38	889	49	1214
28	655	39	917		

STANDARD TEMPERATURE/ PRESSURE CHART FOR R-12

°F	PSI	°F	PSI	°F	PSI	°F	PSI	°F	PSI
65	74	75	87	85	102	95	118	105	136
66	75	76	88	86	103	96	120	106	138
67	76	77	90	87	105	97	122	107	140
68	78	78	92	88	107	98	124	108	142
69	79	79	94	89	108	99	125	109	144
70	80	80	96	90	110	100	127	110	146
71	82	81	98	91	111	101	129	111	148
72	83	82	99	92	113	102	130	112	150
73	84	83	100	93	115	103	132	113	152
74	86	84	101	94	116	104	134	114	154

METRIC TEMPERATURE/ PRESSURE CHART FOR R-12

°C	kg/cm^2	°C	kg/cm^2	°C	kg/cm^2
18	5.2	28	7.0	38	9.0
19	5.3	29	7.1	39	9.2
20	5.5	30	7.2	40	9.4
21	5.6	31	7.5	41	9.6
22	5.8	32	7.7	42	9.9
23	6.0	33	7.9	43	10.0
24	6.1	34	8.1	44	10.4
25	6.3	35	8.3	45	10.7
26	6.6	36	8.5	46	10.9
27	6.8	37	8.7	47	11.0

Transparency 128

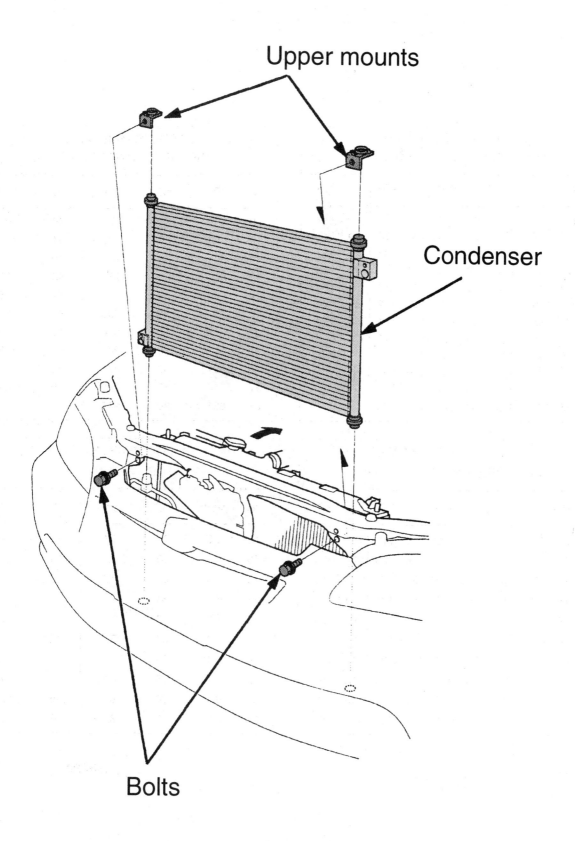

Upper mounts

Condenser

Bolts

Transparency 129

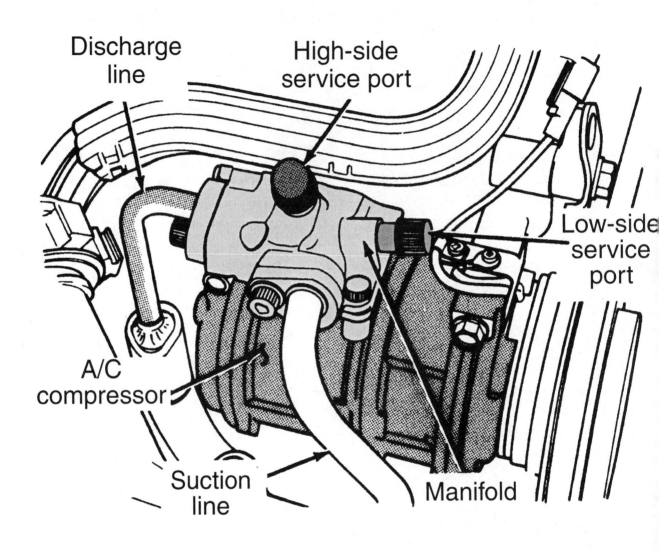

Discharge line

High-side service port

Low-side service port

A/C compressor

Suction line

Manifold

Transparency 130

Automotive Technology: A Systems Approach, 3E

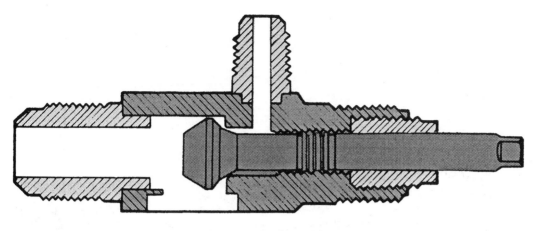

BACK SEATED

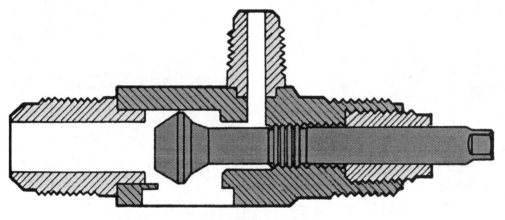

MID POSITION

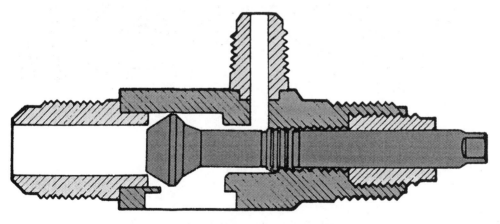

FRONT SEATED

Transparency 131

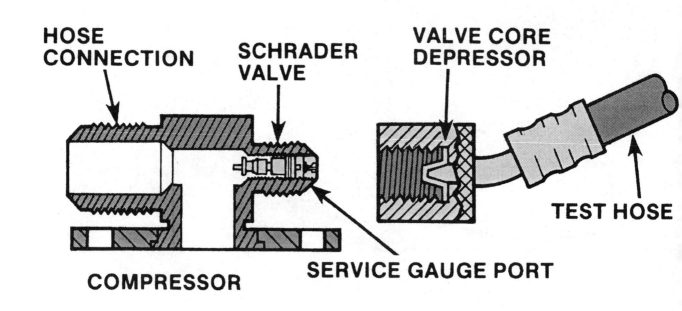

HOSE
CONNECTION

SCHRADER
VALVE

VALVE CORE
DEPRESSOR

TEST HOSE

COMPRESSOR

SERVICE GAUGE PORT

Transparency 132

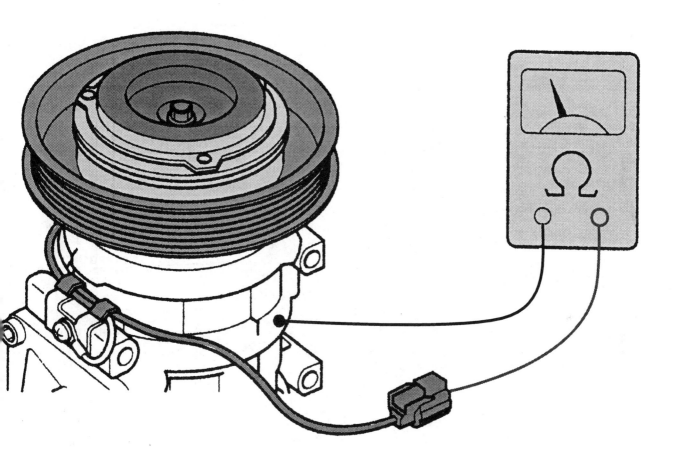

Transparency 133

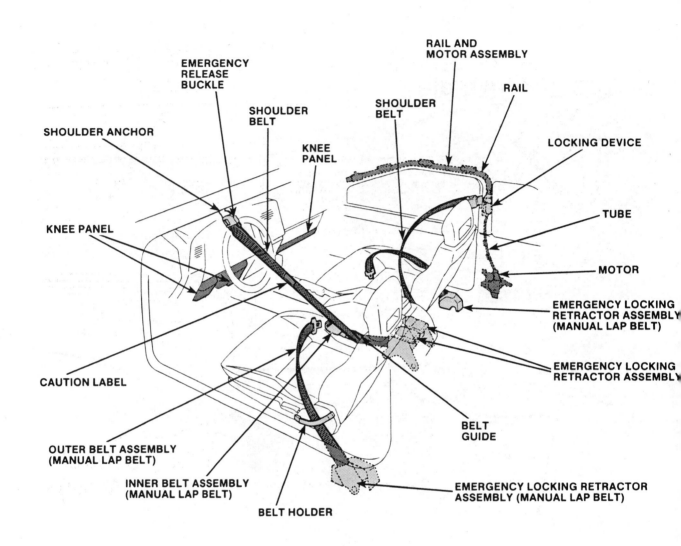

EMERGENCY
RELEASE
BUCKLE

RAIL AND
MOTOR ASSEMBLY

RAIL

SHOULDER
BELT

SHOULDER
BELT

LOCKING DEVICE

SHOULDER ANCHOR

KNEE
PANEL

TUBE

KNEE PANEL

MOTOR

EMERGENCY LOCKING
RETRACTOR ASSEMBLY
(MANUAL LAP BELT)

EMERGENCY LOCKING
RETRACTOR ASSEMBLY

CAUTION LABEL

BELT
GUIDE

OUTER BELT ASSEMBLY
(MANUAL LAP BELT)

INNER BELT ASSEMBLY
(MANUAL LAP BELT)

EMERGENCY LOCKING RETRACTOR
ASSEMBLY (MANUAL LAP BELT)

BELT HOLDER

Transparency 134

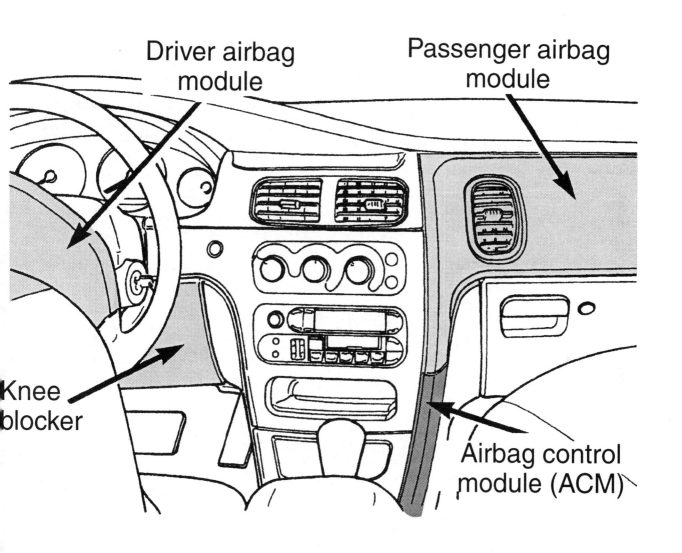

Driver airbag module

Passenger airbag module

Knee blocker

Airbag control module (ACM)

Transparency 135

On back of air bag

In engine compartment

Label on front of driver and passenger sun visors

Label on headliner above driver and passenger sun visors

Label on back side of driver and passenger sun visors

Transparency 136

Automotive Technology: A Systems Approach, 3E

CROSSOVER GUIDE

Crossover Guide. This unique resource will help "make the switch" from your current text to *Automotive Technology* without the toil of locating coverage of the topics you want to teach. The Crossover Guide gives you a topic-by-topic index to the coverage in three of the best-selling texts in this field, and then compares it to the coverage in the third edition of *Automotive Technology*.

ERJAVEC/ AUTOMOTIVE TECHNOLOGY 3rd edition	ERJAVEC/ AUTOMOTIVE TECHNOLOGY 2nd edition	MODERN AUTOMOTIVE TECHNOLOGY Duffy 1998	AUTOMOTIVE TECHNOLOGY Halderman 1999
Ch. 1 The Automotive Industry	*Ch. 1*	*Ch. 2*	*Ch. 1*
Introduction pp. 1 to 8	*pp. 2–7*		*pp. 7–8*
Job Classifications pp. 8 to 10	*pp. 7–8*	*pp. 22–25*	*pp. 5–7*
Related Career Opportunities p. 10	*p. 8*	*pp. 25–26*	
Working as a Technician pp. 10 to 12	*pp. 8–10*	*p. 27*	*pp. 8–9, 12*
Training for a Career in Automotive Service p. 12	*p. 10*	*p. 27*	
ASE Certification pp. 12 to 13	*pp. 10–12*	*pp. 27–31*	*pp. 11–12*
Service Technician Society p. 13			
Ch. 2 Working Safely	*Ch. 2*	*Chs. 5 & 10*	*Chs. 2 & 27*
Personal Safety pp. 16 to 19	*pp. 14–16*	*pp. 64–65*	*pp. 28*
Tool and Equipment Safety pp. 19 to 24	*pp. 16–20*	*pp. 64–65*	*pp. 27, 29–32*
Work Area Safety pp. 24 to 26	*pp. 20–22*		*p. 535*
Manufacturer's Warnings and Government Regulations pp. 26 to 29	*pp. 22–24*		*pp. 32–33 pp. 538–539*
Guidelines for Handling Shop Wastes pp. 29 to 30		*pp. 135–136*	
Ch. 3 Automotive Systems	*Ch. 3*	*Chs. 1 & 10*	*Chs. 1 & 3*
History pp. 33 to 35	*pp. 26–28*		
Modern Power Plants p. 35	*p. 28*		
Design Evolution p. 35 to 36	*pp. 28–29*	*p. 2*	*pp. 2–3*

ERJAVEC/ AUTOMOTIVE TECHNOLOGY 3rd edition	ERJAVEC/ AUTOMOTIVE TECHNOLOGY 2nd edition	MODERN AUTOMOTIVE TECHNOLOGY Duffy 1998	AUTOMOTIVE TECHNOLOGY Halderman 1999
Body Shapes pp. 36 to 39	*pp. 29–31*	*pp. 2, 4*	
The Electronic Revolution p. 39	*p. 31*		
The Basic Engine pp. 39 to 41	*pp. 32–34*	*pp. 5–6*	
Engine Systems pp. 41 to 46	*pp. 34–39*	*pp. 7–13*	
Drivetrain pp. 46 to 50	*pp. 39–44*	*pp. 13–17*	
Running Gear pp. 50 to 52	*pp. 44–47*	*pp. 17–19*	
Preventive Maintenance pp. 52 to 61	*pp. 47–50*	*pp. 123–132*	*pp. 39–42, 45–59*
Ch. 4 Shop Tools	*Chs. 4 & 13*	*Chs. 3, 6, 7 & 9*	*Ch. 2*
Measurement Systems pp. 64 to 65	*pp. 53–54*	*pp. 68–70*	
Fasteners pp. 65 to 68	*pp. 302–309*	*pp. 108–117*	*pp. 15–17*
Measuring Tools pp. 68 to 77	*pp. 54–64*	*pp. 70–77*	*pp. 22, 24*
Hand Tools pp. 77 to 89	*pp. 65–75*	*pp. 34–44*	*pp. 18–27*
Power Tools pp. 89 to 91	*pp. 72–75*	*pp. 46–56*	
Shop (Service) Manuals pp. 91 to 93	*pp. 76–78*	*pp. 83–92*	
Ch. 5 Diagnostic Equipment	*Chs. 5 & 6*	*Chs. 6, 8, 23, 36, 44 & 46*	*Chs. 5, 13, 14, 21, 24, 25 & 26*
Electrical Fundamentals pp. 96 to 98	*p. 81–82*	*p. 94 brief*	*pp. 232–233*
Measuring Electricity pp. 98 to 99	*pp. 82–83*	*pp. 94–97*	*pp. 233–235, 238*
Basic Electrical Diagnosis p. 99	*pp. 83–84*	*p. 97*	*pp. 236–238*
Electrical Test Equipment pp. 100 to 103	*pp. 84–85*	*pp. 102–104*	*pp. 254–257*
Digital Multimeter Usage pp. 103-106	*pp. 85–87*		*pp. 255–259*

ERJAVEC/ AUTOMOTIVE TECHNOLOGY 3rd edition	ERJAVEC/ AUTOMOTIVE TECHNOLOGY 2nd edition	MODERN AUTOMOTIVE TECHNOLOGY Duffy 1998	AUTOMOTIVE TECHNOLOGY Halderman 1999
Ignition System Test Equipment pp. 106 to 109	*pp. 87–91*	*pp. 614, 615, 625*	*pp. 390–393, 399*
Lab Scopes pp. 109 to 113	*p. 91*	*p. 104* *p. 848*	*pp. 402–409, 468–471*
Engine Diagnostic Tools pp. 113 to 120	*Ch. 5, pp. 92–96* *Ch. 6, pp. 118-119*	*pp. 840–843, 863* *pp. 884-888*	*pp. 80–85, 90–93*
Fuel System Test Equipment pp. 120 to 122	*pp. 97–98*	*pp. 840–842* *pp. 368–370*	*pp. 452–454, 459–463, 72–478*
Exhaust Analyzers pp. 122 to 123	*pp. 98–99*	*pp. 802–806*	*pp. 486, 516–518, 524–525*
Computer Scan Tools pp. 123 to 124	*pp. 99–100*	*pp. 843–846*	*pp. 523, 587*
Engine Analyzers pp. 124 to 125	*pp. 100–101*	*pp. 858–864*	*p. 509*
Hydraulic System Testers pp. 125, 127		*p. 77*	
Ch. 6 Automotive Engines	*Ch. 6*	*Chs. 11, 12 & 16*	*Chs. 3, 4, 5 & 7*
Engine Classifications p. 134	*pp. 105–106*	*p. 158*	*pp. 66–69*
Four-Stroke Gasoline Engine pp. 134 to 136	*pp. 106–107*	*pp. 141–142*	*pp. 64–65*
Two-Stroke Gasoline Engine p. 137	*pp. 108–109*	*pp. 166–167*	
Characteristics of Four-Stroke Engine Design pp. 137 to 140	*pp. 110–113*	*pp. 158–162*	*pp. 64–65*
Gasoline Engine Systems pp. 140 to 141	*pp. 113–114*	*pp. 159–160*	
Engine Measurement and Performance pp. 141 to 144	*pp. 114–116*	*pp. 216–222*	*pp. 70–74*
Engine Identification pp. 144 to 145	*pp. 116–117*	*p. 84* *mentioned*	*pp. 37–38*
Engine Diagnostics pp. 145 to 146	*pp. 117–118*	*p. 759*	*pp. 84–85* *pp. 116–118*

ERJAVEC/ AUTOMOTIVE TECHNOLOGY 3rd edition	ERJAVEC/ AUTOMOTIVE TECHNOLOGY 2nd edition	MODERN AUTOMOTIVE TECHNOLOGY Duffy 1998	AUTOMOTIVE TECHNOLOGY Halderman 1999
Evaluating the Engine's Condition p. 146	p. 119		
Noise Diagnosis pp. 146 to 148	pp. 119–121	p. 134 p. 884	pp. 78–80
Other Engine Designs pp. 148 to 152	pp. 121–125	pp. 164–167	
Ch. 7 Engine Disassembly	*Ch. 7*	*Chs. 49 & 51*	*Ch. 6*
Preparing for the Engine for Removal p. 156	p. 128	pp. 899–900	pp. 96–97, 111
Lifting an Engine pp. 156 to 157	pp. 128–129	pp. 900–905	pp. 97, 111–112
Engine Disassembly and Inspection pp. 157 to 162	pp. 130–135	pp. 905–910	pp. 98–102, 106–108, 113
Cleaning Engine Parts pp. 162 to 167	pp. 135–142	pp. 910–913	pp. 103–106
Crack Repair pp. 167 to 168	pp. 142–145	Ch. 51, pp. 941–942	pp. 108–110
Ch. 8 Short Blocks	*Ch. 8*	*Chs. 11, 14, 48 & 50*	*Chs. 10, 11 & 12*
Cylinder Blocks pp. 171 to 172	pp. 147–149	pp. 142–143 pp. 193–194	pp. 194–197
Cylinder Block Reconditioning pp. 172 to 176	pp. 149–154	pp. 916–922	pp. 197–202
Installing Core Plugs pp. 177 to 178	pp. 154–156	p. 922	p. 214
Crankshaft pp. 178 to 180	pp. 156–158	pp. 143–146 pp. 200–206	pp. 202–205
Crankshaft Inspection and Rebuilding pp. 180 to 185	pp. 158–164	p. 893 diagnosis pp. 922, 928–930	pp. 204–205, 208–211, 215–217
Installing Main Bearings and Crankshaft pp. 185 to 190	pp. 164–169	pp. 930–932	pp. 186–189 pp. 214–217
Pistons and Piston Rings pp. 190 to 191	pp. 169–170	pp. 146–148 pp. 194-200	p. 178

ERJAVEC/ AUTOMOTIVE TECHNOLOGY 3rd edition	ERJAVEC/ AUTOMOTIVE TECHNOLOGY 2nd edition	MODERN AUTOMOTIVE TECHNOLOGY Duffy 1998	AUTOMOTIVE TECHNOLOGY Halderman 1999
Installing Pistons and Connecting Rods pp. 192 to 194	*pp. 170–174*	*pp. 891–892 Diagnosis* *pp. 922–928 Service* *pp. 932–934 Installation*	*pp. 189–192 pp. 217–220*
Ch. 9 Cylinder Heads and Valves	*Ch. 9*	*Chs. 11, 12, 13 & 51*	
Introduction p. 198	*pp. 177–178*	*pp. 148–152*	*pp. 136–139*
Combustion Chambers pp. 198 to 199	*pp. 178–180*	*pp. 162–164*	*pp. 135–136*
Intake and Exhaust Valves pp. 200 to 202	*pp. 180–184*	*pp. 176–182*	*pp. 145–148*
Aluminum Cylinder Heads pp. 203 to 204	*pp. 184–185*		*pp. 141, 142 mentioned*
Resurfacing Cylinder Head pp. 204 to 207	*pp. 185–188*	*pp. 940–941*	*pp. 139–142*
Grinding Valves pp. 207 to 208	*pp. 188–191*	*Ch. 51, pp. 943–947*	*pp. 148, 153–154*
Valve Guide Reconditioning pp. 208 to 212	*pp. 191–195*	*Ch. 51, p. 943*	*pp. 142–145*
Reconditioning Valve Seats pp. 212 to 215	*pp. 195–199*	*Ch. 51, pp. 947–951*	*pp. 148, 155–156*
Valve Stem Seals pp. 215 to 218	*pp. 199–205*	*Ch. 51 pp. 951–952, 955*	*pp. 146–151*
Assembling the Cylinder Head pp. 218 to 222	*pp. 205–207*	*Ch. 51, pp. 952–955*	*pp. 150–152*
Ch. 10 Camshafts and Valve Trains	*Ch. 10*	*Chs. 11, 13, 15, 51, 52*	*Chs. 9 & 12*
Camshaft pp. 225 to 232	*pp. 210–217*	*pp. 150–153 pp. 183–188 pp. 210–214*	*pp. 158, 160–166, 169–171*
Camshaft and Valve Train Inspection pp. 232 to 236	*pp. 217–224*	*pp. 955–957 pp. 969–972, 975–979*	*p. 159*
Installing the Camshaft pp. 236 to 237	*pp. 224–225*		*pp. 166–169*

ERJAVEC/ AUTOMOTIVE TECHNOLOGY 3rd edition	ERJAVEC/ AUTOMOTIVE TECHNOLOGY 2nd edition	MODERN AUTOMOTIVE TECHNOLOGY Duffy 1998	AUTOMOTIVE TECHNOLOGY Halderman 1999
Installing Cylinder Head and Valve Train pp. 237 to 238	pp. 225–226	pp. 957–961	pp. 220–224
Adjusting Valves pp. 238 to 239, 242	pp. 226–227	pp. 961–964	pp. 228–229
Installing Timing Components pp. 240 to 242	pp. 227–230	pp. 969–971, 977–979	pp. 172–176
Ch. 11 Lubricating and Cooling Systems	Ch. 11	Chs. 39, 40, 41 & 42	Chs. 3, 7 & 12
Lubrication pp. 246 to 248	pp. 234–237	pp. 740–744 p. 757	pp. 41–44
Lubricating Systems pp. 249 to 253	pp. 237–244	pp. 744–753	pp. 45, 126–132
Oil Pump Inspection and Service pp. 253 to 257	pp. 244–247	pp. 763–767	pp. 128, 255
Installing the Oil Pump pp. 257 to 258	pp. 247–248	p. 767	pp. 224–226
Cooling Systems pp. 258 to 269	pp. 248–261	pp. 697–712	pp. 115–125
Cooling-System Servicing pp. 269 to 275	pp. 261–269	pp. 716–733, 737–738	pp. 45–47 pp. 118, 120–125
Ch. 12 Intake and Exhaust Systems	Ch. 12	Chs. 13 & 28	No Comparable Chapters
Air Induction System pp. 279 to 287	pp. 272–279	pp. 188–189	
Exhaust System Components pp. 288 to 294	pp. 279–286	pp. 459–462	pp. 492–494 catalytic converter
Exhaust System Service pp. 294 to 296	pp. 287–289	pp. 462–465, 481	
Turbochargers and Superchargers pp. 296 to 302	pp. 290–298	pp. 465–477	pp. 74–76
Ch. 13 Engine Sealing and Reassembly	Ch. 13	Chs. 9, 50, 51, 52	Chs. 2 & 12 12 pp.
Torque Principles pp. 305 to 308	pp. 302–307	pp. 109–110, 112–114	pp. 222–223

ERJAVEC/ AUTOMOTIVE TECHNOLOGY 3rd edition	ERJAVEC/ AUTOMOTIVE TECHNOLOGY 2nd edition	MODERN AUTOMOTIVE TECHNOLOGY Duffy 1998	AUTOMOTIVE TECHNOLOGY Halderman 1999
Thread Repair p. 308	*pp. 307–308*	*pp. 114–116*	*pp. 34–35*
Gaskets pp. 308 to 312	*pp. 308–313*	*pp. 117–119* *pp. 958*	*pp. 220–222, 224–225*
Adhesives, Sealants, and Other Sealing Materials pp. 312 to 315	*pp. 315–316*	*Ch. 51, pp. 118–120*	*pp. 223–224*
Oil Seals pp. 315 to 318	*pp. 316–318*	*pp. 931, 965*	*p. 216*
Engine Reassembly pp. 318 to 320	*pp. 319–322*	*p. 935 mentioned* *p. 979 mentioned*	*pp. 214–226*
Reinstalling the Engine p. 320	*pp. 322–323*	*pp. 979–980*	*p. 226*
Ch. 14 Basics of Electrical Systems	*Ch. 14*	*Ch. 8*	*Chs. 13 & 14*
Basics of Electricity pp. 325 to 327	*pp. 327–328*	*p. 94*	*pp. 232–233*
Electrical Terms pp. 327 to 330	*pp. 328–331*	*pp. 94–97*	*pp. 233–241*
Conductors and Insulators pp. 330 to 355	*pp. 331–354*	*p. 94*	*pp. 232–242 pp. 261–265, 269–271*
Testing Basic Electrical Components pp. 355 to 358			*pp. 254–259, 263, 267–269, 271–273*
Electromagnetic Basics pp. 358 to 364	*pp. 354–358*	*p. 96*	*pp. 224–244*
Ch. 15 Basics of Electronics	*Ch. 15*	*Chs. 8, 17, 19*	*Ch. 13*
Introduction pp. 366 to 370	*pp. 361–366*	*Ch. 8, pp. 97–99 diodes, etc.* *Ch. 17, pp. 225–226*	*pp. 233, 244–250*
Integrated Circuits p. 370	*p. 366*	*Ch. 17, p. 229*	*p. 250*
Operation of Microprocessors pp. 371 to 383	*pp. 366–381*	*Ch. 17, pp. 227–246*	
Multiplexing pp. 383 to 384	*p. 381*	*Ch. 17, p. 244*	

ERJAVEC/ AUTOMOTIVE TECHNOLOGY 3rd edition	ERJAVEC/ AUTOMOTIVE TECHNOLOGY 2nd edition	MODERN AUTOMOTIVE TECHNOLOGY Duffy 1998	AUTOMOTIVE TECHNOLOGY Halderman 1999
Protecting Electronic Systems pp. 384 to 385	p. 382	Ch. 19, p. 273	p. 251
Testing Electronic Circuits and Systems pp. 385 to 386	pp. 382–383	Ch. 8, pp. 103–105	
Ch. 16 Batteries: Theory and Service	Ch. 16	Chs. 29 & 30	Ch. 15
Introduction pp. 391 to 392	p. 388	pp. 484–485, 490	p. 275
Conventional Design Battery pp. 392 to 395	pp. 389–392	pp. 483–488	pp. 275–279
Low-Maintenance and Maintenance-Free Batteries pp. 395 to 396	pp. 392–393	p. 489	pp. 275–276
Hybrid Batteries pp. 396 to 397	pp. 393–394		pp. 279–280
Recombination Batteries p. 397	p. 394		
Battery Voltage and Capacity pp. 397 to 398	p. 394	p. 487	pp. 278–279
Battery Rating Methods p. 398	pp. 394–395	p. 489	p. 279
Battery Size Selection pp. 398 to 399	p. 395		
Factors Affecting Battery Life pp. 399 to 400	p. 396		
Safety Procedures pp. 400 to 401	pp. 396–397		p. 280
Routine Inspections p. 401	pp. 397–398	p. 493	p. 280
Routine Cleaning pp. 401 to 405	pp. 398–399	pp. 494–496 cleaning battery terminals only	
Battery Testing pp. 405 to 409	pp. 399–402	pp. 493–499, 502–503	pp. 280–282, 285–286, 288–289
Battery Charging p. 409	pp. 402–403	pp. 499–501	pp. 283–284

ERJAVEC/ AUTOMOTIVE TECHNOLOGY 3rd edition	ERJAVEC/ AUTOMOTIVE TECHNOLOGY 2nd edition	MODERN AUTOMOTIVE TECHNOLOGY Duffy 1998	AUTOMOTIVE TECHNOLOGY Halderman 1999
Jump Starting pp. 409 to 410	*pp. 403–404*	*Ch. 30, pp. 501–502*	*p. 284*
Ch. 17 Starting Systems	*Ch. 17*	*Chs. 31 & 32*	*Ch. 16*
Design and Components pp. 414 to 422	*pp. 408–417*	*pp. 508–517*	*pp. 291–295*
Starter Drives pp. 422 to 423	*pp. 417–418*	*p. 511*	*p. 294*
Control Circuits p. 423	*pp. 418–419*	*pp. 516–517*	*p. 292*
Starting System Testing pp. 424 to 435	*pp. 420–426*	*pp. 520–525*	*pp. 296–302*
Ch. 18 Charging Systems	*Ch. 18*	*Chs. 33 & 34*	*Chs. 13 & 17*
Induced Voltage p. 439	*pp. 429–430*		*pp. 243–244*
Alternating Current Charging Systems pp. 439 to 451	*pp. 430–439*	*pp. 538–550*	*pp. 305–309*
Preliminary Checks (Inspection, Testing and Troubleshooting) pp. 451 to 457	*pp. 439–446*	*pp. 553–561, 570–571*	*pp. 307, 309–323*
AC Generator Service pp. 457 to 460	*pp. 446–447*	*pp. 561–567 includes regulator service*	*p. 316*
Ch. 19 Lighting Systems	*Ch. 19*	*Ch. 37*	*Ch. 18*
Introduction p. 463	*p. 450*	*p. 634*	*p. 403*
Lamps p. 463	*p. 451*		*pp. 329, 331*
Headlights pp. 463 to 476	*pp. 451–460*	*pp. 634–637 theory* *pp. 642–648 service*	*pp. 320–330*
Interior Light Assemblies pp. 476 to 478	*pp. 460–462*	*pp. 641–643 illuminated entry only*	*pp. 332, 333*
Rear Exterior Light Assemblies pp. 478 to 487	*pp. 462–467*	*pp. 637–641*	*p. 332*

ERJAVEC/ AUTOMOTIVE TECHNOLOGY 3rd edition	ERJAVEC/ AUTOMOTIVE TECHNOLOGY 2nd edition	MODERN AUTOMOTIVE TECHNOLOGY Duffy 1998	AUTOMOTIVE TECHNOLOGY Halderman 1999
Light Bulbs pp. 487 to 488	pp. 467–471		
Lighting Maintenance pp. 488 to 489	pp. 469–470	pp. 643–646	
Ch. 20 Electrical Instruments and Accessories	*Ch. 20*	*Chs. 37 & 38*	*Ch. 18*
Body Control Modules pp. 492 to 494			
Instrument Panels pp. 494 to 495	pp. 473–474	pp. 649–650	pp. 332–335
Instrument Gauges pp. 495 to 498	pp. 475–476	pp. 650–652	
Basic Information Gauges pp. 498 to 501	pp. 476–480	pp. 653–654	
Indicators and Warning Devices pp. 501 to 505	pp. 480–484		p. 333 *brake warning light*
Electrical Accessories pp. 505 to 527	pp. 484–500	pp. 656–661 pp. 669–690	pp. 335–343
Ch. 21 Ignition Systems	*Ch. 21*	*Ch. 35*	*Ch. 21*
Purpose of the Ignition System pp. 533 to 534	p. 504	pp. 572–573	
Ignition Timing pp. 534 to 535	pp. 504–506	pp. 586–589, 595	pp. 398–399
Basic Circuitry pp. 535 to 539	pp. 506–507	pp. 573–574	pp. 382–384
Ignition Components pp. 539 to 542	pp. 507–510	pp. 574–577 *ignition coil* pp. 584–586 *spark plugs* p. 583 *secondary wires*	pp. 382–390
Spark Timing Systems pp. 542 to 544	pp. 510–512	pp. 577–581	p. 382 *mentioned*
Switching Systems pp. 544 to 549	pp. 513–521	pp. 579–581	pp. 384–385

ERJAVEC/ AUTOMOTIVE TECHNOLOGY 3rd edition	ERJAVEC/ AUTOMOTIVE TECHNOLOGY 2nd edition	MODERN AUTOMOTIVE TECHNOLOGY Duffy 1998	AUTOMOTIVE TECHNOLOGY Halderman 1999
Distributor Ignition System Operation pp. 549 to 554			pp. 382–387
Electronic Ignition System Operation pp. 555 to 564	pp. 521–529	pp. 578–581, 587–594	pp. 387–390
Ch. 22 Ignition System Service	Ch. 22	Chs. 36 & 46	Ch. 21
Combustion pp. 567 to 568			
General Ignition System Diagnosis pp. 568 to 569		p. 599	
Visual Inspection pp. 569 to 573	pp. 532–537		pp. 391–399
No-Start Diagnosis pp. 573 to 575			p. 390
General Testing pp. 575 to 576		pp. 603–604 pp. 859–863	pp. 505–509 not specific to ignition
Testing with a Scope pp. 577 to 584	pp. 537–547	pp. 599–604, 614 pp. 848–855 using an oscilloscope	pp. 402–409
Effects of Improper Timing pp. 584 to 585		p. 615	pp. 398–399
Setting Ignition Timing pp. 585 to 587	pp. 559–561	pp. 615–618	pp. 399–401
DI and EI Systems pp. 587 to 588	pp. 561, 564	pp. 610, 626	
Primary Circuit Components pp. 588 to 594	pp. 549–553	pp. 610–613, 622–625	p. 393
Distributor Service pp. 594 to 598	pp. 561–562	pp. 607, 619–622	
Secondary Component Tests and Services pp. 598 to 603	pp. 553–558	pp. 604–607	pp. 394–398
Specific EI System Service pp. 603 to 607			
Ch. 23 Fuel Systems	Ch. 23	Chs. 20 & 21	No Chapter on this Topic
Gasoline pp. 610 to 611	pp. 570–571	pp. 291, 293–295	

ERJAVEC/ AUTOMOTIVE TECHNOLOGY 3rd edition	ERJAVEC/ AUTOMOTIVE TECHNOLOGY 2nd edition	MODERN AUTOMOTIVE TECHNOLOGY Duffy 1998	AUTOMOTIVE TECHNOLOGY Halderman 1999
Fuel Performance pp. 611 to 613	pp. 571–573	pp. 291–297	
Basic Fuel Additives pp. 613 to 614	p. 573		
Alternative Fuels pp. 614 to 618	pp. 575–576	pp. 297–302	
Fuel Delivery System pp. 618 to 629	pp. 576–595	pp. 305–314	pp. 433–434
Ch. 24 Fuel System Diagnosis and Service	Ch. 23	Ch. 21	Ch. 24
Alcohol-in-Fuel Test pp. 632 to 633	pp. 574–575		
Fuel System Pressure Relief pp. 633 to 634	pp. 588–589	p. 320	pp. 458–459
Fuel Tanks pp. 634 to 636	pp. 580–581	pp. 315–317	
Fuel Lines pp. 636 to 640	pp. 582–584	pp. 317–319	
Fuel Filters pp. 640 to 641	pp. 586–587	pp. 319–320	
Fuel Pumps pp. 641 to 649	pp. 588–594	pp. 320–324	pp. 452–454, 466–469
Ch. 25 Carburetors	Ch. 24	Chs. 24 & 25	Chs. 22 & 23
Basic Carburetor Design pp. 652 to 654	pp. 599–600	p. 386	
Basic Carburetor Circuits p. 654	pp. 600–607	pp. 386–607	pp. 435–439
Carburetor Systems pp. 654 to 655	pp. 607–609	pp. 394–396	pp. 418–419 throttle position sensor p. 439 vacuum break
Types of Carburetors pp. 655 to 656	pp. 609–610	pp. 396–398	
Feedback Carburetors pp. 656 to 659	pp. 610–613	pp. 399–400	p. 443
Electronic Idle-Speed Control pp. 659 to 661	pp. 613–614	p. 399	p. 445

ERJAVEC/ AUTOMOTIVE TECHNOLOGY 3rd edition	ERJAVEC/ AUTOMOTIVE TECHNOLOGY 2nd edition	MODERN AUTOMOTIVE TECHNOLOGY Duffy 1998	AUTOMOTIVE TECHNOLOGY Halderman 1999
Ch. 26 Carburetor Diagnosis and Service	*Ch. 24*	*Ch. 25*	*Chs. 22 & 23*
Carburetor Diagnosis pp. 664 to 668	*pp. 614–619*	*pp. 403–407, 412–415*	*pp. 420–421 pp. 439–443, 446–447*
Electronic Control Diagnostics pp. 668 to 673		*pp. 415–416*	
Carburetor Service pp. 673 to 674		*pp. 407–412*	
Ch. 27 Electronic Fuel Injection	*Ch. 25*	*Ch. 22*	*Chs. 22 & 24*
Introduction pp. 677 to 678	*p. 623*	*pp. 330–332*	
Types of Fuel Injection p. 678	*pp. 623–629*	*pp. 332–333*	*pp. 451–452*
Continuous Injection Systems pp. 678 to 680	*pp. 624, 635–638*	*pp. 333, 347, 354–356*	
Basic EFI pp. 680 to 683	*pp. 624–625, 629–632*	*pp. 334–339, 346–347*	
Throttle Body Fuel Injection pp. 683 to 685	*pp. 625–626*	*pp. 344–346*	*pp. 454–455*
Port Fuel Injection pp. 685 to 690	*pp. 626–628*	*pp. 347–351*	*p. 456*
Sequential Fuel Injection Systems pp. 690 to 691	*p. 628*		
Central Multi-Port Fuel Injection (CMFI) pp. 691 to 693			
Gasoline Direct-Injection Systems pp. 693 to 694			
Input Sensors pp. 694 to 696	*pp. 629–631*	*pp. 336–342, 351, 354*	*pp. 416–417, 421–422, 427–428*
Other EFI System Sensors pp. 696 to 697	*p. 631*	*pp. 342–343*	*pp. 418–419*
Ch. 28 Fuel Injection System Diagnosis and Service	*Ch. 25*	*Ch. 23*	*Chs. 22 & 24*

ERJAVEC/ AUTOMOTIVE TECHNOLOGY 3rd edition	ERJAVEC/ AUTOMOTIVE TECHNOLOGY 2nd edition	MODERN AUTOMOTIVE TECHNOLOGY Duffy 1998	AUTOMOTIVE TECHNOLOGY Halderman 1999
Preliminary Checks pp. 700 to 702	p. 639	pp. 360–363	
Service Precautions p. 702			
Basic EFI System Checks pp. 702 to 720	pp. 639–650	pp. 365–377	pp. 422–425, 428–431, 452–478
CIS Checks and Tests pp. 720 to 721	p. 650		
Ch. 29 Emission Control Systems	Ch. 26	Ch. 43	Ch. 25
Legislative History pp. 724 to 726	pp. 661–663		
Pollutants pp. 726 to 727	p. 661	pp. 773–775	pp. 481–482
Evaporative Emission Control Systems pp. 727 to 729	pp. 681–683	pp. 778–781	pp. 486–487
Precombustion Systems pp. 729 to 738	pp. 663–664, 666–670, 672–677	pp. 776–778, 781–785, 787–789	pp. 482, 489–490
Post-Combustion Systems pp. 739 to 743	pp. 677–681	pp. 785–787, 789–791	pp. 483–485, 492–493
Ch. 30 Emission Control Diagnosis and Service	Ch. 26	Ch. 44	Chs. 25 & 26
Emissions Testing pp. 746 to 751	pp. 684–685	pp. 802–806	pp. 516–520, 524–525
PCV System Diagnosis and Service pp. 751 to 752	pp. 663–665	pp. 808–809	pp. 482–483
EGR System Diagnosis and Service pp. 753 to 757	pp. 668–672	pp. 811–812	pp. 491–493, 497
Spark Control Systems pp. 757, 759			
Intake Heat Control Diagnosis and Service, p. 759	pp. 673–675	pp. 810–811	
Catalytic Converter Diagnosis pp. 759 to 761		pp. 813–815	pp. 494–496

ERJAVEC/ AUTOMOTIVE TECHNOLOGY 3rd edition	ERJAVEC/ AUTOMOTIVE TECHNOLOGY 2nd edition	MODERN AUTOMOTIVE TECHNOLOGY Duffy 1998	AUTOMOTIVE TECHNOLOGY Halderman 1999
AIR Injection System Diagnosis and Service pp. 761 to 763		*pp. 812–813*	*p. 486*
Evaporative Emission Control System Diagnosis and Service pp. 763 to 765	*pp. 683–684*	*pp. 809–810*	*pp. 487–489*
Ch. 31 On-Board Diagnostic Systems	*Ch. 27*	*Chs. 17 & 18*	*No Chapter on this Topic*
System Functions p. 768	*pp. 689–690*		
System Components pp. 768 to 771	*pp. 690–692*	*pp. 240–244*	
Primary Sensors pp. 771 to 775	*pp. 692–697*	*pp. 238–239*	*pp. 414–429*
Computer Outputs and Actuators pp. 775 to 776	*pp. 697–698*	*pp. 244–246*	
System Operation pp. 776 to 778	*pp. 698–700*	*No general section on this topic, see chapters relating to specific auto. systems*	
OBD-II Standards pp. 778 to 779	*pp. 710–716*		
Monitoring Capabilities pp. 779 to 785			
OBD II Diagnostics pp. 785 to 791		*pp. 251–252*	
OBD II Terms pp. 791 to 792			
Ch. 32 On-Board Diagnostic System Diagnosis and Service	*Ch. 27*	*Ch. 18*	*Chs. 22 & 26*
Electronic Service Precautions pp. 795 to 796			
Basic Diagnosis of Electronic Engine Control Systems pp. 796 to 798	*pp. 700–702*	*pp. 252–254*	*pp. 505–507*

ERJAVEC/ AUTOMOTIVE TECHNOLOGY 3rd edition	ERJAVEC/ AUTOMOTIVE TECHNOLOGY 2nd edition	MODERN AUTOMOTIVE TECHNOLOGY Duffy 1998	AUTOMOTIVE TECHNOLOGY Halderman 1999
Self-Diagnostic Systems pp. 798 to 801	pp. 702–703	pp. 254–262	pp. 505–507
Retrieving Trouble Codes pp. 801 to 806	pp. 703–710	pp. 263–266	pp. 511–514
OBD II System Diagnosis and Service pp. 806 to 808	pp. 710, 716	pp. 254–262	pp. 514–515
OBD II Diagnostics pp. 808 to 817	pp. 710, 716	pp. 251–262	pp. 514–515
Diagnosis of Computer Voltage Supply and Ground Wires pp. 817 to 820			
Testing Input Sensors pp. 820 to 822			
Variable Resistor-Type Sensors pp. 822 to 824			pp. 415–416, 420–421, 430–431
Generating Sensors pp. 824 to 835			pp. 422–424, 417, 428
Testing Actuators pp. 835 to 837		p. 262	
Ch. 33 Clutches	Ch. 28	Chs. 53 & 54	Ch. 39
Operation pp. 843 to 844	pp. 721–722	pp. 985–994	pp. 810–811
Flywheel pp. 844 to 850	pp. 722–728	pp. 987–994	pp. 811–816
Clutch Service Safety Precautions pp. 850 to 851	p. 728		
Clutch Maintenance pp. 851 to 852	pp. 728–729	p. 1006 clutch linkage adjustment	pp. 818–819
Clutch Problem Diagnosis pp. 852 to 854	pp. 729–732	pp. 999–1005 pp. 1014–1015 diagnostic charts	pp. 816–818
Clutch Service pp. 854 to 857	pp. 732–733	pp. 1005–1011 includes installation	pp. 820–822
Ch. 34 Manual Transmissions and Transaxles	Ch. 29	Chs. 55 & 63	Ch. 40

ERJAVEC/ AUTOMOTIVE TECHNOLOGY 3rd edition	ERJAVEC/ AUTOMOTIVE TECHNOLOGY 2nd edition	MODERN AUTOMOTIVE TECHNOLOGY Duffy 1998	AUTOMOTIVE TECHNOLOGY Halderman 1999
Transmission versus Transaxle pp. 861	pp. 736–737	Ch. 55 transmission pp. 1016–1017 Ch. 63 transaxles pp. 1159–1160	p. 825
Gears pp. 861 to 863	pp. 737–739	pp. 1017–1019	pp. 826–827
Basic Gear Theory pp. 863 to 866	pp. 739–741	pp. 1017–1018	pp. 825–826
Transmission/Transaxle Design pp. 866 to 868	pp. 741–744	Ch. 55 transmissions pp. 1019–1023 Ch. 63 transaxles pp. 1160–1164	pp. 827–828, 838
Synchronizers pp. 868 to 870	pp. 744–746	pp. 1023–1025	pp. 834–835
Gearshift Mechanisms pp. 870 to 872	pp. 746–747	pp. 1025–1027	
Transmission Power Flow pp. 872 to 874	pp. 747–750	pp. 1027–1029	p. 826 mentioned
Five-Speed Overdrive p. 874	p. 750	pp. 1028–1029	p. 826 mentioned
Transaxle Power Flows pp. 874 to 876	pp. 750–752	pp. 1164–1167	p. 826 mentioned
Final Drive Gears and Overall Ratios p. 876	pp. 752–755		
Electrical Systems pp. 876 to 878		p. 1033	
Ch. 35 Manual Transmission/ Transaxle Service	Ch. 29 & 30	Chs. 56 & 63	Chs. 3 & 40
Lubricant Check pp. 881 to 884	pp. 758–759	Ch. 64, pp. 1185, 1187 transaxle	p. 55, p. 841
Diagnosing Problems pp. 884 to 889	pp. 759–761	pp. 1037–1039	pp. 835–836, 839
Transmission/Transaxle Removal pp. 889 to 890	pp. 761–762	pp. 1039–1040 transmissions p. 1194 transaxle	pp. 828–829

ERJAVEC/ AUTOMOTIVE TECHNOLOGY 3rd edition	ERJAVEC/ AUTOMOTIVE TECHNOLOGY 2nd edition	MODERN AUTOMOTIVE TECHNOLOGY Duffy 1998	AUTOMOTIVE TECHNOLOGY Halderman 1999
Cleaning and Inspection pp. 890 to 891, 894 to 895	pp. 763–765	pp. 1040–1043 transmissions pp. 1194–1195 transaxles	
Disassembly and Reassembly of the Differential Case p. 895			
Reassembly/ Reinstallation of Transmission/Transaxle pp. 895–898	pp. 765–766	pp. 1043–1045 transmission p. 1195 transaxle	pp. 829–833, 838
Ch. 36 Drive Axles and Differentials	*Ch. 31*	*Chs. 59, 60, 61, 62, 63 & 64*	*Chs. 41 & 42*
FWD Axles p. 901	p. 769	p. 1175	p. 844
Types of CV Joints pp. 901 to 904	pp. 770–772	pp. 1176–1179	p. 855
FWD Applications pp. 904 to 905	pp. 772–774		p. 855
CV Joint Service pp. 905 to 909	pp. 774–780	pp. 1185, 1188–1192	pp. 859–867
CV Joint Service Guidelines pp. 907, 910	pp. 777, 780–781	p. 1191	
Rear-Wheel Drive Shafts pp. 910 to 911	p. 781	pp. 1097–1110	p. 844
Operation of U-Joints pp. 911 to 913	pp. 781–788		pp. 844–847
Types of U-Joints p. 913	pp. 788–789	pp. 1100–1102	p. 844
Diagnosis of Drive Shaft and U-Joint Problems pp. 913 to 915	p. 790	pp. 1110–1113 p. 1121 diagnostic chart	pp. 847–853, 868–869
Differentials and Drive Axles pp. 915 to 922	pp. 791–797	pp. 1123–1128	pp. 872–922
Limited Slip Differentials pp. 922 to 925	pp. 797–799	pp. 1128–1131	pp. 884–887
Axle Shafts pp. 925 to 927	pp. 799–804	pp. 1132–1134	

ERJAVEC/ AUTOMOTIVE TECHNOLOGY 3rd edition	ERJAVEC/ AUTOMOTIVE TECHNOLOGY 2nd edition	MODERN AUTOMOTIVE TECHNOLOGY Duffy 1998	AUTOMOTIVE TECHNOLOGY Halderman 1999
Servicing the Final Drive Assembly pp. 927 to 932	*pp. 804–807*	*pp. 1139–1153*	*pp. 875–884*
Diagnosing Differential Noises pp. 930, 933	*p. 807*	*pp. 1139, 1157–1158*	*p. 876*
Ch. 37 Automatic Transmissions and Transaxles	*Ch. 32*	*Chs. 57 & 63*	*Ch. 44*
Torque Converter pp. 938 to 940	*pp. 812–817*	*pp. 1051–1055, 1061*	*pp. 908–912*
Lockup Torque Converters pp. 941 to 942	*pp. 817–820*	*p. 1054*	*p.909 mentioned*
Planetary Gears pp. 942 to 944	*pp. 820–822*	*pp. 1055–1056*	*pp. 913–914*
Compound Planetary Gearsets pp. 944 to 950	*pp. 826–842*	*p. 1056*	*p. 914*
Planetary Gear Controls pp. 951 to 952	*pp. 823–826*	*pp. 1056–1062*	*p. 916*
Transmission Clutches pp. 952 to 954	*pp. 824–826*	*pp. 1057, 1061*	
Bearings, Bushings, and Thrust Washers pp. 954 to 957			
Snaprings p. 957			
Gaskets and Seals pp. 957 to 960			
Final Drives and Differentials p. 960			
Hydraulic System pp. 960 to 962	*pp. 842–846*	*p. 1062*	*p. 917*
Pumps p. 962	*pp. 846–847*	*p. 1064*	*pp. 917–919*
Valve Body pp. 962 to 963	*pp. 847–848*	*p. 1066*	*pp. 919–922*
Valves pp. 963 to 964	*pp. 848–849*	*pp. 1064–1066*	*p. 919*
Pressure Regulator Valve pp. 964 to 966	*pp. 849–853*	*pp. 1064–1066*	*pp. 919–922*

ERJAVEC/ AUTOMOTIVE TECHNOLOGY 3rd edition	ERJAVEC/ AUTOMOTIVE TECHNOLOGY 2nd edition	MODERN AUTOMOTIVE TECHNOLOGY Duffy 1998	AUTOMOTIVE TECHNOLOGY Halderman 1999
Governor Assembly p. 967	p. 853	pp. 1065–1066	p. 919
Shift Feel pp. 967 to 968		p. 1077	p. 929
Hydraulic Circuits pp. 968 to 973	pp. 853–859		
Electronic Controls pp. 973 to 978	pp. 860–862	pp. 1067, 1070	p. 925
Chrysler Systems pp. 978 to 979	pp. 862–864		
Ford Motor Company Systems p. 979	pp. 865–867		
General Motors Systems pp. 979 to 980	pp. 867–868		p. 925
Honda Systems pp. 980 to 981	pp. 869–870		
Other Common Transmissions pp. 981 to 983	pp. 870–872		
Ch. 38 Automatic Transmission/ Transaxle Service	Ch. 33	Ch. 58	Chs. 3 & 45
Automatic Transmission Fluid pp. 988 to 989	pp. 879–880		pp. 47–48
Diagnostics pp. 989 to 992	pp. 980–983	pp. 1077–1080	pp. 928–929, 933–934, 942
Fluid Leaks pp. 992 to 994	pp. 883–884	p. 1085	
Road Testing the Vehicle pp. 994 to 996	p. 887	p. 1080	pp. 929, 941
Linkages pp. 996 to 997	pp. 884–886	pp. 1080, 1086	p. 935
Electrical Controls pp. 997 to 999	p. 886 Band Adjustment	p. 1086 Band Adjustment	pp. 930–931, 935
Pressure Tests pp. 999 to 1002	Pressure Testing pp. 887 to 890	pp. 1081–1082	p. 933
Torque Converters pp. 1002, 1009			pp. 929–930
Rebuilding a Transmission pp. 1004 to 1009		pp. 1090–1091	pp. 935–945

ERJAVEC/ AUTOMOTIVE TECHNOLOGY 3rd edition	ERJAVEC/ AUTOMOTIVE TECHNOLOGY 2nd edition	MODERN AUTOMOTIVE TECHNOLOGY Duffy 1998	AUTOMOTIVE TECHNOLOGY Halderman 1999
Ch. 39 Four- and All-Wheel Drive	Ch. 34	Chs. 59 & 60	Ch. 43
4WD versus AWD p. 1013	p. 893	p. 1105	
4WD Systems pp. 1013 to 1014	pp. 894–895		p. 890
Transfer Case pp. 1014 to 1015	pp. 895–896	pp. 1103–1105	pp. 895–898
Locking/Unlocking Hubs pp. 1015 to 1018	pp. 896–898		pp. 890–891
Operational Modes pp. 1018 to 1019	pp. 898–900	p. 1105	p. 895
4WD Passenger Cars pp. 1019 to 1020	pp. 900–902		
Servicing 4WD Vehicles pp. 1020 to 1025	pp. 901–906	pp. 1121–1122 diagnostic charts	pp. 899–903
All-Wheel Drive Systems pp. 1021, 1026	pp. 902, 907–908	p. 1105	p. 894 brief
Ch. 40 Tires and Wheels	Ch. 35	Chs. 65 & 66	Chs. 29 &35
Wheels pp. 1031 to 1032	pp. 912–913	pp. 1212–1214	pp. 699–700
Tires pp. 1032 to 1038	pp. 913–921	pp. 1207–1212	pp. 692–698, 704
Tire Repair pp. 1038 to 1041	pp. 922–925	pp. 1222–1226, 1230–1232	pp. 709–712
Tire/Wheel Runout p. 1041	pp. 925–926	p. 1227	pp. 704–707
Tire/Wheel Assembly Service pp. 1041 to 1043	pp. 926–928	pp. 1215–1218 pp. 1227–1232	pp. 707–709, 713–718
Wheel Bearings pp. 1043 to 1046	pp. 928–931	pp. 1215–1219 pp. 1232–1237	pp. 569–586
Ch. 41 Suspension Systems	Ch. 36	Chs. 1, 67 & 68	Chs. 1 & 37
Frames pp. 1049 to 1050	p. 934	p. 2	pp. 2–3
Suspension System Components pp. 1050 to 1056	pp. 934–944	pp. 1243–1249, 1252	pp. 749–755, 761–762

ERJAVEC/ AUTOMOTIVE TECHNOLOGY 3rd edition	ERJAVEC/ AUTOMOTIVE TECHNOLOGY 2nd edition	MODERN AUTOMOTIVE TECHNOLOGY Duffy 1998	AUTOMOTIVE TECHNOLOGY Halderman 1999
MacPherson Strut Suspension Components pp. 1056 to 1059	pp. 944–947	pp. 1249–1251 strut assembly p. 1252 MacPherson	pp. 757–760
Independent Front Suspension pp. 1059 to 1063	pp. 947–952	p. 1244 defined pp. 1247–1252	pp. 735–757
General Front-Suspension Inspection pp. 1063 to 1064	p. 952	p. 1265	pp. 756, 766–769
Front Suspension Component Servicing pp. 1064 to 1071	pp. 952–960	pp. 1265–1279	pp. 770–776
Rear-Suspension Systems p. 1070	p. 958	pp. 1252–1254	pp. 763–766
Live-Axle Rear-Suspension Systems pp. 1070, 1072	pp. 958, 960		p. 763
Semi-Independent Suspension p. 1073	pp. 961–962	p. 1253 mentioned	
Independent Suspension pp. 1073 to 1075	pp. 962–967	pp. 1253–1254 mentioned	p. 763
Electronically Controlled Suspensions pp. 1075 to 1079	pp. 967–971	pp. 1254–1259	pp. 765–766
Servicing Electronic Suspension Components pp. 1079 to 1080	pp. 971–972	pp. 1279–1282	
Active Suspensions pp. 1080 to 1081	pp. 972–974	p. 1260	
Ch. 42 Steering Systems	Ch. 37	Chs. 69 & 70	Ch. 36
Manual Steering Systems pp. 1085 to 1091	pp. 977–984	pp. 1287–1294	pp. 720–726
Power-Steering Systems pp. 1091 to 1096	pp. 988–993	pp. 1294–1302	pp. 726–731
Electronically Controlled Power-Steering Systems pp. 1096 to 1098	pp. 996–998	pp. 1302–1304	
Steering System Diagnosis pp. 1098 to 1101	pp. 985–986, 993–995	pp. 1310–1312	pp. 731–733, 735–741

ERJAVEC/ AUTOMOTIVE TECHNOLOGY 3rd edition	ERJAVEC/ AUTOMOTIVE TECHNOLOGY 2nd edition	MODERN AUTOMOTIVE TECHNOLOGY Duffy 1998	AUTOMOTIVE TECHNOLOGY Halderman 1999
Visual Inspection pp. 1101 to 1108	pp. 986–987, p. 995		p. 732
Four-Wheel Steering Systems pp. 1108 to 1112	pp. 998–1003	pp. 1304–1306	
Ch. 43 Wheel Alignment	Ch. 37	Ch. 74	Ch. 38
Alignment Geometry pp. 1116 to 1120	pp. 1003–1009	pp. 1406–1410	pp. 780–787
Prealignment Inspection p. 1120	p. 1004	pp. 1410–1411	pp. 788–789
Wheel Alignment Equipment pp. 1120 to 1122		pp. 1415–1418	
Alignment Machines pp. 1122 to 1124	p. 1009, 1017–1019	pp. 1418–1421	
Adjusting Wheel Alignment pp. 1124 to 1129	pp. 1009–1016	pp. 1411–1418 *includes descriptions of the various tools and gauges*	
FWD Vehicle Alignment p. 1129	pp. 1016–1019		
Ch. 44 Brake Systems	Ch. 38	Chs. 71 & 72	Chs. 27, 28 & 33
Friction pp. 1133 to 1135	Friction pp. 1024–1026		pp. 530–533, 536
Principles of Hydraulic Brake Systems pp. 1135 to 1137	pp. 1026–1028	pp. 1333–1334	pp. 541–542
Hydraulic Brake System Components pp. 1137 to 1138	pp. 1028–1033	pp. 1331, 1334–1340	pp. 533–535 *brake fluid*
Master Cylinder Operation pp. 1138-1141	p. 1029	pp. 1334–1337	pp. 542–548
Hydraulic Tubes and Hoses pp. 1141 to 1142	pp. 1033–1034	p. 1340	pp. 555–559
Hydraulic System Safety Switches and Valves pp. 1142 to 1145	pp. 1034–1037	pp. 1348–1350	pp. 551–555
Drum and Disc Brake Assemblies pp. 1145 to 1146	pp. 1037–1038	pp. 1331–1332	pp. 531–532

ERJAVEC/ AUTOMOTIVE TECHNOLOGY 3rd edition	ERJAVEC/ AUTOMOTIVE TECHNOLOGY 2nd edition	MODERN AUTOMOTIVE TECHNOLOGY Duffy 1998	AUTOMOTIVE TECHNOLOGY Halderman 1999
Hydraulic System Service pp. 1146 to 1151	pp. 1038–1043	pp. 1356–1365	pp. 551, 555, 560–567
Pushrod Adjustment p. 1151	pp. 1043–1044	p. 1263 mentioned	
Hydraulic Brake Boosters pp. 1151 to 1153	pp. 1044–1045	pp. 1340, 1360–1361	pp. 662–671
Ch. 45 Drum Brakes	Ch. 39	Chs. 71 & 72	Chs. 30 & 32
Drum Brake Operation p. 1156	p. 1050		pp. 588–591
Drum Brake Components pp. 1157 to 1158	pp. 1050–1053	pp. 1344–1348	pp. 588 mentioned
Drum Brake Designs pp. 1158 to 1162	pp. 1053–1059		pp. 588–591
Road Testing Brakes pp. 1162 to 1164	pp. 1059–1061		
Drum Brake Inspection pp. 1164 to 1169	pp. 1041–1067	pp. 1372–1373, 1375–1387	pp. 591–594, 604, 606, 631–636, 645–652
Brake Shoes and Linings pp. 1170 to 1171	pp. 1067–1069	pp. 1376–1378	pp. 594, 599, 604–606
Wheel Cylinder Inspection and Servicing pp. 1171 to 1172	pp. 1069–1070	p. 1373	pp. 598–599
Drum Parking Brakes pp. 1172 to 1173	pp. 1070–1072		pp. 600–602
Integral Parking Brakes pp. 1173 to 1174	p. 1073		pp. 602–603 cable adjustment
Ch. 46 Disc Brakes	Ch. 40	Chs. 71 & 72	Chs. 31 & 32
Disc Brake Components and Their Functions pp. 1178 to 1182	pp. 1080–1084	pp. 1342–1344	pp. 608–612
Disc Brake Diagnosis pp. 1182 to 1184		pp. 1356–1358	pp. 612–613
Service Precautions pp. 1184 to 1185	pp. 1084–1085		
General Caliper Inspecting and Servicing pp. 1185 to 1192	pp. 1085–1094	pp. 1365–1367, 1370	pp. 613–629
Rotor Inspecting and Servicing pp. 1192 to 1194	pp. 1094–1095	pp. 1367–1369	pp. 636–644, 653–660

ERJAVEC/ AUTOMOTIVE TECHNOLOGY 3rd edition	ERJAVEC/ AUTOMOTIVE TECHNOLOGY 2nd edition	MODERN AUTOMOTIVE TECHNOLOGY Duffy 1998	AUTOMOTIVE TECHNOLOGY Halderman 1999
Ch. 47 *Antilock Brake Systems*	*Ch. 41*	*Ch. 73*	*Ch. 34*
Antilock Brakes pp. 1197 to 1199	*pp. 1097–1098*	*pp. 1387–1388*	*pp. 673–680*
ABS Components pp. 1199 to 1201	*pp. 1100–1102*	*pp. 1385–1388*	*pp. 675, 678–680*
Types of ABS pp. 1202 to 1204	*pp. 1098–1100*	*pp. 1389–1390*	*pp. 680–683*
ABS Operation pp. 1204 to 1212	*pp. 1102–1107*	*pp. 1390–1391*	*pp. 680–683*
Automatic Traction Control pp. 1212 to 1213	*pp. 1108–1110*	*pp. 1391–1394 theory* *pp. 1400–1401 service* *p. 1405 diagnostic chart*	*p. 683*
Automatic Stability Control pp. 1213 to 1214			
Antilock Brake System Service pp. 1214 to 1216	*p. 1107*	*pp. 1394–1400*	*pp. 685–686*
Diagnosis and Testing pp. 1216 to 1221	*pp. 1107–1108*	*pp. 1394–1395, 1397–1398* *p. 1405 diagnostic chart*	*pp. 683–688*
Ch. 48 *Heating and Air Conditioning*	*Ch. 42*	*Chs. 75 & 76*	*Ch. 19*
Ventilation System pp. 1225 to 1226	*pp. 1113–1114*		
Automotive Heating Systems pp. 1226 to 1229	*pp. 1114–1117*	*p. 1443*	*pp. 352–353*
Theory of Automotive AC p. 1229	*p. 1117*	*pp. 1429–1431*	*pp. 353–354*
Refrigerants in AC Systems pp. 1229 to 1230	*p. 1118*	*p. 1431*	*pp. 356–357*

ERJAVEC/ AUTOMOTIVE TECHNOLOGY 3rd edition	ERJAVEC/ AUTOMOTIVE TECHNOLOGY 2nd edition	MODERN AUTOMOTIVE TECHNOLOGY Duffy 1998	AUTOMOTIVE TECHNOLOGY Halderman 1999
The AC System and Its Components pp. 1230 to 1237	pp. 1118–1126	pp. 1431–1441 p. 1455 sight glass	pp. 354–360
AC Systems and Controls pp. 1237 to 1240	pp. 1126–1130	pp. 1140–1443	pp. 360–362
Temperature Control Systems pp. 1240 to 1244	pp. 1142–1145	pp. 1443–1446, 1471	pp. 361–362
Ch. 49 Heating and Air Conditioning Service	Ch. 42	Ch. 76	Ch. 20
Maintenance Precautions pp. 1247 to 1248	pp. 1130–1131		
Refrigerant Safety Precautions pp. 1248 to 1249	pp. 1131–1132	p. 1455	
Guidelines for Converting (Retrofitting) R-12 Systems to R-134a pp. 1249 to 1250			pp. 375–376
AC Testing and Servicing Equipment pp. 1250 to 1254	pp. 1132–1135	pp. 1457–1470	pp. 368–378
Service Procedures pp. 1254 to 1259	pp. 1135–1142	pp. 1462–1469	pp. 368–378
Diagnostic and Trouble-shooting Procedures p. 1259	p. 1142	pp. 1453–1455 inspection pp. 1477–1478 diagnostic charts	
Electrical System Inspection pp. 1259 to 1260	pp. 1145–1146		
Heating System Service p. 1260	p. 1117	p. 1470	pp. 367–369
Ch. 50 Other Comfort, Safety, and Security Equipment	Ch. 43	Chs. 38, 77, 78 & 79	Ch. 18

ERJAVEC/ AUTOMOTIVE TECHNOLOGY 3rd edition	ERJAVEC/ AUTOMOTIVE TECHNOLOGY 2nd edition	MODERN AUTOMOTIVE TECHNOLOGY Duffy 1998	AUTOMOTIVE TECHNOLOGY Halderman 1999
Restraint Systems pp. 1264 to 1268	*pp. 1152–1156*	*pp. 1483–1491 theory* *pp. 1494–1495 seatbelt service* *p. 1503 diagnostic chart*	
Air Bags pp. 1268 to 1272	*pp. 1156–1159*	*pp. 1485–1491*	*pp. 343–345*
Servicing the Air Bag System pp. 1272 to 1274	*pp. 1159–1161*	*pp. 1495–1500* *p. 1503 diagnostic chart*	*pp. 345–347*
Security and Antitheft Devices pp. 1274 to 1277	*pp. 1161–1164*	*pp. 1504–1507*	
Other Electronic Equipment pp. 1277 to 1280	*pp. 1164–1167*	*pp. 669–675, 689*	

ASE AND NATEF CORRELATION CHART

ENGINE REPAIR TEST A1	NATEF I. ENGINE REPAIR	AUTOMOTIVE TECHNOLOGY 3E, TEXT	TECH MANUAL
A. GENERAL ENGINE DIAGNOSIS	A. GENERAL ENGINE DIAGNOSIS; REMOVAL AND REINSTALLATION (R &R)	Chs. 5, 6, 7, 11, 12 & 13	Chs. 6, 7, 11 & 12
1. Verify driver's complaint and/or road test vehicle; determine necessary action.	1. Verify and interpret engine concern; determine necessary action.	Ch. 6, p. 146–148 Also see case studies at the end of each chapter Ch. 12, p. 286 Vacuum system troubleshooting	
2. Determine if no-crank, no-start, or hard starting condition is an ignition system, cranking system, fuel system or engine mechanical problem.		Ch. 22, p. 573, 575	
3. Inspect engine assembly for fuel, oil, coolant and other leaks; determine necessary action.	2. Inspect engine assembly for fuel, oil, coolant, and other leaks; determine necessary action.	Ch. 5, p. 113–120 Ch. 7, p. 158–162 Cylinder block inspection	Ch. 11, p. 126, 138–139
4. Listen to engine noises; determine necessary action.	3. Diagnose engine noises and vibrations; determine necessary action.	Ch. 6, p. 146–148	Ch. 11, p. 130 Ch. 12, p. 144
5. Diagnose the cause of excessive oil consumption, coolant consumption, unusual engine exhaust color, odor and sound; determine necessary action.	4. Diagnose the cause of excessive oil consumption, unusual engine exhaust, color, odor, and sound; determine necessary action.	Ch. 11, p. 248, Oil consumption p. 260	Ch. 11, p. 124, 126–127, Oil Consumption
6. Perform engine vacuum tests; determine necessary action.	5. Perform engine vacuum tests; determine necessary action.	Ch. 5, p. 115, 118–119 Ch. 12, p. 286	Ch. 12, p. 146
7. Perform cylinder power balance tests; determine necessary action.	6. Perform cylinder power balance tests; determine necessary action.	Ch. 6, p. 145–146	
8. Perform cylinder compression tests; determine necessary action.	7. Perform cylinder compression tests; determine necessary action.	Ch. 5, p. 113–117 Includes photo sequence	Ch. 6, p. 56–57
9. Perform cylinder leakage tests; determine necessary action.	8. Perform cylinder leakage tests; determine necessary action.	Ch. 5, p. 114–115	Ch. 6, p. 58–60
	9. Remove engine (front-wheel drive); prepare for disassembly.	Ch. 7, p. 156–157 General engine removal information	Ch. 7, p. 65–73
	10. Reinstall engine (front-wheel drive).	Ch. 13, p. 320 Installing the engine Ch. 13, p. 320 General engine removal information	

ENGINE REPAIR TEST A1	NATEF I. ENGINE REPAIR	AUTOMOTIVE TECHNOLOGY TEXT 3E	TECH MANUAL
	11. Remove engine (rear-wheel drive); prepare for disassembly.	Ch. 7, p. 156–157 General engine removal information	Ch. 7, p. 65–73
	12. Reinstall engine (rear-wheel drive).	Ch. 13, p. 320 General engine removal information	
B. CYLINDER HEAD AND VALVE TRAIN DIAGNOSIS AND REPAIR	B. CYLINDER HEAD AND VALVE TRAIN DIAGNOSIS AND REPAIR	Chs. 7, 9, & 10	Chs. 7, 9 & 10
1. Remove cylinder heads, disassemble, clean, and prepare for inspection according to manufacturer's procedures.	1. Remove cylinder head(s); visually inspect cylinder head(s) for cracks; check gasket surface areas for warpage and leakage; check passage condition.	Ch. 7, p. 158–167	Ch. 7, p. 66, 74–76
2. Visually inspect cylinder heads for cracks, gasket surface areas for warpage, corrosion and leakage, and check passage condition.	1. Remove cylinder head(s); visually inspect cylinder head(s) for cracks; check gasket surface areas for warpage and leakage; check passage condition.	Ch. 8, p. 171–174 Ch. 9, p. 200–202	Ch. 9, p. 97–100
3. Inspect and test valve springs for squareness, pressure and free height comparison; replace as necessary.	3. Inspect and test valve springs for squareness, pressure and free height comparison; replace as necessary.	Ch. 9, p. 215–222	Ch. 9, p. 101–102
4. Inspect valve spring retainers, rotators, locks and valve lock grooves.	4. Inspect valve spring retainers, locks and valve lock grooves.	Ch. 9, p. 218	Ch. 9, p. 103
5. Replace valve stem seals.	5. Replace valve stem seals.	Ch. 9, p. 215–217	Ch. 9, p. 104
6. Inspect valve guides for wear; check valve guide height and stem-to-guide clearance; determine needed repairs.	6. Inspect valve guides for wear; check valve guide height and stem-to-guide clearance; recondition or replace as needed	Ch. 9, p. 208–212	Ch. 9, p. 98–100
7. Inspect valves; resurface or replace according to manufacturer's procedures.	7. Resurface valves; perform necessary action.	Ch. 9, p. 207–208	Ch. 9, p. 106–108
8. Inspect and resurface valve seats according to manufacturer's procedures.	8. Resurface valve seats; perform necessary action.	Ch. 9, p. 212–215	
9. Check valve face-to-seat contact and valve seat concentricity (runout).	9. Check valve face-to-seat contact and valve seat concentricity (runout); service seats and valves as needed.	Ch. 9, p. 214 Inspection p. 212–215 Service	
10. Check valve spring installed (assembled) height and valve stem height; service valve and spring assemblies as necessary.	10. Check valve spring installed assembled height and valve stem height; service valve and spring assemblies as necessary.	Ch. 9, p. 217–218	

ENGINE REPAIR TEST A1	NATEF I. ENGINE REPAIR	AUTOMOTIVE TECHNOLOGY 3E, TEXT	TECH MANUAL
11. Inspect pushrods, rocker arms, rocker arm pivots and shafts for wear, bending, cracks, looseness and blocked oil passages; repair or replace as required.	11. Inspect pushrods, rocker arms, rocker arm pivots and shafts for wear, bending, cracks, looseness, and blocked oil passages (orifices); perform necessary action.	Ch. 10, p. 232–234, 238	Ch. 10, p. 120–121
12. Inspect and replace hydraulic or mechanical lifters/lash adjusters.	12. Inspect hydraulic or mechanical lifters; replace as needed.	Ch. 10, p. 233–234 p. 238–239, 242	Ch. 10, p. 120–121
13. Adjust valves on engines with mechanical or hydraulic lifters.	13. Adjust valves (mechanical or hydraulic lifters).	Ch. 10, p. 233–234, 238	Ch. 13, p. 153–154
14. Inspect and replace camshaft drives (includes checking gear wear and backlash, sprocket and chain wear, overhead cam drive sprockets, drive belts, belt tension, tensioners and cam sensor components).	14. Inspect camshaft drives (including gear wear and backlash, sprocket and chain wear); replace as necessary. 15. Inspect and replace timing belt(s), overhead cam drive sprockets, and tensioners; check belt tension; adjust as necessary.	Ch. 10, p. 233–234, 234–237, 240–242	Ch. 10, p. 115–116
15. Inspect and replace timing belt(s), overhead camdrive sprockets, and tensioners; check belt tension; adjust as necessary.	16. Inspect camshaft for runout, journal wear and lobe wear.	Ch. 10, p. 232–233	Ch. 10, p. 117–119
16. Inspect and measure camshaft bore for wear damage, out-of-round and alignment; repair or replace according to mfr's specifications.		Ch. 10, p. 236	
	17. Inspect and measure camshaft bearings for wear, damage, out-of-round, and alignment; determine necessary action.	Ch. 10, p. 226	
17. Time camshaft(s) to crankshaft.	18. Verify camshaft(s) timing according to manufacturer's specifications and procedures.	Ch. 10, p.234–236	
18. Reassemble and install cylinder heads and gaskets; replace and tighten fasteners according to manufacturer's procedures.	2. Install cylinder head(s) and gaskets; tighten according to manufacturer's specifications and procedures.	Ch. 9, p. 218–222	

ENGINE REPAIR TEST A1	NATEF I. ENGINE REPAIR	AUTOMOTIVE TECHNOLOGY 3E, TEXT	TECH MANUAL
C. ENGINE BLOCK DIAGNOSIS AND REPAIR	C. ENGINE BLOCK ASSEMBLY, DIAGNOSIS, AND REPAIR	Chs. 7, 8, 10, 13 & 33	Chs. 4, 7, 8, 10 & 13
1. Disassemble engine block and clean and prepare components for inspection.		Ch. 7, p. 157–158	
2. Visually inspect engine block for cracks, corrosion, passage condition, core and gallery plug holes; and surface warpage; determine necessary action.	2. Inspect engine block for visible cracks, passage condition, core and gallery plug condition, and surface warpage; determine necessary action.	Ch. 7, p. 167–167 Ch. 8, p. 172–178	
3. Inspect and repair damaged threads where allowed; install core and gallery plugs.	3. Inspect internal and external threads; restore as needed (includes installing thread inserts).	Ch. 8, p. 172–176	Ch. 4, p. 28–29
4. Inspect and measure cylinder walls; remove cylinder wall ridges; hone and clean cylinder walls; determine need for further action.	4. Remove cylinder wall ridges. 5. Inspect and measure cylinder walls for damage and wear; determine necessary action.	Ch. 8, p. 174–176	Ch. 7, p. 77–78 Ch. 8, p. 82–84
	6. Deglaze and clean cylinder walls.		
5. Visually inspect crankshaft for surface cracks and journal damage; check oil passage condition; check crankshaft sensor reluctor ring (where applicable); determine necessary action.	8. Inspect crankshaft for surface cracks and journal damage; check oil passage condition; measure journal wear; determine necessary action.	Ch. 8, p. 180–184	Ch. 8, p. 85–87 Measuring crankshaft journals
6. Inspect and measure main bearing bores and cap alignment and fit.	9. Inspect and measure main and connecting rod bearings for damage, clearance, and end play; determine necessary action (includes the proper selection of bearings).	Ch. 8, p. 184–189	
7. Install main bearings and crankshaft; check bearing clearances and endplay; replace/retorque bolts according to manufacturers' procedures.	9. Inspect and measure main and connecting rod bearings for damage, clearance, and end play; determine necessary action (includes the proper selection of bearings).	Ch. 8, p. 184–189	Ch. 8, p. 88–89

ENGINE REPAIR TEST A1	NATEF I. ENGINE REPAIR	AUTOMOTIVE TECHNOLOGY 3E, TEXT	TECH MANUAL
8. Inspect camshaft bearings for unusual wear; remove and replace camshaft bearings; install camshaft timing, timing chain, and gears; check endplay.	7. Inspect and measure camshaft bearings for wear, damage, out-of-round, and alignment; determine necessary action.	Ch. 10, p. 226–277, 234–242	Ch. 10, p. 112–114 Installation
9. Inspect auxiliary (balance, intermediate, idler, counterbalance or silencer) shaft(s) and support bearings for damage and wear; determine necessary action.	15. Inspect auxiliary (balance, intermediate, idler, counterbalancer or silencer) shaft(s); inspect shaft(s) and support bearings for damage and wear; determine necessary action; reinstall and time.	Ch. 8, p. 181–1180 Description of shafts p. 181–182 Bearing inspection	
10. Inspect, measure, service, repair, or replace pistons, piston pins and pin bushings; identify piston and bearing wear patterns that indicate connecting rod alignment problems; determine necessary action.	10. Identify piston and bearing wear patterns that indicate connection rod alignment and main bearing bore problems; inspect rod alignment and bearing bore condition. 11. Inspect, measure, and service pistons and pins; determine necessary action.	Ch. 8, p. 185–194	Ch. 8, p. 81, 90–92
11. Inspect connection rods for damage, alignment, bore condition, and pit fit; determine necessary action.		Ch. 8, p. 186–187 Description of connecting rod	
12. Inspect, measure and install or replace piston rings; assemble piston and connecting rod; install piston/rod assembly; check bearing clearance and sideplay; replace/retorque fasteners according to manufacturers' procedures.	12. Install, measure, and install piston rings. 14. Reassemble engine components using correct gaskets and sealants.	Ch. 8, p. 190–194 Ch. 13, p. 305–318	Ch. 8, p. 90–93
13. Inspect, reinstall, or replace crankshaft vibration damper (harmonic balancer).	13. Inspect, repair or replace crankshaft vibration damper (harmonic balancer).	Ch. 13, p. 318 Installation only	

ENGINE REPAIR TEST A1	NATEF I. ENGINE REPAIR	AUTOMOTIVE TECHNOLOGY 3E, TEXT	TECH MANUAL
14. Inspect crankshaft flange and flywheel mating surfaces; inspect, remove and replace crankshaft pilot bearing/bushing (if applicable); inspect flywheel/flexplate for cracks and wear (includes flywheel ring; measure flywheel runout; determine necessary action		Ch. 8. p. 180–183 Ch. 33, p. 844–845 Pilot bushing	
15. Inspect and replace pans, covers, gaskets and seals.	1. Inspect and replace pans, covers, gaskets, and seals.	Ch. 7, p. 158–162 Inspection Ch. 13, p. 308–320 Replace and reassemble	
16. Assemble engine parts using formed-in-place (tube-applied) sealants or gaskets.		Ch. 13, p. 305–320	Ch. 13, p. 151 Applying RTV silicone sealant
	16. Prime engine lubrication system.	Ch. 13, p. 318	
D. LUBRICATION AND COOLING SYSTEMS DIAGNOSIS AND REPAIR	D. LUBRICATION AND COOLING SYSTEMS DIAGNOSIS AND REPAIR	Chs. 3, 6 & 11	Chs. 3, 6 & 11
1. Perform oil pressure tests; Determine necessary action.	1. Perform oil pressure tests; Determine necessary action.	Ch. 6, p. 145	Ch. 6, p. 61–62
2. Disassemble, inspect, measure and repair oil pump(includes gears, rotors, housing and pickup assembly), pressure relief valves and pump drive; replace oil filter.	2. Inspect oil pump gears or rotors, housing, pressure relief devices, and pump drive; perform necessary action. 13. Perform oil and filter change.	Ch. 3, p. 54–55 Photo sequence Ch. 11, p. 249–258	Ch. 11, p. 131–133
3. Perform cooling system tests; Determine necessary action.	3. Perform cooling system, cap, and recovery system tests (pressure, combustion leakage, and temperature); determine necessary action.	Ch. 11, p. 269–270	Ch. 11, p. 138–139
4. Inspect, replace and adjust drive belts, tensioners, and pulleys.	4. Inspect, replace, and adjust drive belts, tensioners, and pulleys.	Ch. 11, p. 273–274	Ch. 11, p. 134–135
5. Inspect and replace engine cooling and heater system hoses.	5. Inspect and replace engine cooling and heater system hoses.	Ch. 11, pp. 263–264, 271–272	Ch. 3, p. 17
6. Inspect, test and replace thermostat, by-pass and housing.	6. Inspect, test and replace thermostat, by-pass and housing.	Ch. 11, p. 270–271	

ENGINE REPAIR TEST A1	NATEF I. ENGINE REPAIR	AUTOMOTIVE TECHNOLOGY 3E, TEXT	TECH MANUAL
7. Inspect coolant; drain, flush and refill cooling system with recommended coolant and bleed air as required.	7. Test coolant; drain and recover coolant; flush and refill cooling system with recommended coolant; bleed air as required.	Ch. 11, p. 274–275	Ch. 3, p. 17
8. Inspect, test and replace water pump.	8. Inspect, test, remove, and replace water pump.	Ch. 11, p. 272–273	
9. Inspect, test and replace radiator, heater core, pressure cap, and coolant recovery system.	9. Remove and replace radiator.	Ch. 11, p. 270–271	Ch. 11, p. 138–139
10. Clean, inspect, test and replace fan (both electrical and mechanical), fan clutch, fan shroud, air dams and cooling-related temperature sensors.	10. Inspect, and test fan(s) (electrical or mechanical), fan clutch, fan shroud, and air dams. 12. Inspect, test, and replace oil temperature and pressure switches and sensors.	Ch. 11, p. 273	Ch. 11, p. 136–137
11. Inspect, test and repair or replace auxiliary oil coolers.	11. Inspect auxiliary oil coolers; replace as needed.	Ch. 11, p. 250, 269 Description	
E. FUEL, ELECTRICAL, IGNITION, AND EXHAUST SYSTEMS INSPECTION AND SERVICE	NO MATCHING SECTION IN NATEF ENGINE REPAIR TASK LIST	Chs. 12, 16, 17, 22 & 30	Chs. 12, 16, 17, 21/22 & 29/30
1. Inspect, clean or replace fuel and air induction system components, intake manifold, and gaskets.		Ch. 12, p. 279–287 Air induction and vacuum system	Ch. 12, p. 144–146
2. Inspect, service or replace air filters, filter housings and intake ductwork.		Ch. 12, p. 279–282	
3. Inspect turbocharger/supercharger; determine necessary action.		Ch. 12, p. 296–302	
4. Test battery; charge as necessary.		Ch. 16, p. 397–398 Description p. 406–409	Ch. 16, p. 188–191
5. Remove and replace starter.		Ch. 17, p. 427, 430 Removal	Ch. 17, p. 195–198
6. Inspect and replace positive crankcase ventilation (PCV) system components.		Ch. 30, p. 751–752	Ch. 29/30, p. 333–334

ENGINE REPAIR TEST A1	NATEF I. ENGINE REPAIR	AUTOMOTIVE TECHNOLOGY 3E, TEXT	TECH MANUAL
7. Visually inspect and reinstall primary and secondary ignition system components; time distributor.		Ch. 22, p. 588–602 Description	Ch. 21/22, p. 279–283
8. Inspect, service and replace exhaust manifold.		Ch. 12, p. 288–289 Description p. 295 Service	
AUTOMATIC TRANSMISSION/ TRANSAXLE (TEST A2)	**II. AUTOMATIC TRANSMISSION AND TRANSAXLE**		
A. GENERAL TRANSMISSION/ TRANSAXLE DIAGNOSIS	A. GENERAL TRANSMISSION AND TRANSAXLE DIAGNOSIS	Chs. 17, 18, 37 & 38	
1. MECHANICAL/ HYDRAULIC SYSTEMS		Chs. 37 & 38	Ch. 37/38
1. Evaluate driver's concern and road test vehicle to verify mechanical/hydraulic system problems; determine necessary action.	1. Identify and interpret transmission concern; assure proper engine operation; determine necessary action.	Ch. 38, p. 994–996, 1009	Ch. 37/38, p. 439–445
2. Diagnose noise and vibration problems; determine necessary action.	6. Diagnose noise and vibration concerns; determine necessary action.	Ch. 38, p. 990, 994–995	Ch. 37/38, p. 447 Noise
3. Diagnose unusual fluid usage, type, level and condition problems; determine necessary action.	2. Diagnose unusual fluid usage, level, and condition concerns; determine necessary action.	Ch. 38, p. 987–989	Ch. 37/38, p. 440, 443
4. Perform pressure tests; determine necessary action.	3. Perform pressure tests; determine necessary action.	Ch. 38, p. 999–1002	Ch. 37/38, p. 448–450
5. Perform stall tests; determine necessary action.		Ch. 38, p. 1002	Ch. 37/38, p. 446–447
6. Perform torque converter clutch (lock-up converter) mechanical/ hydraulic system tests; determine necessary action.	4. Perform lock-up converter system tests; determine necessary action.	Ch. 37, p. 941–942 Lock-up converter description	Ch. 37/38, p. 441–442 Road test
7. Diagnose mechanical and vacuum control systems; determine necessary action.	5. Diagnose electronic, mechanical, hydraulic, vacuum control system concerns; determine necessary action.	Ch. 38, p. 996–1002	
2. ELECTRONIC SYSTEM		Ch. 37, p. 973–978 Electronic controls system	Chs. 14, 15 & 37/38

AUTOMATIC TRANSMISSION/ TRANSAXLE (TEST A2)	II. AUTOMATIC TRANSMISSION AND TRANSAXLE		
1. Evaluate driver's concern and road test vehicle to verify electronic system problems; determine necessary action.		Ch. 38, p. 994–997, Road test p. 998–999, Electronic defaults	
2. Perform pressure tests on transmissions equipped with electronic pressure control; determine necessary action.		Ch. 38, p. 994–1002	
3. Perform torque converter clutch (lock-up converter) electronic system tests; determine necessary action.		Ch. 38, p. 1002–1003	
4. Diagnose electronic transmission control systems using appropriate test equipment; determine necessary action.		Ch. 5, p. 123–124 Computer scan tools Ch. 15 Covers GENERAL electronic testing Ch. 38, p. 998–999	Ch. 37/38, p. 437–438 Description of the controls Ch. 14, p. 165–172 Basic electrical testing Ch. 15, p. 177–181 Basic electronics testing
5. Verify proper operation of starting and charging systems; check battery, connections and vehicle grounds.		Ch. 17, p. 424 Ch. 18, p. 451–452	
B. TRANSMISSION/ TRANSAXLE MAINTENANCE AND ADJUSTMENT	B. TRANSMISSION AND TRANSAXLE MAINTENANCE AND ADJUSTMENT	Chs. 37 & 38	Chs. 3, 14, 15 & 37/38
1. Inspect, adjust and replace manual valve shift linkage, transmission range sensor/switch, and park/ neutral position switch (inhibitor/neutral safety switch).		Ch. 37, p. 965–967 Description Ch. 38, p. 996–997 Service	
2. Inspect, adjust and replace cables or linkages for throttle valve (TV), kick-down and accelerator pedal.	1. Inspect, adjust or replace throttle (TV) linkages or cables, check gear select indicator (as applicable).	Ch. 37, p. 965–967 Description Ch. 38, p. 996–997 Service	
3. Replace fluid and filter(s); verify proper fluid level.	2. Service transmission; perform visual inspection; replace fluids and filters.	Ch. 38, p. 990–992	Ch.3, p. 15

AUTOMATIC TRANSMISSION/ TRANSAXLE (TEST A2)	II. AUTOMATIC TRANSMISSION AND TRANSAXLE		
C. IN-VEHICLE TRANSMISSION/ TRANSAXLE REPAIR	C. IN-VEHICLE TRANSMISSION and TRANSAXLE REPAIR D. OFF-VEHICLE TRANSMISSION AND TRANSAXLE REPAIR	Chs. 5, 14, 15, 37 & 38	Ch. 37/38
1. Inspect, adjust and replace vacuum modulator, valve, lines and hoses.	C.1. Inspect, adjust or replace (as applicable) vacuum modulator; inspect and repair or replace lines and hoses.	Ch. 37, p. 965–967 Description Ch. 38, p. 996 Service	
2. Inspect, adjust, repair and replace governor cover, seals, sleeve/bore, valve, weight, springs, retainers and gear.	C. 2. Inspect, repair, and replace governor assembly.	Ch. 37, p. 967 Description Ch. 38, p. 1001 Service	
3. Inspect and replace external seals and gaskets.	C. 3. Inspect and replace external seals and gaskets.	Ch. 38, p. 1004–1008, Included in photosequence of transaxle overhaul	
4. Inspect and repair or replace extension housing, bushing, and driveshaft yoke.	C.4. Inspect extension housing, bushings and seals; perform necessary action.	Ch. 38, p. 993	
5. Check condition of engine cooling system; inspect, test, and flush or replace transmission cooler, lines and fittings.	C.5. Inspect, leak test, flush, and replace cooler, lines, and fittings.	Ch. 38, p. 1003, 1009	Ch. 37/38, p. 440
6. Inspect and replace speedometer/speed sensor drive gear, driven gear, and retainers.	C.6. Inspect and replace speedometer drive gear, driven gear, vehicle speed sensor (VSS), and retainers.	Ch. 38, p. 993, 1004–1009	
7. Inspect valve body mating surfaces, bores, valves, springs, sleeves, retainers, brackets, check balls, screens, spacers and gaskets; replace as necessary.	D.1.4. Inspect, measure, clean, and replace valve body (includes surfaces and bores, springs, valves, sleeves, retainers, brackets, check-balls, screens, spacers, and gaskets), and torque valve body bolts.	Ch. 37, p. 962–966 Description of valve body and valves Ch. 38, p. 999–1002 Pressure tests, p. 1004–1009 Transaxle overhaul	
8. Check/adjust valve body bolt torque.	D.1.4. Inspect, measure, clean, and replace valve body (includes surfaces and bores, springs, valves, sleeves, retainers, brackets, check-balls, screens, spacers, and gaskets), and torque valve body bolts.	Ch. 37, p. 963 Ch. 38, p. 1001	Ch. 37/38, p. 452–453

AUTOMATIC TRANSMISSION/ TRANSAXLE (TEST A2)	II. AUTOMATIC TRANSMISSION AND TRANSAXLE		
9. Inspect servo bore, piston, seals, pin, spring, and retainers; repair or replace as necessary and adjust bands.	D.1.5. Inspect servo bore, piston, seals, pin, spring, and retainers; determine necessary action.	Ch. 38, p. 1001–1002	
10. Inspect accumulator bore, piston, seals, spring, and retainers; repair or replace as necessary.	D.1.6. Inspect accumulator bore, piston, seals, spring, and retainer; determine necessary action.	Ch. 38, p. 1004–1008, Included in photosequence of transaxle overhaul	
11. Inspect parking gear, inspect and replace parking pawl, shaft, spring, and retainer.	D.3.9. Inspect and reinstall parking pawl, shaft, spring, and retainer; determine necessary action.	Ch. 38, p. 1002 Parking pawl	
12. Inspect, test, adjust, repair, or replace electrical/electronic components and circuits including computers, solenoids, sensors, relays, terminals, connectors, switches and harnesses.	C.7. Inspect and test, adjust, repair or replace transmission related electrical and electronic components (includes computers, solenoids, sensors, relays, switches, and harnesses).	Ch. 5, p. 123–126 Computer scan tools & engine analyzers Ch. 14 & 15 Cover electrical and electronic testing Ch. 38, p. 998–999	Ch. 37/38, p. 437–438 Description of the controls Ch. 14, p. 165–172 Basic electrical testing Ch. 15, p. 177–181 Basic electronics testing
13. Inspect, replace and align power train mounts.	C.8. Inspect, replace and align power train mounts.	Ch. 38, p. 994, Transaxle mounts	
D. OFF-VEHICLE TRANSMISSION/ TRANSAXLE REPAIR	D. OFF-VEHICLE TRANSMISSION AND TRANSAXLE REPAIR	Chs. 11, 37 & 38	Ch. 37/38
1. REMOVAL, DISASSEMBLY AND ASSEMBLY	1. REMOVAL, DISASSEMBLY AND REINSTALLATION 2. OIL PUMP AND CONVERTER		
1. Remove and replace transmission/transaxle; inspect engine core plugs, rear crankshaft seal, transmission dowel pins, and dowel pin holes.	1.1. Remove and reinstall transmission and torque converter (rear-wheel drive). 1.2. Remove and reinstall transaxle and torque converter assembly.	Ch. 38, p.1004–1009 Transaxle overhaul Ch. 7, p. 157	
2. Disassemble, clean and inspect tramsmission case and subassemblies.	1.3. Disassemble, clean, and inspect transmission/ transaxle.	Ch. 38, p.1004–1009 Transaxle overhaul	
3. Assemble after repair.	1.7. Assemble transmission/transaxle.	Ch. 38, p.1004–1009 Transaxle overhaul	
4. Inspect converter flex (drive) plate, converter attaching bolts, converter pilot, converter pump drive surfaces and crankshaft bore.	2.1. Inspect converter flex plate, attaching parts, pilot, pump drive, and seal areas.	Ch. 37, p. 938–940 Description	

AUTOMATIC TRANSMISSION/ TRANSAXLE (TEST A2)	II. AUTOMATIC TRANSMISSION AND TRANSAXLE		
	2.2. Measure torque converter endplay and check for interference; check stator clutch.		
	2.4. Check torque converter and transmission cooling system for contamination.	Ch. 38, p. 991, 1002–1003	Ch. 37/38, p. 440, 441, 443
2. GEAR TRAIN, SHAFTS, BUSHINGS, OIL PUMP, AND CASE	2. OIL PUMP AND CONVERTER 3. GEAR TRAIN, SHAFTS, BUSHINGS, AND CASE	Chs. 11, 37 & 38	Chs. 11 & 37/38
1. Inspect, measure, and replace oil pump components.	2.3. Inspect, measure, and replace oil pump assembly and components.	Ch. 11, p. 253–258	Ch. 11, p. 131–133
2. Check bearing preload; determine needed service.	3.1. Measure endplay or preload; determine necessary action.	Ch. 38, p. 1006 Transaxle overhaul	
3. Check end play, inspect, measure, and replace thrust washers and bearings as needed.	3.1. Measure endplay or preload; determine necessary action. 3.2. Inspect, measure, and replace thrust washers and bearings.	Ch. 37, p. 956, Endplay description Ch. 38, p. 1005–1008 Transaxle overhaul	
4. Inspect and replace shafts.		Ch. 38, p. 1005–1008 Transaxle overhaul	
5. Inspect oil delivery circuit, including seal rings, ring grooves, sealing surface areas, feed pipes, orifices, and encapsulated check valves (balls).	3.3. Inspect oil delivery seal rings, ring grooves, and sealing surface areas.	Ch. 38, p. 1008 Transaxle overhaul	
6. Inspect and replace bushings.	3.4. Inspect bushings; replace as needed.	Ch. 38, p. 1005–1008 Transaxle overhaul	
7. Inspect and measure planetary gear assembly; replace parts as necessary.	3.5. Inspect and measure planetary gear assembly (includes sun, ring gear, thrust washers, planetary gears, and carrier assembly); replace as needed.	Ch. 37, p. 942–944 Description Ch. 38, p. 1005–1008 Transaxle overhaul	Ch. 37/38, p. 436 Description
8. Inspect, repair, and replace case bores, passages, bushings, vents, mating surfaces, thread condition, and dowel pins.	3.6. Inspect case bores, passages, bushings, vents, and mating surfaces; determine necessary action.	Ch. 38, p. 1005–1008 Transaxle overhaul	
9. Inspect, repair or replace transaxle drive chains, sprockets, gears, bearings, and bushings.	3.7. Inspect transaxle drive, link chains, sprockets, gears, bearings, and bushings; perform necessary action.	Ch. 38, p. 1005–1008 Transaxle overhaul	

AUTOMATIC TRANSMISSION/ TRANSAXLE (TEST A2)	II. AUTOMATIC TRANSMISSION AND TRANSAXLE		
10. Inspect, measure, repair, adjust or replace transaxle final drive components.	3.8. Inspect, measure, repair, adjust or replace transaxle final drive components.	Ch. 38, p. 1005–1008 Transaxle overhaul	
3. FRICTION AND REACTION UNITS	4. FRICTION AND REACTION UNITS	Chs. 37 & 38	Ch. 37/38
1. Inspect hydraulic clutch assembly; replace parts as necessary.	1. Inspect clutch drum, piston, check-balls, springs, retainers, seals, and friction and pressure plates; replace as needed.	Ch. 37, p. 952–954 Description Ch. 38, p. 1005–1008 Transaxle overhaul	Ch. 37/38, p. 454–456
2. Measure and adjust clutch pack clearance.	2. Measure clutch pack clearance; adjust as needed.	Ch. 37, p. 953–954 Description	Ch. 37/38, p. 456
3. Air test the operation of clutch and servo assemblies.	3. Air test operation of clutch and servo assemblies.	Ch. 37, p. 952–954 Clutch and servo description Ch. 38, p. 999–1002 Air tests	
4. Inspect one-way clutch assemblies; replace parts as necessary.	4. Inspect roller and sprag clutch, races, rollers, sprags, springs, cages, and retainers; replace as needed.	Ch. 38, p. 1005–1008 Transaxle overhaul	
5. Inspect and replace bands and drums (housings/cylinders).	5. Inspect bands and drums; adjust or replace as needed.	Ch. 37, p. 951 Description Ch. 38, p. 999 Service	Ch. 37/38, p. 455–456
MANUAL DRIVE TRAIN AND AXLES (TEST A3)	III. MANUAL DRIVE TRAINS AND AXLES		
A. CLUTCH DIAGNOSIS AND REPAIR	A. CLUTCH DIAGNOSIS AND REPAIR	Chs. 8 & 33	Ch. 33
1. Diagnose clutch noise, binding, slippage, pulsation, chatter, pedal feel/effort, and release problems; determine needed repairs.	1. Diagnose clutch noise, binding, slippage, pulsation, and chatter; determine necessary action.	Ch. 33, p. 851–854	Ch. 33, p. 374–380
2. Inspect, adjust, replace clutch pedal linkage, cables and automatic adjuster mechanisms, brackets, bushings, pivots and springs.	2. Inspect clutch pedal linkage, cables, automatic adjuster mechanisms, brackets, bushings, pivots, and springs; perform necessary action.	Ch. 33, p. 844–851	Ch. 33, p. 377, 379–380
3. Inspect, adjust, replace, and bleed hydraulic clutch slave and master cylinders, lines and hoses.	3. Inspect hydraulic clutch slave and master cylinders, lines, and hoses; perform necessary action.	Ch. 33, p. 849–850 Description	

MANUAL DRIVE TRAIN AND AXLES (TEST A3)	III. MANUAL DRIVE TRAINS AND AXLES		
4. Inspect, adjust and replace release (throw-out) bearing, lever and pivot.	4. Inspect relaease (throw-out) bearing, lever, and pivot; perform necessary action.	Ch. 33, p. 845–849 Description	Ch. 33, p. 387
5. Inspect and replace clutch disc and pressure plate assembly.	5. Inspect and replace clutch pressure plate assembly and clutch disc.	Ch. 33 p. 843–847 Description p. 854–856 Service	Ch. 33, p. 387, 389–390
6. Inspect and replace pilot bearing.	6. Inspect, remove or replace crankshaft pilot bearing or bushing (as applicable).	Ch. 33, p. 845 Description	Ch. 33, p. 387–388
7. Inspect and measure flywheel and ring gear; repair or replace as necessary.	7. Inspect flywheel and ring gear for wear and cracks, measure runout; determine necessary action.	Ch. 33, p. 844 Description p. 854–856 Service	Ch. 33, p. 384–385, 387
8. Inspect engine block, clutch (bell) housing, and transmission case mating surfaces; determine needed repairs.	8. Inspect engine block, clutch (bell) housing, and transmission/transaxle case mating surface; determine necessary action.	Ch. 35. p. 896	Ch. 33, p. 389
9. Measure flywheel-to-block runout and crankshaft end play; determine needed repairs.	9. Measure flywheel-to-block runout and crankshaft endplay; determine necessary action.	Ch. 8, p. 181 Ch. 33, p. 856	Ch. 33, p. 385–386
10. Measure clutch (bell) housing bore-to-crankshaft runout and face squareness; determine needed repairs.		Ch. 33, p. 856	Ch. 33, p. 386
11. Inspect, replace and align power train mounts.		Ch. 35, p. 884, 887 Transaxle mounts	
B. TRANSMISSION DIAGNOSIS AND REPAIR	B. TRANSMISSION/ TRANSAXLE DIAGNOSIS AND REPAIR	Chs. 8, 11, 34 & 35	Ch. 34/35
1. Diagnose transmission noise, hard shifting, jumping out of gear, and fluid leakage problems; determine needed repairs.	4. Diagnose noise, hard shifting, jumping out of gear, and fluid leakage concerns; determine necessary action.	Ch. 35, p. 865–870	Ch. 34/35, p. 394, 400, 401–403
2. Inspect, adjust and replace transmission external shifter assembly, shift linkages, brackets, bushings, grommets, pivots and levers.	5. Inspect, adjust, and reinstall shift linkages, brackets, bushings, cables, pivots, and levers.	Ch. 34, p. 870–871 Description	Ch. 34/35, p. 397–400

MANUAL DRIVE TRAIN AND AXLES (TEST A3)	III. MANUAL DRIVE TRAINS AND AXLES		
3. Inspect and replace transmission gaskets, sealants, seals and fasteners; inspect sealing surfaces.	7. Inspect and replace gaskets, seals, and sealants; inspect sealing surfaces.	Ch. 34, p. 866 Description Ch. 35, p. 897–898 Service	
4. Remove and replace transmission; inspect transmission mounts.	1. Remove and reinstall transmission/transaxle 6. Inspect and reinstall powertrain mounts.	Ch. 35, p. 889–891	Ch. 34/35, p. 403, Checking transmission mounts
5. Disassemble and clean transmission components; reassemble transmission.	2. Disassemble, clean, and reassemble transmission/ transaxle components.	Ch. 35, p. 890–897	
6. Inspect, repair and/or replace transmission shift cover and internal shift forks, bushings, levers, shafts, sleeves, detent mechanisms, interlocks and springs.	9. Inspect, adjust, and reinstall shift cover, forks, levers, grommets, shafts, sleeves, detent mechanism, interlocks, and springs.	Ch. 34, p. 870–871 Description Ch. 35, p. 893–894 Disassembly of transaxle Ch. 35, p. 895–896 Assembly of transaxle	
7. Inspect and replace input (clutch) shaft, bearings, and retainers.		Ch. 34, p. 866–867 Description Ch. 35, p. 872 Service p. 893–896 Dissassembly & reassembly of a transaxle	
8. Inspect and replace main shaft, gears, thrust washers, bearings and retainers/snap rings.		Ch. 34, p. 861–867 Description Ch. 35, p. 890–892 Service p. 893–896 Dissassembly & reassembly of a transaxle	
9. Inspect and replace synchronizer hub, sleeve, keys (inserts), springs and blocking (synchronizing) rings; measure blocking ring clearance.	11. Inspect and reinstall synchronizer hub, sleeve, keys (inserts), springs, and blocking rings.	Ch. 34, p. 868–851 Description Ch. 35, p. 891–892 Service p. 893–896 Dissassembly & reassembly of a transaxle	

MANUAL DRIVE TRAIN AND AXLES (TEST A3)	III. MANUAL DRIVE TRAINS AND AXLES		
10. Inspect and replace counter (cluster) gear, shaft, bearings, thrust washers and retainers.		Ch. 34, p. 866–867 Description Ch. 35, p. 891–892 Service p. 893–896 Dissassembly & reassembly of a transaxle	
11. Inspect and replace reverse idler gear, shaft, bearings, thrust washers and retainers/snap rings.		Ch. 35, p. 891–892 Service p. 893–896 Dissassembly & reassembly of a transaxle	
12. Measure and adjust shaft, gear and synchronizer end play.		Ch. 34, p. 866–871 Description of components	
13. Measure and adjust bearing preload.		Ch. 35, p. 892–897	
14. Inspect, repair and replace extension housing and transmission case mating surfaces, bores, bushings and vents.	3. Inspect transmission/ transaxle case, extension housing, case mating surfaces, bores, bushings, and vents; perform necessary action.	Ch. 34, p. 867 Illustration Ch. 35, p. 891–892 Service	
15. Inspect and replace speedometer drive gear, driven gear and retainers.	12. Inspect and reinstall speedometer drive gear, driven gear, vehicle speed sensor (VSS), and retainers.	Ch. 35, p. 891–892 Service	
16. Inspect, test and replace transmission sensors and switches.	16. Inspect, test, and replace transmission/ transaxle sensors and switches.	Ch. 34, p. 876–877 Description Ch. 35, p. 884 Back-up light switch service	
17. Inspect lubrication devices; check fluid level, and refill with proper fluid.	15. Inspect lubrication devices (oil pump or slingers); perform necessary action.	Ch. 11, p. 253–257 Oil pump inspection Ch. 8, p. 183 Oil grooves	Ch. 34/35, p. 395 Fluid check
	8. Remove and replace transaxle final drive.	Ch. 34, p. 857 Description	
	14. Remove, inspect, measure, adjust, and reinstall transaxle final drive pinion gears (spiders), shaft, side gears, side bearings, thrust washers, and case assembly.	Ch. 35, p. 871–879 Disassembly, cleaning, reassembly of a typical transaxle.	

MANUAL DRIVE TRAIN AND AXLES (TEST A3)	III. MANUAL DRIVE TRAINS AND AXLES		
C. TRANSAXLE DIAGNOSIS AND REPAIR	B. TRANSMISSION/ TRANSAXLE DIAGNOSIS AND REPAIR D. DRIVE AXLE DIAGNOSIS AND REPAIR	Chs. 8, 11, 34, 35 & 36	Ch. 34/35, 36
1. Diagnose transaxle noise, hard shifting, jumping out of gear and fluid leakage problems; determine needed repairs.	B.4. Diagnose noise, hard shifting, jumping out of gear, and fluid leakage concerns; determine necessary action. B.13. Diagnose transaxle final drive assembly noise and vibration concerns; determine necessary action.	Ch. 35, p. 865–870	Ch. 34/35, p. 394, 400, 401–403
2. Inspect, adjust and replace transaxle external shift assemblies, linkages, brackets, bushings/ grommets, cables, pivots and levers.	B.5. Inspect, adjust, and reinstall shift linkages, brackets, bushings, cables, pivots, and levers.	Ch. 35, p. 889–898	Ch. 34/35, p. 397–400
3. Inspect and replace transaxle gaskets, sealants, seals and fasteners; inspect sealing surfaces.	B.7. Inspect and replace gaskets, seals, and sealants; inspect sealing surfaces.	Ch. 34, p. 866–867 Description Ch. 35, p. 893–898 Service	
4. Remove and replace transaxle; inspect, replace, and align transaxle mounts.	B.1. Remove and reinstall transmission/transaxle B.6. Inspect and reinstall powertrain mounts	Ch. 35, p. 881–892	Ch. 34/35, p. 304 Transmission mount check
5. Disassemble and clean transaxle components; reassemble transaxle.	B.2. Disassemble, clean, and reassemble transmission/transaxle components.	Ch. 35, p. 889–898	
6. Inspect, repair and/or replace transaxle shift cover, and internal shift forks, levers, bushings, shafts, sleeves, detent mechanisms, interlocks and springs.	B.9. Inspect, adjust, and reinstall shift cover, forks, levers, grommets, shafts, sleeves, detent mechanism, interlocks, and springs.	Ch. 35, p. 893–896 Dissassembly & reassembly of a transaxle	
7. Inspect and replace input shaft and bearings.		Ch. 34, p. 867–868 Description Ch. 35, p. 891 Service	

MANUAL DRIVE TRAIN AND AXLES (TEST A3)	III. MANUAL DRIVE TRAINS AND AXLES		
8. Inspect and replace output shaft, gears, thrust washers, bearings and retainers/snap rings.		Ch. 34, p. 861–848 Description Ch. 35, p. 890–892 Service	
9. Inspect and replace synchronizer hub, sleeve, keys (inserts), springs, and blocking (synchronizing) rings; measure blocking ring clearance.	B.11. Inspect and reinstall synchronizer hub, sleeve, keys (inserts), springs, and blocking rings	Ch. 34, p. 868–870 Description Ch. 35, p. 891–892 Service p. 893–896 Dissassembly & reassembly of a transaxle	
10. Inspect and replace reverse idler gear, shaft, bearings, thrust washers, and retainers/snap rings.		Ch. 35, p. 891–892 Service p. 893–896 Dissassembly & reassembly of a transaxle	
11. Inspect, repair, and replace transaxle case mating surfaces, bores, bushings, and vents.	B.3. Inspect transmission/ transaxle case, extension housing, case mating surfaces, bores, bushings, and vents; perform necessary action.	Ch. 35, p. 891–892 Service p. 893–896 Dissassembly & reassembly of a transaxle	
12. Inspect and replace speedometer drive gear, driven gear, and retainers.	B.12. Inspect and reinstall speedometer drive gear, driven gear, vehicle speed sensor (VSS), and retainers.	Ch. 35, p. 891–892 Service p. 893–896 Dissassembly & reassembly of a transaxle	
13. Inspect, test, and replace transaxle sensors and switches.	B.16. Inspect, test, and replace transmission/ transaxle sensors and switches.	Ch. 34, p. 876–877 Description Ch. 35, p. 884 Back-up light switch service	
14. Diagnose differential assembly noise and vibration problems; determine needed repairs.	D.1.1. Diagnose noise and vibration concerns; determine necessary action.	Ch. 36, p. 930, 933	Ch. 36, p. 424, Noise
15. Remove and replace differential assembly.	D.1.11. Reassemble and reinstall differential case assembly; measure runout; determine necessary action.	Ch. 36, p. 915–925 Description p. 927–929 Service	

MANUAL DRIVE TRAIN AND AXLES (TEST A3)	III. MANUAL DRIVE TRAINS AND AXLES		
16. Inspect, measure, adjust and replace differential pinion gears (spiders), shaft, side gears, thrust washers, and case.	D.1.10. Disassemble, inspect, measure, and adjust or replace differential pinion gears (spiders), shaft, side gears, side bearings, thrust washers, and case.	Ch. 36, p. 915–922 Description p. 927–932 Service	Ch. 36, p. 426–428 Pinion gears
17. Inspect and replace differential side bearings.	D.1.10. Disassemble, inspect, measure, and adjust or replace differential pinion gears (spiders), shaft, side gears, side bearings, thrust washers, and case.	Ch. 36, p. 931–932	
18. Measure shaft end play/preload (shim/spacer selection procedure).	B.10. Measure endplay or preload (shim or spacer selection procedure) on transmission/transaxle shafts; perform necessary action.	Ch. 35, p. 892, 898	
19. Inspect lubrication devices; check fluid level and refill with proper fluid.	B.15. Inspect lubrication devices (oil pump or slingers); perform necessary action.	Ch. 11, p. 253–257 Oil pump Ch. 8, p. 183 Oil groove	
	D.3. Replace front wheel drive (FWD) front wheel bearing.	Ch. 40, p. 1043–1045	
D. DRIVE (HALF) SHAFT AND UNIVERSAL JOINT/CONSTANT VELOCITY (CV) JOINT DIAGNOSIS AND REPAIR (FRONT AND REAR WHEEL DRIVE).	C. DRIVE SHAFT AND HALF SHAFT, UNIVERSAL AND CONSTANT-VELOCITY (CV) JOINT DIAGNOSIS AND REPAIR	Ch. 36	Ch. 36
1. Diagnose shaft and universal/CV joint noise and vibration problems; determine needed repairs.	1. Diagnose constant-velocity (CV) joint noise and vibration concerns; determine necessary action. 2. Diagnose universal joint noise and vibration concerns; perform necessary action.	Ch. 36, p. 901–915, 927, 930	Ch. 36, p. 407–408, 422–423
2. Inspect, service and replace shafts, yokes, boots and universal/CV joints.	4. Inspect, service, and replace shafts, yokes, boots, and CV joints.	Ch. 36, p. 905–910, 913–915	Ch. 36, p. 407–423
3. Inspect, service and replace shaft center support bearings.	5. Inspect, service, and replace shaft center support bearings.	Ch. 36, p. 910 Description	

MANUAL DRIVE TRAIN AND AXLES (TEST A3)	III. MANUAL DRIVE TRAINS AND AXLES		
4. Check and correct propeller shaft balance.	6. Check shaft balance; measure shaft runout; measure and adjust driveline angles.	Ch. 36, 910–911	Ch. 36, p. 421–422
5. Measure shaft runout.	6. Check shaft balance; measure shaft runout; measure and adjust driveline angles.	Ch. 36, p. 914–915	Ch. 36, p. 420–421
6. Measure and adjust shaft angles.	6. Check shaft balance; measure shaft runout; measure and adjust driveline angles.	Ch. 36, p. 915	
E. REAR WHEEL DRIVE AXLE DIAGNOSIS AND REPAIR	D. DRIVE AXLE DIAGNOSIS AND REPAIR		
1. RING AND PINION GEARS	1. RING AND PINION GEARS AND DIFFERENTIAL CASE ASSEMBLY	Ch. 36	Ch. 36
1. Diagnose noise, vibration and fluid leakage problems; determine needed repairs.	1. Diagnose noise and vibration concerns; determine necessary action. 2. Diagnose fluid leakage concerns; determine necessary action.	Ch. 36, p. 927, 930, 933 Noise and vibration	Ch. 36, p. 424
2. Inspect and replace companion flange and pinion seal; measure companion flange runout.	3. Inspect and replace companion flange and pinion seal; measure companion flange runout.	Ch. 36, p. 929 Mentioned	
3. Measure ring gear runout; determine needed repairs.	4. Inspect ring gear and measure runout; determine necessary action.	Ch. 36, p. 928–929	Ch. 36, p. 427
4. Inspect and replace ring and pinion gearset, collapsible spacers, sleeves (shims) and bearings.	5. Remove, inspect, and reinstall drive pinion and ring gear, spacers, sleeves, and bearings.	Ch. 36, p. 929–931	Ch. 36, p. 427
5. Measure and adjust drive pinion depth.	6. Measure and adjust drive pinion depth.	Ch. 36, p. 929	Ch. 36, p. 426–427
6. Measure and adjust drive pinion bearing preload(collapsible spacer or shim type).	7. Measure and adjust drive pinion bearing preload.	Ch. 36, p. 929–930	Ch. 36, p. 427
7. Measure and adjust differential (side) bearing preload, and ring and pinion backlash (threaded cup or shim type).	8. Measure and adjust side bearing preload and ring and pinion gear total backlash and backlash variation on a differential carrier assembly (threaded cup or shim types).	Ch. 36, p. 929–932	Ch. 36, p. 427–428 Backlash

MANUAL DRIVE TRAIN AND AXLES (TEST A3)	III. MANUAL DRIVE TRAINS AND AXLES		
8. Perform ring and pinion tooth contact pattern checks; determine needed adjustments.	9. Check ring and pinion tooth contact patterns; perform necessary action.	Ch. 36, p. 930	Ch. 36, p. 429 Case Study
2. DIFFERENTIAL CASE ASSEMBLY	1. RING AND PINION GEARS AND DIFFERENTIAL CASE ASSEMBLY	Ch. 36	Ch. 36
1. Diagnose differential noise and vibration problems; determine needed adjustments.	1. Diagnose noise and vibration concerns; determine necessary action.	Ch. 36, p. 927, 930, 933	Ch. 36, p. 424
2. Remove and replace differential assembly.	11. Reassemble and reinstall differential case assembly; measure runout; determine necessary action.	Ch. 36, p. 927–929	
3. Inspect, measure, adjust and replace differential pinion gears (spiders), shaft, side gears, thrust washers and case.	10. Disassemble, inspect, measure, and adjust or replace differential pinion gears (spiders), shaft, side gears, side bearings, thrust washers, and case.	Ch. 36, p. 928, 931–932	
4. Inspect and replace differential side bearings.	10. Disassemble, inspect, measure, and adjust or replace differential pinion gears (spiders), shaft, side gears, side bearings, thrust washers, and case.	Ch. 36, p. 930–932 Side bearing preload	
5. Measure differential case runout; determine needed repairs.	11. Reassemble and reinstall differential case assembly; measure runout; determine necessary action.	Ch. 36, p. 928–929	
3. LIMITED SLIP DIFFERENTIAL	2. LIMITED SLIP DIFFERENTIAL	Ch. 36	
1. Diagnose limited slip differential noise, slippage and chatter problems; determine needed repairs.	1. Diagnose noise, slippage, and chatter concerns; determine necessary action.	Ch. 36, p. 924–925, 930, 933	
2. Inspect, flush and refill with correct	2. Inspect and flush differential housing; refill with correct lubricant.	Ch. 36, p. 924 Mentioned	
3. Inspect, adjust and replace clutch (cone/plate) pack.	3. Inspect and reinstall clutch (cone or plate) components.	Ch. 36, p. 922–925 Description p. 930, 933 Service	
	4. Measure rotating torque; determine necessary action.		
4. AXLE SHAFTS	3. DRIVE AXLE SHAFTS	Ch. 36	Ch. 36

MANUAL DRIVE TRAIN AND AXLES (TEST A3)	III. MANUAL DRIVE TRAINS AND AXLES		
1. Diagnose rear axle shaft noise, vibration and fluid leakage problems; determine needed repairs.	1. Diagnose drive axle shafts, bearings, and seals for noise, vibration, and fluid leakage concerns; determine necessary action.	Ch. 36, p. 927, 930, 933	Ch. 36, p. 407–408
2. Inspect and replace rear axle shaft wheel studs.	2. Inspect and replace drive axle shaft wheel studs.	Ch. 40, p. 1040	
3. Remove, inspect, and replace rear axle shafts, seals, bearings and retainers.	3. Remove and replace drive axle shafts. 4. Inspect and replace drive axle shaft seals, bearings, and retainers.	Ch. 36, p. 926–927	Ch. 36, p. 407–408
4. Measure rear axle flange runout and shaft end play; determine needed repairs.	5. Measure drive axle flange runout and shaft endplay; determine necessary action.	Ch. 36, p. 927	
F. FOUR-WHEEL DRIVE COMPONENT DIAGNOSIS AND REPAIR	E. FOUR-WHEEL DRIVE/ ALL-WHEEL DRIVE COMPONENT DIAGNOSIS AND REPAIR	Ch. 39	Chs. 36 & 39
1. Diagnose four-wheel drive assembly noise, vibration, shifting and steering problems; determine needed repairs.	1. Diagnose noise, vibration, and unusual steering concerns; determine necessary action.	Ch. 39, p. 1027 Case Study	Ch. 39, p. 462–463
2. Inspect, adjust and repair transfer case shifting mechanisms, bushings, mounts, levers and brackets.	2. Inspect, adjust, and repair shifting controls (mechanical, electrical, and vacuum), bushings, mounts, levers, and brackets.	Ch. 39, p. 1013–1015 Description p. 1020–1025 Service	Ch. 39, p. 464–466
3. Remove and replace transfer case.	3. Remove and reinstall transfer case.	Ch. 39, p. 1014–1015 Description p. 1020–1025 Service	
4. Disassemble and clean transfer case and components; reassemble transfer case.	4. Disassemble, service, and reassemble transfer case and components.	Ch. 39, p. 1014–1015 Description p. 1020–1025 Service	
5. Inspect and service transfer case and internal components; check lube level.	4. Disassemble, service, and reassemble transfer case and components. 6. Check drive assembly seals and vents; check lube level.	Ch. 39, p. 1014–1015 Description p. 1020–1025 Service	Ch. 39, p. 460 Fluid check

MANUAL DRIVE TRAIN AND AXLES (TEST A3)	III. MANUAL DRIVE TRAINS AND AXLES		
6. Inspect, service and replace front-drive (propeller) shafts and universal/CV joints.		Ch. 39, p. 1024–1025 Shaft installation	Ch. 36, p. 407–420 General information (not specific to front-drive)
7. Inspect, service and replace front-drive axle knuckles and driving shafts.		Ch. 39, p. 1014 Description	
8. Inspect, service and replace front wheel bearings and locking hubs.	5. Inspect front-wheel bearings and locking hubs; perform necessary action.	Ch. 39, p. 1015–1018 Description	Ch. 39, p. 459, Automatic locking hub
9. Check transfer case and front axle seals and remote vents.	6. Check drive assembly seals and vents; check lube level.	Ch. 39, p. 1015 1 paragraph	
10. Diagnose, test, adjust, and replace electrical/ electronic components of 4WD systems.	7. Diagnose, test, adjust, and replace electrical/ electronic components of 4WD systems.	Ch. 39, p. 1017–1019 Description	
SUSPENSION AND STEERING (TEST A4)	IV. SUSPENSION AND STEERING		
A. STEERING SYSEMS DIAGNOSIS AND REPAIR	A. STEERING SYSEMS DIAGNOSIS AND REPAIR	Chs. 42 & 50	
1. STEERING COLUMNS AND MANUAL STEERING GEARS		Chs. 42 & 50	Chs. 3 & 42
1. Diagnose steering column noises and steering effort concerns (including manual and electronic tilt and telescoping mechanisms); determine needed repairs.	3. Diagnose steering column noises, looseness, and binding concerns (including tilt mechanisms); determine necessary action.	Ch. 42, p. 1089–1091 Description	Ch. 42, p. 499–506, 518 General diagnostics
2. Diagnose manual steering gear (non-rack and pinion type) noises, binding, vibration, freeplay, steering effort, and lubricant leakage concerns; determine needed repairs.		Ch. 42, p. 1098–1102 General steering diagnosis	Ch. 42, p. 499–505, 518 General diagnostics
3. Diagnose manual rack and pinion steering gear noises, binding, vibration, freeplay, steering effort, and lubricant leakage concerns; determine needed repairs.		Ch. 42, p. 1098–1102 General steering diagnosis p. 1105–1106	Ch. 42, p. 499–505, Ch. 42, p. 499–505, General diagnostics

SUSPENSION AND STEERING (TEST A4)	IV. SUSPENSION AND STEERING		
4. Inspect and replace steering column, steering shaft U-joint(s), flexible coupling(s), collapsible columns, steering wheels (includes steering wheels with air bags and/or other steering wheel mounted controls and components).	1. Disable and enable supplemental restraint system (SRS) in accordance with manufacturer's procedures. 2. Remove and replace steering wheel; center/ time supplemental restraint system (SRS) coil in accordance with manufacturer's procedures. 6. Inspect steering shaft universal-joint(s), flexible coupling(s), collapsible column, lock cylinder mechanism, and steering wheel; perform necessary action.	Ch. 42, p. 1089–1091 Description p. 1107 Service Ch. 50, p. 1272–1273, 1275 Disabling supplemental restraint system	
5. Remove and replace manual steering gear (non-rack and pinion type) (includes vehicles equipped with air bags and/or other steering wheel mounted controls and components).		Ch. 42, p. 1088–1089, Steering gear description only	
6. Adjust manual steering gear (non-rack and pinion type) worm bearing preload and sector lash.	7. Adjust manual or power non-rack and pinion worm bearing preload and sector lash.	Ch. 42, p. 1106–1107	
7. Remove and replace manual rack and pinion steering gear (includes vehicles equipped with air bags and/or other steering wheel mounted controls and components).	8. Remove and replace manual or power rack and pinion steering gear; inspect mounting bushings and brackets.	Ch. 42, p. 1087–1089 Description p. 1105 Inspection Ch. 50, p. 1272–1273, 1275 Disabling supplemental restraint system	
8. Adjust manual rack and pinion steering gear.	10. Adjust manual or power rack and pinion steering gear.	Ch. 42, p. 1106–1107 General manual steering gear adjustment	
9. Inspect and replace rack and pinion steering gear inner tie rod ends (sockets) and bellows boots.	11. Inspect and replace manual or power rack and pinion steering gear inner tie rod ends (sockets) and bellows boots.	Ch. 42, p. 1105	Ch. 42, p. 517–518 Inspection only

SUSPENSION AND STEERING (TEST A4)	IV. SUSPENSION AND STEERING		
10. Inspect and replace manual rack and pinion steering gear mounting bushings and brackets.	8. Remove and replace manual or power rack and pinion steering gear; inspect mounting bushings and brackets.	Ch. 42, p. 1105	
2. POWER-ASSISTED STEERING UNITS			
1. Diagnose power steering gear (non-rack and pinion type) noises, binding, vibration, freeplay, steering effort, steering pull(lead), and fluid leakage concerns; determine needed repairs.	4. Diagnose power steering gear (non-rack and pinion) binding, uneven turning effort, looseness, hard steering, and fluid leakage concerns; determine necessary action.	Ch. 42, p. 1098–1102 General steering diagnosis	Ch. 42, p. 505–506, 511, 518 General diagnostics
2. Diagnose power rack and pinion steering gear noises, vibration, looseness, hard steering and fluid leakage problems; determine needed repairs.	5. Diagnose power steering gear (rack and pinion) binding, uneven turning effort, looseness, hard steering, and fluid leakage concerns; determine necessary action.	Ch. 42, p. 1098–1102, 1105 General steering diagnosis	Ch. 42, p. 505–506, 511, 518 General diagnostics
3. Inspect power steering fluid level and condition; adjust level in accordance with vehicle manufacturers' recommendations.	12. Inspect power steering fluid levels and condition. 13. Flush, fill, and bleed power steering system.	Ch. 42, p. 1101	Ch. 3, p. 15, 18 Ch. 42, p. 511–512
4. Inspect, adjust, align, and replace power steering pump belt(s) and tensioners.	15. Remove, inspect, replace, and adjust power steering pump belt.	Ch. 42, p. 1101	
5. Diagnose power steering pump noises, vibration, and fluid leakage; determine needed repairs.	14. Diagnose power steering fluid leakage; determine necessary action.	Ch. 42, p. 1098–1102, 1108 General steering diagnosis	Ch. 42, p. 505
6. Remove and replace power steering pump; inspect pump mounting and attaching brackets.	16. Remove, inspect, and replace power steering pump, mounts, seals, and gaskets.	Ch. 42. p. 1107	
7. Inspect and replace power steering pump seals, gaskets, reservoir and valves.	16. Remove, inspect, and replace power steering pump, mounts, seals, and gaskets.	Ch. 42, p. 1093 Description	
8. Inspect and replace power steering pump pulley.	17. Remove, inspect, and replace power steering pump pulley, check alignment.	Ch. 3, p. 53 Ch. 42, p. 1101	

SUSPENSION AND STEERING (TEST A4)	IV. SUSPENSION AND STEERING		
9. Perform power steering system pressure and flow tests; determine needed repairs.		Ch. 42, p. 1104 Ch. 5, p. 127	Ch. 42, p. 513–514
10. Inspect and replace power steering hoses, fittings, O-rings, and coolers.	18. Inspect and replace power steering hoses and fittings.	Ch. 42, p. 1095–1096 Description	
11. Remove and replace power steering gear (non-rack and pinion type)(includes vehicles equipped with air bags and/or other steering wheel mounted controls and components).		Ch. 42, p. 1107	
12. Remove and replace power rack and pinion steering gear; inspect and replace mounting bushings and brackets (includes vehicles equipped with air bags and/or other steering wheel mounted controls and components).	8. Remove and replace manual or power rack and pinion steering gear; inspect mounting bushings and brackets.	Ch. 42, p. 1105 Ch. 50, p. 1272–1273, 1275 Disabling supplemental restraint system	
13. Adjust power steering gear (non-rack and pinion type) worm bearing preload and sector lash.	7. Adjust manual or power non-rack and pinion worm bearing preload and sector lash.	Ch. 42, p. 1106–1107	
14. Inspect and replace power steering gear (non-rack and pinion type) seals and gaskets.		Ch. 42, p. 1104	
15. Adjust power rack and pinion steering gear.	10. Adjust manual or power rack and pinion steering gear.	Ch. 42, p. 1106–1107 General steering gear adjustments	
16. Inspect and replace power rack and pinion steering gear inner tie rod ends (sockets), and bellows boots.	11. Inspect and replace manual or power rack and pinion steering gear inner tie rod ends (sockets) and bellows boots.	Ch. 42, p.1103–1105	Ch. 42, p. 517–518 Inspection Only
17. Flush, fill and bleed power steering system.	13. Flush, fill and bleed power steering system.	Ch. 42, p. 1107–1108	Ch. 42, p. 511–512
18. Diagnose, inspect, repair or replace components of variable-assist steering.		Ch. 42, p. 1096–1098 Description	

SUSPENSION AND STEERING (TEST A4)	IV. SUSPENSION AND STEERING		
19. Diagnose, inspect, repair or replace components of power steering idle speed compensation systems.		Ch. 31, p. 774 Ch. 32, p. 821–822	
	9. Disassemble, inspect, perform necessary action and reassemble rack and pinion steering gear.	Ch. 42, p. 1105, Rack and pinion inspection	Ch. 42, p. 516–518 Rack and pinion inspection
	21. Diagnose and adjust components of electronically controlled steering systems; determine necessary action.	Ch. 42, p. 1096–1098 Description	
3. STEERING LINKAGE			
1. Inspect and adjust (where applicable) front and rear steering linkage geometry including parallelism and vehicle ride height.	C.3. Measure vehicle riding height; determine necessary action.	Ch. 42, p. 1085–1088 Description p. 1102–1104 Service	
2. Inspect and replace pitman arm.	19. Inspect and replace pitman arm, relay (centerlink/intermediate) rod, idler arm and mountings, and steering linkage damper.	Ch. 42, p. 1086, 1102	
3. Inspect and replace center link (relay rod/ drag link/intermediate rod).	19. Inspect and replace pitman arm, relay (centerlink/intermediate) rod, idler arm and mountings, and steering linkage damper.	Ch. 42, p. 1087, 1103	
4. Inspect, adjust (where applicable) and replace idler arm and mountings.	19. Inspect and replace pitman arm, relay (centerlink/intermediate) rod, idler arm and mountings, and steering linkage damper.	Ch. 42, p. 1086, 1102–1103	Ch. 42, p. 507–508
5. Inspect, replace, and adjust tie rods, tie rod sleeves, clamps and tie rod ends (sockets).	20. Inspect, replace, and adjust tie rod ends (sockets), tie rod sleeves, and clamps.	Ch. 42, p. 1087, 1103–1106	Ch. 42, p. 509–510
6. Inspect and replace steering linkage damper.	19. Inspect and replace pitman arm, relay (centerlink/intermediate) rod, idler arm and mountings, and steering linkage damper.	Ch. 42, p. 1104 Service	

SUSPENSION AND STEERING (TEST A4)	IV. SUSPENSION AND STEERING		
B. SUSPENSION SYSTEMS DIAGNOSIS AND REPAIR	B. SUSPENSION SYSTEMS DIAGNOSIS AND REPAIR	Chs. 40 &41	Chs. 40 & 41
1. FRONT SUSPENSIONS	1. FRONT SUSPENSIONS		
1. Diagnose front suspension system noises, body sway/roll, and ride height concerns; determine needed repairs.	1. Diagnose short and long arm suspension system noises, body sway, and uneven riding height concerns; determine necessary action. 2. Diagnose MacPherson strut suspension system noises, body sway, and uneven riding height concerns; determine necessary action.	Ch. 41, p. 1063–1065	Ch. 41, p. 484–485 General diagnosis
2. Inspect and replace upper and lower control arms, bushings, shafts, rebound and jounce bumpers.	3. Remove, inspect, and install upper and lower control arms, bushings, shafts, and rebound bumpers.	Ch. 41, p. 1059–1063, 1069	Ch. 41, p. 487–488 General inspection p. 493–494 Bushings only
3. Inspect, adjust, and replace strut rods/radius arm (compression/ tension) and bushings.	4. Remove, inspect, install, and adjust strut (compression/tension) rods and bushings.	Ch. 41, p. 1069	Ch. 41, p. 487–488 General inspection
4. Inspect and replace upper and lower ball joints (with or without wear indicators).	5. Remove, inspect, and install upper and lower ball joints on short and long arm suspension systems.	Ch. 41, p. 1060–1062, 1066–1067	Ch. 41, p. 487–488 General inspection
5. Inspect and replace kingpins, bearings, and bushings.		Ch. 41, p. 1064, 1069–1070	Ch. 41, p. 487–488 General inspection
6. Inspect and replace steering knuckle/spindle assemblies and steering arms.	6. Remove, inspect, and install steering knuckle assemblies.	Ch. 41, p. 1060, Brief description of knuckle/spindle p. 1071, Removal	Ch. 41, p. 487–488 General inspection
7. Inspect and replace front suspension system coil springs and spring insulators(silencers).	7. Remove, inspect, and install short and long arm suspension system coil springs and spring insulators.	Ch. 41, p. 1050–1059 p. 1063–1066	Ch. 41, p. 487–488 General inspection
8. Inspect and replace front suspension system leaf spring(s), leaf spring insulators (silencers), shackles, brackets, bushings and mounts.		Ch. 41, p. 1070 Description	Ch. 41, p. 487–488 General inspection

SUSPENSION AND STEERING (TEST A4)	IV. SUSPENSION AND STEERING		
9. Inspect, replace and adjust front suspension system torsion bars; inspect mounts.	8. Remove, inspect, install, and adjust suspension system torsion bars; inspect mounts.	Ch. 41, p.1053–1054, 1066	Ch. 41, p. 487–488 General inspection
10. Inspect and replace stabilizer bar (swaybar) bushings, brackets and links.	9. Remove, inspect, and install stabilizer bar bushings, brackets, and links.	Ch. 41, p. 1063, 1069	Ch. 41, p. 487–488 General inspection
11. Inspect and replace strut cartridge or assembly.	10. Remove, inspect, and install MacPherson strut cartridge or assembly, strut coil spring, insulators (silencers), and upper strut bearing mount.	Ch. 41, p. 1056–1059 p. 1070–1071	Ch. 41, p. 489–491
12. Inspect and replace strut bearing and mount.	10. Remove, inspect, and install MacPherson strut cartridge or assembly, strut coil spring, insulators (silencers), and upper strut bearing mount.	Ch. 41, p. 1056–1059, Description of McPherson strut p. 1070, 1071, Service	Ch. 41, p. 490 Mounts only
	11. Lubricate suspension and steering systems.	Ch. 41, p. 1066–1067	
2. REAR SUSPENSIONS	2. REAR SUSPENSIONS		
1. Diagnose suspension system noises, body sway/roll and ride height concerns; determine needed repairs.		Ch. 41, p. 1063–1067	Ch. 41, p. 484–485 General diagnosis
2. Inspect and replace rear suspension system coil springs and spring insulators (silencers).	1. Remove, inspect, and install coil springs and spring insulators.	Ch. 41, p. 1075	Ch. 41, p. 487–488 General inspection p. 493–494 Bushings only
3. Inspect and replace rear suspension system lateral links/arms (track bars), control (trailing) arms, stabilizer bars (sway bars), bushings, and mounts.	2. Remove, inspect, and install transverse links, control arms, bushings, and mounts.	Ch. 41, p. 1075	Ch. 41, p. 487–488 General inspection
4. Inspect and replace rear suspension system leaf spring(s), leaf spring insulators (silencers), shackles, brackets, bushings and mounts.	3. Remove, inspect, and install leaf springs, leaf spring insulators (silencers), shackles, brackets, bushings, and mounts.	Ch. 41, p. 1070, 1072 Description	Ch. 41, p. 487–488 General inspection
5. Inspect and replace rear strut cartridge or assembly, and upper mount assembly.	4. Remove, inspect, and install MacPherson strut cartridge or assembly, strut coil spring, and insulators (silencers).	Ch. 41, p. 1071 General strut service	Ch. 41, p. 489–491

SUSPENSION AND STEERING (TEST A4)	IV. SUSPENSION AND STEERING		
6. Inspect non-independent rear axle assembly for bending, warpage and misalignment.		Ch. 36, p. 927	Ch. 41, p. 487–488 General inspection
7. Inspect and replace rear ball joints and tie rod/toe link assemblies.		Ch. 41, p. 1064–1070	Ch. 41, p. 487–488 General inspection
6. Inspect and replace knuckle/spindle assembly.			Ch. 41, p. 487–488 General inspection
3. MISCELLANEOUS SERVICE	3. MISCELLANEOUS SERVICE		
1. Inspect and replace shock absorbers, mounts, and bushings.	1. Inspect, remove, and replace shock absorbers.	Ch. 41, p. 1054–1056 p. 1069–1070	
2. Inspect and replace air shock absorbers, lines and fittings.		Ch. 41, p. 1055–1056 Description	
3. Diagnose and service front and/or rear wheel bearings.	2. Remove, inspect, and service or replace front and rear wheel bearings.	Ch. 40, p. 1043–1046	Ch. 40, p. 475–478
4. Diagnose, inspect, adjust, repair or replace components of electronically controlled suspension systems (including primary and supplemental air suspension and ride control systems).	3. Diagnose, inspect, adjust, repair or replace components of electronically electronically controlled suspension systems.	Ch. 41, p.1075–1081	
5. Inspect and repair front and/or rear cradle (crossmember/subframe) mountings, bushings, brackets and bolts.		Ch. 35, p. 887–888	
C. WHEEL ALIGNMENT DIAGNOSIS, ADJUSTMENT AND REPAIR	C. WHEEL ALIGNMENT DIAGNOSIS, ADJUSTMENT AND REPAIR	Chs. 41, 42, 43	Chs. 42 & 43
1. Diagnose vehicle wander, drift, pull, hard steering, bump steer (toe curve), memory steer, torque steer, and steering return concerns; determine needed repairs.	1. Diagnose vehicle wander, drift, pull, hard steering, bump steer, memory steer, torque steer, and steering return concerns; determine necessary action.	Ch. 42, p. 1098–1101	Ch. 42, p. 500–506 General Diagnostics
	2. Perform prealignment inspection; perform necessary action.	Ch. 42, p. 1120	Ch. 43, p. 521–522
2. Measure vehicle ride height; determine needed repairs.	3. Measure vehicle riding height; determine necessary action.	Ch.41, p. 1064–1065	Ch. 43, p. 524

SUSPENSION AND STEERING (TEST A4)	IV. SUSPENSION AND STEERING		
3. Check and adjust front and rear wheel camber on suspension systems with a camber adjustment.	4. Check and adjust front and rear wheel camber; perform necessary action.	Ch. 43, p. 1116, 1121, 1124–1127	Ch. 43, p. 523–525
4. Check front and rear wheel camber on non-adjustable suspension systems; determine needed repairs.	4. Check and adjust front and rear wheel camber; perform necessary action.	Ch. 43, p. 1125–1127	Ch. 43, p. 523–525
5. Check and adjust caster on suspension systems with caster adjustment.	5. Check and adjust caster; perform necessary action.	Ch. 43, p. 1116, 1121, 1124–1126	Ch. 43, p. 523–525
6. Check caster on non-adjustable suspension systems; determine needed repairs.		Ch. 43, p. 1125–1127	Ch. 43, p. 523–525
7. Check and adjust front wheel toe.	6. Check and adjust front wheel toe; adjust as needed.	Ch. 43, p. 1116–1117, 1121–1122, 1127–1129	Ch. 43, p. 523–525
8. Center steering wheel.	7. Center steering wheel.	Ch. 42, p. 1089–1091	Ch. 43, p. 527–528
9. Check toe-out-on-turns (turning radius/angle); determine needed repairs.	8. Check toe-out-on-turns (turning radius); determine necessary action.	Ch. 42, p. 1118	Ch. 43, p. 523–525
10. Check SAI/KPI (steering axis inclination/king pin inclination); determine needed repairs.	9. Check SAI (steering axis inclination) and included angle; determine necessary action.	Ch.42, p. 1117–1118	Ch. 43, p. 523–525
11. Check included angle; determine needed repairs.		Ch. 42, p. 1117	
12. Check rear wheel toe; determine needed repairs or adjustments.	10. Check and adjust rear wheel toe.	Ch. 42, p. 1128	Ch. 43, p. 523–525
13. Check rear wheel thrust angle; determine needed repairs or adjustments.	11. Check rear wheel thrust angle; determine necessary action.	Ch. 42, p. 1128–1129	Ch. 43, p. 523–525
14. Check for front wheel setback; determine needed repairs or adjustments.	12. Check for front wheel setback; determine necessary action.	Ch. 43, p. 1128–1129	
15. Check front cradle (crossmember/subframe) alignment; determine needed repairs or adjustments.	13. Check front cradle (subframe) alignment; determine necessary action.		
D. WHEEL AND TIRE DIAGNOSIS AND REPAIR		Ch. 40	Chs. 40, 41 & 42
1. Diagnose tire wear patterns; determine needed repairs.	1. Diagnose tire wear patterns; determine necessary action.	Ch. 40, p. 1038	Ch. 40, p. 473–474

SUSPENSION AND STEERING (TEST A4)	IV. SUSPENSION AND STEERING		
2. Check tire condition, tread pattern, and size; check and adjust air pressure.	2. Inspect tires; check and adjust air pressure.	Ch. 40, p. 1036–1038	Ch. 40, p. 473–474
3. Diagnose wheel/tire vibration, shimmy, and noise concerns; determine needed repairs.	3. Diagnose wheel/tire vibration, shimmy, and noise; determine necessary action.	Ch. 40, p. 1037, 1040, 1045	Ch. 40, p. 472 Ch. 41, p. 484 Ch. 42, p. 503–504
4. Rotate tires/wheels and torque fasteners according to manufacturer's recommendations.	4. Rotate tires according to manufacturer's recommendations.	Ch. 40, p. 1037–1038	
5. Measure wheel, tire, axle flange and hub runout (radial and lateral); determine needed repairs.	5. Measure wheel, tire, axle and hub runout; determine necessary action.	Ch. 40, p. 1041	
6. Diagnose tire pull (lead) problems; determine corrective actions.	6. Diagnose tire pull (lead) problem; determine necessary action.	Ch. 43, p. 116–1120	Ch. 42, p. 501
7. Dismount and mount tire on wheel.	8. Dismount, inspect, repair, and remount tire on wheel.	Ch. 40, p. 1038–1039	Ch. 40, p. 473
8. Balance wheel and tire assembly (static and/or dynamic).	7. Balance wheel and tire assembly (static and dynamic).	Ch. 40, p. 1041–1043	Ch. 40, p. 479–480
	9. Reinstall wheel; torque lug nuts.	Ch. 40, p. 1040–1041	Ch. 40, p. 477–478
BRAKES TEST A5	**V. BRAKES**		
A. HYDRAULIC SYSTEM DIAGNOSIS AND REPAIR	A. HYDRAULIC SYSTEM DIAGNOSIS AND REPAIR	Ch. 44	Ch. 44
1. MASTER CYLINDERS (NON-ABS)			
1. Diagnose poor stopping or dragging caused by problems in the master clyinder; determine needed repairs.	4. Diagnose poor stopping, pulling or dragging concerns caused by problems in the hydraulic system; determine necessary action.	Ch. 44, p. 1147	Ch. 44, p. 536–539 General diagnostics
2. Diagnose poor stopping dragging, high or low pedal, or hard pedal caused by problems in the step bore master cylinder cylinder and interval valves (e.g. volume control devices, quick take-up valve, fast-fill valve, pressure regulating valve); determine needed repairs.	4. Diagnose poor stopping, pulling or dragging concerns caused by problems in the hydraulic system; determine necessary action.	Ch. 44, p. 1147–1149	Ch. 44, p. 536–539 General diagnostics
3. Measure and adjust master cylinder pedal pushrod length.	1. Measure and adjust pedal height.	Ch. 44, p. 1151	

BRAKES TEST A5	V. BRAKES		
4. Check master cylinder for defects by depressing brake pedal; determine needed repairs.		Ch. 44, p. 1147	Ch. 44, p. 540–541
5. Diagnose the cause of master cylinder external fluid leakage.	2. Check master cylinder for internal and external leaks and proper operation; determine necessary action.	Ch. 44, p. 1146	
6. Remove master cylinder from vehicle; install master cylinder in vehicle; test operation of the hydraulic system.	3. Remove, bench bleed, and reinstall master	Ch. 44, p. 1147	
7. Bench bleed (check for function and remove air) all non-ABS master cylinders.	3. Remove, bench bleed, and reinstall master cylinder.		Ch. 44, p. 542–544
2. FLUIDS, LINES AND HOSES			
1. Diagnose poor stopping, pulling, or dragging caused by problems in the brake fluid, lines, and hoses; determine needed repairs.	4. Diagnose poor stopping, pulling or dragging concerns caused by problems in the hydraulic system; determine necessary action.	Ch. 44, p. 1146–1147	Ch. 44, p. 537–539 General diagnostics
2. Inspect brake lines and fittings for leaks, dents, kinks, rust, cracks, or wear; tighten loose fittings and supports.	5. Inspect brake lines, flexible hoses, and fittings for leaks, dents, kinks, rust, cracks, bulging or wear; tighten loose fittings and supports; determine necessary action.	Ch. 44, p. 1141–1142, 1146	Ch. 44, p. 536, 541
3. Inspect flexible brake hoses for leaks, kinks, cracks, bulging, or wear; tighten loose fittings and supports.	5. Inspect brake lines, flexible hoses, and fittings for leaks, dents, kinks, rust, cracks, bulging or wear; tighten loose fittings and supports; determine necessary action.	Ch. 44, p. 1142, 1146–1147	Ch. 44, p. 536, 541
4. Fabricate and/or replace brake lines (double flare and ISO types), hoses, fittings, and supports.	6. Fabricate and install brake lines (double flare and ISO types); replace hoses, fittings, and supports as needed.	Ch. 44, p. 1141–1142	
5. Select, handle, store, and install proper brake fluids (including silicone fluids).	7. Select, handle, store, and install brake fluids to proper level.	Ch. 44, p. 1137	Ch. 44, p. 536, 541
6. Inspect brake lines and hoses for proper routing.		Ch. 44, p. 1141	Ch. 44, p. 536, 541
3. VALVES AND SWITCHES (NON-ABS)			

BRAKES TEST A5	V. BRAKES		
1. Diagnose poor stopping, pulling, or dragging caused by problems in the hydraulic system valve(s); determine needed repairs.	4. Diagnose poor stopping, pulling or dragging concerns caused by problems in the hydraulic system; determine necessary action.	Ch. 44, p. 1142–1145	Ch. 44, p. 537–539 General diagnostics
2. Inspect, test, and replace metering, proportioning, pressure differential, and combination valves.	8. Inspect, test, and replace metering (hold-off), proportioning (balance), pressure differential, and combination valves.	Ch.44, p. 1142–1144, Description	
3. Inspect, test, replace, and adjust load or height sensing-type proportioning valve(s).	9. Inspect, test, replace, and adjust height (load) sensing proportioning valve.	Ch. 44, p. 1143–1144 Description	
4. Inspect, test, and replace brake warning light, switch, and wiring.	10. Inspect, test, and replace components of brake warning light system.	Ch. 20, p. 504 Description	Ch. 44, 536, 541 Inspection only
4. BLEEDING, FLUSHING AND LEAK TESTING (NON-ABS)			
1. Bleed (manual, pressure, vacuum or surge method) and/or flush hydraulic sytem.	11. Bleed (manual, pressure, vacuum or surge) brake system. 12. Flush hydraulic system.	Ch. 44, p. 1147–1149	Ch. 44, p. 542–546
2. Pressure test brake hydraulic system.		Ch. 44, p. 1153	
B. DRUM BRAKE DIAGNOSIS AND REPAIR	B. DRUM BRAKE DIAGNOSIS AND REPAIR	Chs. 40, 44, 45 & 46	Chs. 44 & 45
1. Diagnose poor stopping, pulling or dragging caused by drum brake hydraulic problems; determine needed repairs.	1. Diagnose poor stopping, noise, pulling, grabbing, dragging or pedal pulsation concerns; determine necessary action.	Ch. 45, p. 1162–1164	Ch. 44, p. 537–539 General diagnostics
2. Diagnose poor stopping, noise, pulling, grabbing, dragging or pedal pulsation caused by drum brake mechanical problems; determine needed repairs.	1. Diagnose poor stopping, noise, pulling, grabbing, dragging or pedal pulsation concerns; determine necessary action.	Ch. 45, p. 1162–1164	Ch. 44, p. 537–539 General diagnostics
3. Remove, clean, inspect, and measure brake drums; follow mfr's recommendations in determining need to machine or replace.	2. Remove, clean (using proper safety procedures), inspect, and measure brake drums; service or replace as needed.	Ch. 45, p. 1164–1167	Ch. 45, p. 554–561
4. Machine drum according to mfr's procedures and and specifications.	3. Mount brake drum on lathe; machine braking surface.	Ch. 45, p. 1167	

BRAKES TEST A5	V. BRAKES		
5. Using proper safety procedures, remove, clean and inspect brake shoes/linings, springs, pins, self-adjusters, levers, clips, brake backing (support) plates and other related brake hardware; determine needed repairs.	4. Remove, clean, and inspect brake shoes, springs, pins, clips, leavers adjusters/self-adjusters, other related brake hardware, and backing support plates; lubricate and reassemble.	Ch. 45, p. 1157–1158 p. 1164–1167	Ch. 45, p. 554–561
6. Lubricate brake shoe support pads on backing (support) plate, self-adjuster mechanisms and other brake hardware.	4. Remove, clean, and inspect brake shoes, springs, pins, clips, leavers, adjusters/self-adjusters, other related brake hardware, and backing support plates; lubricate and reassemble.	Ch. 45, p. 1168–1171	Ch. 45, p. 557, 561
7. Install brake shoes and related hardware.	4. Remove, clean, and inspect brake shoes, springs, pins, clips, leavers, adjusters/self-adjusters, other related brake hardware, and backing support plates; lubricate and reassemble.	Ch. 45, p. 1171	Ch. 45, p. 5558–559, 561
	5. Remove, inspect, and install wheel cylinders.	Ch. 45, p. 1171–1172	
8. Pre-adjust brake shoes and parking brake before installing brake drums or drum/hub assemblies and wheel bearings.	6. Pre-adjust brake shoes and parking brake before installing brake drums or drum/hub assemblies and wheel bearings.	Ch. 45, p. 1171	Ch. 45, p. 558
9. Reinstall wheel, torque lug nuts, and make final checks and adjustments.	7. Install wheel, torque lug nuts, and make final checks and adjustments.	Ch. 40, p. 1040	Ch. 45, p. 559, 561
C. DISC BRAKE DIAGNOSIS AND REPAIR	C. DISC BRAKE DIAGNOSIS AND REPAIR	Ch. 46	Chs. 44 & 46
1. Diagnose poor stopping, pulling or dragging caused by disc brake hydraulic problems; determine needed repairs.	1. Diagnose poor stopping, noise, pulling, grabbing, dragging, or pedal pulsation concerns; determine necessary action.	Ch. 46, p. 1182–1184	Ch. 44, p. 537–539 General diagnostics
2. Diagnose poor stopping, noise, pulling, grabbing, dragging, pedal pulsation or pedal travel caused by disc brake mechanical problems; determine needed repairs.	1. Diagnose poor stopping, noise, pulling, grabbing, dragging, or pedal pulsation concerns; action.	Ch. 46, p. 1182–1184	Ch. 44, p. 537–539 General diagnostics

BRAKES TEST A5	V. BRAKES		
3. Retract integral parking brake caliper piston)s) according to manufacturer's recommendations		Ch. 46, p. 1181–1182 Description	Ch. 46, p. 573
4. Remove caliper assembly from mountings; clean and inspect for leaks and damage to caliper housing.	2. Remove caliper assembly from mountings; clean and inspect for leaks and damage to caliper housing; determine necessary action.	Ch. 46, p. 1179–1180 p. 1185–1192	Ch. 46, p. 572–575, 582–583, 585–586 Caliper removal p. 578 Cleaning
5. Clean, inspect, and measure caliper mountings and slides for wear and damage.	3. Clean, inspect, and measure caliper mountings and slides for wear and damage; determine necessary action.	Ch. 46, p. 1185–1186	
6. Remove, clean and inspect pads and retaining hardware; determine needed repairs, adjustments and replacements.	6. Remove, clean and inspect pads and retaining hardware; determine necessary action.	Ch. 46, p. 1181, 1186–1187	Ch. 46, p. 575–576
7. Disassemble and clean caliper assembly; inspect parts for wear, rust, scoring and damage; replace all seals, boots and any damaged or worn parts.	5. Disassemble and clean caliper assembly; inspect parts for wear, rust, scoring and damage; replace seal, boot and any damaged or worn parts.	Ch. 46, p. 1186–1190	Ch. 46, p. 576–580, 583–587
8. Reassemble caliper	6. Reassemble, lubricate, and reinstall caliper, pads, and related hardware; seat pads, and inspect for leaks.	Ch. 46, p. 1187–1192	Ch. 46, p. 578–580, 583–587
9. Clean, inspect and measure rotor with a dial indicator and a micrometer; follow mfr's recommendations in determining need to machine or replace.	7. Clean, inspect and measure rotor with a dial indicator and a micrometer; follow mfr's recommendations in determining need to machine or replace.	Ch. 46, p. 1192–1194	Ch. 46, p. 590
10. Remove and replace rotor.	11. Remove and replace rotor.	Ch. 46, p. 1193	Ch. 46, p. 588–589
11. Machine rotor, using on-car or off-car method, according to mfr's procedures and specifications.	8. Refinish rotor according to manufacturer's recommendations.	Ch. 46, p. 1194	
12. Install pads, calipers and related attaching hardware; bleed system.	6. Reassemble, lubricate, and reinstall caliper, pads, and related hardware; seat pads, and inspect for leaks.	Ch. 46, p. 1187–1192	Ch. 46, p. 578–580, 583–587

BRAKES TEST A5	V. BRAKES		
13. Adjust calipers with integrated parking brakes according to mfr's recommendations.	9. Adjust calipers with integrated parking brake system.	Ch. 46, p. 1181–1182 Description	
14. Fill master cylinder to proper level with recommended fluid; inspect caliper for leaks.		Ch. 46, p.1185, 1192	Ch. 46, p. 580
15. Reinstall wheel, torque lug nuts and make final checks and adjustments.	10. Install wheel, torque lug nuts, and make final checks and adjustments.	Ch. 40, p. 1040 Ch. 46, p. 1185	
D. POWER ASSIST UNITS DIAGNOSIS AND REPAIR	D. POWER ASSIST UNITS DIAGNOSIS AND REPAIR	Ch. 44	Ch. 44
1. Test pedal free travel with and without engine running to check power booster operation.	1. Test pedal free travel with and without engine running; check power booster assist operation.	Ch. 44, p. 1153	Ch. 44, p. 547
2. Check vacuum supply (manifold or auxiliary pump) to vacuum-type power booster.	2. Check vacuum supply (manifold or auxiliary pump) to vacuum-type power booster.	Ch. 44, p. 1149–1150	Ch. 44, p. 547–548
3. Inspect the vacuum-type power booster unit for vacuum leaks and proper operation; inspect the check valve for proper operation; repair, adjust or replace parts as necessary.	3. Inspect the vacuum-type power booster unit for vacuum leaks; inspect the check valve for proper operation; determine necessary action.	Ch.44, p. 1149–1150	Ch. 44, p. 548–549
4. Inspect and test hydro-boost system and accumulator for leaks and proper operation; repair, adjust or replace parts as necessary.	4. Inspect and test hydro-boost system and accumulator for leaks and proper operation; determine necessary action.	Ch. 44, p. 1153	
E. MISCELLANEOUS SYSTEMS (WHEEL BEARINGS, PARKING BRAKES,ELECTRICAL, ETC.) DIAGNOSIS AND REPAIR	E. MISCELLANEOUS SYSTEMS (WHEEL BEARINGS, PARKING BRAKES, ELECTRICAL, ETC.) DIAGNOSIS AND REPAIR	Chs. 40 & 45	Chs. 19, 40 & 45
1. Diagnose wheel bearing noises, wheel shimmy and vibration problems; determine needed repairs.	1. Diagnose wheel bearing noises, wheel shimmy and vibration problems; determine necessary action.	Ch. 40, p. 1043–1045	
2. Remove, clean, inspect, repack wheel bearings or replace wheel bearings and races; replace seals; adjust wheel bearings according to manufacturer's specifications.	2. Remove, clean, inspect, repack, and install wheel bearings and replace seals; install hub and adjust wheel bearings. 7. Replace wheel bearing and race.	Ch.40, p. 1043–1046	Ch. 40, p. 473, 475–477

BRAKES TEST A5	V. BRAKES		
3. Check parking brake system; inspect cables and parts for wear, rusting and corrosion; clean or replace parts as necessary; lubricate assembly.	3. Check parking brake cables and components for wear, rusting, binding, and corrosion; clean, lubricate, and replace as necessary.	Ch. 45, p. 1172–1174	Ch. 45, p. 563–566 Adjust and replace a parking brake cable
4. Adjust parking brake assembly; check operation.	4. Check parking brake operation; adjust as needed.	Ch. 45, p. 1172–1174	
5. Test the service and parking brake indicator and warning light(s), switch(es), and wiring.	5. Check operation of parking brake indicator light system.	Ch. 45, p. 1172–1173	
6. Test, adjust, repair or replace brake stop light switch, lamps, and related circuits.	6. Check operation of brake stop light system; adjust and service as needed.	Ch. 19, p. 484–485 Description p. 489 Service	Ch. 44, p. 1144–1145 Description Ch. 19, p. 238 Stop-light switch
F. ANTILOCK BRAKE SYSTEM (ABS) DIAGNOSIS AND REPAIR	F. ANTILOCK BRAKE SYSTEM	Ch. 47	Chs. 44 & 47
1. Follow accepted service and safety precautions when inspecting, testing and servicing of ABS hydraulic, electrical and mechanical components.	1. Inspect and test anti-lock brake system (ABS) components; determine necessary action.	Ch. 47, p. 1215, 1216	Ch. 47, p. 594
2. Diagnose poor stopping, wheel lock up, pedal feel and travel, pedal pulsation and noise problems caused by the ABS; determine needed repairs.	2. Diagnose poor stopping, wheel lock up, abnormal pedal feel or pulsation and noise concerns caused by the ABS; determine necessary action.	Ch. 47, p. 1216–1219 General diagnostics and testing	Ch. 47, p. 594–597 Ch. 44, p. 537–539 General diagnostics
3. Observe ABS warning light(s) at startup and during road test; determine if further diagnosis is needed.		Ch. 47, p. 1216–1218	Ch. 47, p. 594–595
4. Diagnose ABS electronic control(s), components, and circuits using self diagnosis and/or recommended test equipment; determine needed repairs.	3. Diagnose ABS electronic control(s) and components using self diagnosis and/or recommended test equipment; determine necessary action.	Ch. 47, p. 1216–1221	Ch. 47, p. 594–602
5. Depressurize integral (high pressure) components of the ABS following mfr's recommended safety procedures.	4. Depressurize high-pressure components of the ABS.	Ch. 47, p. 1215–1216	

BRAKES TEST A5	V. BRAKES		
6. Fill the ABS master cylinder with recommended fluid to proper level following mfr's procedures; inspect system for leaks.		Ch. 44, p. 1146 Ch. 47, p. 1218	
7. Bleed the ABS hydraulic circuits following mfr's procedures.	5. Bleed the ABS front and rear hydraulic circuits.	Ch. 47, p. 1221	
8. Perform a fluid pressure (hydraulic boost) diagnosis on integral (high pressure) ABS; determine needed repairs.		Ch. 47, p. 1218	
9. Remove and install ABS components following mfr's procedures and specifications; observe proper placement of components and routing of wiring harness.	6. Remove and install ABS electrical/electronic and hydraulic components.	Ch. 47, p. 1219–1220	
10. Diagnose, service, test and adjust ABS speed sensors and circuits following mfr's recommended procedures (includes voltage output, resistance, shorts to voltage/ground, and frequency data).	7. Service, test, and adjust ABS speed sensors.	Ch. 47, p. 1220–1221	Ch. 47, p. 601–602
11. Diagnose ABS braking problems caused by vehicle modifications (tire size, curb height, final drive ratio etc.) and other vehicle mechanical and electrical/electronic modifications (communication, security, and radio, etc.)	8. Diagnose ABS braking concerns caused by vehicle modifications (tire size, curb height, final drive ratio etc.)	Ch. 47, p. 1216	
12. Repair wiring harness and connectors following manufacturers' procedures.		Ch. 14, p. 357–358 Ch. 47, p. 1220–1221	
ELECTRICAL/ ELECTRONIC SYSTEMS (TEST A6)	**VI. ELECTRICAL/ ELECTRONIC SYSTEMS**		
A. GENERAL ELECTRICAL/ ELECTRONIC SYSTEM DIAGNOSIS	A. GENERAL ELECTRICAL SYSTEM DIAGNOSIS	Chs. 14 & 15	Chs. 5, 14, 15 & 16
1. Check electrical circuits with a test light; determine needed repairs.	2. Check electrical circuits with a test light; determine necessary action.	Ch. 14, p. 353–354, 356	Ch. 5, p. 41–42 Ch. 14, p. 165

ELECTRICAL/ ELECTRONIC SYSTEMS (TEST A6)	VI. ELECTRICAL/ ELECTRONIC SYSTEMS		
2. Check voltages and voltage drops in electrical/electronic circuits with a voltmeter; determine needed repairs.	3. Check voltage and voltage drop in electrical/ electronic circuits using a digital multimeter (DMM); determine necessary action.	Ch. 14, p. 348–350, 356	Ch. 14, p. 167–170 Using a DMM
3. Check current flow in electrical/electronic circuits and components with an ammeter; determine needed repairs.	4. Check current flow in electrical/electronic circuits and components with an ammeter; determine necessary action.	Ch. 14, p. 349, 351	
4. Check continuity and resistances in electrical/ electronic circuits and components with an ohmmeter; determine needed repairs.	5. Check continuity and resistances in electrical/ electronic circuits and components with an ohmmeter; determine necessary action.	Ch. 14, p. 351–352	Ch. 15, p. 177–179
5. Check electrical/ electronic circuits with jumper wires; determine needed repairs.	6. Check electrical circuits with jumper wires; determine necessary action.	Ch. 14, p. 354, 356	
6. Find shorts, grounds, opens and resistance problems in electrical/ electronic circuits; determine needed repairs.	7. Locate shorts, grounds, opens and resistance problems in electrical/ electronic circuits; determine necessary action.	Ch. 14, p.345, 348, 355–357 Ch. 15, p. 385–386	Ch. 14, p. 163 Description
7. Measure and diagnose the cause(s) of abnormal key-off battery drain (parasitic draw); determine needed repairs.	8. Measure and diagnose the cause(s) of abnormal key-off battery drain; determine necessary action.	Ch. 16, p. 407	Ch. 16, p. 184
8. Inspect, test and replace fusible links, circuit breakers, fuses, and other other current limiting devices.	9. Inspect and test fusible links, circuit breakers, and fuses; determine necessary action.	Ch. 14, p. 335–340 Description	Ch. 14, p. 171–172
9. Read and interpret electrical schematic diagrams and symbols.	1. Use wiring diagrams during diagnosis of electrical circuit problems.	Ch. 14, p. 344, 346–347	Ch. 14, p. 173
B. BATTERY DIAGNOSIS AND SERVICE	B. BATTERY DIAGNOSIS AND SERVICE	Ch. 16	Ch. 16
1. Perform battery state-of-charge test; determine needed service.	1. Perform battery state-of-charge test; determine needed service.	Ch. 16, p. 397–398 Description	Ch. 16, p. 188–189
2. Perform battery capacity (load, high-rate discharge) test; determine needed service.	2. Perform battery capacity test; determine needed service.	Ch. 16, p. 397–398 Description p. 407–408 Capacity test	Ch. 16, p. 188–189

ELECTRICAL/ ELECTRONIC SYSTEMS (TEST A6)	VI. ELECTRICAL/ ELECTRONIC SYSTEMS		
3. Maintain or restore electronic memory functions.	3. Maintain or restore electronic memory functions.	Ch. 16, p. 404	Ch. 16, p. 183–184 Maintaining memory
4. Inspect, clean, fill or replace battery.	4. Inspect, clean, fill or replace battery.	Ch. 16, p. 401	Ch. 16, p. 185–187
5. Perform slow/fast battery charge in accordance with mfr's recommendations.	5. Perform slow/fast battery charge.	Ch. 16, p. 409	Ch. 16, p. 190–191 Maintenance-free battery
6. Inspect, clean and repair or replace battery cables, connectors, clamps and hold downs.	6. Inspect and clean battery cables, connectors, clamps and hold downs; repair or replace as needed.	Ch. 16, p. 394–395, 401–405	Ch. 16, p. 185–187
7. Jump start a vehicle with jumper cables and a booster battery or auxiliary power supply.	7. Start a vehicle using jumper cables and a battery or auxiliary power supply according to manufacturers recommended specifications.	Ch. 16, p. 409–410	
C. STARTING SYSTEM DIAGNOSIS AND REPAIR	C. STARTING SYSTEM DIAGNOSIS AND REPAIR	Ch. 17	Ch. 17
1. Perform starter current draw test; determine needed repairs.	1. Perform starter current draw test; determine necessary action.	Ch. 17, p. 424–427 Various tests	Ch. 17, p. 199–200
2. Perform starter circuit voltage drop tests; determine needed repairs.	2. Perform starter circuit voltage drop tests; determine necessary action.	Ch. 17, p. 427	Ch. 17, p. 199–200
3. Inspect, test, and repair or replace switches, connectors and wires of starter control circuits.	6. Inspect and test switches, connectors, and wires of starter control circuits; perform necessary action.	Ch. 17, p.423 Description p. 431 Inspection Ch. 14, p. 357–358, 360–361 Service of wires and connectors	Ch. 17, p. 202–203 Control circuit test
4. Inspect, test and replace starter relays and solenoids.	5. Inspect and test starter relays and solenoids; replace as needed.	Ch. 17, p. 414–417 Description p. 424–435 Service	Ch. 17, 195–197 Solenoid removal, inspection, and replacement
5. Remove and replace starter.	4. Remove and install starter.	Ch. 17, p. 427, 430	Ch. 17, p. 195–197
6. Differentiate between electrical and engine mechanical problems that cause a slow crank or no crank condition.		Ch. 17, p. 424–427	

ELECTRICAL/ ELECTRONIC SYSTEMS (TEST A6)	VI. ELECTRICAL/ ELECTRONIC SYSTEMS		
	5. Perform starter bench tests; determine necessary action.	Ch. 17, p. 430	Ch. 17, p. 193–194
	7. Disassemble, clean, inspect, and test starter components; replace as needed.	Ch. 17, p. 430–435	
D. CHARGING SYSTEM DIAGNOSIS AND REPAIR	**D. CHARGING SYSTEM DIAGNOSIS AND REPAIR**	Ch. 18	Ch. 18
1. Diagnose charging system problems that cause and undercharge, a no-charge or an overcharge condition.	2. Diagnose charging system for the cause of undercharge, no-charge, and overcharge conditions.	Ch. 18, p. 451–457	
2. Inspect, adjust and replace generator (alternator) drive belts, pulleys and tensioners.	3. Inspect and adjust generator (alternator) drive belts; replace as needed.	Ch. 18, p. 452, 454–455	Ch. 18, p. 209–210
3. Perform charging system output test; determine needed repairs.	3. Perform charging system output test; determine necessary action.	Ch. 18, p. 452–453, 456	Ch. 18, p. 214–216 General testing
4. Perform generator (alternator) output test; determine needed repairs.		Ch. 18, p. 453, 456	Ch. 18, p. 214–216 General testing
5. Inspect, test, repair or replace voltage regulator/ regulating circuit; determine needed repairs.	4. Inspect and test voltage regulator/regulating circuit; perform necessary action.	Ch. 18, p. 446–450 Description p. 452–457 Tests	
6. Perform charging circuit voltage drop tests; determine needed repairs.	7. Perform charging circuit voltage drop tests; determine necessary action.	Ch. 14, p. 350	Ch. 18, p. 214–216 General testing
7. Inspect, repair or replace connectors and wires of charging circuits.		Ch. 14, p. 357–358, 360–361 Service of wires and connectors	Ch. 18, p. 207–208
8. Remove, inspect, and replace generator (alternator).	5. Remove, inspect, and install generator (alternator).	Ch. 18, p. 439–445, 457–459	Ch. 18, p. 212–213
9. Disassemble, clean, inspect, test and replace generator (alternator) components.	6. Disassemble generator (alternator), clean, inspect, and test components; determine necessary action.	Ch. 18, p. 439–445 p. 452–459	Ch. 18, p. 217–221
E. LIGHTING SYSTEMS DIAGNOSIS AND REPAIR	**E. LIGHTING SYSTEMS DIAGNOSIS AND REPAIR**	Ch. 19	Ch. 19
1. HEADLIGHTS, PARKING LIGHTS, TAILLIGHTS, DASH LIGHTS AND COURTESY LIGHTS.			

ELECTRICAL/ ELECTRONIC SYSTEMS (TEST A6)	VI. ELECTRICAL/ ELECTRONIC SYSTEMS		
1. Diagnose the cause of brighter than normal, intermittent, dim or no operation of headlight.	E.1. Diagnose the cause of brighter than normal, intermittent, dim or no light operation; determine necessary action.	Ch. 19, p. 488–489	Ch. 19, p. 232
2. Inspect, replace and aim headlights/bulbs.	E.2. Inspect, replace and aim headlights and bulbs.	Ch. 19, p. 463–476	Ch. 19, p. 236–237 Aiming
3. Inspect, test and repair or replace headlight and dimmer switches, relays, control units, sensors, sockets, connectors and wires of headlight circuits.	A.10. Inspect and test switches, connectors, relays, and wires of electrical/electronic circuits; perform necessary action.	Ch. 19, p. 466–468 Description p. 482–483, 488–489 Service	Ch. 19, p. 234–235
	A.11. Repair wiring harnesses and connectors A.12. Perform solder repair of electrical wiring.		
4. Diagnose the cause of intermittent, slow or no operation of retractable headlight assembly.		Ch. 19, p. 469–470 Description	
5. Inspect, test and repair or replace motors, switches, relays, connectors, wires and controllers of retractable headlight assembly	A.10. Inspect and test switches, connectors, relays, and wires of electrical/electronic circuits; perform necessary action. A.11. Repair wiring harnesses and connectors A.12. Perform solder repair of electrical wiring.	Ch. 19, p. 488–489	
6. Diagnose the cause of brighter than normal intermittent, dim or no operation of parking lights and/or taillights.	E.1. Diagnose the cause of brighter than normal, intermittent, dim or no light operation; determine necessary action.	Ch. 19, p. 488–489	Ch. 19, p. 232–233
7. Inspect, test and repair or replace switches, relays, bulbs, sockets, connectors and wires of parking light and taillight circuits.	A.10. Inspect and test switches, connectors, relays, and wires of electrical/electronic circuits; perform necessary action. A.11. Repair wiring harnesses and connectors A.12. Perform solder repair of electrical wiring.	Ch. 19, p. 488–489	

ELECTRICAL/ ELECTRONIC SYSTEMS (TEST A6)	VI. ELECTRICAL/ ELECTRONIC SYSTEMS		
8. Diagnose the cause of intermittent, dim, no lights or no brightness control of instrument lighting circuits.	E.1. Diagnose the cause of brighter than normal, intermittent, dim or no light operation; determine necessary action.	Ch. 19, p. 488–489 Ch. 20, p. 494–495	Ch. 19, p. 230
9. Inspect, test and repair or replace switches, relays, bulbs, sockets, connectors, wires, controllers, and printed circuit boards of instrument lighting circuits.	A.10. Inspect and test switches, connectors, relays, and wires of electrical/ electronic circuits; perform necessary action. A.11. Repair wiring harnesses and connectors A.12. Perform solder repair of electrical wiring.	Ch. 14, p. 355–358	
10. Diagnose the cause of intermittent, dim or no operation of courtesy lights (dome, map, vanity).	E.1. Diagnose the cause of brighter than normal, intermittent, dim or no light operation; determine necessary action.	Ch. 19, p. 477–478, 488–489	Ch. 19, p. 230–231
11. Inspect, test and repair or replace switches, relays, bulbs, sockets, connectors, and wires of courtesy light (dome, map, vanity) circuits.	A.10. Inspect and test switches, connectors, relays, and wires of electrical/ electronic circuits; perform necessary action. A.11. Repair wiring harnesses and connectors A.12. Perform solder repair of electrical wiring.	Ch. 19, p. 488–489	
2. STOPLIGHTS, TURN SIGNALS, HAZARD LIGHTS AND BACK-UP LIGHTS			
1. Diagnose the cause intermittent, dim or no operation of stoplight (brake light).	E.1. Diagnose the cause of brighter than normal, intermittent, dim or no light operation; determine necessary action.	Ch. 19, p. 478, 481, 488–489	Ch. 19, p. 233
2. Inspect, test, adjust and repair or replace switch, bulbs, sockets, connectors and wires of stoplight circuits.	A.10. Inspect and test switches, connectors, relays, and wires of electrical/ electronic circuits; perform necessary action. A.11. Repair wiring harnesses and connectors A.12. Perform solder repair of electrical wiring.	Ch. 19, p. 488–489	Ch. 19, p. 238–239

ELECTRICAL/ ELECTRONIC SYSTEMS (TEST A6)	VI. ELECTRICAL/ ELECTRONIC SYSTEMS		
3. Diagnose the cause of no turn signal and/or hazard lights or lights with no flash on one or both sides.	E.3. Inspect and diagnose incorrect turn signal or hazard light operation; perform necessary action.	Ch. 19, p. 478–481, 488–489	Ch. 19, p. 230–231
4. Inspect, test and repair or replace switches, flasher units, bulbs, sockets, connectors and wires of turn signal and hazard light circuits.	E.3. Inspect and diagnose incorrect turn signal or hazard light operation; perform necessary action.	Ch. 19, p. 478–481	
5. Diagnose the cause of intermittent, dim or no operation of back-up light.	E.1. Diagnose the cause of brighter than normal, intermittent, dim or no light operation; determine necessary action.	Ch. 19, p. 486, 488–489	Ch. 19, p. 230
6. Inspect, test and repair or replace switch, bulbs, sockets, connectors and wires of back-up light circuits.	A.10. Inspect and test switches, connectors, relays, and wires of electrical/ electronic circuits; perform necessary action. A.11. Repair wiring harnesses and connectors A.12. Perform solder repair of electrical wiring.	Ch. 19, p. 488–489	
F. GAUGES, WARNING DEVICES, AND DRIVER INFORMATION SYSTEMS DIAGNOSIS AND REPAIR	F. GAUGES, WARNING DEVICES, AND DRIVER INFORMATION SYSTEMS DIAGNOSIS AND REPAIR	Ch. 20	Ch. 20
1. Diagnose the cause of intermittent, high, low or no gauge readings.	1. Inspect and test gauges and guage sending units for cause of intermittent, high, low, or no gauge readings; determine necessary action.	Ch. 20, p. 493–501, 504 Types of gauges & diagnostics	Ch. 20, p. 243–246
2. Inspect, test and repair or replace gauges, gauge sending units, connectors, wires and printed circuit boards of gauge circuits.	1. Inspect and test gauges and guage sending units for cause of intermittent, high, low, or no gauge readings; determine necessary action.	Ch. 20, p. 495–501 Types of gauges p. 502 Service	Ch. 20, p. 251–252 Temperature sending unit
	2. Inspect and test connectors, wires, and printed circuit boards of gauge circuits; determine necessary action.		
3. Diagnose the cause(s) of intermittent, high, low or no readings on electronic digital instrument clusters.		Ch. 20, p. 493–494, 504 General diagnostics	Ch. 20, p. 245–246

ELECTRICAL/ ELECTRONIC SYSTEMS (TEST A6)	VI. ELECTRICAL/ ELECTRONIC SYSTEMS		
4. Inspect, test, repair or replace sensors, sending units, connectors and wires of electronic instrument circuits.	4. Inspect and test sensors, connectors, and wires of electronic instrument circuits; determine necessary action.	Ch. 20, p. 502	
5. Diagnose the cause of constant, intermittent or no operation of warning lights, indicator lights and other driver information systems.	3. Diagnose the cause of incorrect operation of warning devices and other driver information systems; determine necessary action.	Ch. 20, p. 501–504 Types of warning devices	Ch. 20, p. 244–246
6. Inspect, test and repair or replace bulbs, sockets, connectors, wires, electronic components, and controllers of warning light, indicator light and driver information system circuits.	A.10. Inspect and test switches, connectors, relays, and wires of electrical/ electronic circuits; perform necessary action. A.11. Repair wiring harnesses and connectors A.12. Perform solder repair of electrical wiring.	Ch. 19, p. 474	
7. Diagnose the cause of constant, intermittent or no operation of audible warning devices.		Ch. 20, p. 504	
8. Inspect, test and repair or replace switches, relays, timers, electronic components, controllers, printed circuits, connectors and wires of audible warning device circuits.	A.10. Inspect and test switches, connectors, relays, and wires of electrical/ electronic circuits; perform necessary action. A.11. Repair wiring harnesses and connectors A.12. Perform solder repair of electrical wiring.	Ch. 20, p. 489–504	
G. HORN AND WIPER/ WASHER DIAGNOSIS AND REPAIR	G. HORN AND WIPER/ WASHER DIAGNOSIS AND REPAIR	Ch. 20	Ch. 20
1. Diagnose the cause of constant, intermittent or no operation of horn(s).	1. Diagnose incorrect horn operation; perform necessary action.	Ch. 20, p. 523 Description	Ch. 20, p. 250
2. Inspect, test and repair or replace horn(s), horn relay, horn button (switch), connectors and wires of horn circuits.		Ch. 20, p. 523	

ELECTRICAL/ ELECTRONIC SYSTEMS (TEST A6)	VI. ELECTRICAL/ ELECTRONIC SYSTEMS		
3. Diagnose the cause of wiper problems including constant operation, intermittent operation, poor speed control, no parking or no operation of wiper.	2. Diagnose incorrect wiper operation, diagnose wiper speed control and park problems; perform necessary action.	Ch. 20, p. 505–510 Description p. 511 Service	Ch. 20, p. 246–247
4. Inspect, test and replace intermittent (pulsing) wiper controls.	2. Diagnose incorrect wiper operation, diagnose wiper speed control and park problems; perform necessary action.	Ch. 20, p. 508–509	
5. Inspect, test and replace wiper motor, resistors, switches, relays, controllers, connections and wires of wiper circuits.		Ch. 20, p. 505–511	
6. Diagnose the cause of constant, intermittent or no operation of windshield washer.	3. Diagnose incorrect windshield washer operation; perform necessary action.	Ch. 20, p. 505–510 Description p. 511 Service	Ch. 20, p. 247
7. Inspect, test and repair or replace washer motor, pump assembly, relays, switches, connectors and wires of washer circuits.			
H. ACCESSORIES DIAGNOSIS AND REPAIR	**H. ACCESSORIES DIAGNOSIS AND REPAIR**	Chs. 20 & 43	Chs. 20 & 50
1. BODY			
1. Diagnose the cause of slow, intermittent or no operation of power side windows and power tailgate window.	1. Diagnose incorrect operation of motor-driven accessory circuits; determine necessary action.	Ch. 20, p. 512–515	Ch. 20, p. 247
2. Inspect, test, and repair or replace regulators (linkages), switches, controllers, relays, motors, connectors, and wires of power side window and power tailgate window circuits.		Ch. 20, p. 514	
3. Diagnose the cause of slow, intermittent or no operation of power seat and seat memory controls.	1. Diagnose incorrect operation of motor-driven accessory circuits; determine necessary action.	Ch. 20, p. 515–518	

ELECTRICAL/ ELECTRONIC SYSTEMS (TEST A6)	VI. ELECTRICAL/ ELECTRONIC SYSTEMS		
4. Inspect, test, and repair or replace power seat gearbox, cables, switches, controllers, sensors, relays, solenoids, motors, connectors, and wires of power seat circuits and memory controls.		Ch. 20, p. 515–517	
5. Diagnose the cause of slow, intermittent or no operation of rearwindow defogger.	2. Diagnose incorrect heated glass operation; determine necessary action.	Ch. 20, p. 519–521	Ch. 20, p. 248
6. Inspect, test, and repair or replace switches, relays, timers, controllers, window grid, connectors, and wires of rear window defogger circuits.		Ch. 20, p. 521	Ch. 20, p. 253
7. Diagnose the cause of slow, intermittent or no operation of electric door and hatch/trunk lock.	3. Diagnose incorrect lock operation; determine necessary action.	Ch. 20, p. 511–512 Description	Ch. 20, p. 248
8. Inspect, test, and repair or replace switches, relays, controllers, actuators/ solenoids, connectors, and wires of electric door lock circuits.		Ch. 20, p. 511–512	
9. Diagnose the cause of slow, intermittent or no operation of keyless and remote lock/unlock devices.		Ch. 50, p 1274, 1276 Description	
10. Inspect, test, and repair or replace components, connectors, controllers, and wires of keyless and remote lock/ unlock devices.		Ch. 50, p. 1274–1277	
11. Diagnose the cause of slow, intermittent or no operation of electrical sunroof and convertible top.		Ch. 20, p. 522–523	
12. Inspect, test, and repair or replace motors, switches, controllers, relays, connectors, and wires of electrically-operated sunroof and convertible tops.			

ELECTRICAL/ ELECTRONIC SYSTEMS (TEST A6)	VI. ELECTRICAL/ ELECTRONIC SYSTEMS		
13. Diagnose the cause of slow, intermittent or no operation of electrically operated/heated mirror.	2. Diagnose incorrect heated glass operation; determine necessary action.	Ch. 20, p. 519–520 Description	
14. Inspect, test, and repair or replace motors, heated mirror grids, switches, controllers, relays, connectors, and wires of electrically operated/heated mirror circuits.		Ch. 20, p. 518–520	
2. MISCELLANEOUS			
1. Diagnose the cause of radio static and weak, intermittent, or no radio reception.	1. Diagnose radio static and weak, intermittent, or no radio reception; determine necessary action.	Ch. 50, p. 1277–1279	Ch. 50, p. 640–641
2. Inspect, test, and repair or replace speakers, amplifiers, remote controls, antennas, leads, grounds, connectors, and wires of sound system circuits.		Ch. 50, p. 1279–1280	Ch. 50, p. 648–650 Identify static source
3. Inspect, test, and repair or replace switches, relays, motor, connectors, and wires of power antenna circuits.		Ch. 50, p. 1279–1280	
4. Inspect, test, and replace noise suppression components.		Ch. 50, p. 1279–1280	
5. Identify the component (unit) causing poor sound quality, noisy, erratic, intermittent or no operation of the audio system; remove and reinstall audio system component (unit).		Ch. 50, p. 1279–1280	Ch. 50, p. 641
6. Inspect, test, and repair or replace case, fuse, connectors, relays, and wires of cigar lighter circuits.		Ch. 20, p. 523–524 Briefly described	
7. Inspect, test, and repair or replace clock, connectors, and wires of clock circuits.		Ch. 20, p. 523 Briefly described	
8. Diagnose the cause of unregulated, intermittent, or no operation of cruise control.	4. Diagnose incorrect operation of cruise control systems; repair as needed.	Ch. 20, p. 524–527 Description	Ch. 20, p. 255–257 Road test

ELECTRICAL/ ELECTRONIC SYSTEMS (TEST A6)	VI. ELECTRICAL/ ELECTRONIC SYSTEMS		
9. Inspect, test, adjust, and repair or replace speedometer cables, regulator, servo, hoses, switches, relays, electronic controller, speed sensors, connectors, and wires of cruise control circuits.		Ch. 20, p. 526–528	
10. Diagnose the cause of false, intermittent, or no operation of anti-theft systems.		Ch. 50, p. 1274, 1276–1278 Description	
11. Inspect, test, and repair or replace components, controllers, switches, relays, connectors, sensors, and wires of anti-theft system circuits.		Ch. 50, p. 1274–1277	
12. Diagnose the cause(s) of the airbag warning light staying on or flashing.	5. Diagnose Supplemental Restraint System (SRS) concerns; determine necessary action. (Note: Follow manufacturer's safety procedures to prevent accidental deployment.)	Ch. 20, p. 501 Ch. 50, p. 1269–1270 Mentioned	
13. Inspect, test, and repair or replace the airbag(s), controller, sensors, connectors, and wires of the airbag system circuit(s).		Ch. 50, p. 1268–1274	
14. Diagnose the cause of improper operation of motorized seat belts.	1. Diagnose incorrect operation of motor-driven accessory circuits; determine necessary action.	Ch. 50, p. 1264–1268	
15. Inspect, test, and repair or replace motors, solenoids, switches, tracks, controllers, connectors and wires of motorized seatbelts.		Ch. 50, p. 1267	
HEATING AND AIR CONDITIONING (TEST A7)	VII. HEATING AND AIR CONDITIONING		
A. A/C SYSTEM DIAGNOSIS AND REPAIR	A. A/C SYSTEM DIAGNOSIS AND REPAIR E. REFRIGERANT RECOVERY, RECYCLING AND HANDLING	Chs. 48 & 49	Ch. 48/49

HEATING AND AIR CONDITIONING (TEST A7)	VII. HEATING AND AIR CONDITIONING		
1. Diagnose the cause of unusual operating noises of the A/C system; determine needed repairs.	A.1. Diagnose unusual operating noises in the A/C system; determine necessary action.	Ch. 48, p. 1233–1234 Description	
2. Identify system type and conduct performance test on the A/C system; determine needed repairs.	A.2. Identify refrigerant type; conduct a performance test of the A/C system; determine necessary action.	Ch. 49, p. 1258–1259	Ch. 48/49, p. 619–620, 628–629
3. Diagnose A/C system problems indicated by refrigerant flow past the sight glass (for systems using a sight glass); determine needed repairs.		Ch. 48, p. 1237	Ch. 48/49, p. 616, 625
4. Diagnose A/C system problems indicated by pressure gauge readings; determine needed repairs.		Ch. 49, p. 1250–1251	Ch. 48/49, p. 614, 616, 628–629
5. Diagnose A/C system problems indicated by sight, sound, smell and touch procedures; determine needed repairs.		Ch. 49, p. 1258–1259	
6. Leak test A/C system; determine needed repairs.	A.3. Leak test A/C system; determine necessary action.	Ch. 49, p. 1253–1254	
7. Identify and recover A/C system refrigerant.	E.2. Identify and recover (by label application or use of a refrigerant identifier) A/C system refrigerant.	Ch. 49, p. 1250, 1254–1255	Ch. 48/49, p. 632–633
8. Evacuate A/C system.	E.6. Evacuate and charge A/C system.	Ch. 49, p. 1255–1257	
9. Clean A/C system components and hoses.		Ch. 49, p. 11247–1248	
10. Charge A/C system with refrigerant (liquid or vapor).	E.6. Evacuate and charge A/C system.	Ch. 49, p. 1255–1257	
	A.4. Inspect the condition of discharged oil; determine necessary action.		
11. Identify lubricant type; inspect level in A/C system.	A.5. Select oil type; measure, and add oil to the A/C system as needed.	Ch. 49, p. 1255	
B. REFRIGERATION SYSTEM COMPONENT DIAGNOSIS AND REPAIR	B. REFRIGERATION SYSTEM COMPONENT DIAGNOSIS AND REPAIR	Chs. 48 & 49	Ch. 48/49
1. COMPRESSOR AND CLUTCH	1. COMPRESSOR AND CLUTCH		

HEATING AND AIR CONDITIONING (TEST A7)	VII. HEATING AND AIR CONDITIONING		
1. Diagnose A/C system problems that cause protection devices (pressure, thermal and PCM) to interrupt system operation; determine needed repairs.	1. Diagnose A/C system problems that cause the protection devices (pressure, thermal and PCM) to interrupt system operation; determine necessary action.	Ch. 48, p. 1238–1240 Description of controls	
2. Inspect, test and replace A/C system pressure and thermal protection devices.		Ch. 49, p. 1250–1251	
3. Inspect, adjust and replace A/C compressor drive belts, pulleys and tensioners.	2. Inspect A/C compressor drive belts; replace and adjust as necessary.		
4. Inspect, test, service and replace A/C compressor clutch components or assembly.	3. Inspect, test, and replace A/C compressor clutch components or assembly.	Ch. 48, p. 1233–1234 Description	Ch. 48/49, p. 630–631
5. Identify required lubricant type; inspect and correct level in A/C compressor.		Ch. 49, p. 1255	
6. Inspect, test, service or replace A/C compressor.	4. Remove and replace A/C compressor and mountings		
7. Inspect, repair or replace A/C compressor mounting.	4. Remove and replace A/C compressor and mountings.		
2. EVAPORATOR, CONDENSER, AND RELATED COMPONENTS	2. EVAPORATOR, CONDENSER, AND RELATED COMPONENTS		
1. Inspect, repair or replace A/C system mufflers, hoses, lines, filters, fittings and seals.	1. Determine need for A/C system filter; perform necessary action. 2. Remove and inspect A/C system mufflers, hoses, lines, fittings, o-rings, seals and service valves; perform necessary action.	Ch. 49, p. 1251–1253 Service valves Ch. 48, p. 1236–1237 Lines	Ch. 48/49, p. 624 Inspection
2. Inspect A/C condenser for air flow restrictions.	3. Inspect A/C condenser for air flow restrictions; perform necessary action.	Ch. 49, p. 1258–1259	Ch. 48/49, p. 625 Inspection
3. Inspect, test and replace A/C system condenser and mountings.		Ch. 48, p. 1234 Description	Ch. 48/49, p. 625 Inspection
4. Inspect and replace reciever/drier or accumulator/drier.	4. Remove and install reciever/drier or accumulator/drier.	Ch. 48, p. 1234–1235 Description Ch. 49, p. 1247–1248 Maintenance	Ch. 48/49, p. 625 Inspection

HEATING AND AIR CONDITIONING (TEST A7)	VII. HEATING AND AIR CONDITIONING		
5. Inspect, test and replace expansion valve(s).	5. Remove and install expansion valve or orifice (expansion) tube.	Ch. 48, p. 1235–1236 Description	Ch. 48/49, p. 626 Inspection
6. Inspect and replace orifice tube(s).	5. Remove and install expansion valve or orifice (expansion) tube.	Ch. 48, p. 1235–1236 Description	Ch. 48/49, p. 626 Inspection
7. Inspect, test or replace evaporator(s).		Ch. 48, p. 1236 Description	
8. Inspect, clean and repair evaporator, housing and water drain.	6. Inspect evaporator housing water drain; perform necessary action.		
9. Inspect, test and replace evaporator pressure/temperature control systems and devices.		Ch. 42, p. 1238 Description	
10. Identify, inspect and replace A/C system service alves (gauge connections).		Ch. 49, p. 1251–1253	
11. Inspect and replace A/C system high pressure relief device.		Ch. 48, p. 1240 Mentioned	
C. HEATING AND ENGINE COOLING SYSTEMS DIAGNOSIS AND REPAIR.	C. HEATING, VENTILATION, AND ENGINE COOLING SYSTEMS DIAGNOSIS AND REPAIR.	Chs. 11, 48 & 49	Chs. 11 & 48/49
1. Diagnose the cause of temperature control problems in the heater/ventilation system; determine needed repairs.	1. Diagnose temperature control problems in the heater/ventilation system; determine necessary action.	Ch. 49, p. 1260	Ch. 48/49, p. 612–613, 617
2. Diagnose window fogging problems; determine needed repairs.			
3. Perform cooling system tests; determine needed repairs.	2. Perform cooling system, cap, and recovery system tests (pressure, combustion leakage, and temperature); determine necessary action.	Ch. 11, p. 269–270	Ch. 11, p. 136–139
4. Inspect and replace engine cooling and heater system hoses.	3. Inspect engine cooling and heater system hoses and belts; perform necessary action.	Ch. 11, p. 263–264, 271–272	Ch. 11, p. 138 Inspection
5. Inspect, test and replace radiator, pressure cap, coolant recovery system and water pump.	2. Perform cooling system, cap, and recovery system tests (pressure, combustion leakage, and temperature); determine necessary action.	Ch. 11, p. 260–262, 269–273	

HEADING AND AIR CONDITIONING (TEST A7)	VII. HEATING AND AIR CONDITIONING		
6. Inspect, test and replace thermostat, bypass and housing.	1. Inspect, test and replace thermostat and housing.	Ch. 11, p. 264–265, 270–271	
7. Identify, inspect, recover coolant; flush and refill system with proper coolant.	5. Determine coolant condition; drain and recover coolant. 6. Flush system; refill system with recommended coolant; bleed system.	Ch. 11, p. 274–275	
8. Inspect, test and replace fan (both electrical and mechanical), fan clutch, fan belts, fan shrouds, and air dams.	7. Inspect, test and replace fan, fan clutch (electrical and mechanical), fan shroud, and air dams; perform necessary action.	Ch. 11, p. 273–274	Ch. 11, p. 136–137
9. Inspect, test and replace heater coolant control valve (manual, vacuum and electrical types).	9. Inspect and test heater control valve(s); perform necessary action.	Ch. 48, p. 1227 Description	
10. Inspect, flush and replace heater core.		Ch. 48, p. 1227	
D. OPERATING SYSTEMS AND RELATED CONTROLS DIAGNOSIS AND REPAIR	D. OPERATING SYSTEMS AND RELATED CONTROLS DIAGNOSIS AND REPAIR	Chs. 48 & 49	
1. ELECTRICAL			
1. Diagnose the cause of failures in the electrical control system of heating, ventilating and A/C systems; determine needed repairs.	D.1. Diagnose failures in the electrical control system of heating, ventilating and A/C systems; determine necessary action.	Ch. 49, p. 1259–1260	
2. Inspect, test, repair and replace A/C-heater blower motors, resistors, switches, relay/modules, wiring and protection devices.	D.2. Inspect and test A/C-heater blower motors, resistors, switches, relay, wiring and protection devices; perform necessary action.	Ch. 48, p.1227–1228, 1237–1242 Description Ch. 49, p. 1259–1260	
3. Inspect, test, repair and replace A/C compressor clutch coil, relay/modules, wiring, sensors, switches, diodes and protection devices.		Ch. 49, p. 1259	
4. Inspect, test, repair, replace and adjust A/C-related engine control systems.		Ch. 31, p. 771	

HEATING AND AIR CONDITIONING (TEST A7)	VII. HEATING AND AIR CONDITIONING		
5. Inspect, test, repair, replace and adjust load sensitive A/C compressor cut-off systems.	D.3. Test A/C compressor load cut-off systems; determine necessary action.	Ch. 49, p. 1238–1240 Description	
6. Inspect, test, repair and replace engine cooling/condenser fan motors, relays/modules, switches, sensors, wiring and protection devices.	C.8. Inspect and test electrical fan control system and circuits.	Ch. 11, p. 266–267 Description p. 273 Inspection	
7. Inspect, test, adjust, repair and replace electric actuator motors, relays/ modules, switches, sensors, wiring and protection devices.		Ch. 32, p. 835–837	
8. Inspect, test, service or replace heating, ventilating and A/C control panel assemblies.	D.5. Inspect and test A/C-heater control panel assembly; determine necessary action.	Ch. 48, p. 1240–1242	
2. VACUUM/ MECHANICAL			
1. Diagnose the cause of failures in the vacuum and mechanical switches and controls of the heating, ventilating and A/C systems; determine needed repairs.	D.1. Diagnose failures in the vacuum and mechanical components and controls of the heating, ventilation and A/C (HVAC) system; determine necessary action.	Ch. 48, p. 1237–1240 Description	
2. Inspect, test, service or replace heating, ventilating and A/C control panel assemblies.	D.5. Inspect and test A/C-heater control panel assembly; determine necessary action.	Ch. 48, p. 1240–1242 Description	
3. Inspect, test, adjust and replace heating, ventilating and A/C control cables and linkages.	D.6. Inspect and test A/C-heater control cables and linkages; perform necessary action.	Ch. 48, p. 1227, 1243	
4. Inspect, test and replace heating, ventilating and A/C vacuum actuators (diaphragms/motors) and hoses.	D.7. Inspect and test A/C-heater ducts, doors, hoses, and outlets; perform necessary action.	Ch. 48, p. 1227–1229	
5. Identify, inspect, test and replace heating, ventilating and A/C vacuum reservoir, check valve and restrictors.		Ch. 48, p. 1227–1229	
6. Inspect, test, adjust, repair or replace heating, ventilating and A/C ducts, doors and outlets.	D.7. Inspect and test A/C-heater ducts, doors, hoses, and outlets; perform necessary action	Ch. 48, p. 1228–1229, 1242–1243 Ch. 49, p. 1260	

HEADING AND AIR CONDITIONING (TEST A7)	VII. HEATING AND AIR CONDITIONING		
3. AUTOMATIC AND SEMI-AUTOMATIC HEATING, VENTILATING AND A/C SYSTEMS		Ch. 48	Ch. 48/49
1. Diagnose temperature control system problems; determine needed repairs.	D.8. Check operation of automatic and semi-automatic heating, ventilation, and air-conditioning (HVAC) control systems; determine necessary action.	Ch. 48, p. 1240–1242	
2. Diagnose blower system problems; determine needed repairs.		Ch. 48, p. 1227–1229, 1243	Ch. 48/49, p. 613, 614 General diagnostics
3. Diagnose air distribution problems; determine needed repairs.		Ch. 48, p. 1228, 1242–1243	
4. Diagnose compressor clutch control system; determine needed repairs.		Ch. 48, p. 1238–1240	
5. Inspect, test, adjust or replace climate control and sun-load sensors.		Ch. 48, p. 1240–1242	
6. Inspect, test, adjust and replace temperature blend door actuator(s).		Ch. 48, p. 1228 Description	
7. Inspect, test and replace low engine coolant temperature blower control system.		Ch. 11, p. 266	
8. Inspect, test and replace heater water valve and controls.		Ch. 48, p. 1226–1227 Ch. 49, p. 1260	
9. Inspect, test and replace electric and vacuum motors, solenoids and switches.		Ch. 14, p. 354–358 Ch. 32, p. 820–836	
10. Inspect, test and replace ATC panel.		Ch. 48, p. 1240–1242 Description	
11. Inspect, test, adjust or replace ATC-microprocessor (climate control computer/progammer).		Ch. 48, p. 1240–1242 Description	
12. Check and adjust calibration of ATC system.		Ch. 48, p. 1240–1242 Description	
E. REFRIGERANT RECOVERY, RECYCLING, HANDLING AND RETROFIT	E. REFRIGERANT RECOVERY, RECYCLING, AND HANDLING	Ch. 49	Ch. 48/49

HEATING AND AIR CONDITIONING (TEST A7)	VII. HEATING AND AIR CONDITIONING		
1. Maintain and verify correct operation of certified equipment.	1. Verify correct operation and maintenance of refrigerant handling equipment.	Ch. 49, p. 1248–1249	
2. Identify and recover A/C system refrigerant.	2. Identify (by label application or use of a refrigerant identifier) and recover A/C system refrigerant.	Ch. 49, p. 1254–1255	Ch. 48/49, p. 632–633
3. Recycle or properly dispose of refrigerant.	3. Recycle refrigerant.	Ch. 49, p. 1254–1255	Ch. 48/49, p. 634
4. Label and store refrigerant.	4. Label and store refrigerant.	Ch. 49, p. 1248–1249, 1254–1255	Ch. 48/49, p. 634
5. Test recycled refrigerant for non-condensable gases.	5. Test recycled refrigerant for non-condensable gases.	Ch. 49, p. 1254	
6. Follow Federal and local guidelines for retrofit procedures		Ch. 49, p. 1249	
ENGINE PERFORMANCE (A8)	VII. ENGINE PERFORMANCE		
A. GENERAL ENGINE DIAGNOSIS	A. GENERAL ENGINE DIAGNOSIS F. ENGINE RELATED SERVICES	Chs. 5, 6, 12, 22, 23 & 30	Chs. 3, 4, 5, 6, 11, 12, 13 & 21/22
1. Verify driver's complaint, perform visual inspection, and/or road test vehicle; determine needed action.	A.1. Interpret and verify concern; determine necessary action.	Ch. 6, p. 146–148 Ch. 12, p. 286 Case Studies at the end of chapters.	
	A.2. Inspect engine assembly for fuel, oil, coolant, and other leaks, determine necessary action.	No separate section on leak detection. Specific types of leaks (i.e. fuel) are found in the appropriate chapters.	Ch. 11, p. 126, 138–139
2. Research applicable vehicle information, such as engine management system operation, vehicle service history, service precautions, and technical service bulletins.	B.7. Access and use electronic service information (ESI). B.8. Locate and interpret vehicle and major component identification numbers (VIN, vehicle certification labels, and calibration decals).	Ch. 4, p. 91–93 Plus, specific system, part or calibration decals, labels, and/or numbers are found in the appropriate chapters.	Ch. 4, p. 33–34 Ch. 6, p. 55 Appendix
3. Diagnose the cause of unusual engine noise and/or vibration problems; determine needed action.	A.3. Diagnose unusual engine noise or vibration concerns; determine necessary action.	Ch. 6, p. 146–148	Ch. 11, p. 130 Ch. 12, p. 144

ENGINE PERFORMANCE (A8)	VII. ENGINE PERFORMANCE		
4. Diagnose the cause of unusual exhaust color, odor and sound; determine needed action.	A.4. Diagnose unusual exhaust color, odor and sound; determine necessary action.	Ch. 23, p. 613	
5. Perform engine manifold vacuum or pressure tests; determine needed action.	A.5. Perform engine absolute (vacuum/boost) manifold pressure tests; determine necessary action.	Ch. 5, p. 115, 118–120 Ch. 30, p. 753–754	Ch. 12, p. 146
6. Perform cylinder power balance test; determine needed action.	A.6. Perform cylinder power balance test; determine necessary action.	Ch. 5, p. 115, 118	
7. Perform cylinder cranking compression test; determine needed action.	A.7. Perform cylinder compression test; determine necessary action.	Ch. 5, p.113–114, 117–118	Ch. 6, p. 56–57
8. Perform cylinder leakage test; determine needed action.	A.8. Perform cylinder leakage test; determine necessary action.	Ch. 5, p. 114	Ch. 6, p. 58–60
9. Diagnose engine mechanical, electrical, electronic, fuel and ignition problems with an oscilloscope and/or engine analyzer; determine needed action.	A.9. Diagnose engine mechanical, electrical, electronic, fuel, and ignition concerns with an oscilloscope and engine diagnostic equipment; determine necessary action.	Ch. 5, p. 100–125 Diagnostic equipment Ch. 22, p. 577–585 Oscilliscope testing	Ch. 21/22, p. 270–271 Scope testing of ignition system
10. Prepare and inspect vehicle and analyzer for exhaust gas analysis; interpret HC and CO exhaust gas readings	A.10. Prepare 4 or 5 gas analyzer; inspect and prepare vehicle for test, and obtain exhaust readings; interpret readings, and determine necessary action.	Ch. 5, p. 122–123 Description Ch. 30, p. 746–751	Ch. 5, p. 49–50
11. Verify correct valve adjustment on engines with mechanical or hydraulic lifters.	F.1. Adjust valves on engines with mechanical or hydraulic lifters.	Ch. 10, p. 234–235	Ch. 13, p. 153–154
12. Verify correct camshaft timing; determine needed action.	F.2. Verify correct camshaft timing; determine necessary action.	Ch. 10, p. 235–236	
13. Verify proper engine operating temperature, check coolant level and condition, perform cooling system pressure test; determine needed repairs.	F.3. Verify proper engine operating temperature; determine necessary action. F.4. Perform cooling system pressure tests; check coolant condition; inspect and test radiator, pressure cap, coolant recovery tank, and hoses; perform necessary action.	Ch. 11, p. 274–275	Ch. 3, p. 17 Ch. 11, p. 138–139

ENGINE PERFORMANCE (A8)	VII. ENGINE PERFORMANCE		
	F.5. Inspect and test thermostat, by-pass, and housing; perform necessary action.	Ch. 11, p. 264–265 Description p. 270–272	
14. Inspect, test, and replace mechanical/ electrical fans, fan clutch, fan shroud/ducting, and fan control devices.	F.6. Inspect and test mechanical/electrical fans, fan clutch, fan shroud/ ducting, air dams, and fan control devices; perform necessary action.	Ch. 11, p. 273	Ch. 11, p. 136–137
B. IGNITION SYSTEM DIAGNOSIS AND REPAIR	**C. IGNITION SYSTEM DIAGNOSIS AND REPAIR**	Chs. 21 & 22	Ch. 21/22
1. Diagnose ignition- related problems such as no-starting, hard starting, engine misfire, poor driveability, spark knock, power loss, poor mileage and emissions problems on vehicles with distributor and distributorless ignition systems; determine needed repairs.	1. Diagnose no-starting, driveability, and emissions concerns on vehicles with electronic ignition (EI/DIS) (distributorless) systems; determine necessary action. 2. Diagnose no-starting, driveability, and emissions concerns on vehicles with distributor ignition (DI) systems; determine necessary action.	Ch. 22, p. 568–569, 573–575	
2. Check for possible ignition system related diagnostic trouble codes (DTC).		Ch. 32, p. 798–809, 813	
3. Inspect, test, repair or replace ignition primary circuit wiring and components.	3. Inspect and test ignition primary circuit wiring and components; perform necessary action.	Ch. 21, p. 535–539 Description Ch. 22, p. 569–573	Ch. 21/22, p. 272–277
4. Inspect, test and service distributor.	4. Inspect and test distributor; perform necessary action.	Ch. 22, p. 594–598	
5. Inspect, test, service, repair or replace ignition system secondary circuit wiring and components.	5. Inspect and test ignition system secondary circuit wiring and components; perform necessary action.	Ch. 21, p. 535–539 Description Ch. 22, p. 598–603	Ch. 21/22, p. 277
6. Inspect, test and replace ignition coil(s).	6. Inspect, test and replace ignition coil(s); perform necessary action.	Ch. 21, p. 535–540 Description Ch. 22, p. 580, 582–583, 589–590	Ch. 21/22, p. 272–273 Inspection
7. Check and adjust if necessary, ignition system timing and timing advance/retard.	7. Check and adjust (where applicable) ignition system timing and timing advance/retard.	Ch. 21, p. 548–549 Description Ch. 22, p. 585–587	Ch. 21/22, p. 279–280

ENGINE PERFORMANCE (A8)	VII. ENGINE PERFORMANCE		
8. Inspect, test and replace ignition system pick-up sensor or triggering devices.	8. Inspect and test ignition system pick-up sensor or triggering devices; perform necessary action.	Ch. 22, p. 571	Ch. 21/22, p. 275–276 Inspection
9. Inspect, test and replace ignition control module.	9. Inspect and test ignition control module; perform necessary action.	Ch. 22, p. 571	Ch. 21/22, p. 277 Inspection
C. FUEL, AIR INDUCTION AND EXHAUST SYSTEM DIAGNOSIS AND REPAIR	**C. FUEL, AIR INDUCTION AND EXHAUST SYSTEM DIAGNOSIS AND REPAIR**	Chs. 12, 24, 25, 26, 27, 28	Chs. 12, 23/24, 25/26, 27/28 & 29/30
1. Diagnose fuel system related problems, including hot or cold no-starting, hard starting, poor driveability, incorrect idle speed, poor idle, flooding, hesitation, surging, engine misfire, power loss, stalling, poor mileage, dieseling and emissions problems on vehicles with injection-type or carburetor-type fuel systems; determine needed action.	1. Diagnose hot or cold no-starting, hard starting, poor driveability, incorrect idle speed, poor idle, flooding, hesitation, surging, engine misfire, power loss, stalling, poor mileage, dieseling and emissions problems on vehicles with carburetor-type fuel systems; determine necessary action.

2. Diagnose hot or cold no-starting, hard starting, poor driveability, incorrect idle speed, poor idle, flooding, hesitation, surging, engine misfire, power loss, stalling, poor mileage, dieseling and emissions problems on vehicles with injection-type fuel systems; determine necessary action. | Ch. 12, p. 286–287 Vacuum system

Ch. 24, p. 646–647 Ch. 26, p. 664–665 Ch. 26, p. 666–667 | Ch. 23/24, p. 286

Ch. 27/28, p. 310–313 Fuel injection |
	4. Check fuel for contaminants and quality; determine necessary action.	Ch. 24, p. 632–633	
2. Check for possible fuel or induction system related diagnostic trouble codes (DTCs).		Ch. 26, p. 614 Ch. 28, p. 702	
3. Perform fuel system pressure, volume, or fuel pump current draw tests; determine needed action.		Ch. 24, p. 633–634, 643–645 Fuel pressure test	Ch. 23/24, p. 290–291

ENGINE PERFORMANCE (A8)	VII. ENGINE PERFORMANCE		
4. Inspect fuel tank, filler neck and gas cap; inspect and replace fuel lines, fittings and hoses; check fuel for contaminants and quality.	3. Inspect fuel tank and fuel cap, fuel lines, fittings, and hoses; perform necessary action.	Ch. 24, p. 634–640	
5. Inspect, test and replace mechanical and electrical fuel pumps and pump control systems; inspect, service and replace fuel filters.	5. Inspect and test mechanical and electrical fuel pumps and pump control systems; perform necessary action. 6. Replace fuel filters.	Ch. 24, p. 641–649	
6. Inspect, test and repair or replace fuel pressure regulation system and components of injection-type fuel systems.	7. Inspect and test fuel pressure regulation system and components of injection-type fuel systems; perform necessary action.	Ch. 27, p. 689–693 Description Ch. 28, p. 706, 716	
7. Inspect, test, adjust and repair or replace cold enrichment, acceleration enrichment, and deceleration fuel reduction or shut-off components.	8. Inspect and test cold enrichment system and components; perform necessary action.	Ch. 28, p. 716–720	
8. Remove, clean, and replace throttle body; make related adjustments.	9. Remove, service, and install throttle body; adjust related linkages.	Ch. 28, p. 705–706	
9. Inspect, test, clean and replace fuel injectors.	10. Inspect, test, and clean fuel injectors.	Ch. 28, p. 706–717	Ch. 27/28, p. 308–309, 316–319
10. Inspect, service and repair or replace air filtration system components.	11. Inspect throttle body mounting plates, air induction and filtration system, intake manifold, and gaskets; perform necessary action.	Ch. 12, p. 279–282	
11. Inspect throttle body, air induction system, intake manifold and gaskets for vacuum leaks/unmetered air.	11. Inspect throttle body mounting plates, air induction and filtration system, intake manifold, and gaskets; perform necessary action.	Ch. 12, p. 279–287 Air induction & intake manifold Ch. 28, p. 704	
12. Check/adjust idle speed and fuel mixture where applicable.	12. Check idle speed and fuel mixture. 13. Adjust idle speed and fuel mixture.	Ch. 26, p. 664–666 Ch. 25, p. 717–720	

ENGINE PERFORMANCE (A8)	VII. ENGINE PERFORMANCE		
13. Remove, clean, inspect, test, and repair or replace fuel system vacuum and electrical components and connections.	14. Remove, inspect, and test vacuum and electrical circuits, components and and connections of fuel system; perform necessary action.	Ch. 23, p. 643–649 Electric fuel pump	
14. Inspect, service and replace exhaust manifold, exhaust pipes, mufflers, resonators, catalytic converters, tail pipes and heat shields.	15. Inspect exhaust manifold, exhaust pipes, muffler(s), catalytic converter(s), resonator(s), tail pipe(s), and heat shield(s) ; perform necessary action.	Ch. 12, p. 288–296	Ch. 12, p. 144–146 Ch. 29/30, p. 338–340
15. Perform exhaust system back-pressure test; determine needed action.	16. Perform exhaust system back-pressure test; determine necessary action.	Ch. 12, p. 289–292	
16. Inspect, test, clean and repair or replace turbocharger/supercharger and system components.	17. Test the operation of turbocharger/supercharger systems; determine necessary action.	Ch. 12, p. 296–302	
D. EMISSIONS CONTROL SYSTEMS DIAGNOSIS AND REPAIR	E. EMISSIONS CONTROL SYSTEMS DIAGNOSIS AND REPAIR	Chs. 12 & 30	Ch. 29/30
1. POSITIVE CRANKCASE VENTILATION	1. POSITIVE CRANKCASE VENTILATION		
1. Test and diagnose emissions or driveability problems caused by positive crankcase (PCV) system.	1. Diagnose oil leaks, emissions, and driveability problems resulting from failure of the positive crankcase ventilation (PCV) system; determine necessary action.	Ch. 30, p. 751–753	Ch. 29/30, p. 325–328
2. Inspect, service and replace PCV filter/ breather cap, valve, tubes, orifices and hoses.	2. Inspect and test positive crankcase ventilation (PCV) filter/ breather cap, valve, tubes, orifices and hoses; perform necessary action.	Ch. 30, p. 751–753	Ch. 29/30, p. 333–334
2. EXHAUST GAS RECIRCULATION	2. EXHAUST GAS RECIRCULATION		
1. Test and diagnose emissions or driveability problems caused by the exhaust gas recirculation (EGR) system.	1. Diagnose emissions and driveability problems caused by failure of the exhaust gas recirculation (EGR) system; determine necessary action.	Ch. 30, p. 753–757	Ch. 29/30, p. 328–329
2. Check for possible exhaust gas recirculation (EGR) related diagnostic trouble codes (DTCs).		Ch. 30, p. 757	

ENGINE PERFORMANCE (A8)	VII. ENGINE PERFORMANCE		
	2. Inspect and test valve, valve manifold, and exhaust passages of exhaust gas recirculation (EGR) systems; perform necessary action.	Ch. 30, p. 753–756	Ch. 29/30, p. 335–337
3. Inspect, test, service and replace components of the EGR system, including EGR tubing, exhaust passages, vacuum pressure controls, filters, hoses, electrical/electronic, sensors, controls, solenoids and wiring of exhaust gas recirculation (EGR) systems.	3. Inspect and test vacuum/pressure controls, filters, and hoses of exhaust gas recirculation (EGR) systems; perform necessary action. 4. Inspect and test electrical/electronic sensors, controls, and wiring of exhaust gas recirculation (EGR) systems; perform necessary action.	Ch. 30, p. 753–757	Ch. 29/30, p. 335–337
3. EXHAUST GAS TREATMENT	3. EXHAUST GAS TREATMENT		
1. Test and diagnose emissions or driveability problems caused by the secondary air injection or catalytic converter system.	1. Diagnose emissions and driveability problems resulting from the failure of the secondary air injection and catalytic converter system; determine necessary action.	Ch. 30, p. 759–763	
2. Check for possible secondary air injection system or catalytic converter related diagnostic trouble codes.		Ch. 12, p. 289–290 Ch. 30, p. 762	
3. Inspect, test, service and replace mechanical components and electrical/electronically-operated components and circuits of secondary air injection systems.	2. Inspect and test mechanical components of secondary air injection systems; perform necessary action. 3. Inspect and test electrical/electronically-operated components and circuits of secondary air injection systems; perform necessary action.	Ch.30, p. 761–763	
4. Inspect and test the catalytic converter(s).	4. Inspect and test components of the catalytic converter systems; perform necessary action.	Ch. 12, p. 292 Ch. 30, p. 759–761	Ch. 29/30, p. 338–340

ENGINE PERFORMANCE (A8)	VII. ENGINE PERFORMANCE		
	4. INTAKE AIR TEMPERATURE CONTROLS	Ch. 29, p. 738 Description	
	1. Diagnose emissions and driveability problems resulting from failure of the intake air temperature control system; determine necessary action.	Ch. 12, p. 282–284	
	2. Inspect and test components of intake air temperature control system; perform necessary action.	Ch. 30, p. 759	
	5. EARLY FUEL EVAPORATION (INTAKE MANIFOLD TEMPERATURE) CONTROLS	Ch. 29, p. 738 Description	
	1. Diagnose emissions and driveability problems resulting from failure of early fuel evaporation control system; determine necessary action.	Ch. 12, p. 286	
	2. Inspect and test components of early fuel evaporation control system; perform necessary action.	Ch. 12, p. 286	
4. EVAPORATIVE EMISSIONS CONTROLS	6. EVAPORATIVE EMISSIONS CONTROLS		
1. Test and diagnose emissions or driveability problems caused by the evaporative emissions control system.	1. Diagnose emissions or driveability problems resulting from failure of evaporative emissions control system; determine necessary action.	Ch. 30, p. 763–765	
2. Check for possible evaporative emissions related diagnostic trouble codes (DTCs).		Ch. 30, p. 764	
3. Inspect, test, and replace mechanical and electrical components and hoses of evaporative emissions control systems.	3. Inspect and test components and hoses of evaporative emissions control systems; perform necessary action.	Ch. 30, p. 763–765	
E. COMPUTERIZED ENGINE CONTROLS DIAGNOSIS AND REPAIR	B. COMPUTERIZED ENGINE CONTROLS DIAGNOSIS AND REPAIR	Chs. 14, 22 & 32	Ch. 31/32

ENGINE PERFORMANCE (A8)	VII. ENGINE PERFORMANCE		
1. Retrieve and record stored diagnostic trouble codes.	1. Retrieve and record stored OBD I diagnostic trouble codes; clear codes. 2. Retrieve and record stored OBD II diagnostic trouble codes; clear codes.	Ch. 32, p. 798–814	Ch. 31/32, p. 350–351
2. Diagnose the causes of emissions or driveability problems resulting from failure of computerized engine controls with stored diagnostic trouble codes.	3. Diagnose the causes of emissions or driveability concerns resulting from failure of computerized engine controls with stored diagnostic trouble codes.	Ch. 32, p. 796–837	
3. Diagnose the causes of emissions or driveability problems resulting from failure of computerized engine controls with no stored diagnostic trouble codes.	4. Diagnose emissions or driveability concerns resulting from failure of computerized engine controls with no stored diagnostic trouble codes.	Ch. 32, p. 796–798	
4. Use a scan tool or digital multimeter (DMM) to inspect, test, and adjust, computerized engine control system sensors, actuators, circuits, and powertrain control module(PCM).	5. Inspect and test computerized engine control system sensors, powertrain control module (PCM), actuators, and circuits; perform necessary action. 6. Obtain and interpret digital multimeter (DMM) readings.	Ch. 32, p. 799–801, 806–807, 809–837	Ch. 5, p. 45–46 Use of a DMM Ch. 29/30, p. 348–349, 352–366
5. Measure and interpret voltage, voltage drop amperage, and resistance using digital, multimeter (DMM) readings.	6. Obtain and interpret digital multimeter (DMM) readings.	Ch. 32, p. 806–807, 817–834	Ch. 29/30, p. 352–361
6. Test, remove, inspect, clean, service and repair or replace power and ground distribution circuits and connections.	9. Inspect and test power and ground circuits and connections; service or replace as needed.	Ch. 14, p. 345–358 Electricity basics Ch. 22, p. 569–570 Ignition systems	
7. Practice recommended precautions when handling static sensitive devices and/or replacing the powertrain control module (PCM).	10. Practice recommended precautions when handling static sensitive devices.	Ch. 32, p. 795–796	Ch. 29/30, p. 345–346

ENGINE PERFORMANCE (A8)	VII. ENGINE PERFORMANCE		
8. Diagnose driveability and emissions problems resulting from failures of interrelated systems (cruise control, security alarms, torque controls, suspension controls, traction controls, torque management, A/C, non-OEM installed accessories, and similar systems).	11. Diagnose driveability and emissions problems resulting from failures of interrelated systems (cruise control, security alarms, suspension controls, traction controls, A/C, automatic transmissions, non-OEM-installed accessories, and similar systems); determine necessary action.	Ch. 31, p. 771–776 Description p. 778	
9. Diagnose the causes of emissions or driveability problems resulting from computerized spark timing controls; determine needed repairs.		Ch. 22, p. 584–585	
10. Verify, repair, and clear diagnostic trouble codes (DTCs).	1. Retrieve and record stored OBD I diagnostic trouble codes; clear codes. 2. Retrieve and record stored OBD II diagnostic trouble codes; clear codes.	Ch. 32, p. 817	
F. ENGINES ELECTRICAL SYSTEMS DIAGNOSIS AND REPAIR	VI. ELECTRICAL ELECTRONIC SYSTEMS	Chs. 16, 17 & 18	Chs. 16, 17, 18
1. BATTERY	B. BATTERY		
1. Test and diagnose emissions or driveablility problems caused by battery condition and connections.		Ch. 16, p. 410 Case study	
2. Test and diagnose the cause(s) of abnormal key-off battery drain; determine needed repairs.		Ch. 16, p. 410	Ch. 16, p. 184
2. STARTING SYSTEM	C. STARTING SYSTEM		
1. Perform starter current draw test; determine needed action.	1. Perform starter current draw test; determine necessary action.	Ch. 17, p. 425	Ch. 17, p. 199–200
2. Perform starter circuit voltage drop tests; determine needed action.	2. Perform starter circuit voltage drop tests; determine necessary action.	Ch. 17, p. 427–429	Ch. 17, p. 199–200
3. Inspect, test, and repair or replace components and wires in the starter control circuit.	6. Inspect and test switches, connectors, and wires of starter control system.	Ch. 17, p. 423 Description p. 427 Tests	

ENGINE PERFORMANCE (A8)	VII. ENGINE PERFORMANCE		
3. CHARGING SYSTEM	D. CHARGING SYSTEM		
1. Test and diagnose charging system problems that cause an undercharge, overcharge or no-charge condition, or engine performance problems; determine needed action.	2. Diagnose charging system for the causes of undercharge, no-charge or overcharge conditions.	Ch. 18, p. 451–457	
2. Inspect, adjust and replace alternator (generator) drive belts, pulleys and fans.	3. Inspect and adjust generator (alternator) drive belts; replace as needed.	Ch. 18, p. 451–452, 454–455	Ch. 18, p. 209–210
3. Inspect, test, and repair or replace charging circuit connectors and wires.		Ch. 18, p. 451–457 Inspection and testing	Ch. 18, p. 207 Inspection

53. *Celestial Navigation.* Briefly discuss how you think the benefits and problems of celestial navigation might have affected ancient sailors. For example, how did they benefit from using the north celestial pole to tell directions, and what problems did they experience because of the difficulty in determining longitude? Can you explain why ancient sailors generally hugged coastlines as much as possible on their voyages? What dangers did this type of sailing pose? Why did the Polynesians become the best navigators of their time?

Web Projects

54. *Sundials.* Although they are no longer necessary for timekeeping, sundials remain popular for their cultural and artistic value. Search the Web for pictures and information about sundials around the world. Write a short report about three sundials that you find particularly interesting.

55. *Calendar History.* Investigate the history of the Julian or Gregorian calendar in greater detail. Write a short summary of an interesting aspect of the history you learn from your Web research. (For example, why did Julius Caesar allow one year to have 445 days? How did our months end up with 28, 30, or 31 days?)

56. *Global Positioning System.* Learn more about the global positioning system and its uses. Write a short report summarizing how new uses of GPS may affect our lives over the next 10 years.

Our perspective on the universe has changed dramatically throughout human history. This timeline summarizes some of the key discoveries that have shaped our modern perspective.

Stonehenge

Earth-centered model of the universe

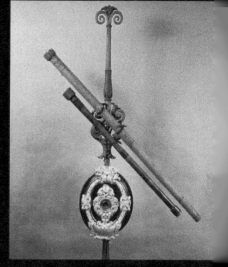

Galileo's telescope

| < 2500 B.C. | 400 B.C. –170 A.D. | 1543–1648 A.D. |

(1) Ancient civilizations recognized patterns in the motion of the Sun, Moon, planets, and stars through our sky. They also noticed connections between what they saw in the sky and our lives on Earth, such as the cycles of seasons and of tides [Section 3.1].

(2) The ancient Greeks tried to explain observed motions of the Sun, Moon, and planets using a model with Earth at the center, surrounded by spheres in the heavens. The model explained many phenomena well, but could explain the apparent retrograde motion of the planets only with the addition of many complex features—and even then, its predictions were not especially accurate [Section 3.2].

(3) Copernicus suggested that Earth is a planet orbiting the Sun. The Sun-centered model explained apparent retrograde motion simply, though it made accurate predictions only after Kepler discovered his three laws of planetary motion. Galileo's telescopic observations confirmed the Sun-centered model, and revealed that the universe contains far more stars than had been previously imagined [Section 3.3].

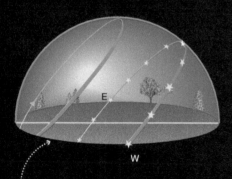

Earth's rotation around its axis leads to the daily east-to-west motions of objects in the sky.

The tilt of Earth's rotation axis leads to seasons as Earth orbits the Sun.

Planets are much smaller than the Sun. At a scale of 1 to 10 billion, the Sun is the size of a grapefruit, Earth is the size of a ball point of a pen, and the distance between them is about 15 meters.

Yerkes Observatory

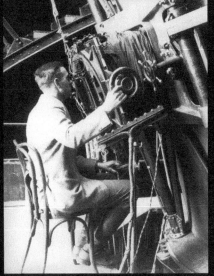

Edwin Hubble at the Mt. Wilson telescope

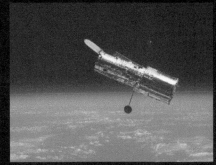

Hubble Space Telescope

1838–1920 A.D. 1924–1929 A.D. 1990 A.D.–present

(4) Larger telescopes and photography made it possible to measure the parallax of stars, offering direct proof that Earth really does orbit the Sun and showing that even the nearest stars are light-years away. We learned that our Sun is a fairly ordinary star in the Milky Way [Sections 2.4, 15.1].

(5) Edwin Hubble measured the distances of galaxies, showing that they lay far beyond the bounds of the Milky Way and proving that the universe is far larger than our own galaxy. He also discovered that more distant galaxies are moving away from us faster, telling us that the entire universe is expanding and suggesting that it began in an event we call the Big Bang [Sections 1.3, 20.2].

(6) Improved measurements of galactic distances and the rate of expansion have shown that the universe is about 14 billion years old. These measurements have also revealed still-unexplained surprises, including evidence for the existence of mysterious "dark matter" and "dark energy" [Sections 1.3, 22.1].

Distances between stars are enormous. At a scale of 1 to 10 billion, you can hold the Sun in your hand, but the nearest stars are thousands of kilometers away.

Our solar system is located about 28,000 light-years from the center of the Milky Way Galaxy.

The Milky Way Galaxy contains over 100 billion stars.

The observable universe contains over 100 billion galaxies.

MAKING SENSE OF THE UNIVERSE
UNDERSTANDING MOTION, ENERGY, AND GRAVITY

LEARNING GOALS

4.1 DESCRIBING MOTION: EXAMPLES FROM DAILY LIFE

- How do we describe motion?
- How is mass different from weight?

4.2 NEWTON'S LAWS OF MOTION

- How did Newton change our view of the universe?
- What are Newton's three laws of motion?

4.3 CONSERVATION LAWS IN ASTRONOMY

- Why do objects move at constant velocity if no force acts on them?
- What keeps a planet rotating and orbiting the Sun?
- Where do objects get their energy?

4.4 THE UNIVERSAL LAW OF GRAVITATION

- What determines the strength of gravity?
- How does Newton's law of gravity extend Kepler's laws?

4.5 ORBITS, TIDES, AND THE ACCELERATION OF GRAVITY

- How do gravity and energy allow us to understand orbits?
- How does gravity cause tides?
- Why do all objects fall at the same rate?

*If I have seen farther than others, it is because
I have stood on the shoulders of giants.*

—Isaac Newton

The history of the universe is essentially a story about the interplay between matter and energy. This interplay began in the Big Bang and continues today in everything from the microscopic jiggling of atoms to gargantuan collisions of galaxies. Understanding the universe therefore depends on becoming familiar with how matter responds to the ebb and flow of energy.

You might guess that it would be difficult to understand the many interactions that shape the universe, but we now know that just a few physical laws govern the movements of everything from atoms to galaxies. The Copernican revolution spurred the discovery of these laws, and Galileo deduced some of them from his experiments. But it was Sir Isaac Newton who put all the pieces together into a simple system of laws describing both motion and gravity.

In this chapter, we'll discuss Newton's laws of motion, the laws of conservation of angular momentum and of energy, and the universal law of gravitation. By understanding these laws, you will be able to make sense of many of the wide-ranging phenomena you will encounter as you study astronomy.

4.1 DESCRIBING MOTION: EXAMPLES FROM DAILY LIFE

Think about what happens when you throw a ball to a dog. The ball leaves your hand, traveling in some particular direction at some particular speed. During its flight, the ball is pulled toward Earth by gravity, slowed by air resistance, and pushed by gusts of wind. Despite the complexity of the ball's motion, the dog still catches it.

We humans can perform an even better trick: We have learned how to figure out where the ball will land even before throwing it. In fact, we can use the same basic trick to predict the motions of objects throughout the universe, and we can perform it with such extraordinary precision that we can land a spaceship on target on Mars after sending it on a journey of hundreds of millions of kilometers.

Our primary goal in this chapter is to understand how humans have learned to make sense of motion in the universe. We all have experience with motion and a natural intuition as to what motion is, but in science we need to define our ideas and terms precisely. In this section, we'll use examples from everyday life to explore some of the fundamental ideas of motion.

How do we describe motion?

You are probably familiar with common terms used to describe motion in science, such as *velocity, acceleration,* and *momentum.* However, their scientific definitions may differ subtly from those you use in casual conversation. Let's investigate the precise meanings of these terms.

Speed, Velocity, and Acceleration A car provides a good illustration of the three basic terms that we use to describe motion:

- The **speed** of the car tells us how far it will go in a certain amount of time. For example, "100 kilometers per hour" (about 60 miles per hour) is a speed, and it tells us that the car will cover a distance of 100 kilometers if it is driven at this speed for an hour.

- The **velocity** of the car tells us both its speed and its direction. For example, "100 kilometers per hour going due north" describes a velocity.

- The car has an **acceleration** if its velocity is changing in any way, whether in speed or direction or both.

Note that while we normally think of *acceleration* as an increase in speed, in science we also say that you are accelerating when you slow down or turn (FIGURE 4.1). Slowing represents a negative acceleration, causing your velocity to decrease. Turning means a change in direction—which therefore means a change in velocity—so turning is a form of acceleration even if your speed remains constant.

You can often feel the effects of acceleration. For example, as you speed up in a car, you feel yourself being pushed back into your seat. As you slow down, you feel yourself being pulled forward. As you drive around a curve, you feel yourself being pushed away from the direction of your turn. In contrast, you don't feel such effects when moving at *constant velocity.* That is why you don't feel any sensation of motion when you're traveling in an airplane on a smooth flight.

The Acceleration of Gravity One of the most important types of acceleration is the acceleration caused by gravity. In a legendary experiment in which he supposedly dropped

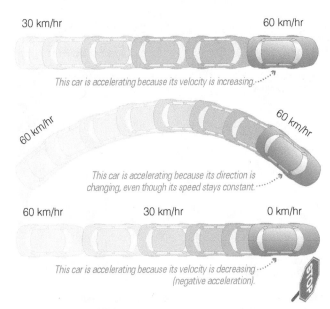

30 km/hr   60 km/hr

This car is accelerating because its velocity is increasing.

60 km/hr   60 km/hr

This car is accelerating because its direction is changing, even though its speed stays constant.

60 km/hr   30 km/hr   0 km/hr

This car is accelerating because its velocity is decreasing (negative acceleration).

FIGURE 4.1 Speeding up, turning, and slowing down are all examples of acceleration.

weights from the Leaning Tower of Pisa, Galileo demonstrated that gravity accelerates all objects by the same amount, regardless of their mass. This fact may be surprising because it seems to contradict everyday experience: A feather floats gently to the ground, while a rock plummets. However, air resistance causes this difference in acceleration. If you dropped a feather and a rock on the Moon, where there is no air, both would fall at exactly the same rate.

The acceleration of a falling object is called the **acceleration of gravity**, abbreviated *g*. On Earth, the acceleration of gravity causes falling objects to fall faster by 9.8 meters per second (m/s), or about 10 m/s, with each passing second. For example, suppose you drop a rock from a tall building. At the moment you let it go, its speed is 0 m/s. After 1 second, the rock will be falling downward at about 10 m/s. After 2 seconds, it will be falling at about 20 m/s. In the absence of air resistance, its speed will continue to increase by about 10 m/s each second until it hits the ground (FIGURE 4.2). We therefore say that the acceleration of gravity is about 10 *meters per second per second,* or 10 *meters per second squared,* which we write as 10 m/s² (more precisely, $g = 9.8$ m/s²).

Momentum and Force The concepts of speed, velocity, and acceleration describe how an individual object moves, but most of the interesting phenomena we see in the universe

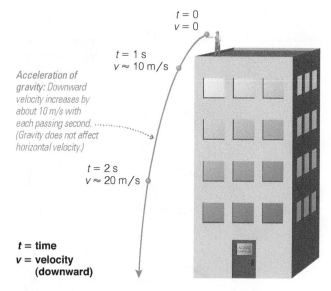

$t = 0$
$v = 0$

$t = 1$ s
$v \approx 10$ m/s

Acceleration of gravity: Downward velocity increases by about 10 m/s with each passing second. (Gravity does not affect horizontal velocity.)

$t = 2$ s
$v \approx 20$ m/s

t = time
v = velocity
    (downward)

FIGURE 4.2 On Earth, gravity causes an unsupported object to accelerate downward at about 10 m/s², which means its downward velocity increases by about 10 m/s with each passing second. (Gravity does not affect horizontal velocity.)

result from interactions between objects. We need two additional concepts to describe these interactions:

- An object's **momentum** is the product of its mass and velocity; that is, momentum = mass × velocity.

- The only way to change an object's momentum is to apply a **force** to it.

We can understand these concepts by considering the effects of collisions. Imagine that you're stopped in your car at a red light when a bug flying at a velocity of 30 km/hr due south slams into your windshield. What will happen to your car? Not much, except perhaps a bit of a mess on your windshield. Next, imagine that a 2-ton truck runs the red light and hits you head-on with the same velocity as the bug. Clearly, the truck will cause far more damage. We can understand why by considering the momentum and force in each collision.

Before the collisions, the truck's much greater mass means it has far more momentum than the bug, even though both the truck and the bug are moving with the same velocity. During the collisions, the bug and the truck each transfer some of their momentum to your car. The bug has very little momentum to give to your car, so it does not exert much of a force. In contrast, the truck imparts enough of its momentum to cause a dramatic and sudden change in your car's momentum. You feel this sudden change in momentum as a force, and it can do great damage to you and your car.

The mere presence of a force does not always cause a change in momentum. For example, a moving car is always affected by forces of air resistance and friction with the road—forces that will slow your car if you take your foot off the gas pedal. However, you can maintain a constant velocity, and hence constant momentum, if you step on the gas pedal hard enough to overcome the slowing effects of these forces.

In fact, forces of some kind are always present, such as the force of gravity or the electromagnetic forces acting between atoms. The **net force** (or *overall force*) acting on an object represents the combined effect of all the individual forces put together. There is no net force on your car when you are driving at constant velocity, because the force generated by the engine to turn the wheels precisely offsets the forces of air resistance and road friction. A change in momentum occurs only when the net force is not zero.

Changing an object's momentum means changing its velocity, as long as its mass remains constant. A net force that is not zero therefore causes an object to accelerate. Conversely, whenever an object accelerates, a net force must be causing the acceleration. That is why you feel forces (pushing you forward, backward, or to the side) when you accelerate in your car. We can use the same ideas to understand many astronomical processes. For example, planets are always accelerating as they orbit the Sun, because their direction of travel constantly changes as they go around their orbits. We can therefore conclude that some force must be causing this acceleration. As we'll discuss shortly, Isaac Newton identified this force as gravity.

Moving in Circles Think about an ice skater spinning in place. She isn't going anywhere, so she has no overall velocity and hence no overall momentum. Nevertheless, every part of her body is moving in a circle as she spins, so these parts have momentum even though her overall momentum is zero. Is there a way to describe the total momentum from each part of her body as she spins? Yes—we say that her spin gives her **angular momentum**, which you can also think of as "circling momentum" or "turning momentum." (The term *angular* arises because a complete circle turns through an *angle* of 360°.)

Any object that is either spinning or moving along a curved path has angular momentum, which makes angular momentum very important in astronomy. For example, Earth has angular momentum due to its rotation (its *rotational angular momentum*) and to its orbit around the Sun (its *orbital angular momentum*).

Because angular momentum is a special type of momentum, an object's angular momentum can change only when a special type of force is applied to it. To see why, consider what happens when you try to open a swinging door. Opening the door means making it rotate on its hinges, which means giving the door some angular momentum. Pushing directly on the hinges will have no effect on the door, even if you push with a very strong force. However, even a light force can make the door rotate if you push on the part of the door that is farthest from the hinges. The type of force that can change an object's angular momentum is called a **torque**, which you can think of as a "twisting force." As the door example shows, the amount of torque depends not only on how much force is applied, but also on where it is applied.

Changing a tire offers another familiar example of torque. Turning the bolts on a tire means making them rotate, which requires giving them some angular momentum. A longer wrench means you can push from farther out than you can with a short wrench, so you can turn the bolts with less force. We will see many more applications of angular momentum in astronomy throughout the rest of the book.

How is mass different from weight?

In daily life, we usually think of *mass* as something you can measure with a bathroom scale, but technically the scale measures your *weight*, not your mass. The distinction between mass and weight rarely matters when we are talking about objects on Earth, but it is very important in astronomy:

- Your **mass** is the amount of matter in your body.

- Your **weight** (or *apparent weight**) is the *force* that a scale measures when you stand on it; that is, weight depends both on your mass and on the forces (including gravity) acting on your mass.

To understand the difference between mass and weight, imagine standing on a scale in an elevator (**FIGURE 4.3**). Your mass will be the same no matter how the elevator moves, but your weight can vary. When the elevator is stationary or moving at constant velocity, the scale reads your "normal" weight. When the elevator accelerates upward, the floor exerts

*Some physics texts distinguish between "true weight," due only to gravity, and "apparent weight," which also depends on other forces (as in an elevator). In this book the word *weight* means "apparent weight."

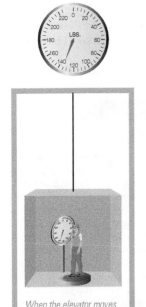

When the elevator moves at constant velocity (or is stationary)...

...your weight is normal.

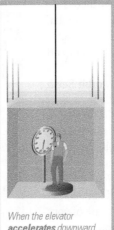

*When the elevator **accelerates** upward...*

...you weigh more.

*When the elevator **accelerates** downward...*

...you weigh less.

*If the cable breaks so that you are in **free-fall**...*

...you are weightless.

FIGURE 4.3

interactive figure
Mass is not the same as weight. The man's mass never changes, but his weight is different when the elevator accelerates.

a greater force than it does when you are at rest. You feel heavier, and the scale verifies your greater weight. When the elevator accelerates downward, the floor and the scale exert a weaker force on you, so the scale registers less weight. Note that the scale shows a weight different from your "normal" weight only when the elevator is *accelerating*, not when it is going up or down at constant speed.

Your mass therefore depends only on the amount of matter in your body and is the same anywhere, but your weight can vary because the forces acting on you can vary. For example, your mass would be the same on the Moon as on Earth, but you would weigh less on the Moon because of its weaker gravity.

Free-Fall and Weightlessness Now consider what happens if the elevator cable breaks (see the last frame in Figure 4.3). The elevator and you are suddenly in **free-fall**—falling without any resistance to slow you down. The floor drops away at the same rate that you fall, allowing you to "float" freely above it, and the scale reads zero because you are no longer held to it. In other words, your free-fall has made you **weightless**.

In fact, you are in free-fall whenever there's nothing to *prevent* you from falling. For example, you are in free-fall when you jump off a chair or spring from a diving board or trampoline. Surprising as it may seem, you have therefore experienced weightlessness many times in your life. You can experience it right now simply by jumping off your chair—though your weightlessness lasts for only the very short time until you hit the ground.

Weightlessness in Space You've probably seen videos of astronauts floating weightlessly in the Space Station. But why are they weightless? Many people guess that there's no gravity in space, but that's not true. After all, it is gravity that makes the Space Station orbit Earth. Astronauts feel weightless for the same reason you are weightless when you jump off a chair: They are in free-fall.

Astronauts are weightless the entire time they orbit Earth because they are in a *constant state of free-fall*. To understand this idea, imagine a tower that reaches all the way to the Space Station's orbit, about 350 kilometers above Earth (FIGURE 4.4). If you stepped off the tower, you would fall downward, remaining weightless until you hit the ground (or until air resistance had a noticeable effect on you). Now, imagine that instead of stepping off the tower, you ran and jumped out of the tower. You'd still fall to the ground, but because of your forward motion, you'd land a short distance away from the base of the tower.

The faster you ran out of the tower, the farther you'd go before landing. If you could somehow run fast enough—about

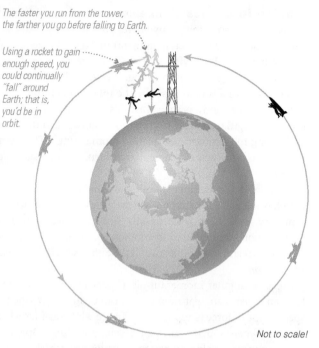

The faster you run from the tower, the farther you go before falling to Earth.

Using a rocket to gain enough speed, you could continually "fall" around Earth; that is, you'd be in orbit.

Not to scale!

FIGURE 4.4 **interactive figure** This figure explains why astronauts are weightless and float freely in space. If you could leap from a tall tower with enough speed, you could travel forward so fast that you'd orbit Earth. You'd then be in a constant state of free-fall, which means you'd be weightless. *Note:* On the scale shown here, the tower extends far higher than the Space Station's orbit; the rocket's orientation shows it rotating once with each orbit. (Adapted from *Space Station Science* by Marianne Dyson.)

28,000 km/hr (17,000 mi/hr) at the orbital altitude of the Space Station—a very interesting thing would happen: By the time gravity had pulled you downward as far as the length of the tower, you'd already have moved far enough around Earth that you'd no longer be going down at all. Instead, you'd be just as high above Earth as you'd been all along, but a good portion of the way around the world. In other words, you'd be orbiting Earth.

The Space Shuttle, the Space Station, and all other orbiting objects stay in orbit because they are constantly "falling around" Earth. Their constant state of free-fall makes these spacecraft and everything in them weightless.

THINK ABOUT IT

In the *Hitchhiker's Guide to the Galaxy* books, author Douglas Adams says that the trick to flying is to "throw yourself at the ground and miss." Although this phrase does not really explain flying, which involves lift from air, it describes *orbit* fairly well. Explain.

 Motion and Gravity Tutorial, Lesson 1

4.2 NEWTON'S LAWS OF MOTION

The complexity of motion in daily life might lead you to guess that the laws governing motion would also be complex. For example, if you watch a falling piece of paper waft lazily to the ground, you'll see it rock back and forth in a seemingly unpredictable pattern. However, the complexity of this motion arises because the paper is affected by a variety of forces, including gravity and the changing forces caused by air currents. If you could analyze the forces individually, you'd find that each force affects the paper's motion in a simple, predictable way. Sir Isaac Newton (1642–1727) discovered the remarkably simple laws that govern motion.

How did Newton change our view of the universe?

Newton was born in Lincolnshire, England, on Christmas Day in 1642. His father, a farmer who never learned to read or write, died 3 months before his birth. Newton had a difficult childhood and showed few signs of unusual talent. He attended Trinity College at Cambridge, where he earned his keep by performing menial labor, such as cleaning the boots and bathrooms of wealthier students and waiting on their tables.

The plague hit Cambridge shortly after Newton graduated, and he returned home. By his own account, he experienced a moment of inspiration in 1666 when he saw an apple fall to the ground. He suddenly realized that the gravity making the apple fall was the same force that held the Moon in orbit around Earth. In that moment, Newton shattered the remaining vestiges of the Aristotelian view of the world, which for centuries had been accepted as unquestioned truth.

Aristotle had made many claims about the physics of motion, using his ideas to support his belief in an Earth-centered cosmos. He had also maintained that the heavens were totally distinct from Earth, so physical laws on Earth did not apply to heavenly motion. By the time Newton saw the apple fall, the Copernican revolution had displaced Earth from a central position, and Galileo's experiments had shown that the laws of physics were not what Aristotle had believed [**Section 3.3**].

Newton's sudden insight delivered the final blow to Aristotle's view. By recognizing that gravity operates in the heavens as well as on Earth, Newton eliminated Aristotle's distinction between the two realms and brought the heavens and Earth together as one *universe*. This insight also heralded the birth of the modern science of *astrophysics* (although the term wasn't coined until much later), which applies physical laws discovered on Earth to phenomena throughout the cosmos.

Over the next 20 years, Newton's work completely revolutionized mathematics and science. He quantified the laws

Sir Isaac Newton (1642–1727)

of motion and gravity, conducted crucial experiments regarding the nature of light, built the first reflecting telescopes, and invented the mathematics of calculus. The compendium of Newton's discoveries is so tremendous that it would take a complete book just to describe them, and many more books to describe their influence on civilization. When Newton died in 1727, at age 84, English poet Alexander Pope composed the following epitaph:

Nature, and Nature's laws lay hid in the Night.
God said, Let Newton be! and all was Light.

What are Newton's three laws of motion?

Newton published the laws of motion and gravity in 1687, in his book *Philosophiae Naturalis Principia Mathematica* ("Mathematical Principles of Natural Philosophy"), usually called *Principia*. He enumerated three laws that apply to all motion, which we now call **Newton's laws of motion**. These laws govern the motion of everything from our daily movements on Earth to the movements of planets, stars, and galaxies throughout the universe. FIGURE 4.5 summarizes the three laws.

Newton's First Law Newton's first law of motion essentially restates Galileo's discovery that objects will remain in motion unless a force acts to stop them. It can be stated as follows:

> **Newton's first law:** *An object moves at constant velocity if there is no net force acting upon it.*

In other words, objects at rest (velocity = 0) tend to remain at rest, and objects in motion tend to remain in motion with no change in either their speed or their direction.

The idea that an object at rest should remain at rest is rather obvious: A car parked on a flat street won't suddenly start moving for no reason. But what if the car is traveling along a flat, straight road? Newton's first law says that the car should keep going at the same speed forever *unless* a force

Newton's first law of motion:
An object moves at constant velocity unless a net force acts to change its speed or direction.

Example: A spaceship needs no fuel to keep moving in space.

Newton's second law of motion:
Force = mass × acceleration

Example: A baseball accelerates as the pitcher applies a force by moving his arm. (Once the ball is released, the force from the pitcher's arm ceases, and the ball's path changes only because of the forces of gravity and air resistance.)

Newton's third law of motion:
For any force, there is always an equal and opposite reaction force.

Example: A rocket is propelled upward by a force equal and opposite to the force with which gas is expelled out its back.

FIGURE 4.5 Newton's three laws of motion.

acts to slow it down. You know that the car eventually will come to a stop if you take your foot off the gas pedal, so one or more forces must be stopping the car—in this case forces arising from friction and air resistance. If the car were in space, and therefore unaffected by friction or air, it would keep moving forever (though gravity would gradually alter its speed and direction). That is why interplanetary spacecraft need no fuel to keep going after they are launched into space, and why astronomical objects don't need fuel to travel through the universe.

Newton's first law also explains why you don't feel any sensation of motion when you're traveling in an airplane on a smooth flight. As long as the plane is traveling at constant velocity, no net force is acting on it or on you. Therefore, you feel no different from the way you would feel at rest. You can walk around the cabin, play catch with someone, or relax and go to sleep just as though you were "at rest" on the ground.

Newton's Second Law Newton's second law of motion tells us what happens to an object when a net force *is* present. We have already seen that a net force will change an object's momentum, accelerating it in the direction of the force.

Newton's second law, which quantifies this relationship, can be written in either of the following two forms:

Newton's second law:

$$force = mass \times acceleration\,(F = ma)$$

or $\quad$ *force* = rate of change in *momentum*

This law explains why you can throw a baseball farther than you can throw a shot in the shot put. The force your arm delivers to both the baseball and the shot equals the product of mass and acceleration. Because the mass of the shot is greater than that of the baseball, the same force from your arm gives the shot a smaller acceleration. Because of its smaller acceleration, the shot leaves your hand with less speed than the baseball and therefore travels a shorter distance before hitting the ground. Astronomically, Newton's second law explains why a large planet such as Jupiter has a greater effect on asteroids and comets than a small planet such as Earth [**Section 12.4**]. Because Jupiter is much more massive than Earth, it exerts a stronger gravitational force on passing asteroids and comets, and therefore sends them scattering with a greater acceleration.

MATHEMATICAL INSIGHT 4.1

Units of Force, Mass, and Weight

Newton's second law, $F = ma$, shows that the unit of force is equal to a unit of mass multiplied by a unit of acceleration. Consider a mass of 1 kilogram accelerating at 10 m/s^2:

$$force = mass \times acceleration$$
$$= 1\ kg \times 10\ \frac{m}{s^2} = 10\ \frac{kg \times m}{s^2}$$
$$= 10\ newtons$$

This example shows that the standard unit of force is called the **newton**, which is equivalent to a *kilogram-meter per second squared*.

We can also use Newton's second law to clarify the difference between mass and weight. Imagine standing on a chair when it is suddenly pulled out from under you. You will immediately begin accelerating downward with the acceleration of gravity, which

means the force of gravity acting on you must be your mass times the acceleration of gravity. We define this force as your weight, and it is the same whether you are falling or standing still:

$$weight = mass \times acceleration\ of\ gravity$$

(Your apparent weight may differ if forces besides gravity are acting on you at the same time and is zero if you are in free-fall.)

Like any force, weight has units of mass times acceleration. Thus, although we commonly speak of weights in *kilograms*, this usage is not technically correct: Kilograms are a unit of mass, not of force. You may safely ignore this technicality as long as you are dealing with objects on Earth that are not accelerating. In space or on other planets, the distinction between mass and weight is important and cannot be ignored.

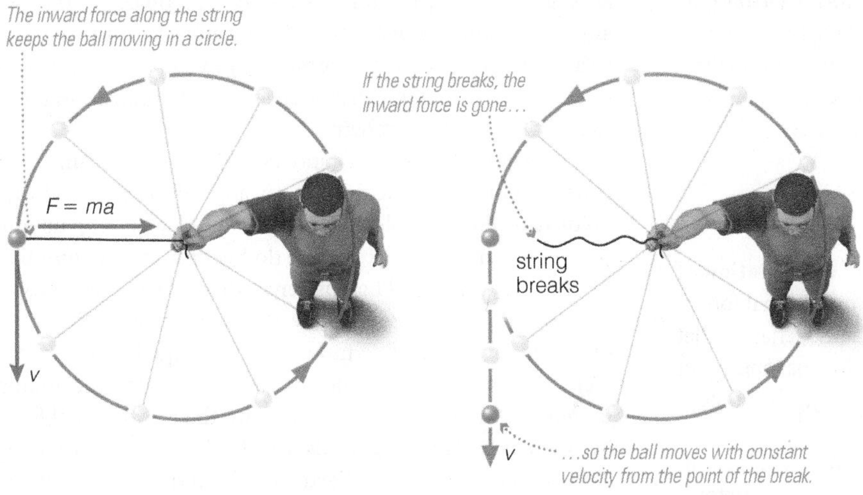

The inward force along the string keeps the ball moving in a circle.

$F = ma$

v

If the string breaks, the inward force is gone...

string breaks

v ...so the ball moves with constant velocity from the point of the break.

a When you swing a ball on a string, the string exerts a force that pulls the ball inward.

b If the string breaks, the ball flies off in a straight line at constant velocity.

FIGURE 4.6 Newton's second law of motion tells us that an object going around a curve has an acceleration pointing toward the inside of the curve.

We can also use Newton's second law of motion to understand acceleration around curves. Suppose you swing a ball on a string around your head (FIGURE 4.6a). The ball is accelerating even if it has a steady speed, because it is constantly changing direction and therefore has a changing velocity. What makes it accelerate? According to Newton's second law, the taut string must be applying a force to the ball. We can understand this force by thinking about what happens when the string breaks (FIGURE 4.6b): With the force gone, the ball flies off in a straight line. Therefore, when the string is intact, the force must be pulling the ball *inward* to keep it from flying off. Because acceleration must be in the same direction as the force, we conclude that the ball has an inward acceleration as it moves around the circle.

The same idea helps us understand the force on a car moving around a curve or a planet orbiting the Sun. In the case of the car, the inward force comes from friction between the tires and the road. The tighter the curve (or the faster the car is going), the greater the force needed to keep the car moving around it. If the inward force due to friction is not great enough, the car skids outward. Similarly, a planet orbiting the Sun always has an acceleration in the direction of the Sun, and gravity is the inward force that causes this acceleration. Indeed, it was Newton's discovery of the precise nature of this acceleration that helped him deduce the law of gravity, which we'll discuss in Section 4.4.

COMMON MISCONCEPTIONS

What Makes a Rocket Launch?

If you've ever watched a rocket launch, it's easy to see why many people believe that the rocket "pushes off" the ground. However, the ground has nothing to do with the rocket launch, which is actually explained by Newton's third law of motion. To balance the force driving gas out the back of the rocket, an equal and opposite force must propel the rocket forward. Rockets can be launched horizontally as well as vertically, and a rocket can be "launched" in space (for example, from a space station) with no need for any solid ground.

Newton's Third Law Think for a moment about standing still on the ground. Your weight exerts a downward force, so if this force were acting alone, Newton's second law would demand that you accelerate downward. The fact that you are not falling means there must be no *net* force acting on you, which is possible only if the ground is exerting an upward force on you that precisely offsets the downward force you exert on the ground. The fact that the downward force you exert on the ground is offset by an equal and opposite force that pushes upward on you is one example of Newton's third law of motion, which tells us that any force is always paired with an equal and opposite reaction force.

> **Newton's third law:** *For any force, there is always an equal and opposite reaction force.*

This law is very important in astronomy, because it tells us that objects always attract *each other* through gravity. For example, your body always exerts a gravitational force on Earth identical to the force that Earth exerts on you, except that it acts in the opposite direction. Of course, the same force means a much greater acceleration for you than for Earth (because your mass is so much smaller than Earth's), which is why you fall toward Earth when you jump off a chair, rather than Earth falling toward you.

Newton's third law also explains how a rocket works: A rocket engine generates a force that drives hot gas out the back, which creates an equal and opposite force that propels the rocket forward.

4.3 CONSERVATION LAWS IN ASTRONOMY

Newton's laws of motion are easy to state, but they may seem a bit arbitrary. Why, for example, should every force be opposed by an equal and opposite reaction force? In the centuries since Newton first stated his laws, we have learned that they are not arbitrary at all, but instead reflect deeper aspects of nature known as *conservation laws*. In this section, we'll explore three of the most important conservation laws for astronomy: *conservation of momentum*, *conservation of angular momentum*, and *conservation of energy*. We'll see some immediate examples of how they apply to astronomy, and then use these laws over and over throughout the rest of the book.

Why do objects move at constant velocity if no force acts on them?

The first of our conservation laws, the law of **conservation of momentum**, states that as long as there are no external forces, the total momentum of interacting objects cannot change; that is, their total momentum is *conserved*. An individual object can gain or lose momentum only if some other object's momentum changes by a precisely opposite amount.

The law of conservation of momentum is implicit in Newton's laws. To see why, watch a game of pool. Newton's second law tells us that when one pool ball strikes another, it exerts a force that changes the momentum of the second ball. At the same time, Newton's third law tells us that the second ball exerts an equal and opposite force on the first one—which means that the first ball's momentum changes by precisely the same amount as the second ball's momentum, but in the opposite direction. The total combined momentum of the two balls remains the same both before and after the collision (**FIGURE 4.7**). Note that no *external* forces are accelerating the balls.

Rockets offer another good example of conservation of momentum in action. When you fire a rocket engine, the total momentum of the rocket and the hot gases it shoots out the back must stay the same. In other words, the amount of forward momentum the rocket gains is equal to the amount of backward momentum in the gas that shoots out the back. That is why forces between the rocket and the gases are always equal and opposite.

From the perspective of conservation of momentum, Newton's first law makes perfect sense. When no net force

acts on an object, there is no way for the object to transfer any momentum to or from any other object. In the absence of a net force, an object's momentum must therefore remain unchanged—which means the object must continue to move exactly as it has been moving.

According to current understanding of the universe, conservation of momentum is an absolute law that always holds true. For example, it holds even when you jump up into the air. You may wonder, Where do I get the momentum that carries me upward? The answer is that as your legs propel you skyward, they are actually pushing Earth in the other direction, giving Earth's momentum an equal and opposite kick. However, Earth's huge mass renders its acceleration undetectable. During your brief flight, the gravitational force between you and Earth pulls you back down, transferring your momentum back to Earth. The total momentum of you and Earth remains the same at all times.

What keeps a planet rotating and orbiting the Sun?

Perhaps you've wondered how Earth manages to keep rotating and going around the Sun day after day and year after year. The answer comes from our second conservation law: the law of **conservation of angular momentum**. Recall that rotating or orbiting objects have angular momentum because they are moving in circles or going around curves, and that angular momentum can be changed only by a "twisting force," or *torque*. The law of conservation of angular momentum states that as long as there is no external torque, the total angular momentum of a set of interacting objects cannot change. An individual object can change its angular momentum only by transferring some angular momentum to or from another object. Because astronomical objects can have angular momentum due to both their rotation and their orbit, let's consider both cases.

Orbital Angular Momentum Consider Earth's orbit around the Sun. A simple formula tells us Earth's angular momentum at any point in its orbit:

$$\text{angular momentum} = m \times v \times r$$

where m is Earth's mass, v is its orbital velocity (or, more technically, the component of velocity perpendicular to r), and r is the "radius" of the orbit, by which we mean its distance from the Sun (**FIGURE 4.8**). Because there are no objects around to give or take angular momentum from Earth as it orbits the Sun, Earth's orbital angular momentum must always stay the same. This explains two key facts about Earth's orbit:

1. Earth needs no fuel or push of any kind to keep orbiting the Sun—it will keep orbiting as long as nothing comes along to take angular momentum away.

2. Because Earth's angular momentum at any point in its orbit depends on the product of its speed and orbital radius (distance from the Sun), Earth's orbital speed must be faster when it is nearer to the Sun (and the radius is smaller) and slower when it is farther from the Sun (and the radius is larger).

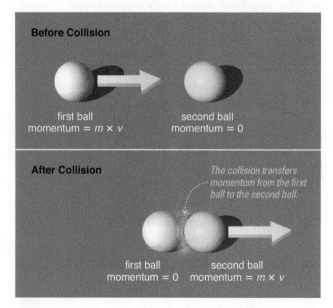

Before Collision

first ball
momentum = $m \times v$

second ball
momentum = 0

After Collision

The collision transfers momentum from the first ball to the second ball.

first ball
momentum = 0

second ball
momentum = $m \times v$

FIGURE 4.7 Conservation of momentum demonstrated with balls on a pool table.

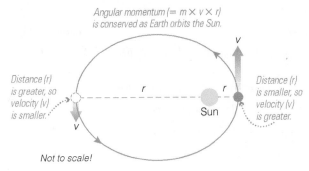

Angular momentum (= m × v × r) is conserved as Earth orbits the Sun.

Distance (r) is greater, so velocity (v) is smaller.

Distance (r) is smaller, so velocity (v) is greater.

Sun

Not to scale!

FIGURE 4.8 Earth's orbital angular momentum stays constant, so Earth moves faster when it is closer to the Sun and slower when it is farther from the Sun.

The second fact is just what Kepler's second law of planetary motion states [**Section 3.3**]. That is, the law of conservation of angular momentum tells us *why* Kepler's law is true.

Rotational Angular Momentum The same idea explains why Earth keeps rotating. As long as Earth isn't transferring any of the angular momentum of its rotation to another object, it keeps rotating at the same rate. (In fact, Earth is very gradually transferring some of its rotational angular momentum to the Moon, and as a result Earth's rotation is gradually slowing down; see Section 4.5.)

Conservation of angular momentum also explains why we see so many spinning disks in the universe, such as the disks of galaxies like the Milky Way and disks of material orbiting young stars. The idea is easy to illustrate with an ice skater spinning in place (**FIGURE 4.9**). Because there is so little friction on ice, the angular momentum of the ice skater remains essentially constant. When she pulls in her extended arms, she decreases her radius—which means her velocity of rotation

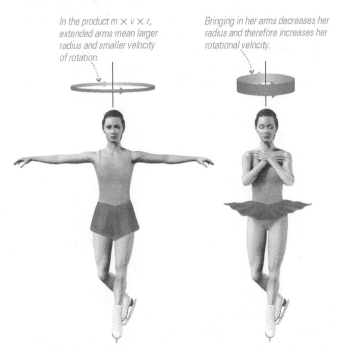

In the product m × v × r, extended arms mean larger radius and smaller velocity of rotation.

Bringing in her arms decreases her radius and therefore increases her rotational velocity.

FIGURE 4.9 A spinning skater conserves angular momentum.

must increase. Stars and galaxies are both born from clouds of gas that start out much larger in size. These clouds almost inevitably have some small net rotation, though it may be imperceptible. Like the spinning skater as she pulls in her arms, they must therefore spin faster as gravity makes them shrink in size. (We'll discuss why the clouds also flatten into disks in Chapter 8.)

THINK ABOUT IT

How does conservation of angular momentum explain the spiraling of water going down a drain?

(MA) Energy Tutorial, Lesson 1

Where do objects get their energy?

Our third crucial conservation law for astronomy is the law of **conservation of energy**. This law tells us that, like momentum and angular momentum, energy cannot appear out of nowhere or disappear into nothingness. Objects can gain or lose energy only by exchanging energy with other objects. Because of this law, the story of the universe is a story of the interplay of energy and matter: All actions involve exchanges of energy or the conversion of energy from one form to another.

Throughout the rest of this book, we'll see numerous cases in which we can understand astronomical processes simply by studying how energy is transformed and exchanged. For example, we'll see that planetary interiors cool with time because they radiate energy into space, and that the Sun became hot because of energy released by the gas that formed it. By applying the laws of conservation of momentum, angular momentum, and energy, we can understand almost every major process that occurs in the universe.

Basic Types of Energy Before we can fully understand the law of conservation of energy, we need to know what energy is. In essence, energy is what makes matter move. Because this statement is so broad, we often distinguish between different types of energy. For example, we talk about the energy we get from the food we eat, the energy that makes our cars go, and the energy a light bulb emits. Fortunately, we can classify nearly all types of energy into just three major categories (**FIGURE 4.10**):

- Energy of motion, or **kinetic energy** (*kinetic* comes from a Greek word meaning "motion"). Falling rocks, orbiting planets, and the molecules moving in the air are all examples of objects with kinetic energy. Quantitatively, the kinetic energy of a moving object is $\frac{1}{2}mv^2$, where m is the object's mass and v is its speed.

- Energy carried by light, or **radiative energy** (the word *radiation* is often used as a synonym for *light*). All light carries energy, which is why light can cause changes in matter. For example, light can alter molecules in our eyes—thereby allowing us to see—or warm the surface of a planet.

Energy can be converted from one form to another.

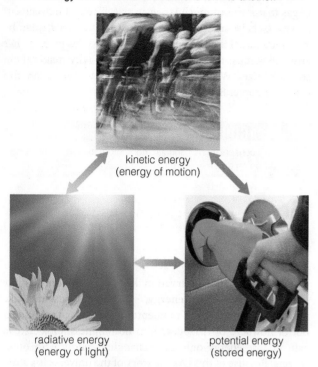

kinetic energy
(energy of motion)

radiative energy
(energy of light)

potential energy
(stored energy)

FIGURE 4.10 The three basic categories of energy. Energy can be converted from one form to another, but it can never be created or destroyed, an idea embodied in the law of conservation of energy.

TABLE 4.1 **Energy Comparisons**

Item	Energy (joules)
Energy of sunlight at Earth (per m² per second)	1.3×10^3
Energy from metabolism of a candy bar	1×10^6
Energy needed to walk for 1 hour	1×10^6
Kinetic energy of a car going 60 mi/hr	1×10^6
Daily food energy need of average adult	1×10^7
Energy released by burning 1 liter of oil	1.2×10^7
Thermal energy of parked car	1×10^8
Energy released by fission of 1 kilogram of uranium-235	5.6×10^{13}
Energy released by fusion of hydrogen in 1 liter of water	7×10^{13}
Energy released by 1-megaton H-bomb	4×10^{15}
Energy released by magnitude 8 earthquake	2.5×10^{16}
Annual U.S. energy consumption	10^{20}
Annual energy generation of Sun	10^{34}
Energy released by a supernova	10^{44}–10^{46}

- Stored energy, or **potential energy**, which might later be converted into kinetic or radiative energy. For example, a rock perched on a ledge has *gravitational* potential energy because it will fall if it slips off the edge, and gasoline contains *chemical* potential energy that can be converted into the kinetic energy of a moving car.

Regardless of which type of energy we are dealing with, we can measure the amount of energy with the same standard units. For Americans, the most familiar units of energy are *Calories,* which are shown on food labels to tell us how much energy our bodies can draw from the food. A typical adult needs about 2500 Calories of energy from food each day. In science, the standard unit of energy is the **joule**. One food Calorie is equivalent to about 4184 joules, so the 2500 Calories used daily by a typical adult is equivalent to about 10 million joules. TABLE 4.1 compares various energies in joules.

Thermal Energy—The Kinetic Energy of Many Particles Although there are only three major categories of energy, we sometimes divide them into various subcategories. In astronomy, the most important subcategory of kinetic energy is **thermal energy**, which represents the collective kinetic energy of the many individual particles (atoms and molecules) moving randomly within a substance like a rock or the air or the gas within a distant star. In such cases, it is much easier to talk about the thermal energy of the object than about the kinetic energies of its billions upon billions of individual particles. Note that all objects contain thermal energy even when they are sitting still, because the particles

within them are always jiggling about randomly. These random motions can contain substantial energy: The thermal energy of a parked car due to the random motion of its atoms is much greater than the kinetic energy of the car moving at highway speed.

Thermal energy gets its name because it is related to temperature, but temperature and thermal energy are not quite the same thing. Thermal energy measures the *total* kinetic energy of all the randomly moving particles in a substance, while **temperature** measures the *average* kinetic energy of the particles. For a particular object, a higher temperature simply means that the particles on average have more kinetic energy and hence are moving faster (FIGURE 4.11). You're probably familiar with temperatures measured in *Fahrenheit* or *Celsius,*

lower temperature

higher temperature

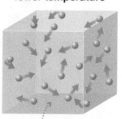

These particles are moving relatively slowly, which means low temperature . . .

. . . and now the same particles are moving faster, which means higher temperature.

FIGURE 4.11 Temperature is a measure of the average kinetic energy of the particles (atoms and molecules) in a substance. Longer arrows represent faster speeds.

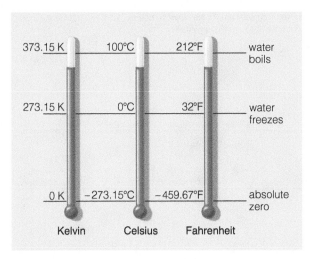

FIGURE 4.12 Three common temperature scales: Kelvin, Celsius, and Fahrenheit. Scientists generally prefer the Kelvin scale. Note that the degree symbol (°) is not usually used with the Kelvin scale.

but in science we often use the **Kelvin** temperature scale (**FIGURE 4.12**). The Kelvin scale does not have negative temperatures, because it starts from the coldest possible temperature, known as *absolute zero* (0 K).

Thermal energy depends on temperature, because a higher average kinetic energy for the particles in a substance means a higher total energy. But thermal energy also depends on the number and density of the particles, as you can see by imagining that you quickly thrust your arm in and out of a hot oven and a pot of boiling water (don't try this!). The air in a hot oven is much higher in temperature than the water boiling in a pot (**FIGURE 4.13**). However, the boiling water would scald your arm almost instantly, while you can safely put your arm into the oven air for a few seconds. The reason for this difference is density. In both cases, because the air or water is hotter than your body, molecules striking your skin transfer thermal energy to molecules in your arm. The higher temperature in the oven means that the air molecules strike your skin harder, on average, than the molecules in

the boiling water. However, because the *density* of water is so much higher than the density of air (meaning water has far more molecules in the same amount of space), many more molecules strike your skin each second in the water. While each individual molecule that strikes your skin transfers a little less energy in the boiling water than in the oven, the sheer number of molecules hitting you in the water means that more thermal energy is transferred to your arm. That is why the boiling water causes a burn almost instantly.

THINK ABOUT IT

In air or water that is colder than your body temperature, thermal energy is transferred from you to the surrounding cold air or water. Use this fact to explain why falling into a 32°F (0°C) lake is much more dangerous than standing naked outside on a 32°F day.

The environment in space provides another example of the difference between temperature and heat. Surprisingly, the temperature in low Earth orbit can be several thousand degrees. However, astronauts working in Earth orbit are at much greater risk of getting cold than hot. The reason is the extremely low density: Although the particles striking an astronaut's space suit may be moving quite fast, there are not enough of them to transfer much thermal energy. (You may wonder how the astronauts become cold given that the low density also means the astronauts cannot transfer much of their own thermal energy to the particles in space. It turns out that they lose their body heat by emitting *thermal radiation*, which we will discuss in Section 5.3.)

Potential Energy in Astronomy Many types of potential energy are important in astronomy, but two are particularly important: *gravitational potential energy* and the potential energy of mass itself, or *mass-energy*.

An object's **gravitational potential energy** depends on its mass and how far it can fall as a result of gravity. An object has more gravitational potential energy when it is higher and less when it is lower. For example, if you throw a ball up into the air, it has more potential energy when it is high up than when it is near the ground. Because energy must be conserved during the ball's flight, the ball's kinetic energy increases when its gravitational potential energy decreases, and vice versa (**FIGURE 4.14a**). That is why the ball travels fastest (has the most kinetic energy) when it is closest to the ground, where it has the least gravitational potential energy. The higher it is, the more gravitational potential energy it has and the slower the ball travels (less kinetic energy). For an object near Earth's surface, its gravitational potential energy is *mgh*, where *m* is its mass, *g* is the acceleration of gravity, and *h* is its height above the ground.

The same general idea explains how stars become hot (**FIGURE 4.14b**). Before a star forms, its matter is spread out in a large, cold cloud of gas. Most of the individual gas particles are far from the center of this large cloud and therefore have a lot of gravitational potential energy. The particles lose gravitational potential energy as the cloud contracts under

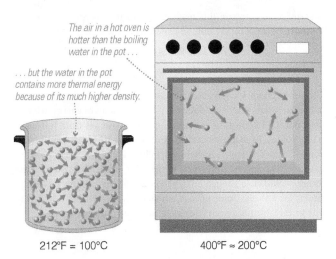

The air in a hot oven is hotter than the boiling water in the pot . . .

. . . but the water in the pot contains more thermal energy because of its much higher density.

212°F = 100°C   400°F ≈ 200°C

FIGURE 4.13 Thermal energy depends on both the temperature and the density of particles in a substance.

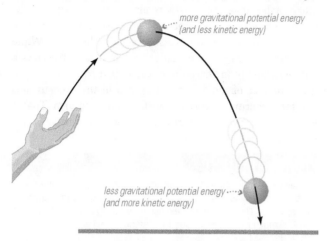

The total energy (kinetic + potential) is the same at all points in the ball's flight.

more gravitational potential energy
(and less kinetic energy)

less gravitational potential energy
(and more kinetic energy)

a The ball has more gravitational potential energy when it is high up than when it is near the ground.

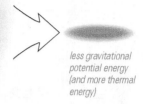

Energy is conserved: As the cloud contracts, gravitational potential energy is converted to thermal energy and radiation.

less gravitational potential energy (and more thermal energy)

more gravitational potential energy (and less thermal energy)

b A cloud of interstellar gas contracting because of its own gravity has more gravitational potential energy when it is spread out than when it shrinks in size.

FIGURE 4.14 Two examples of gravitational potential energy.

its own gravity, and this "lost" potential energy ultimately gets converted into thermal energy, making the center of the cloud hot.

Einstein discovered that mass itself is a form of potential energy, often called **mass-energy**. The amount of potential energy contained in mass is described by Einstein's famous equation

$$E = mc^2$$

where E is the amount of potential energy, m is the mass of the object, and c is the speed of light. This equation tells us that a small amount of mass contains a huge amount of energy. For example, the energy released by a 1-megaton

H-bomb comes from converting only about 0.1 kilogram of mass (about 3 ounces—a quarter of a can of soda) into energy (FIGURE 4.15). The Sun generates energy by converting a tiny fraction of its mass into energy through a similar process of nuclear fusion [**Section 14.2**].

Just as Einstein's formula tells us that mass can be converted into other forms of energy, it also tells us that energy can be transformed into mass. This process is especially important in understanding what we think happened during the early moments in the history of the universe, when some of the energy of the Big Bang turned into the mass from which all objects, including us, are made [**Section 22.1**]. Scientists also use this idea to search for undiscovered particles of matter,

MATHEMATICAL INSIGHT 4.2

Mass-Energy

It's easy to calculate mass-energies with Einstein's formula $E = mc^2$.

EXAMPLE: Suppose a 1-kilogram rock were completely converted to energy. How much energy would it release? Compare this to the energy released by burning 1 liter of oil.

SOLUTION:

Step 1 Understand: We can compute the total mass-energy of the rock from Einstein's formula and then compare it to the energy released by burning a liter of oil, from Table 4.1.

Step 2 Solve: The mass-energy of the rock is

$$E = mc^2 = 1 \text{ kg} \times \left(3 \times 10^8 \, \frac{\text{m}}{\text{s}}\right)^2$$

$$= 1 \text{ kg} \times \left(9 \times 10^{16} \, \frac{\text{m}^2}{\text{s}^2}\right)$$

$$= 9 \times 10^{16} \, \frac{\text{kg} \times \text{m}^2}{\text{s}^2} = 9 \times 10^{16} \text{ joules}$$

We divide to compare this mass-energy to the energy released by burning 1 liter of oil (12 million joules; see Table 4.1):

$$\frac{9 \times 10^{16} \text{ joules}}{1.2 \times 10^7 \text{ joules}} = 7.5 \times 10^9$$

Step 3 Explain: We have found that converting a 1-kilogram rock completely to energy would release 9×10^{16} joules of energy, which is about 7.5 billion times as much energy as we get from burning 1 liter of oil. In fact, the total amount of oil used by all cars in the United States is approximately 7.5 billion liters per week—which means that complete conversion of the mass of a 1-kilogram rock to energy could yield enough energy to power all the cars in the United States for a week. Unfortunately, no technology available now or in the foreseeable future can release all the mass-energy of a rock.

FIGURE 4.15 The energy released by this H-bomb comes from converting only about 0.1 kilogram of mass into energy in accordance with the formula $E = mc^2$.

using large machines called *particle accelerators* to create subatomic particles from energy.

Conservation of Energy We have seen that energy comes in three basic categories—kinetic, radiative, and potential—and explored several subcategories that are especially important in astronomy: thermal energy, gravitational potential energy, and mass-energy. Now we are ready to return to the question of where objects get their energy. Because energy cannot be created or destroyed, objects always get their energy from other objects. Ultimately, we can always trace an object's energy back to the Big Bang [**Section 1.2**], the beginning of the universe in which all matter and energy is thought to have come into existence.

For example, imagine that you've thrown a baseball. It is moving, so it has kinetic energy. Where did this kinetic energy come from? The baseball got its kinetic energy from the motion of your arm as you threw it. Your arm, in turn, got its kinetic energy from the release of chemical potential energy stored in your muscle tissues. Your muscles got this energy from the chemical potential energy stored in the foods you ate. The energy stored in the foods came from sunlight, which plants convert into chemical potential energy through photosynthesis. The radiative energy of the Sun was generated through the process of nuclear fusion, which releases some of the mass-energy stored in the Sun's supply of hydrogen. The mass-energy stored in the hydrogen came from the birth of the universe in the Big Bang. After you throw the ball, its kinetic energy will ultimately be transferred to molecules in the air or ground. It may be difficult to trace after this point, but it will never disappear.

4.4 THE UNIVERSAL LAW OF GRAVITATION

Newton's laws of motion describe how objects in the universe move in response to forces. The laws of conservation of momentum, angular momentum, and energy offer an alternative and often simpler way of thinking about what happens when a force causes some change in the motion of one or more objects. However, we cannot fully understand motion unless we also understand the forces that lead to changes in motion. In astronomy, the most important force is gravity, which governs virtually all large-scale motion in the universe.

 **Motion and Gravity Tutorial, Lesson 2**

What determines the strength of gravity?

Isaac Newton discovered the basic law that describes how gravity works. Newton expressed the force of gravity mathematically with his **universal law of gravitation**. Three simple statements summarize this law:

- Every mass attracts every other mass through the force called *gravity*.

- The strength of the gravitational force attracting any two objects is *directly proportional* to the product of their masses. For example, doubling the mass of *one* object doubles the force of gravity between the two objects.

- The strength of gravity between two objects decreases with the *square* of the distance between their centers. We therefore say that the gravitational force follows an **inverse square law**. For example, doubling the distance between two objects weakens the force of gravity by a factor of 2^2, or 4.

These three statements tell us everything we need to know about Newton's universal law of gravitation. Mathematically, all three statements can be combined into a single equation, usually written like this:

$$F_g = G \frac{M_1 M_2}{d^2}$$

where F_g is the force of gravitational attraction, M_1 and M_2 are the masses of the two objects, and d is the distance between their centers (**FIGURE 4.16**). The symbol G is a constant called

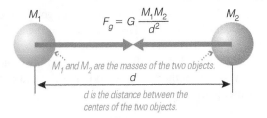

FIGURE 4.16 The universal law of gravitation is an *inverse square law*, which means that the force of gravity declines with the *square* of the distance d between two objects.

the **gravitational constant**, and its numerical value has been measured to be $G = 6.67 \times 10^{-11} \text{ m}^3/(\text{kg} \times \text{s}^2)$.

MA Orbits and Kepler's Law Tutorial, Lessons 1–4

How does Newton's law of gravity extend Kepler's laws?

By the time Newton published *Principia* in 1687, Kepler's laws of planetary motion [**Section 3.3**] had already been known and tested for some 70 years. Kepler's laws had proven so successful that there was little doubt about their validity. However, there was great debate among scientists about *why* Kepler's laws hold true.

Newton resolved the debate by showing that Kepler's laws are consequences of the laws of motion and the universal law of gravitation. In particular, with the aid of the mathematics of calculus that he invented, Newton showed that the inverse square law for gravity leads naturally to elliptical orbits for planets orbiting the Sun (with the Sun at one focus), which is Kepler's first law. As we've seen, Kepler's second law (a planet moves faster when it is closer to the Sun) then arises as a consequence of conservation of angular momentum. Kepler's third law (average orbital speed is slower for planets with larger average orbital distance) arises from the fact that gravity weakens with distance from the Sun. Newton also discovered that he could extend Kepler's laws into a more general set of rules about orbiting objects.

Newton's discoveries sealed the triumph of the Copernican revolution. Prior to Newton, it was still possible to see Kepler's model of planetary motion as "just" another model, though it fit the observational data far better than any previous model. By explaining Kepler's laws in terms of basic laws of physics, Newton removed virtually all remaining doubt about the legitimacy of the Sun-centered solar system. By extending the laws to other orbiting objects, he provided us with a way to explain the motions of objects throughout the universe. Let's explore four crucial ways in which Newton extended Kepler's laws.

Planets Are Not the Only Objects with Elliptical Orbits Kepler wrote his first two laws for planets orbiting the Sun, but Newton showed that any object going around another object will obey these laws. For example, the orbits of a satellite around Earth, of a moon around a planet, and of an asteroid around the Sun are all ellipses in which the orbiting object moves faster at the nearer points in its orbit and slower at the farther points.

Ellipses Are Not the Only Possible Orbital Paths Ellipses (which include circles) are the only possible shapes for **bound orbits**—orbits in which an object goes around

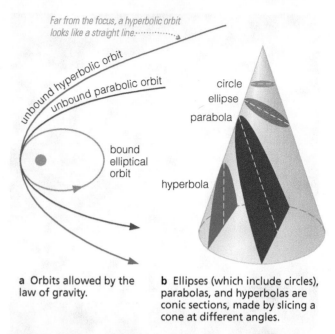

a Orbits allowed by the law of gravity.

b Ellipses (which include circles), parabolas, and hyperbolas are conic sections, made by slicing a cone at different angles.

FIGURE 4.17 Newton showed that ellipses are not the only possible orbital paths. Orbits can also be unbound, taking the mathematical shape of either parabolas or hyperbolas.

another object over and over again. (The term *bound orbit* comes from the idea that gravity creates a *bond* that holds the objects together.) However, Newton discovered that objects can also follow **unbound orbits**—paths that bring an object close to another object just once. For example, some comets that enter the inner solar system follow unbound orbits. They come in from afar just once, loop around the Sun, and never return.

More specifically, Newton showed that orbital paths can be ellipses, parabolas, or hyperbolas (**FIGURE 4.17a**). Bound orbits are ellipses, while unbound orbits can be either parabolas or hyperbolas. Together, these shapes are known in mathematics as the *conic sections*, because they can be made by slicing through a cone at different angles (**FIGURE 4.17b**). Note that objects on unbound orbits still obey the basic principle of Kepler's second law: They move faster when they are closer to the object they are orbiting, and slower when they are farther away.

Objects Orbit Their Common Center of Mass

We usually think of one object orbiting another object, like a planet orbiting the Sun or the Moon orbiting Earth. However, Newton showed that two objects attracted by gravity actually *both* orbit around their common **center of mass**—the point at which the two objects would balance if they were somehow connected (**FIGURE 4.18**). For example, in a binary star system in which both stars have the same mass, we would see both stars tracing ellipses around a point halfway between them. When one object is more massive than the other, the center of mass lies closer to the more massive object.

The idea that objects orbit their common center of mass holds even for the Sun and planets. However, the Sun is so much more massive than the planets that the center of mass between the Sun and any planet lies either inside or nearly

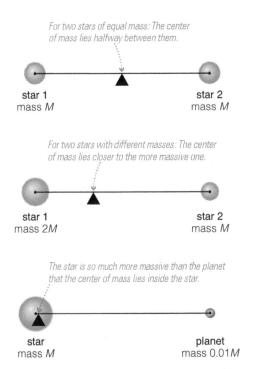

For two stars of equal mass: The center of mass lies halfway between them.

star 1
mass *M*

star 2
mass *M*

For two stars with different masses: The center of mass lies closer to the more massive one.

star 1
mass 2*M*

star 2
mass *M*

The star is so much more massive than the planet that the center of mass lies inside the star.

star
mass *M*

planet
mass 0.01*M*

FIGURE 4.18 Interactive figure Two objects attracted by gravity orbit their common center of mass—the point at which they would balance if they were somehow connected.

FIGURE 4.19 Newton's version of Kepler's third law shows that when one object orbits a much more massive object, the orbital period depends only on its average orbital distance. The astronaut and the Space Shuttle share the same orbit and therefore stay together—even as both orbit Earth at a speed of 25,000 km/hr.

inside the Sun, making it difficult for us to notice the Sun's motion about this center. Nevertheless, with precise measurements we can detect the Sun's slight motion around this center of mass. As we will see in Chapter 13, a stronomers have used this same idea to discover many planets around other stars.

Orbital Characteristics Tell Us the Masses of Distant Objects Recall that Kepler's third law is written $p^2 = a^3$, where p is a planet's orbital period in years and a is the planet's average distance from the Sun in AU. Newton found that this statement is actually a special case of a more general equation that we call **Newton's version of Kepler's third law** (see Mathematical Insight 4.3). This equation allows us to measure orbital period and distance in any units we wish (rather than only in years and AU), and also shows that the relationship between orbital period and average distance depends on the masses of the orbiting objects. When an object is much less massive than the object it orbits, we can calculate the mass of the central object from the orbital period and average distance of the orbiting object.

Newton's version of Kepler's third law is the primary means by which we determine masses throughout the universe. For example, it allows us to calculate the mass of the Sun from Earth's orbital period (1 year) and its average distance from the Sun (1 AU). Similarly, measuring the orbital period and average distance of one of Jupiter's moons allows us to calculate Jupiter's mass, and measuring the orbital periods and average distances of stars in binary star systems allows us to determine their masses.

Newton's version of Kepler's third law also explains another important characteristic of orbital motion. It shows that the orbital period of a *small* object orbiting a much more massive object depends only on its orbital distance, not on its mass. That is why an astronaut does not need a tether to stay close to the spacecraft during a space walk (**FIGURE 4.19**). The spacecraft and the astronaut are both much smaller in mass than Earth, so they stay together because they have the same orbital distance and hence the same orbital period.

4.5 ORBITS, TIDES, AND THE ACCELERATION OF GRAVITY

Newton's universal law of gravitation has applications that go far beyond explaining Kepler's laws. In this final section, we'll explore three important concepts that we can understand with the help of the universal law of gravitation: orbits, tides, and the acceleration of gravity.

How do gravity and energy allow us to understand orbits?

The law of gravitation explains Kepler's laws of planetary motion, which describe the simple and stable orbits of the planets, and Newton's extensions of Kepler's laws explain other stable orbits, such as the orbit of a satellite around Earth or of a moon around a planet. But orbits do not always stay the same. For example, you've probably heard of satellites crashing to Earth from orbit, proving that orbits can sometimes change dramatically. To understand how and why orbits sometimes change, we need to consider the role of energy in orbits.

Orbital Energy Consider the orbit of a planet around the Sun. The planet has both kinetic energy (because it is moving around the Sun) and gravitational potential energy (because it would fall toward the Sun if it stopped orbiting). Its kinetic energy depends on its orbital speed, and its gravitational potential energy depends on its distance from the Sun. Because the planet's distance and speed both vary as it orbits the Sun, its gravitational potential energy and kinetic energy also vary as it orbits (FIGURE 4.20). However, the planet's total **orbital energy**—the sum of its kinetic and gravitational potential energies—stays the same. This fact is a consequence of the law of conservation of energy. As long as no other object causes the planet to gain or lose orbital energy, its orbital energy cannot change and its orbit must remain the same.

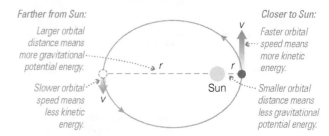

Total orbital energy = gravitational potential energy + kinetic energy

FIGURE 4.20 The total orbital energy of a planet stays constant throughout its orbit, because its gravitational potential energy increases when its kinetic energy decreases, and vice versa.

MATHEMATICAL INSIGHT 4.3

Newton's Version of Kepler's Third Law

Newton's version of Kepler's third law relates the orbital periods, distances, and masses of any pair of orbiting objects, such as the Sun and a planet, a planet and a moon, or two stars in a binary star system. Mathematically, we write it as follows:

$$p^2 = \frac{4\pi^2}{G(M_1 + M_2)} a^3$$

where M_1 and M_2 are the object masses, p is their orbital period, and a is the average distance between their centers. The term $4\pi^2$ is simply a number ($4\pi^2 \approx 4 \times 3.14^2 = 39.44$); G is the gravitational constant, which is measured experimentally.

If we measure the orbital period and distance of one object orbiting another, we can use Newton's equation to calculate the sum $M_1 + M_2$ of the object masses. If one object is much more massive than the other, we essentially learn its mass. For example, when we apply the law to a planet orbiting the Sun, the sum $M_{Sun} + M_{planet}$ is pretty much just M_{Sun} because the Sun is so much more massive than any planet. We can therefore use any planet's orbital period and distance from the Sun to calculate the mass of the Sun.

EXAMPLE 1: Earth orbits the Sun in 1 year at an average distance of 150 million kilometers (1 AU). Calculate the Sun's mass.

SOLUTION:

Step 1 Understand: We will use Newton's version of Kepler's third law. For Earth's orbit around the Sun, this law takes the form

$$(p_{Earth})^2 = \frac{4\pi^2}{G(M_{Sun} + M_{Earth})} (a_{Earth})^3$$

The Sun is much more massive than Earth, so the sum $M_{Sun} + M_{Earth}$ is approximately the Sun's mass alone, M_{Sun}. We therefore rewrite the equation as

$$(p_{Earth})^2 \approx \frac{4\pi^2}{G \times M_{Sun}} (a_{Earth})^3$$

Step 2 Solve: We know Earth's orbital period (p_{Earth}) and average distance (a_{Earth}), so the above equation contains only one unknown: M_{Sun}. To solve for this unknown, we multiply both sides by M_{Sun} and divide both sides by $(p_{Earth})^2$:

$$M_{Sun} \approx \frac{4\pi^2(a_{Earth})^3}{G(p_{Earth})^2}$$

We now plug in the values $p_{Earth} = 1$ yr, which is the same as 3.15×10^7 s; $a_{Earth} \approx 150$ million km, or 1.5×10^{11} m; and the experimentally measured value $G = 6.67 \times 10^{-11}$ m³/(kg × s²). The equation becomes

$$M_{Sun} \approx \frac{4\pi^2}{\left(6.67 \times 10^{-11} \dfrac{m^3}{kg \times s^2}\right)} \frac{(1.5 \times 10^{11} \text{ m})^3}{(3.15 \times 10^7 \text{ s})^2}$$

$$= 2 \times 10^{30} \text{ kg}$$

Step 3 Explain: Simply by knowing Earth's orbital period and average distance, along with the gravitational constant, G, we were able to use Newton's version of Kepler's third law to find that the Sun's mass is about 2×10^{30} kilograms. (Note: G was not measured until more than 100 years after Newton published *Principia*, so Newton was not able to calculate masses in absolute units.)

EXAMPLE 2: A *geosynchronous satellite* orbits Earth with the same period as that of Earth's rotation: 1 sidereal day, or about 23 hours, 56 minutes, 4 seconds [**Section S1.1**]. Calculate the orbital distance of a geosynchronous satellite.

SOLUTION:

Step 1 Understand: We need Newton's version of Kepler's third law in a form that we can apply to this problem. A satellite is much less massive than Earth ($M_{Earth} + M_{satellite} \approx M_{Earth}$), so we put the law in this form:

$$(p_{satellite})^2 \approx \frac{4\pi^2}{G \times M_{Earth}} (a_{satellite})^3$$

Step 2 Solve: To solve for the satellite's distance, $a_{satellite}$, we multiply both sides of the equation by $(G \times M_{Earth})/4\pi^2$ and then take the cube root of both sides:

$$a_{satellite} \approx \sqrt[3]{\frac{G \times M_{Earth}}{4\pi^2} (p_{satellite})^2}$$

If you now plug in the given value $p_{satellite} = 1$ sidereal day $\approx$ 86,164 s, along with Earth's mass and G, you will find that $a_{satellite} \approx$ 42,000 km. (You should try the calculation for yourself.)

Step 3 Explain: We have found that a geosynchronous satellite orbits at a distance of 42,000 kilometers above the *center* of Earth, which is about 35,600 kilometers above Earth's surface.

Generalizing from planets to other objects leads to an important idea about motion throughout the cosmos: *Orbits cannot change spontaneously.* Left undisturbed, planets would forever keep the same orbits around the Sun, moons would keep the same orbits around their planets, and stars would keep the same orbits in their galaxies.

Gravitational Encounters Although orbits cannot change spontaneously, they can change through exchanges of energy. One way that two objects can exchange orbital energy is through a **gravitational encounter**, in which they pass near enough so that each can feel the effects of the other's gravity. For example, in the rare cases in which a comet happens to pass near a planet, the comet's orbit can change dramatically. FIGURE 4.21 shows a comet headed toward the Sun on an unbound orbit. The comet's close passage by Jupiter allows the comet and Jupiter to exchange energy. In this case, the comet loses so much orbital energy that its orbit changes from unbound to bound and elliptical. Jupiter gains exactly as much energy as the comet loses, but the effect on Jupiter is unnoticeable because of its much greater mass.

Spacecraft engineers can use the same basic idea in reverse. For example, on its way to Pluto, the *New Horizons* spacecraft was deliberately sent past Jupiter on a path that allowed it to gain orbital energy at Jupiter's expense. This extra orbital energy boosted the spacecraft's speed; without this boost, it would have needed four extra years to reach Pluto. The effect of the tiny spacecraft on Jupiter was negligible.

A similar dynamic sometimes occurs naturally and may explain why most comets orbit so far from the Sun. Astronomers think that most comets once orbited in the same region of the solar system as the large outer planets

[**Section 12.2**]. Gravitational encounters with Jupiter or the other large planets then caused some of these comets to be "kicked out" into much more distant orbits around the Sun; some may have been ejected from the solar system completely.

Atmospheric Drag Friction can cause objects to lose orbital energy. Consider a satellite orbiting Earth. If the orbit is fairly low—such as a few hundred kilometers above Earth's surface—the satellite experiences a bit of drag from Earth's thin upper atmosphere. This drag gradually causes the satellite to lose orbital energy until it finally plummets to Earth. The satellite's lost orbital energy is converted to thermal energy in the atmosphere, which is why a falling satellite usually burns up.

Friction may also have played a role in shaping the current orbits of some of the small moons of Jupiter and other planets. These moons may once have orbited the Sun independently, and their orbits could not have changed spontaneously. However, the outer planets probably once were surrounded by clouds of gas [**Section 8.2**], and friction would have slowed objects passing through this gas. Some of these small objects may have lost just enough energy to friction to allow them to be "captured" as moons. (Mars may have captured its two small moons in a similar way.)

Escape Velocity An object that gains orbital energy moves into an orbit with a higher average altitude. For example, if we want to boost the orbital altitude of a spacecraft, we can give it more orbital energy by firing a rocket. The chemical potential energy released by the rocket fuel is converted to orbital energy for the spacecraft.

If we give a spacecraft enough orbital energy, it may end up in an unbound orbit that allows it to *escape* Earth completely (FIGURE 4.22). For example, when we send a space probe to Mars, we must use a large rocket that gives the probe enough energy to leave Earth orbit. Although it would probably make more sense to say that the probe achieves "escape energy," we instead say that it achieves **escape velocity**. The escape velocity from Earth's surface is about 40,000 km/hr,

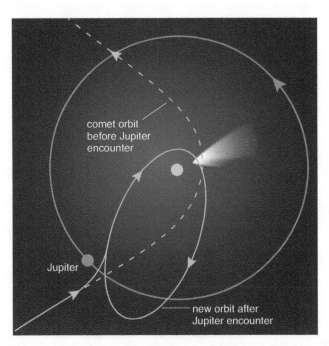

FIGURE 4.21 This diagram shows a comet in an unbound orbit of the Sun that happens to pass near Jupiter. The comet loses orbital energy to Jupiter, changing its unbound orbit to a bound orbit around the Sun.

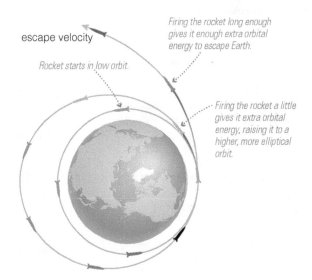

FIGURE 4.22 **interactive figure** An object with escape velocity has enough orbital energy to escape Earth completely.

or 11 km/s, meaning that this is the minimum velocity required to escape Earth's gravity for a spacecraft that starts near the surface.

Note that escape velocity does not depend on the mass of the escaping object—*any* object must travel at a velocity of 11 km/s to escape from Earth, whether it is an individual atom or molecule escaping from the atmosphere, a spacecraft being launched into deep space, or a rock blasted into the sky by a large impact. Escape velocity *does* depend on whether you start from the surface or from someplace high above the surface. Because gravity weakens with distance, it takes less energy—and hence a lower velocity—to escape from a point high above Earth than from Earth's surface.

How does gravity cause tides?

If you've spent time near an ocean, you've probably observed the rising and falling of the tides. In most places, tides rise and fall twice each day. We can understand the basic cause of tides by examining the gravitational attraction between Earth and the Moon. We'll then see how the same ideas explain many other phenomena that we can observe throughout the universe, including the synchronous rotation of our own Moon and many other worlds.

The Moon's Tidal Force Gravity attracts Earth and the Moon toward each other (with the Moon staying in orbit as

The Origin of Tides

Many people believe that tides arise because the Moon pulls Earth's oceans toward it. But if that were the whole story, there would be a bulge only on the side of Earth facing the Moon, and hence only one high tide each day. The correct explanation for tides must account for why Earth has *two* tidal bulges.

Only one explanation works: Earth must be stretching from its center in both directions (toward and away from the Moon). This stretching force, or tidal force, arises from the *difference* in the force of gravity attracting different parts of Earth to the Moon. In fact, stretching due to tides affects many objects, not just Earth. Many moons are stretched into slightly oblong shapes by tidal forces caused by their parent planets, and mutual tidal forces stretch close binary stars into teardrop shapes. In regions where gravity is extremely strong, such as near a black hole, tides can have even more dramatic effects.

it "falls around" Earth), but it affects different parts of Earth slightly differently: Because the strength of gravity declines with distance, the gravitational attraction of each part of Earth to the Moon becomes weaker as we go from the side of Earth facing the Moon to the side facing away from the Moon. This difference in attraction creates a "stretching force," or **tidal force**, that stretches the entire Earth to create two tidal bulges, one facing the Moon and one opposite the

Escape Velocity

A simple formula allows us to calculate the escape velocity from any planet, moon, or star:

$$v_{escape} = \sqrt{2 \times G \times \frac{M}{R}}$$

where M is the object's mass, R is the starting distance above the object's center, and G is the gravitational constant. If you use this formula to calculate the escape velocity from an object's *surface*, replace R with the object's radius.

EXAMPLE 1: Calculate the escape velocity from the Moon's surface. Compare it to the 11 km/s escape velocity from Earth.

SOLUTION:

Step 1 Understand: We use the above formula; because we seek the escape velocity from the Moon's *surface*, we use the Moon's radius as R. From Appendix E, the Moon's mass and radius are $M_{Moon} = 7.4 \times 10^{22}$ kg and $R_{Moon} = 1.7 \times 10^{6}$ m.

Step 2 Solve: We substitute the Moon's mass and radius into the escape velocity formula:

$$v_{escape} = \sqrt{2 \times G \times \frac{M_{Moon}}{R_{Moon}}}$$

$$= \sqrt{2 \times \left(6.67 \times 10^{-11} \frac{m^3}{kg \times s^2}\right) \times \frac{(7.4 \times 10^{22} \text{ kg})}{(1.7 \times 10^6 \text{ m})}}$$

$$\approx 2400 \text{ m/s} = 2.4 \text{ km/s}$$

Step 3 Explain: Escape velocity from the Moon's surface is 2.4 km/s, which is less than one-fourth the escape velocity (11 km/s) from Earth's surface.

EXAMPLE 2: Suppose a future space station orbits Earth in geosynchronous orbit, 42,000 kilometers above the center of Earth (see Mathematical Insight 4.3). At what velocity must a spacecraft be launched from the station to escape Earth?

SOLUTION:

Step 1 Understand: We seek the escape velocity from a satellite orbiting 42,000 kilometers above the center of Earth, so we use the escape velocity formula with the mass of Earth ($M_{Earth} = 6.0 \times 10^{24}$ kg) and R set to the satellite's distance ($R = 42,000$ km $= 4.2 \times 10^7$ m).

Step 2 Solve: With the above values, we find

$$v_{escape} = \sqrt{2 \times G \times \frac{M_{Earth}}{R_{orbit}}}$$

$$= \sqrt{2 \times \left(6.67 \times 10^{-11} \frac{m^3}{kg \times s^2}\right) \times \frac{(6.0 \times 10^{24} \text{ kg})}{(4.2 \times 10^7 \text{ m})}}$$

$$= 4400 \text{ m/s} = 4.4 \text{ km/s}$$

Step 3 Explain: The escape velocity from geosynchronous orbit is 4.4 km/s—considerably lower than the 11 km/s escape velocity from Earth's surface. It would therefore require substantially less fuel to launch a spacecraft from the space station than from Earth, which is why some people propose building future spacecraft at future space stations.

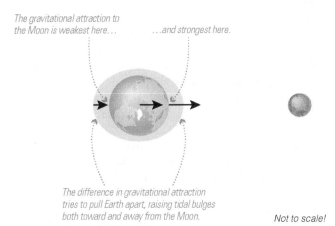

The gravitational attraction to the Moon is weakest here...   *...and strongest here.*

The difference in gravitational attraction tries to pull Earth apart, raising tidal bulges both toward and away from the Moon.

Not to scale!

FIGURE 4.23 Tides are created by the difference in the force of attraction between the Moon and different parts of Earth. The two daily high tides occur as a location on Earth rotates through the two tidal bulges. (The diagram greatly exaggerates the tidal bulges, which raise the oceans only about 2 meters and the land only about a centimeter.)

Moon (**FIGURE 4.23**). If you are still unclear about why there are *two* tidal bulges, think about a rubber band: If you pull on a rubber band, it will stretch in both directions relative to its center, even if you pull on only one side (while holding the other side still). In the same way, Earth stretches on both sides even though the Moon is tugging harder on only one side.

Tides affect both land and ocean, but we generally notice only the ocean tides because water flows much more readily than land. Earth's rotation carries any location through each of the two bulges each day, creating two high tides. Low tides occur when the location is at the points halfway between the two tidal bulges. The two "daily" high tides actually come slightly more than 12 hours apart. Because of its orbital motion around Earth, the Moon reaches its highest point in the sky at any location about every 24 hours 50 minutes, rather than every 24 hours. In other words, the tidal cycle of two high tides and two low tides takes about 24 hours 50 minutes, with each high tide occurring about 12 hours 25 minutes after the previous one.

The height and timing of ocean tides vary considerably from place to place on Earth, depending on factors such as latitude, the orientation of the coastline (such as whether it is north-facing or west-facing), and the depth and shape of any channel through which the rising tide must flow. For example, while the tide rises gradually in most locations, the incoming tide near the famous abbey on Mont-Saint-Michel, France, moves much faster than a person can swim (**FIGURE 4.24**). In centuries past, the Mont was an island twice a day at high tide but was connected to the mainland at low tide. Many pilgrims drowned when they were caught unprepared by the tide rushing in. (Today, a human-made causeway keeps the island connected to the mainland.) Another unusual tidal pattern occurs in coastal states along the northern shore of the Gulf of Mexico, where topography and other factors combine to make only one noticeable high tide and low tide each day.

The Tidal Effect of the Sun The Sun also exerts a tidal force on Earth, causing Earth to stretch along the Sun-Earth line. You might at first guess that the Sun's tidal force would be more than the Moon's, since the Sun's mass is more than a million times that of the Moon. Indeed, the *gravitational* force between Earth and the Sun is much greater than that between Earth and the Moon, which is why Earth orbits the Sun. However, the much greater distance to the Sun (than to the Moon) means that the *difference* in the Sun's pull on the near and far sides of Earth is relatively small.

The overall tidal force caused by the Sun is a little less than half that caused by the Moon (**FIGURE 4.25**). When the tidal forces of the Sun and the Moon work together, as is the case at both new moon and full moon, we get the especially pronounced *spring tides* (so named because the water tends to "spring up" from Earth). When the tidal forces of the Sun and the Moon counteract each other, as is the case at first- and third-quarter moon, we get the relatively small tides known as *neap tides*.

THINK ABOUT IT

Explain why any tidal effects on Earth caused by the other planets would be unnoticeably small.

FIGURE 4.24 Photographs of high and low tide at the abbey of Mont-Saint-Michel, France, one of the world's most popular tourist destinations. Here the tide rushes in much faster than a person can swim. Before a causeway was built (visible at the far left), the Mont was accessible by land only at low tide. At high tide, it became an island.

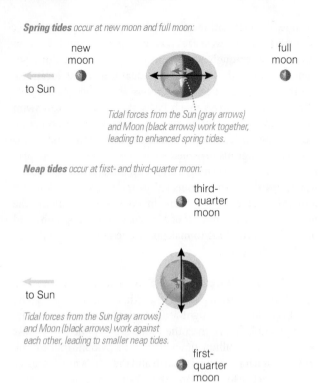

Spring tides occur at new moon and full moon:

new
moon

full
moon

to Sun

Tidal forces from the Sun (gray arrows)
and Moon (black arrows) work together,
leading to enhanced spring tides.

Neap tides occur at first- and third-quarter moon:

third-
quarter
moon

to Sun

Tidal forces from the Sun (gray arrows)
and Moon (black arrows) work against
each other, leading to smaller neap tides.

first-
quarter
moon

FIGURE 4.25 interactive figure The Sun exerts a tidal force on Earth less than half as strong as that from the Moon. When the tidal forces from the Sun and Moon work together at new moon and full moon, we get enhanced *spring tides*. When they work against each other at first- and third-quarter moons, we get smaller *neap tides*.

Tidal Friction So far, we have talked as if Earth rotated smoothly through the tidal bulges. But because tidal forces stretch Earth itself, the process creates friction, called **tidal friction**. **FIGURE 4.26** shows the effects of this friction. In essence, the Moon's gravity tries to keep the tidal bulges on the Earth-Moon line, while Earth's rotation tries to pull the bulges around with it. The resulting "compromise" keeps the bulges just ahead of the Earth-Moon line at all times.

The slight misalignment of the tidal bulges with the Earth-Moon line causes two important effects. First, the Moon's gravity always pulls back on the bulges, slowing Earth's rotation. Second, the gravity of the bulges pulls the Moon slightly ahead in its orbit, causing the Moon to move farther from Earth. These effects are barely noticeable on human time scales—for example, tidal friction increases the length of a day

by only about 1 second every 50,000 years*—but they add up over billions of years. Early in Earth's history, a day may have been only 5 or 6 hours long and the Moon may have been one-tenth or less its current distance from Earth. These changes also provide a great example of conservation of angular momentum and energy: The Moon's growing orbit gains the angular momentum and energy that Earth loses as its rotation slows.

The Moon's Synchronous Rotation Recall that the Moon always shows (nearly) the same face to Earth, a trait called **synchronous rotation** (see Figure 2.23). Synchronous rotation may seem like an extraordinary coincidence, but it is a natural consequence of tidal friction.

Because Earth is more massive than the Moon, Earth's tidal force has a greater effect on the Moon than the Moon's tidal force has on Earth. This tidal force gives the Moon two tidal bulges along the Earth-Moon line, much like the two tidal bulges that the Moon creates on Earth. (The Moon does not have visible tidal bulges, but it does indeed have excess mass along the Earth-Moon line.) If the Moon rotated through its tidal bulges in the same way as Earth, the resulting friction would cause the Moon's rotation to slow down. This is exactly what we think happened long ago.

The Moon probably once rotated much faster than it does today. As a result, it *did* rotate through its tidal bulges, and its rotation gradually slowed. Once the Moon's rotation slowed to the point at which the Moon and its bulges rotated at the same rate—that is, synchronously with the orbital period—there was no further source for tidal friction. The Moon's synchronous rotation was therefore a natural outcome of Earth's tidal effects on the Moon. In fact, if the Moon and Earth stay together long enough (for another few hundred billion years), the gradual slowing of Earth's rotation will eventually make Earth keep the same face to the Moon as well.

Tidal Effects on Other Worlds Tidal forces and tidal friction affect many worlds. Synchronous rotation is especially common. For example, Jupiter's four large moons (Io, Europa, Ganymede, and Callisto) keep nearly the same face toward Jupiter at all times, as do many other moons. Pluto and its moon Charon *both* rotate synchronously: Like two dancers, they

---

*This effect is overwhelmed on short time scales by other effects due to slight changes in Earth's internal mass distribution; these changes can alter Earth's rotation period by a second or more per year, which is why "leap seconds" are occasionally added to or subtracted from the year.

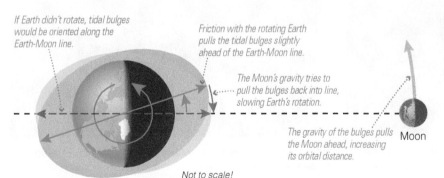

If Earth didn't rotate, tidal bulges
would be oriented along the
Earth-Moon line.

Friction with the rotating Earth
pulls the tidal bulges slightly
ahead of the Earth-Moon line.

The Moon's gravity tries to
pull the bulges back into line,
slowing Earth's rotation.

The gravity of the bulges pulls
the Moon ahead, increasing
its orbital distance.

Moon

Not to scale!

FIGURE 4.26 Earth's rotation pulls its tidal bulges slightly ahead of the Earth-Moon line, leading to gravitational effects that gradually slow Earth's rotation and increase the Moon's orbital energy and distance.

always keep the same face toward each other. Many binary star systems also rotate in this way. Some moons and planets exhibit variations on synchronous rotation. For example, Mercury rotates exactly three times for every two orbits of the Sun. This pattern ensures that Mercury's tidal bulge always aligns with the Sun at perihelion, where the Sun exerts its strongest tidal force.

Tidal forces play other roles in the cosmos as well. They can alter the shapes of objects by stretching them along the line of tidal bulges. In Chapter 11, we'll see how tidal forces also lead to the astonishing volcanic activity of Jupiter's moon Io and the possibility of a subsurface ocean on its moon Europa. As you study astronomy, you'll encounter many more cases where tides and tidal friction play important roles.

Why do all objects fall at the same rate?

We will discuss many more applications of the universal law of gravitation in this book, but for now let's look at just one more: Galileo's discovery that the acceleration of a falling object is independent of its mass.

If you drop a rock, the force acting on the rock is the force of gravity. The two masses involved are the mass of Earth and the mass of the rock, which we'll denote M_{Earth} and M_{rock}, respectively. The distance is the distance from the *center of Earth* to the center of the rock. If the rock isn't too far above Earth's surface, this distance is approximately the radius of Earth, R_{Earth} (about 6400 kilometers), so the force of gravity acting on the rock is

$$F_g = G\frac{M_{Earth}\,M_{rock}}{d^2} \approx G\frac{M_{Earth}\,M_{rock}}{(R_{Earth})^2}$$

According to Newton's second law of motion ($F = ma$), this force is equal to the product of the rock's mass and acceleration. That is,

$$G\frac{M_{Earth}\,M_{rock}}{(R_{Earth})^2} = M_{rock}\,a_{rock}$$

Note that M_{rock} "cancels" because it appears on both sides of the equation (as a multiplier), giving Galileo's result that the acceleration of the rock—or of any falling object—does not depend on the object's mass.

The text shows that the acceleration of a falling rock near the surface of Earth is

$$a_{rock} = G \times \frac{M_{Earth}}{(R_{Earth})^2}$$

Because this formula applies to *any* falling object on Earth, it is the *acceleration of gravity, g*. Calculating g is easy. Simply plug in Earth's mass (6.0×10^{24} kg) and radius (6.4×10^6 m):

$$g_{Earth} = G \times \frac{M_{Earth}}{(R_{Earth})^2}$$

$$= \left(6.67 \times 10^{-11}\frac{m^3}{kg \times s^2}\right) \times \frac{6.0 \times 10^{24}\,kg}{(6.4 \times 10^6\,m)^2} = 9.8\frac{m}{s^2}$$

EXAMPLE 1: What is the acceleration of gravity on the Moon?

SOLUTION:

Step 1 Understand: We want the acceleration of gravity on the Moon's surface, so we use the above formula with the Moon's mass (7.4×10^{22} kg) and radius (1.7×10^6 m).

Step 2 Solve: The formula becomes

$$g_{Moon} = G \times \frac{M_{Moon}}{(R_{Moon})^2}$$

$$= \left(6.67 \times 10^{-11}\frac{m^3}{kg \times s^2}\right) \times \frac{7.4 \times 10^{22}\,kg}{(1.7 \times 10^6\,m)^2} = 1.7\frac{m}{s^2}$$

Step 3 Explain: The acceleration of gravity on the Moon is 1.7 m/s², or about one-sixth that on Earth, so objects on the Moon weigh about one-sixth of what they weigh on Earth.

EXAMPLE 2: The Space Station orbits at an altitude of roughly 350 kilometers above Earth's surface. What is the acceleration of gravity at this altitude?

SOLUTION:

Step 1 Understand: Because the Space Station is significantly above Earth's surface, we cannot use the approximation $d \approx R_{Earth}$ that we used in the text. Instead, we must go back to Newton's second law and set the gravitational force on the Space Station equal to its mass times acceleration. The acceleration in this equation is the acceleration of gravity at the Space Station's altitude.

Step 2 Solve: We write Newton's second law with the force being the force of gravity acting between Earth and the Space Station, which we set equal to the Space Station's mass times its acceleration:

$$G \times \frac{M_{Earth}\,M_{station}}{d^2} = M_{station} \times a_{station}$$

You should confirm that when we solve this equation for the acceleration of gravity, we find

$$a_{station} = G \times \frac{M_{Earth}}{d^2}$$

In this case, the distance d is the 6400-kilometer radius of Earth *plus* the 350-kilometer altitude of the Station, or $d = 6750$ km $= 6.75 \times 10^6$ m. The gravitational acceleration is

$$a_{station} = G \times \frac{M_{Earth}}{d^2}$$

$$= \left(6.67 \times 10^{-11}\frac{m^3}{kg \times s^2}\right) \times \frac{6.0 \times 10^{24}\,kg}{(6.75 \times 10^6\,m)^2} = 8.8\frac{m}{s^2}$$

Step 3 Explain: The acceleration of gravity in low Earth orbit is 8.8 m/s², which is only about 10% less than the 9.8 m/s² acceleration of gravity at Earth's surface. We see again that lack of gravity cannot be the reason astronauts are weightless in orbit; rather, they are weightless because they are in free-fall.

The fact that objects of different masses fall with the same acceleration struck Newton as an astounding coincidence, even though his own equations showed it to be so. For the next 240 years, this seemingly odd coincidence remained just that—a coincidence—in the minds of most scientists. However, in 1915, Einstein showed that it is not a coincidence at all. Rather, it reveals something deeper about the nature of gravity and of the universe. Einstein described the new insights in his *general theory of relativity* (the topic of Chapter S3).

The Big Picture

Putting Chapter 4 into Context

We've covered a lot of ground in this chapter, from the scientific terminology of motion to the overarching principles that govern motion throughout the universe. Be sure you grasp the following "big picture" ideas:

- Understanding the universe requires understanding motion. Motion may seem complex, but it can be described simply using Newton's three laws of motion.

- Today, we know that Newton's laws of motion stem from deeper physical principles, including the laws of conservation of momentum, of angular momentum, and of energy. These principles enable us to understand a wide range of astronomical phenomena.

- Newton also discovered the universal law of gravitation, which explains how gravity holds planets in their orbits and much more—including how satellites can reach and stay in orbit, the nature of tides, and why the Moon rotates synchronously around Earth.

- Newton's discoveries showed that the same physical laws we observe on Earth apply throughout the universe. The universality of physics opens up the entire cosmos as a possible realm of human study.

SUMMARY OF KEY CONCEPTS

4.1 DESCRIBING MOTION: EXAMPLES FROM DAILY LIFE

- **How do we describe motion?** **Speed** is the rate at which an object is moving. **Velocity** is speed in a certain direction. **Acceleration** is a change in velocity, meaning a change in either speed or direction. **Momentum** is mass times velocity. A **force** can change an object's momentum, causing it to accelerate.

- **How is mass different from weight?** An object's mass is  the same no matter where it is located, but its weight varies with the strength of gravity or other forces acting on the object. An object becomes **weightless** when it is in **free-fall**, even though its mass is unchanged.

4.2 NEWTON'S LAWS OF MOTION

- **How did Newton change our view of the universe?** Newton showed that the same physical laws that operate on Earth also operate in the heavens, making it possible to learn about the universe by studying physical laws on Earth.

- **What are Newton's three laws of motion?** (1) An object moves at constant velocity if there is no net force acting upon it. (2) Force = mass × acceleration ($F = ma$). (3) For any force, there is always an equal and opposite reaction force.

4.3 CONSERVATION LAWS IN ASTRONOMY

- **Why do objects move at constant velocity if no force acts on them?** **Conservation of momentum** means that an object's momentum cannot change unless the object transfers momentum to or from other objects. When no force is present, no momentum can be transferred so an object must maintain its speed and direction.

- **What keeps a planet rotating and orbiting the Sun?**  **Conservation of angular momentum** means that a planet's rotation and orbit cannot change unless the planet transfers angular momentum to another object. The planets in our solar system do not exchange substantial angular momentum with each other or anything else, so their orbits and rotation rates remain steady.

- **Where do objects get their energy?** Energy is always  conserved—it can be neither created nor destroyed. Objects received whatever energy they now have from exchanges of energy with other objects. Energy comes in three basic categories—**kinetic**, **radiative**, and **potential**.

kinetic energy

radiative energy   potential energy

4.4 THE UNIVERSAL LAW OF GRAVITATION

- **What determines the strength of gravity?** The **universal**  **law of gravitation** states that every object attracts every other object with a gravitational force that is proportional to the product of the objects' masses and declines with the square of the distance between their centers:

$$F_g = G \frac{M_1 M_2}{d^2}$$

- **How does Newton's law of gravity extend Kepler's laws?** (1) Newton showed that any object going around another object will obey Kepler's first two laws. (2) He showed that ellipses (or circles), which define **bound orbits**, are not the only possible orbital shape—orbits can also be **unbound** and in the form of parabolas or hyperbolas. (3) He showed that two objects actually orbit their common **center of mass**. (4) **Newton's version of Kepler's third law** allows us to calculate the masses of orbiting objects from their orbital periods and distances.

4.5 ORBITS, TIDES, AND THE ACCELERATION OF GRAVITY

- **How do gravity and energy allow us to understand orbits?** Gravity determines orbits, and an object cannot change its orbit unless it gains or loses **orbital energy**—the sum of its kinetic and gravitational potential energies—through energy

- **How does gravity cause tides?** The Moon's gravity a **tidal force** that stretches Earth along the Earth-Moon line, causing Earth to bulge both toward and away from the Moon.

Earth's rotation carries us through the two bulges each day, giving us two daily high tides and two daily low tides. Tidal forces also lead to **tidal friction**, which is gradually slowing Earth's rotation and explains the synchronous rotation of the Moon.

- **Why do all objects fall at the same rate?** Newton's equations show that the acceleration of gravity is independent of the mass of a falling object, so all objects fall at the same rate.

VISUAL SKILLS CHECK

Use the following questions to check your understanding of some of the many types of visual information used in astronomy. Answers are provided in Appendix J. For additional practice, try the Chapter 4 Visual Quiz at MasteringAstronomy®.

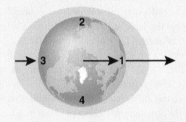

The figure above, based on Figure 4.23, shows how the Moon causes tides on Earth. Note that the North Pole is in the center of the diagram, so the numbers 1 through 4 label points along Earth's equator.

1. What do the three black arrows represent?
   a. the tidal force Earth exerts on the Moon
   b. the Moon's gravitational force at different points on Earth
   c. the direction in which Earth's water is flowing
   d. Earth's orbital motion
2. Where is it high tide?
   a. point 1 only
   b. point 2 only
   c. points 1 and 3
   d. points 2 and 4
3. Where is it low tide?
   a. point 1 only
   b. point 2 only
   c. points 1 and 3
   d. points 2 and 4

4. What time is it at point 1?
   a. noon
   b. midnight
   c. 6 a.m.
   d. cannot be determined from the information in the figure
5. The light blue ellipse represents tidal bulges. In what way are these bulges drawn inaccurately?
   a. There should be only one bulge rather than two.
   b. They should be aligned with the Sun rather than the Moon.
   c. They should be much smaller compared to Earth.
   d. They should be more pointy in shape.

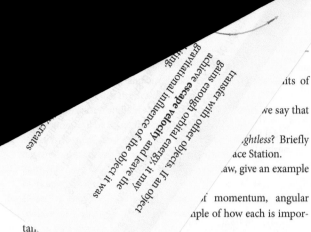

...its of

...we say that

...ghtless? Briefly ...ace Station.

...aw, give an example

...f momentum, angular ...ple of how each is impor-
ta...

6. Define ....ergy, and *potential energy*, with at least two ...

7. Define *tempera...* ....mal energy. How are they related? How are they differe...

8. What do we mean by *mass-energy*? Explain the formula $E = mc^2$.

9. Summarize the *universal law of gravitation* both in words and with an equation.

10. What is the difference between a *bound* and an *unbound orbit*? What orbital shapes are possible?

11. What do we need to know if we want to measure an object's mass with *Newton's version of Kepler's third law*? Explain.

12. Explain why orbits cannot change spontaneously, and how a *gravitational encounter* can cause a change. How can an object achieve *escape velocity*?

13. Explain how the Moon creates tides on Earth. Why do we have two high and low tides each day? How do the tides vary with the phase of the Moon?

14. What is *tidal friction*? What effects does it have on Earth? How does it explain the Moon's synchronous rotation?

TEST YOUR UNDERSTANDING

Does It Make Sense?

Decide whether the statement makes sense (or is clearly true) or does not make sense (or is clearly false). Explain clearly; not all of these have definitive answers, so your explanation is more important than your chosen answer.

15. If you could buy a pound of chocolate on the Moon, using a pound scale from Earth, you'd get more chocolate than if you bought a pound on Earth.

16. Suppose you could enter a vacuum chamber (a chamber with no air in it) on Earth. Inside this chamber, a feather would fall at the same rate as a rock.

17. When an astronaut goes on a space walk outside the Space Station, she will quickly float away from the station unless she has a tether holding her to the station.

18. I used Newton's version of Kepler's third law to calculate Saturn's mass from orbital characteristics of its moon Titan.

19. If the Sun were magically replaced with a giant rock that had precisely the same mass, Earth's orbit would not change.

20. The fact that the Moon rotates once in precisely the time it takes to orbit Earth once is such an astonishing coincidence that scientists probably never will be able to explain it.

21. Venus has no oceans, so it could not have tides even if it had a moon (which it doesn't).

22. If an asteroid passed by Earth at just the right distance, Earth's gravity would capture it and make it our second moon.

23. When I drive my car at 30 miles per hour, it has more kinetic energy than it does at 10 miles per hour.

24. Someday soon, scientists are likely to build an engine that produces more energy than it consumes.

Quick Quiz

Choose the best answer to each of the following. Explain your reasoning with one or more complete sentences.

25. Which one of the following describes an object that is *accelerating*? (a) A car traveling on a straight, flat road at 50 miles per hour. (b) A car traveling on a straight uphill road at 30 miles per hour. (c) A car going around a circular track at a steady 100 miles per hour.

26. Suppose you visited another planet. (a) Your mass and weight would be the same as they are on Earth. (b) Your mass would be the same as on Earth, but your weight would be different. (c) Your weight would be the same as on Earth, but your mass would be different.

27. Which person is weightless? (a) A child in the air as she plays on a trampoline. (b) A scuba diver exploring a deep-sea wreck. (c) An astronaut on the Moon.

28. Consider the statement "There's no gravity in space." This statement is (a) completely false. (b) false if you are close to a planet or moon, but true in between the planets. (c) completely true.

29. To make a rocket turn left, you need to (a) fire an engine that shoots out gas to the left. (b) fire an engine that shoots out gas to the right. (c) spin the rocket clockwise.

30. Compared to its angular momentum when it is farthest from the Sun, Earth's angular momentum when it is nearest to the Sun is (a) greater. (b) less. (c) the same.

31. The gravitational potential energy of a contracting interstellar cloud (a) stays the same at all times. (b) gradually transforms into other forms of energy. (c) gradually grows larger.

32. If Earth were twice as far from the Sun, the force of gravity attracting Earth to the Sun would be (a) twice as strong. (b) half as strong. (c) one quarter as strong.

33. According to the universal law of gravitation, what would happen to Earth if the Sun were somehow replaced by a black hole of the same mass? (a) Earth would be quickly sucked into the black hole. (b) Earth would slowly spiral into the black hole. (c) Earth's orbit would not change.

34. If the Moon were closer to Earth, high tides would (a) be higher than they are now. (b) be lower than they are now. (c) occur three or more times a day rather than twice a day.

PROCESS OF SCIENCE

Examining How Science Works

35. *Testing Gravity.* Scientists are continually trying to learn whether our current understanding of gravity is complete or must be modified. Describe how the observed motion of spacecraft headed out of our solar system (such as the *Voyager* spacecraft) can be used to test the accuracy of our current theory of gravity.

36. *How Does the Table Know?* Thinking deeply about seemingly simple observations sometimes reveals underlying truths that we might otherwise miss. For example, think about holding a golf ball in one hand and a bowling ball in the other. To keep them motionless you must actively adjust the tension in your arm muscles so that each arm exerts a different upward force that

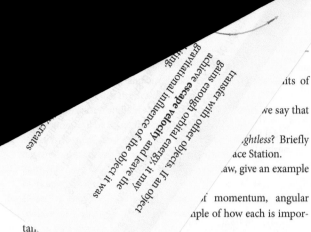
(folded corner text) ...gravitational influence of the object. ... transfer with orbital objects and leave the ... achieve *escape velocity*. If an object ... creates ...

exactly balances the weight of each ball. Now, think about what happens when you set the balls on a table. Somehow, the table also exerts exactly the right amount of upward force to keep the balls motionless, even though their weights are very different. How does a table "know" to make the same type of adjustment that you make when you hold the balls motionless in your hands? (*Hint:* Think about the origin of the force pushing upward on the objects.)

GROUP WORK EXERCISE

37. *Your Ultimate Energy Source.* According to the law of conservation of energy, the energy your body is using right now had to come from somewhere else. Your task in this exercise is to trace the flow of that energy as far back in time as you can. Before you begin, assign the following roles to the people in your group: *Scribe* (takes notes on the group's activities), *Proposer* (proposes explanations to the group), *Skeptic* (points out weaknesses in proposed explanations), and *Moderator* (leads group discussion and makes sure the group works as a team). After you have your roles, make a list going backwards in time describing how the energy you are using right now has proceeded through time. Then, for each item on the list, state whether that energy was in the form of kinetic energy, gravitational potential energy, chemical potential energy, electrical potential energy, mass-energy, or radiative energy.

INVESTIGATE FURTHER

In-Depth Questions to Increase Your Understanding

Short-Answer/Essay Questions

38. *Units of Acceleration.*
   a. If you drop a rock from a very tall building, how fast will it be going after 4 seconds? **b.** As you sled down a steep, slick street, you accelerate at a rate of 4 meters per second squared. How fast will you be going after 5 seconds? **c.** You are driving along the highway at a speed of 60 miles per hour when you slam on the brakes. If your acceleration is at an average rate of −20 miles per hour per second, how long will it take to come to a stop?

39. *Gravitational Potential Energy.* For each of the following, which object has more gravitational potential energy, and how do you know?
   a. A bowling ball perched on a cliff ledge or a baseball perched on the same ledge **b.** A diver on a 10-meter platform or a diver on a 3-meter diving board **c.** A 100-kilogram satellite orbiting Jupiter or a 100-kilogram satellite orbiting Earth (Assume both satellites orbit at the same distance from their planet's center.)

40. *Einstein's Famous Formula.*
   a. What is the meaning of the formula $E = mc^2$? Be sure to define each variable. **b.** How does this formula explain the generation of energy by the Sun? **c.** How does this formula explain the destructive power of nuclear bombs?

41. *The Gravitational Law.*
   a. How does quadrupling the distance between two objects affect the gravitational force between them? **b.** Suppose the Sun were somehow replaced by a star with twice as much mass. What would happen to the gravitational force between Earth and the Sun? **c.** Suppose Earth were moved to one-third of its current distance from the Sun. What would happen to the gravitational force between Earth and the Sun?

42. *Allowable Orbits?*
   a. Suppose the Sun were replaced by a star with twice as much mass. Could Earth's orbit stay the same? Why or why not? **b.** Suppose Earth doubled in mass (but the Sun stayed the same as it is now). Could Earth's orbit stay the same? Why or why not?

43. *Head-to-Foot Tides.* You and Earth attract each other gravitationally, so you should also be subject to a tidal force resulting from the difference between the gravitational attraction felt by your feet and that felt by your head (at least when you are standing). Explain why you can't feel this tidal force.

44. *Synchronous Rotation.* Suppose the Moon had rotated *more slowly* when it formed than it does now. Would it still have ended up in synchronous rotation? Why or why not?

45. *Geostationary Orbit.* A satellite in *geostationary* orbit appears to remain stationary in the sky as seen from any particular location on Earth.
   a. Briefly explain why a geostationary satellite must orbit Earth in 1 *sidereal* day, rather than 1 solar day. **b.** Explain why a geostationary satellite must be in orbit around Earth's equator, rather than in some other orbit (such as around the poles). **c.** Home satellite dishes (such as those used for television) receive signals from communications satellites. Explain why these satellites must be in geostationary orbit.

46. *Elevator to Orbit.* Some people have proposed building a giant elevator from Earth's surface to the altitude of geosynchronous orbit. The top of the elevator would then have the same orbital distance and period as any satellite in geosynchronous orbit.
   a. Suppose you were to let go of an object at the top of the elevator. Would the object fall? Would it orbit Earth? Explain. **b.** Briefly explain why (not counting the huge costs for construction) the elevator would make it much cheaper and easier to put satellites in orbit or to launch spacecraft into deep space.

Quantitative Problems

Be sure to show all calculations clearly and state your final answers in complete sentences.

47. *Energy Comparisons.* Use the data in Table 4.1 to answer each of the following questions.
   a. Compare the energy of a 1-megaton H-bomb to the energy released by a major earthquake. **b.** If the United States obtained all its energy from oil, how much oil would be needed each year? **c.** Compare the Sun's annual energy output to the energy released by a supernova.

48. *Moving Candy Bar.* We can calculate the kinetic energy of any moving object with a very simple formula: kinetic energy $= \frac{1}{2}mv^2$, where m is the object's mass and v is its velocity or speed. Table 4.1 shows that metabolizing a candy bar releases about 10^6 joules. How fast must the candy bar travel to have the same 10^6 joules in the form of kinetic energy? (Assume the candy bar's mass is 0.2 kilogram.) Is your answer faster or slower than you expected?

49. *Spontaneous Human Combustion.* Suppose that all the mass in your body were suddenly converted into energy according to the formula $E = mc^2$. How much energy would be released? Compare this to the energy released by a 1-megaton H-bomb (see Table 4.1). What effect would your disappearance have on your surroundings?

50. *Fusion Power.* No one has yet succeeded in creating a commercially viable way to produce energy through nuclear fusion. However, suppose we could build fusion power plants using the hydrogen in water as a fuel. Based on the data in Table 4.1, how much water would we need each minute to meet U.S. energy needs? Could such a reactor power the entire United States with the water flowing from your kitchen sink? Explain. (*Hint:* Use the annual U.S. energy consumption to find the energy consumption per minute, and then divide by the energy yield from fusing 1 liter of water to figure out how many liters would be needed each minute.)

51. *Understanding Newton's Version of Kepler's Third Law.* Find the orbital period for the planet in each case. (*Hint:* The calculations for this problem are so simple that you will not need a calculator.)
a. A planet with twice Earth's mass orbiting at a distance of 1 AU from a star with the same mass as the Sun **b.** A planet with the same mass as Earth orbiting at a distance of 1 AU from a star with four times the Sun's mass

52. *Using Newton's Version of Kepler's Third Law.*
a. Find Earth's approximate mass from the fact that the Moon orbits Earth in an average time of 27.3 days at an average distance of 384,000 kilometers. (*Hint:* The Moon's mass is only about $\frac{1}{80}$ of Earth's.) **b.** Find Jupiter's mass from the fact that its moon Io orbits every 42.5 hours at an average distance of 422,000 kilometers. **c.** You discover a planet orbiting a distant star that has about the same mass as the Sun, with an orbital period of 63 days. What is the planet's orbital distance? **d.** Pluto's moon Charon orbits Pluto every 6.4 days with a semimajor axis of 19,700 kilometers. Calculate the *combined* mass of Pluto and Charon. **e.** Calculate the orbital period of a spacecraft in an orbit 300 kilometers above Earth's surface. **f.** Estimate the mass of the Milky Way Galaxy from the fact that the Sun orbits the galactic center every 230 million years at a distance of 27,000 light-years. (As we'll discuss in Chapter 23, this calculation actually tells us only the mass of the galaxy *within* the Sun's orbit.)

53. *Escape Velocity.* Calculate the escape velocity from each of the following.
a. The surface of Mars (mass $= 0.11 M_{Earth}$, radius $= 0.53 R_{Earth}$) **b.** The surface of Mars's moon Phobos (mass $= 1.1 \times 10^{16}$ kg, radius $= 12$ km) **c.** The cloud tops of Jupiter (mass $= 317.8 M_{Earth}$, radius $= 11.2 R_{Earth}$) **d.** Our solar system, starting from Earth's orbit (*Hint:* Most of the mass of our solar system is in the Sun; $M_{Sun} = 2.0 \times 10^{30}$ kg.) **e.** Our solar system, starting from Saturn's orbit

54. *Weights on Other Worlds.* Calculate the acceleration of gravity on the surface of each of the following worlds. How much would *you* weigh, in pounds, on each of these worlds?
a. Mars (mass $= 0.11 M_{Earth}$, radius $= 0.53 R_{Earth}$) **b.** Venus (mass $= 0.82 M_{Earth}$, radius $= 0.95 R_{Earth}$) **c.** Jupiter (mass $= 317.8 M_{Earth}$, radius $= 11.2 R_{Earth}$) Bonus: Given that Jupiter has no solid surface, how could you weigh yourself on Jupiter? **d.** Jupiter's moon Europa (mass $= 0.008 M_{Earth}$, radius $= 0.25 R_{Earth}$) **e.** Mars's moon Phobos (mass $= 1.1 \times 10^{16}$ kg, radius $= 12$ km)

55. *Gees.* Acceleration is sometimes measured in *gees*, or multiples of the acceleration of gravity: 1 gee (1g) means $1 \times g$, or 9.8 m/s²; 2 gees (2g) means $2 \times g$, or 2×9.8 m/s² $= 19.6$ m/s²; and so on. Suppose you experience 6 gees of acceleration in a rocket.

a. What is your acceleration in meters per second squared? **b.** You will feel a compression force from the acceleration. How does this force compare to your normal weight? **c.** Do you think you could survive this acceleration for long? Explain.

56. *Extra Moon.* Suppose Earth had a second moon, called Swisscheese, with an average orbital distance double the Moon's and a mass about the same as the Moon's.
a. Is Swisscheese's orbital period longer or shorter than the Moon's? Explain. **b.** The Moon's orbital period is about one month. Apply Kepler's third law to find the approximate orbital period of Swisscheese. (*Hint:* If you form the ratio of the orbital distances of Swisscheese and the Moon, you can solve this problem with Kepler's original version of his third law rather than looking up all the numbers you'd need to apply Newton's version of Kepler's third law.) **c.** In words, describe how tides would differ because of the presence of this second moon. Consider the cases when the two moons are on the same side of Earth, on opposite sides of Earth, and 90° apart in their orbits.

Discussion Questions

57. *Knowledge of Mass-Energy.* Einstein's discovery that energy and mass are equivalent has led to technological developments that are both beneficial and dangerous. Discuss some of these developments. Overall, do you think the human race would be better or worse off if we had never discovered that mass is a form of energy? Defend your opinion.

58. *Perpetual Motion Machines.* Every so often, someone claims to have built a machine that can generate energy perpetually from nothing. Why isn't this possible according to the known laws of nature? Why do you think claims of perpetual motion machines sometimes receive substantial media attention?

Web Projects

59. *Space Station.* Visit a NASA website with pictures from the Space Station. Choose two photos that illustrate some facet of Newton's laws of motion or gravity. Explain how what is going on is related to Newton's laws.

60. *Tide Tables.* Find a tide table or tide chart for a beach town that you'd like to visit. Explain how to read the table and discuss any differences between the actual tidal pattern and the idealized tidal pattern described in this chapter.

61. *Space Elevator.* Read more about space elevators (see Problem 46) and how they might make it easier and cheaper to get to Earth orbit or beyond. Write a short report about the feasibility of building a space elevator, and briefly discuss the pros and cons of such a project.

5 LIGHT AND MATTER
READING MESSAGES FROM THE COSMOS

LEARNING GOALS

May the warp be the white light of morning,
May the weft be the red light of evening,
May the fringes be the falling rain,
May the border be the standing rainbow.
Thus weave for us a garment of brightness.
—*Song of the Sky Loom (Native American)*

Ancient observers could discern only the most basic features of the light that they saw, such as color and brightness. Over the past several hundred years, we have discovered that light carries far more information. Today, we can analyze the light of distant objects to learn what they are made of, how hot they are, how fast they are moving, and much more. Light is truly the cosmic messenger, bringing the stories of distant objects to Earth.

In this chapter, we will focus our attention on learning how to read the messages carried by light. We'll begin with a brief look at the basic interactions of light and matter that create those messages, and then study the properties of light and matter individually and in some detail. With that background, we'll be ready to explore how a spectrum forms, so that we can understand how light can encode so much information about distant objects.

MA Light and Spectroscopy Tutorial, Lesson 1

5.1 LIGHT IN EVERYDAY LIFE

What do you see as you look around you? You may be tempted to list nearby objects, but all you're really seeing is *light* that has interacted with those objects. Through intuition and experience, you're able to interpret the colors and patterns of the light and turn them into information about the objects and substances that surround you.

Astronomers study the universe in much the same way. Telescopes collect the light of distant objects, and we use the light to extract information about those objects. The more we understand about light and its interactions with matter, the more information we can extract. As a first step in developing this understanding, let's take a closer look at our everyday experience with light.

How do we experience light?

You can tell that light is a form of energy even without opening your eyes. Outside on a hot, sunny day you can feel your skin warm as it absorbs sunlight. Because greater warmth means more molecular motion, sunlight must be transferring its energy to the molecules in your skin. The energy that light carries is called *radiative energy*; recall that it is one of the three basic categories of energy, along with kinetic and potential energy (see Figure 4.10).

Energy and Power We measure energy in units of joules [**Section 4.3**], so we can use these energy units to measure the total amount of energy that light transfers to your skin. With light, however, we are usually more interested in the *rate* at which it carries energy toward or away from us than in the

total amount of energy it carries. After all, because light always travels through space at the speed of light, we cannot hold light in our hands in the same way that we can hold a hot potato, which has thermal energy, or a rock, which has gravitational potential energy. The rate of energy flow is called **power**, which we measure in units called **watts**. A power of 1 watt means an energy flow of 1 joule per second:

$$1 \text{ watt} = 1 \text{ joule/s}$$

For example, a 100-watt light bulb requires 100 joules of energy (which you buy from the electric company) for each second it is turned on. Interestingly, the power requirement of an average human—about 10 million joules per day—is about the same as that of a 100-watt light bulb.

Light and Color Everyday experience tells us that light comes in different forms that we call *colors*. You've probably seen a prism split light into the rainbow of light called a **spectrum** (FIGURE 5.1). The basic colors in a rainbowlike spectrum are red, orange, yellow, green, blue, and violet. We see *white* when these colors are mixed in roughly equal proportions. Light from the Sun or a light bulb is often called *white light*, because it contains all the colors of the rainbow. *Black* is what we perceive when there is no light and hence no color.

The wide variety of all possible colors comes from mixtures of just a few colors in varying proportions. Your television takes advantage of this fact to simulate a huge range of colors by combining only red, green, and blue light; these three colors are often called the *primary colors of vision*, because they are the colors directly detected by cells in your eyes. Colors tend to look different on paper, so artists generally work with an alternative set of primary colors: red, yellow, and blue. If you do any graphic design work, you may be familiar with the CMYK process, in which the four colors cyan, magenta, yellow, and black are mixed to produce a great variety of colors; the CMYK process was used to print this book.

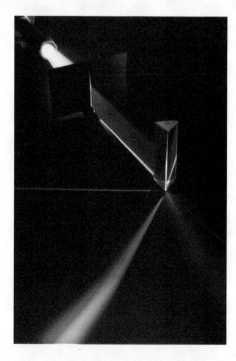

FIGURE 5.1
When we pass white light through a prism, it disperses into a rainbow of color that we call a *spectrum*.

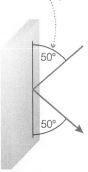

Reflection (mirror): angle of incidence = angle of reflection.

a A mirror *reflects* light along a simple path: The angle at which the light strikes the mirror is the same angle at which it is reflected.

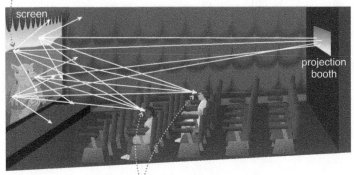

Scattering: The screen scatters light from the projector in many directions...

...*so that every person in the audience sees light from all parts of the screen.*

b A movie screen *scatters* light in many different directions, so that each member of the audience can watch the movie. The pages in a book do the same thing, which is why you can read them from different angles and distances.

FIGURE 5.2 Reflection and scattering.

SEE IT FOR YOURSELF

If you have a magnifying glass handy, hold it close to your TV screen to see the individual red, blue, and green dots. If you don't have a magnifying glass, try splashing a few droplets of water onto your TV screen (carefully!). What do you see when you look closely at the droplets?

You can produce a spectrum with either a prism or a **diffraction grating**, which is a piece of plastic or glass etched with many closely spaced lines. If you have a DVD handy, you can make a spectrum for yourself. The bottom of a DVD is etched with many closely spaced circles and therefore acts like a diffraction grating. That is why you see rainbows of color on the bottom of the disc when you hold it up to light.

How do light and matter interact?

Light can interact with matter in four basic ways, all of which are familiar in everyday life:

- **Emission:** A light bulb *emits* visible light; the energy of the light comes from electrical potential energy supplied to the light bulb.

- **Absorption:** When you place your hand near an incandescent light bulb, your hand *absorbs* some of the light, and this absorbed energy warms your hand.

- **Transmission:** Some forms of matter, such as glass or air, *transmit* light, which means allowing it to pass through.

- **Reflection/scattering:** Light can bounce off matter, leading to what we call *reflection* when the bouncing is all in the same general direction or *scattering* when the bouncing is more random (**FIGURE 5.2**).

Materials that transmit light are said to be *transparent,* and materials that absorb light are called *opaque.* Many materials are neither perfectly transparent nor perfectly opaque. For example, dark sunglasses and clear eyeglasses are both partially

transparent, but the dark glasses absorb more and transmit less light. Materials often interact differently with different colors of light. For example, red glass transmits red light but absorbs other colors, while a green lawn reflects (scatters) green light but absorbs all other colors.

Let's put these ideas together to understand what happens when you walk into a room and turn on the light switch (**FIGURE 5.3**). The light bulb begins to emit white light, which is a mix of all the colors in the spectrum. Some of this light exits the room, transmitted through the windows. The rest of the light strikes the surfaces of objects inside the room, and the material properties of each object determine the colors it absorbs or reflects. The light coming from each object therefore carries an enormous amount of information about the object's location, shape and structure, and composition. You acquire this information when light enters your eyes, where special cells in your retina absorb it and send signals to your brain. Your brain interprets the messages that light carries, recognizing materials and objects in the process we call *vision.*

All the information that light brings us from the cosmos was encoded by the same four basic interactions between light and matter common to our everyday experience. However, our eyes perceive only a tiny fraction of all the information contained in light. Modern instruments can break light into a much wider variety of colors and can analyze those colors in far greater detail. In order to understand how to decode that information, we need to examine the nature of light and matter more closely.

5.2 PROPERTIES OF LIGHT

Light is familiar to all of us, but its nature remained a mystery for most of human history. Experiments performed by Isaac Newton in the 1660s provided the first real insights into the nature of light. It was already known that passing white light through a prism produced a rainbow of color, but many people thought the colors came from the prism rather than

CHAPTER **5** LIGHT AND MATTER **139**

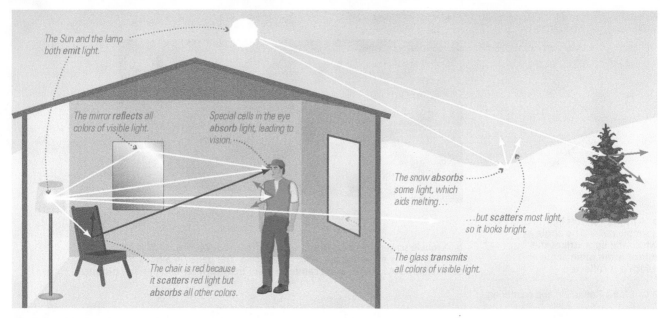

FIGURE 5.3 interactive figure This diagram shows examples of the four basic interactions between light and matter: emission, absorption, transmission, and reflection (or scattering).

from the light itself. Newton proved that the colors came from the light by placing a second prism in front of the light of just one color, such as red, from the first prism. If the rainbow of color had come from the prism itself, the second prism would have produced a rainbow just like the first. But it did not: When only red light entered the second prism, only red light emerged, proving that the color was a property of the light and not of the prism.

What is light?

Newton's work tells us something about the nature of color, but it still does not tell us exactly what light *is*. Newton himself guessed that light is made up of countless tiny particles. However, other scientists soon conducted experiments that demonstrated that light behaves like waves. Thus began one of the most important debates in scientific history: Is light a wave or a particle? To understand this question, and our modern answer to it, we must first understand the differences between particles and waves.

Particles and Waves in Everyday Life Marbles, baseballs, and individual atoms and molecules are all examples of *particles*. A particle of matter can sit still or it can move from one place to another. If you throw a baseball at a wall, it obviously travels from your hand to the wall.

In contrast, think about what happens when you toss a pebble into a pond, creating a set of outward moving ripples, or *waves* (**FIGURE 5.4**). These waves consist of *peaks*, where the water is higher than average, and *troughs*, where the water is lower than average. If you watch as the waves pass by a floating leaf, you'll see the leaf rise up with each peak and drop down with each trough, but the leaf itself will *not* travel across the pond's surface with the wave. We conclude that even though the waves are moving outward, the particles

(molecules) that make up the water are moving primarily up and down (along with a bit of sloshing back and forth). That is, the waves carry *energy* outward from the place where the pebble landed but do not carry matter along with them. In essence, a particle is a *thing*, while a wave is a *pattern* revealed by its interaction with particles.

Let's focus on three basic properties of waves: wavelength, frequency, and speed.* **Wavelength** is the distance from one

---

*There is also a fourth wave property, *amplitude*, defined as half the height from trough to peak. Amplitude is related to the brightness of light.

Wavelength is the distance from one peak to the next (or one trough to the next).

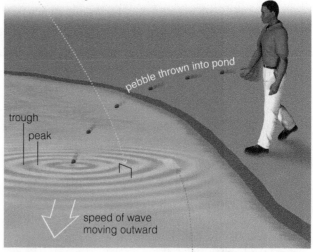

*Leaf bobs up and down with the **frequency** of the waves.*

FIGURE 5.4 interactive figure Tossing a pebble into a pond generates waves. The waves carry energy outward, but matter, such as a floating leaf and the molecules of the water, only bobs up and down (with a bit of sloshing back and forth) as the waves pass by.

peak to the next (or one trough to the next). **Frequency** is the number of peaks passing by any point each second. For example, if the leaf bobs up and down three times each second, then three peaks must be passing by it each second, which means the waves have a frequency of three **cycles per second**. "Cycles per second" are often called **hertz (Hz)**, so we can also describe this frequency as 3 Hz. The **speed** of the waves tells us how fast their peaks travel across the pond. Because the waves carry energy, the speed essentially tells us how fast the energy travels from one place to another.

A simple formula relates the wavelength, frequency, and speed of any wave. Suppose a wave has a wavelength of 1 centimeter and a frequency of 3 hertz. The wavelength tells us that each time a peak passes by, the wave peak has traveled 1 centimeter. The frequency tells us that three peaks pass by each second. The speed of the wave must therefore be 3 centimeters per second. If you try a few more similar examples, you'll find the general rule

$$\text{wavelength} \times \text{frequency} = \text{speed}$$

Light as an Electromagnetic Wave You've probably heard that light is a wave, but it isn't quite like the waves we see in everyday life. More familiar waves always move through some form of matter. For example, the waves on the pond move through the water, causing particles (molecules) of water to vibrate up and down and slosh back and forth, while sound waves move through air, causing air molecules to vibrate back and forth. The vibrations of matter allow the waves to transmit energy from one place to another, even though particles of matter do not travel along with the waves. In contrast to these everyday examples of waves, we do not see anything move up and down when light travels through space. So what, exactly, is "waving" when a light wave passes by?

The answer is what scientists call electric and magnetic fields. The concept of a **field** is a bit abstract, but it is used to describe the strength of force that a particle would experience at any point in space. For example, Earth creates a *gravitational field* that describes the strength of gravity at any distance from Earth, which means that the strength of the field declines with the square of the distance from Earth's center [**Section 4.4**]. Electricity and magnetism also create forces, so their strength in different places can be described in terms of *electric fields* and *magnetic fields*.

Light waves are traveling vibrations of both electric and magnetic fields, so we say that light is an **electromagnetic wave**. Just as the ripples on a pond will cause a leaf to bob up and down, the vibrations of the electric field in an electromagnetic wave will cause any charged particle, such as an electron, to bob up and down. If you could set up electrons in a row, they would wriggle like a snake as light passed by (**FIGURE 5.5a**). The distance between peaks in this row of electrons would tell us the wavelength of the light wave, while the number of times each electron bobbed up and down would tell us the frequency (**FIGURE 5.5b**).

All light travels through empty space at the same speed—the **speed of light** (represented by the letter *c*), which is about 300,000 kilometers per second. Because the speed of

If you could line up electrons, they would bob up and down with the vibrating electric field of a passing light wave.

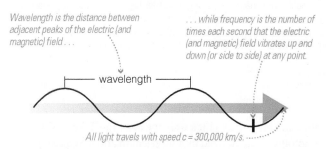

a Electrons move when light passes by, showing that light carries a vibrating electric field.

Wavelength is the distance between adjacent peaks of the electric (and magnetic) field . . .

. . . while frequency is the number of times each second that the electric (and magnetic) field vibrates up and down (or side to side) at any point.

|← wavelength →|

All light travels with speed c = 300,000 km/s.

b The vibrations of the electric field determine the wavelength and frequency of a light wave. Light also has a magnetic field (not shown) that vibrates perpendicular to the direction of the electric field vibrations.

FIGURE 5.5 Interactive figure Light is an electromagnetic wave.

any wave is its wavelength times its frequency, we find a very important relationship between wavelength and frequency for light: *The longer the wavelength, the lower the frequency, and vice versa.* For example, light waves with a wavelength of 1 centimeter must have half the frequency of light waves with a wavelength of $\frac{1}{2}$ centimeter and one-fourth the frequency of light waves with a wavelength of $\frac{1}{4}$ centimeter (**FIGURE 5.6**).

Photons: "Particles" of Light Waves and particles appear distinctly different in everyday life. For example, no one would confuse the ripples on a pond with a baseball. However, experiments have shown that light behaves as *both* a wave and a particle. We say that light comes in individual "pieces," called **photons**, that have properties of both particles and waves. Like baseballs, photons of light can be counted

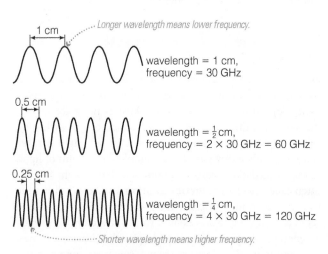

Longer wavelength means lower frequency.

1 cm

wavelength = 1 cm, frequency = 30 GHz

0.5 cm

wavelength = $\frac{1}{2}$ cm, frequency = 2 × 30 GHz = 60 GHz

0.25 cm

wavelength = $\frac{1}{4}$ cm, frequency = 4 × 30 GHz = 120 GHz

Shorter wavelength means higher frequency.

FIGURE 5.6 Because all light travels through space at the same speed, light of longer wavelength must have lower frequency, and vice versa. (GHz stands for gigahertz, or 10^9 Hz.)

individually and can hit a wall one at a time. Like waves, each photon is characterized by a wavelength and a frequency. The idea that light can be both a wave and a particle may seem quite strange, but it is fundamental to our modern understanding of physics. (We will discuss some of the implications of this wave-particle duality in Chapter S4.)

Just as a moving baseball carries a specific amount of kinetic energy, each photon of light carries a specific amount of radiative energy. The shorter the wavelength of the light (or, equivalently, the higher its frequency), the higher the energy of the photons.

To sum up, our modern understanding maintains that (1) light is both a particle and a wave, an idea we describe by saying that light consists of individual photons characterized by wavelength, frequency, and energy, and (2) the wavelength, frequency, and energy of light are simply related because all photons travel through space at the same speed—the speed of light.

THINK ABOUT IT

If you assume that each of the three waves shown in Figure 5.6 represents a photon of light, which one has the most energy? Which one has the least energy? Explain.

What is the electromagnetic spectrum?

Newton's experiments proved that white light is a mix of all the colors in the rainbow. Later scientists found that there is light "beyond the rainbow" as well. Just as there are sounds that our ears cannot hear (such as the sound of a dog whistle), there is light that our eyes cannot see. In fact, light that we can see is only a tiny part of the complete spectrum of light, usually called the **electromagnetic spectrum**; light itself is often called **electromagnetic radiation**. FIGURE 5.7 shows the way the electromagnetic spectrum is commonly divided into regions according to wavelength (or, equivalently, frequency or energy). Keep in mind that despite the different names, everything in the electromagnetic spectrum represents a form of light and therefore consists of photons that travel through space at the speed of light.

The light that our eyes can see, which we call **visible light**, is found near the middle of the spectrum, with wavelengths ranging from about 400 nanometers at the blue or violet end of the rainbow to about 700 nanometers at the red end. (A nanometer [nm] is a billionth of a meter.) Light with wavelengths somewhat longer than red light is called **infrared**, because it lies beyond the red end of the rainbow. **Radio waves** are the longest-wavelength light. Wavelengths of light that fall near the border between infrared and radio waves, where wavelengths range from micrometers to centimeters, are sometimes given the name **microwaves**. In astronomy, you may occasionally hear portions of the microwave band described more specifically by wavelength. For example, the science conducted with telescopes optimized to detect microwaves with wavelengths of around 1 to a few millimeters is often called *millimeter astronomy*, and the science conducted with wavelengths of tenths of a millimeter is often called *submillimeter astronomy*.

On the other side of the spectrum, light with wavelengths somewhat shorter than those of blue light is called **ultraviolet**, because it lies beyond the blue (or violet) end of the rainbow. Light with even shorter wavelengths is called **X rays**, and the shortest-wavelength light is called **gamma rays**. Notice that visible light is an extremely small part of the entire electromagnetic spectrum: The reddest red that our eyes can see has only about twice the wavelength of the bluest blue, but the radio waves from your favorite radio station are a billion times longer than the X rays used in a doctor's office.

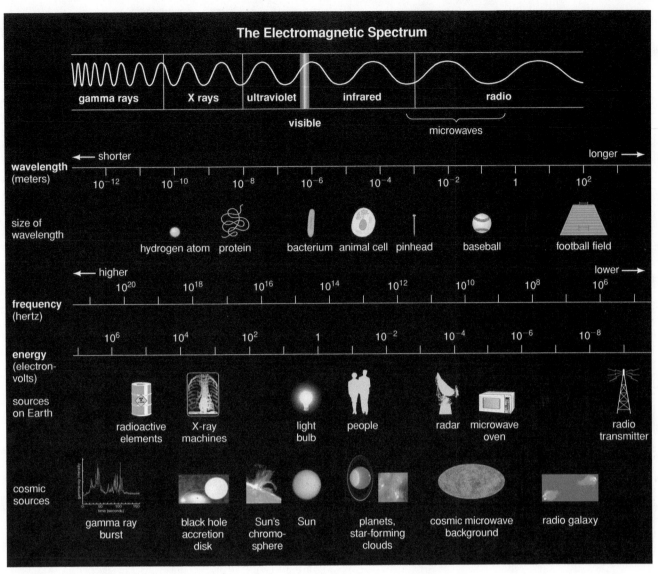

FIGURE 5.7 interactive figure The electromagnetic spectrum. Notice that wavelength increases as we go from gamma rays to radio waves, while frequency and energy increase in the opposite direction. (Energy is given in units of *electron-volts*, eV: 1 eV = 1.60 × 10^{-19} joule.)

The different energies of different forms of light explain many familiar effects in everyday life. Radio waves carry so little energy that they have no noticeable effect on our bodies. However, radio waves can make electrons move up and down in an antenna, which is how your car radio receives the radio waves coming from a radio station. Molecules moving around in a warm object emit infrared light, which is why we sometimes associate infrared light with heat. Receptors in our eyes respond to visible-light photons, making vision possible. Ultraviolet photons carry enough energy to harm cells in our skin, causing sunburn or skin cancer. X-ray photons have enough energy to penetrate through skin and muscle but can be blocked by bones or teeth. That is why doctors and dentists can see our bone structures on photographs taken with X-ray light.

Just as different colors of visible light may be absorbed or reflected differently by the objects we see (see Figure 5.3), the various portions of the electromagnetic spectrum may interact in very different ways with matter. For example, a brick wall is opaque to visible light but transmits radio waves, which is why radios and cell phones work inside buildings. Similarly, glass that is transparent to visible light may be opaque to ultraviolet light. In general, certain types of matter tend to interact more strongly with certain types of light, so each type of light carries different information about distant objects in the universe. That is why astronomers seek to observe light of all wavelengths [**Section 6.4**].

5.3 PROPERTIES OF MATTER

Light carries information about matter across the universe, but we are usually more interested in the matter the light is coming from—such as planets, stars, and galaxies—than we are in the light itself. We must therefore explore the nature of matter if we are to decode the messages carried by light.

What is the structure of matter?

Like the nature of light, the nature of matter remained mysterious for most of human history. Nevertheless, ancient philosophers came up with some ideas that are still with us today.

The ancient Greek philosopher Democritus (c. 470–380 B.C.) wondered what would happen if we could break a piece of matter, such as a rock, into ever smaller pieces. He claimed that the rock would eventually break into particles so small that nothing smaller could be possible. He called these particles *atoms*, a Greek term meaning "indivisible." Building on the beliefs of earlier Greek philosophers, Democritus assumed that all materials were composed from four basic *elements*: fire, water, earth, and air. He proposed that the properties of different elements could be explained by the physical characteristics of their atoms. For example, Democritus suggested that atoms of water were smooth and round, so water flowed and had no fixed shape, while burns were painful because atoms of fire were thorny. He imagined atoms of earth to be rough and jagged, so they could fit together like pieces of a three-dimensional jigsaw puzzle, and he used this idea to suggest that the universe began as a chaotic mix of atoms that slowly clumped together to form our world.

Although Democritus was wrong in his specifics, he was on the right track. All ordinary matter is indeed composed of **atoms**, and the properties of ordinary matter depend on the physical characteristics of its atoms. However, by modern definition, atoms are *not* indivisible because they are composed of even smaller particles.

MATHEMATICAL INSIGHT 5.1

Wavelength, Frequency, and Energy

 Math Review Video: Problem Solving, Part 4

The relationship *wavelength* × *frequency* = *speed* holds for any wave. For light, which travels (in a vacuum) at speed $c = 3 \times 10^8$ m/s, this relationship becomes

$$\lambda \times f = c$$

where λ (the Greek letter *lambda*) stands for wavelength and f stands for frequency. Note that, because c is a constant, frequency must go up when wavelength goes down, and vice versa.

The radiative energy (E) carried by a photon of light is given by

$$E = h \times f$$

where h is *Planck's constant* ($h = 6.626 \times 10^{-34}$ joule × s). Energy therefore increases with frequency.

EXAMPLE 1: A radio station at 93.3 FM broadcasts radio waves with a frequency of 93.3 megahertz (MHz). What is their wavelength?

SOLUTION:

Step 1 Understand: Radio waves are a form of light, so they obey the relationship $\lambda \times f = c$. We are given the frequency (f) and know the speed of light (c), so we can simply solve for the wavelength (λ). There is one subtlety: The units of frequency, called hertz or "cycles per second," are really just "per second," or 1/s; the reason is that "cycles" is just a descriptive term, with no units itself. So we write 93.3 megahertz as 93.3×10^6 1/s.

Step 2 Solve: We solve for wavelength by dividing both sides of $\lambda \times f = c$ by f, which gives $\lambda = c/f$. We now plug in the speed of light and the frequency to find

$$\lambda = \frac{c}{f} = \frac{3 \times 10^8 \, \frac{m}{s}}{93.3 \times 10^6 \, \frac{1}{s}} = 3.2 \text{ m}$$

Step 3 Explain: Radio waves with a frequency of 93.3 MHz have a wavelength of 3.2 meters. That is why radio towers are so large; they must be taller than the waves they are transmitting.

EXAMPLE 2: The middle of the visible spectrum is green light with a wavelength of about 550 nanometers. What is its frequency?

SOLUTION:

Step 1 Understand: All light obeys the relation $\lambda \times f = c$. In this case we are given the wavelength, so we simply solve the equation for the frequency.

Step 2 Solve: Dividing both sides of the equation $\lambda \times f = c$ by λ gives $f = c/\lambda$. We plug in the speed of light and the wavelength ($\lambda = 550 \times 10^{-9}$ m) to find

$$f = \frac{c}{\lambda} = \frac{3 \times 10^8 \, \frac{m}{s}}{550 \times 10^{-9} \, m} = 5.45 \times 10^{14} \, \frac{1}{s}$$

Step 3 Explain: Green visible light has a frequency of about 5.5×10^{14} 1/s, which is 5.5×10^{14} Hz, or 550 trillion Hz. This high frequency is one reason the wave properties of light are not obvious in everyday life.

EXAMPLE 3: What is the energy of a visible-light photon with a wavelength of 550 nanometers?

SOLUTION:

Step 1 Understand: The energy of a photon is $E = h \times f$. We are given the photon's wavelength rather than frequency, so we use the fact that $f = c/\lambda$ to write

$$E = h \times f = h \times \frac{c}{\lambda}$$

Step 2 Solve: We plug in the wavelength and Planck's constant to find

$$E = h \times \frac{c}{\lambda}$$

$$= (6.626 \times 10^{-34} \text{ joule} \times s) \times \frac{3 \times 10^8 \, \frac{m}{s}}{550 \times 10^{-9} \, m}$$

$$= 3.6 \times 10^{-19} \text{ joule}$$

Step 3 Explain: The energy of a single visible-light photon is about 3.6×10^{-19} joule. Note that this is barely a *billion-trillionth* of the 100 joules of energy needed each second by a 100-watt light bulb.

Atoms come in different types, and each type corresponds to a different chemical **element**. Scientists have identified more than 100 chemical elements, and fire, water, earth, and air are *not* among them. Some of the most familiar chemical elements are hydrogen, helium, carbon, oxygen, silicon, iron, gold, silver, lead, and uranium. Appendix D gives the periodic table of all the elements.

Atomic Structure Each chemical element consists of a different type of atom, and atoms are in turn made of particles that we call **protons**, **neutrons**, and **electrons** (FIGURE 5.8). Protons and neutrons are found in the tiny **nucleus** at the center of the atom. The rest of the atom's volume contains electrons, which surround the nucleus. Although the nucleus is very small compared to the atom as a whole, it contains most of the atom's mass, because protons and neutrons are each about 2000 times as massive as an electron. Note that atoms are incredibly small: Millions could fit end to end across the period at the end of this sentence. The number of atoms in a single drop of water (typically, 10^{22} to 10^{23} atoms) may exceed the number of stars in the observable universe.

The properties of an atom depend mainly on the **electrical charge** in its nucleus. Electrical charge is a fundamental physical property that describes how strongly an object will interact with electromagnetic fields; total electrical charge is always

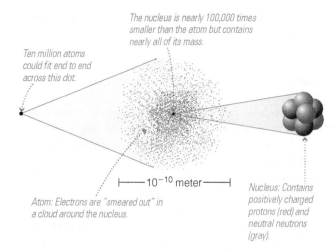

The nucleus is nearly 100,000 times smaller than the atom but contains nearly all of its mass.

Ten million atoms could fit end to end across this dot.

├──── 10^{-10} meter ────┤

Atom: Electrons are "smeared out" in a cloud around the nucleus.

Nucleus: Contains positively charged protons (red) and neutral neutrons (gray).

FIGURE 5.8 The structure of a typical atom. Note that atoms are extremely tiny: The atom shown in the middle is magnified to about 1 billion times its actual size, and the nucleus on the right is magnified to about 100 trillion times its actual size.

conserved, just as energy is always conserved. We define the electrical charge of a proton as the basic unit of positive charge, which we write as $+1$. An electron has an electrical charge that is precisely opposite that of a proton, so we say it has negative charge (-1). Neutrons are electrically neutral, meaning that they have no charge.

What Do Polarized Sunglasses Have to Do with Astronomy?

If you go to the store to buy a pair of sunglasses, you'll face a dizzying array of choices. Sunglasses come in different styles and different tints and with different efficiencies in blocking ultraviolet and infrared light. Most of these choices should make sense to you (well, perhaps not all of the styles), but one option may not be familiar: The labels on some sunglasses say that they are "polarized." What does this mean? The term comes from a property of light, called *polarization*, that has to do with the direction in which a light wave vibrates and how those vibrations change when light bounces off or passes through matter. Polarization is important not only to sunglasses but also to astronomy.

To explore this idea, think about how waves move on a string when you shake one end of it. The string vibrates either up and down or back and forth while the wave itself moves along it in a direction perpendicular to the direction of vibration. Light waves move in a similar way, with the electric and magnetic fields vibrating either up and down or side to side compared with the direction of travel. For example, the wave shown in Figure 5.5b is moving to the right on the page while its electric field vibrates up and down on the page.

The direction of vibration affects the way light interacts with matter. As Figure 5.5a indicates, an electric field that vibrates up and down will make electrons move up and down as the wave passes by. That is, the direction in which the electric field vibrates determines the direction in which charged particles vibrate as the wave passes by. Because the direction of wave vibration matters, we give it a name: the *polarization* of the wave. An individual wave moving toward you can be polarized with its vibrations either up and down or side to side or some combination of those two.

Each light wave (or, more technically, each individual photon) has a particular direction of polarization, although our eyes do not

detect it. If all the waves taken together have no preferential direction of vibration, we say that the light is *unpolarized*. However, some physical processes produce waves with a particular direction of polarization, which is where your sunglasses and astronomy come in.

When light reflects off a flat horizontal surface like the ground or a lake, all the reflected light tends to have its electric field vibrating horizontally. (Light with other directions of vibration is absorbed or transmitted.) In other words, the reflected light is horizontally polarized. Polarized sunglasses are designed to block light with horizontal polarization, which is often the cause of "glare." Of course, the polarized glasses work only if you are wearing them horizontally; if you turn a pair of polarized sunglasses so that the two lenses are no longer horizontal to the ground, they will not block glare effectively.

In astronomy, we aren't worried about glare from distant objects, but if we learn that a light source is producing polarized light, this tells us something about the nature of the source. For example, light that passes through clouds of interstellar dust tends to be polarized, telling us that the dust grains in the cloud must be preferentially absorbing light with electric fields vibrating in a particular direction. More detailed analysis has taught us that the polarization arises because the microscopic dust grains have an elongated shape, and all tend to be aligned in the same way as a result of magnetic fields within the clouds. Polarization arises in many other astronomical contexts as well, including the study of the leftover radiation from the Big Bang. Although polarization has provided important insights into many astronomical processes, its analysis can be fairly technical, and we will not discuss it further in this book.

Oppositely charged particles attract and similarly charged particles repel. The attraction between the positively charged protons in the nucleus and the negatively charged electrons that surround it is what holds an atom together. Ordinary atoms have identical numbers of electrons and protons, making them electrically neutral overall.*

Although we can think of electrons as tiny particles, they are not quite like tiny grains of sand and they don't orbit the nucleus the way planets orbit the Sun. Instead, the electrons in an atom form a kind of "smeared out" cloud that surrounds the nucleus and gives the atom its apparent size. The electrons aren't really cloudy, but it is impossible to pinpoint their positions in the atom. The electrons therefore give the atom a size far larger than that of its nucleus even though they represent only a tiny portion of the atom's mass. If you imagine an atom on a scale that makes its nucleus the size of your fist, its electron cloud would be many kilometers wide.

Atomic Terminology You've probably learned the basic terminology of atoms in past science classes, but let's review it just to be sure. **FIGURE 5.9** summarizes the key terminology we will use in this book.

Each different chemical element contains a different number of protons in its nucleus. This number is its **atomic number**. For example, a hydrogen nucleus contains just one proton, so its atomic number is 1. A helium nucleus contains two protons, so its atomic number is 2. The *combined* number

---

*You may wonder why electrical repulsion doesn't cause the positively charged protons in a nucleus to fly apart from one another. The answer is that an even stronger force, called the *strong force*, overcomes electrical repulsion and holds the nucleus together [**Section S4.2**].

---

atomic number = number of protons
atomic mass number = number of protons + neutrons
(A neutral atom has the same number of electrons as protons.)

Hydrogen (¹H)   **Helium (⁴He)**   **Carbon (¹²C)**

   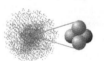   

atomic number = 1   atomic number = 2   atomic number = 6
atomic mass   atomic mass   atomic mass
number = 1   number = 4   number = 12
(1 electron)   (2 electrons)   (6 electrons)

---

*Different **isotopes** of a given element contain the same number of protons, but different numbers of neutrons.*

Isotopes of Carbon

carbon-12   carbon-13   carbon-14

^{12}C ^{13}C ^{14}C
(6 protons   (6 protons   (6 protons
+ 6 neutrons)   + 7 neutrons)   + 8 neutrons)

FIGURE 5.9 Terminology of atoms.

of protons and neutrons in an atom is called its **atomic mass number**. The atomic mass number of ordinary hydrogen is 1 because its nucleus is just a single proton. Helium usually has two neutrons in addition to its two protons, giving it an atomic mass number of 4. Carbon usually has six protons and six neutrons, giving it an atomic mass number of 12.

Every atom of a given element contains exactly the same number of protons, but the number of neutrons can vary. For example, all carbon atoms have six protons, but they may have six, seven, or eight neutrons. Versions of an element with different numbers of neutrons are called **isotopes** of that element. Isotopes are named by listing their element name and atomic mass number. For example, the most common isotope of carbon has six protons and six neutrons, giving it atomic mass number $6 + 6 = 12$, so we call it *carbon-12*. The other isotopes of carbon are carbon-13 (six protons and seven neutrons) and carbon-14 (six protons and eight neutrons). We sometimes write the atomic mass number as a superscript to the left of the element symbol: ^{12}C, ^{13}C, ^{14}C. We read ^{12}C as "carbon-12."

THINK ABOUT IT

The symbol ^{4}He represents helium with an atomic mass number of 4. ^{4}He is the most common form of helium, containing two protons and two neutrons. What does the symbol ^{3}He represent?

Molecules The number of different material substances is far greater than the number of chemical elements because atoms can combine to form **molecules**. Some molecules consist of two or more atoms of the same element. For example, we breathe O_2, oxygen molecules made of two oxygen atoms. Other molecules, such as the water molecule, are made up of atoms of two or more different elements. (Molecules with two or more types of atom are often called *compounds*.) The symbol H_2O tells us that a water molecule contains two hydrogen atoms and one oxygen atom. The chemical properties of a molecule are different from those of its individual atoms. For example, molecular oxygen (O_2) behaves very differently from atomic oxygen (O), and water behaves very differently from pure hydrogen or pure oxygen.

What are the phases of matter?

Interactions between light and matter depend on the physical state of the matter, which we usually describe by the matter's **phase**. For example, molecules of H₂O can exist in three familiar phases: as **solid** ice, as **liquid** water, and as the **gas** we call water vapor. But how can the *same* molecules (H₂O) look and act so different in different phases?

You are probably familiar with the idea of a **chemical bond**, the name we give to the interactions between electrons that hold the atoms in a molecule together. For example, we say that chemical bonds hold the hydrogen and oxygen atoms together in a molecule of H₂O. Similar but much weaker interactions among electrons hold together the many water molecules in a block of ice or a pool of water. We can think of the interactions that keep neighboring atoms or molecules close together as other types of bonds, with the phases of solid, liquid, and gas differing in the strength of the bonds between neighboring atoms and molecules. Phase changes occur when one type of bond is broken and replaced by another. Changes in either pressure or temperature (or both) can cause phase changes, but it's easier to think first about temperature: As a substance is heated, the average kinetic energy of its particles increases, enabling the particles to break the bonds holding them to their neighbors.

Phase Changes in Water Water is the only familiar substance that we see in all three phases (solid, liquid, gas) in everyday life, so let's consider what happens to water as an example of how phase changes occur as a substance heats up.

At low temperatures, water molecules have a relatively low average kinetic energy, allowing them to be tightly bound to their neighbors in the *solid* structure of ice. As long as the temperature remains below freezing, the water molecules in ice remain rigidly held together. However, the molecules within this rigid structure are always vibrating, and higher temperature means greater vibrations. If we start with ice at a very low temperature, the molecular vibrations grow gradually stronger as the temperature rises toward the melting point, which is 0°C at ordinary (sea level) atmospheric pressure.

The melting point is the temperature at which the molecules have enough energy to break the solid bonds of ice. The molecules can then move much more freely among one another, allowing the water to flow as a *liquid*. However, the molecules in liquid water are not completely free of one another, as we can tell from the fact that droplets of water can stay intact. Adjacent molecules in liquid water must therefore still be held together by a type of bond, though it is much looser than the bond that holds them together in solid ice.

If we continue to heat the water, the increasing kinetic energy of the molecules will ultimately break the bonds between neighboring molecules altogether. The molecules will then be able to move freely, and freely moving particles constitute a *gas*. Above the boiling point (100°C at sea level), all the bonds between adjacent molecules are broken so the water can exist only as a gas.

We see ice melting into liquid water and liquid water boiling into gas so often that it's tempting to think that's the end

of the story. However, a little thought should convince you that the reality has to be more complex. For example, you know that Earth's atmosphere contains water vapor that condenses to form clouds and rain. But Earth's surface temperature is well below the boiling point of water, so how is it that our atmosphere can contain water in the gas phase?

The answer lies in the fact that temperature is a measure of the *average* kinetic energy of the particles in a substance [**Section 4.3**]. Individual particles may have substantially lower or higher energies than the average. Even at the low temperatures at which most water molecules are bound together as ice or liquid, a few molecules will always have enough energy to break free of their neighbors and enter the gas phase. In other words, some gas (water vapor) is always present along with solid ice or liquid water. The process by which molecules escape from a solid is called **sublimation**, and the process by which molecules escape from a liquid is called **evaporation**. Higher temperatures lead to higher rates of sublimation or evaporation.

Molecular Dissociation and Ionization Above the boiling point, all the water will have entered the gas phase. What happens if we continue to raise the temperature?

The molecules in a gas move freely, but they often collide with one another. As the temperature rises, the molecules move faster and the collisions become more violent. At high enough temperatures, the collisions become so violent that they can break the chemical bonds holding individual water molecules together. The molecules then split into pieces, a process we call **molecular dissociation**. (In the case of water, molecular dissociation usually frees one hydrogen atom and leaves a negatively charged molecule that consists of one hydrogen atom and one oxygen atom [OH]; at even higher temperatures, the OH dissociates into individual atoms.)

At still higher temperatures, collisions can break the bonds holding electrons around the nuclei of individual atoms, allowing the electrons to go free. The loss of one or more negatively charged electrons leaves the remaining atom with a net positive charge. Charged atoms (whether positive or negative) are called **ions**, and the process of stripping electrons from atoms is called **ionization**. At temperatures of several thousand degrees, the process of ionization turns what once was water into a hot gas consisting of freely moving electrons and positively charged ions of hydrogen and oxygen. This type of hot gas, in which atoms have become ionized, is called a **plasma**. Because a plasma contains many charged particles, its interactions with light are different from those of a gas consisting of neutral atoms, which is one reason plasma is sometimes referred to as "the fourth phase of matter." However, because the electrons and ions are not bound to one another, it is also legitimate to call plasma a gas. That is why we sometimes say that the Sun is made of hot gas and sometimes say that it is made of plasma; both statements are correct.

The degree of ionization in a plasma depends on its temperature and composition. A neutral hydrogen atom contains only one electron, so hydrogen can be ionized only once; the remaining hydrogen ion, designated H^+, is simply a proton. Oxygen, with atomic number 8, has eight electrons when it is neutral, so it can be ionized multiple times. *Singly ionized* oxygen is missing one electron, so it has a charge of +1 and is designated O^+. *Doubly ionized* oxygen, or O^{+2}, is missing two electrons; *triply ionized* oxygen, or O^{+3}, is missing three electrons; and so on. At temperatures of several million degrees, oxygen can be *fully ionized*, in which case all eight electrons are stripped away and the remaining ion has a charge of +8.

FIGURE 5.10 summarizes the changes that occur as we heat water from ice to a fully ionized plasma. Other chemical substances go through similar phase changes, but the changes generally occur at different temperatures for different substances.

Phases and Pressure Temperature is the primary factor determining the phase of a substance and the ways in which light interacts with it, but pressure also plays a role. You're undoubtedly familiar with the idea of pressure in an everyday sense: For example, you can put more pressure on your arm by squeezing it. In science, we use a more precise definition: **Pressure** is the *force per unit area* pushing on an object's surface. You feel more pressure when you squeeze your arm because squeezing increases the force on each square centimeter of your arm's surface. Similarly, piling rocks on a table increases the weight (force) on the table, which therefore increases the pressure on the surface of the table; if the pressure becomes too great, the table breaks. The gas in an atmosphere also creates pressure, because the weight of the gas bears down on everything beneath it. For example, at sea level on Earth, the weight of the atmosphere creates a pressure of about 14.7 pounds per square inch. That is, the total weight of all the air above each square inch of Earth's surface is about 14.7 pounds [**Section 10.1**].

Pressure can affect phases in a variety of ways. For example, deep inside Earth, the pressure is so high that Earth's

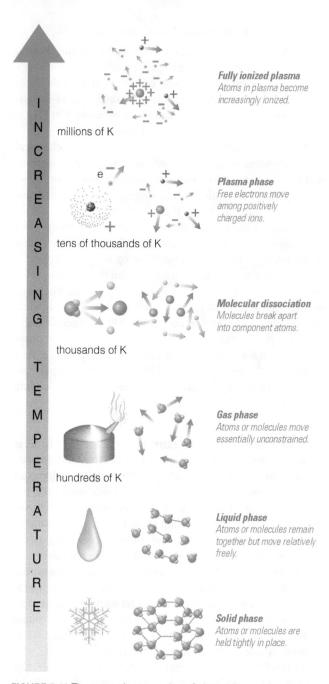

millions of K

Fully ionized plasma
Atoms in plasma become increasingly ionized.

tens of thousands of K

Plasma phase
Free electrons move among positively charged ions.

thousands of K

Molecular dissociation
Molecules break apart into component atoms.

hundreds of K

Gas phase
Atoms or molecules move essentially unconstrained.

Liquid phase
Atoms or molecules remain together but move relatively freely.

Solid phase
Atoms or molecules are held tightly in place.

FIGURE 5.10 The general progression of phase changes in water.

inner metal core remains solid, even though the temperature is high enough that the metal would melt into liquid under less extreme pressure conditions [**Section 9.1**]. On a planetary surface, atmospheric pressure can determine whether water is stable in liquid form.

Remember that liquid water is always evaporating (or ice sublimating) at a low level, because a few molecules randomly get enough energy to break the bonds holding them to their neighbors. On Earth, enough liquid water has evaporated from the oceans to make water vapor an important ingredient of our atmosphere. Some of these atmospheric water vapor molecules collide with the ocean surface, where they can "stick" and rejoin the ocean—essentially the opposite of evaporation (**FIGURE 5.11**). The greater the pressure created

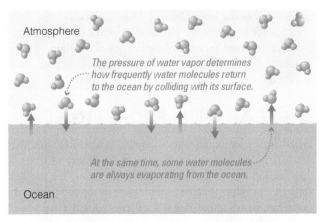

FIGURE 5.11 Evaporation of water molecules from the ocean is balanced in part by molecules of water vapor in Earth's atmosphere returning to the ocean. The rate at which these molecules return is directly related to the pressure created by water vapor in the atmosphere.

by water vapor molecules in our atmosphere,* the higher the rate at which water molecules return to the ocean. This direct return of water vapor molecules from the atmosphere helps keep the total amount of water in Earth's oceans fairly stable.† On the Moon, where the lack of atmosphere means no pressure from water vapor at all, liquid water would evaporate quite quickly (as long as the temperature were high enough that it did not freeze first). The same is true on Mars, because the atmosphere lacks enough water vapor to balance the rate of evaporation.

High pressure can also cause gases to dissolve in liquid water. For example, sodas are made by putting water in contact with high-pressure carbon dioxide gas. Because of the high pressure, many more carbon dioxide molecules enter the water than are released, so the water becomes "carbonated"—that is, it has a lot of dissolved carbon dioxide. When you open a bottle of carbonated water, exposing it to air with ordinary pressure, the dissolved carbon dioxide quickly bubbles up and escapes.

How is energy stored in atoms?

Now that we have reviewed the structure of matter and how its phase depends on temperature and pressure, it is time to return to the primary goal of this chapter: understanding how we learn about distant objects by studying their light. To produce light, these objects must somehow transform energy contained in matter into the vibrations of electric and magnetic fields that we call light. We therefore need to focus on the charged particles within atoms, particularly the electrons, because only particles that have charge can interact with light.

Atoms contain energy in three different ways. First, by virtue of their mass, they possess mass-energy in the amount mc^2.

*Technically, this is known as the *vapor pressure* of water in the atmosphere. We can also measure vapor pressure for other atmospheric constituents, and the total gas pressure is the sum of all the individual vapor pressures.

†Rain and snow also contribute, of course; however, even if Earth's temperature rose enough that raindrops and snowflakes could no longer form, only a small fraction of Earth's ocean water would evaporate before the return rate of water vapor molecules balanced the evaporation rate.

Second, they possess kinetic energy by virtue of their motion. Third, they contain *electrical potential energy* that depends on the arrangement of their electrons around their nuclei. To interpret the messages carried by light, we must understand how electrons store and release this electrical potential energy.

Energy Levels in Atoms The energy stored by electrons in atoms has a strange but important property: The electrons can have only particular amounts of energy, and not other energies in between. As an analogy, suppose you're washing windows on a building. If you use an adjustable platform to reach high windows, you can stop the platform at any height above the ground. But if you use a ladder, you can stand only at *particular* heights—the heights of the rungs of the ladder—and not at other heights in between. The possible energies of electrons in atoms are like the possible heights on a ladder. Only a few particular energies are possible; energies between these special few are not possible. The possible energies are known as the **energy levels** of an atom.

FIGURE 5.12 shows the energy levels of hydrogen, the simplest of all elements. The energy levels are labeled on the left in numerical order and on the right in units of *electronvolts*, or *eV* for short (1 eV = 1.60 × 10⁻¹⁹ joule). The lowest possible energy level—called level 1 or the *ground state*—is defined as an energy of 0 eV. Each of the higher energy levels (sometimes called *excited states*) is labeled with the extra energy of an electron in that level compared to an electron in the ground state.

Energy Level Transitions An electron can rise from a low energy level to a higher one or fall from a high level to a lower one. Such changes are called **energy level transitions**. Because energy must be conserved, energy level transition can occur only when an electron gains or loses the specific

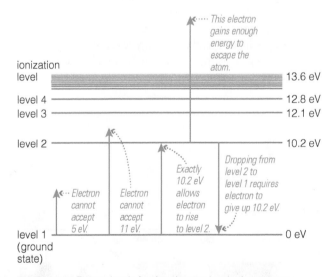

FIGURE 5.12 Energy levels for the electron in a hydrogen atom. The electron can change energy levels only if it gains or loses the amount of energy separating the levels. If the electron gains enough energy to reach the ionization level, it can escape from the atom, leaving behind a positively charged ion. (The many levels between level 4 and the ionization level are not labeled.)

amount of energy separating two levels. For example, an electron in level 1 can rise to level 2 only if it gains 10.2 eV of energy. If you try to give the electron 5 eV of energy, the electron won't accept it because it is not enough energy to reach level 2. Similarly, if you try to give the electron 11 eV, the electron won't accept it because it is too much for level 2 but not enough to reach level 3. Once in level 2, the electron can return to level 1 by giving up 10.2 eV of energy. Figure 5.12 shows several examples of allowed and disallowed energy level transitions.

Notice that the amount of energy separating the various levels gets smaller at higher levels. For example, it takes more energy to raise the electron from level 1 to level 2 than from level 2 to level 3, which in turn takes more energy than the transition from level 3 to level 4. If the electron gains enough energy to reach the *ionization level,* it escapes the atom completely, thereby ionizing the atom. Any excess energy beyond the amount needed for ionization becomes kinetic energy of the free-moving electron.

THINK ABOUT IT

Are there any circumstances under which an electron in a hydrogen atom can lose 2.6 eV of energy? Explain.

Quantum Physics If you think about it, the idea that electrons in atoms are restricted to particular energy levels is quite bizarre. It is as if you had a car that could go around a track only at particular speeds and not at speeds in between. How strange it would seem if your car suddenly changed its speed from 5 miles per hour to 20 miles per hour without first passing through a speed of 10 miles per hour! In scientific terminology, the electron's energy levels in an atom are said to be *quantized,* and the study of the energy levels of electrons (and other particles) is called *quantum physics* (or *quantum mechanics*). We will explore some of the astonishing implications of quantum physics in Chapter S4.

Electrons have quantized energy levels in all atoms, not just in hydrogen. Moreover, the allowed energy levels differ from element to element and from one ion of an element to another ion of the same element. Even molecules have quantized energy levels. As we will see shortly, the different energy levels of different atoms and molecules allow light to carry "fingerprints" that can tell us the chemical composition of distant objects.

5.4 LEARNING FROM LIGHT

Matter leaves its fingerprints whenever it interacts with light. Examining the color of an object is a crude way of studying the clues left by the matter it contains. For example, a red shirt absorbs all visible photons except those in the red part of the spectrum, so we know that it must contain a dye with these special light-absorbing characteristics. If we take light and disperse it into a spectrum, we can see the spectral fingerprints more clearly. The photograph that opens this chapter (page 137) shows the Sun's visible-light spectrum in great detail, with the rainbow of color stretching in horizontal rows from the upper left to the lower right of the photograph. We see similar dark or bright lines when we look at almost any spectrum, whether it is the spectrum of the flame from the gas grill in someone's backyard or the spectrum of a distant galaxy whose light we collect with a gigantic telescope. As long as we collect enough light to see details in the spectrum, we can learn many fundamental properties of the object we are viewing, no matter how far away the object is located.

The process of obtaining a spectrum and reading the information it contains is called **spectroscopy**. If you project a spectrum produced by a prism onto a wall, it looks like a rainbow (at least for visible light). However, it's often more useful to display spectra as graphs that show the amount, or **intensity**, of the light at each wavelength. For example, consider the spectrum in FIGURE 5.13, which plots the intensity of light from an astronomical object at wavelengths ranging from the ultraviolet on the left to the infrared on the right. At wavelengths where a lot of light is coming from the object, the intensity is high, while at wavelengths where there is little light, the intensity is low.*

---

*More technically, intensity is proportional to the total amount of *energy* transmitted by the light at each wavelength.

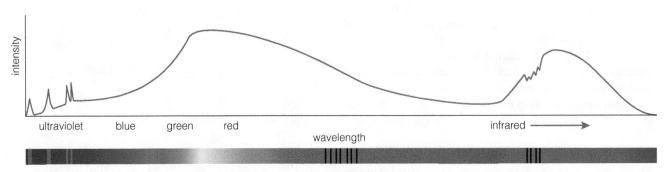

FIGURE 5.13 A schematic spectrum obtained from the light of a distant object. The "rainbow" at bottom shows how the light would appear if viewed with a prism or diffraction grating; of course, our eyes cannot see the ultraviolet or infrared light. The graph shows the corresponding intensity of the light at each wavelength. The intensity is high where the rainbow is bright and low where it is dim (such as in places where the rainbow shows dark lines).

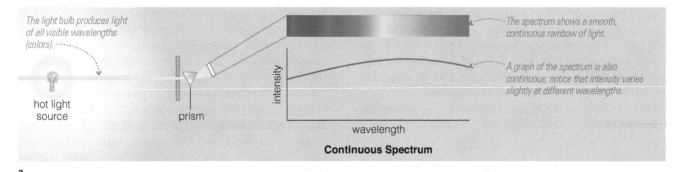

The light bulb produces light of all visible wavelengths (colors).

hot light source

prism

The spectrum shows a smooth, continuous rainbow of light.

A graph of the spectrum is also continuous; notice that intensity varies slightly at different wavelengths.

intensity

wavelength

Continuous Spectrum

a

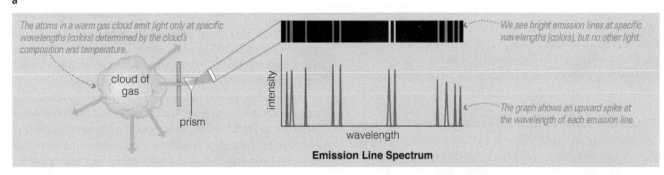

The atoms in a warm gas cloud emit light only at specific wavelengths (colors) determined by the cloud's composition and temperature.

cloud of gas

prism

We see bright emission lines at specific wavelengths (colors), but no other light.

The graph shows an upward spike at the wavelength of each emission line.

intensity

wavelength

Emission Line Spectrum

b

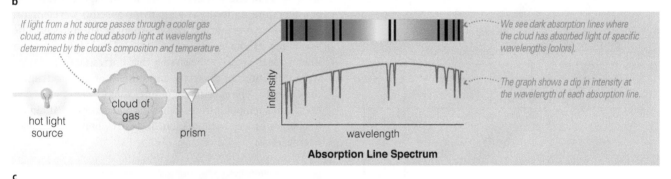

If light from a hot source passes through a cooler gas cloud, atoms in the cloud absorb light at wavelengths determined by the cloud's composition and temperature.

hot light source

cloud of gas

prism

We see dark absorption lines where the cloud has absorbed light of specific wavelengths (colors).

The graph shows a dip in intensity at the wavelength of each absorption line.

intensity

wavelength

Absorption Line Spectrum

c

FIGURE 5.14 interactive figure These diagrams show examples of the conditions under which we see the three basic types of spectra.

Our goal in this section is to learn how to interpret astronomical spectra like the one in Figure 5.13. The bumps and wiggles in that spectrum arise from several different processes, making it a good case study. We'll consider these processes one at a time, then return to interpret the full spectrum at the end of this section.

(MA) Light and Spectroscopy Tutorial, Lessons 2–4

What are the three basic types of spectra?

Laboratory studies show that spectra come in three basic types* (FIGURE 5.14):

1. The spectrum of a traditional, or incandescent, light bulb (which contains a heated wire filament) is a rainbow of color. Because the rainbow spans a broad range of wavelengths without interruption, we call it a **continuous spectrum**.

2. A thin or low-density cloud of gas emits light only at specific wavelengths that depend on its composition and temperature. The spectrum therefore consists of bright **emission lines** against a black background and is called an **emission line spectrum**.

3. If the cloud of gas lies between us and a light bulb, we still see most of the continuous spectrum of the light bulb. However, the cloud absorbs light of specific wavelengths, so the spectrum shows dark **absorption lines** over the background rainbow,* making it what we call an **absorption line spectrum**.

Note that when the spectra are shown as graphs, absorption lines appear as dips on a background of relatively high-intensity light while emission lines look like spikes on a background with little or no intensity.

We can apply these ideas to the solar spectrum that opens this chapter, which shows numerous absorption lines over a

*The rules that specify the conditions producing each type are often called *Kirchhoff's laws*.

*More technically, we'll see an absorption line spectrum as long as the cloud is cooler in temperature than the source of background light, which in this case is the light bulb filament.

background rainbow of color. This tells us that we are essentially looking at a hot light source through gas that is absorbing some of the colors, much as when we look through the cloud of gas to the light bulb in Figure 5.14c. For the solar spectrum, the hot light source is the hot interior of the Sun, while the "cloud" is the relatively cool and low-density layer of gas at the top of the Sun's visible surface, or *photosphere* [**Section 14.1**].

How does light tell us what things are made of?

We have just seen *how* different viewing conditions lead to different types of spectra, so it is time to discuss *why*. Let's start with emission and absorption line spectra, in which the lines form as a direct consequence of the fact that each type of atom, ion, or molecule possesses a unique set of energy levels.

Emission Line Spectra The atoms in any cloud of gas are constantly colliding with one another, exchanging energy in each collision. Most of the collisions simply send the atoms flying off in new directions. However, a few of the collisions

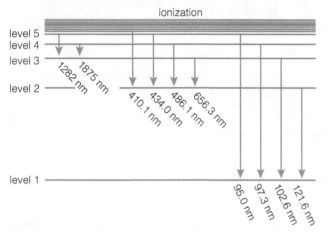

a Energy level transitions in hydrogen correspond to photons with specific wavelengths. Only a few of the many possible transitions are labeled.

410.1 434.0   486.1   656.3
nm   nm   nm   nm

b This spectrum shows emission lines produced by downward transitions between higher levels and level 2 in hydrogen.

410.1 434.0   486.1   656.3
nm   nm   nm   nm

c This spectrum shows absorption lines produced by upward transitions between level 2 and higher levels in hydrogen.

FIGURE 5.15 **interactive figure** An atom emits or absorbs light only at specific wavelengths that correspond to changes in the atom's energy as an electron undergoes transitions between its allowed energy levels.

transfer the right amount of energy to bump an electron from a low energy level to a higher energy level.

Electrons can't stay in higher energy levels for long. They always fall back down to the ground state, level 1, usually in a tiny fraction of a second. The energy the electron loses when it falls to a lower energy level must go somewhere, and often it goes into *emitting* a photon of light. The emitted photon must have the same amount of energy that the electron loses, which means that it has a specific wavelength and frequency. FIGURE 5.15a shows the energy levels in hydrogen that we saw in Figure 5.12, but it is also labeled with the wavelengths of the photons emitted by various downward transitions of an electron from a higher energy level to a lower one. For example, the transition from level 2 to level 1 emits an ultraviolet photon of wavelength 121.6 nm, and the transition from level 3 to level 2 emits a red visible-light photon of wavelength 656.3 nm.*

Although electrons that rise to higher energy levels in a gas quickly return to level 1, new collisions can raise other electrons to higher levels. As long as the gas remains moderately warm, collisions are always bumping some electrons to levels from which they fall back down and emit photons with some of the wavelengths shown in Figure 5.15a. The gas therefore emits light with these specific wavelengths. That is why a warm gas cloud produces an emission line spectrum, as shown in FIGURE 5.15b. The bright emission lines appear at the wavelengths that correspond to downward transitions of electrons, and the rest of the spectrum is dark (black). The specific set of lines that we see depends on the cloud's temperature as well as its composition: At higher temperatures, electrons are more likely to be bumped to higher energy levels.

> **THINK ABOUT IT**
>
> If nothing continues to heat the hydrogen gas, all the electrons eventually will end up at the lowest energy level (the ground state, or level 1). Use this fact to explain why we should *not* expect to see an emission line spectrum from a very cold cloud of hydrogen gas.

Absorption Line Spectra Now, suppose a light bulb illuminates the hydrogen gas from behind (as in Figure 5.14c). The light bulb emits light of all wavelengths, producing a spectrum that looks like a rainbow of color. However, the hydrogen atoms can absorb those photons that have the right amount of energy to raise an electron from a low energy level to a higher one. FIGURE 5.15c shows the result. It is an absorption line spectrum, because the light bulb produces a continuous rainbow of color while the hydrogen atoms absorb light at specific wavelengths.

Given that electrons at high energy levels quickly return to lower levels, you might wonder why photons emitted in downward transitions don't cancel out the effects of those

---

*Astronomers call transitions between level 1 and other levels the *Lyman* series of transitions. The transition between level 1 and level 2 is Lyman α, between level 1 and level 3 is Lyman β, and so on. Similarly, transitions between level 2 and higher levels are called *Balmer* transitions. Other sets of transitions also have names.

helium

sodium

neon

FIGURE 5.16 Visible-light emission line spectra for helium, sodium, and neon. The patterns and wavelengths of lines are different for each element, giving each a unique spectral fingerprint.

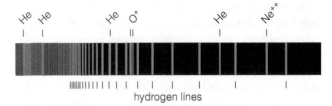

He   He   He   O⁺   He   Ne⁺⁺

hydrogen lines

FIGURE 5.17 The emission line spectrum of the Orion Nebula in a portion of the ultraviolet (about 350–400 nm). The lines are labeled with the chemical elements or ions that produce them (He = helium; O = oxygen; Ne = neon). The many hydrogen lines are all transitions from high levels to level 2.

absorbed in upward transitions. Finding the answer requires looking more deeply at what happens to the absorbed photons. Two things can happen after an electron absorbs a photon and rises to a higher energy level. The first is that the electron quickly returns to its original level, emitting a photon of the same energy as the one that it absorbed. However, the emitted photon can be going in any random direction, which means that we will still see an absorption line because photons that were coming toward us are redirected away from our line of sight. Alternatively, the electron can lose its energy in some other way, either by dropping back down to its original level in multiple steps (and therefore emitting photons with different energies than the originally absorbed photon) or by transferring its energy to another particle in a subsequent collision. Either way, we are left with an absorption line because photons of a specific wavelength have been removed from the spectrum of light that's coming toward us.

You can now see why the dark absorption lines in Figure 5.15c occur at the same wavelengths as the emission lines in Figure 5.15b: Both types of lines represent the same energy level transitions, except in opposite directions. For example, electrons moving downward from level 3 to level 2 in hydrogen can emit photons of wavelength 656.3 nm (producing an emission line at this wavelength), while electrons absorbing photons with this wavelength can rise up from level 2 to level 3 (producing an absorption line at this wavelength).

Chemical Fingerprints The fact that hydrogen emits and absorbs light at specific wavelengths makes it possible to detect its presence in distant objects. For example, imagine that you look through a telescope at an interstellar gas cloud, and its spectrum looks like that shown in Figure 5.15b. Because only hydrogen produces this particular set of lines, you can conclude that the cloud is made of hydrogen. In essence, the spectrum contains a "fingerprint" left by hydrogen atoms.

Real interstellar clouds are not made solely of hydrogen. However, the other chemical constituents in the cloud leave fingerprints on the spectrum in much the same way. Every type of atom has its own unique spectral fingerprint, because it has its own unique set of energy levels. For example, FIGURE 5.16 shows emission line spectra for helium, sodium, and neon. Moreover, different ions (atoms with missing or extra electrons) also produce different fingerprints (FIGURE 5.17). For example, the wavelengths of lines produced by doubly ionized neon (Ne^{+2})

are different from those of singly ionized neon (Ne^+), which in turn are different from those of neutral neon (Ne). These differences can help us determine the temperature of a hot gas or plasma, because more highly charged ions will be present at higher temperatures; this fact enables us to use spectra to measure the surface temperatures of stars [**Section 15.1**].

Molecules also produce spectral fingerprints. Like atoms, molecules can produce spectral lines when their electrons change energy levels. But molecules can also produce spectral lines in two other ways. Because they are made of two or more atoms bound together, molecules can vibrate and rotate (FIGURE 5.18a). Vibration and rotation also require energy, and the possible energies of rotation and vibration in molecules are quantized much like electron energy levels in atoms. A molecule can absorb or emit a photon when it changes its rate of vibration or rotation. The energy changes in molecules are usually smaller than those in atoms and therefore produce lower-energy photons, and the energy levels also tend to be bunched more closely together than in atoms. Molecules therefore produce spectra with many sets of tightly bunched lines, called **molecular bands** (FIGURE 5.18b), that are usually found in the infrared portion of the electromagnetic spectrum.

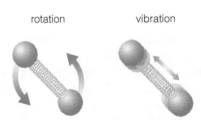

rotation   vibration

a We can think of a two-atom molecule as two balls connected by a spring. Although this model is simplistic, it illustrates how molecules can rotate and vibrate. The rotations and vibrations can have only particular amounts of energy and therefore produce unique spectral fingerprints.

b This spectrum of molecular hydrogen (H_2) consists of lines bunched into broad molecular bands.

FIGURE 5.18 Like atoms and ions, molecules emit or absorb light at specific wavelengths.

Over the past century, scientists have conducted laboratory experiments to identify the spectral lines of every chemical element and of many ions and molecules. As a result, when we see lines in the spectrum of a distant object, we can usually determine what produced them. For example, if we see spectral lines of hydrogen, helium, and carbon in the spectrum of a distant star, we know that all three elements are present in the star. More detailed analysis even allows us to determine the relative proportions of the various elements. That is how we have learned the chemical compositions of objects throughout the universe.

Reflected Light Spectra Some astronomical objects, such as planets and moons, reflect some of the light that falls on them. Reflected light also leaves a mark in spectra that can reveal information about the object, though not with the same level of detail as spectral lines. To understand why, consider the spectrum you would see from a red shirt on a sunny day. The red shirt absorbs blue light and reflects red light, so its visible spectrum will look like the spectrum of sunlight but with blue light missing. Because the shirt itself is too cool in temperature to emit visible light, the missing blue light must be telling you something about the dye in the shirt. In a similar way, the surface materials of a planet determine how much light of different colors is reflected or absorbed. The reflected light gives the planet its color, while the absorbed light heats the surface and helps determine its temperature. Careful study of which colors are absorbed and which are reflected can tell you at least something about the types of minerals on the surface.

How does light tell us the temperatures of planets and stars?

We have seen how emission and absorption line spectra form and how we can use them to determine the composition of a cloud of gas. Now we are ready to turn our attention to continuous spectra. Although continuous spectra can be produced in more than one way, light bulbs, planets, and stars produce a particular kind of continuous spectrum that can help us determine their temperatures.

Thermal Radiation: Every Body Does It In a cloud of gas that produces a simple emission or absorption line spectrum, the individual atoms or molecules are essentially independent of one another. Most photons pass easily through such a gas, except those that cause energy level transitions in the atoms or molecules of the gas. However, the atoms and molecules within most of the objects we encounter in everyday life—such as rocks, light bulb filaments, and people—cannot be considered independent and therefore have much more complex sets of energy levels. These objects tend to absorb light across a broad range of wavelengths, which means that light cannot easily pass through them and light emitted inside them cannot easily escape. The same is true of almost any large or dense object, including planets and stars.

In order to understand the spectra of such objects, let's consider an idealized case in which an object absorbs all photons that strike it and does not allow photons inside it to escape easily. Photons tend to bounce randomly around

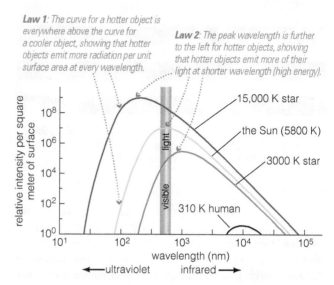

Law 1: The curve for a hotter object is everywhere above the curve for a cooler object, showing that hotter objects emit more radiation per unit surface area at every wavelength.

Law 2: The peak wavelength is further to the left for hotter objects, showing that hotter objects emit more of their light at shorter wavelength (high energy).

FIGURE 5.19 interactive figure Graphs of idealized thermal radiation spectra demonstrate the two laws of thermal radiation: (1) Each square meter of a hotter object's surface emits more light at all wavelengths; (2) hotter objects emit photons with a higher average energy. Notice that the graph uses power-of-10 scales on both axes, so that we can see all the curves even though the differences between them are quite large.

inside such an object, constantly exchanging energy with its atoms or molecules. By the time the photons finally escape the object, their radiative energies have become randomized so that they are spread over a wide range of wavelengths. The wide wavelength range of the photons explains why the spectrum of light from such an object is smooth, or *continuous*, like a pure rainbow without any absorption or emission lines.

Most important, the spectrum from such an object depends on only one thing: the object's *temperature*. To understand why, remember that temperature represents the average kinetic energy of the atoms or molecules in an object [**Section 4.3**]. Because the randomly bouncing photons interact so many times with those atoms or molecules, they end up with energies that match the kinetic energies of the object's atoms or molecules—which means the photon energies depend only on the object's temperature, regardless of what the object is made of. The temperature dependence of this light explains why we call it **thermal radiation** (sometimes known as *blackbody radiation*), and why its spectrum is called a **thermal radiation spectrum**.

No real object emits a perfect thermal radiation spectrum, but almost all familiar objects—including the Sun, the planets, rocks, and even you—emit light that approximates thermal radiation. FIGURE 5.19 shows graphs of the idealized thermal radiation spectra of three stars and a human, each with its temperature given on the Kelvin scale (see Figure 4.12). Be sure to notice that these spectra show the intensity of light *per unit surface area*, not the total amount of light emitted by the object. For example, a very large 3000 K star can emit more total light than a small 15,000 K star, even though the hotter star emits much more light per unit area.

The Two Laws of Thermal Radiation If you compare the spectra in Figure 5.19, you'll see that they obey two laws of thermal radiation:

- **Law 1** (the Stefan-Boltzmann law): *Each square meter of a hotter object's surface emits more light at all wavelengths.* For example, each square meter on the surface of the 15,000 K star emits a lot more light at every wavelength than each square meter of the 3000 K star, and the hotter star emits light at some ultraviolet wavelengths that the cooler star does not emit at all.

- **Law 2** (Wien's [pronounced "veen's"] law): *Hotter objects emit photons with a higher average energy,* which means a shorter average wavelength. That is why the peaks of the spectra are at shorter wavelengths for hotter objects. For example, the peak for the 15,000 K star is in ultraviolet light, the peak for the 5800 K Sun is in visible light, and the peak for the 3000 K star is in the infrared.

You can see these laws in action with a fireplace poker (**FIGURE 5.20**). While the poker is still relatively cool, it emits only infrared light, which we cannot see. As it gets hot (above about 1500 K), it begins to glow with visible light, and it glows more brightly as it gets hotter, demonstrating the first law. Its color demonstrates the second law. At first it glows "red hot," because red light has the longest wavelengths of visible light. As it gets even hotter, the average wavelength of the emitted photons moves toward the blue (short-wavelength) end of the visible spectrum. The mix of colors emitted at this higher temperature makes the poker look white to your eyes, which is why "white hot" is hotter than "red hot."

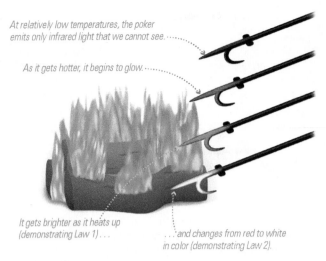

At relatively low temperatures, the poker emits only infrared light that we cannot see. ⋯⋯

As it gets hotter, it begins to glow. ⋯⋯

It gets brighter as it heats up (demonstrating Law 1) . . .

. . . and changes from red to white in color (demonstrating Law 2).

FIGURE 5.20 interactive figure A fireplace poker shows the two laws of thermal radiation in action.

Because thermal radiation spectra depend only on temperature, we can use them to measure the temperatures of distant objects. In many cases we can estimate temperatures simply from the object's color. Notice that while hotter objects emit more light at *all* wavelengths, the biggest difference appears at the shortest wavelengths. At human body temperature of about 310 K, people emit mostly in the infrared and emit no visible light at all—which explains why we don't glow in the dark! A relatively cool star, with a 3000 K surface temperature, emits mostly red light. That is why some bright stars in our sky, such as Betelgeuse (in Orion) and Antares (in Scorpius), appear reddish in color. The Sun's 5800 K surface emits most strongly in green light (around 500 nm), but the Sun looks yellow or white to our eyes because it also emits other colors throughout the visible spectrum. Hotter stars emit mostly in the ultraviolet but appear blue-white in color because our eyes

MATHEMATICAL INSIGHT 5.2

Laws of Thermal Radiation

The two laws of thermal radiation have simple formulas.

Stefan-Boltzmann law (Law 1):

$$\text{emitted power (per square meter of surface)} = \sigma T^4$$

where σ (Greek letter *sigma*) is a constant with a measured value of $\sigma = 5.7 \times 10^{-8} \text{ watt/}(m^2 \times K^4)$ and T is on the Kelvin scale (K).

Wien's law (Law 2): $\quad \lambda_{max} \approx \dfrac{2{,}900{,}000}{T \text{ (Kelvin scale)}} \text{ nm}$

where λ_{max} (read as "lambda-max") is the wavelength (in nanometers) of maximum intensity, which is the peak of a thermal radiation spectrum.

EXAMPLE: Find the emitted power per square meter and the wavelength of peak intensity for a 15,000 K object that emits thermal radiation.

SOLUTION:

Step 1 Understand: We can calculate the emitted power per square meter from the Stefan-Boltzmann law and the wavelength of maximum intensity from Wien's law.

Step 2 Solve: We plug the object's temperature ($T = 15{,}000$ K) into the Stefan-Boltzmann law to find the emitted power per square meter:

$$\sigma T^4 = 5.7 \times 10^{-8} \frac{\text{watt}}{m^2 \times K^4} \times (15{,}000 \text{ K})^4$$

$$= 2.9 \times 10^9 \text{ watt/}m^2$$

We find the wavelength of maximum intensity with Wien's law:

$$\lambda_{max} \approx \frac{2{,}900{,}000}{15{,}000 \text{ (Kelvin scale)}} \text{ nm} \approx 190 \text{ nm}$$

Step 3 Explain: A 15,000 K object emits 2.9 billion watts per square meter of surface. Its wavelength of maximum intensity is 190 nm, which is in the ultraviolet. Note that we can learn about astronomical objects by using these facts in reverse. For example, if an object's thermal radiation spectrum peaks at a wavelength of 190 nm, its surface temperature must be about 15,000 K. We can then divide its total emitted power by the power it emits per square meter of surface to determine its surface area, from which we can calculate its radius.

train stationary

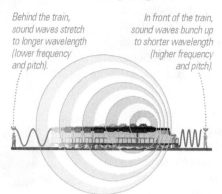

The pitch this person hears . . .

. . . is the same as the pitch this person hears.

a The whistle sounds the same no matter where you stand near a stationary train.

train moving to right

Behind the train, sound waves stretch to longer wavelength (lower frequency and pitch).

In front of the train, sound waves bunch up to shorter wavelength (higher frequency and pitch).

b For a moving train, the sound you hear depends on whether the train is moving toward you or away from you.

light source moving to right

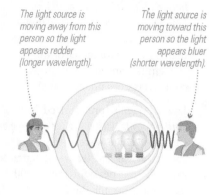

The light source is moving away from this person so the light appears redder (longer wavelength).

The light source is moving toward this person so the light appears bluer (shorter wavelength).

c We get the same basic effect from a moving light source (although the shifts are usually too small to notice with our eyes).

FIGURE 5.21 The Doppler effect. Each circle represents the crests of sound (or light) waves going in all directions from the source. For example, the circles from the train might represent waves emitted 0.001 second apart.

cannot see their ultraviolet light. If an object were heated to a temperature of millions of degrees, it would radiate mostly X rays. Some astronomical objects are indeed hot enough to emit X rays, such as disks of gas encircling exotic objects like neutron stars and black holes (see Chapter 18).

 **MA** The Doppler Effect Tutorial, Lessons 1, 2

How does light tell us the speed of a distant object?

There is still more that we can learn from light. In particular, we can learn about the motion of distant objects (relative to us) from changes in their spectra caused by the **Doppler effect**.

The Doppler Effect You've probably noticed the Doppler effect on the *sound* of a train whistle near train tracks. If the train is stationary, the pitch of its whistle sounds the same no matter where you stand (**FIGURE 5.21a**). But if the train is moving, the pitch sounds higher when the train is coming toward you and lower when it's moving away from you. Just as the train passes by, you can hear the dramatic change from high to low pitch—a sort of "weeeeeeee–ooooooooooh" sound. To understand why, we have to think about what happens to the sound waves coming from the train (**FIGURE 5.21b**). When the train is moving toward you, each pulse of a sound wave is emitted a little closer to you. The result is that waves are bunched up between you and the train, giving them a shorter wavelength and higher frequency (pitch). After the train passes you by, each pulse comes from farther away, stretching out the wavelengths and giving the sound a lower frequency.

The Doppler effect causes similar shifts in the wavelengths of light (**FIGURE 5.21c**). If an object is moving toward us, the light waves bunch up between us and the object, so its entire spectrum is shifted to shorter wavelengths. Because shorter wavelengths of visible light are bluer, the Doppler shift of an object coming toward us is called a **blueshift**. If an object

is moving away from us, its light is shifted to longer wavelengths. We call this Doppler shift a **redshift** because longer wavelengths of visible light are redder. For convenience, astronomers use the terms *blueshift* and *redshift* even when they aren't talking about visible light.

Spectral lines provide the reference points we use to identify and measure Doppler shifts (**FIGURE 5.22**). For example, suppose we recognize the pattern of hydrogen lines in the spectrum of a distant object. We know the **rest wavelengths** of the hydrogen lines—that is, their wavelengths in stationary clouds of hydrogen gas—from laboratory experiments in which a tube of hydrogen gas is heated so that the wavelengths of the spectral lines can be measured. If the hydrogen lines from the object appear at longer wavelengths, then we know they are redshifted and the object is moving away from us. The larger the shift, the faster the object is moving. If the lines appear at shorter wavelengths, then we know they are blueshifted and the object is moving toward us.

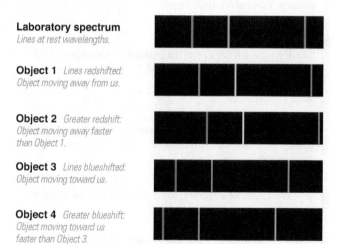

Laboratory spectrum
Lines at rest wavelengths.

Object 1 *Lines redshifted: Object moving away from us.*

Object 2 *Greater redshift: Object moving away faster than Object 1.*

Object 3 *Lines blueshifted: Object moving toward us.*

Object 4 *Greater blueshift: Object moving toward us faster than Object 3.*

FIGURE 5.22 interactive figure Spectral lines provide the crucial reference points for measuring Doppler shifts.

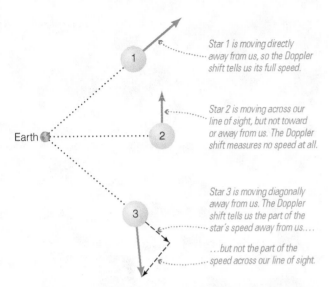

Star 1 is moving directly away from us, so the Doppler shift tells us its full speed.

Star 2 is moving across our line of sight, but not toward or away from us. The Doppler shift measures no speed at all.

Star 3 is moving diagonally away from us. The Doppler shift tells us the part of the star's speed away from us....

...but not the part of the speed across our line of sight.

FIGURE 5.23 **interactive figure** The Doppler shift tells us only the portion of an object's speed that is directed toward or away from us. It does not give us any information about how fast an object is moving across our line of sight.

THINK ABOUT IT

Suppose the hydrogen emission line with a rest wavelength of 121.6 nm (the transition from level 2 to level 1) appears at a wavelength of 120.5 nm in the spectrum of a particular star. Given that these wavelengths are in the ultraviolet, is the shifted wavelength closer to or farther from blue visible light? Why, then, do we say that this spectral line is *blueshifted*?

Components of Motion It's important to note that a Doppler shift tells us only the part of an object's full motion that is directed toward or away from us (the object's *radial* component of motion). Doppler shifts do not give us any information

about how fast an object is moving across our line of sight (the object's *tangential* component of motion). For example, consider three stars all moving at the same speed, with one moving directly away from us, one moving across our line of sight, and one moving diagonally away from us (**FIGURE 5.23**). The Doppler shift will tell us the full speed of only the first star. It will not indicate any speed for the second star, because none of this star's motion is directed toward or away from us. For the third star, the Doppler shift will tell us only the part of the star's velocity that is directed away from us. To measure how fast an object is moving across our line of sight, we must observe it long enough to notice how its position gradually shifts across our sky.

Rotation Rates The Doppler effect not only tells us how fast a distant object is moving toward or away from us but also can reveal information about motion *within* the object. For example, suppose we look at spectral lines of a planet or star that happens to be rotating (**FIGURE 5.24**). As the object rotates, light from the part of the object rotating toward us will be blueshifted, light from the part rotating away from us will be redshifted, and light from the center of the object won't be shifted at all. The net effect, if we look at the whole object at once, is to make each spectral line appear *wider* than it would if the object were not rotating. The faster the object is rotating, the broader in wavelength the spectral lines become. We can therefore determine the rotation rate of a distant object by measuring the width of its spectral lines.

Putting It All Together **FIGURE 5.25** shows the same spectrum we began with in Figure 5.13, but this time with labels indicating the processes responsible for its various features. The thermal emission peaks in the infrared, corresponding to a surface temperature of about 225 K, well below the 273 K freezing point of water. The absorption bands in the

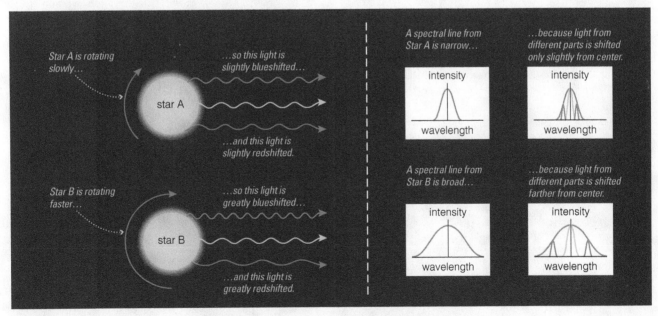

FIGURE 5.24 This diagram shows how the Doppler effect can tell us the rotation rate even of stars that appear as points of light to our telescopes. Rotation spreads the light of any spectral line over a range of wavelengths, so faster-rotating stars have broader spectral lines.

An astronomical spectrum contains an enormous amount of information. This figure shows a schematic spectrum of Mars. It is the same spectrum shown in Figure 5.13, but this time describing what we can learn from it.

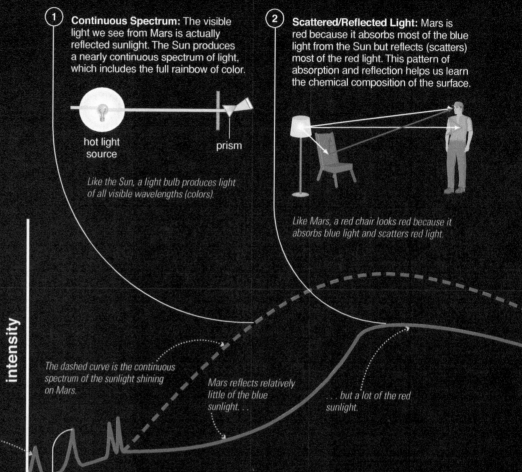

① Continuous Spectrum: The visible light we see from Mars is actually reflected sunlight. The Sun produces a nearly continuous spectrum of light, which includes the full rainbow of color.

Like the Sun, a light bulb produces light of all visible wavelengths (colors).

hot light source

prism

② Scattered/Reflected Light: Mars is red because it absorbs most of the blue light from the Sun but reflects (scatters) most of the red light. This pattern of absorption and reflection helps us learn the chemical composition of the surface.

Like Mars, a red chair looks red because it absorbs blue light and scatters red light.

The dashed curve is the continuous spectrum of the sunlight shining on Mars.

Mars reflects relatively little of the blue sunlight. . .

. . . but a lot of the red sunlight.

The graph and the "rainbow" contain the same information. The graph makes it easier to read the intensity at each wavelength of light. . .

. . . while the "rainbow" shows how the spectrum appears to the eye (for visible light) or instruments (for non-visible light).

intensity

ultraviolet   blue   green   red

wavelength

④ Emission Lines: Ultraviolet emission lines in the spectrum of Mars tell us that the atmosphere of Mars contains hot gas at high altitudes.

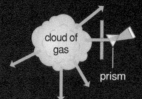

cloud of gas

prism

We see bright emission lines from gases in which collisions raise electrons in atoms to higher energy levels. The atoms emit photons at specific wavelengths as the electrons drop to lower energy levels.

3 **Thermal Radiation:** Objects emit a continuous spectrum of thermal radiation that peaks at a wavelength determined by temperature. Thermal radiation from Mars produces a broad hump in the infrared, with a peak indicating a surface temperature of about 225 K.

All objects—whether a fireplace poker, planet, or star—emit thermal radiation. The hotter the object, (1) the more total light (per unit area), and (2) the higher the average energy (shorter average wavelength) of the emitted photons.

Mars's thermal radiation peaks in the infrared because it is much cooler than the Sun, which peaks in visible light.

infrared

5 **Absorption Lines:** These absorption lines reveal the presence of carbon dioxide in Mars's atmosphere.

hot light source

cloud of gas

prism

When light from a hot source passes through a cooler gas, the gas absorbs light at specific wavelengths that raise electrons to higher energy levels. Every different element, ion, and molecule has unique energy levels and hence its own spectral "fingerprint."

6 **Doppler Effect:** The wavelengths of the spectral lines from Mars are slightly shifted by an amount that depends on the velocity of Mars toward or away from us as it moves

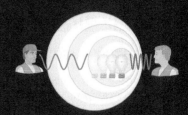

A Doppler shift toward the red side of the spectrum tells us the object is moving away from us. A shift toward the blue side of the spectrum tells us the object is moving toward us. For planets and stars, Doppler shifts are far too small to be detected by eye.

infrared come mainly from carbon dioxide, indicating a carbon dioxide atmosphere. The emission lines in the ultraviolet come from hot gas in a high, thin layer of the object's atmosphere. The reflected light looks like the Sun's 5800 K thermal radiation except that much of the blue light is missing, so the object must be reflecting sunlight and must look red in color. Perhaps by now you have guessed that this figure represents the spectrum of the planet Mars.

MATHEMATICAL INSIGHT 5.3

The Doppler Shift

We can calculate an object's radial (toward or away from us) velocity from its Doppler shift. For speeds small compared to the speed of light (less than a few percent of c), the formula is

$$\frac{v_{rad}}{c} = \frac{\lambda_{shift} - \lambda_{rest}}{\lambda_{rest}}$$

where v_{rad} is the radial velocity of the object, λ_{rest} is the rest wavelength of a particular spectral line, and λ_{shift} is the shifted wavelength of the same line. A positive answer means the object is redshifted and moving away from us; a negative answer means it is blueshifted and moving toward us.

EXAMPLE: One of the visible lines of hydrogen has a rest wavelength of 656.285 nm, but it appears in the spectrum of the star Vega at 656.255 nm. How is Vega moving relative to us?

SOLUTION:

Step 1 Understand: We can calculate the radial velocity from the given formula. Note that the line's wavelength in Vega's spectrum is slightly *shorter* than its rest wavelength, which means it is blueshifted and Vega's radial motion is *toward* us.

Step 2 Solve: We plug in the rest wavelength ($\lambda_{rest} = 656.285$ nm) and the wavelength in Vega's spectrum ($\lambda_{shift} = 656.255$ nm):

$$\frac{v_{rad}}{c} = \frac{\lambda_{shift} - \lambda_{rest}}{\lambda_{rest}}$$

$$= \frac{656.255 \text{ nm} - 656.285 \text{ nm}}{656.285 \text{ nm}}$$

$$= -4.5712 \times 10^{-5}$$

Step 3 Explain: We have found Vega's radial velocity as a fraction of the speed of light; it is negative because Vega is moving toward us. To convert to a velocity in km/s, we multiply by the speed of light:

$$v_{rad} = -4.5712 \times 10^{-5} \times c$$

$$= -4.5712 \times 10^{-5} \times (3 \times 10^{5} \text{ km/s})$$

$$= -13.7 \text{ km/s}$$

Vega is moving *toward* us at 13.7 km/s. This speed is typical of stars in our neighborhood of the galaxy.

The Big Picture

Putting Chapter 5 into Context

This chapter was devoted to one essential purpose: understanding how we learn about the universe by observing the light of distant objects. "Big picture" ideas that will help you keep your understanding in perspective include the following:

■ Light and matter interact in ways that allow matter to leave "fingerprints" on light. We can therefore learn a great deal about the objects we observe by carefully analyzing their light. Most of what we know about the universe comes from information that we receive from light.

■ The visible light that our eyes can see is only a small portion of the complete electromagnetic spectrum. Different portions of the spectrum contain different pieces of the story of a distant object, so it is important to study all forms of light.

■ There is far more to light than meets the eye. By dispersing the light of a distant object into a spectrum, we can determine the object's composition, surface temperature, motion toward or away from us, and more.

SUMMARY OF KEY CONCEPTS

5.1 LIGHT IN EVERYDAY LIFE

■ **How do we experience light?** Light carries radiative energy that it can exchange with matter. **Power** is the *rate* of energy transfer, measured in **watts**: 1 watt = 1 joule/s. The colors of light contain a great deal of information about the matter with which it has interacted.

■ **How do light and matter interact?** Matter can emit, absorb, transmit, or reflect (or scatter) light.

5.2 PROPERTIES OF LIGHT

■ **What is light?** Light is an **electromagnetic wave**, but also comes in individual "pieces" called **photons**. Each photon has a precise wavelength, frequency, and energy: The shorter the wavelength, the higher the frequency and energy.

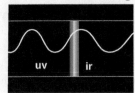

■ **What is the electromagnetic spectrum?** In order of decreasing wavelength (increasing frequency and energy), the forms of light are **radio waves, microwaves, infrared, visible light, ultraviolet, X rays**, and **gamma rays**.

5.3 PROPERTIES OF MATTER

■ **What is the structure of matter?** Ordinary matter is made of **atoms**, which are made of **protons, neutrons**, and **electrons**. Atoms of different chemical **elements** have different numbers of protons. **Isotopes** of a particular chemical element all have the same number of protons but different numbers of neutrons. **Molecules** are made from two or more atoms.

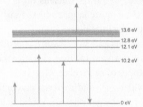

■ **What are the phases of matter?** The appearance of matter depends on its **phase: solid, liquid**, or **gas**. Gas is always present along with solid or liquid phases; solids **sublimate** into gas and liquids **evaporate** into gas. At very high temperatures, **molecular dissociation** breaks up molecules and **ionization** strips electrons from atoms; an ionized gas is called a **plasma**.

■ **How is energy stored in atoms?** Electrons can exist at particular **energy levels** within an atom. **Energy level transitions**, in which an electron moves from one energy level to another, can occur only when the electron gains or loses just the right amount of energy.

5.4 LEARNING FROM LIGHT

■ **What are the three basic types of spectra?** There are three basic types of spectra: a **continuous spectrum**, which looks like a rainbow of light; an **absorption line spectrum**, in which specific colors are missing from the rainbow; and an **emission line spectrum**, in which we see light only with specific colors against a black background.

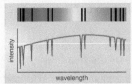

■ **How does light tell us what things are made of?** **Emission** or **absorption lines** occur only at specific wavelengths that correspond to particular energy level transitions in atoms or molecules. Every kind of atom, ion, and molecule produces a unique set of spectral lines, so we can determine composition by identifying these lines.

■ **How does light tell us the temperatures of planets and stars?** Objects such as planets and stars produce **thermal radiation** spectra, the most common type of continuous spectra. We can determine temperature from these spectra because hotter objects emit more total radiation per unit area and emit photons with a higher average energy.

■ **How does light tell us the speed of a distant object?** The **Doppler effect** tells us how fast an object is moving toward or away from us. Spectral lines are shifted to shorter wavelengths (a **blueshift**) in objects moving toward us and to longer wavelengths (a **redshift**) in objects moving away from us.

VISUAL SKILLS CHECK

Use the following questions to check your understanding of some of the many types of visual information used in astronomy. Answers are provided in Appendix J. For additional practice, try the Chapter 5 Visual Quiz at MasteringAstronomy®.

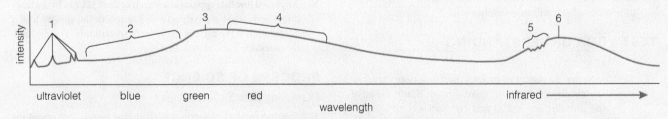

The graph above is a schematic spectrum of the planet Mars; it is the same spectrum shown in Figure 5.13. Keeping in mind that Mars reflects visible sunlight and emits infrared light, refer to the numbered features of the graph and answer the following questions.

1. Which of the six numbered features represents emission lines?
2. Which of the six numbered features represents absorption lines?
3. Which portion(s) of the spectrum represent(s) reflected sunlight?
   a. 1 only   b. 2, 3, and 4   c. 3 and 6   d. the entire spectrum
4. What does the wavelength of the peak labeled 6 tell us about Mars?
   a. its color   b. its surface temperature
   c. its chemical composition   d. its orbital speed

5. What feature(s) of this spectrum indicate(s) that Mars appears red in color?
   a. the wavelength of the peak labeled 3
   b. the wavelength of the peak labeled 6
   c. the fact that the intensity of region 4 is higher than that of region 2
   d. the fact that the peak labeled 3 is higher than the peak labeled 6

REVIEW QUESTIONS

Short-Answer Questions Based on the Reading

1. What is the difference between *energy* and *power*? What units do we use to measure power?

2. What are the four major ways light and matter can interact? Give an example of each from everyday life.

3. What do we mean when we say that light is an *electromagnetic wave*? Describe the relationship among *wavelength, frequency,* and *speed* for light waves.

4. What is a *photon*? In what way is a photon like a particle? In what way is it like a wave?

5. List the different forms of light in order from lowest to highest energy. Would the list be different if you went in order from lowest to highest frequency? From shortest to longest wavelength? Explain.

6. Briefly describe the structure and size of an atom. How big is the *nucleus* in comparison to the entire atom?

7. What determines an atom's *atomic number*? What determines its *atomic mass number*? Under what conditions are two atoms different *isotopes* of the same element? What is a *molecule*?

8. What is *electrical charge*? Will an electron and a proton attract or repel each other? Will two electrons attract or repel each other? Explain.

9. Describe the phase changes of water as you heat it, starting from its solid phase, ice. What happens at very high temperatures? What is a *plasma*?

10. What do we mean when we say that *energy levels* are quantized in atoms? Under what circumstances can *energy level transitions* occur?

11. How do we convert a spectrum shown as a band of light (like a rainbow) into a graph of the spectrum?

12. Describe the conditions that would cause us to see each of the three basic types of spectra. What do we see in the Sun's spectrum shown on the opening page of this chapter?

13. How can we use *emission* or *absorption lines* to determine the chemical composition of a distant object?

14. Describe two ways in which the *thermal radiation spectrum* of an 8000 K star would differ from that of a 4000 K star.

15. Describe the *Doppler effect* for light and what we can learn from it. What does it mean to say that radio waves are *blueshifted*? Why does the Doppler effect widen the spectral lines of rotating objects?

16. Describe each of the key features of the spectrum in Figure 5.25 and explain what it tells us about the object.

TEST YOUR UNDERSTANDING

Does It Make Sense?

Decide whether the statement makes sense (or is clearly true) or does not make sense (or is clearly false). Explain clearly; not all of these have definitive answers, so your explanation is more important than your chosen answer.

17. The walls of my room are transparent to radio waves.

18. Because of their higher frequencies, X rays must travel through space faster than radio waves.

19. If you could see infrared light, you would see a glow from the backs of your eyelids when you closed your eyes.

20. If you had X-ray vision, you could read this entire book without turning any pages.

21. Two isotopes of the element rubidium differ in their number of protons.

22. A "white hot" object is hotter than a "red hot" object.

23. If the Sun's surface became much hotter (while the Sun's size remained the same), the Sun would emit more ultraviolet light but less visible light than it currently emits.

24. If you could view a spectrum of light reflecting off a blue sweatshirt, you'd find the entire rainbow of color (looking the same as a spectrum of white light).

25. Galaxies that show redshifts must be red in color.

26. If a distant galaxy has a substantial redshift (as viewed from our galaxy), then anyone living in that galaxy would see a substantial redshift in a spectrum of the Milky Way Galaxy.

Quick Quiz

Choose the best answer to each of the following. Explain your reasoning with one or more complete sentences.

27. Why is a sunflower yellow? (a) It emits yellow light. (b) It absorbs yellow light. (c) It reflects yellow light.

28. Blue light has higher frequency than red light. Thus, blue light has (a) higher energy and shorter wavelength than red light. (b) higher energy and longer wavelength than red light. (c) lower energy and shorter wavelength than red light.

29. Radio waves are (a) a form of sound. (b) a form of light. (c) a type of spectrum.

30. Compared to an atom as a whole, an atomic nucleus (a) is very tiny but has most of the mass. (b) is quite large and has most of the mass. (c) is very tiny and has very little mass.

31. Some nitrogen atoms have 7 neutrons and some have 8 neutrons, which makes these two forms of nitrogen (a) ions of each other. (b) phases of each other. (c) isotopes of each other.

32. Sublimation is the process by which (a) solid material enters the gas phase. (b) liquid material enters the gas phase. (c) solid material becomes a liquid.

33. If you heat a rock until it glows, its spectrum will be (a) a thermal radiation spectrum. (b) an absorption line spectrum. (c) an emission line spectrum.

34. The set of spectral lines that we see in a star's spectrum depends on the star's (a) interior temperature. (b) chemical composition. (c) rotation rate.

35. Compared to the Sun, a star whose spectrum peaks in the infrared is (a) cooler. (b) hotter. (c) larger.

36. A spectral line that appears at a wavelength of 321 nm in the laboratory appears at a wavelength of 328 nm in the spectrum of a distant object. We say that the object's spectrum is (a) redshifted. (b) blueshifted. (c) whiteshifted.

PROCESS OF SCIENCE

Examining How Science Works

37. *Elements in Space.* Astronomers claim that objects throughout the universe are made of the same chemical elements that exist here on Earth. Given that most of these objects are so far away that we can never hope to visit them, why are astronomers so confident that these objects are made from the same set of chemical elements, rather than some completely different types of materials?

38. *Newton's Prisms.* Look back at the brief discussion in this chapter of how Newton proved that the colors seen when light passed through a prism came from the light itself rather than from the prism. Suppose you wanted to test Newton's findings. Assuming you have two prisms and a white screen, describe how you would arrange the prisms to duplicate Newton's discovery.

39. *Light Around You.* Before you begin, assign the following roles to the people in your group: *Scribe* (takes notes on the group's activities), *Proposer* (proposes explanations to the group), *Skeptic* (points out weaknesses in proposed explanations), and *Moderator* (leads group discussion and makes sure everyone contributes). Look carefully at all the ways in which light and matter are interacting in the room around you to answer the following questions: **a.** What is emitting light? **b.** What is absorbing light? **c.** What is responsible for the colors you see? **d.** What would the room look like if you observed it with an infrared camera? With an ultraviolet camera? With an X-ray camera? **e.** Are there any radio waves in the room? Explain all your answers clearly.

INVESTIGATE FURTHER

In-Depth Questions to Increase Your Understanding

Short-Answer/Essay Questions

40. *Atomic Terminology Practice I.*
    a. The most common form of iron has 26 protons and 30 neutrons. State its atomic number, atomic mass number, and number of electrons (if it is neutral). **b.** Consider the following three atoms: Atom 1 has 7 protons and 8 neutrons; atom 2 has 8 protons and 7 neutrons; atom 3 has 8 protons and 8 neutrons. Which two are *isotopes* of the same element? **c.** Oxygen has atomic number 8. How many times must an oxygen atom be ionized to create an O^{+5} ion? How many electrons are in an O^{+5} ion?

41. *Atomic Terminology Practice II.*
    a. What are the atomic number and atomic mass number of a fluorine atom with 9 protons and 10 neutrons? If we could add a proton to this fluorine nucleus, would the result still be fluorine? What if we added a neutron to the fluorine nucleus? Explain. **b.** The most common isotope of gold has atomic number 79 and atomic mass number 197. How many protons and neutrons does the gold nucleus contain? If the isotope is electrically neutral, how many electrons does it have? If it is triply ionized, how many electrons does it have? **c.** Uranium has atomic number 92. Its most common isotope is ^{238}U, but the form used in nuclear bombs and nuclear power plants is ^{235}U. How many neutrons are in each of these two isotopes of uranium?

42. *The Fourth Phase of Matter.*
    a. Explain why nearly all the matter in the Sun is in the plasma phase. **b.** Based on your answer to part a, explain why plasma is the most common phase of matter in the universe. **c.** If plasma is the most common phase of matter in the universe, why is it so rare on Earth?

43. *Energy Level Transitions.* The following labeled transitions represent an electron moving between energy levels in hydrogen. Answer each of the following questions and explain your answers.

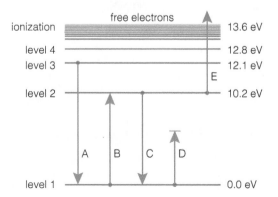

a. Which transition could represent an atom that *absorbs* a photon with 10.2 eV of energy? **b.** Which transition could represent an atom that *emits* a photon with 10.2 eV of energy? **c.** Which transition represents an electron that is breaking free of the atom? **d.** Which transition, as shown, is *not* possible? **e.** Would transition A represent emission or absorption of light? How would the wavelength of the emitted or absorbed photon compare to that of the photon involved in transition C? Explain.

44. *Spectral Summary.* Clearly explain how studying an object's spectrum can allow us to determine each of the following properties of the object.
    a. The object's surface chemical composition **b.** The object's surface temperature **c.** Whether the object is a low-density cloud of gas or something more substantial **d.** Whether the object has a hot upper atmosphere **e.** Whether the object is reflecting blue light from a star **f.** The speed at which the object is moving toward or away from us **g.** The object's rotation rate

45. *Orion Nebula.* Much of the Orion Nebula looks like a glowing cloud of gas. What type of spectrum would you expect to see from the glowing parts of the nebula? Why?

46. *The Doppler Effect.* In hydrogen, the transition from level 2 to level 1 has a rest wavelength of 121.6 nm. Suppose you see this line at a wavelength of 120.5 nm in Star A, 121.2 nm in Star B, 121.9 nm in Star C, and 122.9 nm in Star D. Which stars are coming toward us? Which are moving away? Which star is moving fastest relative to us? Explain your answers without doing any calculations.

Quantitative Problems

Be sure to show all calculations clearly and state your final answers in complete sentences.

47. *Human Wattage.* A typical adult uses about 2500 Calories of energy each day. Use this fact to calculate the typical adult's average *power* requirement, in watts. (*Hint:* 1 Calorie = 4184 joules.)

48. *Electric Bill.* Your electric utility bill probably shows your energy use for the month in units of *kilowatt-hours.* A kilowatt-hour is defined as the energy used in 1 hour at a rate of 1 kilowatt (1000 watts); that is, 1 kilowatt-hour = 1 kilowatt × 1 hour. Use this fact to convert 1 kilowatt-hour into joules. If your bill says you used 900 kilowatt-hours, how much energy did you use in joules?

49. *Radio Station.* What is the wavelength of a radio photon from an AM radio station that broadcasts at 1120 kilohertz? What is its energy?

50. *UV Photon.* What is the energy (in joules) of an ultraviolet photon with wavelength 120 nm? What is its frequency?

51. *X-Ray Photon.* What is the wavelength of an X-ray photon with energy 10 keV (10,000 eV)? What is its frequency? (1 eV = 1.60 × 10^{-19} joule.)

52. *How Many Photons?* Suppose that all the energy from a 100-watt light bulb came in the form of photons with wavelength 600 nm. (This is not quite realistic; see Problem 57.)
    a. Calculate the energy of a *single* photon with wavelength 600 nm. **b.** How many 600-nm photons must be emitted each second to account for all the light from this 100-watt light bulb? **c.** Based on your answer to part b, explain why we don't notice the particle nature of light in our everyday lives.

53. *Thermal Radiation Laws.*
    a. Find the emitted power per square meter and wavelength of peak intensity for a 3000 K object that emits thermal radiation. **b.** Find the emitted power per square meter and wavelength of peak intensity for a 50,000 K object that emits thermal radiation.

54. *Hotter Sun.* Suppose the surface temperature of the Sun were about 12,000 K, rather than 6000 K.

a. How much more thermal radiation would the Sun emit? **b.** What would happen to the Sun's wavelength of peak emission? **c.** Do you think it would still be possible to have life on Earth? Explain.

55. *Taking the Sun's Temperature.* The Sun radiates a total power of about 4×10^{26} watts into space. The Sun's radius is about 7×10^8 meters.

    a. Calculate the average power radiated by each square meter of the Sun's surface. (*Hint:* The formula for the surface area of a sphere is $A = 4\pi r^2$.) **b.** Using your answer from part a and the Stefan-Boltzmann law, calculate the average surface temperature of the Sun. (*Note:* The temperature calculated this way is called the Sun's *effective temperature.*)

56. *Doppler Calculations.* In hydrogen, the transition from level 2 to level 1 has a rest wavelength of 121.6 nm. Find the speed and direction (toward or away from us) for a star in which this line appears at wavelength

    a. 120.5 nm. **b.** 121.2 nm. **c.** 121.9 nm. **d.** 122.9 nm.

57. *Understanding Light Bulbs.* A traditional incandescent light bulb uses a hot tungsten coil to produce a thermal radiation spectrum. The temperature of this coil is typically about 3000 K.

    a. What is the wavelength of maximum intensity for this light bulb? Compare to the 500-nm wavelength of maximum intensity for the Sun. **b.** Overall, do you expect the light from this bulb to be the same as, redder than, or bluer than light from the Sun? Why? Use your answer to explain why professional photographers use a different type of film for indoor photography than for outdoor photography. **c.** Do incandescent light bulbs emit all their energy as visible light? Use your answer to explain why these light bulbs are usually hot to touch. **d.** *Fluorescent* light bulbs primarily produce emission line spectra rather than thermal radiation spectra. Explain why, if the emission lines are in the visible part of the spectrum, a fluorescent bulb can emit more visible light than a standard bulb of the same wattage. **e.** *Compact fluorescent* light bulbs are designed to produce so many emission lines in the visible part of the spectrum that their light looks very similar to the light of incandescent bulbs. However, they are much more energy efficient: A 15-watt compact fluorescent bulb typically emits as much visible light as a traditional incandescent 75-watt bulb. Although compact fluorescent bulbs generally cost more than incandescent bulbs, is it possible that they could save you money? Besides initial cost and energy efficiency, what other factors must be considered?

Discussion Questions

58. *The Changing Limitations of Science.* In 1835, French philosopher Auguste Comte stated that science would never allow us to learn the composition of stars. Although spectral lines had been seen in the Sun's spectrum by that time, not until the middle of the 19th century did scientists recognize that spectral lines give clear information about chemical composition (primarily through the work of Foucault and Kirchhoff). Why might our present knowledge have seemed unattainable in 1835? Discuss how new discoveries can change the apparent limitations of science. Today, other questions seem beyond the reach of science, such as the question of how life began on Earth. Do you think such questions will ever be answerable through science? Defend your opinion.

59. *Your Microwave Oven.* A microwave oven emits microwaves that have just the right wavelength to cause energy level changes in water molecules. Use this fact to explain how a microwave oven cooks your food. Why doesn't a microwave oven make a plastic dish get hot? Why do some clay dishes get hot in the microwave? Why do dishes that aren't themselves heated by the microwave oven sometimes still get hot when you heat food on them? (*Note:* It's not a good idea to put dishes without food or liquid in a microwave.)

60. *Democritus and the Path of History.* Besides his belief in atoms, Democritus held several other strikingly modern notions. For example, he maintained that the Moon was a world with mountains and valleys and that the Milky Way was composed of countless individual stars—ideas that weren't generally accepted until the time of Galileo, more than 2000 years later. Unfortunately, we know of Democritus's work only secondhand because none of the 72 books he is said to have written survived the destruction of the Library of Alexandria. Do you think history might have been different if the work of Democritus had not been lost? Defend your opinion.

Web Projects

61. *Kids and Light.* Visit one of the many websites designed to teach middle and high school students about light. Read the content and try the activities. If you were a teacher, would you find the site useful for your students? Why or why not? Write a one-page summary of your conclusions.

62. *Light Bulbs.* To save energy, in 2007 the U.S. Congress passed legislation designed to phase out the use of traditional incandescent light bulbs by 2014. Find out about the status of this phaseout; is it still on track? What types of alternative bulbs are available? Write a short report summarizing the advantages and disadvantages of each technology.

63. *Medical Imaging.* Learn about CT scans or other technologies for medical imaging of the human body. How do they work? How are such technologies similar to those used by astronomers to learn about the universe? Write a short report summarizing your findings.

8 FORMATION OF THE SOLAR SYSTEM

LEARNING GOALS

The evolution of the world may be compared to a display of fireworks that has just ended: some few red wisps, ashes and smoke. Standing on a cooled cinder, we see the slow fading of the suns, and we try to recall the vanished brilliance of the origin of the worlds.

—G. Lemaître (1894–1966),
astronomer and Catholic priest

How did Earth come to be? How old is it? Is it unique? Our ancestors could do little more than guess at the answers to these questions, but today we are able to address them scientifically. As we'll discuss in this chapter, careful study of the major features of our solar system has enabled scientists to put together a detailed theory of how Earth and our solar system were born.

Our theory of solar system formation is important not only because it helps us understand our cosmic origins, but also because it holds the key to understanding the nature of planets. If the planets in our solar system all formed together, then their differences must be attributable to physical processes that occurred during the birth and subsequent evolution of the solar system. Our study of the solar system's birth will therefore form the basis for our comparative study of the planets in subsequent chapters. It will also help us extend these ideas to the myriad of other planetary systems now known to exist, a topic we will study in Chapter 13.

8.1 THE SEARCH FOR ORIGINS

The development of any scientific theory is an interplay between observations and attempts to explain those observations [**Section 3.4**]. Hypotheses that seem to make sense at one time might later be dismissed because they fail to explain new data. For example, ancient Greek ideas about Earth's origins probably seemed quite reasonable when people assumed that Earth was the center of the universe, but they no longer made sense after Kepler and Galileo proved that Earth is a planet orbiting the Sun.

By the end of the 17th century, the Copernican revolution [**Section 3.3**] and Newton's discovery of the universal law of gravitation [**Section 4.4**] had given us a basic understanding of the layout and motion of the planets and moons in our solar system. It was only natural that scientists would begin to speculate about how this system came to be.

How did we arrive at a theory of solar system formation?

Recall that a hypothesis can rise to the status of a scientific theory only if it offers a detailed physical model that explains a broad range of observed facts. For our solar system, the most important facts to explain are the four major features discussed in Chapter 7. If a hypothesis fails to explain even one of the four features, then it cannot be correct. If it successfully

explains all four, then we might reasonably assume it is on the right track. We therefore arrive at the following four criteria for the success of a solar system formation theory:

1. It must explain the patterns of motion discussed in Chapter 7.

2. It must explain why planets fall into two major categories: small, rocky *terrestrial* planets near the Sun and large, hydrogen-rich *jovian* planets farther out.

3. It must explain the existence of huge numbers of asteroids and comets and why these objects reside primarily in the regions we call the *asteroid belt*, the *Kuiper belt*, and the *Oort cloud*.

4. It must explain the general patterns while at the same time making allowances for exceptions to the general rules, such as the odd axis tilt of Uranus and the existence of Earth's large Moon.

From Hypothesis to Theory Although it took time to learn all four of the major features, scientists began speculating about how our solar system formed as soon as the basic patterns of motion were known. We generally credit two 18th-century scientists with proposing the hypothesis that ultimately blossomed into our modern scientific theory of the origin of the solar system. Around 1755, German philosopher Immanuel Kant proposed that our solar system formed from the gravitational collapse of an interstellar cloud of gas. About 40 years later, French mathematician Pierre-Simon Laplace put forth the same idea independently. Because an interstellar cloud is usually called a *nebula* (Latin for "cloud"), their idea became known as the *nebular hypothesis*.

The nebular hypothesis remained popular throughout the 19th century. By the early 20th century, however, scientists had found a few aspects of our solar system that the nebular hypothesis did not seem to explain well—at least in its original form as described by Kant and Laplace. While some scientists sought to modify the nebular hypothesis, others looked for different ways to explain how the solar system might have formed.

During much of the first half of the 20th century, the nebular hypothesis faced stiff competition from a hypothesis proposing that the planets represent debris from a near-collision between the Sun and another star. According to this *close encounter hypothesis,* the planets formed from blobs of gas that had been gravitationally pulled out of the Sun during the near-collision.

Today, the close encounter hypothesis has been discarded. It began to lose favor when calculations showed that it could not account for either the observed orbital motions of the planets or the neat division of the planets into two major categories (terrestrial and jovian). Moreover, the close encounter hypothesis required a highly improbable event: a near-collision between our Sun and another star. Given the vast separation between star systems in our region of the galaxy, the chance of such an encounter is so small that it would be difficult to imagine it happening even once in order to form our solar system. It certainly could not account for the many other planetary systems that we have discovered in recent years.

While the close encounter hypothesis was losing favor, new discoveries about the physics of planet formation led to modifications of the nebular hypothesis. Using more sophisticated models of the processes that occur in a collapsing cloud of gas, scientists found that the nebular hypothesis offered natural explanations for all four general features of our solar system. By the latter decades of the 20th century, so much evidence had accumulated in favor of the nebular hypothesis that it achieved the status of a scientific *theory* [**Section 3.4**]—the **nebular theory** of our solar system's birth.

Putting the Theory to the Test Recall that in science, a theory is never really complete and we must put it to continual tests and modify it as necessary. In the case of a theory that claims to explain the origin of *our* solar system, one critical set of tests involves its ability to predict and explain the characteristics of other solar systems. The nebular theory has clearly passed the most important of these tests: Because it claims that planets are a natural outgrowth of the star formation process, it predicts that other planetary systems ought to be common, a prediction that has now been borne out by observations. Other observations have presented greater challenges; many of the recently discovered planetary systems are organized in ways somewhat different from our own. Nevertheless, as we'll discuss in Chapter 13, scientists have not found any major flaws in the nebular theory, and with relatively minor modifications it seems capable of explaining the diversity of planetary systems that we observe. As a result, the nebular theory today stands on stronger ground than ever. We'll therefore devote the rest of this chapter to understanding the basic theory and how it explains the major features of our solar system.

Where did the solar system come from?

The nebular theory begins with the idea that our solar system was born from the gravitational collapse of an interstellar cloud of gas, called the **solar nebula**, that collapsed under its own gravity. As we'll discuss in more detail in the next section, this cloud gave birth to the Sun at its center and the planets in a spinning disk that formed around the young Sun.

Where did the gas that made up the solar nebula come from? According to modern science, it was the product of billions of years of galactic recycling that occurred before the Sun and planets were born. Recall that the universe as a whole is thought to have been born in the Big Bang [**Section 1.2**], which essentially produced only two chemical elements: hydrogen and helium. Heavier elements were produced later by massive stars, and released into space when the stars died. The heavy elements then mixed with other interstellar gas that formed new generations of stars (**FIGURE 8.1**).

Although this process of creating heavy elements in stars and recycling them within the galaxy has probably gone on

FIGURE 8.1 This figure, which is a portion of Figure 1.10, summarizes the galactic recycling process.

for most of the 14-billion-year history of our universe, only a small fraction of the original hydrogen and helium has been converted into heavy elements. By studying the composition of the Sun, other stars of the same age, and interstellar gas clouds, we have learned that the gas that made up the solar nebula contained (by mass) about 98% hydrogen and helium and 2% all other elements combined. The Sun and planets were born from this gas, and Earth and the other terrestrial worlds were made primarily from the heavier elements mixed within it. As we discussed in Chapter 1, we are "star stuff" because we and our planet are made of elements forged in stars that lived and died long ago.

THINK ABOUT IT

Could a solar system like ours have formed with the first generation of stars after the Big Bang? Explain.

Strong observational evidence supports this scenario. Spectroscopy shows that old stars have a smaller proportion of heavy elements than younger ones, just as we would expect if they were born at a time before many heavy elements had been manufactured. Moreover, visible and infrared telescopes allow us to study stars that are in the process of formation today. **FIGURE 8.2** shows the Orion Nebula, in which many stars are in various stages of formation. Just as our scenario predicts, the forming stars are embedded within gas clouds like our solar nebula, and the characteristics of these clouds match what we expect if they are collapsing due to gravity.

100,000 AU

FIGURE 8.2 interactive figure The Orion Nebula, an interstellar cloud in which new star systems are forming. Over the next few million years, thousands of stars will be born in this gas cloud. Some of these stars may end up with their own planetary systems. This image combines an infrared view from the Spitzer Space Telescope and visible data from the Hubble Space Telescope.

(MA) Formation of the Solar System Tutorial, Lessons 1–2

8.2 EXPLAINING THE MAJOR FEATURES OF THE SOLAR SYSTEM

We are now ready to look at the nebular theory in somewhat more detail. In the process, we'll see how it successfully accounts for all four major features of our solar system.

What caused the orderly patterns of motion?

The solar nebula probably began as a large, roughly spherical cloud of very cold and very low-density gas. Initially, this gas was probably so spread out—perhaps over a region a few light-years in diameter—that gravity alone may not have been strong enough to pull it together and start its collapse. Instead, the collapse may have been triggered by a cataclysmic event, such as the impact of a shock wave from the explosion of a nearby star (a supernova).

Once the collapse started, gravity enabled it to continue. Remember that the strength of gravity follows an inverse square law with distance [**Section 4.4**]. The mass of the cloud remained the same as it shrank, so the strength of gravity increased as the diameter of the cloud decreased.

Because gravity pulls inward in all directions, you might at first guess that the solar nebula would have remained spherical as it shrank. Indeed, the idea that gravity pulls in all directions explains why the Sun and the planets are spherical. However, we must also consider other physical laws that apply to a collapsing gas cloud in order to understand how orderly motions arose in the solar nebula.

Heating, Spinning, and Flattening As the solar nebula shrank in size, three important processes altered its density, temperature, and shape, changing it from a large, diffuse (spread-out) cloud to a much smaller spinning disk (**FIGURE 8.3**):

- **Heating.** The temperature of the solar nebula increased as it collapsed. Such heating represents energy conservation in action [**Section 4.3**]. As the cloud shrank, its gravitational potential energy was converted to the kinetic energy of individual gas particles falling inward. These particles crashed into one another, converting the kinetic energy of their inward fall to the random motions of thermal energy (see Figure 4.14b). The Sun formed in the center, where temperatures and densities were highest.

- **Spinning.** Like an ice skater pulling in her arms as she spins, the solar nebula rotated faster and faster as it shrank in radius. This increase in rotation rate represents conservation of angular momentum in action [**Section 4.3**]. The rotation of the cloud may have been imperceptibly slow before its collapse began, but the cloud's shrinkage made fast rotation inevitable. The rapid rotation helped ensure that not all the material in the solar nebula collapsed into the center: The greater the angular momentum of a rotating cloud, the more spread out it will be.

- **Flattening.** The solar nebula flattened into a disk. This flattening is a natural consequence of collisions between particles in a spinning cloud. A cloud may start with any size or shape, and different clumps of gas within the cloud may be moving in random directions at random speeds. These clumps collide and merge as the cloud collapses, and each new clump has the average velocity of the clumps that formed it. The random motions of the original cloud therefore become more orderly as the cloud collapses, changing the cloud's original lumpy shape into a rotating, flattened disk. Similarly, collisions between clumps of material in highly elliptical orbits reduce their eccentricities, making the orbits more circular.

The formation of the spinning disk explains the orderly motions of our solar system today. The planets all orbit the Sun in nearly the same plane because they formed in the flat disk. The direction in which the disk was spinning became the direction of the Sun's rotation and the orbits of the planets. Computer models show that planets would have tended to rotate in this same direction as they formed—which is why most planets rotate the same way—though the small sizes of planets compared to the entire disk allowed some exceptions to arise. The fact that collisions in the disk tended to make orbits more circular explains why the planets in our solar system have nearly circular orbits.

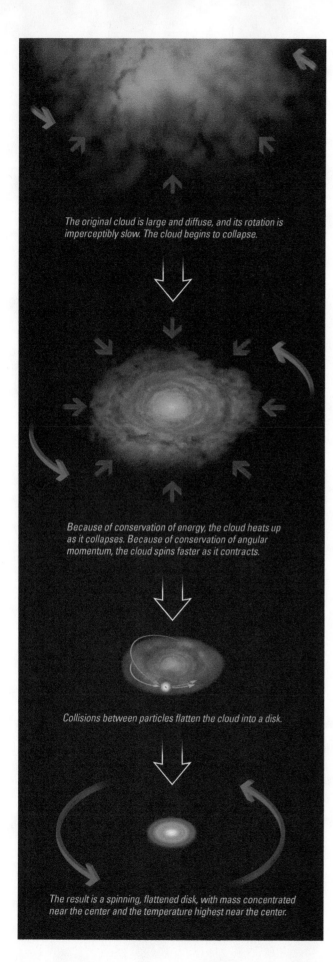

The original cloud is large and diffuse, and its rotation is imperceptibly slow. The cloud begins to collapse.

Because of conservation of energy, the cloud heats up as it collapses. Because of conservation of angular momentum, the cloud spins faster as it contracts.

Collisions between particles flatten the cloud into a disk.

The result is a spinning, flattened disk, with mass concentrated near the center and the temperature highest near the center.

FIGURE 8.3 Interactive figure This sequence of illustrations shows how the gravitational collapse of a large cloud of gas causes it to become a spinning disk of matter. The hot, dense central bulge becomes a star, while planets can form in the surrounding disk.

Testing the Model Because the same processes should affect other collapsing gas clouds, we can test our model by searching for disks around other forming stars. Observational evidence does indeed support our model of spinning, heating, and flattening.

The heating that occurs in a collapsing cloud of gas means the gas should emit thermal radiation [**Section 5.4**], primarily in the infrared. We've detected infrared radiation from many nebulae where star systems appear to be forming. More direct evidence comes from flattened, spinning disks around other stars (**FIGURE 8.4**), some of which appear to be ejecting jets of material perpendicular to their disks [**Section 16.2**]. These jets are thought to result from the flow of material from the disk onto the forming star, and they may influence the solar system formation processes.

Other support for the model comes from computer simulations of the formation process. A simulation begins with a set of data representing the conditions we observe in interstellar clouds. Then, with the aid of a computer, we apply the laws of physics to predict the changes that should occur over time. Computer simulations successfully reproduce most of the general characteristics of motion in our solar system, suggesting that the nebular theory is on the right track.

Additional evidence that our ideas about the formation of flattened disks are correct comes from many other structures in the universe. We expect flattening to occur anywhere orbiting particles can collide, which explains why we find so many cases of flat disks, including the disks of spiral galaxies like the Milky Way, the disks of planetary rings, and the *accretion disks* that surround neutron stars and black holes in close binary star systems [**Section 18.3**].

Why are there two major types of planets?

The planets began to form after the solar nebula had collapsed into a flattened disk of perhaps 200 AU in diameter (about twice the present-day diameter of Pluto's orbit). The churning and mixing of gas in the solar nebula should have ensured that the nebula had the same composition throughout: 98% hydrogen and helium plus 2% heavier elements.

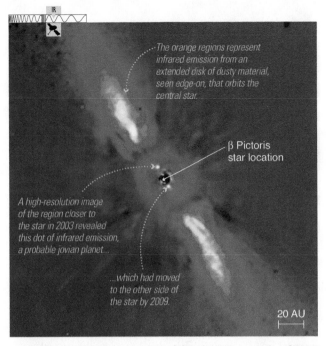

The orange regions represent infrared emission from an extended disk of dusty material, seen edge-on, that orbits the central star.

β Pictoris star location

A high-resolution image of the region closer to the star in 2003 revealed this dot of infrared emission, a probable jovian planet...

...which had moved to the other side of the star by 2009.

20 AU

a This infrared image composite from the European Southern Observatory Very Large Telescope shows a large debris disk orbiting the star Beta Pictoris and a probable jovian planet that has formed in the disk. Images were taken with the star itself blocked; the star's position has been added digitally.

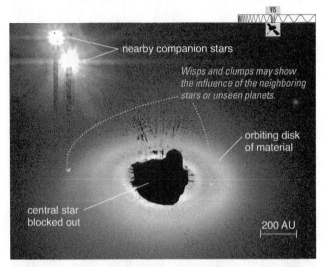

nearby companion stars

Wisps and clumps may show the influence of the neighboring stars or unseen planets.

orbiting disk of material

central star blocked out

200 AU

b This Hubble Space Telescope image shows a disk around the star HD141569A. The colors are not real; a black-and-white image has been tinted red to bring out faint detail.

FIGURE 8.4 These images show flattened, spinning disks of material around other stars.

How, then, did the terrestrial planets end up so different in composition from the jovian planets? The key clue comes from their locations: Terrestrial planets formed in the warm, inner regions of the swirling disk, while jovian planets formed in the colder, outer regions.

Condensation: Sowing the Seeds of Planets

In the center of the collapsing solar nebula, gravity drew together enough material to form the Sun. In the surrounding disk, however, the gaseous material was too spread out for gravity alone to clump it together. Instead, material had to begin clumping in some other way and then grow in size until gravity could start pulling it together into planets. In essence, planet formation required the presence of "seeds"—solid bits of matter from which gravity could ultimately build planets.

The basic process of seed formation was probably much like the formation of snowflakes in clouds on Earth: When the temperature is low enough, some atoms or molecules in a gas may bond and solidify. The general process in which solid (or liquid) particles form in a gas is called **condensation**—we say that the particles *condense* out of the gas. (Pressures in the solar nebula were generally too low to allow the condensation of liquid droplets.) These particles start out microscopic in size, but they can grow larger with time.

Different materials condense at different temperatures. As summarized in **TABLE 8.1**, the ingredients of the solar nebula fell into four major categories:

- **Hydrogen and helium gas (98% of the solar nebula).** These gases never condense in interstellar space.

TABLE 8.1 Materials in the Solar Nebula

A summary of the four types of materials present in the solar nebula. The squares represent the relative proportions of each type (by mass).

	Examples	Typical Condensation Temperature	Relative Abundance (by mass)
Hydrogen and Helium Gas	hydrogen, helium	do not condense in nebula	98%
Hydrogen Compounds	water (H_2O), methane (CH_4), ammonia (NH_3)	<150 K	1.4%
Rock	various minerals	500–1300 K	0.4%
Metal	iron, nickel, aluminum	1000–1600 K	0.2%

- **Hydrogen compounds (1.4% of the solar nebula).** Materials such as water (H_2O), methane (CH_4), and ammonia (NH_3) can solidify into **ices** at low temperatures (below about 150 K under the low pressure of the solar nebula).

- **Rock (0.4% of the solar nebula).** Rocky material is gaseous at very high temperatures, but condenses into solid bits of mineral at temperatures between about 500 K and 1300 K, depending on the type of rock. (A *mineral* is a type of rock with a particular chemical composition and structure.)

- **Metal (0.2% of the solar nebula).** Metals such as iron, nickel, and aluminum are also gaseous at very high temperatures, but condense into solid form at higher temperatures than rock—typically in the range of 1000 K to 1600 K.

Because hydrogen and helium gas made up 98% of the solar nebula's mass and did not condense, the vast majority of the nebula remained gaseous at all times. However, other materials could condense wherever the temperature allowed (**FIGURE 8.5**). Close to the forming Sun, where the temperature was above 1600 K, it was too hot for any material to condense. Near what is now Mercury's orbit, the temperature was low enough for metals and some types of rock to condense into tiny, solid particles, but other types of rock and all the hydrogen compounds remained gaseous. More types of rock could condense, along with the metals, at the distances from the Sun where Venus, Earth, and Mars would form. In the region where the asteroid belt would eventually be located, temperatures were low enough to allow dark, carbon-rich minerals to condense, along with minerals containing small amounts of water. Hydrogen compounds could condense into ices only beyond the **frost line**—the distance at which it was cold enough for ices to condense—which lay between the present-day orbits of Mars and Jupiter.

THINK ABOUT IT

Consider a region of the solar nebula in which the temperature was about 1300 K. Based on the data in Table 8.1, what fraction of the material in this region was gaseous? What were the solid particles in this region made of? Answer the same questions for a region with a temperature of 100 K. Would the 100 K region be closer to or farther from the Sun? Explain.

The frost line marked the key transition between the warm inner regions of the solar system where terrestrial planets formed and the cool outer regions where jovian planets formed. Inside the frost line, only metal and rock could condense into solid "seeds," which is why the terrestrial planets ended up being made of metal and rock. Beyond the frost line, where it was cold enough for hydrogen compounds to condense into ices, the solid seeds were built of ice along with metal and rock. Moreover, because hydrogen compounds were nearly three times as abundant in the nebula as metal

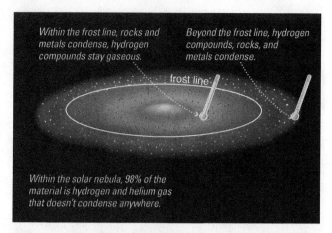

FIGURE 8.5 interactive figure Temperature differences in the solar nebula led to different kinds of condensed materials at different distances from the Sun, sowing the seeds for two kinds of planets.

and rock combined (see Table 8.1), the total amount of solid material was far greater beyond the frost line than within it. The stage was set for the birth of two types of planets: planets born from seeds of metal and rock in the inner solar system and planets born from seeds of ice (as well as metal and rock) in the outer solar system.

Building the Terrestrial Planets From this point, the story of the inner solar system seems fairly clear. The solid seeds of metal and rock in the inner solar system ultimately grew into the terrestrial planets we see today, but these planets ended up relatively small in size because rock and metal made up such a small amount of the material in the solar nebula.

The process by which small "seeds" grew into planets is called **accretion** (**FIGURE 8.6**). Accretion began with the microscopic solid particles that condensed from the gas of the solar nebula. These particles orbited the forming Sun with the same orderly, circular paths as the gas from which they condensed. Individual particles therefore moved at nearly the same speed as neighboring particles, so "collisions" were more like gentle touches. Although the particles were far too small to attract each other gravitationally at this point, they were able to stick together through electrostatic forces—the same "static electricity" that makes hair stick to a comb. Small particles thereby began to combine into larger ones. As the particles grew in mass, gravity began to aid the process of

COMMON MISCONCEPTIONS

Solar Gravity and the Density of Planets

Some people guess that it was the Sun's gravity that pulled the dense rocky and metallic materials to the inner part of the solar nebula, or that gases escaped from the inner nebula because gravity couldn't hold them. But this is not the case—all the ingredients were orbiting the Sun together under the influence of the Sun's gravity. The orbit of a particle or a planet does *not* depend on its size or density, so the Sun's gravity cannot be the cause of the different kinds of planets. Rather, the different temperatures in the solar nebula are the cause.

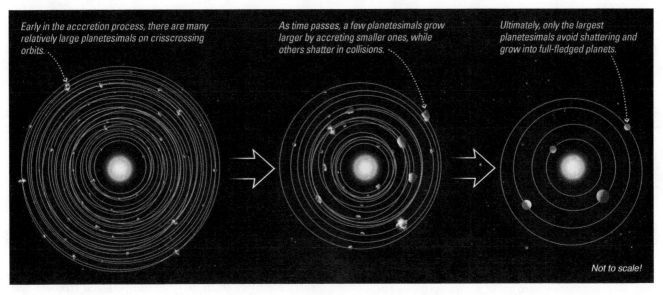

Early in the acccretion process, there are many relatively large planetesimals on crisscrossing orbits.

As time passes, a few planetesimals grow larger by accreting smaller ones, while others shatter in collisions.

Ultimately, only the largest planetesimals avoid shattering and grow into full-fledged planets.

Not to scale!

FIGURE 8.6 These diagrams show how planetesimals gradually accrete into terrestrial planets.

their sticking together, accelerating their growth into boulders large enough to count as **planetesimals**, which means "pieces of planets."

The planetesimals grew rapidly at first. As they grew larger, they had both more surface area to make contact with other planetesimals and more gravity to attract them. Some planetesimals probably grew to hundreds of kilometers in size in only a few million years—a long time in human terms, but only about *one-thousandth* of the present age of the solar system. However, once the planetesimals reached these relatively large sizes, further growth became more difficult.

Gravitational encounters [**Section 4.5**] between planetesimals tended to alter their orbits, particularly those of the smaller planetesimals. With different orbits crossing each other, collisions between planetesimals tended to occur at higher speeds and hence became more destructive. Such collisions tended to shatter planetesimals rather than help them grow. Only the largest planetesimals avoided being shattered and could grow into terrestrial planets.

Theoretical evidence in support of this model comes from computer simulations of the accretion process. Observational evidence comes from **meteorites**, rocks that have fallen to Earth from space. Meteorites that appear to be surviving fragments from the period of condensation contain metallic grains embedded in rocky minerals (**FIGURE 8.7**), just as we would expect if metal and rock condensed in the inner solar system. Meteorites thought to come from the outskirts of the asteroid belt contain abundant carbon-rich materials, and some contain water—again as we would expect for planetesimals that formed in that region.

Making the Jovian Planets Accretion should have occurred similarly in the outer solar system, but condensation of ices meant both that there was more solid material and that this material contained ice in addition to metal and rock. The solid objects that reside in the outer solar system today, such as comets and the moons of the jovian planets,

still show this ice-rich composition. However, the growth of icy planetesimals cannot be the whole story of jovian planet formation, because the jovian planets contain large amounts of hydrogen and helium gas.

The leading model for jovian planet formation holds that these planets formed as gravity drew gas around ice-rich planetesimals much more massive than Earth. Because of their large masses, these planetesimals had gravity strong enough to capture some of the hydrogen and helium gas that made up the vast majority of the surrounding solar nebula. This added gas made their gravity even stronger, allowing them to capture even more gas. Ultimately, the jovian planets accreted so much gas that they bore little resemblance to the icy seeds from which they grew.

FIGURE 8.7 Shiny flakes of metal are clearly visible in this slice through a meteorite (a few centimeters across), mixed in among the rocky material. Such metallic flakes are just what we would expect to find if condensation really occurred in the solar nebula as described by the nebular theory.

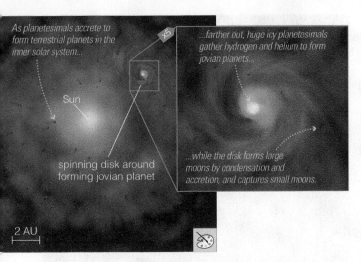

As planetesimals accrete to form terrestrial planets in the inner solar system...

...farther out, huge icy planetesimals gather hydrogen and helium to form jovian planets...

Sun

spinning disk around forming jovian planet

...while the disk forms large moons by condensation and accretion, and captures small moons.

2 AU

FIGURE 8.8 The young jovian planets were surrounded by disks of gas, much like the disk of the entire solar nebula but smaller in size. According to the leading model, the planets grew as large, ice-rich planetesimals captured hydrogen and helium gas from the solar nebula. This painting shows the gas and planetesimals surrounding one jovian planet in the larger solar nebula.

This model also explains most of the large moons of the jovian planets. The same processes of heating, spinning, and flattening that made the disk of the solar nebula should also have affected the gas drawn by gravity to the young jovian planets. Each jovian planet came to be surrounded by its own disk of gas, spinning in the same direction as the planet rotated (**FIGURE 8.8**). Moons that accreted from ice-rich planetesimals within these disks ended up with nearly circular orbits going in the same direction as their planet's rotation and lying close to their planet's equatorial plane.

Clearing the Nebula The vast majority of the hydrogen and helium gas in the solar nebula never became part of any planet. So what happened to it? Apparently, it was cleared away by a combination of intense radiation from the young Sun and the **solar wind**—a stream of charged particles (such as protons and electrons) continually blown outward in all directions from the Sun. Although the solar wind is fairly weak today, observations show that stars tend to have much stronger winds when they are young. The young Sun therefore also should have had a strong solar wind—strong enough to have swept huge quantities of gas out of the solar system.

The clearing of the gas sealed the compositional fate of the planets. If the gas had remained longer, it might have continued to cool until hydrogen compounds could have condensed into ices even in the inner solar system. In that case, the terrestrial planets might have accreted abundant ice, and perhaps hydrogen and helium gas as well, changing their basic nature. At the other extreme, if the gas had been blown out earlier, the raw materials of the planets might have been swept away before the planets could fully form. Although these extreme scenarios did not occur in our solar system, they may sometimes occur around other stars. Planet formation may also sometimes be interrupted when radiation from hot neighboring stars drives away material in a solar nebula.

The clearing of the nebula also helps explain what was once considered a surprising aspect of the Sun's rotation. According to the law of conservation of angular momentum, the spinning disk of the solar nebula should have spun fastest near its center, where most of the mass became concentrated. We therefore expect the young Sun to have rotated very fast. But the Sun rotates quite slowly today, with each full rotation taking about a month. If the young Sun really did rotate fast, as the nebular theory seems to demand, how did its rotation slow down?

Angular momentum cannot simply disappear, but it can be transferred from one object to another—and then the other object can be pushed away. A spinning skater can slow her spin by grabbing her partner and then pushing him away. The Sun probably lost angular momentum in a similar way.

The young Sun's rapid rotation would have generated a magnetic field far stronger than that of the Sun today, which in turn would have led to the strong solar wind and to strong surface activity (such as large sunspots and frequent solar flares [**Section 14.3**]) that would have caused the young Sun to emit intense ultraviolet and X-ray radiation. This high-energy radiation ionized gas in the solar nebula, creating many charged particles, while the magnetic field swept through the nebula with the Sun's rapid rotation. Because charged particles and magnetic fields tend to move together, the magnetic field dragged the charged particles along faster than the rest of the nebula, effectively slowing the Sun's rotation and transferring some of the Sun's angular momentum to the nebula. When the nebula was cleared into interstellar space, the gas carried the angular momentum away, leaving the Sun with the greatly diminished angular momentum and slow rotation that we see today (**FIGURE 8.9**).

Although we cannot prove that the young Sun really did lose angular momentum in this way, support for the idea comes

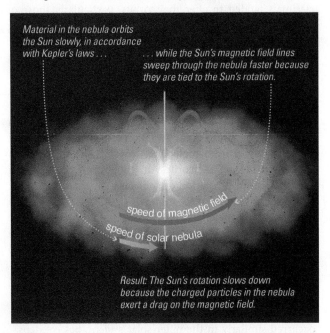

Material in the nebula orbits the Sun slowly, in accordance with Kepler's laws . . .

. . . while the Sun's magnetic field lines sweep through the nebula faster because they are tied to the Sun's rotation.

speed of magnetic field

speed of solar nebula

Result: The Sun's rotation slows down because the charged particles in the nebula exert a drag on the magnetic field.

FIGURE 8.9 The young Sun should have rotated rapidly, but today the Sun rotates quite slowly. As shown in this diagram, the Sun probably lost angular momentum because of drag between slow-moving charged particles in the solar nebula and the Sun's rotating magnetic field (represented by purple loops).

from observations of other stars. When we look at young stars in interstellar clouds, we find that nearly all of them rotate rapidly and have strong magnetic fields and strong winds [**Section 16.2**]. Older stars almost invariably rotate slowly, like our Sun. This suggests that nearly all stars have their original rapid rotations slowed by transferring angular momentum to charged particles in their disks—particles that are later swept away—just as we suspect happened with the Sun.

Where did asteroids and comets come from?

The process of planet formation also explains the origin of the many asteroids and comets that populate our solar system (including those large enough to qualify as dwarf planets): They are "leftovers" from the era of planet formation. Asteroids are the rocky leftover planetesimals of the inner solar system, while comets are the icy leftover planetesimals of the outer solar system. We'll see in Chapter 12 why most asteroids ended up grouped in the asteroid belt while most comets ended up split between two regions (the Kuiper belt and the Oort cloud).

Evidence that asteroids and comets are leftover planetesimals comes from analysis of meteorites, spacecraft visits to comets and asteroids, and theoretical models of solar system formation. In fact, the nebular theory allowed scientists to make predictions about the locations of comets that weren't verified until decades later, when we discovered large comets orbiting in the vicinity of Neptune and Pluto.

The asteroids and comets that exist today probably represent only a small fraction of the leftover planetesimals that roamed the young solar system. The rest are now gone. Some of these "lost" planetesimals may have been flung into deep space by gravitational encounters, but many others must have collided with the planets. When impacts occur on solid worlds, they leave behind **impact craters** as scars. Impacts have thereby transformed planetary landscapes and, in the case of Earth, have altered the course of evolution. For example, an impact is thought to have been responsible for the death of the dinosaurs [**Section 12.4**].

Although impacts occasionally still occur, the vast majority of these collisions occurred in the first few hundred million years of our solar system's history, during the period we call the **heavy bombardment**. Every world in our solar system must have been pelted by impacts during the heavy bombardment (**FIGURE 8.10**), and most of the craters we see on the Moon and other worlds date from this period. These impacts did more than just batter the planets. They also brought materials from other regions of the solar system—a fact that is critical to our existence on Earth today.

The metal and rock planetesimals that built the terrestrial planets probably contained no water or other hydrogen compounds at all, because it was too hot for these compounds to condense in our region of the solar nebula. How, then, did Earth come to have the water that makes up our oceans and the gases that first formed our atmosphere? The likely answer is that water, along with other hydrogen compounds, was brought to Earth and other terrestrial planets by the impacts of water-bearing planetesimals that formed farther from

FIGURE 8.10 Around 4 billion years ago, Earth, its Moon, and the other planets were heavily bombarded by leftover planetesimals. This painting shows the young Earth and Moon, with an impact in progress on Earth.

the Sun. We don't yet know whether these planetesimals came primarily from the outer asteroid belt, where rocky planetesimals contained small amounts of water and other hydrogen compounds, or whether they were comets containing huge amounts of ice. Either way, the water we drink and the air we breathe probably originated beyond the orbit of Mars.

How do we explain "exceptions to the rules"?

We have now explained all the major features of our solar system except the exceptions to the rules, including our surprisingly large Moon. Today, we think that most of these exceptions arose from collisions or close gravitational encounters.

Captured Moons We have explained the orbits of most large jovian planet moons by their formation in a disk that swirled around the forming planet. But how do we explain moons with less orderly orbits, such as those that go in the "wrong" direction (opposite their planet's rotation) or that have large inclinations to their planet's equator? These moons are probably leftover planetesimals that originally orbited the Sun but were then captured into planetary orbit.

It's not easy for a planet to capture a moon. An object cannot switch from an unbound orbit (for example, an asteroid whizzing by Jupiter) to a bound orbit (for example, a moon orbiting Jupiter) unless it somehow loses orbital energy [**Section 4.5**]. For the jovian planets, captures probably occurred when passing planetesimals lost energy to drag in the extended and relatively dense gas that surrounded these planets as they formed. The planetesimals would have been slowed by friction with the gas, just as artificial satellites are slowed by drag in encounters with Earth's atmosphere. If friction reduced its orbital energy enough, a planetesimal

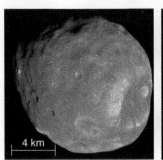
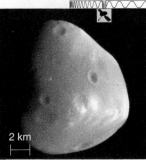

a Phobos   **b** Deimos

FIGURE 8.11 The two moons of Mars are probably captured asteroids. Phobos is only about 13 kilometers across, and Deimos is only about 8 kilometers across—making each of these two moons small enough to fit within the boundaries of a typical large city. (Images from the *Mars Reconnaissance Orbiter*.)

could have become an orbiting moon. Because of the random nature of the capture process, captured moons would not necessarily orbit in the same direction as their planet or in its equatorial plane. Computer models suggest that this capture process would have worked only on objects up to a few kilometers in size. Most of the small moons of the jovian planets are a few kilometers across, supporting the idea that they were captured in this way. Mars may have similarly captured its two small moons, Phobos and Deimos, at a time when the planet had a much more extended atmosphere than it does today (**FIGURE 8.11**).

The Giant Impact Formation of Our Moon Capture processes cannot explain our own Moon, because it is much too large to have been captured by a small planet like Earth. We can also rule out the possibility that our Moon formed simultaneously with Earth, because if both had formed together, they would have accreted from planetesimals of the same type and would therefore have approximately the same composition and density. But this is not the case: The Moon's density is considerably lower than Earth's, indicating that it has a very different average composition. So how did we get our Moon? Today, the leading hypothesis suggests that it formed as the result of a **giant impact** between Earth and a huge planetesimal.

According to models, a few leftover planetesimals may have been as large as Mars. If one of these Mars-size objects struck a young planet, the blow might have tilted the planet's axis, changed the planet's rotation rate, or completely shattered the planet. The giant impact hypothesis holds that a Mars-size object hit Earth at a speed and angle that blasted Earth's outer layers into space. According to computer simulations, this material could have collected into orbit around our planet, and accretion within this ring of debris could have formed the Moon (**FIGURE 8.12**).

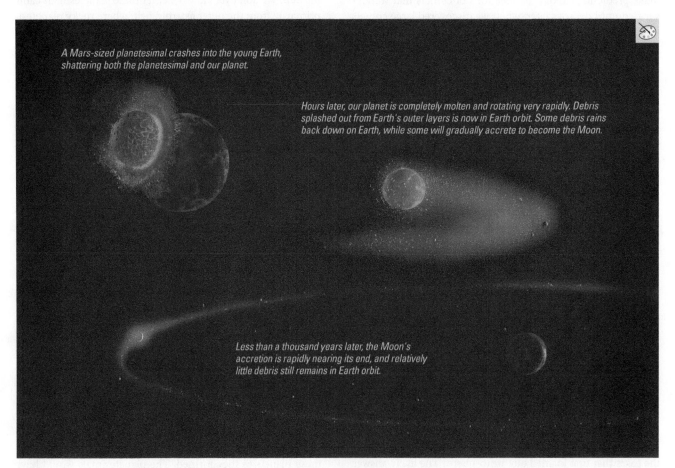

A Mars-sized planetesimal crashes into the young Earth, shattering both the planetesimal and our planet.

Hours later, our planet is completely molten and rotating very rapidly. Debris splashed out from Earth's outer layers is now in Earth orbit. Some debris rains back down on Earth, while some will gradually accrete to become the Moon.

Less than a thousand years later, the Moon's accretion is rapidly nearing its end, and relatively little debris still remains in Earth orbit.

FIGURE 8.12 Artist's conception of the giant impact hypothesis for the formation of our Moon. The fact that ejected material came mostly from Earth's outer rocky layers explains why the Moon contains very little metal. The impact must have occurred more than 4.4 billion years ago, since that is the age of the oldest Moon rocks. As shown, the Moon formed quite close to a rapidly rotating Earth, but over billions of years, tidal forces have slowed Earth's rotation and moved the Moon's orbit outward (see Figure 4.26).

Strong support for the giant impact hypothesis comes from two features of the Moon's composition. First, the Moon's overall composition is quite similar to that of Earth's outer layers—just as we would expect if it were made from material blasted away from those layers. Second, the Moon has a much smaller proportion of easily vaporized ingredients (such as water) than Earth. This fact supports the hypothesis because the heat of the impact would have vaporized these ingredients. As gases, they would not have participated in the subsequent accretion of the Moon.

Other Exceptions Giant impacts may also explain other exceptions to the general trends. For example, Pluto's moon Charon shows signs of having formed in a giant impact similar to the one thought to have formed our Moon. Mercury has a metal core extending to 85% of its radius—the largest of any planet—which may be the result of a giant impact that blasted away its outer, rocky layers. Giant impacts could have been responsible for tilting the axes of many planets (including Earth) and perhaps for tipping Uranus on its side. Venus's slow and backward rotation could also be the result of a giant impact, though some scientists suspect it is a consequence of processes attributable to Venus's thick atmosphere.

Although we cannot definitively explain these exceptions to the general rules, the overall lesson is clear: The chaotic processes that accompanied planet formation, including the many collisions that surely occurred, are *expected* to have led to at least a few exceptions. We therefore conclude that the nebular theory can account for all four of the major features of our solar system. FIGURE 8.13 summarizes what we have discussed. Computer models of planetary formation suggest that the entire process took no more than about 50 million years, which is only about 1% of the current age of the solar system.

Planetary Destiny We've now seen that the nebular theory accounts for all the major features of our solar system. Of course, that does not mean that it explains *everything* about the formation of our solar system. As we'll discuss in Chapter 13, discoveries of other planetary systems have already forced us to revise parts of the theory to allow for a wider range of possibilities than we observe in our own solar system. Nevertheless, the basic theory is widely accepted today because it is so strongly supported by the available evidence.

Assuming the nebular theory is correct, was it inevitable that our solar nebula would form the solar system we see today? Probably not. The first stages of planet formation were orderly and inevitable according to the nebular theory. The creation of a spinning disk, condensation within that disk, and the first stages of accretion were relatively gradual processes that probably would happen again if we turned back the clock. However, the final stages of accretion, and giant impacts in particular, are inherently random and probably would not happen again in the same way. A larger or smaller planet might form at Earth's location and might suffer from a larger giant impact or from no giant impact at all. We don't yet know whether these differences would fundamentally alter the solar system or simply change a

few "minor" details—such as the possibility of life on Earth. What we do know is that, among the billions of star systems in our galaxy, it's unlikely that any other is exactly like ours.

THINK ABOUT IT

Make a brief list of characteristics of Earth that arose through apparently random processes in our solar system. Overall, how likely do you think it was that a planet like Earth would form? Defend your opinion, and discuss how your answer relates to the possibility of finding Earth-like planets in other star systems.

8.3 THE AGE OF THE SOLAR SYSTEM

The nebular theory seems to explain *how* our solar system was born. But *when* was it born, and how do we know? The answer is that the planets began to form through accretion just over $4\frac{1}{2}$ billion years ago, a fact we learned by determining the age of the oldest rocks in the solar system.

How do we measure the age of a rock?

The first step in understanding how we learned the age of our solar system is to understand exactly what we mean by the age of a rock. A rock is a collection of a great many atoms held together in solid form. The atoms must be older than Earth, having been forged in the Big Bang or in stars that lived long ago. We cannot determine the ages of the individual atoms, because old atoms are indistinguishable from young ones. However, some atoms undergo changes with time that allow us to determine how long they have been held in place within the rock's solid structure. In other words, the age of a rock is the time since its atoms became locked together in their present arrangement, which in most cases means the time *since the rock last solidified.*

Radiometric Dating The method by which we measure a rock's age is called **radiometric dating**, and it relies on careful measurement of the rock's proportions of various atoms and isotopes. Recall that each chemical element is uniquely characterized by the number of protons in its nucleus, and that different *isotopes* of the same element differ in their number of neutrons [**Section 5.3**]. The key to radiometric dating lies in the fact that some isotopes are radioactive, which is just a fancy way of saying that their nuclei tend to undergo some type of spontaneous change (also called *decay*) with time, such as breaking into two pieces or having a neutron turn into a proton. Decay can change one element into an entirely different one, with different chemical properties.

As a specific example, consider the radioactive isotope potassium-40 (nuclei consisting of 19 protons and 21 neutrons), which decays when one of its protons turns into a neutron, thereby transforming it into argon-40 (18 protons and 22 neutrons). We say that potassium-40 is the *parent isotope*, because it is the original isotope before the decay, and argon-40 is the *daughter isotope* left behind by the decay process.

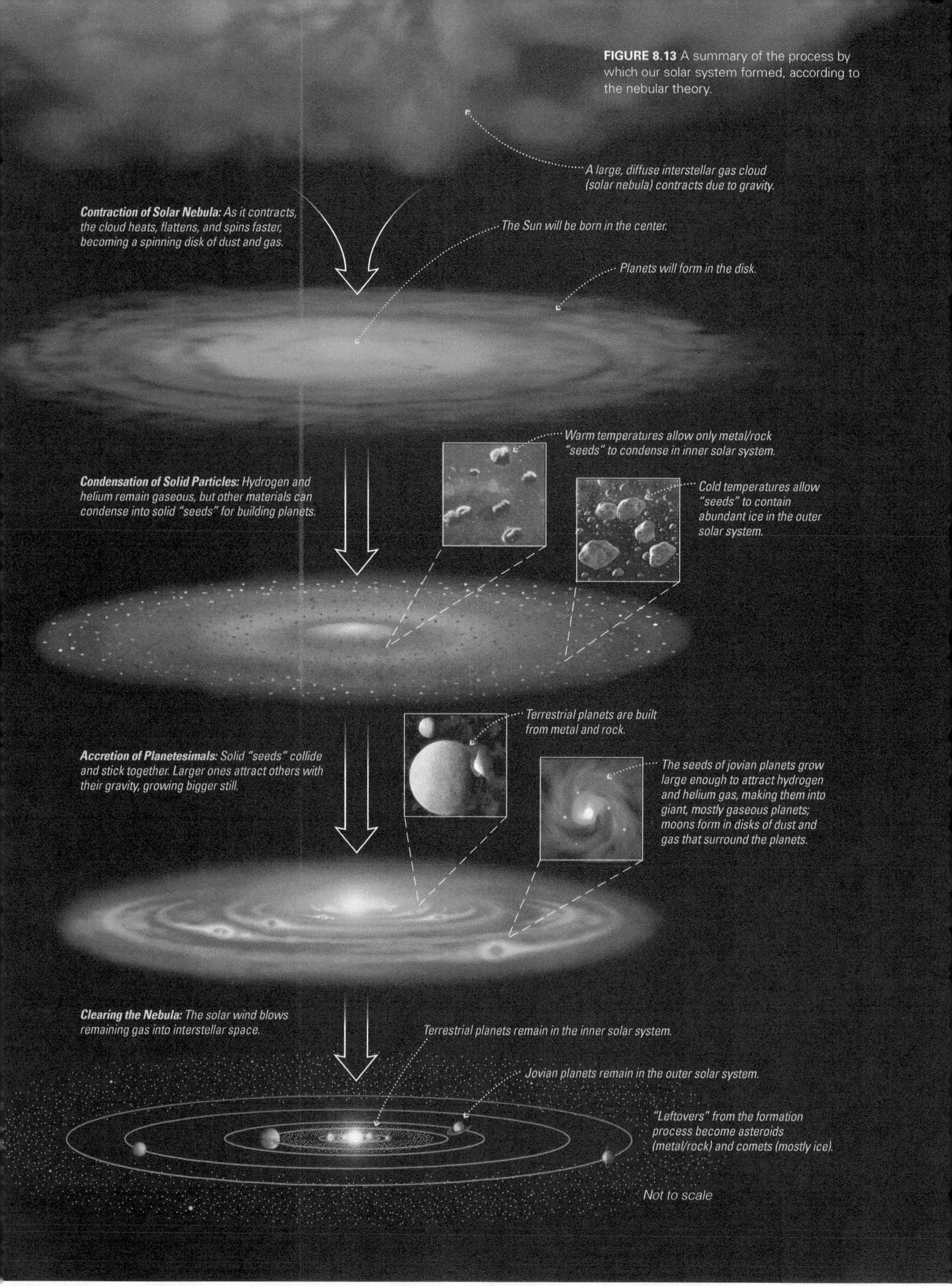

FIGURE 8.13 A summary of the process by which our solar system formed, according to the nebular theory.

A large, diffuse interstellar gas cloud (solar nebula) contracts due to gravity.

Contraction of Solar Nebula: As it contracts, the cloud heats, flattens, and spins faster, becoming a spinning disk of dust and gas.

The Sun will be born in the center.

Planets will form in the disk.

Warm temperatures allow only metal/rock "seeds" to condense in inner solar system.

Condensation of Solid Particles: Hydrogen and helium remain gaseous, but other materials can condense into solid "seeds" for building planets.

Cold temperatures allow "seeds" to contain abundant ice in the outer solar system.

Terrestrial planets are built from metal and rock.

Accretion of Planetesimals: Solid "seeds" collide and stick together. Larger ones attract others with their gravity, growing bigger still.

The seeds of jovian planets grow large enough to attract hydrogen and helium gas, making them into giant, mostly gaseous planets; moons form in disks of dust and gas that surround the planets.

Clearing the Nebula: The solar wind blows remaining gas into interstellar space.

Terrestrial planets remain in the inner solar system.

Jovian planets remain in the outer solar system.

"Leftovers" from the formation process become asteroids (metal/rock) and comets (mostly ice).

Not to scale

(Potassium-40 also decays by other paths, but we will focus only on decay into argon-40 to keep the discussion simple.)

While the decay of any single nucleus is an instantaneous event, laboratory studies show that a modest amount (millions of atoms or more, which is still only a tiny fraction of a gram) of any radioactive parent isotope will gradually transform itself into the daughter isotope at a very steady rate. You don't have to watch for all that long—rarely longer than a few years at most—before you can measure the rate. You can then use this rate to calculate what we call the **half-life**, which is the time it would take for half of the parent nuclei to decay. Every radioactive isotope has its own unique half-life, which may be anywhere from a fraction of a second to many billions of years. Laboratory measurements show that the half-life for the transformation of potassium-40 into argon-40 is 1.25 billion years.

To understand the idea of half-life better, imagine a small piece of rock that contained 1 microgram of potassium-40 and no argon-40 when it solidified long ago. The half-life of 1.25 billion years means that half the original potassium-40 had decayed into argon-40 by the time the rock was 1.25 billion years old, so at that time the rock contained $\frac{1}{2}$ microgram of potassium-40 and $\frac{1}{2}$ microgram of argon-40. Half of this remaining potassium-40 had then decayed by the end of the next 1.25 billion years, so after 2.5 billion years the rock contained $\frac{1}{4}$ microgram of potassium-40 and $\frac{3}{4}$ microgram of argon-40. After three half-lives, or 3.75 billion years, only $\frac{1}{8}$ microgram of potassium-40 remained, while $\frac{7}{8}$ microgram had become argon-40. **FIGURE 8.14** summarizes the gradual

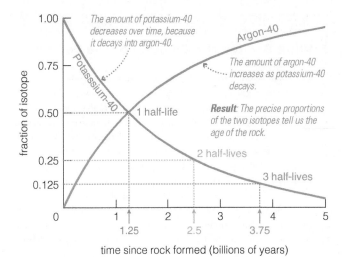

FIGURE 8.14 Potassium-40 is radioactive, decaying into argon-40 with a half-life of 1.25 billion years. The red line shows the decreasing amount of potassium-40, and the blue line shows the increasing amount of argon-40. The remaining amount of potassium-40 drops by half with each successive half-life.

decrease in the amount of potassium-40 and the corresponding rise in the amount of argon-40.

You can now see the essence of radiometric dating. Suppose you find a rock that contains equal numbers of atoms of potassium-40 and argon-40. If you assume that all the argon came from potassium decay (and if the rock shows no evidence of subsequent heating that could have allowed any argon to escape), then it must have taken precisely one half-life for the rock to

MATHEMATICAL INSIGHT 8.1

Radiometric Dating

The amount of a radioactive substance decreases by half with each half-life, so we can express the decay process with a simple formula relating the current and original amounts of a radioactive substance in a rock:

$$\frac{\text{current amount}}{\text{original amount}} = \left(\frac{1}{2}\right)^{t/t_{\text{half}}}$$

where t is the time since the rock formed and t_{half} is the half-life of the radioactive material. We can solve this equation for the age t by taking the base-10 logarithm of both sides and rearranging the terms. The resulting general equation for the age is

$$t = t_{\text{half}} \times \frac{\log_{10}\left(\dfrac{\text{current amount}}{\text{original amount}}\right)}{\log_{10}\left(\dfrac{1}{2}\right)}$$

EXAMPLE: You heat and chemically analyze a small sample of a meteorite. Potassium-40 and argon-40 are present in a ratio of approximately 0.85 unit of potassium-40 atoms to 9.15 units of gaseous argon-40 atoms. (The units are unimportant, because only the relative amounts of the parent and daughter materials matter.) How old is the meteorite?

SOLUTION:

Step 1 Understand: The formula above allows us to find the meteorite's age from the current and original amounts of a parent isotope. We are given that the current amount of the parent isotope potassium-40 is 0.85 unit. We are not told the original amount, but we can figure it out from the fact that the sample now has 9.15 units of the daughter isotope argon-40. As discussed in the text, we can assume that *all* the trapped argon-40 in the meteorite is a decay product of potassium-40, which means that the 9.15 units of argon-40 must originally have been potassium-40. Therefore, the original amount of potassium-40 was $0.85 + 9.15 = 10$ units.

Step 2 Solve: We use the formula above with current amount = 0.85 unit and original amount = 10 units:

$$t = 1.25 \text{ billion yr} \times \frac{\log_{10}\left(\dfrac{0.85}{10}\right)}{\log_{10}\left(\dfrac{1}{2}\right)}$$

$$= 1.25 \text{ billion yr} \times \left(\frac{-1.07}{-0.301}\right)$$

$$= 4.45 \text{ billion yr}$$

Step 3 Explain: We have used radiometric dating to determine that the meteorite's age is 4.45 billion years, which means it solidified 4.45 billion years ago. (*Note:* This example captures the essence of radiometric dating, but real cases generally require more detailed analysis.)

What Started the Collapse of the Solar Nebula?

The solar nebula probably could not have started collapsing on its own, because gravity was too weak when the gas was still spread out over a large region of space. We therefore suspect that some cataclysmic event triggered the collapse. But what type of event? Although we may never know for sure, radioactive elements and their decay products give us some clues. Radioactive elements are made in the violent stellar explosions called *supernovae*, so their presence in meteorites and on Earth underscores the fact that our solar system is made from the remnants of past generations of stars.

Some meteorites contain the rare isotope xenon-129. Xenon is gaseous even at extremely low temperatures, so it could not have condensed and become trapped in the meteorites as they condensed

in the solar nebula. Instead, it must be a product of radioactive decay, and laboratory studies show that its parent isotope is iodine-129. This is a crucial clue, because iodine-129 has a relatively short half-life of 17 million years. We conclude that the xenon-129 we observe in meteorites today is the product of radioactive decay of iodine-129 produced in a supernova that occurred no more than a few tens of millions of years before the collapse of the solar nebula began.

The relatively short time between a supernova and the birth of our solar system suggests that a shock wave from the exploding star may have been the trigger for the nebula's collapse. Once this shock wave got the collapse started, gravity took over and made the rest of the collapse inevitable.

end up with equal amounts of the two isotopes. You can therefore conclude that the rock is 1.25 billion years old. The only question is whether you are right in assuming that the rock lacked argon-40 when it formed. In this case, knowing a bit of "rock chemistry" helps. Potassium-40 is a natural ingredient of many minerals in rocks, but argon-40 is a gas that does not combine with other elements and did not condense in the solar nebula. Therefore, if you find argon-40 gas trapped inside minerals, it must have come from radioactive decay of potassium-40.

Validity of the Method Radiometric dating is possible with many other radioactive isotopes as well. In many cases, a rock contains more than one radioactive isotope, and agreement between the ages calculated from the different isotopes gives us confidence that we have dated the rock correctly. We can also check results from radiometric dating against those from other methods of measuring or estimating ages. For example, some archaeological artifacts have original dates printed on them, and these dates agree with ages found by radiometric dating. The same agreement is found for wood artifacts that can be dated both by counting tree rings and by the radiometric method.

We can validate the $4\frac{1}{2}$-billion-year radiometric age for the solar system as a whole by comparing it to an age based on detailed study of the Sun. Theoretical models of the Sun, along with observations of other stars, show that stars slowly expand and brighten as they age. The model ages are not nearly as precise as radiometric ages, but they confirm that the Sun is between about 4 and 5 billion years old. Overall, the technique of radiometric dating has been checked in so many ways and relies on such basic scientific principles that there is no serious scientific debate about its validity.

How do we know the age of the solar system?

Radiometric dating tells us how long it has been since a rock solidified, which is not the same as the age of a planet as a whole. For example, we find rocks of many different ages on Earth. Some rocks are quite young because they formed recently from molten lava; others are much older. The oldest Earth rocks are about 4 billion years old, and some small

mineral grains date to almost 4.4 billion years ago, but even these are not as old as Earth itself, because Earth's entire surface has been reshaped through time.

Moon rocks brought back by the *Apollo* astronauts have also been dated, and many are older than the oldest Earth rocks, demonstrating that parts of the Moon's surface have not changed since very early in its history. The oldest Moon rocks contain minerals with a small amount of uranium-238, which decays (in several steps) into lead-206 with a half-life of about 4.5 billion years. Lead and uranium have very different chemical behaviors, and some minerals start with virtually no lead. Laboratory analysis of such minerals in lunar rocks shows that they now contain almost equal proportions of atoms of uranium-238 and lead-206, which means they are about one half-life old. More precise work shows them to be about 4.4 billion years old.

THINK ABOUT IT

If future scientists examine the same lunar rocks 4.5 billion years from now, what proportions of uranium-238 and lead-206 will they find? Explain.

Although the oldest Moon rocks are older than the oldest Earth rocks, the rocks must still be younger than the Moon and Earth as a whole. In fact, their age tells us that the giant impact thought to have created the Moon must have occurred more than 4.4 billion years ago. But how do we determine when the planets first began to form?

To go all the way back to the origin of the solar system, we must find rocks that have not melted or vaporized since they first condensed in the solar nebula. Meteorites that have fallen to Earth are our source of such rocks. Many meteorites appear to have remained unchanged since they condensed and accreted in the early solar system. Careful analysis of radioactive isotopes in these meteorites shows that the oldest ones formed about 4.55 billion years ago, so this time must mark the beginning of accretion in the solar nebula. Because the planets apparently accreted within about 50 million (0.05 billion) years after that, Earth and the other planets had formed by about 4.5 billion years ago. In other words, the age of our solar system is only about a third of the 14-billion-year age of our universe.

Putting Chapter 8 into Perspective

This chapter described the current scientific theory of our solar system's formation, and how this theory explains the major features we observe. As you continue your study of the solar system, keep in mind the following "big picture" ideas:

- The nebular theory of solar system formation gained wide acceptance because of its success in explaining the major characteristics of our solar system.

- Most of the general features of the solar system were determined by processes that occurred very early in the solar system's history.

- Chance events may have played a large role in determining how individual planets turned out. No one knows how different our solar system might be if the process started over.

- We have learned the age of our solar system—about $4\frac{1}{2}$ billion years—from radiometric dating of the oldest meteorites. This age agrees with ages estimated through a variety of other techniques, making it clear that we are recent arrivals on a very old planet.

SUMMARY OF KEY CONCEPTS

8.1 THE SEARCH FOR ORIGINS

- **How did we arrive at a theory of solar system formation?** A successful theory must explain four major features of our solar system: patterns of motion, the existence of two types of planets (terrestrial and jovian), the presence of asteroids and comets, and exceptions to the rules. Developed over a period of more than two centuries, the **nebular theory** explains all four features and also can account for other planetary systems.

- **Where did the solar system come from?** The nebular

theory holds that the solar system formed from the gravitational collapse of an interstellar cloud known as the **solar nebula**. This cloud was the product of recycling of gas through many generations of stars within our galaxy. This material consisted of 98% hydrogen and helium and 2% all other elements combined.

8.2 EXPLAINING THE MAJOR FEATURES OF THE SOLAR SYSTEM

- **What caused the orderly patterns of motion?** As the

solar nebula collapsed under gravity, natural processes caused it to heat up, spin faster, and flatten out as it shrank. The orderly motions we observe today all came from the orderly motion of this spinning disk.

- **Why are there two major types of planets?** The inner

regions of the solar nebula were relatively hot, so only metal and rock could condense into tiny, solid grains; these grains accreted into larger **planetesimals** that ultimately merged to make the terrestrial planets. Beyond the

frost line, cooler temperatures also allowed more abundant **hydrogen compounds** to condense into ice, building ice-rich planetesimals; some of these grew large enough for their gravity to draw in hydrogen and helium gas, forming the jovian planets.

- **Where did asteroids and comets come from?** Asteroids are the rocky leftover planetesimals of the inner solar system, and comets are the ice-rich leftover planetesimals of the outer solar system. These objects still occasionally collide with planets or moons, but the vast majority of impacts occurred during the **heavy bombardment** in the solar system's first few hundred million years.

- **How do we explain "exceptions to the rules"?** Most

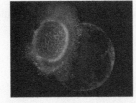

of the exceptions probably arose from collisions or close encounters with leftover planetesimals. Our Moon is most likely the result of a **giant impact** between a Mars-size planetesimal and the young Earth.

8.3 THE AGE OF THE SOLAR SYSTEM

- **How do we measure the age of a rock?** **Radiometric**

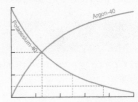

dating is based on carefully measuring the proportions of radioactive isotopes and their decay products within rocks. The ratio of the isotopes changes with time in a steady and predictable way that we characterize by an isotope's **half-life**, the time it takes for half the atoms in a collection to decay.

- **How do we know the age of the solar system?** Radiometric dating of the oldest meteorites tells us that accretion began in the solar nebula about 4.55 billion years ago, with the planets forming by about 4.5 billion years ago.

Use the following questions to check your understanding of some of the many types of visual information used in astronomy. Answers are provided in Appendix J. For additional practice, try the Chapter 8 Visual Quiz at MasteringAstronomy®.

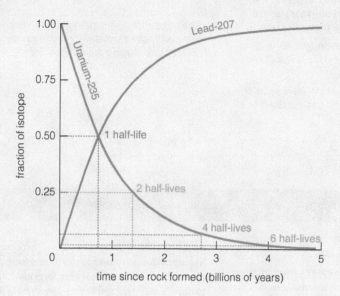

The graph above, similar to Figure 8.14, shows the radioactive decay of uranium-235 to lead-207. (Uranium-235 also decays to lead-206, but we'll ignore that reaction for the sake of clarity in this example.)

1. Compare the graph above to Figure 8.14, which shows the decay of potassium-40. Which element is more radioactive (undergoes radioactive decay more quickly)?
   a. uranium-235
   b. potassium-40
   c. Both are equally radioactive.

2. What fraction of the original uranium-235 should be left after 3.5 billion years?
   a. $\frac{1}{2}$
   b. $\frac{1}{4}$
   c. $\frac{1}{8}$
   d. $\frac{1}{32}$
   e. $\frac{1}{64}$

3. You find a mysterious rock on the ground and determine that 60% of its uranium-235 has been converted into lead-207. What is the most likely origin of the rock, based on its radiometric age?
   a. It's older than our solar system, so it must have come from another solar system.
   b. It's a meteorite dating back to the formation of the solar system.
   c. It's a volcanic rock nearly a billion years old.
   d. It was just formed this year during the eruption of a nearby volcano.

MasteringAstronomy®

For instructor-assigned homework go to MasteringAstronomy®.

REVIEW QUESTIONS

Short-Answer Questions Based on the Reading

1. Briefly describe the four major features of our solar system that a formation theory must explain.

2. What is the *nebular theory*, and why is it widely accepted by scientists today?

3. What do we mean by the *solar nebula*? What was it made of, and where did it come from?

4. Describe the three key processes that led the solar nebula to take the form of a spinning disk. What observational evidence supports this scenario?

5. List the approximate condensation temperature and abundance for each of the four categories of materials in the solar nebula. Which ingredients are present in terrestrial planets? In jovian planets? In comets and asteroids?

6. What was the *frost line*? Which ingredients condensed inside and outside the frost line? What role did it play in the formation of two distinct types of planets?

7. Briefly describe the process by which terrestrial planets are thought to have formed.

8. How was the formation of jovian planets similar to that of the terrestrial planets? How was it different? Why did the jovian planets end up with so many moons?

9. What is the *solar wind,* and what roles did it play in the early solar system?

10. How did planet formation lead to the existence of asteroids and comets?

11. What was the *heavy bombardment,* and when did it occur?

12. What is the leading hypothesis for the Moon's formation, and what evidence supports this hypothesis?

13. Describe the technique of *radiometric dating.* What is a *half-life?*

14. How old is the solar system, and how do we know?

TEST YOUR UNDERSTANDING

Surprising Discoveries?

Suppose we found a solar system with the property described. (These are not real discoveries.) In light of what you've learned about the formation of our own solar system, decide whether the discovery should be considered reasonable or surprising. Explain your reasoning.

15. A solar system has five terrestrial planets in its inner solar system and three jovian planets in its outer solar system.

16. A solar system has four large jovian planets in its inner solar system and seven small terrestrial planets in its outer solar system.

17. A solar system has ten planets that all orbit the star in approximately the same plane. However, five planets orbit in one direction (e.g., counterclockwise), while the other five orbit in the opposite direction (e.g., clockwise).

18. A solar system has 12 planets that all orbit the star in the same direction and in nearly the same plane. The 15 largest moons in this solar system orbit their planets in nearly the same direction and plane as well. However, several smaller moons have highly inclined orbits around their planets.

19. A solar system has six terrestrial planets and four jovian planets. Each of the six terrestrial planets has at least five moons, while the jovian planets have no moons at all.

20. A solar system has four Earth-size terrestrial planets. Each of the four planets has a single moon that is nearly identical in size to Earth's Moon.

21. A solar system has many rocky asteroids and many icy comets. However, most of the comets orbit in the inner solar system, while the asteroids orbit in far-flung regions much like the Kuiper belt and Oort cloud of our solar system.

22. A solar system has several planets similar in composition to the jovian planets of our solar system but similar in mass to the terrestrial planets of our solar system.

23. A solar system has several terrestrial planets and several larger planets made mostly of ice. (*Hint:* What would happen if the solar wind started earlier or later than in our solar system?)

24. Radiometric dating of the oldest meteorites from another solar system shows that they are a billion years younger than rocks from the terrestrial planets of the same system.

Quick Quiz

Choose the best answer to each of the following. Explain your reasoning with one or more complete sentences.

25. How many of the planets orbit the Sun in the same direction as Earth does? (a) a few (b) most (c) all

26. What fraction of the large moons of the planets orbit in the same direction as their planets rotate? (a) some (b) most (c) all

27. The solar nebula was 98% (a) rock and metal. (b) hydrogen compounds. (c) hydrogen and helium.

28. Which of the following did *not* occur during the collapse of the solar nebula? (a) spinning faster (b) heating up (c) concentrating denser materials nearer the Sun

29. What is Jupiter's main ingredient? (a) rock and metal (b) hydrogen compounds (c) hydrogen and helium

30. Which lists the major steps of solar system formation in the correct order? (a) collapse, accretion, condensation (b) collapse, condensation, accretion (c) accretion, condensation, collapse

31. Which of the following is *not* true about the young Sun? (a) It rotated much faster than it does today. (b) It was much brighter and hotter than it is today. (c) It had a much stronger solar wind than it does today.

32. Leftover ice-rich planetesimals are called (a) comets. (b) asteroids. (c) meteorites.

33. What's the leading hypothesis for the origin of the Moon? (a) It formed along with Earth. (b) It formed from material ejected from Earth in a giant impact. (c) It split out of a rapidly rotating Earth.

34. About how old is the solar system? (a) 4.5 million years (b) 4.5 billion years (c) 4.5 trillion years

PROCESS OF SCIENCE

Examining How Science Works

35. *Explaining the Past.* Is it really possible for science to inform us about things that may have happened billions of years ago? To address this question, test the nebular theory against each of the three hallmarks of science discussed in Chapter 3. Be as detailed as possible in explaining whether the theory does or does not satisfy these hallmarks. Use your findings to decide whether the theory can really tell us about how our solar system formed. Defend your opinion.

36. *Unanswered Questions.* As discussed in this chapter, the nebular theory explains many but not all questions about the origin of our solar system. Choose one important but unanswered question about the origin of our solar system and write two or three paragraphs in which you discuss how we might answer this question in the future. Be as specific as possible, focusing on the type of evidence necessary to answer the question and how the evidence could be gathered. What are the benefits of finding answers to this question?

GROUP WORK EXERCISE

37. *A Cold Solar Nebula.* In this chapter, you've learned that the nature of the planets in our solar system was determined by the location of the frost line when the era of planet formation ended. In our solar system, the frost line was located between Mars and Jupiter, but study of other solar systems suggests that our solar system could have turned out differently. Here we examine what would have happened if the entire solar nebula had cooled to 50 K before the solar wind cleared it away. Before you begin, assign the following roles to the people in your group: *Scribe* (takes notes on the group's activities), *Proposer* (proposes explanations to the group), *Skeptic* (points out weaknesses in proposed explanations), and *Moderator* (leads group discussion and makes sure everyone contributes).
a. Make a list of ingredients that will condense at 50 K, and another list of the main ingredients of a typical jovian planet and terrestrial planet. **b.** Use your lists to suggest ways in which jovian and/or terrestrial planets would be different from the ones in our solar system under this alternative formation scenario. Be sure to consider differences in size and composition, and assess whether any differences would be minor or major. **c.** Discuss the likelihood that your predicted changes would match the actual characteristics of this alternative solar system. What factors limit the degree to which you can make successful predictions? **d.** Come up with additional "what if" scenarios, discussing various ways in which planets might have turned out differently.

INVESTIGATE FURTHER

In-Depth Questions to Increase Your Understanding

Short-Answer/Essay Questions

38. *An Early Solar Wind.* Suppose the solar wind had cleared away the solar nebula before the seeds of the jovian planets could gravitationally draw in hydrogen and helium gas. How would the planets of the outer solar system be different? Would they still have many moons? Explain your answer in a few sentences.

39. *Angular Momentum.* Suppose our solar nebula had begun with much more angular momentum than it did. Do you think planets could still have formed? Why or why not? What if the solar nebula had started with zero angular momentum? Explain your answers in one or two paragraphs.

40. *Two Kinds of Planets.* The jovian planets differ from the terrestrial planets in a variety of ways. Using sentences that members of your family would understand, explain why the jovian planets differ from the terrestrial planets in each of the following: composition, size, density, distance from the Sun, and number of satellites.

41. *Two Kinds of Planetesimals.* Why are there two kinds of "leftovers" from solar system formation? List as many differences between comets and asteroids as you can.

42. *History of the Elements.* Our bodies (and most living things) are made mostly of water: H_2O. Summarize the "history" of a typical hydrogen atom from its creation to the formation of Earth. Do the same for a typical oxygen atom. (*Hint:* Which elements were created in the Big Bang, and where were the others created?)

43. *Understanding Radiometric Dating.* Imagine you had the good fortune to find a rocky meteorite in your backyard. Qualitatively, how would you expect its ratio of potassium-40 to argon-40 to be different from that of other rocks in your yard? Explain why, in a few sentences.

44. *Rocks from Other Solar Systems.* Many "leftovers" from planetary formation were likely ejected from our solar system, and the same has presumably happened in other star systems. Given that fact, should we expect to find meteorites that come from other star systems? How rare or common would you expect them to be? (Be sure to consider the distances between stars.) Suppose that we *did* find a meteorite identified as a leftover from another stellar system. What could we learn from it?

Quantitative Problems

Be sure to show all calculations clearly and state your final answers in complete sentences.

45. *Radiometric Dating.* You are dating rocks by their proportions of parent isotope potassium-40 (half-life 1.25 billion years) and daughter isotope argon-40. Find the age for each of the following. **a.** A rock that contains equal amounts of potassium-40 and argon-40 **b.** A rock that contains three times as much argon-40 as potassium-40

46. *Lunar Rocks.* You are dating Moon rocks based on their proportions of uranium-238 (half-life of about 4.5 billion years) and its ultimate decay product, lead. Find the age for each of the following.
a. A rock for which you determine that 55% of the original uranium-238 remains, while the other 45% has decayed into lead
b. A rock for which you determine that 63% of the original uranium-238 remains, while the other 37% has decayed into lead

47. *Carbon-14 Dating.* The half-life of carbon-14 is about 5700 years. **a.** You find a piece of cloth painted with organic dye. By analyzing the dye, you find that only 77% of the carbon-14 originally in the dye remains. When was the cloth painted? **b.** A well-preserved piece of wood found at an archaeological site has 6.2% of the carbon-14 it must have had when it was living. Estimate when the wood was cut. **c.** Is carbon-14 useful for establishing Earth's age? Why or why not?

48. *Collapsing Cloud.* The time it takes for a cloud 100,000 AU in diameter to collapse in "free fall" to form a new star is *half* the time it would take an object to orbit the star on an elliptical orbit with a semimajor axis of 50,000 AU (half the 100,000 AU diameter). Use Kepler's third law to find the collapse time, assuming the star has the same mass as the Sun.

49. *Icy Earth.* How massive would Earth have been if it had accreted hydrogen compounds in addition to rock and metal? Assume the same proportions of the ingredients as listed in Table 8.1. What would Earth's mass be if it had been possible to capture hydrogen and helium gas in the proportion listed in the table?

50. *What Are the Odds?* The fact that all the planets orbit the Sun in the same direction is cited as support for the nebular hypothesis. Imagine that there's a different hypothesis in which planets can be created orbiting the Sun in either direction. Under this hypothesis, what is the probability that eight planets would end up traveling in the same direction? (*Hint:* It's the same probability as that of flipping a coin eight times and getting all heads.)

51. *Spinning Up the Solar Nebula.* The orbital speed of the material in the solar nebula at Pluto's average distance from the Sun was about 5 km/s. What was the orbital speed of this material when it was 40,000 AU from the Sun (before it fell inward with the collapse of the nebula)? Use the law of conservation of angular momentum (see Section 4.3).

Discussion Questions

52. *Theory and Observation.* Discuss the interplay between theory and observation that has led to our modern theory of solar system formation. What role does technology play in allowing us to test this theory?

53. *Lucky to Be Here?* Considering the overall process of solar system formation, do you think formation of a planet like Earth was likely? Could random events in the early history of the solar system have prevented our being here today? What implications do your answers have for the possibility of Earth-like planets around other stars? Defend your opinions.

Web Projects

54. *Spitzer Space Telescope.* NASA's Spitzer Space Telescope operates at the infrared wavelengths especially useful for studies of star and planet formation. Visit the Spitzer website to see what such studies have told us about how planets form. Summarize your findings in a one- to two-page report.

55. *The Stardust Puzzle.* Search the Internet for recent progress in explaining the *Stardust* mission's discovery of minerals from a comet nucleus that must have formed very close to the Sun. Write a one- to two-page report, describing how the result has affected our ideas about the processes in the early solar nebula.

56. *Dating the Past.* The method of radiometric dating that tells us the age of our solar system is also used to determine when many other past events occurred. For example, it is used to determine ages of fossils that tell us when humans first evolved and ages of relics that teach us about the rise of civilization. Research one key aspect of human history in which radiometric dating helps us piece the story together. Write two or three paragraphs on how radiometric dating is used in this case (such as what materials are dated and what radioactive elements are used) and what these studies have concluded. Does your understanding of the method lead you to accept the results? Why or why not?

PLANETARY GEOLOGY
EARTH AND THE OTHER TERRESTRIAL WORLDS

LEARNING GOALS

Nothing is rich but the inexhaustible wealth of nature. She shows us only surfaces, but she is a million fathoms deep.

—Ralph Waldo Emerson

It's easy to take for granted the qualities that make Earth so suitable for human life: a temperature neither boiling nor freezing, abundant water, a protective atmosphere, and a relatively stable environment. But we need look only as far as our neighboring terrestrial worlds to see how fortunate we are. The Moon is airless and barren, and Mercury is much the same. Venus is a searing hothouse, while Mars has an atmosphere so thin and cold that liquid water cannot last on its surface today.

How did the terrestrial worlds come to be so different, and why did Earth alone develop conditions that permit abundant life? We'll explore these questions through careful, comparative study of the planets, focusing on the geology of the terrestrial worlds in this chapter and on their atmospheres in Chapter 10. As we will see, the histories of the terrestrial worlds have been determined largely by properties endowed at their births.

(MA) Formation of the Solar System Tutorial, Lesson 1

9.1 CONNECTING PLANETARY INTERIORS AND SURFACES

Earth's surface seems solid and steady, but every so often it offers us a reminder that nothing about it is permanent. If you live in Alaska or California, you've probably felt the ground shift beneath you in an earthquake. In Washington State, you may have witnessed the rumblings of Mount St. Helens. In Hawaii, a visit to the active Kilauea volcano will remind you that you are standing on mountains of volcanic rock protruding from the ocean floor.

Volcanoes and earthquakes are not the only processes acting to reshape Earth's surface. They are not even the most dramatic: Far greater change can occur on the rare occasions when an asteroid or a comet slams into Earth. More gradual processes can also have spectacular effects. The Colorado River causes only small changes in the landscape from year to year, but its unrelenting flow over the past few million years carved the Grand Canyon. The Rocky Mountains were once twice as tall as they are today, but they have been cut down in size through tens of millions of years of erosion by wind, rain, and ice. Entire continents even move slowly about, completely rearranging the map of Earth every few hundred million years.

Earth is not alone in having undergone tremendous change since its birth. The surfaces of all five terrestrial worlds—Mercury, Venus, Earth, the Moon, and Mars—must have looked quite similar when they were young. All five were made of rocky material that condensed in the solar nebula, and all five were subjected early on to the impacts of the heavy bombardment [**Section 8.2**]. The great differences in their present-day appearances must therefore be the result of changes that have occurred through time. Ultimately, these changes must be traceable to fundamental properties of the planets.

FIGURE 9.1 shows global views of the terrestrial surfaces to scale, as well as sample surface views from orbit. Profound differences among these worlds are immediately obvious. Mercury and the Moon show the scars of their battering during the heavy bombardment: They are densely covered by craters, except in areas that appear to be volcanic plains. Bizarre bulges and odd volcanoes dot the surface of Venus. Mars, despite its middling size, has the solar system's largest volcanoes and a huge canyon cutting across its surface, along with numerous features that appear to have been shaped by liquid water. Earth has surface features similar to all those on the other terrestrial worlds, and more—including a

Venus   Earth

Mercury   Mars   Earth's Moon

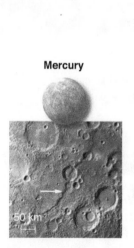
Heavily cratered Mercury has long steep cliffs (arrow).

Cloud-penetrating radar revealed this twin-peaked volcano on Venus.

A portion of Earth's surface as it appears without clouds.

The Moon's surface is heavily cratered in most places.

Mars has features that look like dry riverbeds; note the impact craters.

FIGURE 9.1 Global views to scale, along with sample close-ups viewed from orbit, of the five terrestrial worlds. All the images were taken with visible light except those for Venus, which are based on radar data.

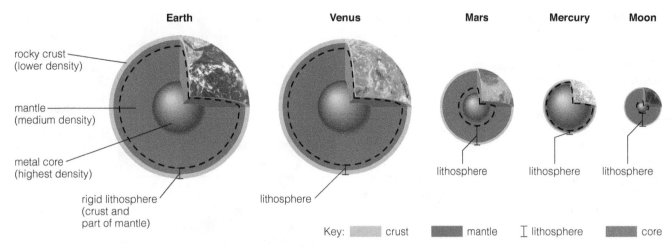

Labels: Earth, Venus, Mars, Mercury, Moon

rocky crust (lower density)

mantle (medium density)

metal core (highest density)

rigid lithosphere (crust and part of mantle)

lithosphere

lithosphere   lithosphere   lithosphere

Key: ▮ crust   ▮ mantle   ⊺ lithosphere   ▮ core

FIGURE 9.2 Interior structures of the terrestrial worlds, with sizes shown to scale from largest to smallest. Color coding shows the core-mantle-crust layering by density; a dashed circle represents the inner boundary of the lithosphere, defined by the strength of the rock rather than by density. The thicknesses of the crust and lithosphere on Venus and Earth are exaggerated to make them visible in this figure.

unique layer of living organisms that covers almost the entire surface of the planet.

Our goal in this chapter is to understand how these differences among the terrestrial planets came to be. This type of study is called **planetary geology**; geology is literally the study of Earth (*geo* means "Earth"), so planetary geology is the extension of this science to other worlds. Note that we use the term *planetary* geology for the study of any solid world, even if it is a moon rather than a planet. Because most geological features are shaped by processes that take place deep beneath the surface, we'll begin our study of planetary geology by examining what planets are like on the inside.

What are terrestrial planets like on the inside?

We cannot see inside Earth or any other planet, but a variety of clues tell us about their internal structures. For Earth, our most detailed information comes from **seismic waves**, vibrations that travel both through the interior and along the surface after an earthquake (*seismic* comes from the Greek word for "shake"). In much the same way that shaking a box containing a gift offers clues about what's inside, seismic vibrations offer clues about what's inside Earth. We also have seismic data for the Moon, thanks to monitoring stations left on the Moon by the *Apollo* astronauts.

For other worlds, we can learn about their interiors in a variety of ways. For example, comparing a world's overall density (found by dividing its total mass by its total volume) to the density of its surface rock tells us how much more dense it must be inside; precise measurements of a world's gravity from spacecraft can tell us about how its mass is distributed inside it; study of magnetic fields tells us about the interior layers in which these fields are generated; and observations of surface rocks that have emerged from the interior (such as volcanic rock) can tell us about interior composition.

Layering by Density All the terrestrial worlds have layered interiors. You are probably familiar with the idea of dividing the interior into three layers by density:

- **Core.** The highest-density material, consisting primarily of metals such as nickel and iron, resides in the central core.

- **Mantle.** Rocky material of moderate density—mostly minerals that contain silicon, oxygen, and other elements—forms the thick mantle that surrounds the core.

- **Crust.** The lowest-density rock, such as granite and basalt (a common form of volcanic rock), forms the thin crust, essentially representing the world's outer skin.

FIGURE 9.2 shows these layers for the five terrestrial worlds. Although not shown in the figure, Earth's metallic core actually consists of two distinct regions: a solid *inner core* and a molten (liquid) *outer core*.* Venus may have a similar core structure, but without seismic data we cannot be sure.

We can understand *why* the interiors are layered by thinking about what happens in a mixture of oil and water: Gravity pulls the denser water to the bottom, driving the less dense oil to the top, in a process called **differentiation** (because it results in layers made of *different* materials). The layered interiors of the terrestrial worlds tell us that they underwent differentiation at some time in the past, which means all these worlds must once have been hot enough inside for their interior rock and metal to melt. Dense metals like iron sank toward the center, driving less dense rocky material toward the surface.

Comparing the terrestrial worlds' interiors provides important clues about their early histories. Models indicate that the relative proportions of metal and rock should have been similar throughout the inner solar system at the time the terrestrial

*Because temperature increases with depth in a planet, it may seem surprising that Earth's inner core is solid while its outer core is molten. The inner core is kept solid by the higher pressure at its greater depth, even though the temperature is also higher.

planets formed, which means we should expect smaller worlds to have correspondingly smaller metal cores. We do indeed see this general pattern in Figure 9.2, but the pattern is not perfect: Mercury's core seems surprisingly big, while the Moon's core seems surprisingly small. These surprises are a major reason scientists suspect that giant impacts affected both worlds [**Section 8.2**]. In Mercury's case, a giant impact that blasted away its outer rocky layers while leaving its core intact could explain why the core is so large compared to the rest of the planet. We can explain the Moon's small core by assuming the Moon formed from debris blasted out of Earth's rocky outer layers (see Figure 8.12): The debris would have contained relatively little high-density metal and therefore would have accreted into an object with a very small metal core.

Layering by Rock Strength In geology, it's often more useful to categorize interior layers by rock strength than by density. The idea that rock can vary in strength may seem surprising, since we often think of rock as the very definition of strength. However, like all matter built of atoms, rock is mostly empty space; its apparent solidity arises from electrical bonds between its atoms and molecules [**Section 5.3**]. Although these bonds are strong, they can still break and re-form when subjected to heat or sustained stress, which means that even solid rock can slowly deform and flow over millions and billions of years. The long-term behavior of rock is much like that of Silly Putty, which breaks like a brittle solid when you pull it sharply but deforms and stretches when you pull it slowly (**FIGURE 9.3**). Also like Silly Putty, rock becomes softer and easier to deform when it is warmer.

In terms of rock strength, a planet's outer layer consists of relatively cool and rigid rock, called the **lithosphere** (*lithos* is Greek for "stone"), that essentially "floats" on the warmer, softer rock beneath. As shown by the dashed circles in Figure 9.2, the lithosphere encompasses the crust and part of the mantle of each world.

FIGURE 9.3 Silly Putty stretches when pulled slowly but breaks cleanly when pulled rapidly. Rock behaves just the same way, but on a longer time scale.

Notice that lithospheric thickness is closely related to a world's size: Smaller worlds tend to have thicker lithospheres. The two largest terrestrial planets, Earth and Venus, have thin lithospheres that extend only a short way into their upper mantles. The smaller worlds—Mars, Mercury, and the Moon—have thick lithospheres that extend nearly to their cores. The thickness of the lithosphere is very important to geology. A thin lithosphere is brittle and can crack easily. A thick lithosphere is much stronger and inhibits the passage of molten rock from below, making volcanic eruptions and the formation of mountain ranges less likely.

Why Big Worlds Are Round The fact that rock can deform and flow also explains why large worlds are spherical while small moons and asteroids are "potato-shaped." The weak gravity of a small object is unable to overcome the rigidity of its rocky material, so the object retains the shape it had when it was born. For a larger world, gravity can overcome the strength of solid rock, slowly deforming and molding it into a spherical shape. Gravity will make any rocky object bigger than about 500 kilometers in diameter into a sphere within about 1 billion years. Larger worlds become spherical more quickly, especially if they are molten (or gaseous) at some point in their history.

What causes geological activity?

The most interesting aspects of planetary geology are those that cause the surfaces of the terrestrial worlds to change with time. We use the term **geological activity** to describe ongoing changes. For example, we say that Earth is geologically active, because volcanic eruptions, earthquakes, erosion, and other geological processes continually reshape its surface. In contrast, the Moon and Mercury have virtually no geological activity, which is why their surfaces today look essentially the same as they did billions of years ago.

Interior heat is the primary driver of geological activity. For example, volcanoes can erupt only if the interior is hot enough to melt at least some rock into molten lava. But what makes some planetary interiors hotter than others? To find the answer, we must investigate how interiors heat up and cool off. As we'll see, we can ultimately trace a planet's internal heat, and hence its geological activity, back to its size.

How Interiors Get Hot A hot interior contains a lot of thermal energy, and the law of conservation of energy tells us that this energy must have come from somewhere [**Section 4.3**]. Although you might first guess that the Sun would be the heat source, this is not the case: Sunlight is the primary heat source for the *surfaces* of the terrestrial planets, but virtually none of this solar energy penetrates more than a few meters into the ground. Internal heat is a product of the planets themselves, not of the Sun. Three sources of energy explain nearly all the interior heat of the terrestrial worlds (FIGURE 9.4):

- **Heat of accretion.** Accretion deposits energy brought in from afar by colliding planetesimals. As a planetesimal

approaches a forming planet, its gravitational potential energy is converted to kinetic energy, causing it to accelerate. Upon impact, much of the kinetic energy is converted to heat, adding to the thermal energy of the planet.

- **Heat from differentiation.** When a world undergoes differentiation, the sinking of dense material and rising of less-dense material means that mass moves inward, losing gravitational potential energy. This energy is converted to thermal energy by the friction generated as materials separate by density. The same thing happens when you drop a brick into a pool: As the brick sinks to the bottom, friction with the surrounding water heats the pool—though the amount of heat from a single brick is too small to be noticed.

- **Heat from radioactive decay.** The rock and metal that built the terrestrial worlds contained radioactive isotopes of elements such as uranium, potassium, and thorium. When radioactive nuclei decay, subatomic particles fly off at high speeds, colliding with neighboring atoms and heating them. In essence, this transfers some of the mass-energy ($E = mc^2$) of the radioactive nuclei to the thermal energy of the planetary interior.

How Do We Know What's Inside Earth?

Our deepest drills have barely pricked Earth's surface, penetrating much less than 1% of the way into the interior. How, then, can we claim to know what our planet is like on the inside?

For Earth, much of our information about the interior comes from *seismic waves,* vibrations created by earthquakes. Seismic waves come in two basic types, analogous to the two ways you can generate waves in a Slinky (FIGURE 1). Pushing and pulling on one end of a Slinky (while someone holds the other end still) generates a wave in which the Slinky is bunched up in some places and stretched out in others. Waves like this in rock are called P waves. The *P* stands for *primary,* because these waves travel fastest and are the first to arrive

after an earthquake, but it is easier to think of *P* as meaning *pressure* or *pushing.* P waves can travel through almost any material—whether solid, liquid, or gas—because molecules can always push on their neighbors no matter how weakly they are bound together. (Sound travels as a pressure wave quite similar to a P wave.)

Shaking a Slinky slightly up and down or side to side generates a different type of wave; in rock, such waves are called S waves. The *S* stands for *secondary* but is easier to remember as meaning *shear* or *side to side.* S waves travel only through solids, because the bonds between neighboring molecules in a liquid or gas are too weak to transmit up-and-down or sideways forces.

The speeds and directions of seismic waves depend on the composition, density, pressure, temperature, and phase (solid or liquid) of the material they pass through. For example, P waves reach the side of the world opposite an earthquake, but S waves do not. This tells us that a liquid layer has stopped the S waves, which is how we know that Earth has a liquid outer core (FIGURE 2). More careful analysis of seismic waves has allowed geologists to develop a detailed picture of Earth's interior structure.

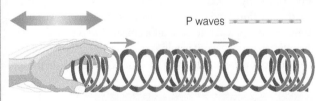

P waves result from compression and stretching in the direction of travel.

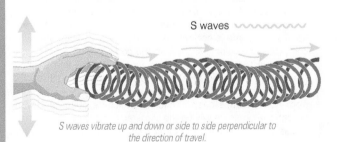

S waves vibrate up and down or side to side perpendicular to the direction of travel.

FIGURE 1 Slinky examples demonstrating P and S waves.

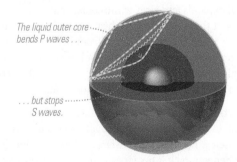

The liquid outer core bends P waves . . .

. . . but stops S waves.

FIGURE 2 Because S waves do not reach the side of Earth opposite an earthquake, we infer that part of Earth's core is liquid.

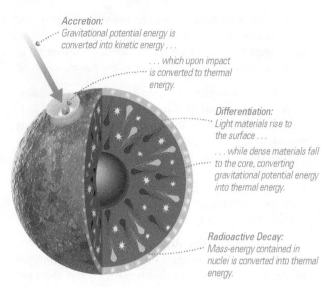

Accretion:
Gravitational potential energy is converted into kinetic energy . . .

. . . which upon impact is converted to thermal energy.

Differentiation:
Light materials rise to the surface . . .

. . . while dense materials fall to the core, converting gravitational potential energy into thermal energy.

Radioactive Decay:
Mass-energy contained in nuclei is converted into thermal energy.

FIGURE 9.4 The three main heat sources for terrestrial planet interiors are accretion, differentiation, and radioactive decay. Only the last is still a major heat source today.

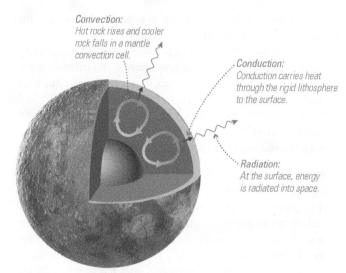

Convection:
Hot rock rises and cooler rock falls in a mantle convection cell.

Conduction:
Conduction carries heat through the rigid lithosphere to the surface.

Radiation:
At the surface, energy is radiated into space.

FIGURE 9.5 The three main cooling processes in planets. Convection can occur only in a planet that is still hot inside.

Note that accretion and differentiation deposited heat into planetary interiors only when the planets were very young. In contrast, radioactive decay provides an ongoing source of heat. Over billions of years, the total amount of heat deposited by radioactive decay has been comparable to or greater than the amount that was deposited initially by accretion and differentiation. However, the rate of radioactive decay has declined with time, so it was an even more significant heat source when the planets were young than it is today.

The combination of the three heat sources explains how the terrestrial interiors ended up with their core-mantle-crust structures. The many violent impacts that occurred during the latter stages of accretion deposited so much energy that the outer layers of the young planets began to melt. This started the process of differentiation, which then released its own additional heat. This heat, along with the substantial heat from early radioactive decay, made the interiors hot enough to melt and differentiate throughout.

How Interiors Cool Off Cooling a planetary interior requires transporting heat outward. Just as there are three basic heating processes for planetary interiors, there are also three basic cooling processes (**FIGURE 9.5**):

- **Convection.** Convection is the process by which hot material expands and rises while cooler material contracts and falls. It therefore transfers heat upward and can occur whenever there is strong heating from below. You can see convection in a pot of soup on a hot burner, and you may be familiar with it in weather: Warm air near the ground tends to rise while cool air above tends to fall.

- **Conduction.** Conduction is the transfer of heat from hot material to cooler material through contact; it is operating when a hot potato transfers its heat to your cooler hand when you pick it up. Conduction occurs through the microscopic collisions of individual atoms or molecules. Molecules of materials in close contact are constantly colliding with one another, so the faster-moving molecules in hot material tend to transfer some of their energy to the slower-moving molecules of cooler material.

- **Radiation.** Planets ultimately lose heat to space through radiation. Remember that objects emit *thermal radiation* characteristic of their temperatures [**Section 5.4**]; this radiation (light) carries energy away and therefore cools an object. Because of their relatively low temperatures, planets radiate primarily in the infrared.

For Earth, convection is the most important heat transfer process in the interior. Hot rock from deep in the mantle gradually rises, slowly cooling as it makes its way upward. By the time it reaches the top of the mantle, the rock has transferred its excess heat to its surroundings, so it is now cool and it begins to fall. This ongoing process creates individual **convection cells** within the mantle, shown as small circles in Figure 9.5; arrows indicate the direction of flow. Keep in mind that mantle convection primarily involves solid rock, not molten rock. Because solid rock flows quite slowly, mantle convection takes a long time. At the typical rate of mantle convection on Earth—about 1 centimeter per year—it would take about 100 million years for a piece of rock to be carried from the base of the mantle to the top.

COMMON MISCONCEPTIONS

Pressure and Temperature

Some people think that Earth's interior should be hot just because the internal pressure is so high. After all, if we compress a gas from low pressure to high pressure, it heats up. But the same is not necessarily true of rock. High pressure compresses rock only slightly, so the compression causes little increase in temperature. Although high pressures and temperatures sometimes go together in planets, they don't have to. In fact, after all the radioactive elements decay (billions of years from now), Earth's deep interior will become quite cool even though the pressure will be the same as it is today. The temperatures inside Earth and the other planets can remain high only if there is a source of heat for the interior, such as accretion, differentiation, or radioactive decay.

Mantle convection stops at the base of the lithosphere, where the rock is too strong to flow as readily as it does lower down. From the base of the lithosphere to the surface, heat continues upward primarily through conduction. (Some heat also reaches the surface through volcanic eruptions that directly carry hot rock upward.) When the heat finally reaches Earth's surface, it is radiated away into space.

Planetary Size Controls Geological Activity Size is the single most important factor in planetary cooling: Just as a hot potato remains hot inside much longer than a hot pea, a large planet can stay hot inside much longer than a small one. You can see why size is the critical factor by picturing a large planet as a smaller planet wrapped in extra layers of rock. The extra rock acts as insulation, so it takes much longer for interior heat to reach the surface.

Size is therefore the primary factor in determining geological activity. The relatively small sizes of the Moon and Mercury probably allowed their interiors to cool within a billion years or so after they formed. As they cooled, their lithospheres thickened and mantle convection was confined to deeper and deeper layers. Ultimately, the mantle convection probably stopped altogether. With insufficient internal heat to drive any further movement of interior rock, the Moon and Mercury are now geologically "dead," meaning they have little or no heat-driven geological activity today.

In contrast, the much larger size of Earth has allowed our planet to stay quite hot inside. Mantle convection keeps interior rock in motion and the heat keeps the lithosphere thin, which is why geological activity can continually reshape the surface. Venus probably remains nearly as active as Earth, thanks to its very similar size. Mars, with a size in between those of the other terrestrial worlds, probably represents an intermediate case: It has cooled significantly during its history, but it probably still retains enough internal heat for at least some geological activity.

MATHEMATICAL INSIGHT 9.1

The Surface Area–to–Volume Ratio

The total amount of heat contained in a planet depends on its volume, but this heat can escape into space only from its *surface*. As heat escapes, more heat flows upward from the interior to replace it until the interior is no hotter than the surface. The time it takes a planet to lose its internal heat is related to the ratio of the *surface area* through which it loses heat to the *volume* that contains heat, or the *surface area–to–volume ratio*:

$$\text{surface area–to–volume ratio} = \frac{\text{surface area}}{\text{volume}}$$

A spherical planet (radius r) has surface area $4\pi r^2$ and volume $\frac{4}{3}\pi r^3$, so the ratio becomes

$$\underset{\text{(for a sphere)}}{\text{surface area–to–volume ratio}} = \frac{4\pi r^2}{\frac{4}{3}\pi r^3} = \frac{3}{r}$$

Because r appears in the denominator, we conclude that *larger objects have smaller surface area-to-volume ratios*. Note that this idea holds for objects of any shape, which is why the larger of two objects that start at the same temperature retains heat longer. It also explains why crushed ice cools a drink more quickly than an equal amount of ice cubes: The crushed ice pieces have a greater combined surface area than the ice cubes, which means faster cooling because more ice surface is in direct contact with the surrounding liquid.

EXAMPLE: Compare and interpret the surface area–to–volume ratios of the Moon and Earth.

SOLUTION:

Step 1 Understand: We compare the two surface area–to–volume ratios by dividing the Moon's ratio (which is larger, because the Moon is smaller) by Earth's. The result tells us the relative rates at which the two worlds would lose heat if they started with the same internal temperature.

Step 2 Solve: We've already found that the surface area–to–volume ratio for a spherical world is $3/r$. Therefore, we find

$$\frac{\text{surface area–to–volume ratio (Moon)}}{\text{surface area–to–volume ratio (Earth)}} = \frac{3/r_{\text{Moon}}}{3/r_{\text{Earth}}} = \frac{r_{\text{Earth}}}{r_{\text{Moon}}}$$

From Appendix E, the radii are $r_{\text{Moon}} = 1738$ km and $r_{\text{Earth}} = 6378$ km. Substituting these values into our equation, we find

$$\frac{\text{surface area–to–volume ratio (Moon)}}{\text{surface area–to–volume ratio (Earth)}} = \frac{6378 \text{ km}}{1738 \text{ km}} = 3.7$$

Step 3 Explain: The Moon's surface area–to–volume ratio is nearly four times as large as Earth's, which means the Moon would cool four times as fast if both worlds started with the same temperature. However, Earth's larger size also gave it much more internal heat to begin with, which amplifies the difference in heat loss found from the surface area–to–volume ratio alone. Overall, we expect the Moon to have cooled many times faster than Earth, which explains why the Moon's interior is so much cooler than Earth's interior today.

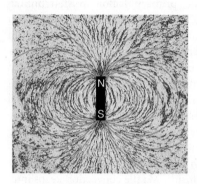

a This photo shows how a bar magnet influences iron filings (small black specks) around it. The *magnetic field lines* (red) represent this influence graphically.

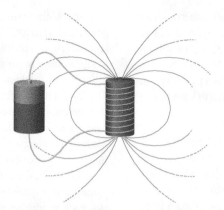

b A similar magnetic field is created by an electromagnet, which is essentially a wire wrapped around a metal bar and attached to a battery. The field is created by the battery-forced motion of charged particles (electrons) along the wire.

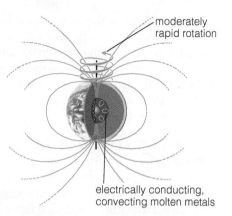

moderately
rapid rotation

electrically conducting,
convecting molten metals

c Earth's magnetic field also arises from the motion of charged particles. The charged particles move within Earth's liquid outer core, which is made of electrically conducting, convecting molten metals.

FIGURE 9.6 Sources of magnetic fields.

Why do some planetary interiors create magnetic fields?

Interior heat plays another important role: It can help create a global **magnetic field.** Earth's magnetic field determines the direction in which a compass needle points, but it also plays many other important roles. As we'll discuss in Chapter 10, the magnetic field helps create a *magnetosphere* (see Figure 10.11) that surrounds our planet and diverts the paths of high-energy charged particles coming from the Sun. The magnetic field therefore protects Earth's atmosphere from being stripped away into space by these particles; many scientists suspect that this protection has been crucial to the long-term habitability of Earth, and hence to our own existence.

You are probably familiar with the pattern of the magnetic field created by an iron bar (**FIGURE 9.6a**). Earth's magnetic field is generated by a process more like that of an *electromagnet,* in which the magnetic field arises as a battery forces charged particles (electrons) to move along a coiled wire (**FIGURE 9.6b**). Earth does not contain a battery, but charged particles move with the molten metal in its liquid outer core (**FIGURE 9.6c**). Internal heat causes the liquid metal to rise and fall (convection), while Earth's rotation twists and distorts the convection pattern. The result is that electrons in the molten metal move within Earth's outer core in much the same way as they move in an electromagnet, generating Earth's magnetic field.

We can generalize these ideas to other worlds. There are three basic requirements for a global magnetic field:

1. An interior region of electrically conducting fluid (liquid or gas), such as molten metal

2. Convection in that layer of fluid

3. At least moderately rapid rotation

Earth is the only terrestrial world that meets all three requirements, which is why it is the only terrestrial world with a strong magnetic field. The Moon has no magnetic field, presumably because its core has long since cooled and ceased convecting. Mars's core probably still retains some heat, but not enough to drive core convection, which is why it also lacks a magnetic field today. Venus probably has a molten core layer much like that of Earth, but either its convection or its 243-day rotation period is too slow to generate a magnetic field. Mercury remains an enigma: It possesses a measurable magnetic field despite its small size and slow, 59-day rotation. The reason for this may be Mercury's huge metal core, which may still be partially molten and convecting.

The same three requirements for a magnetic field also apply to jovian planets and stars. For example, Jupiter's strong magnetic field comes from its rapid rotation and its layer of convecting metallic hydrogen that conducts electricity [**Section 11.1**]. The Sun's magnetic field is generated by the combination of convection of ionized gas (plasma) in its interior and rotation.

THINK ABOUT IT

Recall that the Sun had a strong solar wind when it was young (which cleared out the remaining gas of the solar nebula [**Section 8.2**]) because its magnetic field was much stronger than it is today. What single factor explains why the young Sun's magnetic field was so strong?

(MA) Shaping Planetary Surfaces Tutorial, Lessons 1–3

9.2 SHAPING PLANETARY SURFACES

Now that we have discussed how Earth and other terrestrial worlds work on the inside, we are ready to turn to their surfaces. The surfaces of the planets are remarkably flat. For example, the tallest mountains on Earth rise only about 10 kilometers above sea level, less than 1/600 of Earth's radius—which means they could be represented by grains of sand on a typical globe. Nevertheless, surface features tell us a great deal about the histories of the planets.

FIGURE 9.7 **interactive figure** Artist's conception of the impact process.

What processes shape planetary surfaces?

Although we find a huge variety of geological surface features on Earth and the other terrestrial worlds, nearly all of them can be explained by just four major geological processes:

- **Impact cratering**: the creation of bowl-shaped *impact craters* by asteroids or comets striking a planet's surface
- **Volcanism**: the eruption of molten rock, or *lava,* from a planet's interior onto its surface
- **Tectonics**: the disruption of a planet's surface by internal stresses
- **Erosion**: the wearing down or building up of geological features by wind, water, ice, and other phenomena of planetary weather

Let's examine each of these processes in a little more detail.

Impact Cratering The scarred faces of the Moon and Mercury (see Figure 9.1) attest to the battering that the terrestrial worlds have taken from leftover planetesimals, such as comets and asteroids. They also immediately reveal an important feature of impact cratering: Small craters far outnumber large ones, confirming that many more small asteroids and comets orbit the Sun than large ones. While the Moon and Mercury bear the most obvious scars, all the terrestrial worlds have suffered similar impacts.

An impact crater forms when an asteroid or comet slams into a solid surface (FIGURE 9.7). Impacting objects typically hit the surface at a speed between about 40,000 and 250,000 km/hr (10–70 km/s). At such tremendous speed, the impact releases enough energy to vaporize solid rock and blast out a *crater* (the Greek word for "cup"). Debris from the blast shoots high above the surface and then rains down over a large area. If the impact is large enough, some of the ejected material can escape into space.

Craters are usually circular, because an impact blasts out material in all directions, regardless of the incoming object's direction. Laboratory experiments show that craters are typically about 10 times as wide as the objects that create them and about 10–20% as deep as they are wide. For example, an asteroid 1 kilometer in diameter will blast out a crater about 10 kilometers wide and 1–2 kilometers deep. A large crater may have a central peak, which forms when the center rebounds after impact in much the same way that water rebounds after you drop a pebble into it. FIGURE 9.8 shows two typical impact craters, one on Earth and one on the Moon.

a Meteor Crater in Arizona is more than a kilometer across and almost 200 meters deep. It was created around 50,000 years ago by the impact of a metallic asteroid about 50 meters across.

FIGURE 9.8 Impact craters.

b This photo shows a crater, named Tycho, on the Moon. Note the classic shape and central peak.

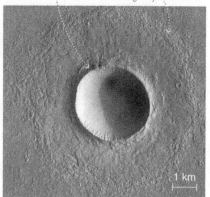
A simple bowl-shaped crater, showing a sharp rim . . .

. . . and a ring of ejected debris.

`1 km`

a A crater with a typical bowl shape.

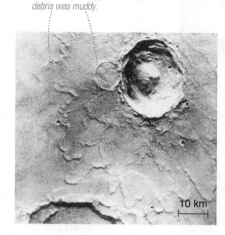
Unusual ridges suggest the impact debris was muddy.

`10 km`

b This crater was probably made by an impact into icy ground.

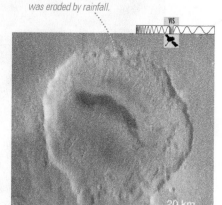
This crater rim looks like it was eroded by rainfall.

`20 km`

c This crater shows evidence of erosion.

FIGURE 9.9 Crater shapes on Mars tell us about Martian geology. (Photos from *Mars Global Surveyor* (a) and *Viking* spacecraft (b and c).)

Details of crater shapes provide clues about geological conditions. For example, **FIGURE 9.9** contrasts three craters on Mars. The crater in Figure 9.9a has a simple bowl shape, as we expect from the basic cratering process. The crater in Figure 9.9b has an extra large bump in its center and appears to be surrounded by mud flows, suggesting that underground water (or ice) melted or vaporized on impact; the muddy debris then flowed across the surface and hardened into the pattern we see today. The crater in Figure 9.9c shows obvious signs of erosion: It lacks a sharp rim and its floor no longer has a well-defined bowl shape. This suggests that ancient rainfall eroded the crater and that the crater bottom was once a lake. Studies of crater shapes on other worlds provide similar clues to their surface conditions and history.

Volcanism We use the term *volcanism* to refer to any eruption of molten lava, whether the lava comes from a tall volcano or simply rises to the surface through a crack in a planet's lithosphere. Volcanism occurs when underground molten rock, technically called *magma*, finds a path to the surface (**FIGURE 9.10**).

Molten rock tends to rise for three main reasons. First, molten rock is generally less dense than solid rock, and lower-density materials tend to rise when surrounded by higher-density materials. Second, because most of Earth's interior is *not* molten, the solid rock surrounding a chamber of molten rock (a *magma chamber*) can squeeze the molten rock, driving it upward under pressure. Third, molten rock often contains trapped gases that expand as it rises, which can make it rise much faster and lead to dramatic eruptions. The same molten rock that is called magma when it is underground is called *lava* once it erupts onto the surface.

The result of an eruption depends on how easily the lava flows across the surface. Lava that is "runny" can flow far before cooling and solidifying, while "thick" lava tends to collect in one place.* Broadly speaking, lava can shape three different types of volcanic features:

■ The runniest lavas flow far and flatten out before solidifying, creating vast **volcanic plains** (**FIGURE 9.11a**).

■ Somewhat thicker lavas tend to solidify before they completely spread out, creating **shield volcanoes** (so named because of their shape). Shield volcanoes can be very tall

molten rock in upper mantle

FIGURE 9.10 Volcanism. This photo shows the eruption of an active volcano on the flanks of Kilauea on the Big Island of Hawaii. The inset shows the underlying process: Molten rock collects in a magma chamber and can erupt upward.

---

*The "thickness" of a liquid is described by the technical term *viscosity*, which refers to how much internal friction it has. For example, liquid water has a low viscosity that allows it to flow quickly and easily; honey and molasses flow more slowly because they have higher viscosities.

Lava plains (maria) on the Moon

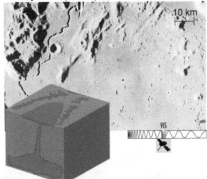

10 km

a Very runny lava makes flat lava plains like these on the Moon. The long, winding channel near the upper left was made by a river of molten lava.

Olympus Mons (Mars)

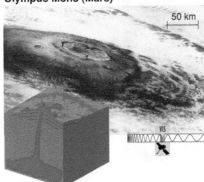

50 km

b Slightly thicker lava makes shallow-sloped shield volcanoes, such as Olympus Mons on Mars.

Mount Hood (Earth)

c The thickest lavas make steep-sloped stratovolcanoes like Oregon's Mount Hood.

FIGURE 9.11 The shapes of volcanic structures depend on whether the lava is runny or thick.

but are not very steep. Examples include the mountains of the Hawaiian Islands on Earth and Olympus Mons on Mars (FIGURE 9.11b).

■ The thickest lavas cannot flow very far before solidifying and therefore build up tall, steep **stratovolcanoes** (FIGURE 9.11c). Examples include Mount Fuji (Japan), Mount Kilimanjaro (Tanzania), and Mount Hood (Oregon).

SEE IT FOR YOURSELF

Your kitchen and bathroom probably contain jars, bottles, and tubes with materials that are runny, thick, or in between. By squeezing or pouring these materials, can you match the shapes of the three volcanic features in Figure 9.11?

Lava plains and shield volcanoes are made of **basalt,** a mixture of many different minerals that erupts from volcanoes as a high-density but fairly runny lava. All the terrestrial worlds and some jovian moons show evidence of volcanic plains and shield volcanoes, telling us that basalt is common throughout the solar system. Stratovolcanoes are made by lower-density volcanic rock that erupts as a thicker lava; this type of lava is common on Earth but rare in the rest of the solar system.

Volcanic mountains are the most obvious result of volcanism, but volcanism has had a much more profound effect on our planet: It explains the existence of our atmosphere and oceans. Recall that Earth accreted from rocky and metallic planetesimals, while water and other ices were brought in by planetesimals from more distant reaches of the solar system that crashed into the growing planets [**Section 8.2**]. Water and gases became trapped in the interiors of the planets in much the same way that the gas in a carbonated beverage is trapped in a pressurized bottle. Volcanic eruptions later released some of this gas into the atmosphere in a process known as **outgassing**. Outgassing can range from dramatic, as during a volcanic eruption (FIGURE 9.12a), to more gradual, as when

gas escapes from volcanic vents (FIGURE 9.12b). The same type of outgassing also occurred on other terrestrial worlds. That is, virtually all the gas that made the atmospheres of Venus, Earth, and Mars—and the water vapor that rained down to form Earth's oceans—originally was released from the planetary interiors by outgassing.

Tectonics The term *tectonics* comes from the Greek word *tekton*, for "builder"; notice the same root in the word *architect*, which means "master builder." In geology, tectonics refers to the "building" of surface features by stretching, compression, or other forces acting on the lithosphere.

Tectonic features arise in a variety of ways. For example, the weight of a volcano can bend or crack the lithosphere beneath it, while a rising plume of hot material can push up on the lithosphere to create a bulge. However, most tectonic activity is a direct or indirect result of mantle convection (FIGURE 9.13). The crust can be compressed in places where adjacent convection cells push rock together; this type of compression helped create the Appalachian Mountains of the eastern United States. Cracks and valleys form in places where adjacent convection cells pull the crust apart; examples of such cracks and valleys include the Guinevere Plains on Venus, the Ceraunius Valleys on Mars, and New Mexico's Rio Grande Valley. (The river named the Rio Grande came *after* the valley formed from tectonic processes.)

On Earth, the ongoing stress of mantle convection ultimately fractured Earth's lithosphere into more than a dozen pieces, or **plates**. These plates move over, under, and around each other in a process we call **plate tectonics**. The movements of the plates explain nearly all Earth's major geological features, including the arrangement of the continents, the nature of the seafloor, and the origin of earthquakes. Because plate tectonics appears to be unique to Earth, we'll save further discussion of it for Section 9.6. (Because the term *plate tectonics* refers to a process, it is generally considered to be singular rather than plural, despite the *-s* on *tectonics*.)

a The eruption of Mount St. Helens, May 18, 1980.

b More gradual outgassing from a volcanic vent in Volcanoes National Park, Hawaii.

FIGURE 9.12 Examples of outgassing, which released the gases that ultimately made the atmospheres of Venus, Earth, and Mars.

Erosion The last of the four major geological processes is *erosion*, which refers to the breakdown or transport of surface rock through the action of ice, liquid, or gas (**FIGURE 9.14**). The shaping of valleys by glaciers (ice), the carving of canyons by rivers (liquid), and the shifting of sand dunes by wind (gas) are all examples of erosion. Note that although we often associate erosion with breakdown, it also builds things such as sand

dunes, river deltas, and lake-bed deposits. Indeed, the most common type of rock on Earth's surface is **sedimentary rock**, which has been built over long periods of time as erosion piled sediments into layers on the floors of oceans and seas. You can see layered sedimentary rock in almost any canyon wall, including the walls of the Grand Canyon, which were built up from sediments long before the Colorado River carved the canyon.

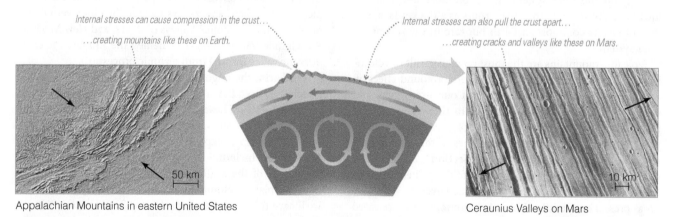

Internal stresses can cause compression in the crust...

...creating mountains like these on Earth.

Internal stresses can also pull the crust apart...

...creating cracks and valleys like these on Mars.

50 km

Appalachian Mountains in eastern United States

10 km

Ceraunius Valleys on Mars

FIGURE 9.13 interactive figure Tectonic forces produce a wide variety of features, including mountain ranges and fractured plains. The Mars image is a visible-light photo from orbit. The Earth image was computer generated from topographical data.

a The Colorado River has been carving the Grand Canyon for millions of years.

b Glaciers created Yosemite Valley during ice ages.

c Wind erosion wears away rocks and builds up sand dunes.

d This river delta is built from sediments worn away by wind and rain and then carried downstream.

FIGURE 9.14 A few examples of erosion on Earth.

How do impact craters reveal a surface's geological age?

Notice that impact cratering is the only one of the four processes with an external cause: the random impacts of objects from space. This fact leads to one of the most useful insights in planetary geology: *We can estimate the geological age of any surface region from its number of impact craters, with more craters indicating an older surface.* By "geological age" we mean the age of the surface as it now appears; a geologically young surface is dominated by features that have formed relatively recently in the history of the solar system, while a geologically old surface still looks about the same today as it did billions of years ago.

You can understand this idea by thinking about why the Moon has so many more impact craters than Earth. Recall that all the terrestrial worlds, regardless of their size or distance from the Sun, were battered by impacts during the heavy bombardment that occurred early in our solar system's history [**Section 8.2**]. Most impact craters were made during that time, and relatively few impacts have occurred since. In places where we see numerous craters, such as on much of the Moon's surface, we must be looking at a surface that has stayed virtually unchanged for billions of years. In contrast, when we see very few craters, as we do on Earth, we must be looking at a younger surface, one on which the scars of ancient impacts have been erased over time by other geological processes, such as volcanic eruptions or erosion.

Careful studies of the Moon have allowed planetary scientists to be more precise about surface ages. The degree of crowding among craters varies greatly from place to place on the Moon (**FIGURE 9.15**). In the **lunar highlands**, craters

a This *Apollo* photograph of the Moon shows that some areas are much more heavily cratered than others. (This view of the Moon is *not* the one we see from Earth.)

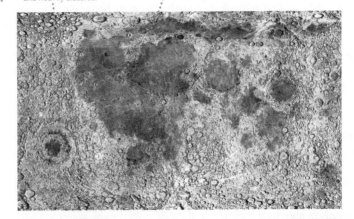

Lunar maria are huge impact basins that were flooded by lava. Only a few small craters appear on the maria.

Lunar highlands are ancient and heavily cratered.

b This map shows the entire surface of the Moon in the same way a flat map of Earth represents the entire globe. Radiometric dating shows the heavily cratered lunar highlands to be a half-billion or more years older than the darkly colored lunar maria, telling us that the impact rate dropped dramatically after the end of the heavy bombardment.

FIGURE 9.15 These photos of the Moon show that crater crowding is closely related to surface age.

are so crowded that we see craters on top of other craters. In the **lunar maria**, we see only a few craters on top of generally smooth volcanic plains. Radiometric dating of rocks brought back by the *Apollo* astronauts indicates that those from the lunar highlands are about 4.4 billion years old, telling us that the heavy cratering occurred early in the solar system's history. Rocks from the maria date to 3.0–3.9 billion years ago, telling us that the lava flows that made these volcanic plains had occurred by that time. Because the maria contain only about 3% as many craters as the highlands, we conclude that the heavy bombardment must have ended by about 4 billion years ago, and relatively few impacts have occurred since that time.

In fact, radiometric dating of Moon rocks has allowed scientists to reconstruct the rate of impacts during much of the Moon's history. Because impacts are essentially random events, the same changes in impact rate over time must apply to all the terrestrial worlds. The degree of crater crowding therefore allows us to estimate the geological age of a planetary surface to within a few hundred million years. Although this is nowhere near as accurate as radiometric dating, it has the advantage of requiring nothing more than orbital photos.

THINK ABOUT IT

Mercury is heavily cratered, much like the lunar highlands. Venus has relatively few craters. Which planet has the older surface? Is there any difference between the ages of the two planets as a whole? Explain how the surfaces of Mercury and Venus can have different ages while the planets themselves are the same age.

Why do the terrestrial planets have different geological histories?

The same four geological processes operate on all solid worlds, yet the terrestrial worlds have had very different geological histories. For example, the surfaces of the Moon and Mercury are dominated by impact craters, but show virtually no features of erosion. Volcanic and tectonic features are found on all the worlds, but we find tall volcanoes only on Earth, Venus, and Mars. And Earth is the only terrestrial world on which features of erosion dominate the landscape. Why do the processes operate so differently on different worlds? Ultimately, we can trace the answer back to three fundamental planetary properties: size, distance from the Sun, and rotation rate (FIGURE 9.16).

Planetary Properties Controlling Volcanism and Tectonics Volcanism and tectonics both require internal heat, which means they depend on planetary size. As shown in Figure 9.16, larger planets have more internal heat and hence more volcanic and tectonic activity.

All the terrestrial worlds probably had some degree of volcanism and tectonics when their interiors were young and hot. As an interior cools, volcanic and tectonic activity subsides. The Moon and Mercury lack ongoing volcanism and tectonics because their small sizes allowed their interiors to cool long ago. Earth has active volcanism and tectonics because it is large enough to still have a hot interior. Venus, nearly the same size as Earth, must still be hot inside and probably also

has active volcanism and tectonics, though we lack conclusive evidence of volcanic eruptions in the past few tens of millions of years. Mars, with its smaller size, has much less volcanism and tectonic activity today than it did in the distant past.

Planetary Properties Controlling Erosion Erosion arises from weather phenomena such as wind and rain. Figure 9.16 shows that erosion therefore has links with all three fundamental planetary properties. Planetary size is important because erosion requires an atmosphere, and a terrestrial world can have an atmosphere only if it is large enough to have had significant volcanic outgassing and if its gravity is strong enough to have prevented the gas from escaping to space. Distance from the Sun is important because of its role in temperature: If all else is equal (such as planetary size), the higher temperatures on a world closer to the Sun will make it easier for atmospheric gases to escape into space, while the colder temperatures on a world farther from the Sun may cause atmospheric gases to freeze out. Distance is also important because water erosion is much more effective with liquid water than with water vapor or ice and therefore is strongest when moderate temperature allows water vapor to condense into liquid form. Rotation rate is important because it is the primary driver of winds and other weather [**Section 10.2**]: Faster rotation means stronger winds and storms.

The Moon and Mercury lack significant atmospheres and erosion because they lack outgassing today, and any atmospheric gases they had in the distant past have been lost to space. Mars has limited erosion at the present time; it has only a thin atmosphere because much of the water vapor and carbon dioxide outgassed in its past either escaped into space or lies frozen in its polar caps or beneath the surface. Venus and Earth probably had similar amounts of outgassing, but cooler temperatures on Earth led to condensation and the formation of oceans, allowing wind and weather to drive strong erosion. Most of Venus's gas remained in its atmosphere, making its atmosphere much thicker than Earth's, but Venus has little erosion because its slow rotation rate means that it has very little surface wind and its high temperature means that rain never falls to the surface.

Planetary Properties Controlling Impact Cratering Impacts are random events and therefore the *creation* of craters is not "controlled" by fundamental planetary properties. However, because impact craters can be *destroyed* over time, the number of remaining impact craters on a world's surface *is* controlled by fundamental properties. The primary factor is size: Larger worlds have more volcanism and tectonics (and in some cases erosion), processes that tend to cover up or destroy ancient impact craters over time. Mercury and the Moon are heavily cratered today because their small sizes have supported relatively little geological activity, so we can still see most of the impact craters that formed during the heavy bombardment. Mars has had more geological activity and therefore has somewhat fewer impact craters remaining today. The active geologies of Venus and Earth have erased nearly all ancient craters, leaving only those that have formed relatively recently (within the last billion years or so).

The Role of Planetary Size

Small Terrestrial Planets

Large Terrestrial Planets

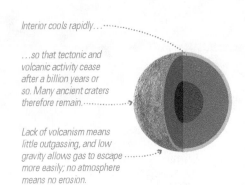

Interior cools rapidly...

...so that tectonic and volcanic activity cease after a billion years or so. Many ancient craters therefore remain.

Lack of volcanism means little outgassing, and low gravity allows gas to escape more easily; no atmosphere means no erosion.

Warm interior causes mantle convection...

...leading to ongoing tectonic and volcanic activity; most ancient craters have been erased.

Outgassing produces an atmosphere and strong gravity holds it, so that erosion is possible.

Core may be molten, producing a magnetic field if rotation is fast enough.

The Role of Distance from the Sun

Planets Close to the Sun

Planets at Intermediate Distances from the Sun

Planets Far from the Sun

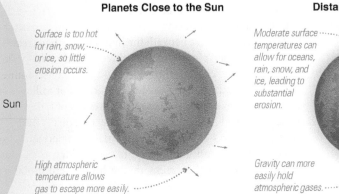

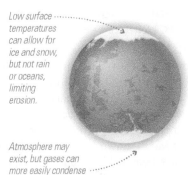

Sun

Surface is too hot for rain, snow, or ice, so little erosion occurs.

High atmospheric temperature allows gas to escape more easily.

Moderate surface temperatures can allow for oceans, rain, snow, and ice, leading to substantial erosion.

Gravity can more easily hold atmospheric gases.

Low surface temperatures can allow for ice and snow, but not rain or oceans, limiting erosion.

Atmosphere may exist, but gases can more easily condense to make surface ice.

The Role of Planetary Rotation

Slow Rotation

Rapid Rotation

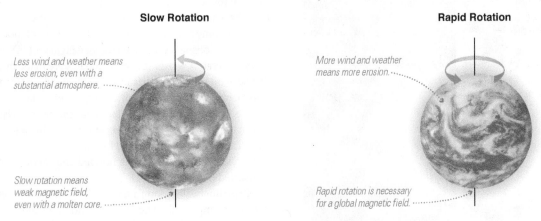

Less wind and weather means less erosion, even with a substantial atmosphere.

Slow rotation means weak magnetic field, even with a molten core.

More wind and weather means more erosion.

Rapid rotation is necessary for a global magnetic field.

FIGURE 9.16 A planet's fundamental properties of size, distance from the Sun, and rotation rate are responsible for its geological history. This illustration shows the role of each key property separately, but a planet's overall geological evolution depends on the combination of all these effects.

9.3 GEOLOGY OF THE MOON AND MERCURY

In the rest of this chapter we will investigate the geological histories of the terrestrial worlds, with the goal of explaining why each ended up as it did. Because smaller worlds have simpler geological histories, we'll start with the smallest worlds, the Moon and Mercury (FIGURE 9.17).

The similar appearances of the Moon and Mercury should not be surprising: Their small sizes mean that most of their internal heat was lost long ago, leaving them without ongoing volcanism or tectonics. They therefore still show the craters made by most of the objects that have hit them during the past $4\frac{1}{2}$ billion years. Small size also explains their lack of significant atmospheres and erosion: Their gravity is too weak to hold gas for long periods of time, and without ongoing volcanism they lack the outgassing needed to replenish gas lost in the past. Nevertheless, both worlds have a few volcanic or tectonic features, indicating that they had geological activity in the past. This also makes sense: Long ago, before they had a chance to cool, even these relatively small worlds were hot enough inside to support some volcanism and tectonics.

What geological processes shaped our Moon?

The familiar face of the full moon reveals some of the surface distinctions we've already discussed (FIGURE 9.18). The bright, heavily cratered regions are lunar highlands. The smooth dark regions are the lunar maria, which got their name because they look much like oceans when seen from afar; *maria* (singular, *mare*) is Latin for "seas." But the entire surface of the Moon should have been packed with craters during the heavy bombardment. So what happened to the craters that must once have been located in the regions where we now see the maria?

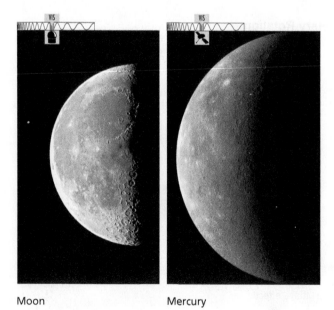

Moon   Mercury

FIGURE 9.17 Views of the Moon and Mercury, shown to scale. The Mercury photo is from *MESSENGER*.

FIGURE 9.18 The familiar face of the Moon shows numerous dark smooth maria.

Volcanism and Tectonics in the Lunar Maria

FIGURE 9.19 shows how the maria probably formed. During the heavy bombardment, craters covered the Moon's entire surface. The largest impacts were violent enough to fracture the Moon's lithosphere beneath the huge craters they created. However, the Moon's interior had already cooled since its formation, so there was no molten rock to flood these craters immediately. Instead, the lava floods came hundreds of millions of years later, thanks to heat released by the decay of radioactive elements in the Moon's interior. This heat gradually built up during the Moon's early history, until mantle material melted between about 3 and 4 billion years ago. Molten rock then welled up through the cracks in the lithosphere, flooding the largest impact craters with lava. The maria are generally circular because they are essentially flooded craters (and craters are almost always round). Their dark color comes from the dense, iron-rich rock (basalt) that rose up from the lunar mantle as molten lava. The flat surfaces of the maria tell us that the lunar lava spread easily and far, which means that it must have been among the runniest lava in the solar system. It was so runny that in places it flowed like rivers of molten rock, carving out long, winding channels (see Figure 9.11a). The relatively few craters within the maria today were made by impacts that occurred after the maria formed, when the heat from radioactive decay was no longer sufficient to produce lava flows.

The Moon's relatively few tectonic features are also found within the maria. These features, which look much like surface wrinkles, probably were created by small-scale tectonic stresses that arose when the lava that flooded the maria cooled and contracted (FIGURE 9.20).

Surprisingly, the Moon's far side looks quite different from the side facing Earth. The far side landscape consists almost entirely of heavily cratered highlands, with very few maria (see Figure 9.15); indeed, the entire far side essentially has a higher altitude than the near side. No one knows what caused this difference in altitude between the two sides, but it apparently allowed lava to well up and create maria much more easily on the near side.

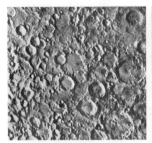

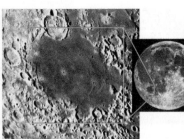

a This illustration shows the Mare Humorum region as it probably looked about 4 billion years ago, when it would have been completely covered in craters.

b Around that time, a huge impact excavated the crater that would later become Mare Humorum. The impact fractured the Moon's lithosphere and erased the many craters that had existed earlier.

c A few hundred million years later, heat from radioactive decay built up enough to melt the Moon's upper mantle. Molten lava welled up through the lithospheric cracks, flooding the impact crater.

d This photo shows Mare Humorum as it appears today, and the inset shows its location on the Moon.

FIGURE 9.19 The lunar maria formed between 3 and 4 billion years ago, when molten lava flooded large craters that had formed hundreds of millions of years earlier. This sequence of diagrams represents the formation of Mare Humorum.

The Moon Today The Moon's era of geological activity is long gone. Today, the Moon is a desolate and nearly unchanging place. Impacts may occur from time to time, but we are unlikely ever to witness a major one. The only ongoing geological change on the Moon is a very slow "sandblasting" of the surface by *micrometeorites,* sand-size particles from space. These tiny particles burn up as meteors in the atmospheres of Earth, Venus, and Mars but rain directly onto the surface of the airless Moon. The micrometeorites gradually pulverize the surface rock, which explains why the lunar surface is covered by a thin layer of powdery "soil." You can see this powdery surface in photos from the *Apollo* missions to the Moon (**FIGURE 9.21**). Pulverization by micrometeorites is a very slow process, so the rover tracks and astronaut footprints could remain for millions of years.

Aside from the micrometeorite sandblasting and rare larger impacts, the Moon has been "geologically dead" since the maria formed more than 3 billion years ago. Nevertheless, the Moon remains a prime target of exploration, because study of lunar geology can help us understand both the Moon's history and the history of our solar system. Several robotic missions are currently studying the Moon, and more are planned. In the future, humans may return to the Moon, and lunar resources may someday prove valuable.

THINK ABOUT IT

It has now been more than 40 years since the last time humans walked on the Moon. Do you favor a return of humans to the Moon? Why or why not?

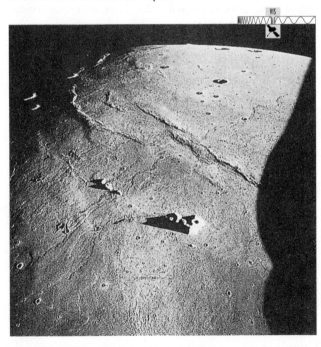

FIGURE 9.20 The wrinkles within the maria were probably made when the lava that flooded the maria cooled and contracted. (This photo shows Mare Imbrium.)

a Astronaut Gene Cernan takes the Lunar Roving Vehicle for a spin during the final *Apollo* mission to the Moon (*Apollo 17,* December 1972).

b The *Apollo* astronauts left footprints, like this one, in the Moon's powdery "soil." Micrometeorites will eventually erase the footprints, but not for millions of years.

FIGURE 9.21 The Moon today is geologically dead, but it can still tell us a lot about the history of our solar system.

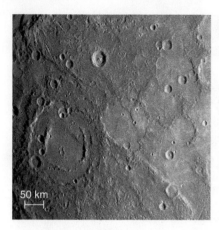

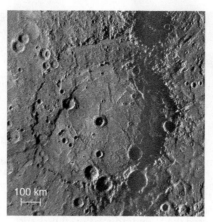

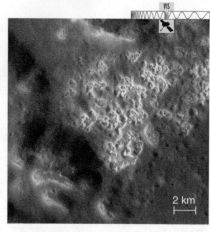

a A close-up view of Mercury's surface, showing impact craters and smooth regions where lava apparently covered up craters.

b The Rembrandt Basin, a large impact crater on Mercury.

c The light-colored "hollows" on this crater floor (shown with colors enhanced) are thought to have formed as easy-to-vaporize materials escaped over millions of years, causing the rock to crumble and make hollowed-out pits.

FIGURE 9.22 *MESSENGER* images of geological features of Mercury.

What geological processes shaped Mercury?

Mercury looks so much like the Moon that it's often difficult to tell which world you are looking at in surface photos. Nevertheless, the two worlds have a few important differences.

Impact Craters and Volcanism on Mercury Impact craters are visible almost everywhere on Mercury, indicating an ancient surface. However, Mercury's craters are less crowded together than the craters in the most ancient regions of the Moon, suggesting that molten lava later covered up some of the craters that formed on Mercury during the heavy bombardment (FIGURE 9.22). As on the Moon, these lava flows probably occurred when heat from radioactive decay accumulated enough to melt part of the mantle. Although we have not found evidence of lava flows as large as those that created the lunar maria, the lesser crater crowding and the many smaller lava plains suggest that Mercury had at least as much volcanism as the Moon.

The largest surface features on Mercury are huge impact craters called *basins.* The impacts were so large and so violent that the craters filled with molten rock heated by the impact. The *Caloris Basin* spans more than half of Mercury's radius. Many of these basins have few craters within them, indicating that they must have formed at a time when the heavy bombardment was already subsiding.

Tectonic Evidence of Planetary Shrinking The most surprising features of Mercury are its many tremendous cliffs—evidence of a type of tectonics quite different from anything we have found on any other terrestrial world (FIGURE 9.23). Mercury's cliffs have vertical faces up to 3 or more kilometers high and typically run for hundreds of kilometers across the surface. They probably formed when

tectonic forces compressed the crust, causing the surface to crumple. Because crumpling would have shrunk the portions of the surface it affected, Mercury as a whole could not have stayed the same size unless other parts of the surface expanded. However, we find no evidence of similar global-scale "stretch marks" on Mercury. Could the whole planet have shrunk?

Apparently so. Recall that in addition to being larger than the Moon, Mercury also has a surprisingly large iron core; Mercury therefore gained and retained more internal heat from accretion and differentiation than the Moon. This heat caused Mercury's core to swell in size. Later, as the core cooled,

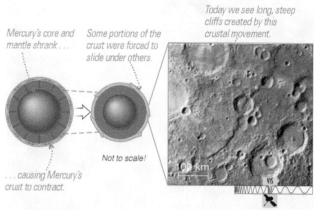

a This diagram shows how Mercury's cliffs probably formed as the core shrank and the surface crumpled.

b This cliff extends about 100 kilometers in length, and its vertical face is as much as 2 kilometers tall. (Photo from *Mariner 10.*)

FIGURE 9.23 Long cliffs on Mercury offer evidence that the entire planet shrank early in its history, perhaps by as much as 20 kilometers in radius.

it contracted by perhaps as much as 20 kilometers in radius. The mantle and lithosphere must have contracted along with the core, generating the tectonic stresses that created the great cliffs. The contraction probably also closed off any remaining volcanic vents, ending Mercury's period of volcanism.

Mercury Today Because Mercury is larger than the Moon, it probably retained its internal heat a bit longer. Nevertheless, it is still small enough that its interior should have cooled relatively quickly. Crater counts on Mercury suggest that most of its volcanic and tectonic activity ceased within 1 to 2 billion years after its formation, though some features may be more recent. For most practical purposes, Mercury is geologically "dead" today, a fact traceable to its small size.

Although there is no active volcanism on Mercury today, its surface still displays one odd form of geological activity: Some crater floors appear to be releasing easily vaporized materials from the rock, causing the rock to crumble and make pits nicknamed "hollows" (see Figure 9.22c). The release of the vaporized gases leaves behind a light-colored coating, whose composition remains unknown. Scientists hope that ongoing *MESSENGER* studies will tell us more about its nature.

Mercury has always seemed an unusual case in our solar system, but the discovery of numerous planets in other solar systems that are rocky and very close to their stars suggests that Mercury may be representative of a class of planets more common elsewhere.

9.4 GEOLOGY OF MARS

As we turn our attention to Mars, it's worth noting that Mars has long held a special place in the human imagination. Its bright reddish color made it a part of many ancient myths and legends. Then, starting more than 200 years ago, Mars became a prime example of scientific enthusiasm gone astray.

Have you ever wondered why people often speak of Martians but rarely of, say, Venusians or Jupiterians? The story begins with observations of Mars made in the late 18th century by brother and sister astronomers William and Caroline Herschel, who are also famous for discovering the planet Uranus. They discovered several features of Mars that resemble features of Earth, including a similar axis tilt, a day just slightly longer than 24 hours, the presence of polar caps, and seasonal variations in appearance over the course of the Martian year (about 1.9 Earth years). By 1784, taking these resemblances to an unwarranted extreme, William Herschel had begun speaking with confidence about "inhabitants" of Mars.

The hypothetical Martians got a bigger break about a century later. In 1879, Italian astronomer Giovanni Schiaparelli reported seeing a network of linear features on Mars through his telescope. He named these features *canali*, by which he meant the Italian word for "channels," but it was frequently translated as "canals." Excited by what sounded like evidence of intelligent life, wealthy American astronomer Percival Lowell commissioned the building of an observatory for the study of Mars.

The Lowell Observatory opened in 1894 in Flagstaff, Arizona. Barely a year later, Lowell published detailed maps of the Martian canals and the first of three books in which

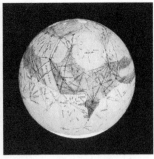
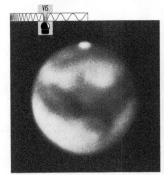

FIGURE 9.24 The image at left is a telescopic photo of Mars. The image at right is a drawing of Mars made by Percival Lowell. As you can see, Lowell had a vivid imagination. Nevertheless, if you blur your eyes while looking at the photo, you might see how some of the features resemble what Lowell thought he saw.

he argued that the canals were the work of an advanced civilization. He suggested that Mars was falling victim to unfavorable climate changes and that the canals had been built to carry water from the poles to thirsty cities elsewhere. Lowell's work drove rampant speculation about Martians and inspired science fiction fantasies such as H. G. Wells's *The War of the Worlds* (published in 1898). Other scientists were skeptical of Lowell's claims, but the public imagination kept them alive until 1965, when NASA's *Mariner 4* spacecraft flew past Mars and sent back photos of a barren, cratered surface. Lowell's canals were nowhere to be seen, confirming that they had been the work of a vivid imagination upon blurry telescopic images (FIGURE 9.24).

The reality may have dampened the enthusiasm of science fiction writers, but scientists find Mars as intriguing as ever. Indeed, although we now know there have never been Martian cities, it's possible that Mars has harbored more primitive life. The search for past or present life on Mars is one of the major goals of Mars exploration, and a first step in this search is understanding Martian geology.

What geological processes have shaped Mars?

Mars is much larger than the Moon or Mercury (see Figure 9.1), so we expect it to have had a more interesting and varied geological history. However, it is much smaller than Venus or Earth, so we expect it to be less geologically active than our own world. Observations confirm this basic picture, though its geology has also been influenced by the fact that it is about 50% farther than Earth from the Sun.

Interestingly, although Mars has only about one-fourth the surface area of Earth, both planets have nearly the same amount of *land* area, because Earth's surface is about three-fourths covered by water. For context, FIGURE 9.25 shows the full surface of Mars (and the locations of particular features we will discuss later), which reveals extensive evidence of all four geological processes.

Impact Cratering on Mars Aside from the polar caps, the most striking feature of Figure 9.25 is the dramatic difference in terrain around different parts of Mars. Much of

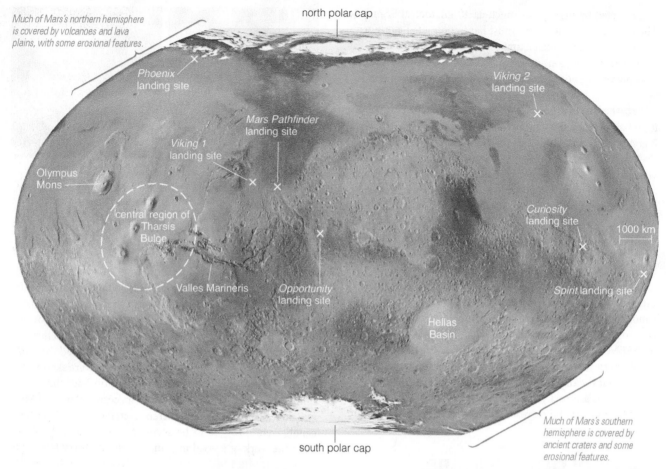

Much of Mars's northern hemisphere is covered by volcanoes and lava plains, with some erosional features.

north polar cap

Phoenix landing site

Viking 2 landing site

Mars Pathfinder landing site

Viking 1 landing site

Olympus Mons

central region of Tharsis Bulge

Curiosity landing site

1000 km

Valles Marineris

Opportunity landing site

Spirit landing site

Hellas Basin

Much of Mars's southern hemisphere is covered by ancient craters and some erosional features.

south polar cap

FIGURE 9.25 Interactive figure This image showing the full surface of Mars is a composite made by combining more than 1000 images with more than 200 million altitude measurements from the *Mars Global Surveyor* mission. Several key geological features are labeled, and landing sites of Mars missions are marked.

the southern hemisphere has relatively high elevation and is scarred by numerous large impact craters, including the very large crater known as the Hellas Basin. In contrast, the northern plains tend to be below the average Martian surface level and show few impact craters. The differences in cratering tell us that the southern highlands are an older surface than the northern plains, which must have had their early craters erased by other geological processes.

THINK ABOUT IT

Which fundamental planetary property (size, distance from the Sun, or rotation rate) explains why Earth does not have any terrain that is as heavily cratered as the southern highlands of Mars?

Volcanism and Olympus Mons Further study suggests that volcanism was the most important process in erasing craters on the northern plains, although tectonics and erosion also played a part. However, no one knows why volcanism affected the northern plains so much more than the southern highlands or why the two regions differ so much in elevation.

More dramatic evidence of volcanism on Mars comes from several towering shield volcanoes. One of these, Olympus Mons, is the tallest known volcano in the solar system (FIGURE 9.26; see also Figure 9.11b). Its base is some 600 kilometers across, large enough to cover an area the size of Arizona. Its peak stands about 26 kilometers above the average Martian surface level, or about three times as high as Mount Everest stands above sea level on Earth. Much of Olympus Mons is rimmed by a cliff that in places is 6 kilometers high.

Olympus Mons and several other large volcanoes are concentrated on or near the continent-size *Tharsis Bulge* (see Figure 9.25). Tharsis is some 4000 kilometers across, and most of it rises several kilometers above the average Martian surface level. It was probably created by a long-lived plume of rising mantle material that bulged the surface upward and provided the molten rock for the eruptions that built the giant volcanoes.

Is there any ongoing volcanism on Mars? Until recently, we didn't think so. We expect Mars to be much less volcanically active than Earth, because its smaller size has allowed its interior to cool much more, and Martian volcanoes show enough impact craters on their slopes to suggest that they have been inactive for at least tens of millions of years. However, geologically speaking, tens of millions of years is

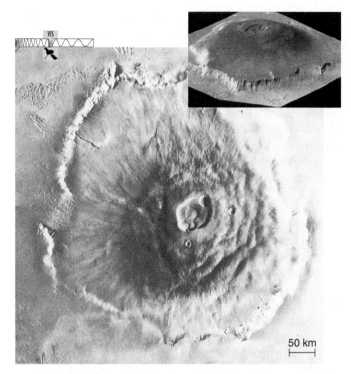

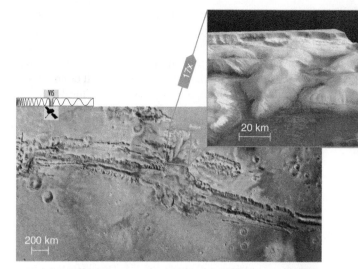

FIGURE 9.27 Valles Marineris is a huge system of valleys on Mars created in part by tectonic stresses. The inset shows a perspective view looking north across the center of the canyon, obtained by *Mars Express*.

FIGURE 9.26 Olympus Mons, photographed from orbit; note the tall cliff around its rim and the central volcanic crater from which lava erupted. The inset shows a 3-D perspective on this immense volcano.

not that long. In addition, radiometric dating of meteorites that appear to have come from Mars (so-called *Martian meteorites* [**Section 24.2**]) shows some of them to be made of volcanic rock that solidified from molten lava as little as 180 million years ago—quite recently in the $4\frac{1}{2}$-billion-year history of the solar system. Given this evidence of geologically recent volcanic eruptions, it is likely that Martian volcanoes will erupt again someday. In addition, scientists suspect the presence of methane in the Martian atmosphere, which might also point to ongoing volcanic activity [**Section 24.2**]. Nevertheless, the Martian interior is presumably cooling and its lithosphere thickening. Within a few billion years, Mars will become as geologically dead as the Moon and Mercury.

Tectonics and Valles Marineris Mars also has tectonic features, though none on a global scale like the plate tectonics of Earth. The most prominent tectonic feature is the long, deep system of valleys called *Valles Marineris* (**FIGURE 9.27**). Named for the *Mariner 9* spacecraft that first imaged it, Valles Marineris extends almost a fifth of the way along the planet's equator. It is as long as the United States is wide and almost four times as deep as Earth's Grand Canyon. No one knows exactly how Valles Marineris formed. Parts of the canyon are completely enclosed by high cliffs on all sides, so neither flowing lava nor water could have been responsible. However, extensive cracks on its western end run up against the Tharsis Bulge (see Figure 9.25), suggesting a connection between the two features. Perhaps it formed through tectonic stresses accompanying the uplift that created Tharsis, cracking the surface and leaving the tall cliff walls of the valleys.

Erosion on Mars Impacts, volcanism, and tectonics explain most of the major geological features of Mars, but closer examination shows extensive evidence of erosion by liquid water. For example, **FIGURE 9.28** shows what appears to be a dried-up riverbed (see also Figure 9.1) that was almost certainly carved by running water, although we cannot yet say whether the water came from runoff after rainfall, from erosion by water-rich debris flows, or from an underground source. Regardless of the specific mechanism, water is the only substance that could have been liquid under past Martian conditions and that is sufficiently abundant to have created such extensive erosion features. We must therefore look more carefully at the evidence suggesting that Mars once had abundant surface water.

What geological evidence tells us that water once flowed on Mars?

No liquid water exists anywhere on the surface of Mars today. We know this in part because orbiting spacecraft have photographed most of the surface in high resolution and have seen

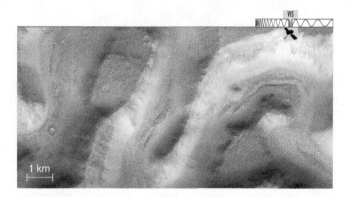

FIGURE 9.28 This photo, taken by *Mars Reconnaissance Orbiter*, shows what appears to be a dried-up meandering riverbed, now filled with dunes of windblown dust. Notice the numerous small impact craters scattered about the image.

no lakes, rivers, or even puddles. More important, current surface conditions do not allow liquid water to remain stable on Mars. In most places and at most times, Mars is so cold that any liquid water would immediately freeze into ice. Even when the temperature rises above freezing, as it often does at midday near the equator, the air pressure is so low that liquid water would quickly evaporate [**Section 5.3**]. If you put on a spacesuit and took a cup of water outside your pressurized spaceship, the water would rapidly either freeze or boil away (or some combination of both).

When we combine the clear evidence of water erosion with the fact that liquid water is unstable on Mars today, we conclude that Mars must once have had very different surface conditions—conditions such as warmer temperatures and greater air pressure that would have allowed water to flow and rain to fall. Geological evidence indicates that this warmer and wetter period must have ended long ago. For example, notice the impact craters that lie on top of the channels in Figure 9.28. Counts of these craters suggest that no water has flowed through these channels for at least about 3 billion years.

Evidence for Ancient Water Flows Strong evidence that Mars had rain and surface water in the distant past comes from both orbital and surface studies. FIGURE 9.29a shows a broad region of the ancient, heavily cratered southern highlands. Notice the indistinct rims of many large craters and the relative lack of small craters. Both facts argue for ancient rainfall, which would have eroded crater rims and erased small craters altogether. FIGURE 9.29b shows a three-dimensional perspective of the surface that suggests water once flowed between two ancient crater lakes. FIGURE 9.29c shows what looks like a river delta where water flowed into an ancient crater. Further evidence that the crater was once a lake comes from images and spectra indicating the presence of clay minerals on the crater floor, presumably deposited by sediments flowing down the river. Some studies even suggest that the northern plains may once have held a vast ocean, though the evidence is less definitive than the evidence for smaller lakes. The evidence for the ocean comes from features that look like an ancient shoreline, along with radar data suggesting that the rock along the proposed shoreline is sedimentary rather than volcanic, just as we would expect if there had once been an ocean; this rock may even contain water ice in its pores and cracks.

Surface studies further strengthen the case for past water. In 2004, the robotic rovers *Spirit* and *Opportunity* landed on opposite sides of Mars. *Spirit* landed in Gusev Crater, the site of a possible ancient lake (see Figure 9.29b). *Opportunity* landed in the Meridiani Plains, where orbital spacecraft had detected spectroscopic hints of minerals that form in water. The rovers carried cameras, instruments to identify rock composition, and a grinder to expose fresh rock for analysis. The rovers long outlasted their design lifetime of 3 months, with *Spirit* lasting more than 6 years and *Opportunity* still going as this book was being written, more than 8 years after arrival.

The rovers provided clinching evidence through identification of several minerals known to form only in the presence of liquid water. Immediately after landing, *Opportunity* found tiny spheres—nicknamed "blueberries" — that contain the iron-rich mineral hematite, and nearby rocks containing the sulfur-rich mineral jarosite. Terrestrial examples of these minerals form in standing water or water seeping through rock (FIGURE 9.30). Detailed chemical analysis suggests these

a This photo shows a broad region of the southern highlands on Mars. The eroded rims of large craters and the relative lack of small craters suggest erosion by rainfall.

b This computer-generated perspective view shows how a Martian valley forms a natural passage between two possible ancient lakes (shaded blue). Vertical relief is exaggerated 14 times to reveal the topography.

landing site of *Spirit* rover

100 km

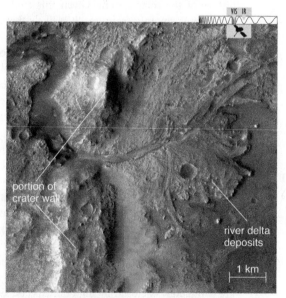

portion of crater wall

river delta deposits

1 km

c Combined visible/infrared image of an ancient river delta that formed where water flowing down a valley emptied into a lake filling a large crater (portions of the crater wall are identified). Clay minerals are identified in green.

FIGURE 9.29 More evidence of past water on Mars.

Mars (Endurance Crater)   **Earth (Utah)**

FIGURE 9.30 "Blueberries" on two planets. In both cases the foreground shows hematite "blueberries," which formed within sedimentary rock layers like those in the background, then eroded out and rolled downhill; the varying tilts of the rock layers hint at changing wind or waves during formation. The background rocks are about twice as far away from the camera in the Earth photo as in the Mars photo (taken by the *Opportunity* rover).

minerals formed in a salty environment such as a sea or ocean. In 2012, after 20 miles of roving, *Opportunity* came across mineral outcrops made of gypsum, another sulfur-rich mineral that only forms in water (FIGURE 9.31); on Earth it's the main ingredient in drywall building material. *Opportunity* team leaders called the discovery a "slam-dunk story that water flowed through underground fractures in the rock."

Scientists expect to learn much more about the history of Martian water as the *Curiosity* rover explores Gale Crater,

FIGURE 9.31 This enhanced-color image shows a layer of the mineral gypsum filling a crack in Martian rock. As on Earth, the gypsum formed from mineral-rich water flowing through a crack in the rock.

where it landed in 2012 (FIGURE 9.32). The landing site was chosen in large part because orbital images of the crater's central mountain—the 5-kilometer-tall Mount Sharp—indicate that it is built from sedimentary rock layers dating to many different times over the past several billion years. *Curiosity* carries the most powerful suite of scientific instruments ever landed on another world, including cameras, drills, microscopes, rock and soil analyzers, a laser to vaporize rock, and a spectrograph to analyze the vaporized material.

FIGURE 9.32 The view of Mount Sharp in Gale Crater, taken from the Bradbury landing site by NASA's *Curiosity* rover (see Figure 9.25). In the main image, parts of the rover and its shadow are visible in the foreground. The zoom-in on Mount Sharp, more than 20 km away, shows the tilted sedimentary rock layers that scientists hope will reveal whether Mars was once habitable.

Evidence for More Recent Water Flows Taken together, the orbital and surface studies provide convincing evidence for abundant liquid water in Mars's distant past. But could water have flowed more recently? As we'll discuss in Chapter 10, abundant water ice still remains on Mars at the polar caps and underground over much of the planet. Although this ice probably represents only a fraction of the water that once existed on Mars, it is still enough that if it all melted, it could make an ocean about 10 meters deep over the entire planet. The atmospheric pressure on Mars is too low today for significant melting to occur on the surface, but it is possible that some liquid water exists underground, near sources of volcanic heat. If so, this liquid water could potentially provide a home for microscopic life. Moreover, if there is enough volcanic heat, ice might occasionally melt and flow along the surface for the short time until it freezes or evaporates. Although we have found no geological evidence to suggest that any large-scale water flows have occurred on Mars in the past billion years, orbital photographs offer tantalizing hints of smaller-scale water flows in much more recent times.

The strongest evidence comes from photos of gullies on crater and channel walls (**FIGURE 9.33**). These gullies look strikingly similar to the gullies we see on almost any eroded slope on Earth, and spacecraft images show that new gullies are still forming. One hypothesis suggests that the gullies form when snow accumulates on the crater walls in winter and melts away from the base of the snowpack in spring. If

this hypothesis is correct, the water at the base could melt (rather than sublimating directly to water vapor, as ice normally does on Mars) because of the angle of sunlight and the pressure of the overlying snow; the melting may have occurred during a time within the past million years or so when Mars's axis tilt was slightly different than it is today. Alternatively, the gullies may be formed by landslides, which have been seen to occur elsewhere on Mars with the change of seasons [**Section 10.4**].

If any liquid water does sometimes flow on Mars, the amount must be a tiny fraction of the water that flowed when riverbeds and lakes were formed long ago. Mars clearly was much warmer and wetter in the past than it is today. Ironically, Percival Lowell's supposition that Mars was drying up has turned out to be basically correct, although in a very different way than he imagined. We'll discuss the reasons for Mars's dramatic climate change in Chapter 10.

9.5 GEOLOGY OF VENUS

The surface of Venus is searing hot with brutal pressure [**Section 7.1**], making it seem quite unlike the "sister planet" to Earth it is sometimes called. However, beneath the surface, Venus and Earth must be quite similar. The two planets are nearly the same size—Venus is only about 5% smaller than Earth in radius—and their similar densities (see Table 7.1) suggest similar overall compositions. We therefore expect the interiors of Venus and Earth to have the same structure and to retain about the same level of internal heat today. Nevertheless, we see ample evidence of "skin-deep" differences in surface geology.

What geological processes have shaped Venus?

Venus's thick cloud cover prevents us from seeing through to its surface with visible light, but we can study its geological features with radar because radio waves can pass through clouds. **Radar mapping** bounces radio waves off the surface and uses the reflections to create three-dimensional images of the surface. From 1990 to 1993, the *Magellan* spacecraft used radar to map Venus's surface with resolution good enough to permit identification of features as small as 100 meters across (**FIGURE 9.34**). Scientists have named most of the major geological features on Venus for goddesses and famous women. Three elevated "continents" (the three "Terra" in Figure 9.34) are the largest surface features.

Impact Cratering on Venus Figure 9.34 shows that Venus has many geological similarities to Earth. Like Earth, Venus has a relatively small number of impact craters, indicating that its ancient craters were erased by other geological processes. Moreover, while Venus has a few large craters, it lacks the small craters that are most common on other worlds—probably because the small objects that could make such craters burn up completely as they enter Venus's thick atmosphere. But even this thick atmosphere has little effect on objects large enough to make the craters we can see in global views like Figure 9.34.

FIGURE 9.33 This *Mars Reconnaissance Orbiter* image supports the hypothesis that running water has etched gullies into crater walls. The image below shows the crater, and the close-up shows details of a gully network that has carried sediments downward. The lack of small impact craters on the sediment deposits indicates that the gullies formed within the last million years or so.

100 m

VIS

6x

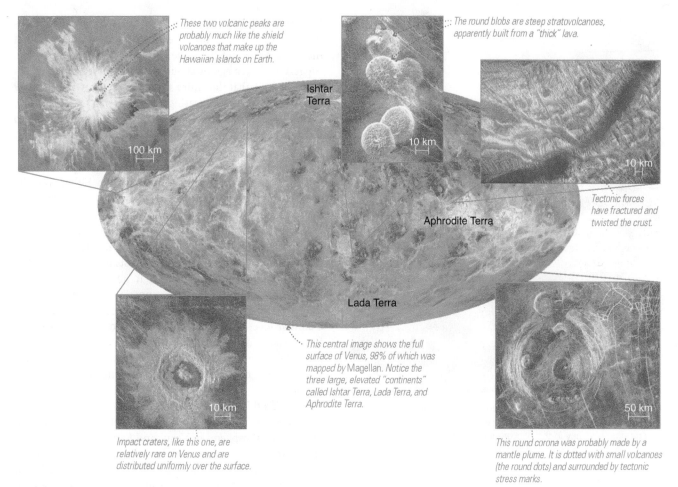

These two volcanic peaks are probably much like the shield volcanoes that make up the Hawaiian Islands on Earth.

100 km

Ishtar Terra

The round blobs are steep stratovolcanoes, apparently built from a "thick" lava.

10 km

10 km

Tectonic forces have fractured and twisted the crust.

Aphrodite Terra

Lada Terra

This central image shows the full surface of Venus, 98% of which was mapped by Magellan. Notice the three large, elevated "continents" called Ishtar Terra, Lada Terra, and Aphrodite Terra.

10 km

Impact craters, like this one, are relatively rare on Venus and are distributed uniformly over the surface.

50 km

This round corona was probably made by a mantle plume. It is dotted with small volcanoes (the round dots) and surrounded by tectonic stress marks.

FIGURE 9.34 These images show the surface of Venus as revealed by radar observations from the *Magellan* spacecraft. Bright regions in the radar images represent rough areas or higher altitudes.

Volcanic and Tectonic Features Volcanism has clearly been important on Venus. Like Earth, Venus shows evidence of having had volcanic flows with a variety of lava types, since we see both lava plains and volcanic mountains. Some mountains are shield volcanoes, indicating eruptions in which the lava was about as runny as that which formed the Hawaiian Islands on Earth. A few volcanoes have steeper sides, indicating eruptions of a thicker lava.

Tectonics has also been very important on Venus, as the entire surface appears to have been extensively contorted and fractured by tectonic forces. Some of these features, including the large circular *coronae* (Latin for "crowns"), provide strong evidence for mantle convection beneath the lithosphere. The coronae were probably pushed upward by hot, rising plumes of rock in the mantle. The plumes probably also forced lava to the surface, which would explain why numerous volcanoes are found near coronae.

Venus almost certainly remains geologically active today, since it should still retain nearly as much internal heat as Earth. Although we have not witnessed any volcanic eruptions, at least two lines of evidence suggest recent volcanic activity. First, Venus's clouds contain sulfuric acid. Sulfuric acid is made from sulfur dioxide (SO_2) and water, and the sulfur dioxide must have entered the atmosphere through volcanic outgassing. Because sulfur dioxide is gradually removed from the atmosphere by chemical reactions with surface rocks, the

existence of sulfuric acid clouds means that volcanic outgassing must have occurred within about the past 100 million years. The second line of evidence narrows the time scale further. The European Space Agency's *Venus Express* spacecraft (orbiting Venus since 2006) detected an infrared spectral feature on three volcanoes that suggests their rocks are "fresh," erupted within about the past 250,000 years (FIGURE 9.35).

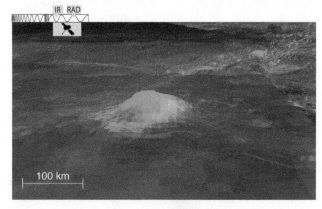

FIGURE 9.35 This composite image shows a volcano called Idunn Mons on Venus. Surface topography details are from NASA's *Magellan* radar mapper (enlarged about 30 times to make the volcano easier to see), and colors represent infrared data from the *Venus Express* spacecraft. Red colors indicate relatively new rock that has not been chemically altered by Venus's harsh atmosphere, suggesting that lava flows occurred within the past 250,000 years.

FIGURE 9.36 This photo from one of the former Soviet Union's *Venera* landers shows Venus's surface; part of the lander is in the foreground, with sky in the background. Many volcanic rocks are visible, hardly affected by erosion despite their presumed age of about 750 million years (the age of the entire surface).

Weak Erosion We might naively expect Venus's thick atmosphere to produce strong erosion, but the view both from orbit and on the surface suggests otherwise. The former Soviet Union sent several landers to Venus in the 1970s and early 1980s. Before the intense surface heat destroyed them, the probes returned images of a bleak, volcanic landscape with little evidence of erosion (FIGURE 9.36). We can trace the lack of erosion on Venus to two simple facts. First, Venus is far too hot for any type of rain or snow on its surface. Second, as we discussed earlier, Venus's slow rotation means it has very little surface wind.

THINK ABOUT IT

Suppose Venus rotated as fast as Earth. How would this change its relative levels of volcanism, tectonics, and erosion? Explain.

Does Venus have plate tectonics?

We can easily explain the lack of erosion on Venus, but another "missing feature" of its geology is more surprising: Venus shows no evidence of Earth-like plate tectonics. As we'll discuss in the next section, plate tectonics shapes nearly all of Earth's major geological features, including mid-ocean ridges, deep ocean trenches, and long mountain ranges like the Rockies and Himalayas. Venus lacks any similar features.

Instead, Venus shows evidence of a very different type of global geological change. On Earth, plate tectonics resculpts the surface gradually, so different regions have different ages.

In contrast, Venus's relatively few impact craters are distributed fairly uniformly over the entire planet, suggesting that the surface is about the same age everywhere; crater counts suggest a surface age of about 750 million years. We therefore conclude that the entire surface of Venus was somehow "repaved" at that time, erasing all craters that formed earlier.

We do not know how much of the repaving was due to tectonic processes and how much was due to volcanism, but both probably were important. It is even possible that plate tectonics played a role before and during the repaving, only to stop after the repaving episode was over. Either way, the absence of present-day plate tectonics on Venus poses a major mystery.

Earth's lithosphere was broken into plates by forces due to the underlying mantle convection. The lack of plate tectonics on Venus therefore suggests either that it has weaker mantle convection or that its lithosphere somehow resists fracturing. The first possibility seems unlikely: Venus's similar size to that of Earth means it should have a similar level of mantle convection. Most scientists therefore suspect that Venus's lithosphere resists fracturing into plates because it is thicker and stronger than Earth's lithosphere, though we have no direct evidence to support this hypothesis.

Even if a thicker and stronger lithosphere explains the lack of plate tectonics on Venus, we are still left with the question of why the lithospheres of Venus and Earth differ. One possible answer is Venus's high surface temperature. Venus is so hot that any water in its crust and mantle has probably been baked out over time. Water tends to soften and lubricate rock, so its loss would have tended to thicken and strengthen Venus's lithosphere. If this idea is correct, then Venus might have had plate tectonics if it had not become so hot in the first place.

The mystery of plate tectonics is just one of many reasons scientists would like to explore Venus in greater detail. Unfortunately, the harsh surface conditions make it difficult for robotic landers to survive, and sending astronauts to Venus seems almost completely out of the question. We are therefore limited to studies from orbit.

9.6 THE UNIQUE GEOLOGY OF EARTH

Most aspects of Earth's geology should make sense in light of what we have found for other terrestrial worlds. Earth's size—largest of the five terrestrial worlds—explains why our planet retains internal heat and remains volcanically and tectonically active. Earth's rampant erosion by water and wind is explained by the combination of our planet's size, distance from the Sun, and rotation rate: Earth is large enough for volcanism and outgassing to have produced an atmosphere while its distance from the Sun allowed water vapor to condense and fall to the surface as rain, and Earth's moderately rapid rotation drives wind and other weather.

However, Earth's geology stands apart from that of the other terrestrial worlds in one important way: Earth is the only planet shaped primarily by ongoing plate tectonics. The importance of this fact goes far beyond basic geology. As we'll discuss in

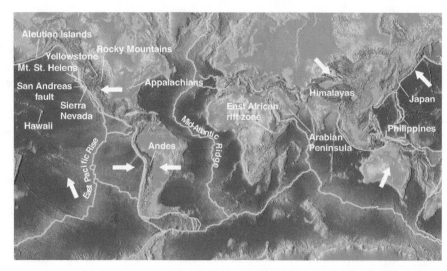

FIGURE 9.37 This relief map shows known plate boundaries (solid yellow lines), with arrows to represent directions of plate motion. Color represents elevation, progressing from blue (lowest) to red (highest). Labels identify some of the geological features discussed in the text.

Chapter 10, plate tectonics plays a crucial role in the stability of Earth's climate. Without this climate stability, it is unlikely that we could be here today.

How is Earth's surface shaped by plate tectonics?

The term *plate tectonics* refers to the scientific theory that explains much of Earth's surface geology as a result of the slow motion of *plates* that essentially "float" over the mantle, gradually moving over, under, and around each other as convection moves Earth's interior rock. Earth's lithosphere is broken into more than a dozen plates (FIGURE 9.37). The plate motions are barely noticeable on human time scales: On average, plates move only a few centimeters per year—about the rate at which your fingernails grow. Nevertheless, over millions of years these motions can completely reshape the surface of our planet.

The Discovery of Continental Motion We usually trace the origin of the theory of plate tectonics to a slightly different hypothesis proposed in 1912 by German meteorologist and geologist Alfred Wegener: *continental drift,* the idea that continents gradually drift across the surface of Earth. Wegener got his idea in part from the puzzle-like fit of continents such as South America and Africa (FIGURE 9.38). He also noted that similar types of distinctive rocks and rare fossils were found in eastern South America and western Africa, suggesting that these two regions once had been close together.

FIGURE 9.38 The puzzle-like fit of South America and Africa.

Despite this evidence, no one at the time knew of a mechanism that could allow the continents to move about. Wegener suggested that Earth's gravity and tidal forces from the Sun and Moon were responsible, but other scientists quickly showed that these forces were too weak to move entire continents. As a result, Wegener's idea of continental drift was widely rejected by geologists for decades after he proposed it.

In the mid-1950s, scientists began to observe geological features that suggested a mechanism for continental motion. In particular, they discovered *mid-ocean ridges* (such as the Mid-Atlantic Ridge shown in Figure 9.37) along which mantle material erupts onto the ocean floor, pushing apart the existing seafloor on either side. This **seafloor spreading** helped explain how the continents could move apart with time. In addition, as more fossil evidence was gathered, it became clear that the continents really were arranged differently in the past, and Wegener's idea of a "continental fit" for Africa and South America ultimately gained acceptance.

Today, geologists can directly measure the slow plate motions by comparing readings taken with the global positioning system (GPS) [**Section S1.3**] on either side of plate boundaries. We also now understand that continental motion is coupled to the underlying mantle convection, driven by the heat released from Earth's interior. Because this idea is quite different from Wegener's original notion of continents plowing through the solid rock beneath them, geologists no longer use the term *continental drift* and instead consider continental motion within the context of plate tectonics.

Seafloor Crust and Continental Crust Another key piece of evidence for plate tectonics came with the discovery that Earth's surface has two distinct types of crust, one type found on seafloors and the other on continents (FIGURE 9.39). **Seafloor crust** is thinner, denser, and younger than **continental crust**. No other planet shows evidence of such distinct differences in crust from place to place.

Seafloor crust is typically 5–10 kilometers thick and is made primarily of the relatively high-density mineral mixture called basalt. Recall that basalt lava is very runny, so it spreads outward when it erupts from volcanoes along mid-ocean

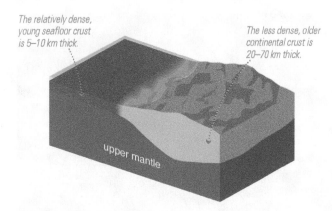

FIGURE 9.39 Earth has two distinct kinds of crust.

ridges. Radiometric dating shows that seafloor basalt is quite young—usually less than 200 million years old—indicating that it erupted to the surface relatively recently in geological history. Further evidence of the young age of seafloors comes from studies of impact craters. Large impacts should occur more or less uniformly over Earth's surface, and the oceans are not deep enough to prevent a large asteroid or comet from making a seafloor crater. However, we find far fewer large craters on the seafloor than on the continents, which means that seafloor crust must have been created more recently.

Continental crust is much thicker—typically between 20 and 70 kilometers thick—but it sticks up only slightly higher than seafloor crust because its sheer weight presses it down farther into the mantle below. It is made mostly of granite and other types of rock that are less dense than basalt. Continental crust spans a wide range of ages and in some places contains rocks that are up to 4 billion years old.

The Conveyor Belt of Plate Tectonics The theory of plate tectonics explains continental motion, seafloor spreading, and the existence of two types of crust as direct results of the way plates move about on Earth. Over millions of years, the movements involved in plate tectonics act like a giant conveyor belt for Earth's lithosphere (FIGURE 9.40).

Mid-ocean ridges occur at places where mantle material rises upward, creating new seafloor crust and pushing plates apart. The newly formed basaltic crust cools and contracts as it spreads sideways from the central ridge, giving seafloor spreading regions their characteristic ridged shape. Along the mid-ocean ridges worldwide, new crust covers an area of about 2 square kilometers every year, enough to replace the entire seafloor within about 200 million years—and thereby explaining the less-than-200-million-year age of seafloor crust.

Over tens of millions of years, any piece of seafloor crust gradually makes its way across the ocean bottom, then finally gets recycled into the mantle in the process we call **subduction**. Subduction occurs where a seafloor plate meets a continental plate, which is generally somewhat offshore at the edge of a sloping continental shelf. As the dense seafloor crust of one plate pushes under the less dense continental crust of another plate, it can pull the entire surface downward to form a deep *ocean trench*. At some trenches, the ocean depth is more than 8 kilometers (5 miles).

Beneath a subduction zone, the descending seafloor crust heats up and may begin to melt as it moves deeper into the mantle. If enough melting occurs, the molten rock may erupt upward. This melting tends to occur under the edges of the continents, which is why so many active volcanoes are found along those edges. Moreover, the lowest-density material tends to melt more easily, which is why the continental crust emerging from these landlocked volcanoes is lower in density than seafloor crust. This fact also explains why steep-sided stratovolcanoes, made from low-density but thick lava (see Figure 9.11c), are common on Earth but rare on other worlds: Without plate tectonics to recycle crust, other worlds generally have only volcanic plains or shield volcanoes made from basalt.

The conveyor-like process of plate tectonics is undoubtedly driven by the heat flow from mantle convection, although the precise relationship between the convection cells and the plates remains an active topic of research. For example, it is not clear whether mantle convection simply pushes plates apart at

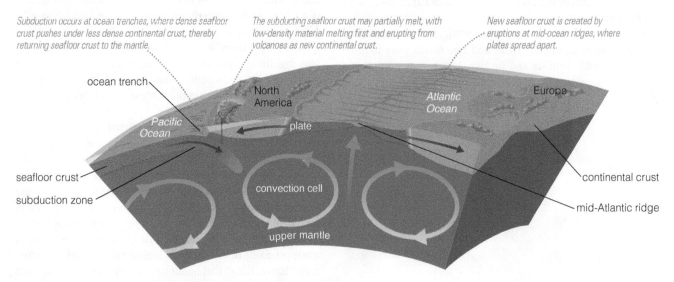

FIGURE 9.40 Plate tectonics acts like a giant conveyor belt for Earth's lithosphere.

the sites of seafloor spreading or whether the plates are denser than the underlying material and pull themselves down at subduction zones.

Building Continents Unlike seafloor crust, continental crust does not get recycled back into the mantle. As a result, present-day continents have been built up over billions of years. However, their histories are not just a simple "piling up" of continental crust. Instead, the continents are continually reshaped by volcanism and stresses associated with plate tectonics, as well as by erosion. FIGURE 9.41 shows some of the complex geological history of North America, which we can use as an example of how the continents have been built.

The west coast regions of Alaska, British Columbia, Washington, Oregon, and most of California began as numerous volcanic islands in the Pacific. Long ago, plate motion carried these islands from their ocean birthplaces toward the North American mainland, where subduction continues to take the seafloor crust downward into the mantle (see Figure 9.40). Because these islands were made of lower-density continental crust, they remained on the surface and attached themselves to the edge of North America, even as the seafloor crust beneath them slid back into the mantle. Similar processes affect other islands today. Alaska's Aleutian Islands, a string of volcanoes located over a region where one seafloor plate is subducting under another (see the plate boundaries in Figure 9.37), are gradually growing and will someday merge together. Japan and the Philippines represent a later stage in this process; each once contained many small islands that merged into the fewer islands we see today. As these islands continue to grow and merge, they may eventually create a new continent or merge with an existing one.

Other portions of North America have been shaped by erosion. The Great Plains and the Midwest once were ancient seas. Erosion gradually filled these seas with sediment that hardened into sedimentary rock. The Deep South formed from the buildup of sediments that were carried to these regions after eroding from other parts of the continent. Northeastern Canada features some of the oldest continental crust on Earth, worn down over time by erosion.

Tectonic processes are responsible for long mountain ranges. The Sierra Nevada range in California, which lies over the region where the Pacific plate subducts under North America, formed when partially molten granite rose up from the mantle and pushed the surface rock higher. The original surface rock was sedimentary, but erosion gradually wore it away and left the granite exposed, which is why the Sierra Nevada mountains are made largely of granite.

Mountain ranges can also form through collisions of continent-bearing plates. The Himalayas, the tallest mountains on Earth, offer the most famous example of this process (FIGURE 9.42). They are still growing taller as the plate carrying the Indian subcontinent rams into the plate carrying Eurasia. Because both colliding plates are made of low-density continental crust, neither plate can subduct under the other. Instead, they push into each other and the resulting compression pushes the land upward to make mountains. The Appalachian range in the eastern United States was built through multiple collisions of continental plates: Over a period of a few hundred million years, North America apparently collided twice with South America and then with western Africa. The Appalachians probably were once as tall as the Himalayas are now, but tens of millions of years of erosion transformed them into the fairly modest mountain range we see today. Similar processes contributed to the formation of the Rocky Mountains in the United States and Canada.

Rifts, Faults, and Earthquakes So far, we have discussed features formed in places where plates are colliding, either with a seafloor plate subducting under a continental

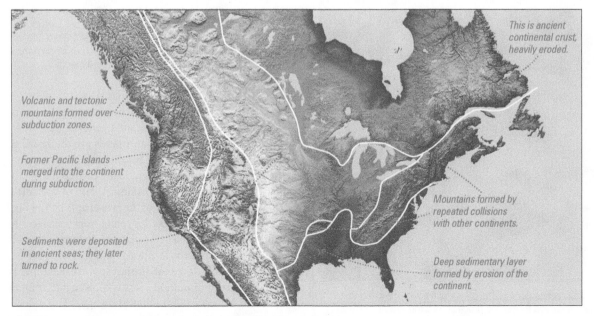

This is ancient continental crust, heavily eroded.

Volcanic and tectonic mountains formed over subduction zones.

Former Pacific Islands merged into the continent during subduction.

Sediments were deposited in ancient seas; they later turned to rock.

Mountains formed by repeated collisions with other continents.

Deep sedimentary layer formed by erosion of the continent.

FIGURE 9.41 The major geological features of North America record the complex history of plate tectonics. Only the basic processes behind the largest features are shown.

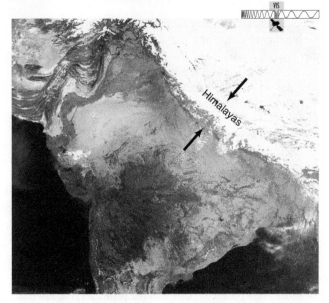

FIGURE 9.42 This satellite photo shows the Himalayas, which are still slowly growing as the plate carrying India pushes into the Eurasian plate. Arrows indicate directions of plate motion.

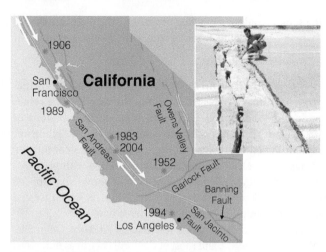

FIGURE 9.44 California's San Andreas Fault marks a boundary where plates are sliding sideways, as shown by the white arrows; asterisks indicate recent earthquakes. The inset photo shows a place along the San Andreas Fault where the painted lines in a road allow us to see how far the two sides of the fault moved in an earthquake.

plate or with two continental plates pushing into each other. Different types of features occur in places where plates pull apart or slide sideways relative to each other.

In places where continental plates are pulling apart, the crust thins and can create a large *rift valley*. The East African rift zone is an example (see Figure 9.37). This rift is slowly growing and will eventually tear the African continent apart. At that point, rock rising upward with mantle convection will begin to erupt from the valley floor, creating a new zone of seafloor spreading. A similar process tore the Arabian Peninsula from Africa, creating the Red Sea (FIGURE 9.43).

Places where plates slip sideways relative to each other are marked by what we call **faults**—fractures in the lithosphere.

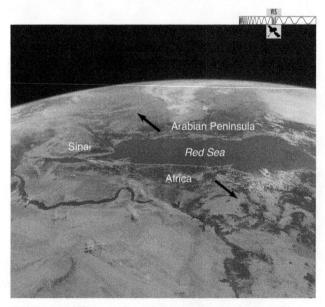

FIGURE 9.43 When continental plates pull apart, the crust thins and deep rift valleys form. This process tore the Arabian Peninsula from Africa, forming the Red Sea. Arrows indicate directions of plate motion.

The San Andreas Fault in California marks a line where the Pacific plate is moving northward relative to the continental plate of North America (FIGURE 9.44). In about 20 million years, this motion will bring Los Angeles and San Francisco together. The two plates do not slip smoothly against each other; instead, their rough surfaces catch. Stress builds up until it is so great that it forces a rapid and violent shift, causing an earthquake. In contrast to the usual motion of plates, which proceeds at a few centimeters per year, an earthquake can move plates by several *meters* in a few seconds. The movement can raise mountains, level cities, set off destructive tsunamis, and make the whole planet vibrate with seismic waves.

THINK ABOUT IT

By studying the plate boundaries in Figure 9.37, explain why California, Oregon, and Washington have more earthquakes and volcanoes than the rest of the continental United States. Find the locations of recent earthquakes and volcanic eruptions worldwide. Do the locations fit the pattern you expect?

Hot Spots Not all volcanoes occur near plate boundaries. Sometimes, a plume of hot mantle material rises in what we call a **hot spot**. The Hawaiian Islands are the result of a hot spot that has been erupting basaltic lava for tens of millions of years. Plate tectonics has gradually carried the Pacific plate over the hot spot, thereby forming a chain of volcanic islands (FIGURE 9.45). Today, most of the lava erupts on the Big Island of Hawaii, giving this island a young, rocky surface. About a million years ago, the Pacific plate lay farther to the southeast (relative to its current location), and the hot spot built the island of Maui. Before that, the hot spot created other islands, including Oahu (3 million years ago), Kauai (5 million years ago), and Midway (27 million years ago). The older islands are more heavily eroded. Midway has eroded so much that it barely rises above sea level. If plate tectonics were not moving

Midway: island eroded down to sea level

A mantle plume created Hawaii and other islands (many now undersea) as the Pacific plate moved over it.

The kink in the chain occurred when the plate direction shifted about 40 million years ago.

Hawaiian Islands

Kauai: heavily eroded valleys

Hawaii: recent lava flows

Loihi: future Hawaiian Island (in about a million years)

FIGURE 9.45 The Hawaiian Islands are just the most recent of a very long string of volcanic islands made by a mantle hot spot. The image of Loihi (lower right) was obtained by sonar, as it is still entirely under water.

the plate relative to the hot spot, a single huge volcano would have formed—perhaps looking somewhat like Olympus Mons on Mars (see Figure 9.26).

The movement of the plate over the hot spot continues today, building underwater volcanoes that eventually will rise above sea level to become new Hawaiian Islands. The growth of a future island, named Loihi, is already well under way—prime beach real estate should be available there in a million years or so. Hot spots can also occur beneath continental crust. For example, a hot spot is responsible for the geysers and hot springs of Yellowstone National Park.

THINK ABOUT IT

Find your hometown or current home on the map in Figure 9.37 or Figure 9.41 (or both). Based on what you have learned about Earth's geology, describe the changes your home has undergone over millions (or billions) of years.

Plate Tectonics Through Time We can use the current motions of the plates to project the arrangement of continents millions of years into the past or the future. For example, at a speed of 2 centimeters per year, a plate will travel 2000 kilometers in 100 million years. **FIGURE 9.46** shows two past arrangements of the continents, along with one future arrangement. Note that about 200 million years ago the present-day continents were together in a single "supercontinent," sometimes called *Pangaea* (which means "all lands").

Studies of magnetized rocks (which record the orientation of ancient magnetic fields) and comparisons of fossils found in different places around the world have allowed geologists to map the movement of the continents even further into the past. It seems that, over the past billion years or more, the continents have slammed together, pulled apart, spun around, and changed places on the globe. Central Africa once lay at

Earth's South Pole, and Antarctica once was near the equator. The continents continue to move, and their current arrangement is no more permanent than any past arrangement.

Was Earth's geology destined from birth?

Now that we have completed our geological tour of the terrestrial worlds, let's consider whether fundamental planetary properties shape all geological destinies. If so, then we should be able to predict the geological features of terrestrial worlds we find around other stars. If not, then we still have more to learn before we'll know whether other worlds could have Earth-like geology.

FIGURE 9.47 summarizes the key trends we've seen among the terrestrial worlds. All the worlds were heavily cratered during the heavy bombardment, but the extent of volcanism and tectonics has depended on planetary size. The interiors of the smallest worlds cooled quickly, so they have not had volcanism or tectonics for billions of years. The interiors of the larger worlds have stayed hot longer, allowing volcanism and tectonics to continue for much longer time periods.

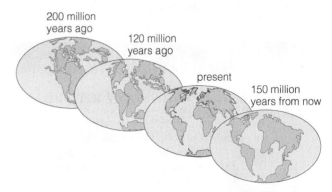

200 million years ago

120 million years ago

present

150 million years from now

FIGURE 9.46 Past, present, and future arrangements of Earth's continents. The present continents were all combined into a single "supercontinent" about 200 million years ago.

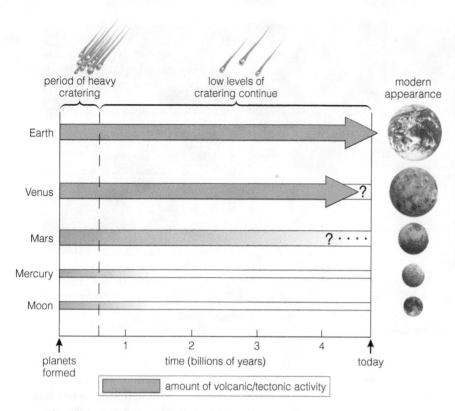

period of heavy cratering

low levels of cratering continue

modern appearance

Earth

Venus ?

Mars ? · · · ·

Mercury

Moon

planets formed

time (billions of years)

today

amount of volcanic/tectonic activity

FIGURE 9.47 This diagram summarizes the geological histories of the terrestrial worlds. The brackets along the top indicate that impact cratering has affected all worlds similarly. The arrows represent volcanic and tectonic activity. A thicker and darker arrow means more volcanic/tectonic activity, and the arrow length tells us how long this activity persisted. Notice this trend's relationship to planetary size: Earth remains active today; Venus has also been active, though we are uncertain whether it remains so; Mars has had an intermediate level of activity and might still have low-level volcanism; Mercury and the Moon have had very little volcanic/tectonic activity. Erosion is not shown, because it has played a significant role only on Earth (ongoing) and Mars (in the past and at low levels today).

The major remaining question concerns whether fundamental properties can also explain Earth's unique plate tectonics. The lack of plate tectonics on Venus tells us that we cannot attribute plate tectonics solely to size, since Venus is so similar in size to Earth. However, if we are correct in guessing that Venus lacks plate tectonics because its high surface temperature led to loss of water and lithospheric thickening, then a lower surface temperature might have led to plate tectonics on Venus as well as Earth. As we'll discuss in the next chapter, we can ultimately trace Venus's high surface temperature to its nearness to the Sun. While plenty of uncertainty still remains, it seems likely that the broad geological histories of Earth and the other terrestrial worlds were indeed destined from birth by the fundamental properties of size, distance from the Sun, and rate of rotation.

The Big Picture

Putting Chapter 9 into Perspective

In this chapter, we have explored the geology of the terrestrial worlds. As you continue your study of the solar system, keep the following "big picture" ideas in mind:

- The terrestrial worlds all looked much the same when they were born, so their present-day differences are a result of geological processes that occurred in the ensuing 4½ billion years.

- The extent to which different geological processes operate on the different worlds depends largely on their fundamental properties, especially their size.

- A planet's geology is largely destined from its birth—which means we should be able to predict the geology of as-yet-undiscovered planets once we know their fundamental properties.

- Earth has been affected by the same geological processes affecting the other terrestrial worlds. However, erosion is far more important on Earth than on any other terrestrial world, and Earth's unique plate tectonics may be very important to our existence.

SUMMARY OF KEY CONCEPTS

9.1 CONNECTING PLANETARY INTERIORS AND SURFACES

- **What are terrestrial planets like on the inside?**

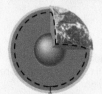

In order of decreasing density and depth, the interior structure consists of **core, mantle,** and **crust.** The crust and part of the mantle together make up the rigid **lithosphere.** In general, a thinner lithosphere allows more geological activity.

- **What causes geological activity?** Interior heat drives

geological activity by causing mantle convection, keeping the lithosphere thin, and keeping the interior partially molten. All the terrestrial interiors were once hot, but larger planets cool slowly, retaining more interior heat and staying geologically active longer.

- **Why do some planetary interiors create magnetic fields?** A planetary **magnetic field** requires three things: an interior layer of electrically conducting fluid, convection of that fluid, and rapid rotation. Among the terrestrial planets, only Earth has all three characteristics.

9.2 SHAPING PLANETARY SURFACES

- **What processes shape planetary surfaces?** The four major geological processes are **impact cratering, volcanism, tectonics**, and **erosion**.

- **How do impact craters reveal a surface's geological age?** More craters indicate an older surface. All the terrestrial worlds were battered by impacts when they were young, so those that still have many impact craters must look much the same as they did long ago. Those with fewer impact craters must have had their ancient craters erased by other geological processes.

- **Why do the terrestrial planets have different geological histories?** Fundamental planetary properties, especially size, determine a planet's geological history. Larger worlds have 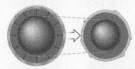 more volcanism and tectonics, and these processes erase more of the world's ancient impact craters. Erosion depends on a planet's size, distance from the Sun, and rotation rate.

9.3 GEOLOGY OF THE MOON AND MERCURY

- **What geological processes shaped our Moon?** The lunar surface is a combination of extremely ancient, heavily  cratered terrain and somewhat younger lava plains called the lunar **maria**. Some small tectonic features are also present. The Moon lacks erosion because it has so little atmosphere.

- **What geological processes shaped Mercury?** Mercury's surface resembles that of the Moon in being shaped   by impact cratering and volcanism. It also has tremendous tectonic cliffs that probably formed when the whole planet cooled and contracted in size.

9.4 GEOLOGY OF MARS

- **What geological processes have shaped Mars?** Mars 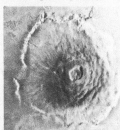 shows evidence of all four geological processes. It has the tallest volcano and the biggest canyon in the solar system, evidence of a period of great volcanic and tectonic activity. It also has abundant craters and evidence of erosion by wind and flowing water.

- **What geological evidence tells us that water once flowed on Mars?** Images of dry river channels and eroded  craters, along with chemical analysis of Martian rocks, show that water once flowed on Mars. Any periods of rainfall seem to have ended at least 3 billion years ago. Mars still has water ice underground and in its polar caps and could possibly have pockets of underground liquid water.

9.5 GEOLOGY OF VENUS

- **What geological processes have shaped Venus?** Venus's surface shows evidence of major volcanic and tectonic  activity in the past billion years, as expected for a planet nearly as large as Earth. This activity explains the relative lack of craters. Despite Venus's thick atmosphere, erosion is only a minor factor because of the high temperature (no rainfall) and slow rotation (little wind). Venus almost certainly remains geologically active today.

- **Does Venus have plate tectonics?** Venus appears to have undergone planetwide resurfacing, but we do not see evidence of ongoing plate tectonics. The lack of plate tectonics probably means that Venus has a stiffer and stronger lithosphere than Earth, perhaps because the high surface temperature has baked out any water that might have softened the lithospheric rock.

9.6 THE UNIQUE GEOLOGY OF EARTH

- **How is Earth's surface shaped by plate tectonics?** On  Earth, the lithosphere is broken into **plates** that move around in the special type of tectonics that we call **plate tectonics**. Plate tectonics works much like a giant conveyor belt. New seafloor **crust** emerges from **mid-ocean ridges** and is recycled into the mantle at **subduction zones**, near which lower-density **continental crust** can erupt to build up the continents. Over time, the shifting of plates rearranges the continents on Earth's surface.

- **Was Earth's geology destined from birth?** It seems likely that the geological histories of Earth and the other terrestrial worlds were indeed destined from birth by the fundamental properties of size, distance from the Sun, and rate of rotation.

Use the following questions to check your understanding of some of the many types of visual information used in astronomy. Answers are provided in Appendix J. For additional practice, try the Chapter 9 Visual Quiz at MasteringAstronomy®.

This image from a MESSENGER flyby shows evidence of impact cratering, volcanism, and tectonic activity on Mercury. Answer the following questions based on the image. Remember that craters are bowl-shaped and rough-floored when they form, and wipe out any preexisting features in the area. Lava on Mercury appears to be fairly runny and makes flat smooth plains as it spreads out.

1. Label 1a lies on the rim of a large crater, and label 1b lies on the rim of a smaller one. Which crater must have formed first?
   a. crater 1a
   b. crater 1b
   c. Cannot be determined
2. The region around 2b has far fewer craters than the region around 2c. The crater floor at 2a is also flat and smooth, without many smaller craters on it. Why are regions 2a and 2b so smooth?
   a. Few small craters ever formed in these regions.
   b. Erosion erased craters that once existed in these regions.
   c. Lava flows covered craters that once existed in these regions.
3. A tectonic ridge appears to connect points 3a and 3b, crossing several craters. From its appearance, we can conclude that it must have formed
   a. before the area was cratered
   b. after the area was cratered
   c. at the same time the area was cratered

4. Using your answers to questions 1–3, list the following features in order from oldest to youngest:
   a. the tectonic ridge from 3a to 3b
   b. crater 1a
   c. the smooth floor of crater 1b

MasteringAstronomy®

For instructor-assigned homework go to MasteringAstronomy®.

REVIEW QUESTIONS

Short-Answer Questions Based on the Reading

1. Describe the core-mantle-crust structures of the terrestrial worlds. What is *differentiation*? What do we mean by the *lithosphere*? How does lithospheric thickness vary among the five terrestrial worlds?
2. Summarize the processes by which planetary interiors get hot and cool off. Why do large planets retain internal heat longer than smaller planets?
3. Why does Earth have a global magnetic field? Why don't the other terrestrial worlds have similarly strong magnetic fields?
4. Define each of the four major geological processes, and give examples of features shaped by each process.
5. What is *outgassing*, and why is it so important to our existence?
6. Why is the Moon so much more heavily cratered than Earth? Explain how crater counts tell us the age of a surface.
7. Summarize the ways in which a terrestrial world's size, distance from the Sun, and rotation rate each affect its relative level of impact cratering, volcanism, tectonics, and erosion.
8. Briefly summarize the geological history of the Moon. How did the lunar maria form?
9. Briefly summarize the geological history of Mercury. How are Mercury's great cliffs thought to have formed?
10. Choose five features on the global map of Mars (Figure 9.25) and explain the nature and likely origin of each.
11. Why isn't liquid water stable on Mars today, and why do we nonetheless think it flowed on Mars in the distant past?

12. Choose at least three major geological features of Venus and explain how we think each one formed.
13. What evidence tells us that Venus was "repaved" about 750 million years ago? What might account for the lack of plate tectonics on Venus?
14. Describe the conveyor-like action of plate tectonics on Earth, and how it explains the differences between seafloor and continental crust.
15. Briefly explain how each of the following geological features of Earth is formed: seafloors, continents, islands, mountain ranges, rift valleys, and faults.
16. To what extent do we think the geologies of the terrestrial worlds were destined from their birth? Explain.

TEST YOUR UNDERSTANDING

Surprising Discoveries?

Suppose we were to make the following discoveries. (These are not real discoveries.) In light of your understanding of planetary geology, decide whether the discovery should be considered reasonable or surprising. (In some cases, both views can be defended.) Explain your answer, if possible tracing your logic back to the terrestrial worlds' fundamental properties of size, distance from the Sun, and rotation rate.

17. New photographs reveal sand dunes on Mercury.
18. Seismographs placed on the surface of Mercury record frequent and violent earthquakes.

19. A new orbiter observes a volcanic eruption on Venus.

20. A Venus radar mapper discovers extensive regions of layered sedimentary rocks.

21. Radiometric dating of rocks brought back from one lunar crater shows that the crater was formed only a few tens of millions of years ago.

22. New high-resolution orbital photographs of Mars show many crater bottoms filled with pools of liquid water.

23. Drilling into the surface, a robotic spacecraft discovers liquid water beneath the slopes of a Martian volcano.

24. Clear-cutting in the Amazon rain forest on Earth exposes terrain that is as heavily cratered as the lunar highlands.

25. Seismic studies on Earth reveal a "lost continent" that held great human cities just a few thousand years ago but is now buried deep under water off the western coast of Europe.

26. We find a planet in another solar system that has Earth-like plate tectonics; the planet is the size of the Moon and orbits 1 AU from its star.

27. We find a planet in another solar system that is as large as Earth but as heavily cratered as the Moon.

28. We find a planet in another solar system that has Earth-like seafloor crust and continental crust but apparently lacks plate tectonics or any other kind of crustal motion.

Quick Quiz

Choose the best answer to each of the following. Explain your reasoning with one or more complete sentences.

29. What is the longest-lasting internal heat source responsible for geological activity? (a) accretion (b) radioactive decay (c) sunlight

30. In general, what kind of planet would you expect to have the thickest lithosphere? (a) a large planet (b) a small planet (c) a planet far from the Sun

31. Which of a planet's fundamental properties has the greatest effect on its level of volcanic and tectonic activity? (a) size (b) distance from the Sun (c) rotation rate

32. What is the name of the rigid outer layer of a planet? (a) crust (b) mantle (c) lithosphere

33. Which describes our understanding of flowing water on Mars? (a) It was never important. (b) It was important once, but is no longer. (c) It is a major process on the Martian surface today.

34. What do we conclude if a planet has few impact craters of any size? (a) The planet was never bombarded by asteroids or comets. (b) Its atmosphere stopped impactors of all sizes. (c) Other geological processes have wiped out craters.

35. How many of the five terrestrial worlds have surfaces being continually reshaped by plate tectonics? (a) one (b) two (c) three or more

36. On how many of the five terrestrial worlds has erosion been an important process? (Be sure that you explain *why* erosion is important on this many worlds and not more.) (a) one (b) two (c) three or more

37. How many of the terrestrial worlds have lava plains or shield volcanoes? (a) one (b) three (c) five

38. How many of the five terrestrial worlds are considered "geologically dead"? (a) none (b) two (c) four

PROCESS OF SCIENCE

Examining How Science Works

39. *Mars Attracts.* William Herschel, Giovanni Schiaperelli, and Percival Lowell were all respected astronomers who made important and widely accepted discoveries, yet all three jumped to incorrect conclusions about Mars. Scientifically, where do you think each went wrong, and how seriously? Try to frame your answer in terms of the hallmarks of science discussed in Chapter 3. Do you think their mistakes had any long-term impact on the study of Mars?

40. *What Is Predictable?* Briefly explain why much of a planet's geological history is destined from its birth, and discuss the level of detail that is predictable. For example, was Mars's general level of volcanism predictable? Could we have predicted a mountain as tall as Olympus Mons or a canyon as long as Valles Marineris? Explain.

41. *Unanswered Questions.* Our current understanding of the terrestrial worlds allows us to paint a broad-brush overview of their geological histories, but we still have much more to learn. Choose one important but unanswered question related to the geology of the terrestrial worlds, and describe why the question is important and how we might answer it in the future. Be as specific as possible, focusing on the type of evidence necessary to answer the question and how the evidence could be gathered.

GROUP WORK EXERCISE

42. *Real and Imaginary Planets.* Before you begin, assign the following roles to the people in your group: *Scribe* (takes notes on the group's activities), *Proposer* (proposes explanations to the group), *Skeptic* (points out weaknesses in proposed explanations), and *Moderator* (leads group discussion and makes sure everyone contributes).
    a. Figure 9.16 shows the general principles for planetary behavior for "generic" planets. For each of the seven example worlds shown, decide which planet or planets in our solar system match the listed characteristics (large or small; close, intermediate, or far; etc.). b. For at least one of the blue annotations on each of the seven worlds in this figure, find an image in the chapter that exemplifies the principle. For example, which image supports the principle that slow rotation leads to less erosion? c. Next, select one of the planet examples you chose in part a, and imagine a significant change in the property listed. How would the planet's geological history have been different? d. Now propose two imaginary planets, whose size, distance from the Sun, and rotation rates are different from each other and different from those of any terrestrial world. Give them names, and predict their geological histories, emphasizing comparisons with the other planets.

INVESTIGATE FURTHER

In-Depth Questions to Increase Your Understanding

Short-Answer/Essay Questions

43. *Dating Planetary Surfaces.* We have discussed two basic techniques for determining the age of a planetary surface: studying the abundance of impact craters and radiometric dating of surface rocks. Which technique seems more reliable? Which technique is more practical? Explain.

44. *Comparative Erosion.* Of Mercury, Venus, the Moon, and Mars, which world has the greatest erosion? Why? Write a paragraph explaining each world's level of erosion, tracing it back to fundamental properties.

45. *Miniature Mars.* Suppose Mars had turned out to be significantly smaller than its current size—say, the size of our Moon. How would this have affected the number of geological features due to each of the four major geological processes? Do you think Mars would be a better or worse candidate for harboring extraterrestrial life? Summarize your answers in two or three paragraphs.

46. *Change in Fundamental Properties.* Choose one property of Earth—either size or distance from the Sun—and suppose that it had been different (for example, smaller size or greater distance). Describe

how this change might have affected Earth's subsequent geological history and the possibility of our existence today on Earth.

47. *Predictive Geology.* Suppose another star system has a rocky terrestrial planet twice as large as Earth but at the same distance from its star (which is just like our Sun) and with a similar rotation rate. In one or two paragraphs, describe the type of geology you would expect it to have.

48. *Mystery Planet.* It's the year 2098, and you are designing a robotic mission to a newly discovered planet around a nearby star that is nearly identical to our Sun. The planet is as large in radius as Venus, rotates with the same daily period as Mars, and lies 1.2 AU from its star. Your spacecraft will orbit but not land on the planet. **a.** Some of your colleagues believe that the planet has no metallic core. How could you support or refute their hypothesis? **b.** Other colleagues suspect that the planet has no atmosphere, but the instruments designed to study the planet's atmosphere fail because of a software error. However, the spacecraft can still photograph geological features. How could you use the spacecraft's photos of geological features to determine whether a significant atmosphere is (or was) present on this planet?

49. *Experiment: Planetary Cooling in a Freezer.* Fill two small plastic containers of similar shape but different sizes with cold water and put both into the freezer at the same time. Every hour or so, record the time and estimate the thickness of the "lithosphere" (the frozen layer) in the two tubs. How long does it take the water in each tub to freeze completely? Describe the relevance of your experiment to planetary geology. Extra credit: Plot your results on a graph with time on the *x*-axis and lithospheric thickness on the *y*-axis. What is the ratio of the two freezing times?

50. *Amateur Astronomy: Observing the Moon.* Any amateur telescope has resolution adequate for identifying geological features on the Moon. The light highlands and dark maria should be evident, and shadowing should be visible near the line between night and day. Try to observe the Moon near the first- or third-quarter phase. Sketch or photograph the Moon at low magnification, and then zoom in on a region of interest. Again sketch or photograph your field of view, labeling its features and identifying the geological process that created them. Look for craters, volcanic plains, and tectonic features. Estimate the size of each feature by comparing it to the size of the entire Moon (radius = 1738 km).

Quantitative Problems

Be sure to show all calculations clearly and state your final answers in complete sentences.

51. *Surface Area–to–Volume Ratio.* Compare the surface area–to–volume ratios of the following:
    a. the Moon and Mars; **b.** Earth and Venus. In each case, use your answer to discuss differences in internal heat on the two worlds.

52. *Doubling Your Size.* Just as the surface area–to–volume ratio depends on size, so can other properties. To see how, suppose that your size suddenly doubled—that is, your height, width, and depth all doubled. (For example, if you were 5 feet tall before, you now are 10 feet tall.)
    a. By what factor has your waist size increased? **b.** How much more material will be required for your clothes? (*Hint:* Clothes cover the surface *area* of your body.) **c.** By what factor has your weight increased? (*Hint:* Weight depends on the *volume* of your body.) **d.** The pressure on your weight-bearing joints depends on how much *weight* is supported by the *surface area* of each joint. How has this pressure changed?

53. *Lunar Footprints.* Assume that the Moon is hit by about 25 million micrometeorite impacts each day (this number comes from observa-

tions of meteors in Earth's atmosphere) and that these impacts strike randomly around the Moon's surface. Also assume that it takes about 20 such impacts to destroy a footprint. About how long would it take for one of the footprints left by the *Apollo* astronauts to be erased? (*Hints:* Use the Moon's surface area to determine the impact rate per square centimeter, and estimate the size of a footprint.)

54. *Geological Proportions.* Express the approximate height and width of Olympus Mons (26 km tall and 600 km wide) as percentages of Mars's radius. Repeat for Valles Marineris (7 km deep and 4000 km long). Then compare the height of Mt. Everest (9 km tall) and the height and width of the Grand Canyon (1.8 km deep and 450 km long) to Earth's radius, and comment on the relative sizes of geological features on the two planets.

55. *Internal versus External Heating.* In daylight, Earth's surface absorbs about 400 watts per square meter. Earth's internal radioactivity produces a total of 30 trillion watts that leak out through our planet's entire surface. Calculate the amount of heat from radioactive decay that flows outward through each square meter of Earth's surface (your answer should have units of watts per square meter). Compare quantitatively to solar heating, and comment on why internal heating drives geological activity.

56. *Plate Tectonics.* Typical motion of one plate relative to another is 1 centimeter per year. At this rate, how long would it take for two continents 3000 kilometers apart to collide? What are the global consequences of motion like this?

57. *More Plate Tectonics.* Consider a seafloor spreading zone creating 1 centimeter of new crust over its entire 2000-kilometer length every year. How many square kilometers of surface will be created in 100 million years? What fraction of Earth's surface does this constitute?

Discussion Questions

58. *Worth the Effort?* Politicians often argue over whether planetary missions are worth the expense involved. If you were in Congress, would you support more or fewer missions? Why?

59. *Evidence of Our Civilization.* Discuss how the geological processes will affect the evidence of our current civilization in the distant future. For example, what evidence of our current civilization will survive in 100,000 years? in 100 million years? Do you think that future archaeologists or alien visitors will be able to know that we existed here on Earth?

Web Projects

60. *"Coolest" Surface Photo.* Visit the Astronomy Picture of the Day website, and search for past images of the terrestrial worlds. Look at many of them, and choose the one you think is the "coolest." Write a short description of what it shows, and explain what you like about it.

61. *Water on Mars.* Go to the home page for NASA's Mars Exploration Program, and look for the latest evidence concerning recent water flows on Mars. Write a few paragraphs describing the new evidence and what it tells us. How will future missions help resolve the questions?

62. *Planetary Geology.* Choose one of the terrestrial worlds, and do a Web search to learn about at least two geological features on it that were *not* highlighted in this chapter. Are the features consistent with what we would expect based on the ideas of "geological destiny" discussed in this chapter? Explain.

63. *Volcanoes and Earthquakes.* Learn about one major earthquake or volcanic eruption that occurred during the past decade. Report on the geological conditions that led to the event, as well as on its geological and human consequences.

10 PLANETARY ATMOSPHERES
EARTH AND THE OTHER TERRESTRIAL WORLDS

LEARNING GOALS

For the first time in my life, I saw the horizon as a curved line. It was accentuated by a thin seam of dark blue light—our atmosphere. Obviously this was not the ocean of air I had been told it was so many times in my life. I was terrified by its fragile appearance.

—Ulf Merbold, astronaut (Germany)

Life as we know it would be impossible on Earth without our atmosphere. This thin layer of gas supplies the oxygen we breathe, shields us from harmful ultraviolet and X-ray radiation from the Sun, protects us from continual bombardment by micrometeorites, generates rain-giving clouds, and traps just enough heat to keep Earth habitable.

How did Earth end up with atmospheric conditions that are so favorable to life? In this chapter, we'll explore the answers—and learn why the other terrestrial worlds ended up so different, despite having formed under similar conditions. We'll also discuss why Earth's climate remains relatively stable and how human activity may be threatening that stability, with potential consequences that we are only beginning to understand.

10.1 ATMOSPHERIC BASICS

The atmospheres of the terrestrial worlds are even more varied than their geologies. **FIGURE 10.1** shows global and surface views of each world. **TABLE 10.1** lists general characteristics of their atmospheres. You'll notice vast differences between the worlds.

The Moon and Mercury have so little atmosphere that it's reasonable to call them "airless"; they have no wind or weather of any kind. At the other extreme, Venus is enshrouded by a thick atmosphere composed almost entirely of carbon dioxide, giving it surface conditions so hot and harsh that not even robotic space probes can survive there for long. Mars also has a carbon dioxide atmosphere, but its air

is so thin that your body tissues would bulge painfully if you stood on the surface without a pressurized spacesuit. Only Earth has the "just right" conditions that allow liquid water on the surface, making it hospitable to life.

Despite these great differences among the terrestrial atmospheres, the same basic processes are at work in all cases. In fact, the same processes are at work on any world with an atmosphere, and in later chapters we'll see how they apply to the atmospheres of the jovian planets, of moons with atmospheres, and even of planets around other stars. Let's begin our comparative study of planetary atmospheres by discussing the basic nature of an atmosphere.

What is an atmosphere?

An *atmosphere* is a layer of gas that surrounds a world. In most cases, it is a surprisingly thin layer. On Earth, for example, about two-thirds of the air in the atmosphere lies within 10 kilometers of the surface (**FIGURE 10.2**). You could represent this air on a standard globe (to scale) with a layer only as thick as a dollar bill.

Atmospheric air is a mixture of gases that may consist either of individual atoms or of molecules. Temperatures in the terrestrial atmospheres are generally low enough (even on Venus) for atoms to combine into molecules. For example, the air we breathe consists of *molecular* nitrogen (N_2) and oxygen (O_2), as opposed to individual atoms (N or O). Other common molecules in terrestrial atmospheres include water (H_2O) and carbon dioxide (CO_2).

Atmospheric Pressure Collisions of individual atoms or molecules in an atmosphere create *pressure* [**Section 5.3**] that pushes in all directions. On Earth, for example, the nitrogen and oxygen molecules in the air fly around at average speeds of about 500 meters per second—fast enough to cross your bedroom a hundred times in 1 second. Given that a single breath of air contains more than a billion trillion molecules, you can imagine how frequently molecules collide. On average,

FIGURE 10.1 Views of the terrestrial worlds and their atmospheres from orbit and from the surface. The surface views for Mercury and Venus are artists' conceptions; the others are photos. The global views are visible-light photos taken from spacecraft. (Venus appears in gibbous phase as it was seen by the *Galileo* spacecraft during its Venus flyby en route to Jupiter.)

TABLE 10.1   Atmospheres of the Terrestrial Worlds

World	Composition of Atmosphere	Surface Pressure*	Average Surface Temperature	Winds, Weather Patterns	Clouds, Hazes
Mercury	helium, sodium, oxygen	10^{-14} bar	day: 425°C (797°F) night: −175°C (−283°F)	none: too little atmosphere	none
Venus	96% carbon dioxide (CO_2) 3.5% nitrogen (N_2)	90 bars	470°C (878°F)	slow winds, no violent storms, acid rain	sulfuric acid clouds
Earth	77% nitrogen (N_2) 21% oxygen (O_2) 1% argon H_2O (0.4%, but variable) 0.04% carbon dioxide (CO_2)	1 bar	15°C (59°F)	winds, hurricanes, rain, snow	H_2O clouds, pollution
Moon	helium, sodium, argon	10^{-14} bar	day: 125°C (257°F) night: −175°C (−283°F)	none: too little atmosphere	none
Mars	95% carbon dioxide (CO_2) 2.7% nitrogen (N_2) 1.6% argon	0.007 bar	−50°C (−58°F)	winds, dust storms	H_2O and CO_2 clouds, dust

*1 bar = the atmospheric pressure at sea level on Earth.

each molecule in the air around you will suffer a million collisions in the time it takes to read this paragraph. These collisions create pressure that pushes in all directions, and this pressure holds up the atmosphere so that it does not collapse under its own weight.

A balloon offers a good example of how pressure works in a gas. The air molecules inside a balloon exert pressure, pushing outward as they constantly collide with the balloon's inside surface. At the same time, outside air molecules collide with the balloon's outer surface, exerting pressure that by itself would make the balloon collapse. A balloon

FIGURE 10.2 Earth's atmosphere, visible in this photograph from the Space Shuttle, is a very thin layer over Earth's surface. Most of the air is in the lowest 10 kilometers of the atmosphere, visible along the edge of the planet.

stays inflated when the inward and outward pressures are balanced (**FIGURE 10.3a**). (We are ignoring the tension in the rubber of the balloon walls.) Imagine that you blow more air into the balloon (**FIGURE 10.3b**). The extra molecules inside mean more collisions with the balloon wall, momentarily making the pressure inside greater than the pressure outside. The balloon therefore expands until the inward and outward pressures are again in balance.

If you heat the balloon (**FIGURE 10.3c**), the gas molecules begin moving faster and collide harder and more frequently with the inside surface, which also momentarily increases the inside pressure until the balloon expands. As it expands, the pressure inside it decreases and the balloon comes back into pressure balance. Conversely, cooling a balloon makes it contract, because the outside pressure momentarily exceeds the inside pressure.

We can understand **atmospheric pressure** by applying similar principles. Gas in an atmosphere is held down by gravity. The atmosphere above any given altitude therefore has some weight that presses downward, tending to compress the atmosphere beneath it. At the same time, the fast-moving molecules exert pressure in all directions, including upward, which tends to make the atmosphere expand. Planetary atmospheres exist in a perpetual balance between the downward weight of their gases and the upward push of their gas pressure.

The higher you go in an atmosphere, the less the weight of the gas above you, and less weight means less pressure. That is why the pressure decreases as you climb a mountain or ascend

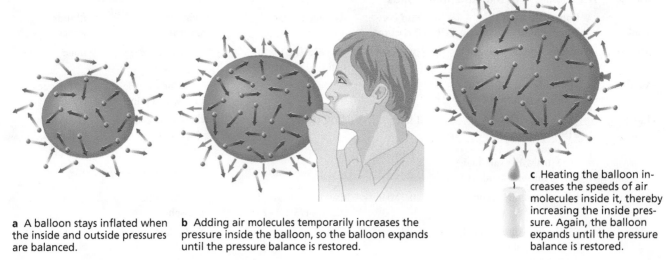

a A balloon stays inflated when the inside and outside pressures are balanced.

b Adding air molecules temporarily increases the pressure inside the balloon, so the balloon expands until the pressure balance is restored.

c Heating the balloon increases the speeds of air molecules inside it, thereby increasing the inside pressure. Again, the balloon expands until the pressure balance is restored.

FIGURE 10.3 Gas pressure in a balloon depends on both density and temperature.

in an airplane. You can visualize this concept by imagining the atmosphere as a very big stack of pillows (**FIGURE 10.4**). The pillows at the bottom are highly compressed because of the weight of all the pillows above. Going upward, the pillows are less and less compressed because less weight lies on top of them.

In planetary science, we usually measure atmospheric pressure in a unit called the **bar** (as in *barometer*). One bar is roughly equal to Earth's atmospheric pressure at sea level. It is also equivalent to 1.03 kilograms per square centimeter or

14.7 pounds per square inch. In other words, if you gathered up all the air directly above any 1 square inch of Earth's surface, you would find that it weighed about 14.7 pounds.

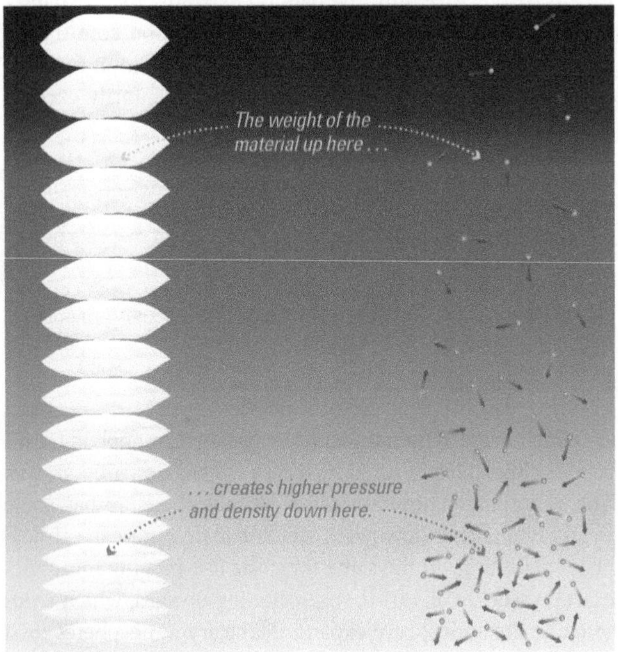

> **THINK ABOUT IT**
>
> Suppose Mars had exactly the same total amount of air above each square inch of surface as Earth. Would the atmospheric pressure be higher, lower, or the same as on Earth? Explain. (*Hint:* Remember that weight depends on the strength of gravity [**Section 4.1**], and that surface gravity is weaker on Mars than on Earth.)

You might wonder why you don't feel Earth's atmospheric weight bearing down on you. After all, if we placed 14.7 pounds of weight on every square inch of your shoulders, you'd certainly feel the downward pressure. You don't notice the atmospheric pressure for two reasons: First, the pressure pushes in all directions, so it pushes upward and inward on you as well as downward. Second, the fluids in your body push outward with an equivalent pressure, so there is no net pressure trying to compress or expand your body. You can tell that the pressure is there, however, because you'll quickly notice any pressure changes. For example, even slight changes in pressure as you go up or down in altitude can cause your ears to "pop." More extreme changes, such as those that affect deep-sea divers when they rise too rapidly, can be deadly. You'd face even greater pressure differences if you visited other planets; as shown in Table 10.1, atmospheric pressure varies by a factor of 10^{16} among the terrestrial worlds.

Where Does an Atmosphere End? If you study Figure 10.4, you'll see that there is no clear boundary between the atmosphere and space above, because pressure and density decrease gradually with increasing altitude. At some point, the density becomes so low that we can't really think of the gas as "air" anymore. Collisions between atoms or molecules are rare at these altitudes, and the gas is so thin that it would

The weight of the material up here . . .

. . . creates higher pressure and density down here.

FIGURE 10.4 Atmospheric density and pressure decrease with altitude for the same reason that a giant stack of pillows would be more compressed at the bottom than at the top. The pressure in each layer is enough to hold up the weight of layers above, counteracting the force of gravity.

FIGURE 10.5 Low-density gas extends into what we often think of as "space," as you can see from the visible glow of gas around a Space Shuttle's tail in this photograph. Notice the aurora in the background, created by interactions between charged particles and atmospheric gas at altitudes above 100 kilometers, well below the Shuttle. Most of Earth's atmospheric gas lies below 10 kilometers.

look and feel as if you had already entered space. On Earth, this occurs at an altitude of about 100 kilometers; above that, the sky is black even in the daytime, much like the sky on the Moon. This altitude is often described as "the edge of space."

However, some gas is still present above 100 kilometers. Earth's tenuous upper atmosphere extends for several hundred kilometers above Earth's surface. The Space Station and many satellites orbit Earth within these outer reaches of the atmosphere (FIGURE 10.5). The low-density gas may be barely noticeable under most conditions, but it still exerts drag on orbiting spacecraft. That is why satellites in low-Earth orbit slowly spiral downward, eventually burning up as they reenter the denser layers of the atmosphere [Section 4.5].

How Atmospheres Affect Planets Earth's atmosphere is obviously important to our existence, but the full range of atmospheric effects is greater than most people realize. To provide context for our study of planetary atmospheres, here is a brief list of key effects of atmospheres that we will study in this chapter:

- As we've seen, atmospheres create pressure that determines whether liquid water can exist on the surface.

- Atmospheres absorb and scatter light. Scattering can make daytime skies bright and absorption can prevent dangerous radiation from reaching the ground.

- Atmospheres can create wind and weather and play a major role in long-term climate change.

- Interactions between atmospheric gases and the solar wind can create a protective *magnetosphere* around planets with strong magnetic fields.

- Atmospheres can make planetary surfaces warmer than they would be otherwise via the **greenhouse effect**.

The greenhouse effect is arguably the most important effect that an atmosphere can have on its planet, and we'll therefore focus our attention on it first.

How does the greenhouse effect warm a planet?

You've probably heard of the greenhouse effect, because it is an important part of the environmental problem known as *global warming* [**Section 10.6**]. But you may be surprised to learn that the greenhouse effect is also critical to the existence of life on Earth. Without the greenhouse effect, Earth's surface would be too cold for liquid water to flow and for life to flourish. Let's explore how the greenhouse effect can warm planetary surfaces.

How the Greenhouse Effect Works FIGURE 10.6 shows the basic idea behind the greenhouse effect. Some of the visible light that reaches the ground is reflected and some is absorbed. The absorbed energy must be returned to space, but planetary surfaces are too cool to emit visible light. (Recall that the type of thermal radiation an object emits depends on its temperature [**Section 5.4**].) Instead, planetary surface temperatures are in the range in which they emit mostly infrared light. The greenhouse effect works by temporarily "trapping" some of this infrared light, slowing its return to space.

The greenhouse effect occurs only when an atmosphere contains gases that can absorb the infrared light. Gases that are particularly good at absorbing infrared light are called **greenhouse gases**, and they include water vapor (H_2O), carbon dioxide (CO_2), and methane (CH_4). These gases absorb

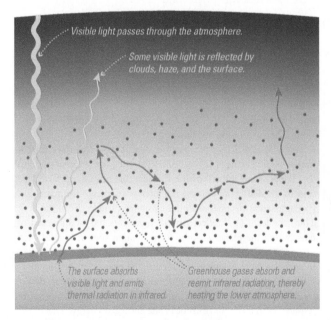

Visible light passes through the atmosphere.

Some visible light is reflected by clouds, haze, and the surface.

The surface absorbs visible light and emits thermal radiation in infrared.

Greenhouse gases absorb and reemit infrared radiation, thereby heating the lower atmosphere.

FIGURE 10.6 The greenhouse effect. The lower atmosphere becomes warmer than it would be if it had no greenhouse gases such as water vapor, carbon dioxide, and methane.

infrared light effectively because their molecular structures begin rotating or vibrating when they absorb an infrared photon (see Figure 5.18).

A greenhouse gas molecule that absorbs an infrared photon does not retain this energy for long; instead, it quickly reemits it as another infrared photon, which may head off in any random direction. This photon can then be absorbed by another greenhouse gas molecule, which does the same thing. The net result is that greenhouse gases tend to slow the escape of infrared radiation from the lower atmosphere, while their molecular motions heat the surrounding air. In this way, the greenhouse effect makes the surface and the lower atmosphere warmer than they would be from sunlight alone. The more greenhouse gases present, the greater the degree of surface warming.

Note that the greenhouse effect does *not* alter a planet's overall energy balance. The total amount of energy that a planet receives from the Sun must be precisely balanced with the amount of energy it returns to space through reflection and radiation. Otherwise, the planet would either rapidly heat up (if it received more energy than it returned) or rapidly cool down (if it returned more energy than it received). All the energy "trapped" by the greenhouse effect still escapes to space, just not as directly as it would otherwise. A blanket offers a good analogy: You stay warmer under a blanket not because the blanket itself provides any heat, but because it slows the escape of your body heat into the cold outside air. In summary, the greenhouse effect makes the total amount of energy in the lower atmosphere greater than it would be otherwise—making it warmer—while leaving the total amount of energy that escapes to space unchanged.

THINK ABOUT IT

Clouds on Earth are made of water (H_2O), which acts as a very effective greenhouse gas even when the water vapor condenses into droplets in clouds. Use this fact to explain why clear nights tend to be colder than cloudy nights.

Incidentally, the name *greenhouse effect* is a bit of a misnomer. The name comes from botanical greenhouses, but greenhouses actually trap heat through a different mechanism than planetary atmospheres: Rather than absorbing infrared radiation, greenhouses stay warm by preventing warm air from rising.

Greenhouse Warming of the Terrestrial Worlds

We can better appreciate the importance of the greenhouse effect by comparing each planet's average surface temperature—or **global average temperature**—with and without it. Recall that a terrestrial planet's interior heat has very little effect on its surface temperature, so sunlight is the only significant energy source for the surface [Section 9.1]. Therefore, without the greenhouse effect, a planet's global average surface temperature would depend on only two things:

- *The planet's distance from the Sun,* which determines the amount of energy received from sunlight. The closer a planet is to the Sun, the greater the intensity of the incoming sunlight.

- *The planet's overall reflectivity,* which determines the relative proportions of incoming sunlight that the planet reflects and absorbs. The higher the reflectivity, the less light absorbed and the cooler the planet.

MATHEMATICAL INSIGHT 10.1

"No Greenhouse" Temperatures

The "no greenhouse" temperature of a planet depends only on its distance from the Sun, its overall reflectivity, and the Sun's brightness. It can be calculated with the following formula:

$$T_{\text{"no greenhouse"}} = 280 \text{ K} \times \sqrt[4]{\frac{(1 - \text{reflectivity})}{d^2}}$$

where d is the distance from the Sun in AU; reflectivity should be stated as a fraction (such as 0.2 rather than 20%). The symbol $\sqrt[4]{}$ means the fourth root, or $\frac{1}{4}$ power.

We will not derive the formula here, but you can see how it makes sense. The term (1 − reflectivity) is the proportion of sunlight that the planet absorbs, which is the light that heats its surface. This term is divided by d^2 because the amount of energy from sunlight (per unit area) declines with the square of distance from the Sun. Thus, the term (1 − reflectivity)/d^2 represents the total amount of energy that the planet absorbs from sunlight (per unit area) each second. This energy warms the surface, which returns the energy to space as thermal radiation. Because the energy emitted by thermal radiation depends on temperature raised to the fourth power (see Mathematical Insight 5.2), calculating the planet's temperature requires taking the fourth root of the absorbed energy. The 280 K in the formula is the temperature of a perfectly black planet at 1 AU from the Sun.

EXAMPLE: Calculate the "no greenhouse" temperature of Mercury.

SOLUTION:

Step 1 Understand: We can use the "no greenhouse" formula with Mercury's distance and reflectivity from Table 10.2; its distance is 0.387 AU and we write the reflectivity of 12% as 0.12.

Step 2 Solve: We substitute the values to find

$$T_{\text{"no greenhouse"}} = 280 \text{ K} \times \sqrt[4]{\frac{(1 - \text{reflectivity})}{d^2}}$$

$$= 280 \text{ K} \times \sqrt[4]{\frac{(1 - 0.12)}{0.387^2}} = 436 \text{ K}$$

Step 3 Explain: Mercury's "no greenhouse" temperature is 436 K. We subtract 273 to convert it to Celsius, finding that 436 K is equivalent to 436 − 273 = 163°C. Note that this agrees with the value in Table 10.2. It also makes sense: Because Mercury has no greenhouse effect, its "no greenhouse" temperature should be roughly midway between its day and night temperatures. The precise halfway point of the day and night temperatures shown in Table 10.2 is 125°C; although this is not an exact match to 163°C, it is close enough for us to be confident that we have the right general idea.

TABLE 10.2 The Greenhouse Effect on the Terrestrial Worlds

World	Average Distance from Sun (AU)	Reflectivity	"No Greenhouse" Average Surface Temperature*	Actual Average Surface Temperature	Greenhouse Warming (actual temperature minus "no greenhouse" temperature)
Mercury	0.387	12%	163°C	day: 425°C night: −175°C	—
Venus	0.723	75%	−40°C	470°C	510°C
Earth	1.00	29%	−16°C	15°C	31°C
Moon	1.00	12%	−2°C	day: 125°C night: −175°C	—
Mars	1.524	16%	−56°C	−50°C	6°C

*The "no greenhouse" temperature is calculated by assuming no change to the atmosphere other than lack of greenhouse warming. For example, Venus has a lower "no greenhouse" temperature than Earth even though it is closer to the Sun, because the high reflectivity of its bright clouds means that it absorbs less sunlight than Earth.

Note that a planet's reflectivity (sometimes called its *albedo*) depends on its composition and color; darker colors reflect less light. For example, clouds, snow, and ice reflect more than 70% of the light that hits them, absorbing only about 30%, while rocks typically reflect only about 20% of the light that hits them and absorb the other 80%.

Both distance from the Sun and reflectivity have been measured for all the terrestrial worlds. With a little mathematics, these measurements can be used to calculate the "no greenhouse" temperature that each world would have without greenhouse gases (see Mathematical Insight 10.1). TABLE 10.2 shows the results. The "no greenhouse" temperatures for Mercury and the Moon lie between their actual day and night temperatures, since they have little atmosphere and hence no greenhouse effect. Mars has a weak greenhouse effect that makes its global average temperature only 6°C higher than its "no greenhouse" temperature. Venus is the extreme case, with a greenhouse effect that bakes its surface to a temperature more than 500°C hotter than it would be otherwise.

We can also see why the greenhouse effect is so important to life on Earth. Without the greenhouse effect, our planet's global average temperature would be a chilly −16°C (+3°F), well below the freezing point of water. With it, the global average temperature is about 15°C (59°F), or about 31°C warmer than the "no greenhouse" temperature. This greenhouse warming is even more remarkable when you realize that it is caused by gases, such as water vapor and carbon dioxide, that are only trace constituents of Earth's atmosphere. Most of the atmosphere consists of nitrogen (N_2) and oxygen (O_2) molecules, which have no effect on infrared light and do not contribute to the greenhouse effect. (Molecules with only two atoms, especially those with two of the same kind of atom, such as N_2 and O_2, are poor infrared absorbers because they have very few ways to vibrate and rotate.)

Why do atmospheric properties vary with altitude? The greenhouse effect can warm a planet's surface and lower atmosphere, but other processes affect the temperature at higher altitudes. The way in which temperature varies with altitude determines what is often called the **atmospheric structure**. Earth's atmospheric structure has four basic layers (FIGURE 10.7), each of which affects the planet in a distinct way:

- The **troposphere** is the lowest layer, in which temperature drops with altitude (something you've probably noticed if you've ever climbed a mountain).

- The **stratosphere** begins where the temperature stops dropping and instead begins to rise with altitude. High in the stratosphere, the temperature falls again.*

- The **thermosphere** begins where the temperature again starts to rise at high altitude.

- The **exosphere** is the uppermost region, in which the atmosphere gradually fades away into space.

Interactions Between Light and Atmospheric Gases The key to understanding atmospheric structure lies in interactions between atmospheric gases and energy from the Sun. Although most light coming from the Sun is visible light, the Sun also emits significant amounts of ultraviolet light

---

*Technically, the region where the temperature falls again is called the *mesosphere*, but we will not make that distinction in this book.

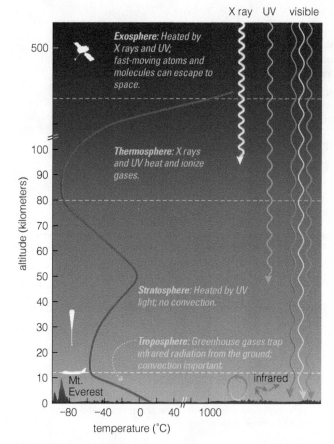

FIGURE 10.7 Earth's average atmospheric structure. The curve shows average temperature for each altitude. The squiggly arrows to the right represent light of different wavelengths and show where it is typically absorbed.

and X rays. In addition, the planetary surface emits infrared light. Atmospheric gases interact with each of these forms of light in different ways (FIGURE 10.8):

- X rays have enough energy to *ionize* (knock electrons from) almost any atom or molecule. They can therefore be absorbed by virtually all atmospheric gases.

- Ultraviolet photons generally do not have enough energy to cause ionization, but they can sometimes break molecules apart. For example, ultraviolet photons can split water (H_2O) molecules, and are even more likely to be absorbed by weakly bonded molecules, such as ozone (O_3), which split apart in the process.

COMMON MISCONCEPTIONS

Temperatures at High Altitude

Many people think that the low temperatures in the mountains are just the result of lower pressures, but Figure 10.7 shows that it's not that simple. The higher temperatures near sea level on Earth are a result of the greenhouse effect, which traps more heat at lower altitudes. If Earth had no greenhouse gases, mountaintops wouldn't be so cold—or, more accurately, sea level wouldn't be so warm.

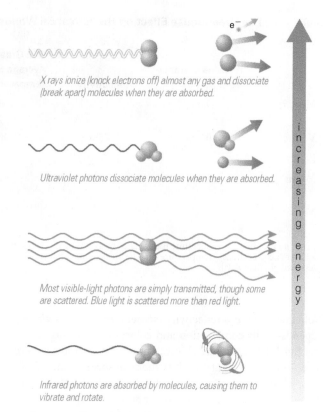

FIGURE 10.8 The primary effects when light of different energies strikes common atmospheric gases.

- Visible-light photons generally pass through atmospheric gases without being absorbed, but some are *scattered* so that their direction changes.

- As we've already discussed, infrared photons can be absorbed by greenhouse gases, which are molecules that easily begin rotating and vibrating.

With these ideas in mind, we are ready to examine the reasons for Earth's atmospheric structure, working our way from the ground up.

Visible Light: Warming the Surface and Coloring the Sky Most visible sunlight reaches the ground and warms the surface, but the small amount that is scattered has two important effects.

First, scattering makes the daytime sky bright, which is why we can't see stars in the daytime. Without scattering, sunlight would travel only in perfectly straight lines, which means we'd see the Sun against an otherwise black sky, just as it appears on the Moon. Scattering also prevents shadows on Earth from being pitch black. On the Moon, shadows receive little scattered sunlight and are extremely cold and dark.

Second, scattering explains why our sky is blue. Visible light consists of all the colors of the rainbow, but not all the colors are scattered equally. Gas molecules scatter blue light (higher energy) much more effectively than red light (lower energy). The difference in scattering is so great that, for practical purposes, we can imagine that only the blue light gets scattered. When the Sun is overhead, this scattered blue light reaches our eyes from all directions and the sky appears blue (FIGURE 10.9).

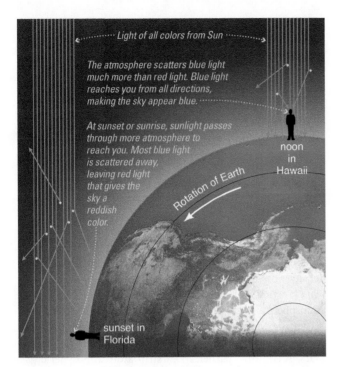

Light of all colors from Sun

The atmosphere scatters blue light much more than red light. Blue light reaches you from all directions, making the sky appear blue.

At sunset or sunrise, sunlight passes through more atmosphere to reach you. Most blue light is scattered away, leaving red light that gives the sky a reddish color.

noon in Hawaii

Rotation of Earth

sunset in Florida

FIGURE 10.9 This diagram summarizes why the daytime sky is blue and sunsets (and sunrises) are red.

COMMON MISCONCEPTIONS

Why Is the Sky Blue?

If you ask around, you'll find a wide variety of misconceptions about why the sky is blue. Some people guess that the sky is blue because of light reflecting from the oceans, but that could not explain blue skies over inland areas. Others claim that "air is blue," a vague statement that is also wrong: If air molecules emitted blue light, then air would glow blue even in the dark; if they were blue because they reflected blue light and absorbed red light, then no red light could reach us at sunset. The real explanation for the blue sky is light scattering, as shown in Figure 10.9, which also explains our red sunsets.

temperature tends to *increase* with altitude as we go upward from the base of the stratosphere. This temperature structure prevents convection in the lower stratosphere, because heat cannot rise if the air above is hotter. The lack of convection makes the air relatively stagnant and *stratified* (layered), with layers of warm air overlying cooler air; this stratification explains the name *stratosphere*. The lack of convection also means that the stratosphere has essentially no weather and no rain. Pollutants that reach the stratosphere, including the ozone-destroying chemicals known as chlorofluorocarbons (CFCs), remain there for decades.

Note that a planet can have a stratosphere *only* if its atmosphere contains molecules that are particularly good at absorbing ultraviolet photons. Ozone (O_3) plays this role on Earth, but the lack of oxygen in the atmospheres of the other terrestrial worlds means that they also lack ozone. As a result, Earth is the only terrestrial world with a stratosphere, at least in our solar system. (The jovian planets have stratospheres due to other ultraviolet-absorbing molecules [**Section 11.1**].)

At sunset or sunrise, the sunlight must pass through a greater amount of atmosphere on its way to us. Most of the blue light is scattered away, leaving only red light to color the sky.

Infrared Light and the Troposphere The ground returns the energy it absorbs by radiating in the infrared. Greenhouse gases absorb this infrared light and warm the troposphere. Because the infrared light comes from the surface, more is absorbed closer to the ground than at higher altitudes, which is why the temperature drops with altitude in the troposphere. (The relatively small amount of infrared light coming from the Sun does not have a significant effect on the atmosphere.)

The drop in temperature with altitude, combined with the relatively high density of air in the troposphere, explains why the troposphere is the only layer of the atmosphere with storms. The primary cause of storms is the churning of air by convection [**Section 9.1**], in which warm air rises and cool air falls. Recall that convection occurs only when there is strong heating from below; in the troposphere, the heating from the ground can drive convection. In fact, the troposphere gets its name from convection; *tropos* is Greek for "turning."

Ultraviolet Light and the Stratosphere Above the troposphere, the air density is too low for greenhouse gases to have much effect, so infrared light from below can travel unhindered through higher layers of the atmosphere and into space. Heating from below therefore has little effect on the stratosphere. Instead, the primary source of heating in the stratosphere is the absorption of solar ultraviolet light by ozone.

Most of this ultraviolet absorption and heating occurs at moderately high altitudes in the stratosphere, which is why

X Rays and the Thermosphere Because nearly all gases are good X-ray absorbers, X rays from the Sun are absorbed by the first gases they encounter as they enter the atmosphere. The density of gas in the exosphere is too low for it to absorb significant amounts of these X rays, so most X rays are absorbed in the thermosphere. The absorbed energy makes temperatures quite high in the thermosphere (*thermos* is Greek for "hot"), but you wouldn't feel much heat because the density and pressure are so low [**Section 4.3**]. Virtually no X rays penetrate beneath the thermosphere, which is why X-ray telescopes are useful only on very high-flying balloons, rockets, and spacecraft.

Solar X rays also ionize a small but important fraction of the thermosphere's gas. The portion of the thermosphere that contains most of the ionized gas is called the *ionosphere*. The ionosphere is very important to radio communication, because it reflects most radio broadcasts back to Earth's surface. Without this reflection, radio communication would work only between locations in sight of each other.

The Exosphere The exosphere is the extremely low-density gas that forms the gradual and fuzzy boundary between the atmosphere and space (*exo* means "outermost" or "outside"). The gas density in the exosphere is so low that collisions between

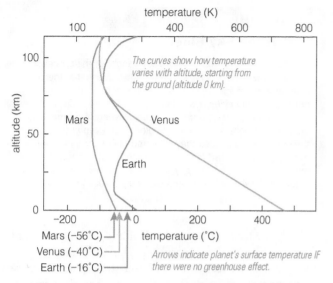

The curves show how temperature varies with altitude, starting from the ground (altitude 0 km).

Mars (−56°C)
Venus (−40°C)
Earth (−16°C)

Arrows indicate planet's surface temperature IF there were no greenhouse effect.

FIGURE 10.10 Venus, Earth, and Mars all have tropospheres and thermospheres (and exospheres, not shown), but only Earth has middle-atmosphere heating to make a stratosphere. The graph also shows that Venus and Earth are considerably warmer than they would be without the greenhouse effect.

atoms or molecules are very rare, although the high temperature means that gas particles move quite rapidly. Lightweight atoms and molecules sometimes reach escape velocity [**Section 4.5**] and fly off into space.

Comparative Structures of Terrestrial Atmospheres

We can now understand the structures of all the terrestrial atmospheres. The Moon and Mercury have so little gas that they essentially contain only an exosphere and have no structure to speak of. **FIGURE 10.10** contrasts the atmospheric

structures of Venus, Earth, and Mars. Notice that all three planets have a troposphere warmed by the greenhouse effect, and all three have a thermosphere heated by solar X rays. However, only Earth has the extra "bump" of a stratosphere, because it is the only planet with a layer of ultraviolet-absorbing gas (ozone). Without ozone, the middle altitudes of Earth's atmosphere would be almost as cold as those on Mars.

THINK ABOUT IT

Would astronauts on the Moon need protection from solar X rays? What about astronauts on Mars? Explain.

Magnetospheres and the Solar Wind There is one other important type of energy coming from the Sun: the low-density flow of subatomic charged particles called the *solar wind* [**Section 8.2**]. The solar wind does not significantly affect atmospheric structure, but it has other important effects.

On the Moon and Mercury, solar wind particles hit the surface, where they can blast atoms free. On Venus and Mars, solar wind particles can strip away atmospheric gas. In contrast, Earth's strong magnetic field creates a **magnetosphere** that acts like a protective bubble surrounding our planet, deflecting most solar wind particles around our planet (**FIGURE 10.11a**).

The magnetosphere still allows a few solar wind particles to get through, especially near the magnetic poles. Once inside the magnetosphere, these particles move along magnetic field lines, collecting in **charged particle belts** (or *Van Allen belts*, after their discoverer) that encircle our planet. The high energies of the particles in these belts can be hazardous to spacecraft and astronauts passing through them.

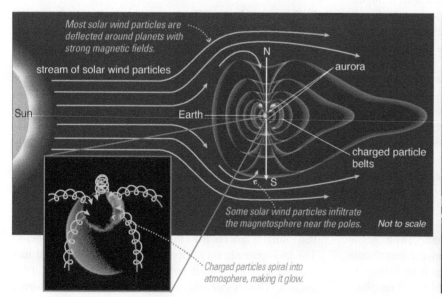

a This diagram shows how Earth's magnetosphere deflects solar wind particles. Some particles accumulate in charged particle belts encircling our planet. The inset is a photo of a ring of auroras around the North Pole; the bright crescent at its left is part of the day side of Earth.

b This photograph shows the aurora near Yellowknife, Northwest Territories, Canada. In a video, you would see these lights dancing about in the sky.

FIGURE 10.11 Earth's magnetosphere acts like a protective bubble, shielding our planet from the charged particles of the solar wind.

Charged particles trapped in the magnetosphere also create the beautiful light of the **aurora** (FIGURE 10.11b). Variations in the solar wind can buffet the magnetosphere and give energy to particles trapped there. If a trapped particle gains enough energy, it can follow the magnetic field all the way down to Earth's atmosphere, where it collides with atmospheric atoms and molecules. These collisions cause the atoms and molecules to radiate and produce the moving lights of the aurora. Because the charged particles follow the magnetic field, auroras are most common near the magnetic poles and are best viewed at high latitudes. In the Northern Hemisphere, the aurora is often called the *aurora borealis,* or northern lights. In the Southern Hemisphere, it is called the *aurora australis,* or southern lights. The aurora can also be seen from space, where the lights look much like surf in the upper atmosphere (see Figure 10.5).

(MA) Surface Temperature of Terrestrial Planets Tutorial, Lesson 1

10.2 WEATHER AND CLIMATE

So far, we've talked mostly about *average* conditions in planetary atmospheres, such as the global average temperature and the average atmospheric structure. However, experience tells us that surface and atmospheric conditions constantly change through weather and climate.

Weather and climate are closely related, but they are not quite the same thing. **Weather** refers to the ever-varying combination of winds, clouds, temperature, and pressure that makes some days hotter or cooler, clearer or cloudier, or calmer or stormier than others. **Climate** refers to the average of weather over many years. For example, we say that Antarctic deserts have a cold, dry climate, even though it might sometimes rain or snow. Geological records show that climates can change, but these changes usually occur gradually over decades, centuries, or millennia.

Weather and climate can be hard to distinguish on a human time scale. For example, a drought lasting a few years may be the result of either random weather fluctuations or the beginning of a gradual change to a drier climate. The difficulty in distinguishing between random weather and real climate trends is an important part of the debate about human influences on the climate. We'll return to this topic in Section 10.6; for now, let's focus on understanding weather and climate generally.

What creates wind and weather?

Wind, rain, and other weather phenomena are all driven by energy in the atmosphere, which means only planets with atmospheres can have weather. Even then, weather varies dramatically among different worlds. Earth has the most diverse weather of the terrestrial planets, so we'll use it as our example of how weather works.

The complexity of weather makes it difficult to predict, and at best the local weather can be predicted only a week or so in advance (see Special Topic, page 280). Nevertheless, when we look at Earth as a whole, we can identify certain general characteristics of weather.

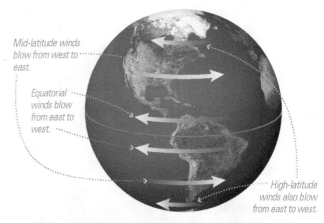

FIGURE 10.12 Schematic of Earth's global wind patterns. Notice that mid-latitude winds blow from west to east, explaining why storms generally move across the United States from the West Coast toward the East Coast.

Global Wind Patterns The wind's direction and strength can change rapidly in any particular place, but we find distinctive patterns on a more global scale. For example, winds generally cause storms moving in from the Pacific to hit the West Coast of the United States first and then make their way eastward across the Rocky Mountains and the Great Plains, heading to the East Coast.

FIGURE 10.12 shows Earth's major **global wind patterns** (or *global circulation*). Notice that the wind direction varies with latitude: Equatorial winds blow from east to west, mid-latitude winds blow from west to east, and high-latitude winds blow like equatorial winds from east to west. Two factors explain this pattern: atmospheric heating and planetary rotation. Let's examine each in turn.

THINK ABOUT IT

Hurricanes usually form over warm, equatorial waters. Based on the wind patterns shown in Figure 10.12, in which direction will a hurricane move after forming off the northeastern coast of South America? Explain why these wind patterns make the Caribbean and the southeastern United States especially vulnerable to hurricanes.

Atmospheric Heating and Circulation Cells

Atmospheric heating affects global wind patterns because equatorial regions receive more heat from the Sun than polar regions. Warm equatorial air therefore rises upward and flows toward the poles, where cool air descends and flows toward the equator. If Earth's rotation did not influence this process, the result would be two huge **circulation cells** (or *Hadley cells*, after the man who first suggested their existence), one in each hemisphere (FIGURE 10.13).

The circulation cells transport heat both from lower to higher altitudes and from the equator to the poles. They therefore make Earth's polar regions much warmer than they would be in the absence of circulation. The same idea applies to different extents on Venus and Mars. On Venus, the dense atmosphere allows the circulation cells to transport so much thermal energy that temperatures are nearly the same at the

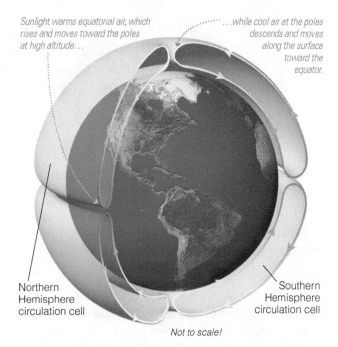

Sunlight warms equatorial air, which rises and moves toward the poles at high altitude...

...while cool air at the poles descends and moves along the surface toward the equator.

Northern Hemisphere circulation cell

Southern Hemisphere circulation cell

Not to scale!

FIGURE 10.13 Interactive figure Atmospheric heating creates a circulation cell in each hemisphere that carries warm equatorial air toward the poles while cool polar air moves toward the equator. This diagram shows how the circulation cells would work if our planet's rotation didn't affect them. The vertical extent of the circulation cells is greatly exaggerated; in reality, the tops of the cells are only a few kilometers above Earth's surface.

equator and the poles. On Mars, the circulation cells transport very little heat because the atmosphere is so thin, so the poles remain much colder than the equator.

Rotation and the Coriolis Effect Planetary rotation affects global wind patterns through the **Coriolis effect** (named for the French physicist who first explained it), which you can understand by thinking about a spinning merry-go-round (**FIGURE 10.14**). The outer parts of the merry-go-round move at a faster speed than the inner parts, because they have a greater distance to travel around the axis with each rotation. If you sit near the edge and roll a ball toward the center, the ball begins with your relatively high speed around the axis. As it rolls inward, the ball's high speed makes it move ahead of the slower-moving inner regions. On a merry-go-round rotating counterclockwise, the ball therefore deviates *to the right* instead of heading straight inward. The Coriolis effect also makes the ball deviate to the right if you roll it outward from a position near the center. In that case, the ball starts with your slower speed around the center and lags behind as it rolls outward to faster-moving regions, again deviating to the right. (If the merry-go-round rotates clockwise rather than counterclockwise, the deviations go to the left instead of the right.)

The Coriolis effect alters the path of air on the rotating Earth in much the same way (**FIGURE 10.15**). Equatorial regions circle around Earth's rotation axis faster than polar regions (see Figure 1.12). Air moving away from the equator therefore

SPECIAL TOPIC

Weather and Chaos

Scientists today have a very good understanding of the physical laws and mathematical equations that govern the behavior of the atmosphere and oceans. Why, then, do we have so much trouble predicting the weather? To understand the answer, we must look at the nature of scientific prediction.

Prediction always requires knowing two things: (1) the current state of a system, sometimes called its *initial conditions*, and (2) how the system is changing. This is easy for something simple, like a car; if you know where a car is and how fast and in what direction it is traveling, you can predict where it will be a few minutes from now. Weather prediction is more difficult because weather is created by the motions of countless individual atoms and molecules. Scientists therefore attempt to predict the weather by creating a "model world." For example, suppose you overlay a globe of Earth with graph paper and specify the current temperature, pressure, cloud cover, and wind within each square; these are your initial conditions, which you can input into a computer along with a set of equations (physical laws) describing the processes that can change weather from one moment to the next. You can now use your computer model to predict the weather for the next month in New York City. The model might tell you that tomorrow will be warm and sunny, with cooling during the next week and a major storm passing through a month from now.

Now, suppose you run the model again, but you make one minor change in the initial conditions—say, a small change in the wind speed somewhere over Brazil. This slightly different initial condition will not change the weather prediction for tomorrow in New York City, and

may only slightly affect the prediction for next week's weather. For next month's weather, however, the two predictions may not agree at all!

The disagreement between the two predictions arises because the laws governing weather can cause tiny changes in initial conditions to be greatly magnified over time. This extreme sensitivity to initial conditions is sometimes called the *butterfly effect*: If initial conditions change by as much as the flap of a butterfly's wings, the resulting long-term prediction may be very different. That is why it is possible to predict the weather with reasonable accuracy a few days in advance, but not a few months in advance.

The butterfly effect is a hallmark of *chaotic systems*. Simple systems are described by linear equations in which, for example, increasing a cause produces a proportional increase in an effect. In contrast, chaotic systems are described by nonlinear equations, which allow for subtler and more intricate interactions. For example, the economy is nonlinear because a rise in interest rates does not automatically produce a corresponding change in consumer spending. Weather is nonlinear because a change in the wind speed in one location does not automatically produce a corresponding change in another location.

Despite their name, chaotic systems are not necessarily random. In fact, many chaotic systems have a kind of underlying order that explains the general features of their behavior even though details at any particular moment remain unpredictable. In a sense, many chaotic systems—like the weather—are "predictably unpredictable."

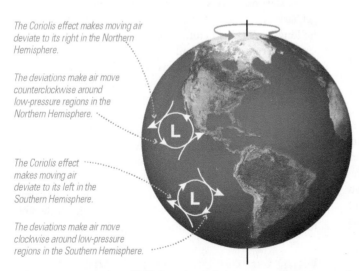

Outer regions rotate faster around the axis than inner regions, because they travel farther with each rotation.

A ball that starts near the center has a slow speed around the axis; it falls behind the overall rotation as it rolls outward.

starting direction

A ball that starts near the edge has a higher speed around the axis, so it gets ahead of the rotation as it rolls inward.

FIGURE 10.14 **interactive figure** The Coriolis effect on a merry-go-round rotating counterclockwise. Notice that the ball's path deviates to the *right* regardless of whether the ball is rolled inward or outward. If the merry-go-round were rotating clockwise, in both cases the ball would veer to the left.

has "extra" speed that causes it to move ahead of Earth's rotation to the east, while air moving toward the equator lags behind Earth's rotation to the west. In either case, moving air turns to the *right* in the Northern Hemisphere and to the *left* in the Southern Hemisphere, which explains why storms circulate in opposite directions in the two hemispheres. Uneven heating and cooling of Earth's surface creates regions of slightly higher pressure ("H" on weather maps) or lower pressure ("L" on weather maps) than average. Storms generally occur around low-pressure regions, which draw air inward from surrounding regions; as shown in Figure 10.15a, the Coriolis effect makes the inward-flowing air rotate counterclockwise in the Northern Hemisphere and clockwise in the Southern Hemisphere. This rotation around a low-pressure

zone can be quite stable, which is why storms can persist for days or weeks while being carried across the globe.

The Coriolis effect plays an even more important role in shaping Earth's global wind patterns: It splits each of the two huge circulation cells shown in Figure 10.13 into three

The Coriolis effect makes moving air deviate to its right in the Northern Hemisphere.

The deviations make air move counterclockwise around low-pressure regions in the Northern Hemisphere.

The Coriolis effect makes moving air deviate to its left in the Southern Hemisphere.

The deviations make air move clockwise around low-pressure regions in the Southern Hemisphere.

Notice the opposite directions of storm circulation in the Northern and Southern Hemispheres.

a Low-pressure regions ("L") draw in air from surrounding areas, and the Coriolis effect causes this air to circulate counterclockwise in the Northern Hemisphere and clockwise in the Southern Hemisphere.

b This photograph shows the opposite directions of storm circulation in the two hemispheres.

FIGURE 10.15 **interactive figure** The Coriolis effect works on the rotating Earth much as it does on a merry-go-round, because regions near the equator move at faster speed around the axis than regions near the poles.

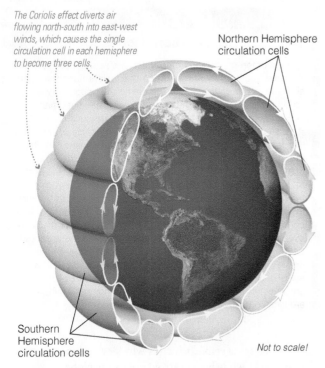

Northern Hemisphere circulation cells

Southern Hemisphere circulation cells

Not to scale!

FIGURE 10.16 interactive figure On Earth, the Coriolis effect causes each of the two large circulation cells that would be present without rotation (see Figure 10.13) to split into three smaller cells.

smaller circulation cells (**FIGURE 10.16**). You can understand why by considering air flowing southward along the surface from the North Pole. Without rotation, this air would travel 10,000 kilometers due south to the equator. But as Earth rotates, the Coriolis effect diverts this air to the right (westward) well before it reaches the equator, forcing the single large circulation cell to split. The three resulting cells circulate the air somewhat like three interlocking gears. These motions explain the global wind directions: Notice that surface air moves toward the equator in the cells near the equator and near the poles, so the Coriolis effect diverts this air into west-ward winds (see Figure 10.12). In contrast, surface air moves toward the poles in the mid-latitude cells, so the Coriolis effect diverts it into winds that blow eastward. In essence, the Coriolis effect on a rotating planet tends to divert air moving north or south into east-west winds.

The Coriolis effect operates to some extent on all planets. Its strength depends on a planet's size and rotation rate: Larger size and faster rotation both contribute to a stronger Coriolis effect. Among the terrestrial planets, Earth is the only one with a Coriolis effect strong enough to split the two large circulation cells. Venus has a very weak Coriolis effect because of its slow rotation, while Mars has a weak Coriolis effect because of its small size. The Coriolis effect is much stronger on the large and fast-rotating jovian planets, and it can therefore split their circulation cells into numerous smaller cells [**Section 11.1**].

Clouds and Precipitation In addition to winds, the other key components of weather are rain, snow, and hail, which together are called **precipitation** in weather reports.

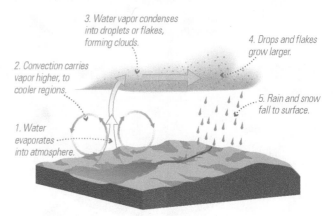

FIGURE 10.17 The cycle of water on Earth's surface and in the atmosphere.

Precipitation requires clouds. We may think of clouds as imperfections on a sunny day, but they have profound effects on Earth and other planets, despite being made from minor ingredients of the atmosphere (see Table 10.1). Besides being the source of precipitation, clouds can alter a planet's energy balance. Clouds reflect sunlight back to space, thereby reducing the amount of sunlight that warms a planet's surface, but they also tend to be made from greenhouse gases that contribute to planetary warming.

On Earth, clouds are made from tiny droplets of liquid water or flakes of ice, which you can feel if you walk through a cloud on a mountaintop. Clouds are produced by condensation of water vapor (**FIGURE 10.17**). The water vapor enters the atmosphere through evaporation of surface water (or sublimation of ice and snow). Convection then carries the water vapor to high, cold regions of the troposphere, where it can condense to form clouds. Clouds can also form as winds blow over mountains, because the mountains force the air high enough to allow condensation. The condensed droplets or ice flakes start out very small, but gradually grow larger. If they get large enough that the upward convection currents can no longer hold them aloft, then they begin to fall toward the surface as rain, snow, or hail.

Stronger convection means more clouds and precipitation. That is why thunderstorms are common on summer afternoons, when the sunlight-warmed surface drives strong convection. The linkage between clouds and convection also explains why Earth has lush jungles near the equator and deserts at latitudes of 20°–30° north or south. Equatorial regions experience high rainfall because they receive more sunlight, which causes more convection. This high rainfall depletes the air of moisture as Earth's circulation cells carry it away from the equator (see Figure 10.16), leaving little moisture to fall as rain at the latitudes of the deserts.

What factors can cause long-term climate change?

We now turn our attention to climate, which varies much more slowly than weather. Scientists have identified four major factors that can lead to long-term climate change on the terrestrial worlds:

Solar brightening: As the Sun brightens with time, the increasing sunlight tends to warm the planets.

Changes in reflectivity: Higher reflectivity tends to cool a planet, while lower reflectivity leads to warming.

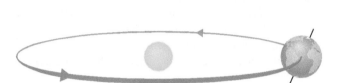

Changes in axis tilt: Greater tilt makes more extreme seasons, while smaller tilt keeps polar regions colder.

Changes in greenhouse gas abundance: An increase in greenhouse gases slows escape of infrared radiation, warming the planet, while a decrease leads to cooling.

FIGURE 10.18 Four major factors affecting long-term climate change.

- **Solar brightening.** The Sun has grown gradually brighter with time, increasing the amount of solar energy reaching the planets.

- **Changes in axis tilt.** The tilt of a planet's axis may change over long periods of time.

- **Changes in reflectivity.** An increase in a planet's reflectivity means a decrease in the amount of sunlight it absorbs, and vice versa.

- **Changes in greenhouse gas abundance.** More greenhouse gases tend to make a planet warmer, and less make it cooler.

FIGURE 10.18 summarizes these four factors, which we now investigate in a little more detail. Keep in mind that more than one factor may be acting at any given time.

Solar Brightening Both theoretical models of the Sun and observations of other Sun-like stars tell us that the Sun has gradually brightened with age [**Section 14.2**]: The Sun today is probably about 30% brighter than it was when our solar system was young. This brightening tends to warm climates with time, though we'd expect the effects to be noticeable only over periods of tens of millions of years or longer. Moreover, the brightening is so gradual that other climate change factors can easily overwhelm it. For example, while solar brightening alone would mean that all planets should be warmer today than they were in the past, both Mars and Earth are cooler than they were at times in their early histories.

Changes in Axis Tilt Small gravitational tugs from moons, other planets, and the Sun can change a planet's axis tilt over thousands or millions of years. For example, while Earth's current axis tilt is about $23\frac{1}{2}°$, the tilt has varied

over tens of thousands of years between about 22° and 25° (**FIGURE 10.19**). These small changes affect the climate by making seasons more or less extreme. Greater tilt means more extreme seasons, with warmer summers and colder winters. The extra summer warmth tends to prevent ice from building up, which reduces the planet's reflectivity and thereby makes the whole planet warmer. Conversely, a smaller tilt means less extreme seasons, which can allow ice to build up and make a planet cooler.

Earth's past periods of smaller axis tilt correlate well with the times of past ice ages, especially when considered along with other small changes in Earth's rotation and orbit. They

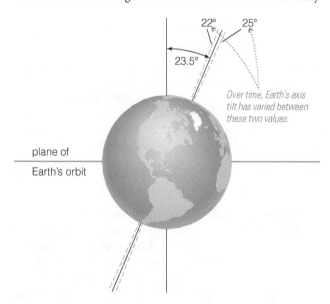

FIGURE 10.19 Earth's axis tilt is currently about $23\frac{1}{2}°$, but it has varied between about 22° and 25° over tens of thousands of years.

are therefore thought to be a primary factor in climate changes on Earth. (The cyclical changes in Earth's axis tilt and orbit are often called *Milankovitch cycles,* after the Serbian scientist who suggested their role in climate change.) As we'll discuss shortly, Mars probably experiences much more extreme changes in axis tilt and climate than Earth, and similar climate cycles may occur on some of the icy moons of the outer solar system.

Changes in Reflectivity

Changes in reflectivity affect climate because they change the proportions of sunlight absorbed and reflected. If a planet reflects more sunlight, it must absorb less, which can lead to planetwide cooling. Microscopic dust particles (called *aerosols*) released by volcanic eruptions can reflect sunlight and cool a planet. Small but measurable planetwide cooling has been detected on Earth following a major volcanic eruption. The cooling can continue for years if the dust particles reach the stratosphere.

Human activity is currently altering Earth's reflectivity, although we are not sure in which direction or by precisely how much. Smog particles can act like volcanic dust, reflecting sunlight before it reaches the ground. Deforestation also increases reflectivity because it removes sunlight-absorbing plants. On the other hand, roads and cities tend to decrease reflectivity, which is why they tend to be hotter than surrounding areas of vegetation.

Changes in Greenhouse Gas Abundance

Perhaps the most important factor in long-term climate change is a change in the abundance of greenhouse gases, which strengthens or weakens the greenhouse effect. If the abundance of greenhouse gases increases, the planet generally will warm. If the planet warms enough, increased evaporation and sublimation may add substantial amounts of gas to the planet's atmosphere, leading to an increase in atmospheric pressure. Conversely, if the abundance of greenhouse gases decreases, the planet generally will cool, and atmospheric pressure may decrease as gases freeze.

How does a planet gain or lose atmospheric gases?

Of the factors that affect planetary climate, changes in greenhouse gas concentrations appear to have had the greatest effect on the long-term climates of Venus, Earth, and Mars. Such changes generally occur as part of more general changes in the abundances of atmospheric gases. We must therefore investigate how atmospheres gain and lose gas.

Sources of Atmospheric Gas

Terrestrial atmospheres can gain gas in three basic ways (FIGURE 10.20):

- **Outgassing.** Volcanic *outgassing* has been the primary source of gases for the atmospheres of Venus, Earth, and Mars. Recall that the terrestrial worlds were built primarily of metal and rock, but impacts of ice-rich planetesimals (from beyond the frost line [**Section 8.2**]) brought in water and gas that became trapped in their interiors during accretion. Studies of volcanic eruptions show that the most common gases released by outgassing are water (H_2O),

carbon dioxide (CO_2), nitrogen (N_2), and sulfur-bearing gases (H_2S and SO_2).*

- **Evaporation/sublimation.** After outgassing creates an atmosphere, some atmospheric gases may condense to become surface liquids or ices. The subsequent evaporation or sublimation of these surface liquids and ices therefore represents a secondary source of atmospheric gas. For example, if a planet warms, the rates of evaporation and sublimation will increase, adding gas to the atmosphere.

- **Surface ejection.** The tiny impacts of micrometeorites, solar wind particles, and high-energy solar photons can knock individual atoms or molecules free from the surface. This *surface ejection* process explains the small amounts of gas that surround the Moon and Mercury. It is not a source process for planets that already have substantial atmospheres, because the atmospheres prevent small particles and high-energy solar photons from reaching the surface.

Losses of Atmospheric Gas

Planets can also lose atmospheric gas, and there are four major loss processes (FIGURE 10.21). Note that the first two of these processes simply recycle gas from the atmosphere to the planet's surface or interior, while the latter two lead to permanent loss of gas.

- **Condensation.** The condensation of gases that then fall as rain, hail, or snow is essentially the reverse of the release of gas by evaporation or sublimation. On Mars, for example, it is cold enough for carbon dioxide to condense into dry ice (frozen carbon dioxide), especially at the poles.

- **Chemical reactions.** Some chemical reactions incorporate gas into surface metal or rock. Rusting is a familiar example: Iron rusts when it reacts with oxygen, thereby removing oxygen from the atmosphere and incorporating it into the metal.

- **Solar wind stripping.** For any world without a protective magnetosphere, particles from the solar wind can gradually strip away gas particles into space.

- **Thermal escape.** If an atom or a molecule of gas in a planet's exosphere achieves escape velocity [**Section 4.5**], it will fly off into space. The relative importance of thermal escape on any world depends on its size, distance from the Sun, and atmospheric composition. In general, more thermal escape will occur if a planet is small (so that it has a low escape velocity) or close to the Sun (which makes it hotter, so that atoms and molecules of atmospheric gas are moving faster). Lightweight gases, such as hydrogen and helium, escape more easily than heavier gases, such as carbon dioxide, nitrogen, and oxygen.

SEE IT FOR YOURSELF

You can see some atmospheric gain and loss processes in your freezer. Look for loose ice cubes that are gradually shrinking away, or look for the buildup of frost. What process is occurring in each case, and where do these processes occur in the solar system?

---

*Among these materials, only water existed in modest quantities in the solar nebula. The others were created by chemical reactions that occurred *inside* the planets after gas became trapped.

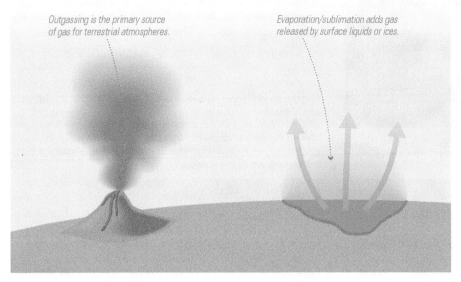

Outgassing is the primary source of gas for terrestrial atmospheres.

Evaporation/sublimation adds gas released by surface liquids or ices.

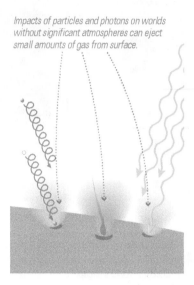

Impacts of particles and photons on worlds without significant atmospheres can eject small amounts of gas from surface.

FIGURE 10.20 Three processes that can provide gas to terrestrial atmospheres.

How Atmospheres Lose Gas

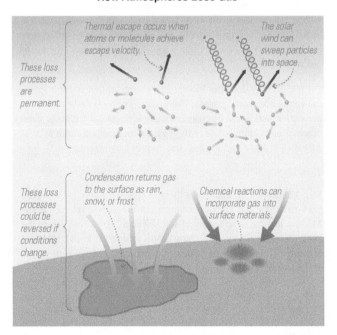

These loss processes are permanent.

Thermal escape occurs when atoms or molecules achieve escape velocity.

The solar wind can sweep particles into space.

These loss processes could be reversed if conditions change.

Condensation returns gas to the surface as rain, snow, or frost.

Chemical reactions can incorporate gas into surface materials.

FIGURE 10.21 Four processes that can remove gas from terrestrial atmospheres.

All the terrestrial planets are small enough and warm enough for hydrogen and helium to escape. That is why they were unable to hold on to any hydrogen or helium gas that they may have captured from the solar nebula when they were very young. Venus, Earth, and Mars have been able to retain heavier gases released later by outgassing, which is why they have substantial atmospheres today. However, the compositions and densities of their atmospheres have changed with time because of other source and loss processes.

10.3 ATMOSPHERES OF THE MOON AND MERCURY

We have now covered the basic ideas needed to understand the atmospheric histories of the terrestrial worlds. In the rest of this chapter, we'll use these to learn how and why each world ended up with its current atmosphere. As we did in Chapter 9, we'll begin with the smallest worlds, the Moon and Mercury.

Do the Moon and Mercury have any atmosphere?

We usually don't think of the Moon and Mercury as having atmospheres, but they are not totally devoid of gas. However, their gas densities are far too low for sunlight to be scattered or absorbed. The lack of scattering means that, even in broad daylight, you would see a pitch-black sky surrounding the bright Sun. The lack of absorption means that their atmospheres do not have a troposphere, stratosphere, or thermosphere. In essence, the Moon and Mercury have only extremely low-density exospheres, without any other atmospheric layers.

The total amount of gas in the exospheres of the Moon and Mercury is very small. If you could condense the entire atmosphere of either the Moon or Mercury into solid form, you would have so little material that you could almost store it in a dorm room. The low density of the gas means that collisions between atoms or molecules are rare. The gas particles therefore can rise as high as their speeds allow—sometimes even escaping to space. As a result, the exospheres of the Moon and Mercury extend thousands of kilometers above their surfaces (**FIGURE 10.22**).

Source and Loss Processes on the Moon and Mercury The Moon and Mercury may once have had some gas released by volcanic outgassing, but they no longer have any volcanic activity, and any gas released in the distant past is long gone. Some of the gas released long ago was probably lost through stripping by the solar wind, but it would have been

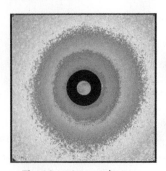

a The Moon's exosphere, which extends high above the surface.

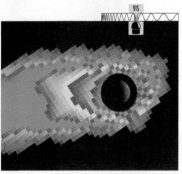

b Mercury's exosphere, much of which is escaping in this image.

lost to thermal escape anyway. Mercury cannot hold much of an atmosphere because its small size and high daytime temperature mean that nearly all gas particles eventually achieve escape velocity. The Moon is cooler than Mercury,

FIGURE 10.22 These "images" of the atmospheres of the Moon and Mercury—which are essentially exospheres only—are based on data collected with instruments sensitive to emission lines from sodium atoms; the colors represent gas density from highest (red) to lowest (blue). The inset photos of the Moon and Mercury are on the same scale as the images.

MATHEMATICAL INSIGHT 10.2

Thermal Escape from an Atmosphere

Thermal escape depends on the speeds of gas particles (atoms or molecules), because a particle can escape to space only if it reaches or exceeds a world's escape velocity. The fact that gas particles continually collide with one another means that individual particles move at a wide range of speeds. However, these speeds are not totally random; instead, their distribution has a characteristic shape that depends on the temperature and the particle masses. **FIGURE 1** shows this characteristic shape for sodium atoms in the Moon's daytime exosphere ($T = 400$ K). The peak in the figure represents the most common speed, or *peak thermal velocity*, which is given by the following formula:

$$v_{thermal} = \sqrt{\frac{2kT}{m}}$$

where m is the mass of a single gas particle, T is the temperature on the Kelvin scale, and $k = 1.38 \times 10^{-23}$ joule/K is *Boltzmann's constant*. Note that the peak thermal velocity increases with temperature (because higher temperature means higher average kinetic energy for gas particles), and decreases with particle mass (because at any particular temperature, particles of lighter gases, with smaller m, move at faster speeds than particles of heavier gases).

If a gas's peak thermal velocity is greater than the escape velocity, most of the gas particles will quickly escape to space. However, some gas particles can escape even if the peak thermal velocity is much lower. For example, Figure 1 shows that a small fraction of the sodium atoms have speeds exceeding the Moon's escape velocity

(about 2.4 km/s), even though the peak thermal velocity (about 0.5 km/s) is well below it. These atoms can escape if they are moving in the right direction (upward) and don't collide with other particles on their way out. (Once these atoms escape, ongoing collisions redistribute the speeds of the remaining atoms, so that the shape of the distribution remains the same and the same small fraction always exceeds escape velocity.) The time it takes for a gas to completely escape depends on how its peak thermal velocity compares to the escape velocity. As a rule of thumb, a peak thermal velocity above about 20% of the escape velocity will allow the gas to be completely lost to space within a few billion years—which is less than the age of our solar system.

EXAMPLE: Why does the Moon's exosphere contain sodium atoms but virtually no hydrogen gas? Useful data: The Moon's daytime temperature is 400 K and its escape velocity is about 2.4 km/s; the mass of a hydrogen atom is 1.67×10^{-27} kg; the mass of a sodium atom is 3.84×10^{-26} kg (about 23 times the mass of a hydrogen atom).

SOLUTION:

Step 1 Understand: The rate of thermal escape depends on how each gas's peak thermal velocity compares to the escape velocity at the Moon's daytime temperature of 400 K. From Figure 1, we know the peak thermal velocity for sodium atoms (about 0.5 km/s). We need to find the peak thermal velocity for hydrogen atoms at the same temperature.

Step 2 Solve: We use the given formula and data to calculate the peak thermal velocity for hydrogen atoms at a temperature of 400 K:

$$v_{thermal\ (H\ atoms)} = \sqrt{\frac{2kT}{m_{H\ atom}}}$$

$$= \sqrt{\frac{2 \times (1.38 \times 10^{-23}\ \frac{joule}{K}) \times (400\ K)}{1.67 \times 10^{-27}\ kg}}$$

$$\approx 2600\ m/s = 2.6\ km/s$$

Step 3 Explain: The peak thermal velocity of the hydrogen atoms is 2.6 km/s, which is slightly *greater* than the Moon's escape velocity of 2.4 km/s. This tells us that hydrogen atoms quickly escape, which is why the Moon cannot retain hydrogen in its atmosphere. In contrast, the peak thermal velocity for sodium atoms (about 0.5 km/s) is only about 20% of the Moon's escape velocity, so their escape rate is slow, and they are continually replenished as micrometeorites, solar wind particles, and high-energy photons eject new sodium atoms from the Moon's surface. That is why the Moon has a thin sodium exosphere.

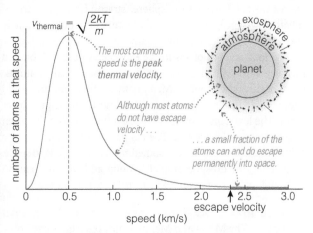

FIGURE 1 interactive figure In a gas at a given temperature, different atoms are always moving at different speeds. This plot shows the range of speeds of sodium atoms in the lunar atmosphere.

but its smaller size gives it a lower escape velocity; as a result, gases escape about as easily on both worlds.

The only ongoing source of gas on the Moon and Mercury is the surface ejection that occurs when micrometeorites, solar wind particles, or high-energy solar photons knock free surface atoms and molecules. This gas never accumulates because it is lost as quickly as it is gained. Some of the relatively few particles released from the surface are blasted upward fast enough to achieve escape velocity and therefore escape directly to space. The rest bounce around like tiny rubber balls, arcing hundreds of kilometers into the sky before crashing back down to the surface. Each gas particle typically bounces a few dozen times before being absorbed back into the surface.

Ice in Polar Craters There cannot be liquid water on the Moon or Mercury, because the lack of significant atmospheric pressure means that water cannot remain stable in liquid form. Daytime temperatures on both worlds are generally high enough that any water ice would long ago have sublimated into gas and escaped to space. However, scientists long wondered whether water ice might reside in permanently shadowed craters near the poles, deposited by comet impacts over millions of years.

For the Moon, the presence of polar ice was confirmed in 2009, when scientists sent the rocket from the *LCROSS* spacecraft crashing into a crater near the south pole. The debris that splashed upward revealed the presence of water vaporized from ice in the lunar soil. A radar sensor aboard India's *Chandrayaan-1* spacecraft detected ice deposits in similar craters near the Moon's north pole (**FIGURE 10.23**). More

surprisingly, other missions detected small amounts of water mixed into the upper layer of lunar soil over much of the lunar surface; the origin of this water is unknown. The evidence for ice in polar craters on Mercury is more limited, but scientists hope to learn more from ongoing observations by the *MESSENGER* spacecraft, which has been orbiting Mercury since 2011.

10.4 THE ATMOSPHERIC HISTORY OF MARS

One of our key goals in this chapter is to understand how and why the atmospheres of Venus, Earth, and Mars came to differ so profoundly, despite the fact that all three worlds must have had similar early atmospheres supplied by outgassing. We are now ready to focus on this question as we continue our atmospheric tour with Mars. Recall that Mars is only about 40% larger in radius than Mercury, but its surface reveals a much more fascinating and complex atmospheric history.

What is Mars like today?

The present-day surface of Mars looks much like deserts or volcanic plains on Earth (for example, see Figure 7.6). However, its thin atmosphere makes Mars quite different. The low atmospheric pressure—less than 1% of that on Earth's surface—explains why liquid water is unstable on the Martian surface [**Section 9.4**] and why visiting astronauts could not survive without a pressurized spacesuit. The atmosphere is made mostly of carbon dioxide, but the total amount of gas is so small that it creates only a weak greenhouse effect. The temperature is usually well below freezing, with a global average of about −50°C (−58°F). The lack of oxygen means that Mars lacks an ozone layer, so much of the Sun's damaging ultraviolet radiation passes unhindered to the surface.

While axis tilt is the only important influence on Earth's seasons, Mars's seasons are also affected by its orbit (**FIGURE 10.24**). Mars's more elliptical orbit puts it significantly closer to the Sun during southern hemisphere summer (and farther from the Sun during southern hemisphere winter), giving its southern hemisphere more extreme seasons—that is, shorter, warmer summers and longer, colder winters—than its northern hemisphere.

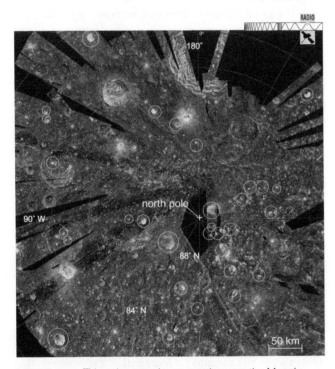

FIGURE 10.23 This radar map shows a region near the Moon's north pole, imaged by a NASA instrument on India's *Chandrayaan-1* spacecraft. The green circles represent craters in which water ice was detected. The ice lies at the bottoms of craters that are in perpetual shadow. Shadows are not visible since radar was used to take the image.

Seasons on Mars

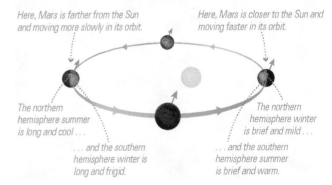

Here, Mars is farther from the Sun and moving more slowly in its orbit.

Here, Mars is closer to the Sun and moving faster in its orbit.

The northern hemisphere summer is long and cool . . .

The northern hemisphere winter is brief and mild . . .

. . . and the southern hemisphere winter is long and frigid.

. . . and the southern hemisphere summer is brief and warm.

FIGURE 10.24 The ellipticity of Mars's orbit makes seasons more extreme in the southern hemisphere than in the northern hemisphere.

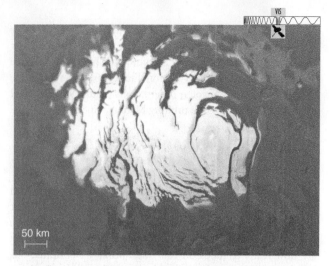

FIGURE 10.25 This image from the *Mars Global Surveyor* shows the residual south polar cap during summer. A layer of frozen carbon dioxide around 8 meters thick overlies a much thicker cap of water ice. In winter, the whole area shown in the image is covered in CO_2 frost.

Seasonal changes lead to several major features of Martian weather. Temperatures at the winter pole drop so low (about −130°C) that carbon dioxide condenses into "dry ice" at the winter polar cap. Meanwhile, frozen carbon dioxide at the summer pole sublimates into carbon dioxide gas, and by the peak of summer only a residual cap of water ice remains (FIGURE 10.25). The atmospheric pressure therefore increases at the summer pole and decreases at the winter pole. Overall, as much as one-third of the total carbon dioxide of the Martian atmosphere moves seasonally between the north and south polar caps.

The Martian Winds The strong winds associated with the cycling of carbon dioxide gas can initiate huge dust storms, particularly when the more extreme summer approaches in the southern hemisphere (FIGURE 10.26). At times, the Martian surface becomes almost completely obscured by airborne dust. As the dust settles out, it can change the surface appearance over vast areas (for example, by covering dark regions with brighter dust); such changes fooled astronomers of the past into thinking they were seeing seasonal changes in vegetation.

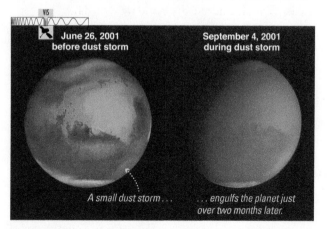

June 26, 2001
before dust storm

September 4, 2001
during dust storm

A small dust storm . . .

. . . engulfs the planet just over two months later.

FIGURE 10.26 These two Hubble Space Telescope photos contrast the appearance of the same face of Mars in the absence (left) and presence (right) of a global dust storm.

FIGURE 10.27 **interactive figure** This photograph shows a dust devil on Mars, photographed by the *Spirit* rover.

Martian winds can also spawn *dust devils*, swirling winds that you may have seen over desert sands or dry dirt on Earth. Dust devils look much like miniature tornadoes, but they rise up from the ground rather than coming down from the sky. The air in dust devils is heated from below by the sunlight-warmed ground; it swirls because of the way it interacts with prevailing winds. Dust devils on Mars are especially common during summer in either hemisphere. While many are quite small (FIGURE 10.27), some can be far larger than their counterparts on Earth.

Martian winds and dust storms leave Mars with perpetually dusty air, which helps explain the colors of the Martian sky. The air on Mars is so thin that, without suspended dust, the sky would be essentially black even in daytime. However, light scattered by the suspended dust tends to give the sky a yellow-brown color. Different hues can occur as the amount of suspended dust varies, and in the mornings and evenings.

Water Ice on Mars Although there is no liquid water on Mars today, there is a fair amount of water ice. The polar caps are made mostly of water ice, overlaid with a thin layer (at most a few meters thick) of CO_2 ice (see Figure 10.25). Radar instruments on *Mars Express* and the *Mars Reconnaissance Orbiter* have found substantial quantities of water frozen in vast layers of dusty ice surrounding both poles. Radar has even detected some icy glaciers well away from the poles; a protective layer of rocks and dust prevents the ice from sublimating away. Scientists sent the *Phoenix* lander to explore the north polar region in 2008 (FIGURE 10.28), and were surprised to discover that the spacecraft's landing rockets had exposed a patch of water ice, despite being hundreds of kilometers away from the polar cap itself. If all the water ice now known on Mars melted, it could make an ocean averaging about 10 meters deep over the planet. The fact that plenty of frozen water still remains on Mars makes it conceivable that some water is present in liquid form in underground locations where it is kept warm by volcanic heat.

Mars Climate and Axis Tilt The weather on Mars does not change much from one year to the next. However,

a The *Phoenix* lander used a robotic arm to scoop up Martian soil for analysis by on-board instruments. Results will help scientists determine whether and when Mars's polar regions may have been habitable.

b The robotic arm camera of the *Phoenix* lander found a bright patch of water ice underneath it. The spacecraft's landing rockets (visible at top) blasted away an overlying layer of dust.

FIGURE 10.28 The *Phoenix* lander.

FIGURE 10.29 The *Mars Reconnaissance Orbiter* captured this image of a landslide in layered terrain in the north polar region. Despite the dark appearance, water makes up the bulk of the material. Layers of dusty ice more than 700 meters thick built up over many cycles of climate change. During the northern spring of 2010, warming conditions apparently weakened the cliff walls and triggered landslides.

changes in its axis tilt probably cause Mars to undergo longer-term cycles of climate change. Theoretical calculations suggest that Mars's axis tilt varies far more than Earth's—from as little as 0° to 60° or more on time scales of hundreds of thousands to millions of years. This extreme variation arises for two reasons. First, Jupiter's gravity has a greater effect on the axis of Mars than on that of Earth, because Mars's orbit is closer to Jupiter's orbit. Second, Earth's axis is stabilized by the gravity of our relatively large Moon. Mars's two tiny moons, Phobos and Deimos (see Figure 8.11), are far too small to offer any stabilizing influence on its axis.

As we discussed earlier, changes in axis tilt affect both the severity of the seasons and the global average temperature. When Mars's axis tilt is small, the poles may stay in a perpetual deep freeze for tens of thousands of years. With more carbon dioxide frozen at the poles, the atmosphere becomes thinner, lowering the pressure and weakening the greenhouse effect. When the axis is highly tilted, the summer pole becomes much warmer, allowing substantial amounts of water ice to sublimate, along with carbon dioxide, into the atmosphere. The pressure therefore increases, and Mars becomes warmer as the greenhouse effect strengthens—although probably not by enough to allow liquid water to become stable at the surface. Changes in axis tilt may therefore destroy existing glaciers and create new ones at different latitudes. The Martian polar regions show layering of dust and

ice that probably reflects changes in climate due to the changing axis tilt (**FIGURE 10.29**). Small changes in the tilt over the last few million years may also be responsible for the formation of the gullies seen on many crater walls (see Figure 9.33).

Why did Mars change?

Mars's varying axis tilt may have had important effects on its climate, but it does not explain the most dramatic climate change in Martian history: the change from a world of flowing water to the cold and dry world we see today.

Past Climate on Mars The geological evidence discussed in Chapter 9 leaves little doubt that Mars had wetter and warmer periods, probably with rainfall, before about 3 billion years ago. The full extent of these periods is a topic of considerable scientific debate. Some scientists think that Mars may have been continuously warm and wet for much of its first billion years of existence. Others think that Mars may have had only intermittent periods of rainfall, perhaps triggered by the heat of large impacts, and that ancient lakes, ponds, or oceans may have been completely ice-covered. Either way, rain could have fallen only if temperatures were warm enough to keep water from freezing and the atmospheric pressure were high enough for liquid water to be stable. We conclude that Mars once must have had a much thicker atmosphere, with a much stronger greenhouse effect.

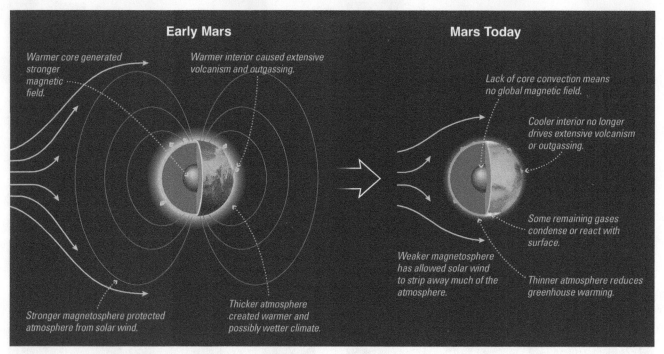

Early Mars

Warmer core generated stronger magnetic field.

Warmer interior caused extensive volcanism and outgassing.

Stronger magnetosphere protected atmosphere from solar wind.

Thicker atmosphere created warmer and possibly wetter climate.

Mars Today

Lack of core convection means no global magnetic field.

Cooler interior no longer drives extensive volcanism or outgassing.

Some remaining gases condense or react with surface.

Weaker magnetosphere has allowed solar wind to strip away much of the atmosphere.

Thinner atmosphere reduces greenhouse warming.

FIGURE 10.30 Some 3 billion years ago, Mars underwent dramatic climate change, ensuring that rain could never fall again.

The idea that Mars once had a much thicker atmosphere and stronger greenhouse effect makes sense. Calculations suggest that Martian volcanoes should have outgassed enough carbon dioxide to make the atmosphere about 400 times as dense as it is today, and enough water to fill oceans tens or even hundreds of meters deep. Moreover, computer simulations show that if Mars had that much carbon dioxide today, its greenhouse effect would make it warm enough to allow for liquid water, and the pressure would be great enough for the water to remain stable. However, because the Sun was dimmer in the distant past (see Figure 10.18), even more greenhouse warming would have been needed to allow for liquid water when Mars was young. Current models are unable to account for the necessary additional warming with carbon dioxide gas alone, but additional greenhouse warming may have been provided by carbon dioxide ice clouds or atmospheric methane.

Loss of Atmospheric Gas The bigger question is not whether Mars once had a denser atmosphere, but what happened to it. Mars must somehow have lost most of its carbon dioxide gas. This loss would have weakened the greenhouse effect until the planet essentially froze over. Some of the carbon dioxide condensed and became part of the polar caps. Some may be chemically bound into **carbonate rocks** (rocks rich in carbon and oxygen), according to recent finds by Mars orbiters and rovers. But the bulk of the gas was probably lost to space.

The precise way in which Mars lost its carbon dioxide gas is not clear, but the leading hypothesis suggests a close link to a change in Mars's magnetic field (**FIGURE 10.30**). Early in its history, Mars probably had molten, convecting metals in its core, much like Earth today. The combination of this convecting metal with Mars's rotation should have

produced a magnetic field and a protective magnetosphere. However, the magnetic field would have weakened as the small planet cooled and core convection ceased, leaving atmospheric gases vulnerable to being stripped into space by solar wind particles. This hypothesis will be put to the test by the orbiting *MAVEN* mission, scheduled for launch in late 2013, which will measure the escape of gases from Mars's atmosphere today and thereby help us understand past gas loss as well.

With regard to water, although some lies frozen in the polar caps and underground, much of the water once present on Mars is also probably gone for good. Like the carbon dioxide, some water vapor may have been stripped away by the solar wind. However, Mars also lost water in another way. Because Mars lacks an ultraviolet-absorbing stratosphere, atmospheric water molecules would have been easily broken apart by ultraviolet photons. The hydrogen atoms that broke away from the water molecules would have been lost rapidly to space through thermal escape. With these hydrogen atoms gone, the water molecules could not be made whole again. Initially, oxygen from the water molecules would have remained in the atmosphere, but over time this oxygen was lost, too. Some was probably stripped away by the solar wind, and the rest was drawn out of the atmosphere through chemical reactions with surface rock. This process literally rusted the Martian rocks, giving the "red planet" its distinctive tint.

THINK ABOUT IT

Some people have proposed "terraforming" Mars—that is, making it more Earth-like—by finding a way to release all the carbon dioxide frozen in its polar caps into its atmosphere. If Mars had oceans in the distant past, could this release of gas allow it to have oceans again? Why or why not?

Size as the Critical Factor Summarizing these ideas, we conclude that Mars's fate was shaped primarily by its relatively small size. It was big enough for volcanism and outgassing to release plenty of water and atmospheric gas early in its history, but too small to maintain the internal heat needed to keep this water and gas. As its interior cooled, its volcanoes quieted and released far less gas, while its relatively weak gravity and the loss of its magnetic field allowed existing gas to be stripped away to space. If Mars had been as large as Earth, so that it could still have outgassing and a global magnetic field, it might still have a moderate climate today. Mars's distance from the Sun helped seal its fate: Even with its small size, Mars might still have some flowing water if it were significantly closer to the Sun, where the extra warmth could melt the water that remains frozen underground and at the polar caps.

The history of the Martian atmosphere holds important lessons for us on Earth. Mars apparently was once a world with more moderate temperatures and streams, rain, glaciers, lakes, and possibly oceans. It had all the necessities for life as we know it. But this once-hospitable planet turned into a frozen and barren desert at least 3 billion years ago, and it is unlikely that Mars will ever again be warm enough for its frozen water to flow. Any life that may have existed on Mars is either extinct or hidden away in a few choice locations, such as in underground water near not-quite-dormant volcanoes. As we consider the possibility of future climate change on Earth, Mars presents us with an ominous example of how drastically things can change.

10.5 THE ATMOSPHERIC HISTORY OF VENUS

Venus (**FIGURE 10.31**) presents a stark contrast to Mars, but it is easy to understand why: Its larger size allowed it to retain more interior heat, leading to greater volcanism. The associated outgassing released the vast quantities of carbon dioxide that create Venus's strong greenhouse effect.

Venus becomes more mysterious when we compare it to Earth. Because Venus and Earth are so similar in size, we might naively expect both planets to have had similar atmospheric histories. Clearly, this is not the case. In this section, we'll explore how Venus's atmosphere ended up so different from Earth's, and in the process we'll learn important lessons about the habitability of our own planet.

What is Venus like today?

If you stood on the surface of Venus, you'd feel a searing heat hotter than that of a self-cleaning oven and a tremendous pressure 90 times greater than that on Earth. A deep-sea diver would have to go nearly 1 kilometer (0.6 mile) beneath the ocean surface on Earth to feel comparable pressure. Venus's atmosphere consists almost entirely of carbon dioxide (CO_2). It has virtually no molecular oxygen (O_2), so you could not breathe the air even if you cooled it to a comfortable temperature.

Moving through the thick air near Venus's surface would feel like a cross between swimming and flying: Its density is

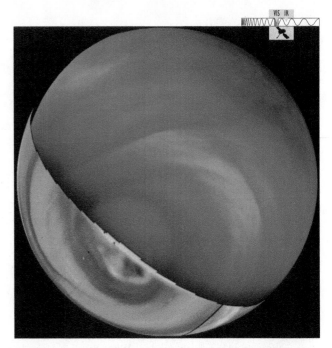

FIGURE 10.31 This composite image from the *Venus Express* spacecraft combines a visible-wavelength image of the day side (left, shaded red) and an infrared image of the night side (right, shaded blue). Venus's south pole lies at the center. At most wavelengths, clouds completely prevent any view of the surface.

about 10% that of water. Looking upward, you'd see a perpetually overcast sky, with only weak sunlight filtering through the thick clouds above. Because the thick atmosphere scatters nearly all the blue light away, the dimly lit sky appears reddish-orange in color.

The weather forecast for the surface of Venus today and every day is dull, dull, dull. Venus's slow rotation (243 Earth days) means a very weak Coriolis effect. As a result, Venus has little wind on its surface and never has hurricane-like storms. The top wind speeds measured by the Soviet Union's *Venera* landers were only about 6 kilometers per hour. No rain falls, because droplets that form and fall from the cool upper atmosphere evaporate long before they reach the ground. The weak Coriolis effect also means that Venus's atmosphere has just two large circulation cells, much like what Earth would have if rotation didn't split its cells (see Figure 10.13). The thick atmosphere makes the circulation so efficient at transporting heat from the equator to the poles that the surface temperature is virtually the same everywhere: The poles are no cooler than the equator, and night is just as searingly hot as day. Moreover, Venus has no seasons because it has virtually no axis tilt,* so temperatures are the same year-round.

The weather is much more interesting at high altitudes. Strong convection drives hot air upward; high in the troposphere, where the temperature is 400°C cooler than on the surface (see Figure 10.10), sulfuric acid (H_2SO_4) condenses into droplets that create Venus's bright, reflective clouds. The droplets sometimes fall through the upper troposphere as

---

*In tables (such as Table 7.1), Venus's axis tilt is usually written as 177.3°. This may sound large, but notice that it is nearly 180°—the same tilt as 0° but "upside down." It is written this way because Venus rotates backward compared to its orbit, and backward rotation is equivalent to forward rotation that is upside down.

sulfuric acid rain, but they evaporate at least 30 kilometers above the surface. Moreover, high-altitude winds circle the planet in just 4 days—much faster than the planet rotates. No one knows why these fast winds blow, but they are responsible for the dynamic cloud patterns visible in Figure 10.31.

How did Venus get so hot?

It's tempting to attribute Venus's high surface temperature solely to the fact that Venus is closer than Earth to the Sun, but Venus would actually be quite cold without its strong greenhouse effect, because its bright clouds reflect much more sunlight than Earth (see Table 10.2). The real question is why Venus has such a strong greenhouse effect.

The simple answer is that Venus has a huge amount of carbon dioxide in its atmosphere—nearly 200,000 times as much as in Earth's atmosphere. However, a deeper question still remains. Given their similar sizes and compositions, we expect Venus and Earth to have had similar levels of volcanic outgassing, and the released gas ought to have had about the same composition on both worlds. Why, then, is Venus's atmosphere so different from Earth's?

The Fate of Outgassed Water and Carbon Dioxide

We expect that huge amounts of water vapor and carbon dioxide should have been outgassed into the atmospheres of both Venus and Earth. Venus's atmosphere does indeed have an enormous amount of carbon dioxide, but it has virtually no water. Earth's atmosphere has very little of either gas. We conclude that Venus must have somehow lost its outgassed water, while Earth lost both water vapor and carbon dioxide. But how were these gases lost?

We can easily account for the missing gases on Earth. The huge amounts of water vapor released into our atmosphere condensed into rain, forming our oceans. In other words, the water is still here, but mostly in liquid rather than gaseous form. The huge amount of carbon dioxide released into our atmosphere is also still here, but in solid form: Carbon dioxide dissolves in water, where it can undergo chemical reactions to make carbonate rocks such as limestone. Earth has about 170,000 times as much carbon dioxide locked up in rocks as in its atmosphere—which means that Earth does indeed have almost as much total carbon dioxide as Venus. Of course, the fact that Earth's carbon dioxide is mostly in rocks rather than in the atmosphere makes all the difference in the world: If this carbon dioxide were in our atmosphere, our planet would be nearly as hot as Venus and certainly uninhabitable.

We are left with the question of what happened to Venus's water. Venus today is incredibly dry. It is far too hot to have any liquid water or ice on its surface; it is even too hot for water to be chemically bound in surface rock, and any water deeper in its crust or mantle was probably baked out long ago. Measurements also show very little water in the atmosphere. Overall, the total amount of water on Venus is about 10,000 times smaller than the total amount on Earth, a fact that explains why Venus retains so much carbon dioxide in its atmosphere: Without oceans, carbon dioxide cannot dissolve or become locked away in carbonate rocks. If it is true that a huge amount of water was outgassed on Venus, it has somehow disappeared.

The leading hypothesis for the disappearance of Venus's water invokes one of the same processes thought to have removed water from Mars. Ultraviolet light from the Sun broke apart water molecules in Venus's atmosphere. The hydrogen atoms then escaped to space (through thermal escape), ensuring that the water molecules could never re-form. The oxygen from the water molecules was lost to a combination of chemical reactions with surface rocks and stripping by the solar wind; Venus's lack of a magnetic field leaves its atmosphere vulnerable to the solar wind.

Acting over billions of years, the breakdown of water molecules and the escape of hydrogen can easily explain the loss of an ocean's worth of water from Venus, and careful study of Venus's atmospheric composition offers evidence that such a loss really occurred. Recall that most hydrogen nuclei contain just a single proton, but a tiny fraction of all hydrogen atoms (about 1 in 6400 measured in Earth's oceans) contain a neutron in addition to the proton, making the isotope of hydrogen that we call *deuterium*. Water molecules that contain one or two atoms of deuterium instead of hydrogen (called *heavy water*) behave chemically just like ordinary water and can be broken apart by ultraviolet light just as easily. However, a deuterium atom is twice as heavy as an ordinary hydrogen atom and therefore does not escape to space as easily when the water molecule is broken apart. If Venus lost a huge amount of hydrogen from water molecules to space, the rare deuterium atoms would have been more likely to remain behind than the ordinary hydrogen atoms. Measurements show that this is the case: The fraction of deuterium among hydrogen atoms is a hundred times higher on Venus than on Earth, suggesting that a substantial amount of water was lost by having its molecules broken apart and its hydrogen lost to space. We cannot determine exactly how much water Venus has lost, but it seems plausible that Venus really did outgas as much water as Earth and then lost virtually all of it.

Of course, Venus could have lost all this water only if it had been in the atmosphere as water vapor, where ultraviolet light could break the molecules apart, rather than in liquid oceans like the water on Earth. Our quest to understand Venus's high temperature therefore leads to one more question: Why didn't Venus, like Earth, end up with oceans to trap its carbon dioxide in carbonate rocks and prevent its water from being lost to space?

The Runaway Greenhouse Effect To understand why Venus does not have oceans, we need to consider the role of **feedback processes**—processes in which a change in one property amplifies (positive feedback) or counteracts (negative feedback) the behavior of the rest of the system. You are probably familiar with feedback processes in daily life. For example, if someone brings a microphone too close to a loudspeaker, it picks up and amplifies small sounds from the speaker. These amplified sounds are again picked up by the microphone and further amplified, causing a loud screech.

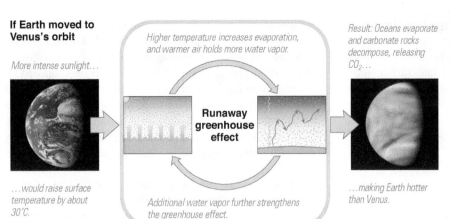

If Earth moved to Venus's orbit

More intense sunlight...

...would raise surface temperature by about 30°C.

Higher temperature increases evaporation, and warmer air holds more water vapor.

Runaway greenhouse effect

Additional water vapor further strengthens the greenhouse effect.

Result: Oceans evaporate and carbonate rocks decompose, releasing CO₂...

...making Earth hotter than Venus.

FIGURE 10.32 This diagram shows how, if Earth were placed at Venus's distance from the Sun, the runaway greenhouse effect would cause the oceans to evaporate completely.

This sound feedback is an example of *positive feedback,* because it automatically amplifies itself. The screech usually leads to a form of *negative feedback:* The embarrassed person holding the microphone moves away from the loudspeaker, thereby stopping the positive sound feedback.

THINK ABOUT IT

Think of at least one other everyday example each for positive feedback and negative feedback.

With the idea of feedback in mind, let's consider what would happen if we could magically move Earth to the orbit of Venus (**FIGURE 10.32**). The greater intensity of sunlight would almost immediately raise Earth's global average temperature by about 30°C, from its current 15°C to about 45°C (113°F). Although this is still well below the boiling point of water, the higher temperature would lead to increased evaporation of water from the oceans. The higher temperature would also allow the atmosphere to hold more water vapor before the vapor condensed to make rain. The combination of more evaporation and greater atmospheric capacity for water vapor would substantially increase the total amount of water vapor in Earth's atmosphere. Now, remember that water vapor, like carbon dioxide, is a greenhouse gas. The added water vapor would therefore strengthen the greenhouse effect, driving temperatures a little higher. The higher temperatures, in turn, would lead to even more ocean evaporation and more water vapor in the atmosphere, strengthening the greenhouse effect even further. In other words, we'd have a positive feedback process in which each little bit of additional water vapor in the atmosphere would lead to higher temperature and even more water vapor. The process would rapidly spin out of control, resulting in a **runaway greenhouse effect**.

The runaway greenhouse effect would cause Earth to heat up until the oceans were completely evaporated and the carbonate rocks had released all their carbon dioxide back into the atmosphere. By the time the runaway process was complete, temperatures on our "moved Earth" would be even higher than they are on Venus today, thanks to the combined greenhouse effects of carbon dioxide and water vapor in the atmosphere. The water vapor would then gradually disappear, as ultraviolet light broke

water molecules apart and the hydrogen escaped to space. In short, moving Earth to Venus's orbit would essentially turn our planet into another Venus.

We have arrived at a simple explanation of why Venus is so much hotter than Earth. Even though Venus is only about 30% closer to the Sun than Earth is, this difference was critical. On Earth, it was cool enough for water to rain down to make oceans. The oceans dissolved carbon dioxide and chemical reactions locked it away in carbonate rocks, leaving our atmosphere with only enough greenhouse gases to make our planet pleasantly warm. On Venus, the greater intensity of sunlight made it just warm enough that oceans either never formed or soon evaporated, leaving Venus with a thick atmosphere full of greenhouse gases.

The next time you see Venus shining brightly as the morning or evening "star," consider the radically different path it has taken from Earth—and thank your lucky star. If Earth had formed a bit closer to the Sun, or if the Sun had been slightly hotter, our planet might have suffered the same greenhouse-baked fate.

THINK ABOUT IT

We've seen that moving Earth to Venus's orbit would cause our planet to become Venus-like. If we could somehow move Venus to Earth's orbit, would it become Earth-like? Why or why not?

A Pleasant Early Venus? Venus's closeness to the Sun may have sealed its ultimate fate, but it's possible that Venus might have been more moderate in its early history. Recall that the Sun has gradually brightened with age; some 4 billion years ago, the intensity of sunlight shining on the young Venus was not much greater than it is on Earth today. Rain might have fallen, and oceans could have formed. It's even conceivable that life could have arisen on the young Venus.

As the Sun gradually brightened, however, any liquid water or life on Venus was doomed. The runaway greenhouse effect raised the temperature so high that all the water evaporated. In the upper atmosphere, ultraviolet light broke apart the water molecules, and the hydrogen escaped to space. If Venus had oceans in its youth, the water is now gone forever.

We'll probably never know for sure whether Venus ever had oceans. The global "repaving" of Venus's surface by tectonics and volcanism [**Section 9.5**] would long ago have covered up any shorelines or other geological evidence of past oceans, and the high surface temperatures would have baked out any gases that might once have been incorporated into surface rock. If the climate once was pleasant, it's unlikely that any evidence survives to tell the tale.

10.6 EARTH'S UNIQUE ATMOSPHERE

Earth's atmosphere, composed mostly of nitrogen and oxygen, makes our lives possible. It provides our planet with just enough warmth and pressure to enable water to cycle among all three phases (solid ice, liquid water, and gaseous water vapor), it protects us from harmful solar radiation, and it produces the weather patterns that variously bring us days of sunshine, clouds, and rain or snow. In this section, we'll discuss how and why our atmosphere is so hospitable—and how we humans may be altering the very balances upon which we depend for survival.

How did Earth's atmosphere end up so different?

As we've seen, most of the major physical differences in the atmospheres of the terrestrial planets are easy to understand. For example, the Moon and Mercury lack substantial atmospheres because of their small sizes, while a very strong greenhouse effect causes the high surface temperature on Venus. In contrast, differences in atmospheric composition seem more surprising, because outgassing should have released the same gases on Venus, Earth, and Mars. How, then, did Earth's atmosphere end up so different? We can break down this general question into four separate questions:

1. Why did Earth retain most of its outgassed water—enough to form vast oceans—while Venus and Mars lost theirs?

2. Why does Earth have so little carbon dioxide (CO_2) in its atmosphere compared to Venus, when Earth should have outgassed about as much of it as Venus?

3. Why is Earth's atmosphere composed primarily of nitrogen (N_2) and oxygen (O_2), when these gases are only trace constituents in the atmospheres of Venus and Mars?

4. Why does Earth have an ultraviolet-absorbing stratosphere, while Venus and Mars do not?

Water and Carbon Dioxide We have already answered the first two questions in our discussions of the atmospheres of Mars and Venus. On Mars, some of the outgassed water was lost after solar ultraviolet light broke water vapor molecules apart, and the rest froze and may remain in the polar caps or underground. On Venus, it was too hot for water vapor to condense, so virtually all the water molecules were ultimately broken apart, allowing the hydrogen atoms to escape to space. Earth retained its outgassed water because temperatures were low enough for water vapor to condense into rain and

form oceans. Evidence from tiny mineral grains suggests that Earth may have had oceans as early as 4.3–4.4 billion years ago. The oceans, in turn, explain the low level of carbon dioxide in our atmosphere. Most of the carbon dioxide outgassed by volcanism on Earth dissolved in the oceans, where chemical reactions turned it into carbonate rocks. Even today, about 60 times as much carbon dioxide is dissolved in the oceans as is present in the atmosphere, and carbonate rocks contain some 170,000 times as much CO_2 as the atmosphere.

Nitrogen, Oxygen, and Ozone Turning our attention to the third question, it's relatively easy to explain the substantial nitrogen content (77%) of our atmosphere. Nitrogen is the third most common gas released by outgassing, after water vapor and carbon dioxide. Because most of Earth's water ended up in the oceans and most of the carbon dioxide ended up in rocks, our atmosphere was left with nitrogen as its dominant ingredient.

The oxygen content (21%) is a little more mysterious. Molecular oxygen (O_2) is not a product of outgassing or any other geological process. Moreover, oxygen is a highly reactive chemical that is easily removed from the atmosphere. Fire, rust, and the discoloration of freshly cut fruits and vegetables are everyday examples of chemical reactions that remove oxygen from the atmosphere (called *oxidation reactions*). Similar reactions between oxygen and surface materials (especially iron-bearing minerals) give rise to the reddish appearance of much of Earth's rock and clay, including the beautiful reds of Arizona's Grand Canyon. Without continual replenishment, these types of chemical reactions would remove all the oxygen in Earth's atmosphere in just a few million years. We must therefore explain not only how oxygen got into Earth's atmosphere in the first place, but how it is replenished as chemical reactions remove it.

The answer to the oxygen mystery is *life* (FIGURE 10.33). Plants and many microorganisms release oxygen through photosynthesis. Photosynthesis takes in CO_2 and, through a complex chain of chemical reactions, releases O_2. Because chemical reactions can remove oxygen, it took a long time for oxygen to accumulate in Earth's atmosphere. According

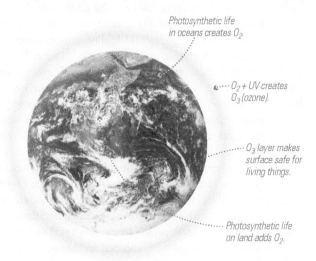

Photosynthetic life in oceans creates O_2.

O_2 + UV creates O_3 (ozone).

O_3 layer makes surface safe for living things.

Photosynthetic life on land adds O_2.

FIGURE 10.33 The origin of oxygen and ozone in Earth's atmosphere.

to present evidence, it took at least a billion years of photosynthesis before the buildup of atmospheric oxygen began, and Earth's atmosphere probably has had enough oxygen for us to breathe only for the past few hundred million years [**Section 24.1**]. If you had a time machine and spun the dial to arrive randomly at any point in Earth's past, there's only about a 1 in 10 chance that you would arrive at a time when you'd be able to breathe the air. Today, plants and single-celled photosynthetic organisms return oxygen to the atmosphere in approximate balance with the rate at which animals and chemical reactions consume oxygen, keeping the oxygen levels relatively steady.

THINK ABOUT IT

Suppose that, somehow, all photosynthetic life on Earth died out. What would happen to the oxygen in our atmosphere? Could animals, including us, still survive?

Life and oxygen also explain the presence of Earth's ultraviolet-absorbing stratosphere. In the upper atmosphere, chemical reactions involving solar ultraviolet light transform some of the O_2 into molecules of O_3, or ozone. The O_3 molecule is more weakly bound than the O_2 molecule, which allows it to absorb solar ultraviolet energy even better. The absorption of solar energy by ozone heats the upper atmosphere, creating the stratosphere. This ozone layer prevents harmful ultraviolet radiation from reaching the surface. Mars and Venus lack photosynthetic life and therefore have too little O_2, and consequently too little ozone, to form a stratosphere.

Maintaining Balance We have answered all four basic questions about Earth's atmosphere. However, a deeper look at what we have learned still leaves us with a major mystery. Our oceans exist because Earth has a greenhouse effect that is "just right" to keep them from either freezing or boiling away, and the presence of liquid water allowed life to arise and produce oxygen. But *why* does the amount of carbon dioxide in our atmosphere stay "just right"? For example, why didn't the chemical reactions either remove *all* the carbon dioxide or leave so much of it that the oceans would boil away? The long-term existence of Earth's oceans tells us that our planet has enjoyed remarkable climate stability—presenting a stark contrast to the dramatic climate changes that apparently occurred on Mars and Venus.

Why does Earth's climate stay relatively stable?

Earth's long-term climate stability has clearly been important to the ongoing evolution of life—and hence to our own relatively recent arrival as a species (see Figure 1.11). Had our planet undergone a runaway greenhouse effect like Venus, life would certainly have been extinguished. If Earth had suffered loss of atmosphere and a global freezing like Mars, any surviving life would have been driven to hide in underground pockets of liquid water.

Earth's climate is not perfectly stable—our planet has endured numerous ice ages and warm periods in the past. Nevertheless, even in the coldest ice ages and warmest warm periods, Earth's temperature has remained in a range in which some liquid water could still exist and harbor life. This long-term climate stability is even more remarkable when you remember that the Sun has brightened substantially over the past 4 billion years, yet Earth's temperature has managed to stay in nearly the same range throughout this time. Apparently, the strength of the greenhouse effect self-adjusts to keep the climate stable. How does it do this?

The Carbon Dioxide Cycle The mechanism by which Earth self-regulates its temperature is called the **carbon dioxide cycle**, or the **CO_2 cycle** for short. Let's follow the cycle as illustrated in FIGURE 10.34, starting at the top center:

- Atmospheric carbon dioxide dissolves in rainwater, creating a mild acid.
- The mildly acidic rainfall erodes rocks on Earth's continents, and rivers carry the broken-down minerals to the oceans.
- In the oceans, calcium from the broken-down minerals combines with dissolved carbon dioxide and falls to the ocean floor, making carbonate rocks such as limestone.*
- Over millions of years, the conveyor belt of plate tectonics (see Figure 9.39) carries the carbonate rocks to subduction zones, where they are carried downward.
- As they are pushed deeper into the mantle, some of the subducted carbonate rocks melt and release their carbon dioxide, which then outgasses back into the atmosphere through volcanoes.

*During the past half billion years or so, the carbonate minerals have been made by shell-forming sea animals, falling to the bottom in the seashells left after the animals die. Without the presence of animals, chemical reactions would do the same thing—and apparently did for most of Earth's history.

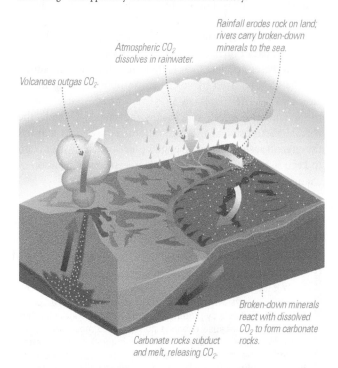

Rainfall erodes rock on land; rivers carry broken-down minerals to the sea.

Atmospheric CO_2 dissolves in rainwater.

Volcanoes outgas CO_2.

Broken-down minerals react with dissolved CO_2 to form carbonate rocks.

Carbonate rocks subduct and melt, releasing CO_2.

FIGURE 10.34 This diagram shows how the CO_2 cycle continually moves carbon dioxide from the atmosphere to the ocean to rock and back to the atmosphere. Note that plate tectonics (subduction in particular) plays a crucial role in the cycle.

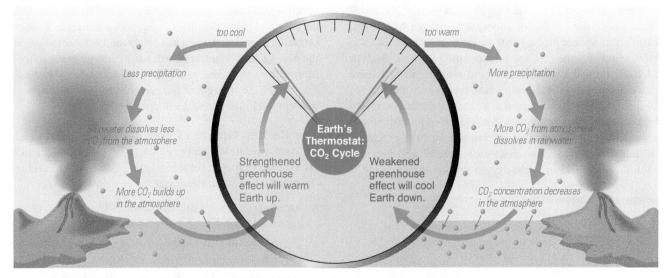

Strengthened greenhouse effect will warm Earth up.

Weakened greenhouse effect will cool Earth down.

Earth's Thermostat: CO₂ Cycle

too cool

Less precipitation

Rainwater dissolves less CO₂ from the atmosphere

More CO₂ builds up in the atmosphere

too warm

More precipitation

More CO₂ from atmosphere dissolves in rainwater

CO₂ concentration decreases in the atmosphere

FIGURE 10.35 The carbon dioxide cycle acts as a thermostat for Earth through negative feedback processes. Cool temperatures cause atmospheric CO_2 to increase, and warm temperatures cause atmospheric CO_2 to decline.

The CO_2 cycle acts as a long-term thermostat for Earth, because it has a built-in form of negative feedback that returns Earth's temperature toward "normal" whenever it warms up or cools down (FIGURE 10.35). The negative feedback occurs because the overall rate at which carbon dioxide is pulled from the atmosphere is very sensitive to temperature: the higher the temperature, the higher the rate at which carbon dioxide is removed.

Consider first what happens if Earth warms up a bit. The warmer temperature means more evaporation and rainfall, pulling more CO_2 out of the atmosphere. The reduced atmospheric CO_2 concentration leads to a weakened greenhouse effect, which counteracts the initial warming and cools the planet back down. Similarly, if Earth cools a bit, precipitation decreases and less CO_2 is dissolved in rainwater, allowing the CO_2 released by volcanism to build back up in the atmosphere. The increased CO_2 concentration strengthens the greenhouse effect and warms the planet. Overall, the natural thermostat of the carbon dioxide cycle has allowed the greenhouse effect to strengthen or weaken just enough to keep Earth's climate fairly stable, regardless of what other changes have occurred on our planet.

COMMON MISCONCEPTIONS

Ozone—Good or Bad?

Ozone often generates confusion, because in human terms it is sometimes good and sometimes bad. Near the ground, ozone is one of the main ingredients in urban air pollution, produced as a by-product of automobiles and industry. This is bad for us, because ozone is poisonous to most living creatures. In contrast, the ozone that exists naturally high above the ground, in the stratosphere, serves as a protective shield from the Sun's ultraviolet radiation. This ozone is therefore crucial to our survival, which is why the release of chemicals (such as chlorofluorocarbons, or CFCs) that destroy stratospheric ozone has been a significant environmental problem.

Ice Ages and Other Long-Term Climate Change

While Earth's climate has remained stable enough for the oceans to stay at least partly liquid throughout history, significant variations have still occurred. Such variations are possible because the CO_2 cycle does not act instantly. When something begins to change the climate, it takes time for the feedback mechanisms of the CO_2 cycle to come into play because of their dependence on the gradual actions of plate tectonics and mineral formation in the oceans. Calculations show that it takes hundreds of thousands of years for atmospheric CO_2 to stabilize through the CO_2 cycle. That is, if the amount of CO_2 in the atmosphere were to rise as a result of, say, increased volcanism, it would take some 400,000 years for the CO_2 cycle to restore temperatures to their current values.[*]

Ice ages occur when the global average temperature drops by a few degrees. The slightly lower temperatures lead to increased snowfall, which may cover continents with ice down to fairly low latitudes. For example, the northern United States was entirely covered with glaciers during the peak of the most recent ice age, which ended only about 10,000 years ago. The causes of ice ages are complex and not fully understood. Over periods of tens or hundreds of millions of years, the Sun's gradual brightening and the changing arrangement of the continents around the globe have at least in part influenced the climate. During the past few million years—a period too short for solar changes or continental motion to have a significant effect—the ice ages appear to have been strongly influenced by small changes in Earth's axis tilt and other characteristics of Earth's rotation and orbit (the Milankovitch cycles noted earlier).

---

[*]This time scale applies to ocean/atmosphere equilibrium only. The time scale for crust recycling is much longer, while shorter-term climate variations in atmospheric CO_2 concentration can occur through factors besides the inorganic CO_2 cycle, such as cycling of carbon dioxide by life.

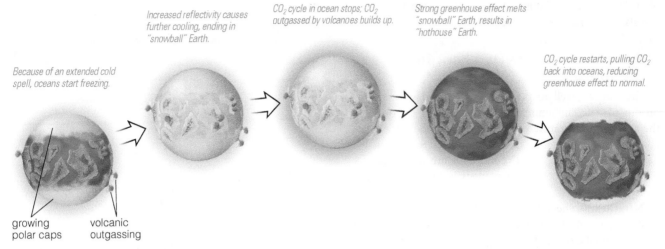

Because of an extended cold spell, oceans start freezing.

Increased reflectivity causes further cooling, ending in "snowball" Earth.

CO_2 cycle in ocean stops; CO_2 outgassed by volcanoes builds up.

Strong greenhouse effect melts "snowball" Earth, results in "hothouse" Earth.

CO_2 cycle restarts, pulling CO_2 back into oceans, reducing greenhouse effect to normal.

growing polar caps   volcanic outgassing

FIGURE 10.36 The CO_2 cycle rescues Earth from a "snowball" phase.

Geological evidence also points to several particularly long and deep ice ages between about 750 and 580 million years ago. During these periods, glaciers appear to have advanced all the way to the equator. Because ice can reflect up to about 90% of the sunlight hitting it, this increase in global ice would have set up a positive feedback process that would have cooled Earth even further. Geologists suspect that in this way our planet may have entered the periods we now call **snowball Earth** (FIGURE 10.36). We do not know why these episodes occurred or precisely how extreme the cold became. Some models suggest the positive feedback may have driven the global average temperature as low as –50°C (–58°F), causing the oceans to freeze to a depth of 1 kilometer or more. Other models suggest the oceans never froze completely, making Earth more of a "slushball" than a snowball. Either way, it seems that Earth became far colder during these periods than in more recent ice ages.

How did Earth recover from a "snowball" phase? The drop in surface temperature would not have affected Earth's interior heat, so volcanic outgassing would have continued to add CO_2 to the atmosphere. Oceans covered by ice would have been unable to absorb this CO_2 gas, which therefore would have accumulated in the atmosphere and strengthened the greenhouse effect. Eventually (perhaps after as long as 10 million years), the strengthening greenhouse effect would have warmed Earth enough to start melting the ice. The feedback processes that started the snowball Earth episode then moved in reverse. As the ice melted, more sunlight would have been absorbed (because liquid water absorbs more and reflects less sunlight than ice), warming the planet further. In fact, because the CO_2 concentration was so high, the warming would have continued well past current temperatures—perhaps taking the global average temperature to higher than 50°C (122°F). In just a few centuries, Earth would have emerged from a "snowball" phase into a "hothouse" phase. Geological evidence supports the occurrence of dramatic increases in temperature at the end of each snowball Earth episode. Earth then recovered over hundreds of thousands of years as the CO_2 cycle removed carbon dioxide from the atmosphere.

The snowball Earth episodes must have had severe consequences for any life on Earth at the time. Indeed, the end of the snowball Earth episodes roughly coincides with a dramatic increase in the diversity of life on Earth (the *Cambrian explosion* [**Section 24.1**]). Some scientists suspect that the environmental pressures caused by the snowball Earth periods may have led to a burst of evolution. If so, we might not be here today if not for Earth's dramatic climate changes.

Earth's Long-Term Future Climate Despite going through periods of ice ages, snowball Earth episodes, and hothouse phases, Earth's climate has remained suitable for life for some 4 billion years. However, the continuing brightening of the Sun will eventually overheat our planet.

According to some climate models, the warming Sun could cause Earth to begin losing its water as soon as a billion or so years from now. If so, then life on Earth has already completed about 75% of its history on this planet. However, there are enough uncertainties in the models to make it possible that they are wrong, and that the CO_2 cycle will keep the climate steady much longer. Either way, by about 3–4 billion years from now, the Sun will have grown so warm that sunlight on Earth will be as intense as it is on Venus today. The effect will be the same as if we moved Earth to Venus's orbit (see Figure 10.32)—a runaway greenhouse effect. Our planet will become a Venus-like hothouse, with temperatures far too high for liquid water to exist and all the CO_2 baked out of the rocks into the atmosphere.

In summary, Earth's habitability will cease between 1 and 4 billion years from now. Although this may seem depressing, remember that a billion years is a very long time—equivalent to some 10 million human lifetimes and far longer than humans have existed so far. If you want to lose sleep worrying about the future, there are far more immediate threats, including those that we will discuss next.

How is human activity changing our planet?

We humans are well adapted to the present-day conditions on our planet. The amount of oxygen in our atmosphere, the average temperature of our planet, and the ultraviolet-absorbing ozone layer are just what we need to survive. We have seen that these "ideal" conditions are no accident—they are consequences of our planet's unique geology and biology.

Nevertheless, the stories of the dramatic and permanent climate changes that occurred on Venus and Mars should teach us to take nothing for granted. Our planet may regulate its own climate quite effectively over long time scales, but fossil and geological evidence tells us that substantial and rapid changes in global climate can occur on shorter ones. In some cases, Earth's climate appears to have warmed several degrees Celsius in just decades. Evidence also shows that these past climate changes have had dramatic effects on local climates by raising or lowering sea level as much as tens of meters, altering ocean currents that keep coastlines warm, and transforming rainforests into deserts.

These past climate changes have been due to "natural" causes, such as small changes in Earth's tilt, major volcanic eruptions, the release of trapped carbon dioxide from oceans, and a variety of other geological processes. Today, however, Earth is apparently undergoing climate change for a new reason: Human activity is rapidly increasing the atmospheric concentration of carbon dioxide and other greenhouse gases. (The carbon dioxide cycle operates much too slowly to absorb these emissions on human time scales.) Effects of this increase in greenhouse gas concentration are already apparent: Global average temperatures have risen by about 0.8°C (1.4°F) in the past century (FIGURE 10.37). This **global warming** is one of the most important issues of our time.

Global Warming Global warming has been a hot political issue, both because some people debate its cause and because efforts to slow or stop the warming would require finding

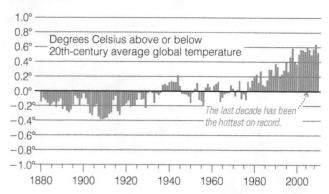

FIGURE 10.37 Average global temperatures from 1860 through 2011. Notice the clear global warming trend of the past few decades. (Data from the National Climate Data Center.)

new energy sources and making other changes that would dramatically affect the world's economy. However, a major research effort has gradually added to our understanding of the potential threat, particularly in the past two decades. The case linking global warming with human activity rests on three basic facts:

1. The greenhouse effect is a simple and well-understood scientific model. We can be confident in our understanding of it because it so successfully explains the observed surface temperatures of other planets. Given this basic model, there is no doubt that a rising concentration of greenhouse gases would make our planet warm up more than it would otherwise; the only debate is about how soon and how much.

2. The burning of fossil fuels and other human activities are clearly increasing the amounts of greenhouse gases in the atmosphere. Observations show that currently the atmospheric concentration of carbon dioxide is significantly higher (about 30%) than it has been at any time during the past million years, and it is rising rapidly (FIGURE 10.38). We can be confident that the rise is a result of human activity, because the atmosphere is becoming enriched in molecules of CO_2 carrying the distinct ratio of isotopes present in fossil fuels.

3. Climate models that ignore human activity fail to match the observed rise in global temperatures. In contrast, climate models that include the enhanced greenhouse effect from human production of greenhouse gases match the observed temperature trend quite well (FIGURE 10.39). Comparisons between observations and models therefore clearly indicate that global warming results from human activity.

These facts, summarized in FIGURE 10.40, offer convincing evidence that we humans are now tinkering with the climate in a way that may cause major changes not just in the distant future, but in our own lifetimes. The same models that convince scientists of the reality of human-induced global warming tell us that if current trends in the greenhouse gas concentration continue—that is, if we do nothing to slow our emissions of carbon dioxide and other greenhouse gases—the warming trend will continue to accelerate. By the end of this century, the models predict that the global average temperature would be

COMMON MISCONCEPTIONS

The Greenhouse Effect

The greenhouse effect is often in the news, usually in discussions about environmental problems, but in itself the greenhouse effect is not a bad thing. In fact, we could not exist without it, because it is responsible for keeping our planet warm enough for liquid water to flow in the oceans and on the surface. The "no greenhouse" temperature of Earth is well below freezing. Why, then, is the greenhouse effect discussed as an environmental problem? The reason is that human activity is adding more greenhouse gases to the atmosphere—and scientists agree that the additional gases are changing Earth's climate. While the greenhouse effect makes Earth livable, it is also responsible for the searing 470°C temperature of Venus—proving that it's possible to have too much of a good thing.

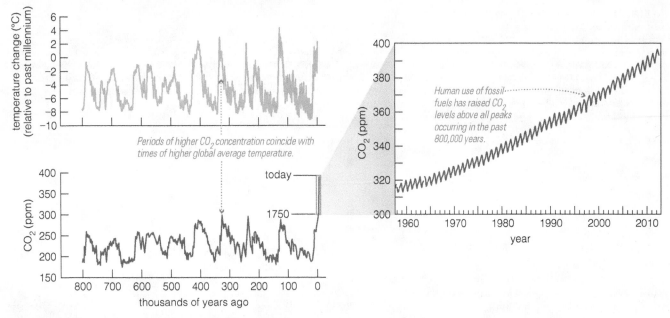

FIGURE 10.38 This diagram shows the atmospheric concentration of carbon dioxide and global average temperature over the past 800,000 years. Data for the past few decades come from direct measurements; earlier data come from studies of air bubbles trapped in Antarctic ice (ice core samples). The CO_2 concentration is measured in parts per million (ppm), which is the number of CO_2 molecules among every 1 million air molecules.

$3°C–5°C$ ($6°F–10°F$) higher than it is now, giving our children and grandchildren the warmest climate that any generation of *Homo sapiens* has ever experienced.

THINK ABOUT IT

Use Figure 10.38 to estimate the current rate at which the carbon dioxide concentration is rising. If the rise continues at the same rate, how long will it be until we reach a doubling of the pre-industrial-age concentration of 280 ppm? What if the rate of increase also rises, as it has over the past few years? Discuss the implications of your answer.

While the models tell us what general trends to expect, we do not expect them to precisely match Earth's behavior because of the complexity of the climate system. In particular, numerous feedback mechanisms can counter or enhance greenhouse warming on time scales of years, decades, and even centuries, and we don't yet understand all these mechanisms. For example, increased evaporation of ocean water can enhance the greenhouse effect because water vapor is also a greenhouse gas, but it can counter global warming if it causes the formation of more clouds (which can block sunlight from reaching the ground). Melting of polar ice, on the other hand, makes global warming even worse, because it changes the reflectivity of part of Earth's surface from high to low, leading to more absorption of solar energy.

Consequences of Global Warming A temperature increase of a few degrees might not sound so bad, but small changes in *average* temperature can lead to much more dramatic changes in climate patterns. These changes will cause some regions to warm much more than the average, while other regions may actually cool. Some regions might experience more rainfall or might become deserts.

Polar regions will warm the most, causing ice to melt. This is clearly threatening to the species of these regions (polar bears, which depend on an abundance of ice floes, are already endangered), but it also warms the oceans everywhere and changes their salt content as melting ice pours more fresh water into the sea. The fact that the waters of the Gulf of

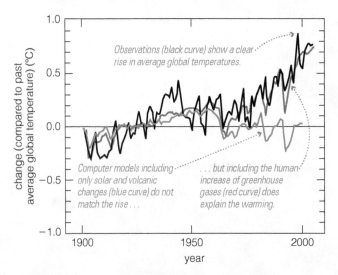

FIGURE 10.39 This graph compares observed temperature changes (black curve) with the predictions of climate models that include only natural factors such as changes in the brightness of the Sun and effects of volcanoes (blue curve) and models that also include the human contribution to increasing greenhouse gas concentration (red curve). Only the red curve matches the observations well. (The red and blue model curves are averages of many scientists' independent models of global warming, which generally agree with each other within $0.1°C–0.2°C$.)

Scientific studies of global warming apply the same basic approach used in all areas of science: We create models of nature, compare the predictions of those models with observations, and use our comparisons to improve the models. We have found that climate models agree more closely with observations if they include human production of greenhouse gases like carbon dioxide, making scientists confident that human activity is indeed causing global warming.

(1) The greenhouse effect makes a planetary surface warmer than it would be otherwise because greenhouse gases such as carbon dioxide, methane, and water vapor slow the escape of infrared light radiated by the planet. Scientists have great confidence in models of the greenhouse effect because they successfully predict the surface temperatures of Venus, Earth, and Mars.

(2) Human activity is adding carbon dioxide and other greenhouse gases to the atmosphere. While the carbon dioxide concentration also varies naturally, its concentration is now much higher than it has been at any time in the previous million years, and it is continuing to rise rapidly.

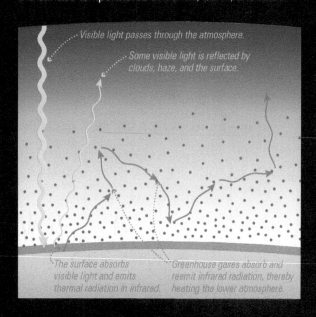

Visible light passes through the atmosphere.

Some visible light is reflected by clouds, haze, and the surface.

The surface absorbs visible light and emits thermal radiation in infrared.

Greenhouse gases absorb and reemit infrared radiation, thereby heating the lower atmosphere.

The graph shows that today's CO_2 levels are higher than at any point in the past 800,000 years.

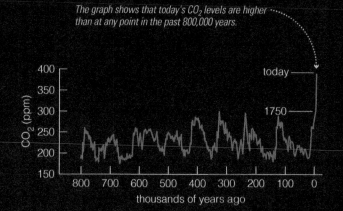

today

1750

thousands of years ago

Global Average Surface Temperature

Planet	Temperature Without Greenhouse Effect	Temperature With Greenhouse Effect
Venus	−40°C	470°C
Earth	−16°C	15°C
Mars	−56°C	−50°C

This table shows planetary temperatures as they would be without the greenhouse effect and as they actually are with it. The greenhouse effect makes Earth warm enough for liquid water and Venus hotter than a pizza oven.

3 Observations show that Earth's average surface temperature has risen during the last several decades. Computer models of Earth's climate show that an increased greenhouse effect triggered by CO_2 from human activities can explain the observed temperature increase.

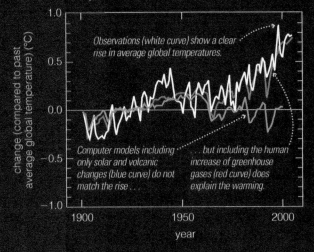

Observations (white curve) show a clear rise in average global temperatures.

Computer models including only solar and volcanic changes (blue curve) do not match the rise . . .

. . . but including the human increase of greenhouse gases (red curve) does explain the warming.

HALLMARK OF SCIENCE **Science progresses through creation and testing of models of nature that explain the observations as simply as possible.** Observations showing a rise in Earth's temperature demand a scientific explanation. Models that include an increased greenhouse effect due to human activity explain those observations better than models without human activity.

4 Models can also be used to predict the consequences of a continued rise in greenhouse gas concentrations. These models show that, without significant reductions in greenhouse gas emissions, we should expect further increases in global average temperature, rising sea levels, and more intense and destructive weather patterns.

This diagram shows the change in Florida's coastline that would occur if sea levels rose by 1 meter. Some models predict that this rise could occur within a century. The light blue regions show portions of the existing coastline that would be flooded.

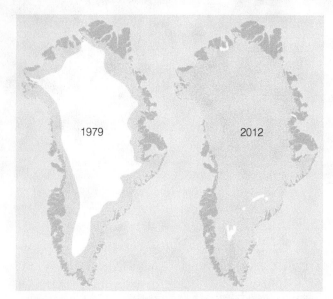

FIGURE 10.41 These maps contrast the extent of the year-round Greenland ice sheet, shown in white, in 1979 and 2012. The pink area indicates the region in which at least some melting occurred during the warm season. The melt region spanned at least 97% of the ice sheet during the extreme warming of 2012.

Mexico are at their warmest level in at least a century may be contributing to the greater strength of hurricanes that have recently blown through the Caribbean, though it is difficult to cite causes for specific storms. More generally, the greater overall warmth of the atmosphere will increase evaporation from the oceans, leading to more numerous and more intense storms; ironically, this fact means that global warming can lead to more severe winter blizzards. In some regions, spring is arriving earlier, which can lead to drier summers and greater wildfire risk. Some researchers also worry that the influx of large quantities of fresh water into the oceans may alter major ocean currents, such as the Gulf Stream—a "river" within the ocean that regulates the climate of western Europe and parts of the United States.

Melting polar ice may significantly increase sea level in the future, but global warming has already caused a rise in sea level for a different reason. Water expands very slightly as it warms—so slightly that we don't notice the change in a glass of water, but enough that sea level has risen some 20 centimeters in the past hundred years. This effect alone is likely to cause sea level to rise another 30 centimeters during this century, with potentially devastating effect on coastal communities and low-lying countries such as Bangladesh. The oceans are slow to

warm and expand; depending on how long it takes to stabilize greenhouse gases, the expansion could raise sea levels another 3 meters in subsequent centuries. The added effect of melting ice could increase sea level much more. While the melting of ice in the Arctic Ocean does not affect sea level—it is already floating—melting of landlocked ice does. Such melting appears to be occurring already. For example, the famous "snows" (glaciers) of Mount Kilimanjaro are rapidly retreating and may be gone within the next decade or so. More ominously, recent data suggest that the Greenland ice sheet is melting much more rapidly than models have predicted (**FIGURE 10.41**). If this trend continues, sea level could rise as much as several *meters*—enough to flood most of Florida—by the end of this century (see item 4 in Figure 10.40). Looking further ahead, complete melting of the polar ice caps would increase sea level by some 70 meters (more than 200 feet). Although such melting would probably take centuries or millennia, it suggests the disconcerting possibility that future generations will have to send deep-sea divers to explore the underwater ruins of many of our major cities.

Fortunately, most scientists believe that we still have time to avert the most serious consequences of global warming, provided that we dramatically and rapidly curtail our greenhouse gas emissions. The most obvious way to reduce these emissions is to improve energy efficiency. Doubling the average gas mileage of cars—which we could do easily with current technology—would immediately cut automobile-related carbon dioxide emissions in half. Other tactics could include replacing fossil fuels with alternative energy sources—such as biofuels, solar, wind, or nuclear energy—or finding ways to bury the carbon dioxide by-products of the fossil fuels that we still use. The key idea to keep in mind is that global warming is a global problem, and significant international cooperation will be required if we hope to solve it. But there is precedent for success: In the 1980s and 1990s, as we learned that human-produced chemicals (known as CFCs) were causing great damage to the ozone layer, the nations of the world agreed on a series of treaties that ultimately phased those chemicals out of production. As a result, the ozone layer is beginning to recover from its earlier damage, and we learned that people can be moved to act in the face of a threat to the environment on which we depend for survival.

THINK ABOUT IT

If you were a political leader, how would *you* deal with the threat of global warming?

The Big Picture

Putting Chapter 10 into Perspective

This chapter and the previous chapter have given us a complete "big picture" view of how the terrestrial worlds started out so similar yet ended up so different. As you continue your studies, keep in mind the following important ideas:

■ Atmospheres affect planets in many ways. They absorb and scatter light, distribute heat, and create the weather that can lead to erosion. Perhaps most important, the greenhouse effect

allows atmospheres to make a planet warmer than it would be otherwise.

■ Atmospheric properties differ widely among the terrestrial worlds, but we can trace these differences to root causes. For example, only the larger worlds have significant atmospheres. The smaller worlds lack the internal heat needed for volcanism and the outgassing that releases atmospheric gases, and they also lack the gravity necessary to retain these gases.

- The histories of Venus and Mars suggest that major climate change is the rule, not the exception. Mars was once warm and wet, but its small size and lack of a magnetic field caused it to lose gas and freeze over 3 billion or more years ago. Venus may once have had oceans, but its proximity to the Sun doomed it to a runaway greenhouse effect.

- We are here to talk about these things today only because Earth has managed to be the exception, a planet whose climate has remained relatively stable. We humans are ideally adapted to Earth today, but we have no guarantee that Earth will remain as hospitable in the future, especially as we tinker with the balance of greenhouse gases that has kept our climate stable.

SUMMARY OF KEY CONCEPTS

10.1 ATMOSPHERIC BASICS

- **What is an atmosphere?** An atmosphere is a layer of gas  that surrounds a world. It can create pressure, absorb and scatter sunlight, create wind and weather, interact with the solar wind to create a magnetosphere, and cause a **greenhouse effect** that can make a planet's surface warmer than it would be otherwise.

- **How does the greenhouse effect warm a planet?** 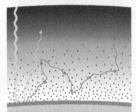 **Greenhouse gases** such as carbon dioxide, methane, and water vapor absorb infrared light emitted from a planet's surface. The absorbed photons are quickly reemitted, but in random directions. The result acts much like a blanket, warming the planet's surface.

- **Why do atmospheric properties vary with altitude?**  **Atmospheric structure** is determined by the way atmospheric gases interact with sunlight. On Earth, the basic structure consists of the **troposphere**, where most greenhouse warming occurs; the **stratosphere**, where **ozone** absorbs ultraviolet light from the Sun; the **thermosphere**, where solar X rays are absorbed; and the **exosphere**, the extremely low-density outer layer of the atmosphere.

10.2 WEATHER AND CLIMATE

- **What creates wind and weather?** **Global wind patterns** are shaped by atmospheric heating and the **Coriolis effect** caused by a planet's rotation. Convection in the troposphere can lead to the formation of clouds and rain, hail, or snow.

- **What factors can cause long-term climate change?** The four factors that cause climate change are solar brightening (noticeable only over many millions of years), changes in axis tilt, changes in reflectivity, and changes in greenhouse gas abundance.

- **How does a planet gain or lose atmospheric gases?**  Three sources of atmospheric gas are outgassing, evaporation or sublimation, and—on worlds with little atmosphere—surface ejection by tiny impacts of particles and photons. Four loss processes are condensation, chemical reactions with surface materials, the stripping of gas by the solar wind, and **thermal escape**.

10.3 ATMOSPHERES OF THE MOON AND MERCURY

- **Do the Moon and Mercury have any atmosphere?** The Moon and Mercury have only very thin exospheres consisting of gas particles released through surface ejection by micrometeorites, solar wind particles, and high-energy solar photons.

10.4 THE ATMOSPHERIC HISTORY OF MARS

- **What is Mars like today?** Mars is cold and dry, with an atmospheric pressure so low that liquid water is unstable; however, a substantial amount of water is frozen in and near the polar caps. Martian weather is driven largely by seasonal changes that cause carbon dioxide alternately to condense and sublimate at the poles, creating pole-to-pole winds and sometimes leading to huge dust storms.

- **Why did Mars change?** Mars's atmosphere must once have been much thicker with a stronger greenhouse effect, so change must have occurred due to loss of atmospheric gas. Much of the 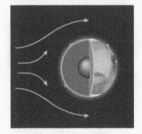 gas probably was stripped away by the solar wind, which was able to reach the atmosphere as Mars cooled and lost its magnetic field. Water was probably lost as ultraviolet light broke apart water molecules in the atmosphere, and the lightweight hydrogen then escaped to space.

10.5 THE ATMOSPHERIC HISTORY OF VENUS

- **What is Venus like today?** Venus has a thick carbon dioxide atmosphere that creates its strong greenhouse effect, explaining why it is so hot. It rotates slowly and therefore has a weak Coriolis effect and weak winds, and is far too hot for rain to fall. Its atmospheric circulation keeps temperatures about the same day and night, and its lack of axis tilt means no seasonal changes.

- **How did Venus get so hot?** Venus's distance from the Sun ultimately led to a **runaway greenhouse effect**: Venus became too hot to develop liquid oceans like those on Earth. Without oceans to dissolve outgassed carbon dioxide and lock it away in carbonate rocks, all of Venus's carbon dioxide remained in its atmosphere, creating its intense greenhouse effect.

10.6 EARTH'S UNIQUE ATMOSPHERE

■ **How did Earth's atmosphere end up so different?**
Temperatures on Earth were just right for outgassed water vapor to condense and form oceans. The oceans dissolve carbon dioxide and ultimately lock it away in carbonate rocks, keeping the greenhouse effect moderate. Nitrogen from outgassing remained in the atmosphere. Oxygen and ozone were produced by photosynthesis, which was possible because the moderate conditions allowed the origin and evolution of abundant life.

■ **Why does Earth's climate stay relatively stable?**

Earth's long-term climate is remarkably stable because of feedback processes that tend to counter any warming or cooling that occurs. The most important feedback process is the **carbon dioxide cycle**, which naturally regulates the strength of the greenhouse effect.

■ **How is human activity changing our planet?** Human activity is releasing carbon dioxide and other greenhouse gases into the atmosphere, and scientific evidence confirms that this

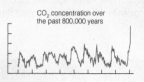

is causing **global warming**. This warming may have many consequences, including a rise in sea level, an increase in severity of storms, and dramatic changes in local climates.

VISUAL SKILLS CHECK

Use the following questions to check your understanding of some of the many types of visual information used in astronomy. Answers are provided in Appendix J. For additional practice, try the Chapter 10 Visual Quiz at MasteringAstronomy®.

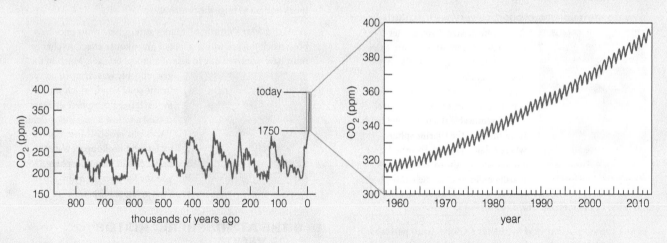

The graph above, a portion of Figure 10.38, shows the atmospheric concentration of carbon dioxide for the past 800,000 years. Use the information in the graph to answer the following questions.

1. Based on the graph, when was the maximum abundance of CO_2 over the past 800,000 years?
   a. about 300,000 years ago
   b. about 125,000 years ago
   c. 1750
   d. now

2. Today's CO_2 abundance is approximately ____ times the average value over the last 800,000 years.
   a. 17   b. 1.7   c. 1.17   d. 0.17

3. How would you describe the rapid variations in CO_2 on the inset graph on the right?
   a. The variations occur randomly every few years.
   b. The variations occur randomly every few months.

   c. The variations occur regularly every few years.
   d. The variations occur regularly every year.
   e. The variations occur regularly every few months.

4. Which physical mechanism is consistent with your answer to question 3?
   a. Major volcanic eruptions every decade or so place additional CO_2 in the atmosphere.
   b. Every few years, another huge coal-powered power plant opens up and produces more CO_2.
   c. Seasonal changes in plant growth produce a regular yearly variation in CO_2 levels, with the Northern Hemisphere (with much more land area) causing almost all the variation.

The graph below, the same as Figure 10.37, shows average global temperatures from 1860 through 2011 relative to the average temperature from the last century. Compare the graph below with the graph of CO_2 levels from questions 1–4.

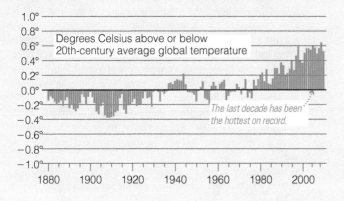

Degrees Celsius above or below 20th-century average global temperature

The last decade has been the hottest on record.

5. What is the relationship between the graph of global average temperatures and the graph of CO_2 levels? Focus on the period since about 1960.
   a. The warmest years correlate exactly with the years of greatest CO_2 abundance, indicating that CO_2 is the single most important factor controlling global temperature changes.
   b. The warmest years correlate roughly with the years of greatest CO_2 abundance, indicating that CO_2 is important but other factors also contribute to global temperature changes.
   c. The warmest years are not correlated with years of high CO_2 abundance, indicating that factors other than CO_2 have the most important effect on global temperature changes.

EXERCISES AND PROBLEMS

MasteringAstronomy®

For instructor-assigned homework go to MasteringAstronomy®.

REVIEW QUESTIONS

Short-Answer Questions Based on the Reading

1. Briefly describe the basic atmospheric characteristics of each of the five terrestrial worlds.
2. Use the balloon analogy to explain the origin of gas pressure. What is *atmospheric pressure*, and why does it decrease with altitude? What is 1 *bar* of pressure?
3. Is there any atmosphere at the orbital altitude of the Space Station? Explain.
4. What is the *greenhouse effect*? Describe how it warms a planet.
5. What factors determine a world's "no greenhouse" surface temperature? Explain the difference between "no greenhouse" and actual temperatures for each of the terrestrial worlds.
6. Describe Earth's basic *atmospheric structure*, from the ground up. How do interactions of sunlight and gases explain the existence of each of the atmospheric layers?
7. Why is the sky blue? Why are sunrises and sunsets red?
8. Why does convection occur in the *troposphere*, leading to active weather, but not in the *stratosphere*?
9. What is ozone? How does the absence of ozone on Venus and Mars explain why these planets lack a stratosphere?
10. What is a *magnetosphere*? Describe its role in protecting any atmosphere from the solar wind and in creating *auroras*.
11. What is the difference between *weather* and *climate*?
12. Describe Earth's *global wind patterns* and the role of *circulation cells*. How does rotation affect these cells?
13. What are clouds made of? How does rain or snow form?
14. Describe each of the four factors that can lead to long-term climate change.
15. Describe each process by which atmospheres gain or lose gas. What factors control *thermal escape*?
16. Why do the Moon and Mercury have so little atmospheric gas?
17. How and why do seasons on Mars differ from seasons on Earth?
18. Describe the leading hypothesis for how Mars lost atmospheric gas. What role does Mars's size play in this process?

19. What do we mean by a *runaway greenhouse effect*? Explain why this process occurred on Venus but not on Earth.
20. Describe four ways in which Earth's atmosphere is unique among the terrestrial worlds, and how each is important to our existence.
21. What is the *carbon dioxide cycle*, and why is it so crucial to life on Earth?
22. Briefly summarize the evidence linking human activity to *global warming*. What are its potential consequences?

TEST YOUR UNDERSTANDING

Does It Make Sense?

Decide whether the statement makes sense (or is clearly true) or does not make sense (or is clearly false). Explain clearly; not all these have definitive answers, so your explanation is more important than your chosen answer.

23. If Earth's atmosphere did not contain molecular nitrogen, X rays from the Sun would reach the surface.
24. If the molecular oxygen content of Earth's atmosphere increases, it will cause our planet to warm up.
25. Earth's oceans must have formed at a time when no greenhouse effect operated on Earth.
26. In the distant past, when Mars had a thicker atmosphere, it also had a stratosphere.
27. If Earth rotated faster, hurricanes would be more common and more severe.
28. Mars would still have seasons even if its orbit around the Sun were perfectly circular rather than elliptical.
29. Mars once may have been warmer than it is today, but it could never have been warmer than Earth.
30. If the solar wind were much stronger, Mercury might develop a carbon dioxide atmosphere.
31. If Earth had as much carbon dioxide in its atmosphere as Venus, our planet would not have oceans.
32. A planet in another solar system has no life but has an Earth-like atmosphere with plentiful oxygen.

Choose the best answer to each of the following. Explain your reasoning with one or more complete sentences.

33. Which terrestrial world has the most atmosphere? (a) Venus (b) Earth (c) Mars

34. The greenhouse effect occurs in the (a) troposphere. (b) stratosphere. (c) lithosphere.

35. What kind of light warms the stratosphere? (a) infrared (b) visible (c) ultraviolet

36. Which of the following is a strong greenhouse gas? (a) nitrogen (b) water vapor (c) oxygen

37. In which direction do hurricanes in the Southern Hemisphere rotate? (a) clockwise (b) counterclockwise (c) either direction

38. What is the leading hypothesis for Venus's lack of water? (a) Venus formed closer to the Sun and accreted very little water. (b) Its water is locked away in the crust. (c) Its water molecules were broken apart, and hydrogen was lost to space.

39. What kind of gas is most affected by thermal escape? (a) greenhouse gases (b) light gases (c) all gases equally

40. About what fraction of Earth's atmosphere is CO_2? (a) 90% (b) 1% (c) less than 0.1%

41. What causes the release of oxygen into Earth's atmosphere? (a) outgassing (b) evaporation/sublimation (c) photosynthesis

42. Where is most of the CO_2 that has outgassed from Earth's volcanoes? (a) in the atmosphere (b) in space (c) in rocks

PROCESS OF SCIENCE

Examining How Science Works

43. *Science with Consequences.* A small but vocal group of people still dispute that humans are causing global warming. Do some research to find the basis of their claims. Then defend or refute their findings based on your own studies and your understanding of the hallmarks of science discussed in Chapter 3.

44. *Unanswered Questions.* Choose one important but unanswered question about Mars's past, and write two or three paragraphs in which you discuss how we might answer this question in the future. Be as specific as possible, focusing on the type of evidence necessary to answer the question and how the evidence could be gathered. What are the benefits of finding answers to this question?

GROUP WORK EXERCISE

45. *Are We Causing Global Warming?* This exercise is intended to help you understand the scientific evidence behind the issue of global warming. Before you begin, assign the following roles to the people in your group: *Scribe* (takes notes on the group's activities), *Advocate* (argues in favor of the claim that human activity is causing global warming), *Skeptic* (points out weaknesses in the arguments made by the *Advocate*), and *Moderator* (leads group discussion and makes sure everyone contributes). **a.** Work together to make a list of scientific observations that have been proposed as evidence that humans are causing global warming. Your list should include, but is not limited to, the evidence in Figures 10.37–10.40. **b.** *Advocate* presents the case that humans are causing global warming, drawing on the evidence from part a. **c.** *Skeptic* attempts to refute *Advocate*'s case using scientific arguments. **d.** After hearing these arguments, *Moderator* and *Scribe* decide whose arguments were more persuasive and explain their reasoning. **e.** Each person in the group writes up a summary of the discussion.

INVESTIGATE FURTHER

In-Depth Questions to Increase Your Understanding

Short-Answer/Essay Questions

46. *Clouds of Venus.* Table 10.2 shows that Venus's surface temperature in the absence of the greenhouse effect is lower than Earth's, even though Venus is closer to the Sun.
    a. Explain this unexpected result in one or two sentences. **b.** Suppose Venus had neither clouds nor greenhouse gases. What do you think would happen to the surface temperature of Venus? Why? **c.** How are clouds and volcanoes linked on Venus? What change in volcanism might result in the disappearance of clouds? Explain.

47. *Atmospheric Structure.* Study Earth's average atmospheric structure (Figure 10.7). Sketch a similar curve for each of the following cases, and explain how and why the structure would be different in each case.
    a. Suppose Earth had no greenhouse gases. **b.** Suppose the Sun emitted no ultraviolet light. **c.** Suppose the Sun had a higher output of X rays.

48. *Magic Mercury.* Suppose we could magically give Mercury the same atmosphere as Earth. Assuming this magical intervention happened only once, would Mercury be able to keep its new atmosphere? Explain.

49. *A Swiftly Rotating Venus.* Suppose Venus rotated as rapidly as Earth. Briefly explain how and why you would expect it to be different in terms of each of the following: geological processes, atmospheric circulation, magnetic field, and climate history.

50. *Coastal Winds.* During the daytime, heat from the Sun tends to make the air temperature warmer over land near the coast than over the water offshore. At night, land cools off faster than the sea, so temperatures tend to be cooler over land. Use these facts to predict the directions in which winds generally blow during the day and at night in coastal regions. Explain your reasoning in a few sentences. (Diagrams might help.)

51. *Sources and Losses.* Choose one process by which atmospheres can gain gas and one by which they can lose gas. For each process, write a few sentences that describe it and how it depends on each of the following fundamental planetary properties: size, distance from the Sun, and rotation rate.

52. *Two Paths Diverged.* Briefly explain how the different atmospheric properties of Earth and Venus can be explained by the fundamental properties of size and distance from the Sun.

53. *Change in Fundamental Properties.* Choose one property of Earth—either size or distance from the Sun—and suppose that it had been different (for example, smaller size or greater distance). Describe how this change would have affected Earth's subsequent atmospheric history and the possibility of life on Earth.

54. *Feedback Processes in the Atmosphere.* As the Sun gradually brightens in the future, how can the CO_2 cycle respond to reduce the warming effect? Which parts of the cycle will be affected? Is this an example of positive or negative feedback?

55. *Earth to Mars.* Section 10.5 discusses what might happen to Earth if it were suddenly moved to the orbit of Venus. What do you think would happen to Earth if it were suddenly moved to the orbital distance of Mars? Write a few sentences explaining your answer.

56. *Global Warming.* What, if anything, should we be doing that we are not doing already to alleviate the threat of global warming? Write a one-page editorial summarizing and defending your opinion.

Quantitative Problems

57. *The Mass of an Atmosphere.* What is the total mass of Earth's atmosphere? You may use the fact that 1 bar is the pressure exerted

by 10,000 kilograms pushing down on a square meter in Earth's gravity. Remember that every square meter of Earth experiences this pressure from the atmosphere above it. Alternatively, you may start with the English unit value for pressure of 14.7 pounds per square inch and convert to kilograms for your final answer. Remember that the surface area of a sphere of radius r is $4\pi r^2$.

58. *The Role of Reflectivity.* By assuming 0% and 100% reflectivity (respectively), find the maximum and minimum possible "no greenhouse" temperatures for a planet at 1 AU. What reflectivity would be necessary to keep the average temperature exactly at the freezing point? Compare to Earth's actual reflectivity in Table 10.2.

59. *The Cooling Clouds of Venus.* Table 10.2 shows that Venus's temperature in the absence of the greenhouse effect is lower than Earth's, even though Venus is closer to the Sun. What would Venus's "no greenhouse" temperature be if its clouds were more transparent, giving a reflectivity the same as Earth's? What would the actual surface temperature be in this case if the greenhouse effect increased the surface temperature by the same number of degrees that it does today?

60. *Mars's Elliptical Orbit.* Mars's distance from the Sun varies from 1.38 AU to 1.66 AU. How much does this affect its "no greenhouse" surface temperature at different times of year? Comment on how this affects Mars's seasons.

61. *Escape from Venus.*
    a. Calculate the escape velocity from Venus's exosphere, which begins about 200 kilometers above the surface. (*Hint:* See Mathematical Insight 4.4.) **b.** Calculate and compare the thermal speeds of hydrogen and deuterium atoms at the exospheric temperature of 350 K. The mass of a hydrogen atom is 1.67×10^{-27} kilogram, and the mass of a deuterium atom is about twice the mass of a hydrogen atom. **c.** In a few sentences, comment on the relevance of these calculations to the question of whether Venus has lost large quantities of water.

Discussion Questions

62. *Lucky Earth.* The climate histories of Venus and Mars make it clear that getting a pleasant climate like that of Earth isn't easy. How does this affect your opinion about whether Earth-like planets might exist around other stars? Explain.

63. *Terraforming Mars.* Some people have suggested that we might be able to engineer Mars in a way that would cause its climate to warm and its atmosphere to thicken. This type of planet engineering is called *terraforming*, because its objective is to make a planet more Earth-like and easier for humans to live on. Discuss possible ways to terraform Mars. Do any of these ideas seem practical? Do they seem like good ideas? Defend your opinions.

64. *Terraforming Venus.* Can you think of ways in which it would be possible to terraform Venus? Discuss the possibilities as well as their practicality.

Web Projects

65. *Human Threats to Earth.* Write a three- to five-page research report about current understanding and controversy regarding global warming. Be sure to address both the latest knowledge about the issue and proposals for alleviating any dangers associated with it. End your report by making your own recommendations about what, if anything, needs to be done to prevent damage to Earth.

66. *Spacecraft Study of Atmospheres.* Learn about a current or planned mission to study the atmosphere of one of the terrestrial worlds (including Earth). Write a one- to two-page essay describing the mission and what we hope to learn from it.

67. *Martian Weather.* Find the latest weather report for Mars from spacecraft and other satellites. What season is it in the northern hemisphere? When was the most recent dust storm? What surface temperature was most recently reported from Mars's surface, and at what location? Summarize your findings by writing a 1-minute script for a television news update on Martian weather.

The photo of Saturn was taken by the *Cassini* spacecraft while it was in Saturn's shadow. The small blue dot of light just inside Saturn's rings at the left (about the 10 o'clock position) is Earth, far in the distance.

11 JOVIAN PLANET SYSTEMS

LEARNING GOALS

11.1 A DIFFERENT KIND OF PLANET
- Are jovian planets all alike?
- What are jovian planets like on the inside?
- What is the weather like on jovian planets?
- Do jovian planets have magnetospheres like Earth's?

11.2 A WEALTH OF WORLDS: SATELLITES OF ICE AND ROCK
- What kinds of moons orbit the jovian planets?
- Why are Jupiter's Galilean moons so geologically active?

- What is remarkable about Titan and other major moons of the outer solar system?
- Why are small icy moons more geologically active than small rocky planets?

11.3 JOVIAN PLANET RINGS
- What are Saturn's rings like?
- How do other jovian ring systems compare to Saturn's?
- Why do the jovian planets have rings?

Do there exist many worlds, or is there but a single world? This is one of the most noble and exalted questions in the study of Nature.

—St. Albertus Magnus (1206–1280)

In Roman mythology, the namesakes of the jovian planets are rulers among gods: Jupiter is the king of the gods, Saturn is Jupiter's father, Uranus is the lord of the sky, and Neptune rules the sea. However, our ancestors could not have foreseen the true majesty of the four jovian planets. The smallest, Neptune, is large enough to contain the volume of more than 50 Earths. The largest, Jupiter, has a volume some 1400 times that of Earth. These worlds are totally unlike the terrestrial planets. They are essentially giant balls of gas, with no solid surface.

Why should we care about a set of worlds so different from our own? Apart from satisfying natural curiosity, studies of the jovian planets and their moons help us understand the birth and evolution of our solar system—which in turn helps us understand our own planet Earth. In addition, the jovian planets provide stepping stones to understanding other planetary systems, which may have a wider range of planetary types than we find in our own solar system. In this chapter, we'll explore the jovian planet systems, focusing first on the planets themselves, then on their many moons, and finally on their beautifully complex rings.

 Formation of the Solar System Tutorial, Lesson 1

11.1 A DIFFERENT KIND OF PLANET

The great differences between the terrestrial and the jovian planets are a relatively recent discovery in human history. Jupiter and Saturn are easily visible in the night sky, but the naked eye cannot discern any details about their nature. Uranus and Neptune were discovered in 1781 and 1846, respectively (see Special Topic, page 312), so they were unknown even during the Copernican revolution.

Astronomers first recognized the immense sizes of Jupiter and Saturn about 250 years ago. Recall that we need to know both angular size and distance to calculate an object's true size (see Mathematical Insight 2.1). Although Copernicus had figured out the *relative* distances to the known planets in astronomical units (AU), scientists did not establish the absolute scale of the solar system until the 1760s, when they were able to measure the true length of an astronomical unit with data from a transit of Venus (see Special Topic, page 207). Only then could scientists calculate the true sizes of Jupiter and Saturn from their distances and angular sizes (measured through telescopes). Knowing the scale of the solar system also told scientists the distances of orbiting moons, and because the orbital periods of the moons were easy to measure, the orbital distances allowed scientists to use Newton's version of Kepler's third law [**Section 4.4**] to calculate the masses of the jovian planets. Together, the measurements of size and mass revealed the low densities of the jovian planets, proving that these worlds are very different in nature from Earth.

The real revolution in understanding jovian planet systems began with the first spacecraft sent to visit them: *Pioneer 10* and *Pioneer 11*, which flew past Jupiter and Saturn in the early 1970s. The *Voyager* missions followed soon thereafter; *Voyager 1* flew past Jupiter and Saturn, and *Voyager 2* flew past all four jovian planets. More recently, we've learned much more about Jupiter from the *Galileo* spacecraft, which orbited Jupiter from 1995 to 2003, and *New Horizons*, which flew past Jupiter in 2007 on its way to Pluto; the *Juno* mission is scheduled to begin orbiting Jupiter in August 2016. Much of our current understanding of Saturn comes from *Cassini*, which has been orbiting Saturn since 2004.

Are jovian planets all alike?

FIGURE 11.1 shows a montage of the jovian planets compiled by the *Voyager* spacecraft, along with basic data; Earth is included for scale. The immense sizes of the jovian worlds are apparent. But while all four are enormous, there are important differences between them. In particular, they differ substantially in mass, density, and overall composition.

Jovian Planet Composition Jupiter and Saturn are made almost entirely of hydrogen and helium, with just a few percent of their masses in the form of hydrogen compounds and even smaller amounts of rock and metal. In fact, their overall compositions are much more similar to the composition of the Sun than to the compositions of the terrestrial planets. Some people even call Jupiter a "failed star" because it has a starlike composition but lacks the nuclear fusion needed to make it shine. This is a consequence of its size: Although Jupiter is large for a planet, it is much less massive than any star. As a result, its gravity is too weak to compress its interior to the extreme temperatures and densities needed for nuclear fusion. (Jupiter would have needed to grow to about 80 times its current mass to have become a star.) Of course, where some people see a failed star, others see an extremely successful planet.

Uranus and Neptune are much smaller than Jupiter and Saturn, and also contain smaller proportions of hydrogen and helium gas. Instead, they are made primarily of hydrogen compounds such as water (H_2O), methane (CH_4), and ammonia (NH_3), along with smaller amounts of metal and rock.

The differences in composition among the jovian planets can probably be traced to their origins. Recall that the jovian planets formed in the outer solar system, where it was cold enough for hydrogen compounds to condense into ices [**Section 8.2**]. Because hydrogen compounds were so much more abundant than metal and rock, some of the ice-rich planetesimals of the outer solar system grew to great size. Once these planetesimals became sufficiently massive, their gravity allowed them to draw in the hydrogen and helium gas that surrounded them. All four jovian planets are thought to have grown from ice-rich planetesimals of about the same mass—roughly 10 times the mass of Earth—but they captured different amounts of hydrogen and helium gas from the surrounding solar nebula.

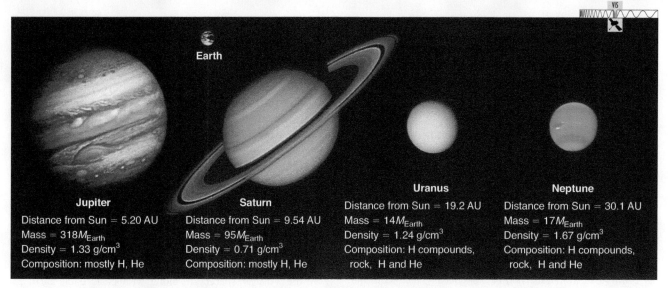

Earth

Jupiter
Distance from Sun = 5.20 AU
Mass = 318M_{Earth}
Density = 1.33 g/cm^3
Composition: mostly H, He

Saturn
Distance from Sun = 9.54 AU
Mass = 95M_{Earth}
Density = 0.71 g/cm^3
Composition: mostly H, He

Uranus
Distance from Sun = 19.2 AU
Mass = 14M_{Earth}
Density = 1.24 g/cm^3
Composition: H compounds,
  rock, H and He

Neptune
Distance from Sun = 30.1 AU
Mass = 17M_{Earth}
Density = 1.67 g/cm^3
Composition: H compounds,
  rock, H and He

FIGURE 11.1 Jupiter, Saturn, Uranus, and Neptune, shown to scale with Earth for comparison.

Jupiter and Saturn captured so much hydrogen and helium gas that these gases now make up the vast majority of their masses. The ice-rich planetesimals from which they grew now represent only about 3% of Jupiter's mass and about 10% of Saturn's mass.

Uranus and Neptune pulled in much less hydrogen and helium gas. Notice in Figure 11.1 that Uranus's mass is about 14 times Earth's mass. Since Uranus is thought to have grown around an ice-rich planetesimal that had about 10 times Earth's mass, the captured hydrogen and helium gas must make up only about a third of Uranus's total mass. The bulk of its mass consists of material from the original ice-rich planetesimal: hydrogen compounds mixed with smaller amounts of rock and metal. The same is true for Neptune, though its higher density suggests that it may have formed around a slightly more massive ice-rich planetesimal.

Why did the different planets capture different amounts of gas? The answer probably lies in their distances from the Sun as they formed. The solid particles that condensed farther from the Sun should have been more widely spread out than those that condensed nearer to the Sun, which means it would have taken longer for them to accrete into large, icy planetesimals. As the nearest jovian planet to the Sun, Jupiter would have been the first to get a planetesimal large enough for its gravity to start drawing in gas, followed by Saturn, Uranus, and Neptune. Because all the planets stopped accreting gas at the same time—when the solar wind blew all the remaining gas into interstellar space—the more distant planets had less time to capture gas and ended up smaller in size.

Density Differences Figure 11.1 shows that Saturn is considerably less dense than Uranus or Neptune. This should make sense when you compare compositions, because the hydrogen compounds, rock, and metal that make up Uranus and Neptune are normally much more dense than hydrogen or helium gas. By the same logic, we'd expect Jupiter to be even less dense than Saturn—but it's not. To understand Jupiter's surprisingly high density, we need to think about how massive planets are affected by their own gravity.

Saturn's average density of 0.71 g/cm^3 is less than that of water. As a result, it is sometimes said that Saturn could float on a giant ocean. Suppose there really were a gigantic planet with a gigantic ocean and we put Saturn on the ocean's surface. Would it float? If not, what would happen?

Building a planet of hydrogen and helium is a bit like making one out of fluffy pillows. Imagine assembling a planet pillow by pillow. As each new pillow is added, those on the bottom are compressed more by those above. As the lower layers are forced closer together, their mutual gravitational attraction increases, compressing them even further. At first the stack grows substantially with each pillow, but eventually the growth slows until adding pillows barely increases the height of the stack (FIGURE 11.2a).

Measure the thickness of your pillow, and then put it at the bottom of a stack of other pillows, folded blankets, or clothing. How much has the stack above the pillow compressed it? Insert your hand between the different layers to feel the pressure differences—and imagine the kind of pressures and compression you'd find in a stack tens of thousands of kilometers tall.

This analogy explains why Jupiter is only slightly larger than Saturn in radius even though it is more than three times as massive. The extra mass of Jupiter compresses its interior to a much higher density. More precise calculations show that Jupiter's radius is almost the maximum possible radius for a jovian planet. If much more gas were added to Jupiter, its weight would actually compress the interior enough to make the planet *smaller* rather than larger (FIGURE 11.2b). Some extrasolar planets that are larger in mass than Jupiter are therefore smaller in size. In fact, the smallest stars are significantly smaller in radius than Jupiter, even though they are at least 80 times as massive.

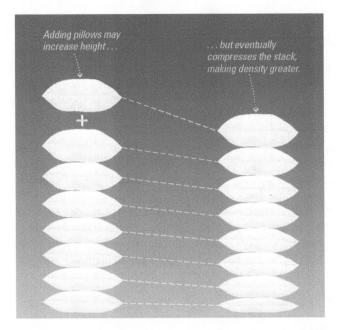

Adding pillows may increase height . . .

+

. . . but eventually compresses the stack, making density greater.

a Adding pillows to a stack may increase its height at first but eventually just compresses the stack, making its density greater. Similarly, adding mass to a jovian planet eventually will increase its density rather than increasing its radius.

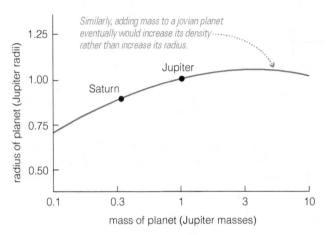

Similarly, adding mass to a jovian planet eventually would increase its density rather than increase its radius.

b This graph shows how radius depends on mass for a hydrogen/helium planet. Notice that Jupiter is only slightly larger in radius than Saturn, despite being three times as massive. Gravitational compression of a planet much more massive than Jupiter would actually make it smaller in size.

FIGURE 11.2 The relationship between mass and radius for a planet made of hydrogen and helium.

Jovian Planet Rotation and Shape The jovian planets rotate much more rapidly than any of the terrestrial worlds. However, precisely defining their rotation rates can be difficult because they lack solid surfaces. We can observe the rotation of clouds, but these observations can be deceptive, because the speeds at which we observe clouds to move are affected by winds as well as by planetary rotation. Nevertheless, observations of clouds at different latitudes suggest that the jovian planets do not rotate like solid balls. Instead, their rotation rates vary with latitude: Equatorial regions complete each rotation in less time than polar regions. (The Sun rotates similarly [**Section 14.1**].)

We can measure the rotation rates of the jovian *interiors* by tracking emissions from charged particles trapped in their magnetospheres. This technique tells us the rotation period of the magnetosphere, which should be the same as the rotation period deep in the interior, where the magnetic field is generated. These measurements show that the jovian "day" ranges from about 10 hours on Jupiter and Saturn to 16–17 hours on Uranus and Neptune. Note that, because the jovian planets are much larger in radius than Earth, their surface rotation speeds are much greater compared to Earth than the periods alone would suggest.

The rapid rotation rates of the jovian planets affect their shapes (**FIGURE 11.3**). Gravity alone would make the jovian planets into perfect spheres. Rotation makes them less like perfect spheres, because it makes material bulge outward. Material near the equator, where speeds around the rotation axis are highest, is flung outward in the same way you feel yourself flung outward when you ride on a merry-go-round. The size of the equatorial bulge depends on the balance between the strength of gravity (which pulls material inward) and the rate of rotation (which pushes material outward).

The balance tips most strongly toward flattening on Saturn: With its rapid 10-hour rotation period and relatively weak surface gravity, Saturn is about 10% larger in diameter at its equator than from pole to pole. In addition to altering a planet's shape, the equatorial bulge exerts an extra gravitational pull that helps keep moons and rings aligned with the equator.

What are jovian planets like on the inside?

The jovian planets are often called "gas giants," making it sound as if they were entirely gaseous like air on Earth. Based on their compositions, Jupiter and Saturn may seem to deserve this name; after all, they became giants primarily by capturing

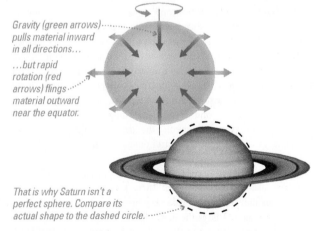

Gravity (green arrows) pulls material inward in all directions . . .

. . . but rapid rotation (red arrows) flings material outward near the equator.

That is why Saturn isn't a perfect sphere. Compare its actual shape to the dashed circle.

FIGURE 11.3 interactive figure Because of their rapid rotation, the jovian planets are not quite spherical. Saturn shows the biggest difference between its actual shape and a perfect sphere.

so much hydrogen and helium gas. The name may seem less fitting for Uranus and Neptune, since they are made mostly of materials besides pure hydrogen and helium. However, closer inspection shows that the name is a little misleading even for Jupiter and Saturn, because their strong gravity compresses most of the "gas" into forms of matter quite unlike anything we are familiar with in everyday life on Earth.

You may wonder how we can claim to know what the jovian planets are like on the inside. The answer is a combination of theoretical modeling and laboratory experiments. Just as with the terrestrial planets, detailed observations of the strength of a planet's gravity and of its magnetic field can help us put together a model of the planet's interior structure. We then use the model to predict observable phenomena, such as a planet's average density, and modify it until the predictions match the data. Today, advanced computer models

successfully explain the observed sizes, densities, atmospheric compositions, and precise shapes of the jovian planets. We are therefore confident that the interior structure found by the models is fairly close to reality. Laboratory studies also provide important data, such as showing us how hydrogen and helium behave under the tremendous temperatures and pressures that exist deep beneath the jovian cloudtops.

Inside Jupiter Let's begin discussion of the jovian interiors by using Jupiter as a prototype. Jupiter's lack of a solid surface makes it tempting to think of the planet as "all atmosphere," but you could not fly through Jupiter's interior in the way airplanes fly through air. A spacecraft plunging into Jupiter would find increasingly higher temperatures and pressures as it descended. The *Galileo* spacecraft dropped a scientific probe into Jupiter (in 1995) that collected measurements for about

SPECIAL TOPIC

How Were Uranus, Neptune, and Pluto Discovered?

The planets Mercury, Venus, Mars, Jupiter, and Saturn are all easily visible to the naked eye and hence were well known to ancient people. In contrast, Uranus, Neptune, and the solar system's many small bodies were discovered relatively recently.

Uranus is actually visible to the naked eye, but it is so faint and moves so slowly in its 84-year orbit of the Sun that ancient people did not recognize it as a planet. It was even recorded as a star on some detailed early sky charts. Uranus was discovered as a planet in 1781 by brother-and-sister astronomers William and Caroline Herschel. William is the more famous of the pair by far, partly because Caroline's gender made many scientists of the time unwilling to take her seriously, but also because he was nearly 12 years older than his sister and had been the one who drew her into astronomical research. William Herschel originally suggested naming the new planet *Georgium Sidus*, Latin for "George's Star," in honor of his patron, King George III. Fortunately, the idea of "Planet George" never caught on. Instead, many 18th- and 19th-century astronomers referred to the new planet as Herschel. The modern name, Uranus (after the mythological father of Saturn), was first suggested by one of Herschel's contemporaries, astronomer Johann Bode. This name was generally accepted by the middle of the 19th century.

Neptune's discovery more than 60 years later represented an important triumph for Newton's universal law of gravitation and the young science of astrophysics. By that time, careful observations of Uranus had shown its orbit to be slightly inconsistent with that predicted by Newton's law—at least if it were being influenced only by the Sun and the other known planets. In the early 1840s in England, a student named John Adams suggested that the inconsistency could be explained if there were an unseen "eighth planet" orbiting the Sun beyond Uranus. According to the official story, he used Newton's theory to predict the location of the planet but was unable to convince British astronomers to carry out a telescopic search. However, documents from the time suggest his prediction may not have been as precise as the official history claims. Meanwhile, in the summer of 1846, French astronomer Urbain Leverrier independently made very precise calculations. He sent a letter to Johann Galle of the Berlin Observatory, suggesting a search for the eighth planet. On the night of September 23, 1846, Galle pointed his telescope to the position suggested by Leverrier. There,

within 1° of its predicted position, he saw the planet Neptune. Hence, Neptune's discovery truly was made by mathematics and physics and was only confirmed with a telescope.

As a side note to this story, Leverrier had such faith in Newton's universal law of gravitation that he also suggested a second unseen planet, this one orbiting closer to the Sun than Mercury. He got this idea because other astronomers had identified slight discrepancies between Mercury's actual orbit and the orbit predicted by Newton's theory. He assumed that no one had yet seen the planet, which he called Vulcan, because it was so close to the Sun. Leverrier died in 1877, still believing that Vulcan would someday be discovered. But Vulcan does not exist. Mercury's actual orbit does not match the orbit predicted by Newton's law because Newton's theory is not the whole story of gravity. About 40 years after Leverrier's death, Einstein showed that Newton's theory is only an approximation of a broader theory of gravity, known today as Einstein's *general theory of relativity*. Einstein's theory predicts an orbit for Mercury that matches its actual orbit. This match was one of the first key pieces of evidence in favor of Einstein's theory [**Section S3.4**].

Pluto was discovered in 1930 by American astronomer Clyde Tombaugh, culminating a search that began when astronomers analyzed the orbit of Neptune. The story of Pluto's discovery at first seemed similar to Neptune's. Just as discrepancies between the predicted orbit and the actual orbit of Uranus led to the prediction that Neptune must exist, lingering discrepancies between the updated prediction for Uranus's orbit and its actual orbit suggested the existence of an even more distant "ninth planet." Tombaugh found Pluto just 6° from the position in the sky where this ninth planet had been predicted to lie, so it seemed that the search had been successful. However, while initial estimates suggested that Pluto was much larger than Earth, we now know that Pluto has a radius of only 1160 kilometers and a mass of just 0.002 Earth mass— making it far too small to affect the orbit of Neptune. In retrospect, the supposed orbital irregularities of Neptune appear to have been errors in measurement; no "ninth planet" is needed to explain the orbits of Uranus or Neptune. As we now know from the fact that many similar objects orbit in the same region of the solar system [**Section 12.3**], Pluto's discovery was just a coincidence, and its small size is why we now call it a *dwarf planet*.

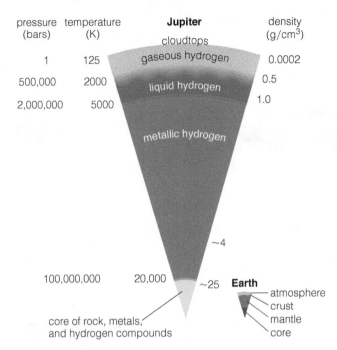

pressure (bars)	temperature (K)		density (g/cm³)
		Jupiter	
		cloudtops	
1	125	gaseous hydrogen	0.0002
500,000	2000	liquid hydrogen	0.5
2,000,000	5000		1.0
		metallic hydrogen	
			~4
100,000,000	20,000		~25

core of rock, metals, and hydrogen compounds

Earth
— atmosphere
— crust
— mantle
— core

FIGURE 11.4 Jupiter's interior structure, labeled with the pressure, temperature, and density at various depths. Earth's interior structure is shown to scale for comparison. (The thickness of Earth's crust and atmosphere are exaggerated.) Note that Jupiter's core is only slightly larger than Earth but is about 10 times as massive.

an hour before the ever-increasing pressures and temperatures destroyed it. *Galileo* provided valuable data about Jupiter's atmosphere, but didn't last long enough to sample the interior: It survived only to a depth of about 200 kilometers, or about 0.3% of Jupiter's radius.

Computer models tell us that Jupiter has fairly distinct interior layers (**FIGURE 11.4**). The layers do not differ much in composition—all except the core are mostly hydrogen and helium. Instead they differ in the phase (such as liquid or gas) of their hydrogen. To get a better sense of this layering, imagine plunging head-on into Jupiter in a futuristic spacesuit that allows you to survive the extreme interior conditions.

Near the cloudtops, you'll find the temperature to be a brisk 125 K (–148°C), the density to be a low 0.0002 g/cm³, and the atmospheric pressure to be about 1 bar (the same as the pressure at sea level on Earth [**Section 10.1**]). As you plunge downward, conditions quickly become more extreme.

By a depth of 7000 kilometers, about 10% of the way to the center, you'll find that the temperature has increased to a scorching 2000 K and the pressure has reached 500,000 bars. The density is about 0.5 g/cm³, or about half that of water. Under these conditions, hydrogen acts more like a liquid than a gas, which is why the layer that begins at this depth is labeled *liquid hydrogen* in Figure 11.4. Of course, like the rest of Jupiter, the layer also contains helium and hydrogen compounds.

At a depth of 14,000 kilometers, about 20% of the way to the center, the density has become about as high as that of water (1.0 g/cm³). The temperature is near 5000 K, almost as hot as the surface (but not the interior) of the Sun. The pressure has reached 2 million bars. This extreme pressure forces hydrogen into a compact, metallic form. Just as is the case with everyday

metals, electrons are free to move around in *metallic hydrogen*, so it conducts electricity quite well. This layer extends through most of the rest of Jupiter's interior and, as we'll see shortly, it is where Jupiter's magnetic field is generated.

You'll finally reach Jupiter's core at a depth of 60,000 kilometers, about 10,000 kilometers from the center. The core temperature is some 20,000 K and the pressure is about 100 million bars. The density of the core is about 25 g/cm³, much denser than any material you'll find on Earth's surface. The core is a mix of hydrogen compounds, rock, and metals, but these materials bear little resemblance to familiar solids or liquids because of the combination of high temperature and extreme pressure. Moreover, while the rock and metal of the terrestrial planets have separated into layers by composition (that is, core, mantle, and crust), Jupiter's core materials are probably all mixed together. The core contains about 10 times as much mass as the entire Earth, but it is only about the same size as Earth because it is compressed to such high density.

Comparing Jovian Interiors Because all four jovian planets have cores of about the same mass, their interiors differ mainly in the hydrogen/helium layers that surround their cores. **FIGURE 11.5** contrasts the four jovian interiors. Remember that while the outer layers are named for the phase of their hydrogen, they also contain helium and hydrogen compounds.

Saturn is the most similar to Jupiter, just as we should expect given its similar size and composition. Its four interior layers differ from those of Jupiter only because of its lower mass and weaker gravity. The lower mass makes the weight of the overlying layers less on Saturn than on Jupiter, so you must look deeper into Saturn to find each level where pressure changes hydrogen from one phase to another. That is, Saturn has thicker layers of gaseous and liquid hydrogen and a thinner and more deeply buried layer of metallic hydrogen.

Pressures within Uranus and Neptune are not high enough to form liquid or metallic hydrogen at all. Each of these two planets has only a thick layer of gaseous hydrogen surrounding its core of hydrogen compounds, rock, and metal. This core material may be liquid, making for very odd "oceans" buried deep inside Uranus and Neptune. The cores of Uranus and Neptune are larger in radius than the cores of Jupiter and Saturn, even though they have about the same mass, because they are less compressed by their lighter-weight overlying layers. The less extreme interior conditions also allowed Uranus's and Neptune's cores to differentiate, so hydrogen compounds reside in a layer around a center of rock and metal.

Internal Heat Recall that internal heat drives surface geology on the terrestrial worlds. The jovian planets do not have surface geology, because they have no solid surfaces, but internal heat still plays an important role.

Jupiter has a tremendous amount of internal heat, and like any hot object, it gradually loses this heat to space by emitting thermal radiation [**Section 5.4**]. In fact, Jupiter emits almost twice as much energy as it receives from the Sun. This heat contributes significant energy to Jupiter's upper atmosphere. (For comparison, Earth's internal heat contributes only 0.005% as much energy to the surface as sunlight does.)

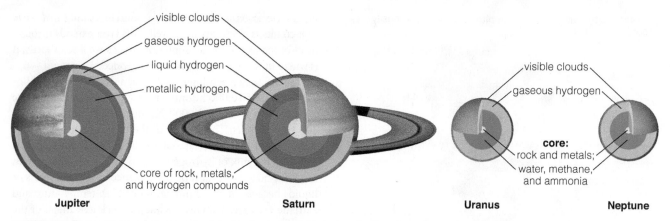

FIGURE 11.5 These diagrams compare the interior structures of the jovian planets, shown approximately to scale. All four planets have cores of rock, metals, and hydrogen compounds, with masses about 10 times the mass of Earth's core. They differ primarily in the thicknesses of the hydrogen/helium layers that surround their cores. Notice that the cores of Uranus and Neptune are differentiated into a layer of hydrogen compounds around a center of rock and metals.

What keeps Jupiter so hot inside? Jupiter's large size means it loses internal heat very slowly (see Mathematical Insight 9.1), and calculations show that the remaining heat of accretion and differentiation is not enough to explain Jupiter's present-day heat loss. Radioactive decay also adds heat, but still not enough to account for all the internal heat. The most likely explanation for Jupiter's excess heat is that the planet is still slowly contracting. Contraction converts gravitational potential energy to thermal energy, so continued contraction would be an ongoing source of internal heat. Although we have not measured any such contraction, theoretical models suggest that it is probably occurring. Moreover, calculations tell us that contraction could easily explain Jupiter's internal heat, even if the contraction is so gradual that we have little hope of ever measuring it directly.

Regardless of the specific mechanism, Jupiter has undoubtedly lost substantial heat during the 4.5 billion years since its formation. Jupiter's interior must have been much warmer in the distant past, and this heat would have "puffed up" its atmosphere. With a larger size, Jupiter would have reflected more sunlight, so in the distant past Jupiter must have been even more prominent in Earth's sky than it is today.

Saturn also emits nearly twice as much energy as it receives from the Sun, suggesting that it, too, must have some ongoing source of heat. However, Saturn's mass is too small for it to be generating heat by contracting like Jupiter. Instead, Saturn's pressure and its lower interior temperatures may allow helium to condense into liquid form at relatively high levels within the interior. The helium droplets slowly rain down to the deeper interior. This gradual helium rain represents a sort of ongoing *differentiation* [**Section 9.1**], because it means that higher-density material (the liquid helium) is still sinking inside the planet. Spacecraft measurements have confirmed that Saturn's atmosphere has less helium than Jupiter's, just as we would expect if helium has been raining down into Saturn's interior for billions of years.

Neither Uranus nor Neptune has internal conditions that should allow helium rain to form, and most of their original heat from accretion should have escaped long ago. This

explains why Uranus emits virtually no excess internal energy. Neptune, however, is more mysterious. Like Jupiter and Saturn, Neptune emits nearly twice as much energy as it receives from the Sun. The only reasonable explanation for this internal heat is that Neptune is somehow still contracting, somewhat like Jupiter, thereby converting gravitational potential energy into thermal energy. However, we do not yet know why a planet of Neptune's size would still be contracting more than 4 billion years after its formation.

What is the weather like on jovian planets?

Jovian atmospheres, by which we mean the portions of the planets that are visible to telescopes and spacecraft, have dynamic winds and weather, with colorful clouds and enormous storms. These atmospheres are made mostly of hydrogen and helium gas, mixed with small amounts of various hydrogen compounds. Because oxygen, carbon, and nitrogen are among the most common elements in the universe besides hydrogen and helium, the most common hydrogen compounds are methane (CH_4), ammonia (NH_3), and water (H_2O). Spectroscopy also reveals the presence of small amounts of more complex hydrogen compounds, such as acetylene (C_2H_2), ethane (C_2H_6), and propane (C_3H_8). Although all these hydrogen compounds together make up only a minuscule fraction of the jovian planets' atmospheres, they are responsible for virtually all aspects of their appearances. Some of these compounds condense to form the clouds that are so prominent in telescope and spacecraft images. Others are responsible for the great variety of colors we see among the jovian planets. Without these compounds in their atmospheres, the jovian planets would be uniform, colorless balls of gas.

THINK ABOUT IT

Several gases in Jupiter's atmosphere—including methane, propane, and acetylene—are highly flammable here on Earth. Jupiter has plenty of lightning to provide sparks, so why don't these gases ignite in Jupiter's atmosphere? (*Hint:* What's missing from Jupiter's atmosphere that's necessary for ordinary fire?)

We can understand the jovian atmospheres using the same basic principles that we used with the terrestrial atmospheres. As we did for the jovian planet interiors, let's examine different aspects of the jovian atmospheres by starting with Jupiter as the prototype for each feature.

Atmospheric Structure and Clouds Telescopic observations of Jupiter, along with data returned from the *Galileo* probe during its 1995 plunge into Jupiter, tell us that the temperature structure of Jupiter's atmosphere is very similar to that of Earth's atmosphere (see Figure 10.7). High above the cloudtops, Jupiter's *thermosphere* consists of very low-density gas heated to about 1000 K by solar X rays and by energetic particles from Jupiter's magnetosphere. Below the thermosphere but still above the clouds, we find Jupiter's *stratosphere*. Recall that a planet can have a stratosphere only if it has a gas that can absorb ultraviolet light from the Sun. Ozone plays this role on Earth. Jupiter lacks molecular oxygen and ozone, but has a few minor atmospheric ingredients that absorb solar ultraviolet photons. This absorption gives the stratosphere a peak temperature of around 200 K (−73°C). Chemical reactions driven by the solar ultraviolet photons create a smog-like haze that masks the color and sharpness of the clouds below. Below the stratosphere lies Jupiter's *troposphere,* where the temperature rises with depth because greenhouse gases trap both solar heat and Jupiter's own internal heat. FIGURE 11.6 shows how temperature varies with altitude in Jupiter's atmosphere.

In the troposphere, the warmer temperatures below drive strong convection. This convection is responsible for the thick clouds that enshroud Jupiter. Recall that clouds form when a gas condenses to make tiny liquid droplets or solid flakes. Water vapor is the only gas that can condense in Earth's atmosphere, which is why clouds on Earth are made of water droplets or ice flakes that can produce rain or snow. In contrast, Jupiter's atmosphere has several gases that can condense to form clouds. Each of these gases condenses at a different temperature, leading to distinctive cloud layers at different altitudes.

Jupiter has three primary cloud layers, which are also shown in Figure 11.6. We can understand them by imagining that we could watch gases rising through the troposphere with convection. Deep in the troposphere, the gases include three ingredients that will condense when temperatures are low enough: water (H_2O), ammonium hydrosulfide (NH_4SH), and ammonia (NH_3). The rising gas first encounters temperatures cool enough for water vapor to condense into liquid water but not cool enough for the other gases to condense. Therefore, the lowest layer of clouds contains water droplets. As the remaining gas continues its rise, it next reaches an altitude at which ammonium hydrosulfide condenses to make the second cloud layer. After rising another 50 kilometers, the gas reaches an altitude at which ammonia condenses to make the upper cloud layer.

Data from telescopic and spacecraft observations tell us that the atmospheric structures of the other three jovian planets are quite similar to that of Jupiter (FIGURE 11.7). The primary difference among them is that the atmospheres get progressively cooler with increasing distance from the Sun. These temperature differences lead the planets to have their cloud layers at different altitudes.

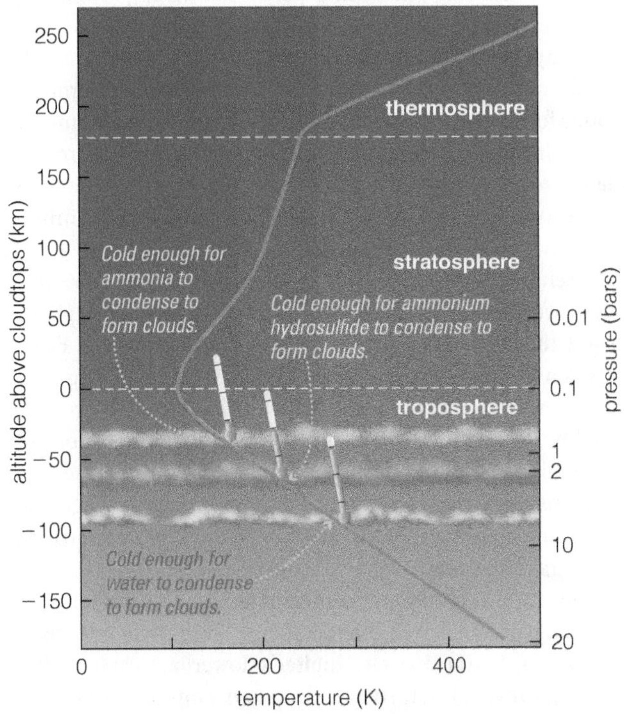

FIGURE 11.6 This graph shows the temperature structure of Jupiter's atmosphere. Jupiter has at least three distinct cloud layers because different atmospheric gases condense at different temperatures and hence at different altitudes.

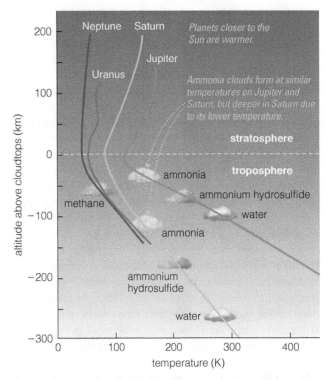

FIGURE 11.7 The figure contrasts the atmospheric structures and cloud layers of the four jovian planets. Note that the altitude scale is different on this figure than on Figure 11.6, allowing us to see the troposphere and stratospheres only.

Saturn has the same set of three cloud layers as Jupiter, but the lower overall temperatures cause these layers to lie deeper in Saturn's atmosphere. For example, to find the relatively warm temperatures at which water vapor can condense to form water clouds, we must look about 200 kilometers deeper into Saturn than into Jupiter. Saturn's cloud layers are also separated by greater vertical distances than Jupiter's, because Saturn's weaker gravity causes less atmospheric compression.

Uranus and Neptune are so cold that any cloud layers similar to those of Jupiter or Saturn would be buried too deep in their atmospheres for us to see. Therefore, we do not know whether such clouds exist on these two planets. However, high in the atmospheres of Uranus and Neptune, we see clouds made from flakes of methane snow. Methane can condense in the very cold upper tropospheres of Uranus and Neptune but not in the warmer tropospheres of Jupiter and Saturn.

Clouds and Colors The spectacular colors of the jovian planets are probably the first thing that jumps out at you when you look at the photos in Figure 11.1. Many mysteries remain about precisely why the jovian planets are so colorful, but clouds are responsible for many of the color features. Different types of clouds reflect light of different colors. For example, Earth's clouds look white from space because they are made of water that reflects the white light of the Sun.

Water clouds on Jupiter and Saturn probably also reflect white light, as do the upper-layer clouds made of ammonia. In contrast, the mid-layer clouds of ammonium hydrosulfide reflect brown and red light, although no one knows exactly why. Most likely, the colors in these clouds come from as-yet-unidentified compounds that are produced by chemical reactions deeper in the atmosphere and are then carried upward by convection. The fact that Saturn's clouds lie deeper in its atmosphere than Jupiter's probably explains Saturn's more subdued colors: Less light penetrates to the depths at which Saturn's clouds are found, and the light they reflect is more obscured by the atmosphere above them.

The blue colors of Uranus and Neptune come from methane gas, which is at least 20 times as abundant (by percentage) on these planets as on Jupiter or Saturn. Methane gas in the upper atmospheres of Uranus and Neptune absorbs red light, allowing only blue light to penetrate to the level at which the methane clouds exist. The methane clouds reflect this blue light upward, giving the planets their blue colors (FIGURE 11.8). Uranus has a lighter blue color than Neptune, probably because it has more smog-like haze to scatter sunlight before it reaches the level of the methane clouds. The extra haze is probably a result of Uranus's "sideways" axis tilt, which leads to extreme seasons. With one hemisphere remaining sunlit for decades, gases have plenty of time to interact with solar ultraviolet light and to make the chemical ingredients of the haze. Continuous sunlight may also explain why Uranus has a surprisingly hot thermosphere that extends thousands of kilometers above its cloudtops.

Global Winds and Storms on Jupiter Jupiter has dynamic weather, with strong winds and powerful storms. To understand Jupiter's weather, we must think about how its rapid rotation affects its global winds.

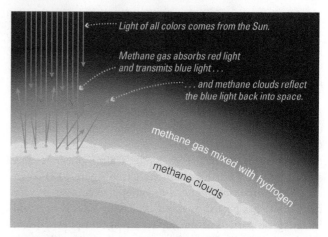

Light of all colors comes from the Sun.

Methane gas absorbs red light and transmits blue light . . .

. . . and methane clouds reflect the blue light back into space.

methane gas mixed with hydrogen

methane clouds

FIGURE 11.8 Neptune and Uranus look blue because methane gas absorbs red light but transmits blue light. Clouds of methane snowflakes reflect the transmitted blue light back to space.

Jupiter has planetwide circulation cells similar to those on Earth (see Figure 10.16). As on Earth, solar heat causes equatorial air to expand and spill toward the poles, while cooler polar air flows toward the equator. Also as on Earth, the Coriolis effect splits the large equator-to-pole circulation cells into smaller cells. However, Jupiter's greater size and faster rotation make the Coriolis effect much stronger on Jupiter than on Earth. Instead of being split into just three smaller cells encircling each hemisphere, Jupiter's circulation cells split into many alternating bands of rising and falling air. These bands are visible as the stripes of alternating color in photographs of Jupiter.

The alternating colors come from differences in the clouds that form in rising and falling air. As shown in FIGURE 11.9, the entire planet is blanketed with the reddish-brown ammonium hydrosulfide clouds that make up Jupiter's middle cloud layer. In contrast, the upper layer of white ammonia clouds forms only in places where rising air carries ammonia gas to altitudes high enough and cold enough for the ammonia to condense. In other words, the white bands (sometimes called *zones*) represent regions of rising air with cold ammonia clouds, while the darker bands (sometimes called *belts*) represent regions of falling air in which we can see down to a lower, warmer cloud level. This distinction between Jupiter's bright and dark bands is analogous to the difference on Earth between cloudy, rainy equatorial regions (regions of generally rising air) and the clear desert skies found at latitudes roughly 20°–30° north and south of the equator (regions of descending air). The infrared photo of Jupiter in Figure 11.9 confirms this idea: Warmer air emits more infrared light, so the warmer reddish bands appear brighter in the infrared photograph than the cooler white bands.

You might wonder why ammonia clouds form only in the rising air and not in the falling air. The answer goes back to the clouds themselves. Jupiter's lower atmosphere has ammonia throughout, so there's always ammonia in the air rising upward. However, once the ammonia condenses to form clouds of ammonia ice, these ice flakes fall back down as ammonia "snow," so the air that continues to rise above the clouds has very little ammonia left in it. Therefore, when

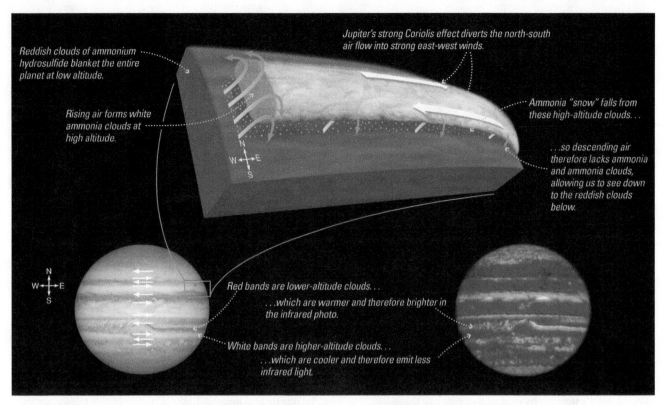

Reddish clouds of ammonium hydrosulfide blanket the entire planet at low altitude.

Jupiter's strong Coriolis effect diverts the north-south air flow into strong east-west winds.

Rising air forms white ammonia clouds at high altitude.

Ammonia "snow" falls from these high-altitude clouds...

...so descending air therefore lacks ammonia and ammonia clouds, allowing us to see down to the reddish clouds below.

Red bands are lower-altitude clouds...

...which are warmer and therefore brighter in the infrared photo.

White bands are higher-altitude clouds...

...which are cooler and therefore emit less infrared light.

FIGURE 11.9 interactive figure Jupiter's bands of color represent alternating regions of rising and falling air: We see white ammonia clouds in regions of rising air, and see down to the underlying layer of reddish ammonium hydrosulfide clouds in regions of falling air. The white arrows on the visible-light photo indicate wind directions. The infrared photo at the right, taken nearly simultaneously with the visible-light photo, confirms that the red bands represent warmer, deeper clouds and the white bands represent cooler, higher-altitude clouds.

this ammonia-depleted air spills to the north and south and returns downward in the bands of falling air, there is not enough ammonia to form clouds. It's analogous to the way that air descending over Earth's desert latitudes is usually depleted of water by precipitation over the equator, leaving it dry.

The alternating bands of rising and falling air shape Jupiter's global wind patterns. As on Earth, the rising and falling air drives slow winds that are directed north or south, but Jupiter's strong Coriolis effect diverts these winds into fast east or west winds. The east-west winds have peak speeds above 400 km/hr, making hurricane winds on Earth seem mild by comparison. The winds are generally strongest at the equator and at the boundaries between bands of rising and falling air.

Jupiter's global wind patterns are sometimes interrupted by powerful storms, much as storms can interrupt Earth's global wind patterns, but Jupiter's storms dwarf those that we see on Earth. Jupiter's most famous feature—the **Great Red Spot**—is a giant storm more than twice as wide as all of planet Earth. It is somewhat like a hurricane, except that its winds circulate around a high-pressure region rather than a low-pressure region (**FIGURE 11.10**). It is also extremely long-lived: Astronomers have seen it throughout the three centuries during which telescopes have been powerful enough to detect it. Other, smaller storms are constantly brewing in Jupiter's atmosphere. Brown ovals are low-pressure storms with their cloudtops deeper in Jupiter's atmosphere, and white ovals are high-pressure storms topped with ammonia clouds.

No one knows what drives Jupiter's storms, why Jupiter has only one Great Red Spot, or why the Great Red Spot has persisted so much longer than storms on Earth. Storms on Earth lose their strength when they pass over land, so perhaps Jupiter's biggest storms last for centuries simply because no solid surface is present to sap their energy. In fact, two long-lived storms have recently (one in 2006 and one in 2008)

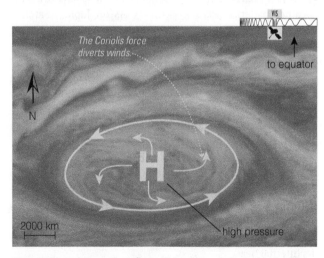

The Coriolis force diverts winds...

to equator

N

H

2000 km

high pressure

FIGURE 11.10 interactive photo This photograph shows Jupiter's Great Red Spot, a huge high-pressure storm that is large enough to swallow two Earths. The overlaid diagram shows a weather map of the region.

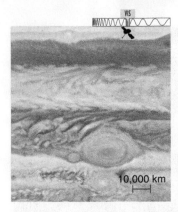   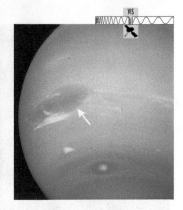

a This Hubble Space Telescope image shows Jupiter's southern hemisphere with the Great Red Spot, "Baby Red" (to its left), and "Red Jr." (below). Baby Red was torn apart by the Great Red Spot a few days later.

b Saturn's atmosphere, photographed by *Voyager 1*. Its banded appearance is very similar to that of Jupiter, but it has even faster winds.

c This infrared image of Uranus from the Keck Telescope shows several storms (the bright blotches) and Uranus's thin rings (red).

d Neptune's atmosphere, viewed from *Voyager 2*, shows bands and occasional strong storms. The large storm (white arrow) was called the Great Dark Spot.

FIGURE 11.11 Selected views of weather patterns on the four jovian planets.

been observed to undergo mysterious change, turning red. The more recent one was torn apart by the Great Red Spot as it passed nearby (FIGURE 11.11a). Scientists hope to learn more about Jupiter's weather by studying storms like these.

The bright colors of the Great Red Spot also pose a mystery: We might expect its high-altitude clouds to be white like the high-altitude ammonia clouds elsewhere, but instead, of course, they are red. The colors may be the result of chemicals formed by interactions between the storm's high-altitude gas and solar ultraviolet light, but no one really knows for sure.

Jupiter does not have seasons, because it has no appreciable axis tilt. In fact, Jupiter's polar temperatures are quite similar to its equatorial temperatures, presumably because heat from Jupiter's interior keeps the planet uniformly warm.

Global Winds and Storms on Saturn, Uranus, and Neptune The other jovian planets also have dramatic weather patterns (FIGURE 11.11b–d). As on Jupiter, Saturn's rapid rotation creates alternating bands of rising and falling air, along with rapid east-west winds. In fact, Saturn's winds are even faster than Jupiter's—a surprising finding that scientists have yet to explain. We might expect seasons on Saturn, because it has an axis tilt similar to that of Earth. Some seasonal weather changes have been observed, but Saturn's internal heat keeps temperatures about the same year-round and planetwide.

Neptune's atmosphere is also banded, and we have seen a high-pressure storm, called the *Great Dark Spot,* similar to Jupiter's Great Red Spot. However, the Great Dark Spot did not last as long, disappearing from view just 6 years after its discovery. Like Saturn, Neptune has an axis tilt similar to Earth's, but it has relatively little seasonal change because of its internal heat.

The greatest surprise in jovian weather comes from Uranus. When *Voyager 2* flew past Uranus in 1986, photographs revealed virtually no clouds and no banded structures like those found on the other jovian planets. Scientists attributed the lack of weather to the lower internal heat of Uranus. However, more recent observations from the Hubble Space Telescope and ground-based adaptive optics telescopes show storms raging in Uranus's atmosphere. The storms may be brewing because of the changing seasons: Thanks to Uranus's extreme axis tilt and 84-year orbit of the Sun [**Section 7.1**], its northern hemisphere began to see sunlight only in 2007 after decades of night.

Do jovian planets have magnetospheres like Earth's?

Recall that Earth has a global magnetic field generated by the movements of charged particles in our planet's metallic outer core (see Figure 9.6c). The jovian planets also have global magnetic fields generated by motions of charged particles deep in their interiors. Just as with Earth, these magnetic fields create bubble-like *magnetospheres* that surround the planets and shield them from the solar wind.

Jupiter's Magnetosphere Of the four jovian planets, Jupiter has by far the strongest magnetic field; it is some 20,000 times as strong as Earth's magnetic field. As discussed in Chapter 9, a planet can have a global magnetic field if it has (1) an interior region of electrically conducting fluid, (2) convection in that layer of fluid, and (3) at least moderately rapid rotation. In Jupiter's case, the electrically conducting fluid region is its thick layer of metallic hydrogen (see Figure 11.4). The great extent of this region, combined with Jupiter's rapid rotation, explains Jupiter's strong magnetic field.

Jupiter's strong magnetic field gives it an enormous magnetosphere that begins to deflect the solar wind some 3 million kilometers (about 40 Jupiter radii) in front of Jupiter (FIGURE 11.12). If we could see Jupiter's magnetosphere, it would be larger than the full moon in our sky.

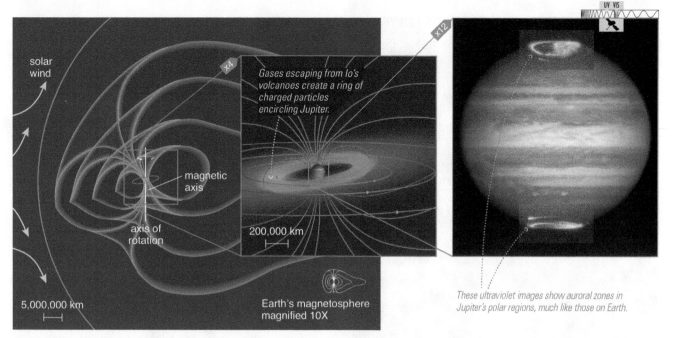

solar
wind

magnetic
axis

axis of
rotation

5,000,000 km

Gases escaping from Io's volcanoes create a ring of charged particles encircling Jupiter.

200,000 km

Earth's magnetosphere
magnified 10X

UV VIS

These ultraviolet images show auroral zones in Jupiter's polar regions, much like those on Earth.

FIGURE 11.12 Jupiter's strong magnetic field gives it an enormous magnetosphere. Gases escaping from Io feed the donut-shaped torus, and particles entering Jupiter's atmosphere near its magnetic poles contribute to auroras on Jupiter. The image at the right is a composite of ultraviolet images of the polar regions overlaid on a visible image of the whole planet, all taken by the Hubble Space Telescope.

Jupiter's magnetosphere traps far more charged particles than Earth's, largely because it has a source of particles that Earth's lacks. Nearly all the charged particles in Earth's magnetosphere come from the solar wind, but in Jupiter's case its volcanically active moon, Io, contributes many additional particles. These particles help create auroras on Jupiter. They also create belts of intense radiation around Jupiter, which can cause damage to orbiting spacecraft.

Jupiter's magnetosphere, in turn, has important effects on Io and the other moons of Jupiter. The charged particles bombard the surfaces of Jupiter's icy moons, with each particle blasting away a few atoms or molecules. This process alters the surface materials and can even generate thin atmospheres, much like the thin atmospheres of Mercury and the Moon [**Section 10.3**]. On Io, bombardment by charged particles leads to the continuous escape of gases that were released by volcanic outgassing. The escaping gases are ionized and feed a donut-shaped charged particle belt, called the *Io torus*, that approximately traces Io's orbit (the red "donut" in Figure 11.12). Scientists hope to learn much more about Jupiter's interior, atmosphere, and magnetosphere through NASA's *Juno* mission, which will orbit Jupiter for about a year after its arrival in 2016.

Comparing Jovian Magnetospheres The other jovian planets also have magnetic fields and magnetospheres, but theirs are much weaker than Jupiter's (although still much stronger than Earth's). The strength of each planet's magnetic field depends primarily on the size of the electrically conducting layer buried in its interior. Saturn's magnetic field is weaker than Jupiter's because it has a thinner layer of electrically conducting metallic hydrogen. Uranus and Neptune, smaller still, have no metallic hydrogen at all. Their relatively weak magnetic fields must be generated in their core "oceans" of hydrogen compounds, rock, and metals.

The size of a planet's magnetosphere depends not only on the magnetic field strength, but also on the pressure of the solar wind against it. The pressure of the solar wind is weaker at greater distances from the Sun, so the magnetospheric "bubbles" surrounding more distant planets are larger than they would be if these planets were closer to the Sun. That is why Uranus and Neptune have moderate-size magnetospheres despite their weak magnetic fields (**FIGURE 11.13**). No other magnetosphere is as full of charged particles as Jupiter's, primarily because no other jovian planet has a satellite like Io. Because trapped particles generate auroras, Jupiter has the brightest auroras, while those of the more distant jovian planets are progressively weaker.

We still have much to learn about the jovian magnetic fields and magnetospheres. For example, we generally expect magnetic fields to be closely aligned with planetary rotation, because the magnetic fields are generated within the rotating interiors of planets. However, while this is the case for Jupiter and Saturn (whose magnetic fields are inclined to their rotation axes by 10° and 0°, respectively), it is not the case for Uranus and Neptune. *Voyager* observations showed that the magnetic field of Uranus is tipped by a whopping 60° relative to its rotation axis, and the magnetic field's center is also significantly offset from the planet's center. Neptune's magnetic field is inclined by 46° to its rotation axis. No one has yet explained these surprising observations.

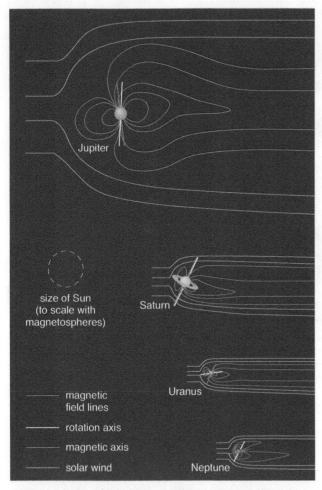

FIGURE 11.13 Comparison of jovian planet magnetospheres. Note the significant tilts of the magnetic fields of Uranus and Neptune compared to their rotation axes. (Planet sizes exaggerated compared to scale of magnetospheres.)

11.2 A WEALTH OF WORLDS: SATELLITES OF ICE AND ROCK

The jovian planets are majestic and fascinating, but they are only the beginning of our exploration of jovian planet *systems*. Each of the four jovian systems includes numerous moons and a set of rings. The total mass of all the moons and rings put together is minuscule compared to that of any one of the jovian planets, but the remarkable diversity of these satellites makes up for their lack of size. In this section, we'll explore a few of the most interesting aspects of the jovian moons.

What kinds of moons orbit the jovian planets?

We now know of more than 170 moons orbiting the jovian planets. Jupiter and Saturn have the most, each with more than 60 moons known to date. It's helpful to organize these moons into three groups by size: small moons less than about 300 kilometers in diameter, medium-size moons ranging from about 300 to 1500 kilometers in diameter, and large moons more than 1500 kilometers in diameter. These categories

are useful because size relates to geological activity. In general, larger moons are more likely to show evidence of past or present geological activity.

FIGURE 11.14 shows a montage of all the medium-size and large moons. These moons resemble the terrestrial planets in many ways. Each is spherical with a solid surface and its own unique geology. Some possess atmospheres, hot interiors, and even magnetic fields. The two largest—Jupiter's moon Ganymede and Saturn's moon Titan—are larger than the planet Mercury, while four others (Jupiter's moons Io, Europa, and Callisto and Neptune's moon Triton) are larger than the largest known dwarf planets, Pluto and Eris. However, they differ from terrestrial worlds in their compositions: Because they formed in the cold outer solar system, most of these worlds contain substantial amounts of ice in addition to metal and rock.

Most of the medium-size and large moons probably formed by accretion within the disks of gas surrounding individual jovian planets [**Section 8.2**]. That explains why their orbits are almost circular and lie close to the equatorial plane of their parent planet, and also why these moons orbit in the same direction in which their planet rotates. Nearly all

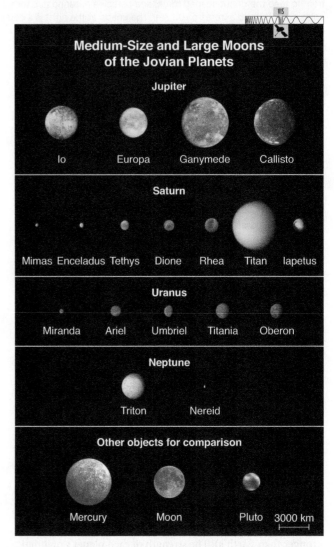

FIGURE 11.14 The medium-size and large moons of the jovian planets, with sizes shown to scale. The moons are shown in order of distance from their planet, from left (nearest) to right (farthest).

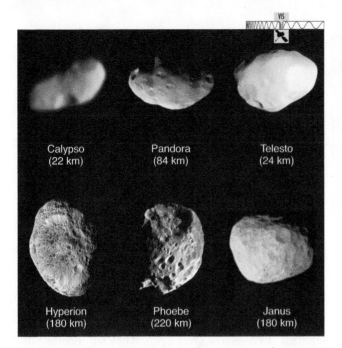

FIGURE 11.15 These photos from the *Cassini* spacecraft show six of Saturn's smaller moons. All are much smaller than the smallest moons shown in Figure 11.14. Their irregular shapes are due to their small size, which makes their gravities too weak to force them into spheres. The sizes in parentheses represent approximate lengths along their longest axes.

Calypso (22 km)   Pandora (84 km)   Telesto (24 km)

Hyperion (180 km)   Phoebe (220 km)   Janus (180 km)

The small moons have irregular shapes, much like potatoes (FIGURE 11.15), because their gravities are too weak to force their rigid material into spheres. We have not studied these moons in depth, but we expect their small sizes to allow for little if any geological activity. For the most part, the small moons are just chunks of ice and rock held captive by the gravity of a massive jovian planet.

In case you are wondering, scientists originally named Jupiter's moons for the mythical lovers of the Roman god Jupiter. However, Jupiter has so many moons that more recent discoveries are named for more distant mythological relations. Saturn's moon Titan is named for the Greek gods called the Titans, who ruled before Zeus (Jupiter); other moons of Saturn are named for individual Titans. Moons of Uranus all take their names from characters in the works of William Shakespeare and Alexander Pope, while moons of Neptune are all characters related to the sea in Greek and Roman mythology.

Why are Jupiter's Galilean moons so geologically active?

We are now ready to embark on a brief tour of the most interesting moons of the jovian planets. Our first stop is Jupiter. Jupiter's four largest moons, known as the *Galilean moons* because Galileo discovered them [**Section 3.3**], are all large enough that they would count as planets or dwarf planets if they orbited the Sun (FIGURE 11.16).

Io: The Most Volcanically Active World in the Solar System

For anyone who thinks of moons as barren, geologically dead places like our own Moon, Io shatters the stereotype. When the *Voyager* spacecraft first photographed Io up close about three decades ago, we discovered a world with a surface so young that not a single impact crater has survived. Moreover, *Voyager* cameras recorded volcanic eruptions in progress as the spacecraft passed by. We now know that Io is by far the most volcanically active world in our solar system. Large volcanoes pockmark its entire surface

these moons also share an uncanny trait: They always keep the same face turned toward their planet, just as our Moon always shows the same face to Earth. This synchronous rotation arose from the strong tidal forces [**Section 4.5**] exerted by the jovian planets, which caused each moon to end up with equal periods of rotation and orbit regardless of how fast the moon rotated when it formed.

The medium-size and large moons tend to have more interesting geology, but small moons are more numerous. Many small moons are probably captured asteroids or comets, and thus do not follow any particular orbital patterns. Dozens of the smallest moons have been discovered only within the past few years, and many more may yet be discovered. (See Table E.3 in Appendix E for a current list.)

1000 km

Io   Europa   Ganymede   Callisto

FIGURE 11.16 This set of photos, taken by the *Galileo* spacecraft, shows global views of the four Galilean moons. Sizes are shown to scale; Io is about the size of Earth's Moon. Colors have been enhanced to show detail.

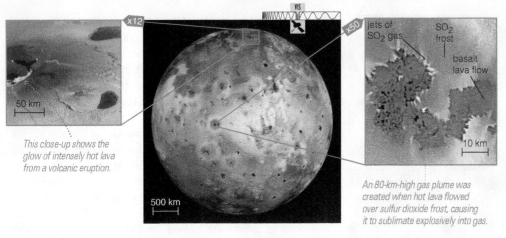

This close-up shows the
glow of intensely hot lava
from a volcanic eruption.

50 km

500 km

jets of
SO₂ gas

SO₂
frost

basalt
lava flow

10 km

An 80-km-high gas plume was
created when hot lava flowed
over sulfur dioxide frost, causing
it to sublimate explosively into gas.

FIGURE 11.17 interactive photo Io is the most volcanically active body in the solar system. Most of the black, brown, and red spots on the surface are recently active volcanic features. White and yellow areas are sulfur dioxide and sulfur deposits, respectively, from volcanic gases. (Photographs from the *Galileo* spacecraft; some colors slightly enhanced or altered.)

(**FIGURE 11.17**), and eruptions are so frequent that they constantly repave the surface. Io probably also has tectonic activity, because tectonics and volcanism generally go hand in hand. However, debris from volcanic eruptions has probably buried most tectonic features.

Many of Io's frequent eruptions are surprisingly similar to those of volcanoes on Earth. Some of the taller volcanoes appear to be shield volcanoes built from flows of basalt lava, and the eruptions are accompanied by outgassing. The primary gases released from Io's volcanoes are sulfur dioxide (SO₂), sulfur, and a hint of sodium. Some of this gas escapes into space, where it supplies ionized gas (plasma) to the Io torus and Jupiter's magnetosphere, and some of it gives Io a very thin atmosphere. Much of the gas condenses and falls back to the surface, where the sulfur gives Io its distinctive red and orange colors and the sulfur dioxide makes a white frost (**FIGURE 11.18**). As hot lava flows across the surface, it can re-vaporize the sulfur dioxide surface ice in much the same way that lava flowing into the ocean vaporizes water on Earth. Io's low gravity and thin atmosphere allow tall plumes of this vaporized sulfur dioxide to rise upward to altitudes of

hundreds of kilometers. Over a period of a few months, fallout from these tall volcanic plumes can blanket an area the size of Arizona.

Io's active volcanoes tell us that it must be quite hot inside. However, Io is only about the size of our geologically dead Moon, so it should have long ago lost any heat from its birth and it is too small for radioactivity to provide much ongoing heat. How, then, can Io be so hot inside? The only possible answer is that some other ongoing process must be heating Io's interior. Scientists have identified this process and call it **tidal heating**, because it arises from effects of tidal forces exerted by Jupiter.

Just as Earth exerts a tidal force that causes the Moon to keep the same face toward us at all times [**Section 4.5**], a tidal force from Jupiter makes Io keep the same face toward Jupiter as it orbits. But Jupiter's mass makes this tidal force far larger than the tidal force that Earth exerts on the Moon. Moreover, Io's orbit is slightly elliptical, so its orbital speed and distance from Jupiter vary. This variation means that the strength and direction of the tidal force change slightly as Io moves through each orbit, which in turn changes the size and orientation of Io's tidal bulges (**FIGURE 11.19a**). The result is that Io is continuously being flexed in different directions, which generates friction inside it. The flexing heats the interior in the same way that flexing warms Silly Putty. Tidal heating generates tremendous heat on Io—more than 200 times as much heat (per gram of mass) as the radioactive heat driving much of Earth's geology. This heat explains Io's volcanic activity. The energy for tidal heating ultimately comes from Jupiter's rotation, which is gradually slowing, although at a rate too small to be observed.

VIS IR

Three large plumes lit by the Sun
blanket the surface in sulfur-rich
snow . . .

. . . while many more eruptions
are visible on Io's night side
glowing in the infrared.

FIGURE 11.18 Two views of Io's volcanoes taken by *New Horizons* on its way to Pluto. Io rotated a little between these images, so the eruption at the top is the same one in both cases.

SEE IT FOR YOURSELF

Pry apart the overlapping ends of a paper clip so that you can hold one end in each hand. Flex the ends apart and together until the paper clip breaks. Lightly touch the broken end to your finger or lips—can you feel the warmth produced by flexing? How is this heating similar to the tidal heating of Io?

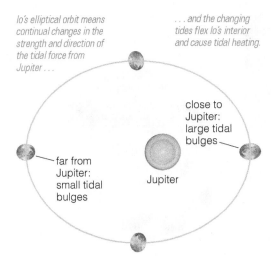

Io's elliptical orbit means continual changes in the strength and direction of the tidal force from Jupiter . . .

. . . and the changing tides flex Io's interior and cause tidal heating.

close to Jupiter: large tidal bulges

far from Jupiter: small tidal bulges

Jupiter

a Tidal heating arises because Io's elliptical orbit (exaggerated in this diagram) causes varying tides.

FIGURE 11.19 interactive figure These diagrams explain the cause of tidal heating on Io. Tidal heating has a weaker effect on Europa and Ganymede, because they are farther from Jupiter and tidal forces weaken with distance.

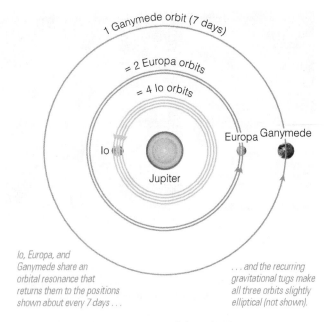

1 Ganymede orbit (7 days)

= 2 Europa orbits

= 4 Io orbits

Io   Europa Ganymede

Jupiter

Io, Europa, and Ganymede share an orbital resonance that returns them to the positions shown about every 7 days . . .

. . . and the recurring gravitational tugs make all three orbits slightly elliptical (not shown).

b Io's orbit is elliptical because of the orbital resonance Io shares with Europa and Ganymede.

However, we are still left with a deeper question: Why is Io's orbit slightly elliptical, when almost all other large satellites have nearly circular orbits? The answer lies in an interesting dance executed by Io and its neighboring moons (**FIGURE 11.19b**). During the time Ganymede takes to complete one orbit of Jupiter (about 7 days), Europa completes exactly two orbits and Io completes exactly four orbits. The three moons therefore line up periodically, and the gravitational tugs they exert on one another add up over time.* Because the tugs are always in the same direction with each alignment, they tend to stretch out the orbits, making them slightly elliptical. The effect is much like that of pushing a child on a swing. If timed properly, a series of small pushes can add up to a *resonance* that causes the child to swing quite high. For the three moons, the resonance that makes their orbits elliptical comes from the small gravitational tugs that repeat at each alignment.

The phenomenon of orbital periods falling into a simple mathematical relationship is called an **orbital resonance**. Resonances are quite common in planetary systems. For example, they affect not only the Galilean moons but also planetary rings, the asteroid belt, and the Kuiper belt in our solar system, and they affect the orbits of some of the planets known around other stars.

Europa: The Water World? Europa offers a striking contrast to Io. Instead of having active volcanoes dotting its surface, Europa is covered by water ice (see Figure 11.16). Nevertheless, its fractured, frozen surface must hide an interior made hot by the same type of tidal heating that powers Io's volcanoes, though tidal heating is weaker on Europa because it lies farther from Jupiter.

Key evidence about how the hot interior affects the icy surface comes from the fact that Europa has only a handful of impact craters. This fact tells us that some type of ongoing geological activity must have erased the evidence of nearly all past impacts. But what is doing the erasing?

Scientists suspect that the answer is either liquid water rising up from an ocean that lies beneath the icy crust or interior water ice that is just warm enough to undergo convection, so that some of it rises up and flows across the surface. Close-up photos of the surface, combined with the fact that Europa has enough internal heat to melt subsurface ice into liquid water, support the ocean hypothesis. For example, **FIGURE 11.20** shows some of the many double-ridged cracks visible on Europa's surface. As the model at the right shows, these cracks are best explained by assuming that the icy crust can slide on a softer or liquid layer below. The double ridges may form as tidal stresses force parts of the icy crust to scrape past each other, warming and possibly melting the ice along the fault.

Other *Galileo* data provide additional support for the ocean hypothesis. Theoretical models based on *Galileo* measurements of the strength of gravity over different parts of the surface indicate that Europa has a metallic core and a rocky mantle surrounded by enough water to make a layer of ice about 100 kilometers thick. The models suggest that the upper 5 to 25 kilometers of the water should be solidly frozen as an icy crust, but that tidal heating should provide enough warmth to turn the underlying ice into a layer of either liquid water or relatively warm, convecting ice. Evidence favoring the idea that the underlying layer consists of liquid water comes from magnetic field data collected by the *Galileo* spacecraft. Europa is one of only a few moons in the solar system to have a magnetic field, and its magnetic field changes as Jupiter rotates. The simplest way to explain this change is if Europa's magnetic field is created (or *induced*)

---

*You may wonder why periodic alignments occur. Like synchronous rotation, they are not a coincidence but rather a consequence of feedback from the tides that the moons raise on Jupiter. The periodic tugs the moons exert on one another actually work to sustain the recurring alignments.

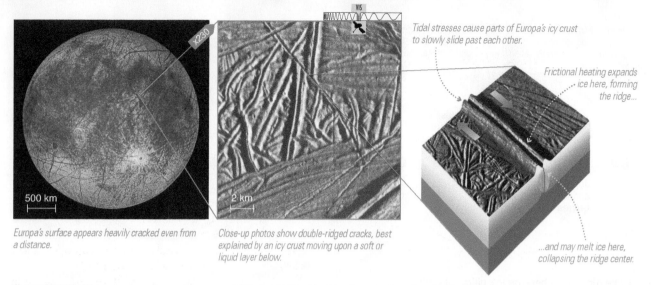

Tidal stresses cause parts of Europa's icy crust to slowly slide past each other.

Frictional heating expands ice here, forming the ridge...

...and may melt ice here, collapsing the ridge center.

Europa's surface appears heavily cracked even from a distance.

Close-up photos show double-ridged cracks, best explained by an icy crust moving upon a soft or liquid layer below.

FIGURE 11.20 This sequence shows how some of the many double-ridged cracks found on Europa's surface may have formed. (Photos are from the *Galileo* spacecraft; colors are enhanced in the global view.)

in response to the rotation of Jupiter's strong magnetic field. This type of response is possible only if Europa has a *liquid* layer of electrically conducting material. A salty ocean would fit the bill, but convecting ice would not. The data also suggest that Europa's liquid ocean must be global in extent, and that it is about as salty as Earth's oceans. Further support for this idea comes from another of *Galileo's* instruments, which found evidence for salty compounds on Europa's surface—possible seepage from a briny deep.

Taken together, the evidence from surface photos, gravitational measurements, and magnetic fields makes a strong case for a deep ocean of liquid water on Europa (**FIGURE 11.21**). Because Europa must have a hot interior from tidal heating, it seems reasonable to imagine that volcanic vents dot the seafloor and sometimes erupt, creating rising plumes of warm water. These plumes may lead to the formation of subsurface lakes within the icy crust, which could cause cracking of the icy

surface above. Surface features that look like jumbled icebergs, such as the region shown on the right of Figure 11.21, may be explained by such cracking.

If these ideas are correct, then Europa may have a hidden ocean containing more than twice as much liquid water as all of Earth's oceans combined, along with a seafloor dotted with the same types of volcanic vents around which life thrives in Earth's oceans. That is why scientists are so interested in the possibility that Europa might also be home to life—a possibility we'll explore further in Chapter 24.

Ganymede: King of the Moons Ganymede is the largest moon in the solar system, and its surface tells of a complex geological history. Like Europa, Ganymede has a surface of water ice. However, while Europa's surface appears relatively young everywhere, Ganymede's surface appears to have a dual personality (**FIGURE 11.22**). Some regions are dark

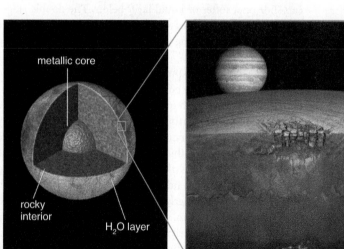

metallic core

rocky interior

H_2O layer

Europa may have a 100-km-thick ocean under an icy crust.

Rising plumes of warm water may sometimes create lakes within the ice, causing the crust above to crack . . .

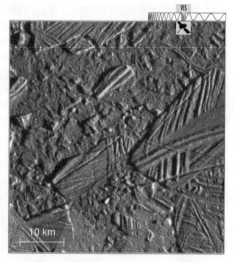

. . . explaining surface terrain that looks like a jumble of icebergs suspended in a place where liquid or slushy water froze.

FIGURE 11.21 This sequence shows a model of Europa's interior structure based on *Galileo* data, along with a *Galileo* surface photo that may tell us about processes occurring in the ice and ocean below. (The layer thicknesses are not to scale in the central panel.)

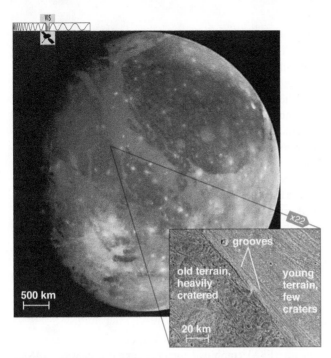

FIGURE 11.22 Ganymede, the largest moon in the solar system, has both old and young regions on its surface of water ice. The dark regions are heavily cratered and must be billions of years old, while the light regions are younger landscapes where eruptions of water have presumably erased ancient craters; the long grooves in the light regions were probably formed by water erupting along surface cracks. Notice that the boundary between the two types of terrain can be quite sharp.

and densely cratered, suggesting that they look much the same today as they did billions of years ago. Other regions are light-colored with very few craters. In some cases, fairly sharp boundaries separate the two types of terrain.

The young terrain argues for occasional upwelling of liquid water or icy slush to the surface. This material would cover craters before refreezing, explaining why there are so few craters in this terrain. The long grooves are probably made by the eruption of water or slush along a crack in the surface. As the water in the crack freezes, it expands and pushes outward, creating the groove.

If liquid water occasionally wells up to the surface, could it mean that Ganymede has a subsurface ocean like that thought to exist on Europa? The case for an ocean on Ganymede is less strong than the case for an ocean on Europa, but magnetic field measurements indicate that such an ocean is possible. Like Europa, Ganymede has a magnetic field that varies with Jupiter's rotation, suggesting the presence of a salty ocean beneath the surface.

One difficulty with the idea of an ocean on Ganymede is figuring out the source of the heat needed to melt subsurface ice. Because Ganymede is farther from Jupiter than Europa or Io, its tidal heating is weaker and could not by itself supply enough heat to melt ice today. However, Ganymede's larger size means it should retain more heat from radioactive decay. Perhaps tidal heating and radioactive decay together provide enough heat to make a liquid layer beneath the icy surface. If so, the lesser heating on Ganymede means that its ocean probably lies at least 150 kilometers beneath the surface—much deeper than Europa's potential ocean.

Callisto: Last of the Galilean Moons The outermost Galilean moon, Callisto, looks most like what scientists originally expected for an outer solar system satellite: a heavily cratered iceball (FIGURE 11.23). The bright, circular patches on its surface are impact craters. They are probably bright because large impacts blast out "clean" ice from deep underground, and this ice reflects more light than the dirtier ice that has been on the surface longer.

Craters make sense on an old surface like Callisto's, but other features are more difficult to interpret. For example, close-up photos show a dark, powdery substance concentrated in low-lying areas, leaving ridges and crests bright white (small photo in Figure 11.23). The dark powder may be debris left behind when ice sublimates into gas from Callisto's surface, much as dark material is left behind on a comet's nucleus when ice sublimates away [**Section 12.2**].

Despite its relatively large size (the third-largest moon in the solar system), Callisto lacks volcanic and tectonic features. This tells us that it lacks any significant source of internal heat. In fact, gravity measurements by the *Galileo* spacecraft showed that Callisto never underwent differentiation: Dense rock and lighter ice are mixed throughout most of its interior, which means that its interior never warmed significantly. The lack of heat is not surprising: Callisto has no tidal heating because it does not participate in the orbital resonances that affect the other three Galilean moons, and we do not expect its icy interior to contain enough radioactive material to supply much heat through radioactive decay.

Nevertheless, it is possible that Callisto, too, may hide a subsurface ocean. Like Europa and Ganymede, Callisto has a magnetic field that suggests the presence of a salty interior ocean. Perhaps Callisto's surface provides just enough

Callisto is heavily cratered, indicating an old surface that nonetheless may hide a deeply buried ocean.

Close-up photo shows a dark powder overlaying the low areas of the surface.

FIGURE 11.23 Callisto, the outermost of the four Galilean moons, has a heavily cratered, icy surface.

insulation for heat from radioactive decay to melt water beneath the thick, icy crust. If so, we face the intriguing possibility that there could be oceans on three worlds orbiting Jupiter—with far more total ocean than we find here on Earth.

What is remarkable about Titan and other major moons of the outer solar system?

Leaving Jupiter behind, we will continue our tour of moons by discussing the major moons of Saturn, Uranus, and Neptune. We'll go in planetary order, first focusing special attention on Saturn's enigmatic Titan, the second-largest moon in the solar system after Ganymede.

Saturn's Moon Titan: Piercing the Veil Titan is unique among the moons of our solar system in having a thick atmosphere—so thick that it hides the surface from view, except at a few specific wavelengths of light (**FIGURE 11.24**). Titan's color comes from chemicals in its atmosphere, which act much like those that make smog over cities on Earth. The atmosphere is about 90% molecular nitrogen (N_2), not that different from the 77% nitrogen content of Earth's atmosphere. However, on Earth the rest of the atmosphere is mostly oxygen, while the rest of Titan's atmosphere consists of argon, methane (CH_4), ethane (C_2H_6), and other hydrogen compounds.

Titan's atmospheric composition can be understood in terms of our general understanding of atmospheric production and loss processes [**Section 10.2**]. Titan's icy composition supplies methane and ammonia gas through evaporation, sublimation, and possibly volcanic eruptions. Solar ultraviolet light breaks down some of those molecules, releasing hydrogen atoms and leaving highly reactive compounds containing carbon and nitrogen. The hydrogen atoms can leave Titan forever by thermal escape, while the remaining molecular fragments can react to make the other ingredients of Titan's

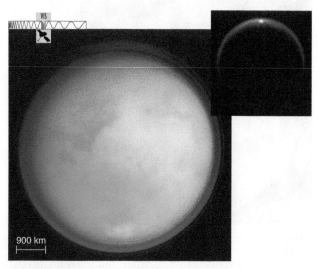

FIGURE 11.24 Titan, as photographed by the *Cassini* spacecraft, is enshrouded by a thick atmosphere with clouds and haze. *Cassini* was outfitted with filters designed to peer through the atmosphere at specific near-infrared wavelengths of light. The inset shows sunlight reflecting off Kraken Mare, Titan's largest lake.

atmosphere. For example, the abundant molecular nitrogen is made after ultraviolet light breaks down ammonia (NH_3) molecules, and ethane is made from methane.

The methane and ethane in Titan's atmosphere are both greenhouse gases and therefore give Titan an appreciable greenhouse effect [**Section 10.1**] that makes it warmer than it would be otherwise. Still, because of its great distance from the Sun, its surface temperature is a frigid 93 K (−180°C). The surface pressure on Titan is about 1.5 times the sea level pressure on Earth, which would be fairly comfortable if not for the lack of oxygen and the cold temperatures.

A moon with a thick atmosphere would be intriguing enough, but we have at least two other reasons for special interest in Titan. First, its complex atmospheric chemistry probably produces numerous organic chemicals—the chemicals that are the basis of life. Second, although it is far too cold for liquid water to exist on Titan's surface, conditions are right for methane or ethane rain, perhaps making rivers that feed into lakes or oceans.

Titan is so intriguing that NASA and the European Space Agency (ESA) combined forces to explore it, with NASA's *Cassini* "mother ship" releasing the ESA-built probe called *Huygens* (pronounced "Hoy-guns"), which parachuted to Titan's surface in 2005 (**FIGURE 11.25**). During its descent, the probe photographed river valleys merging together, flowing down to what looks like a shoreline. On landing, instruments on the probe discovered that the surface has a hard crust but is a bit squishy below, perhaps like sand with liquid mixed in, and photos showed "ice boulders" rounded by erosion. All these results support the idea of a wet climate—but wet with liquid methane rather than liquid water.

Cassini observations of Titan have also taught us a lot. The brighter regions in the photographs are icy hills, perhaps made by ice volcanoes. The dark valleys were probably created when methane rain carried down "smog particles" that concentrated on river bottoms. The vast plains into which the valleys appear to empty are low-lying regions, but they do not appear to be liquid. Instead, they are probably covered by smog particles carried down by the rivers and then sculpted into vast dune fields by Titan's global winds. All in all, conditions in Titan's equatorial regions appear to be analogous to those of the desert southwest of the United States, where infrequent rainfall carves valleys and creates vast dry lakes called *playas* where the water evaporates or soaks into the ground.

The polar regions of Titan, revealed by *Cassini* radar, contain numerous lakes of liquid methane or ethane (**FIGURE 11.26**). Images also reveal polar storm clouds and riverbeds leading into the lakes, suggesting that Titan has a methane/ethane cycle resembling the water cycle on Earth. Interestingly, while almost all of the lakes lie at high northern latitudes, most of the storm clouds have been seen in the south. The reason is probably traceable to Titan's seasons. Titan shares Saturn's 27° axis tilt, which gives it seasons, and Saturn's 29-year orbit of the Sun makes the four seasons last about 7 years each. So far, *Cassini*'s observations have been mostly during Titan's southern hemisphere summer, and the summer warmth explains the rising air responsible for the methane storm clouds seen there. On Earth, the warmth of a summer afternoon or of

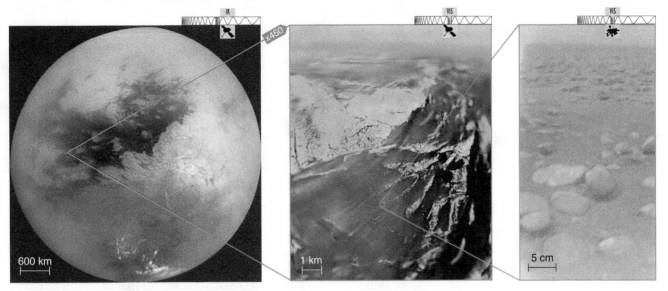

FIGURE 11.25 **Interactive photo** This sequence zooms in on the *Huygens* landing site on Titan. Left: A global view taken by the *Cassini* orbiter. Center: An aerial view from the descending probe. Right: A surface view taken by the probe after landing; the "rocks," which are 10 to 20 centimeters across, are presumably made of ices. Keep in mind that you are looking at the surface of a world more than a billion kilometers away.

Earth's equatorial region creates storm clouds that produce intense rainfall, but Titan's southern hemisphere storms apparently don't produce enough rainfall to create many lakes in the south. The situation may differ for the northern hemisphere, because Saturn's elliptical orbit brings it (and Titan) closer to the Sun during northern summer. The more intense northern summer may create stronger circulation and storms with enough rainfall to fill the northern hemisphere lakes. This hypothesis is being tested now: Spring has begun in Titan's northern hemisphere, and *Cassini* is monitoring the storms and lake depths.

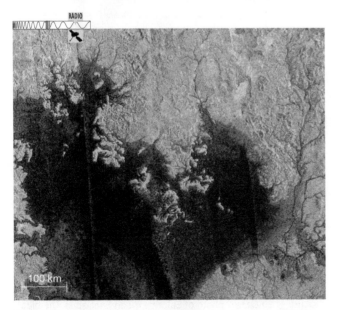

FIGURE 11.26 Radar image of Ligeia Mare near Titan's north pole showing lakes of liquid methane and ethane at a temperature of −180°C. Most solid surfaces reflect radar well, and these regions are artificially shaded tan to suggest land. The liquid surfaces reflect radar poorly, and these regions are shaded blue and black to suggest lakes.

Perhaps the most astonishing result from the *Cassini/Huygens* mission is how familiar the landscape looks in this alien environment with these unfamiliar materials. Instead of liquid water, Titan has liquid methane and ethane. Instead of rock, Titan has ice. Instead of molten lava, Titan has a slush of water ice mixed with ammonia. Instead of surface dirt, Titan's surface has smog-like particles that rain out of the sky and accumulate on the ground. Evidently, the similarities between the physical processes that occur on Titan and Earth are far more important in shaping the landscapes than the fact that the two worlds have very different compositions and temperatures.

THINK ABOUT IT

What other geological features might you expect on Titan, given its similarities to Earth? How might those features be different, given its differences?

The abundance of organic molecules on Titan, along with the similarity of its surface geology to that of Earth, makes it natural to wonder whether Titan could be home to life. Although we cannot rule it out, most scientists think it unlikely that Titan's surface could support life because of the combination of the very low temperatures and the fact that chemical properties of liquid methane and ethane make them seem less suited to supporting biology than liquid water [**Section 24.2**]. Another possibility is subsurface life. *Cassini* observations of small changes in Titan's surface gravity and shape as it orbits Saturn indicate that it probably has a subsurface ocean of liquid water, much like the subsurface ocean on Europa. However, theoretical models of Titan's interior suggest that the bottom of its ocean would be in contact with a layer of high-density ice, rather than with a rocky layer like that thought to exist at the bottom of Europa's ocean. Scientists are unsure whether this difference would have any effect on the potential habitability of Titan's subsurface ocean.

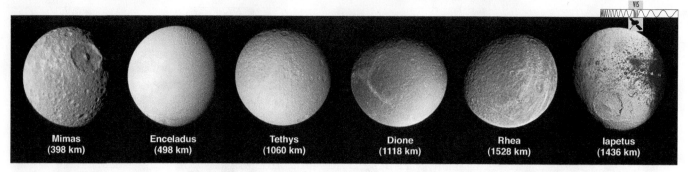

FIGURE 11.27 Portraits taken by the *Cassini* spacecraft of Saturn's medium-size moons (not to scale). All but Mimas show evidence of past volcanism and/or tectonics.

| Mimas (398 km) | Enceladus (498 km) | Tethys (1060 km) | Dione (1118 km) | Rhea (1528 km) | Iapetus (1436 km) |

Saturn's Medium-Size Moons The *Cassini* mission is also teaching us more about Saturn's other moons, especially its six medium-size moons (FIGURE 11.27). The photographs suggest that these moons have had a complex history.

Only Mimas, the smallest of these six moons, shows little evidence of past volcanism or tectonics. It is essentially a heavily cratered iceball. The huge crater visible at Mimas's upper right in Figure 11.27 is sometimes called "Darth Crater" because of Mimas's resemblance to the Death Star in the *Star Wars* movies. (The crater's official name is *Herschel*.) The impact that created this crater probably came close to breaking Mimas apart.

Most of Saturn's other medium-size moons also have heavily cratered surfaces, confirming that they lack global geological activity today. However, we find abundant evidence of volcanism and/or tectonics that must have occurred more recently. Smooth regions appear to be places where icy lava once flowed, and close-up views of the bright streaks (such as the long streaks visible on Dione) show them to be vast sets of tectonic cliffs running parallel to one another.

Iapetus is particularly bizarre (FIGURE 11.28). It has an astonishing ridge more than 10 kilometers high that spans nearly half its circumference, curiously aligned along the equator. No one knows its origin, but it is likely the result of tectonic activity. Moreover, half of Iapetus appears coated in very dark dust (some is visible at the right of the Iapetus image in Figure 11.27). The dust apparently comes from Phoebe, a dark and dusty moon which orbits Saturn in a backwards orbit at a great distance (see Figure 11.15). Small impacts easily eject dust because of Phoebe's low gravity, and the dust forms a ring as it spirals inward toward Iapetus.

Enceladus provided an even bigger surprise: This moon is barely 500 kilometers across—small enough to fit inside the borders of Colorado—and yet it shows clear evidence of *ongoing* geological activity (FIGURE 11.29). Scientists knew

FIGURE 11.28 Saturn's moon Iapetus has a 10-kilometer equatorial ridge (white arrow) that spans nearly half its circumference. The inset shows a portion of the ridge in perspective.

FIGURE 11.29 *Cassini* photo of Saturn's moon Enceladus. The blue "tiger stripes" near the bottom of the main photo are regions of fresh ice that must have recently emerged from below. The colors are exaggerated; the image is a composite made at near-ultraviolet, visible, and near-infrared wavelengths. The inset shows Enceladus backlit by the Sun, with fountains of ice particles (and water vapor) clearly visible as they spray out of the south polar region.

that Enceladus undergoes some tidal heating through an orbital resonance, but were surprised to learn that the heating is enough to make this moon active today. Its surface has very few impact craters—and some regions have none at all—telling us that recent geological activity has erased older craters. Moreover, the strange grooves near its south pole are measurably warmer than the surrounding terrain, and photographs show this region venting huge clouds of water vapor and ice crystals. These fountains must have some subsurface source, which could potentially mean the existence of an ocean beneath the icy crust. In that case, there would be at least a slim possibility that Enceladus could harbor life [**Section 24.2**].

The Medium-Size Moons of Uranus

Uranus does not have any moons that fall into our large category, but it has five medium-size moons: Miranda, Ariel, Umbriel, Titania, and Oberon (see Figure 11.14). Like other jovian moons, these moons are made largely of ice. Because of Uranus's great distance from the Sun, this ice includes a great deal of ammonia and methane as well as water.

Our only close look at these moons came during the *Voyager* flyby in 1986, which left us with many unanswered questions. For example, Ariel and Umbriel are virtual twins in size, yet Ariel shows evidence of volcanism and tectonics, while the heavily cratered surface of Umbriel suggests a lack of geological activity. Titania and Oberon also are twins in size, but Titania appears to have had much more geological activity than Oberon. No one knows why these two pairs of similar-size moons should vary so greatly in geological activity.

Miranda, the smallest of Uranus's medium-size moons, is the most surprising (FIGURE 11.30). We might expect Miranda to be a cratered iceball like Saturn's similar-size moon, Mimas. Instead, *Voyager* images of Miranda show tremendous tectonic features and relatively few craters. Why should Miranda be so much more geologically active than Mimas? Our best guess is that Miranda had an episode of tidal heating billions of years ago, perhaps during a temporary orbital resonance with another moon of Uranus. Mimas apparently never had such an episode of tidal heating and thus lacks similar features.

Neptune's Triton: A Captured Moon

The last stop on our tour is Neptune, so distant that only two of its moons (Triton and Nereid) were known to exist before the *Voyager 2* spacecraft visited it. Nereid is Neptune's only medium-size moon, and Triton is its only large moon. Triton is one of the coldest worlds in the solar system, even colder than Pluto because it reflects more of the weak sunlight that reaches the outskirts of the solar system.

Triton may appear to be a typical moon, but it is not. It orbits Neptune "backward" (opposite to Neptune's rotation) and at a high inclination to Neptune's equator. These are telltale signs of a moon that was captured rather than having formed in the disk of gas around its planet. No one knows how a moon as large as Triton could have been captured, but models suggest one possible mechanism: Triton may have once been a member of a binary Kuiper belt object that passed so close to Neptune that Triton lost energy and was captured while its companion gained energy and was flung away at high speed.

Triton's geology is just as surprising as its origin. Triton is smaller than our own Moon, yet its surface shows evidence of relatively recent geological activity (FIGURE 11.31). Some regions show evidence of past volcanism, perhaps an icy equivalent to the volcanism that shaped the lunar maria. Other regions show wrinkly ridges (nicknamed "cantaloupe terrain") that appear tectonic in nature; apparently, blobs of ice of different density have risen and fallen, contorting the crust. Triton even has a very thin atmosphere that has left wind streaks on its surface.

What could have generated the heat needed to drive Triton's geological activity? The best guess is tidal heating. Triton probably had a very elliptical orbit and a more rapid rotation when Neptune first captured it. Tidal forces would have circularized its orbit, brought it into synchronous rotation, and perhaps heated its interior enough to cause its geological activity. This idea would also explain why the geological activity has subsided with time.

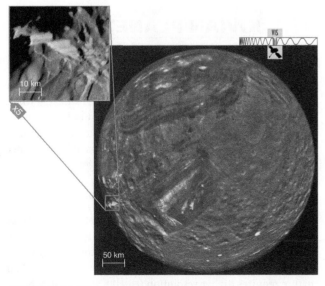

FIGURE 11.30 The surface of Miranda shows astonishing tectonic activity despite its small size. The cliff walls seen in the inset are higher than those of the Grand Canyon on Earth.

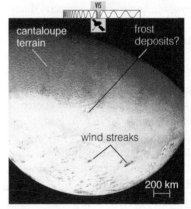

cantaloupe terrain

frost deposits?

wind streaks

200 km

Triton's southern hemisphere as seen by *Voyager 2.*

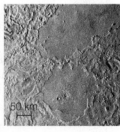

50 km

This close-up shows lava-filled impact basins similar to the lunar maria, but the lava was water or slush rather than molten rock.

FIGURE 11.31 Neptune's moon Triton shows evidence of a surprising level of past geological activity.

Terrestrial Planet Geology

- Internal heat, primarily from radioactive decay, can cause volcanic and tectonic activity.
- Only large planets retain enough internal heat to stay geologically active today.
- Example: Mars (photo above) probably retains some internal heat. If it had been smaller, like Mercury, it would be geologically "dead" today. If it had been larger, like Earth, it would probably have much more active and ongoing tectonics and volcanism.

Jovian Moon Geology

- Tidal heating can cause tremendous geological activity on moons with elliptical orbits around massive planets.
- Even without tidal heating, icy materials can melt and deform at lower temperatures than rock, increasing the likelihood of geological activity.
- Together, these effects explain why icy moons are much more likely to have ongoing geological activity than rocky terrestrial worlds of the same size.
- Example: Ganymede (photo above) shows evidence of recent geological activity, even though it is similar in size to the geologically dead terrestrial planet Mercury.

FIGURE 11.32 Jovian moons can be much more geologically active than terrestrial worlds of similar size because of their icy compositions and tidal heating, which is not important on the terrestrial worlds.

Why are small icy moons more geologically active than small rocky planets?

Based on what we learned when studying the geology of the terrestrial worlds, the active geology of the jovian moons seems out of character with their sizes. Numerous jovian moons remained geologically active far longer than Mercury or our Moon, yet they are no bigger and in many cases are much smaller in size. However, there are two crucial differences between the jovian moons and the terrestrial worlds: icy compositions and tidal heating.

Because they formed far from the Sun, most of the jovian moons contain ices that can melt or deform at far lower temperatures than rock. As a result, they can experience geological activity even when their interiors have cooled to temperatures far below those of rocky worlds. Indeed, except on Io, most of the volcanism that has occurred in the outer solar system probably did not produce any hot lava at all. Instead, it produced icy lava that was essentially liquid water, perhaps mixed with methane and ammonia.

The major lesson, then, is that "ice geology" is possible at far lower temperatures than "rock geology." This fact, combined in many cases with tidal heating, explains how the jovian moons have had such interesting geological histories despite their small sizes. In essence, the same physical properties that

allowed hydrogen compounds to condense as ices in the outer solar system also allowed the worlds made from these ices to stay geologically active for long periods of time. FIGURE 11.32 summarizes the differences between the geology of jovian moons and that of the terrestrial worlds.

11.3 JOVIAN PLANET RINGS

The jovian planet systems have three major components: the planets themselves, the moons, and the rings that encircle the planets. We have already studied the planets and their moons, so we now turn our attention to their amazing rings. For a long time, Saturn's rings were thought to be unique in the solar system. We now know that all four jovian planets have rings. We'll begin by exploring the rings of Saturn, since they are by far the most spectacular.

What are Saturn's rings like?

Saturn's rings have dazzled and puzzled astronomers since Galileo first saw them through his small telescope and suggested that they resembled "ears" on Saturn. You can see the rings through a backyard telescope, but learning their nature requires higher resolution (FIGURE 11.33). Earth-based views make the rings appear to be continuous, concentric sheets of material separated by a large gap (called the

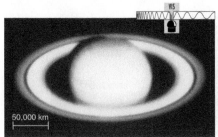

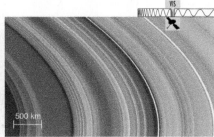

a This Earth-based telescopic view of Saturn makes the rings look like large, concentric sheets. The dark gap within the rings is called the *Cassini division*.

b This image of Saturn's rings from the *Cassini* spacecraft reveals many individual rings separated by narrow gaps.

c Artist's conception of particles in a ring system. Particles clump together because of gravity, but small random velocities cause collisions that break them up.

FIGURE 11.33 Interactive figure Zooming in on Saturn's rings.

Cassini division). Spacecraft images reveal these "sheets" to be made of many individual rings, each separated from the next by a narrow gap. But even these appearances are somewhat deceiving. If we could wander into Saturn's rings, we'd find that they are made of countless icy particles ranging in size from dust grains to large boulders, sometimes clumped together by their mutual gravity. All are far too small to be photographed even from spacecraft passing nearby.

Ring Particle Characteristics Spectroscopy reveals that Saturn's ring particles are made of relatively reflective water ice. The rings look bright where they contain enough particles to intercept sunlight and scatter it back toward us. We see gaps in places where there are few particles to reflect sunlight.

Each individual ring particle orbits Saturn independently in accord with Kepler's laws, so the rings are much like myriad tiny moons. The individual ring particles are so close together that they collide frequently. In the densest parts of the rings, each particle collides with another every few hours. However, the collisions are fairly gentle: Despite the high orbital speeds of the ring particles, nearby ring particles are moving at nearly the same speed and touch only gently when they collide.

THINK ABOUT IT

Which ring particles travel faster: those closer to Saturn or those farther away? Explain why. (*Hint*: Review Kepler's third law.)

The frequent collisions explain why Saturn's rings are perhaps the thinnest known astronomical structure. They span more than 270,000 kilometers in diameter but are only a few tens of *meters* thick. The rings are so thin that they disappear from view when we see Saturn edge-on, as we do around the equinoxes of its 29.5-year orbit of the Sun.

To understand how collisions keep the rings thin, imagine what would happen to a ring particle on an orbit slightly inclined to the central ring plane. The particle would collide with other particles every time its orbit intersected the ring plane, and its orbital tilt would be reduced with every collision. Before long, these collisions would force the particle to conform to the orbital pattern of the other particles, and any particle that moved away from the narrow ring plane would

soon be brought back within it. A similar idea explains why ring particles have almost perfectly circular orbits: Any particle with an elliptical orbit would quickly suffer enough collisions to force it into an orbit matching that of its neighbors.

Rings and Gaps Close-up photographs show an astonishing number of rings, gaps, ripples, and other features—as many as 100,000 altogether. Scientists are still struggling to explain all the features, but some general ideas are now clear.

Rings and gaps are caused by particles bunching up at some orbital distances and being forced out at others. This bunching happens when gravity nudges the orbits of ring particles in some particular way. One source of nudging comes from small moons located within the gaps in the rings themselves, sometimes called *gap moons*. The gravity of a gap moon can effectively keep the gap clear of smaller ring particles while creating ripples in the ring edges (**FIGURE 11.34a**). The ripples appear to move in opposite directions on the two sides of the gap, because ring particles on the inner side orbit Saturn slightly faster than the gap moon, while those on the outer side orbit slightly slower than the gap moon. In some cases, two nearby gap moons can force particles between them into a very narrow ring (**FIGURE 11.34b**). The gap moons are often called *shepherd moons* in those cases, because they act like a shepherd forcing particles into line.

Ring particles also may be nudged by the gravity from larger, more distant moons. For example, a ring particle orbiting about 120,000 kilometers from Saturn's center will circle the planet in exactly half the time it takes the moon Mimas to orbit. Every time Mimas returns to a certain location, the ring particle will also be at its original location and therefore will experience the same gravitational nudge from Mimas. The periodic nudges reinforce one another and clear a gap in the rings—in this case, the large gap visible from Earth (the Cassini division). This type of reinforcement due to repeated gravitational tugs is another example of an *orbital resonance*, much like the orbital resonances that make Io's orbit elliptical (see Figure 11.19). Some resonances create vast numbers of ripples and waves that travel great distances through the rings (**FIGURE 11.35**). Other orbital resonances, caused by moons both within the rings and farther out from Saturn, probably explain most of the intricate structures visible in ring photos.

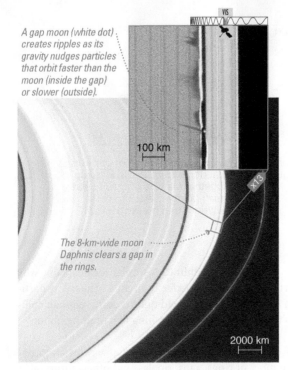

A gap moon (white dot) creates ripples as its gravity nudges particles that orbit faster than the moon (inside the gap) or slower (outside).

100 km

The 8-km-wide moon Daphnis clears a gap in the rings.

2000 km

a Some small moons create gaps within the rings.

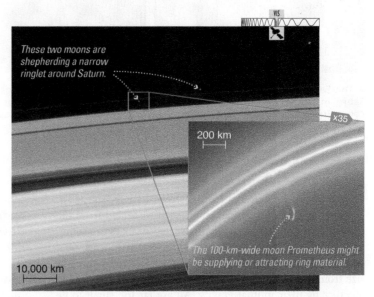

These two moons are shepherding a narrow ringlet around Saturn.

200 km

The 100-km-wide moon Prometheus might be supplying or attracting ring material.

10,000 km

b Some moons force particles between them into a very narrow ring, as is the case with the two shepherd moons shown here. The inset shows a close-up of one of them.

FIGURE 11.34 Small moons within the rings have important effects on ring structure (*Cassini* photos).

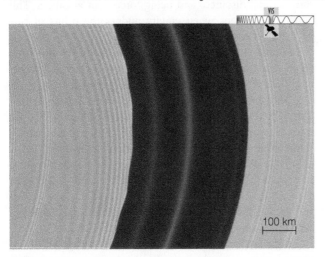

100 km

FIGURE 11.35 This *Cassini* image of a gap in Saturn's rings shows how gravitational tugs from the moon Pan create waves that shape the rings over vast distances.

How do other jovian ring systems compare to Saturn's?

The rings of Jupiter, Uranus, and Neptune are so much fainter than Saturn's that it took almost four centuries longer to discover them. Ring particles in these three systems are far less numerous, generally smaller, and much darker. Despite these differences, a family portrait of the jovian ring systems shows many similarities (FIGURE 11.36). All rings lie in their planet's equatorial plane. Particle orbits are nearly circular, with small orbital tilts relative to the equator. Individual rings and gaps are probably shaped by gap moons, shepherd moons, and orbital resonances.

Uranus's rings were discovered in 1977 during observations of a *stellar occultation*—a star passing behind Uranus as

seen from Earth. During the occultation, the star "blinked" on and off nine times before it disappeared behind Uranus and nine more times as it emerged. Scientists concluded that these nine "blinks" were caused by nine thin rings encircling Uranus. Similar observations of stars passing behind Neptune yielded more confounding results: Rings appeared to be present at some times but not at others. Could Neptune's rings be incomplete or transient?

The *Voyager* spacecraft provided some answers. *Voyager* cameras first discovered thin rings around Jupiter in 1979. After next providing incredible images of Saturn's rings, *Voyager 2* photographed the rings of Uranus as it flew past in 1986. In 1989, *Voyager 2* passed by Neptune and found that it does, in fact, have partial rings—at least when seen from Earth. The space between the ring segments is filled with dust not detectable from Earth. In addition to the dust within the rings of Neptune, *Voyager 2* detected vast dust sheets between the widely separated rings of both Uranus and Neptune.

The differences among the ring systems present us with unsolved mysteries. The larger size, higher reflectivity, and much greater number of particles in Saturn's rings compel us to wonder whether different processes might be at work there. We do not know why Uranus's thin rings have a slight tilt and slightly eccentric orbits, nor do we know why Neptune's rings contain dusty regions that make them appear as partial rings when viewed from Earth. Scientists hope that we may someday learn the answers with new missions to visit Uranus and Neptune, but none are yet under development. Meanwhile, advances in ground-based observing, including the new technology of adaptive optics [**Section 6.3**], are providing views that in some cases rival those obtained from the *Voyager* spacecraft.

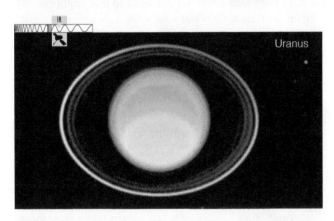

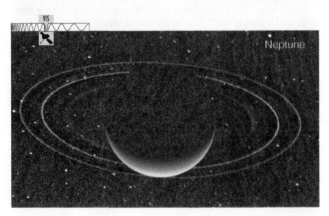

FIGURE 11.36 Four ring systems (not to scale). The rings differ in appearance and in the composition and sizes of the ring particles. (Jupiter: Keck Telescope, infrared; Saturn: *Cassini*, visible; Uranus: Hubble Space Telescope, infrared; Neptune: *Voyager*, visible.)

Why do the jovian planets have rings?

Where do rings come from? Did they form together with the planets out of the solar nebula, or are they a more recent phenomenon? An important clue is that the rings lie close to their planet in a region where tidal forces are very strong.

Within two to three planetary radii of any planet, the tidal forces tugging apart an object become comparable to the gravitational forces holding it together. (This region is often called the *Roche tidal zone*.) Only relatively small objects held together by nongravitational forces—such as the electromagnetic forces that hold solid rock, spacecraft, and human beings together—can avoid being ripped apart by the strong tidal forces in this region. Because a large moon would be ripped apart by tidal forces in the region of the rings, scientists once suspected that Saturn's rings formed after a large moon came too close to the planet. However, moons don't simply "wander" away from their orbits, and a large moon could have been deflected toward Saturn only by a close gravitational encounter with an unusually large asteroid or comet that happened to pass nearby. Such encounters should be extremely rare. Back in the days when Saturn was the only planet known to have rings, it might have seemed possible that such a rare encounter was responsible for the rings. The discovery of rings around the other jovian planets all but ruled out this possibility, because it seems inconceivable that such an unlikely event could have occurred in all four cases.

If the rings did not originate with the destruction of a large moon, where did all the ring particles come from? Another idea that once seemed reasonable was that the ring particles might be leftover chunks of rock and ice that condensed in the disks of gas that orbited each jovian planet when it was young. This would explain why all four jovian planets have rings, because tidal forces near each planet would have prevented these chunks from accreting into a full-fledged moon. However, we now know that the ring particles cannot be leftovers from the births of the planets, because they could not have survived for billions of years. Ring particles are continually being ground down in size, primarily by the impacts of the countless sand-size particles that orbit the Sun—the same types of particles that become meteors in Earth's atmosphere and cause micrometeorite impacts on the Moon [**Section 9.3**]. Millions of years of such tiny impacts would have ground the existing ring particles to dust long ago. The dust particles could not have survived either, because over time they are slightly slowed in their orbits by the pressure of sunlight, and this slowing eventually causes them to spiral into their planet. Ring particles may also be lost in other ways. For example, the thermosphere of Uranus extends up into the ring region, exerting atmospheric drag that also causes ring particles to spiral slowly into the planet. Between the effects of micrometeorite impacts and other processes, *none* of the abundant small particles that now occupy the jovian rings can have been there since the solar system formed more than 4 billion years ago.

We are left with only one reasonable possibility: New particles must be continually supplied to the rings to replace those that are destroyed. These new particles must come from a source that lies in each planet's equatorial plane. The most likely source is numerous small "moonlets"—moons the size

jovian planet

Tidal forces near the planet prevent small moonlets from accreting into larger moons.

Moonlets are occasionally disrupted by impacts.

Ongoing small impacts blast off dust and debris to form the rings.

FIGURE 11.37 This illustration summarizes the origin of rings around the jovian planets.

of gap moons (see Figure 11.34)—that formed in the disks of material orbiting the young jovian planets. As with the ring particles themselves, tiny impacts are gradually grinding away these small moons, but they are large enough to still exist despite $4\frac{1}{2}$ billion years of such sandblasting.

The small moons contribute ring particles in two ways. First, each tiny impact releases particles from a small moon's surface, and these released particles become new, dust-size ring particles. Ongoing impacts ensure that some ring particles are present at all times. Second, occasional larger impacts can shatter a small moon completely, creating a supply of boulder-size ring particles. The frequent tiny impacts then slowly grind these boulders into smaller ring particles. Some of these particles are "recycled" by forming into small clumps, only to come

apart again later on; others are ground down to dust and slowly spiral onto their planet. In summary, all ring particles ultimately come from the gradual dismantling of small moons that formed during the birth of the solar system (**FIGURE 11.37**).

The collisions that shatter small moons and generate large ring particles must occur only occasionally and at essentially random times, which means that the numbers and sizes of particles in any particular ring system may vary dramatically over millions and billions of years. Rings could be broad and bright when they are full of particles and almost invisible when particles are few. The brilliant spectacle of Saturn's rings could be a special treat of our epoch, one that might not have been seen a billion years ago and that might not last long on the time scale of our solar system.

The Big Picture

Putting Chapter 11 into Context

In this chapter, we saw that the jovian planets really are a different kind of planet and, indeed, a different kind of planet system. As you continue your study of the solar system, keep in mind the following "big picture" ideas:

- The jovian planets dwarf the terrestrial planets. Even some of their moons are as large as terrestrial worlds.

- The jovian planets may lack solid surfaces on which geology can occur, but they are interesting and dynamic worlds with rapid winds, huge storms, strong magnetic fields, and interiors in which common materials behave in unfamiliar ways.

- Despite their relatively small sizes and frigid temperatures, many jovian moons are geologically active by virtue of their icy compositions—a result of their formation in the outer regions of the solar nebula—and tidal heating.

- Ring systems probably owe their existence to small moons formed in the disks of gas that produced the jovian planets billions of years ago. The rings we see today are composed of particles liberated from those moons quite recently.

- Understanding the jovian planet systems forced us to modify many of our earlier ideas about the solar system by adding the concepts of ice geology, tidal heating, and orbital resonances. Each new set of circumstances that we discover offers new opportunities to learn how our universe works.

11.1 A DIFFERENT KIND OF PLANET

- **Are jovian planets all alike?** Jupiter and Saturn are made almost entirely of hydrogen and helium, while Uranus and Neptune are made mostly of hydrogen compounds mixed with metals and rock. These differences arose because all four planets started from ice-rich planetesimals of about the same size, but captured different amounts of hydrogen and helium gas from the solar nebula.

- **What are jovian planets like on the inside?** The jovian planets have layered interiors with very high internal temperatures and pressures. All have a core about 10 times as massive as Earth, consisting of hydrogen compounds, metals, and rock. They differ mainly in their surrounding layers of hydrogen and helium, which can take on unusual forms under the extreme internal conditions of the planets.

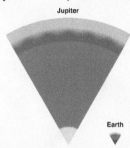

- **What is the weather like on jovian planets?** The jovian planets all have multiple cloud layers that give them distinctive colors, fast winds, and large storms. Some storms, such as Jupiter's **Great Red Spot,** can apparently rage for centuries or longer.

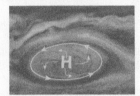

- **Do jovian planets have magnetospheres like Earth's?** Jupiter has a magnetic field 20,000 times stronger than Earth's, which leads to an enormous magnetosphere. Many of the particles in Jupiter's magnetosphere come from volcanic eruptions on Io. Other jovian planets also have magnetic fields and magnetospheres, but they are weaker and smaller than Jupiter's.

11.2 A WEALTH OF WORLDS: SATELLITES OF ICE AND ROCK

- **What kinds of moons orbit the jovian planets?** We can categorize the more than 170 known moons as small, medium-size, or large. Most of the medium-size and large moons probably formed with their planet in the disks of gas that surrounded the jovian planets when they were young. Smaller moons are often captured asteroids or comets.

- **Why are Jupiter's Galilean moons so geologically active?** Io is the most volcanically active object in the solar system, thanks to an interior kept hot by **tidal heating**—which occurs because Io's close orbit is made elliptical by **orbital resonances** with other moons. Europa (and possibly Ganymede) may have a deep, liquid water ocean under its icy crust, also thanks to tidal heating. Callisto is the least geologically active, since it has no orbital resonance or tidal heating.

- **What is remarkable about Titan and other major moons of the outer solar system?** Many medium-size and large moons show a surprisingly high level of past or present volcanism or tectonics. Titan has a thick atmosphere and ongoing erosion, and Enceladus is also geologically active today. Triton, which apparently was captured by Neptune, also shows signs of recent geological activity.

- **Why are small icy moons more geologically active than small rocky planets?** Ices deform and melt at much lower temperatures than rock, allowing icy volcanism and tectonics at surprisingly low temperatures. In addition, some jovian moons have a heat source—tidal heating—that is not important for the terrestrial worlds.

11.3 JOVIAN PLANET RINGS

- **What are Saturn's rings like?** Saturn's rings are made up of countless individual particles, each orbiting Saturn independently like a tiny moon. The rings lie in Saturn's equatorial plane, and they are extremely thin. Moons within and beyond the rings create many ringlets and gaps in part through orbital resonances.

- **How do other jovian ring systems compare to Saturn's?** The other jovian planets have ring systems that are much fainter in photographs. Their ring particles are generally smaller, darker, and less numerous than Saturn's ring particles.

- **Why do the jovian planets have rings?** Ring particles probably come from the dismantling of small moons formed in the disks of gas that surrounded the jovian planets billions of years ago. Small ring particles come from countless tiny impacts on the surfaces of these moons, while larger ones come from impacts that shatter the moons.

Use the following questions to check your understanding of some of the many types of visual information used in astronomy. Answers are provided in Appendix J. For additional practice, try the Chapter 11 Visual Quiz at MasteringAstronomy®.

visible light

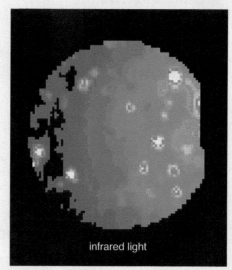

infrared light

Left: Approximate colors of Io in visible light; black spots are volcanoes that are active or have recently gone inactive. Right: Infrared thermal emission from Io; bright spots are active volcanoes. (Both images are from Galileo data, but taken at different times.)

1. What do the colors in the right image represent?
   a. the actual colors of Io's surface
   b. the colors we would see if we had infrared vision
   c. the intensity of the infrared light
   d. regions of different chemical composition on the surface
2. Which color in the right image represents the highest temperatures?
   a. blue   b. green   c. orange   d. red   e. white
3. The right image was obtained when only part of Io was in sunlight. Based on the colors which part of the surface was in sunlight?
   a. the left side
   b. the right side
   c. only the peaks of the volcanoes

4. By comparing the two images, what can you conclude about Io's volcanoes?
   a. Every black spot in the visible image has a bright spot in the infrared image, so all of Io's volcanoes were active when the photos were taken.
   b. There are more black spots in the visible image than bright spots in the infrared image, so many of Io's volcanoes were inactive when the photos were taken.
   c. There are more bright spots in the infrared image than black spots in the visible image, so new eruptions must have started after the visible photo was taken.

EXERCISES AND PROBLEMS

MasteringAstronomy®

For instructor-assigned homework go to MasteringAstronomy®.

REVIEW QUESTIONS

Short-Answer Questions Based on the Reading

1. Briefly describe how differences in composition among the jovian planets can be traced to their formation.
2. Why is Jupiter so much more dense than Saturn? Could a planet be smaller in size than Jupiter but greater in mass?
3. Briefly describe the interior structure of Jupiter and why it is layered in this way. How do the interiors of the other jovian planets compare to that of Jupiter?
4. Why does Jupiter have so much internal heat? What generates internal heat on other jovian planets?
5. Briefly describe Jupiter's atmospheric structure and cloud layers. How do the structures and clouds differ on the other jovian planets?
6. How do clouds contribute to Jupiter's colors? Why are Saturn's colors more subdued? Why are Uranus and Neptune blue?
7. Briefly describe Jupiter's weather patterns. What is the *Great Red Spot*?
8. Why does Jupiter have such a strong magnetic field? Describe a few features of Jupiter's magnetosphere and compare it to the magnetospheres of the other jovian planets.
9. Briefly describe how we categorize jovian moons by size. What is the origin of most of the medium-size and large moons? What is the origin of many of the small moons?
10. Describe key features of Jupiter's four Galilean moons, and the role of *tidal heating* and *orbital resonances* in shaping these features.
11. Describe the atmosphere and surface features of Titan. How is Titan's landscape similar to Earth's? How is it different?

12. Summarize the evidence for and some of the mysteries of past or present geological activity on the medium-size moons of Saturn and Uranus.
13. Why do we think Triton is a captured moon?
14. Briefly explain why icy moons can have active geology at much smaller sizes than rocky worlds.
15. What are planetary rings made of, and how do they differ among the four jovian planets? Briefly describe the effects of gap moons and orbital resonances on ring systems.
16. Explain why we think that ring particles must be replenished over time. Will the jovian planet rings always look the same?

TEST YOUR UNDERSTANDING

Surprising Discoveries?

Suppose someone claimed to make the discoveries described below. (These are not real discoveries.) Decide whether each discovery should be considered reasonable or surprising. More than one right answer may be possible, so explain your answer clearly.

17. Saturn's core is pockmarked with impact craters and dotted with volcanoes erupting basaltic lava.
18. Neptune's deep blue color is not due to methane, as previously thought, but instead is due to its surface being covered with an ocean of liquid water.
19. A jovian planet in another star system has a moon as big as Mars.
20. An extrasolar planet is made primarily of hydrogen and helium. It has approximately the same mass as Jupiter but is the same size as Neptune.
21. A previously unknown moon orbits Jupiter outside the orbits of other known moons. It is the smallest of Jupiter's moons but has several large, active volcanoes.
22. A previously unknown moon orbits Neptune in the planet's equatorial plane and in the same direction that Neptune rotates, but it is made almost entirely of metals such as iron and nickel.
23. An icy, medium-size moon orbits a jovian planet in a star system that is only a few hundred million years old. The moon shows evidence of active tectonics.
24. A jovian planet is discovered in a star system that is much older than our solar system. The planet has no moons but has a system of rings as spectacular as the rings of Saturn.
25. Future observations discover rainfall of liquid water on Titan.
26. During a future mission to Uranus, scientists discover that it is orbited by another 20 previously unknown moons.

Quick Quiz

Choose the best answer to each of the following. Explain your reasoning with one or more complete sentences.

27. Which lists the jovian planets in order of increasing distance from the Sun? (a) Jupiter, Saturn, Uranus, Pluto (b) Saturn, Jupiter, Uranus, Neptune (c) Jupiter, Saturn, Uranus, Neptune
28. Why does Neptune appear blue and Jupiter red? (a) Neptune is hotter, which gives bluer thermal emission. (b) Methane in Neptune's atmosphere absorbs red light. (c) Neptune's air molecules scatter blue light, much as Earth's atmosphere does.
29. Why is Jupiter denser than Saturn? (a) It has a larger proportion of rock and metal. (b) It has a larger proportion of hydrogen. (c) Its higher mass and gravity compress its interior.
30. Some jovian planets give off more energy than they receive because of (a) fusion in their cores. (b) tidal heating. (c) ongoing contraction or differentiation.
31. The main ingredients of most satellites of the jovian planets are (a) rock and metal. (b) hydrogen compound ices. (c) hydrogen and helium.

32. Why is Io more volcanically active than our moon? (a) Io is much larger. (b) Io has a higher concentration of radioactive elements. (c) Io has a different internal heat source.
33. What is unusual about Triton? (a) It orbits its planet backward. (b) It does not keep the same face toward its planet. (c) It is the only moon with its own rings.
34. Which moon shows evidence of rainfall and erosion by some liquid substance? (a) Europa (b) Titan (c) Ganymede
35. Saturn's many moons affect its rings through (a) tidal forces. (b) orbital resonances. (c) magnetic field interactions.
36. Saturn's rings (a) have looked basically the same since they formed along with Saturn. (b) were created long ago when tidal forces tore apart a large moon. (c) are continually supplied with new particles by impacts with small moons.

PROCESS OF SCIENCE

Examining How Science Works

37. *Europan Ocean.* Scientists strongly suspect that Europa has a subsurface ocean, even though we cannot see through the surface ice. Briefly explain why scientists think the ocean exists. Is this "belief" in a Europan ocean scientific? Explain.
38. *Breaking the Rules.* As discussed in Chapter 9, the geological "rules" for the terrestrial worlds tell us that a world as small as Io should not have any geological activity. However, the *Voyager* images of Io's volcanoes proved that the old "rules" had been wrong. Based on your understanding of the nature of science [**Section 3.4**], should this be seen as a failure in the process of the science? Defend your opinion.
39. *Unanswered Questions.* Choose one unanswered question about one of the jovian planets or its moons. Write a few paragraphs discussing the question and the specific types of evidence we would need to answer it.

GROUP WORK EXERCISE

40. *Comparing Jovian Moons.* Comparing the masses, radii, and densities of jovian moons reveals clues about their composition and their history. In this exercise, your team will draw on the data in Appendix E to develop a hypothesis about the moons of Jupiter. Before you begin, assign the following roles to the people in your group: *Scribe* (collects data and takes notes on the group's activities), *Proposer* (proposes hypotheses and explanations of the data), *Skeptic* (points out weaknesses in the hypotheses and explanations), *Moderator* (leads group discussion and makes sure everyone contributes). Each person should write down the answers for each part of the exercise.
    a. *Scribe* collects data on Jupiter's four largest moons from Table E.2 in Appendix E and determines which of Jupiter's moons has the greatest density. **b.** *Moderator* uses Table E.2 to determine what other solar system moon most resembles the moon from part a in mass, radius, and density. **c.** *Proposer* proposes a hypothesis about the composition of the moon from part a, based on its resemblance to the moon from part b. **d.** *Skeptic* questions the hypothesis from part c, stating concerns about its viability. **e.** *Scribe* and *Moderator* use Table E.2 to determine whether there is a trend in density with orbital distance among the major moons of Jupiter and briefly describe any trends they discover. **f.** *Proposer* offers a hypothesis that accounts for any trend found in part e. **g.** *Skeptic* raises questions about the revised hypothesis, stating any reasons to doubt it. **h.** Together, the team develops and describes an experiment that could test the hypotheses in parts c and f.

INVESTIGATE FURTHER

In-Depth Questions to Increase Your Understanding

Short-Answer/Essay Questions

41. *The Importance of Rotation.* Suppose the material that formed Jupiter came together without any rotation so that no "jovian nebula" formed and the planet today wasn't spinning. How else would the jovian system be different? Think of as many effects as you can, and explain each in a sentence.

42. *The Great Red Spot.* Based on the infrared and visible images in Figure 11.9, is Jupiter's Great Red Spot warmer or cooler than nearby clouds? Is it higher or lower in altitude than the nearby clouds? Explain.

43. *Comparing Jovian Planets.* You can do comparative planetology armed only with telescopes and an understanding of gravity.
    a. The small moon Amalthea orbits Jupiter at about the distance in kilometers at which Mimas orbits Saturn, yet Mimas takes almost twice as long to orbit. From this observation, what can you conclude about how Jupiter and Saturn differ? Explain. **b.** Jupiter and Saturn are not very different in radius. When you combine this information with your answer to part a, what can you conclude? Explain.

44. *Minor Ingredients Matter.* Suppose the jovian planets' atmospheres were composed only of hydrogen and helium, with no hydrogen compounds at all. How would the atmospheres be different in terms of clouds, color, and weather? Explain.

45. *Galilean Moon Formation.* Look up the densities of Jupiter's four Galilean moons in Appendix E, and notice that they follow a trend with distance from Jupiter. Based on what you've learned about condensation in the solar nebula, can you suggest a reason for this trend among the Galilean moons? Next, compare the densities of the moons with the planetary densities in Table E.1. Based on the comparison, do you think it was as hot toward the center of the nebula surrounding Jupiter as it was at the center of the solar nebula? Explain.

46. *Super Jupiter.* Suppose that the solar wind had not cleared the solar nebula until much later in our solar system's history, so that Jupiter accumulated 40 times as much mass as it actually has today.
    a. Make a sketch showing how the interior layers of this "Super Jupiter" would compare to the interior layers of the real Jupiter shown in Figure 11.4. **b.** How would you expect the cloud layers and colors to differ on Super Jupiter? Explain. **c.** How would you expect the wind speeds to be different on Super Jupiter? Explain. **d.** How would you expect the magnetic field to be different on Super Jupiter? Explain. **e.** Do you think Super Jupiter would have more or less excess heat than the real Jupiter? Explain.

47. *Observing Project: Jupiter's Moons.* Using binoculars or a small telescope, view the moons of Jupiter. Make a sketch of what you see, or take a photograph. Repeat your observations several times (nightly, if possible) over a period of a couple of weeks. Can you determine which moon is which? Can you measure the moons' orbital periods? Can you determine their approximate distances from Jupiter? Explain.

48. *Observing Project: Saturn's Rings.* Using binoculars or a small telescope, view the rings of Saturn. Make a sketch of what you see, or take a photograph. What season is it in Saturn's northern hemisphere? How far do the rings extend above Saturn's atmosphere? Can you identify any gaps in the rings? Describe any other features you notice.

Quantitative Problems

Be sure to show all calculations clearly and state your final answers in complete sentences.

49. *Disappearing Moon.* Io loses about a ton (1000 kilograms) of sulfur dioxide per second to Jupiter's magnetosphere.
    a. At this rate, what fraction of its mass would Io lose in 4.5 billion years? **b.** Suppose sulfur dioxide currently makes up 1% of Io's mass. When will Io run out of this gas at the current loss rate?

50. *Ring Particle Collisions.* Each ring particle in the densest part of Saturn's rings collides with another about every 5 hours. If a ring particle survived for the age of the solar system, how many collisions would it undergo?

51. *Prometheus and Pandora.* These two moons orbit Saturn at 139,350 and 141,700 kilometers, respectively.
    a. Using Newton's version of Kepler's third law, find their two orbital periods. Find the percent difference in their distances from Saturn and in their orbital periods. **b.** Consider the two in a race around Saturn: In one Prometheus orbit, how far behind is Pandora (in units of time)? In how many Prometheus orbits will Pandora have fallen behind by one of its own orbital periods? Convert this number of periods back into units of time. This is how often the satellites pass by each other.

52. *Orbital Resonances.* Using the data in Appendix E, identify the orbital resonance relationship between Titan and Hyperion. (*Hint:* If the orbital period of one were 1.5 times the orbital period of the other, we would say that they were in a 3:2 resonance.) Which medium-size moon is in a 2:1 resonance with Enceladus?

53. *Titanic Titan.* What is the ratio of Titan's mass to that of the other satellites of Saturn whose masses are listed in Appendix E? Calculate the strength of gravity on Titan compared to that on Mimas. Comment on how this affects the possibility of an atmosphere on each.

54. *Titan's Evolving Atmosphere.* Titan's exosphere lies nearly 1400 kilometers above its surface. What is the escape velocity from this altitude? What is the thermal speed of a hydrogen atom at the exospheric temperature of about 200 K? Use these answers (and the method of Mathematical Insight 10.2) to comment on whether thermal escape of hydrogen is likely to be important for Titan.

55. *Saturn's Thin Rings.* Saturn's ring system is more than 270,000 kilometers wide and only a few tens of meters thick; let's assume 50 meters thick for this problem. Assuming the rings could be shrunk down so that their diameter was the width of a dollar bill (6.6 cm), how thick would the rings be? Compare your answer to the actual thickness of a dollar bill (0.01 cm).

Discussion Questions

56. *Jovian Planet Mission.* We can study terrestrial planets up close by landing on them, but jovian planets have no surfaces to land on. Suppose that you were in charge of planning a long-term mission to "float" in the atmosphere of a jovian planet. Describe the technology you would use and how you would ensure survival for any people assigned to this mission.

57. *Pick a Moon.* Suppose you could choose any one moon to visit in the solar system. Which one would you pick, and why? What dangers would you face in your visit to this moon? What kinds of scientific instruments would you want to bring along for studies?

Web Projects

58. *News from Cassini.* Find the latest news about the *Cassini* mission to Saturn. What is the current mission status? Write a short report about the mission's status and recent findings.

59. *Ocean of Europa.* Investigate plans for future study of Europa's ocean, either from Earth or with spacecraft. Write a short summary of the plans, how they might help us learn whether Europa really has an ocean, and what the ocean might contain if it exists.

Comet McNaught and the Milky Way over Patagonia, Argentina (2007). The fuzzy patches above the comet tail are the Magellanic Clouds, satellite galaxies of the Milky Way.

12 ASTEROIDS, COMETS, AND DWARF PLANETS
THEIR NATURE, ORBITS, AND IMPACTS

LEARNING GOALS

12.1 ASTEROIDS AND METEORITES
- What are asteroids like?
- Why is there an asteroid belt?
- How are meteorites related to asteroids?

12.2 COMETS
- What are comets like?
- Where do comets come from?

12.3 PLUTO: LONE DOG NO MORE
- How big can a comet be?
- What are the large objects of the Kuiper belt like?

12.4 COSMIC COLLISIONS: SMALL BODIES VERSUS THE PLANETS
- Have we ever witnessed a major impact?
- Did an impact kill the dinosaurs?
- Is the impact threat a real danger or media hype?
- How do the jovian planets affect impact rates and life on Earth?

As we look out into the Universe and identify the many accidents of physics and astronomy that have worked to our benefit, it almost seems as if the Universe must in some sense have known that we were coming.

—Freeman Dyson

Asteroids and comets might at first seem insignificant compared to the planets and moons we've discussed so far, but there is strength in numbers, and small bodies probably number in the trillions. The appearance of a comet has more than once altered the course of human history when our ancestors acted on superstitions related to the sighting. More profoundly, asteroids or comets falling to Earth have scarred our planet with impact craters and have altered the course of biological evolution. Asteroids and comets are also important scientifically: As remnants from the birth of our solar system, they teach us about how our solar system formed.

In this chapter, we will explore the small bodies of our solar system. We'll consider asteroids and the pieces of them that fall to Earth as meteorites, comets, and dwarf planets like Pluto and Eris. We'll also explore the dramatic effects of the occasional collisions between small bodies and large planets.

12.1 ASTEROIDS AND METEORITES

The objects we've studied so far—terrestrial planets, jovian planets, and large moons—have changed dramatically since their formation. We have used these objects to infer much about the history of our solar system, but they no longer hold direct clues to what the solar system was like when it was born. In contrast, many small bodies remain much as they were when they first formed, some 4.5 billion years ago. Comets, asteroids, and meteorites therefore have the story of our solar system's birth encoded in their compositions, locations, and numbers.

Using these small bodies to understand planetary formation is a bit like picking through the trash in a carpenter's shop to see how furniture is made. By studying the scraps, sawdust, paint chips, and glue, we can develop some understanding of how the carpenter builds furniture. Asteroids, comets, and meteorites are the "scraps" left over from the formation of our solar system, so their study can give us an understanding of how the planets and larger moons came to exist.

We'll begin our study of small bodies by focusing on asteroids and meteorites, which are closely related. As we discussed in Chapter 8, asteroids are planetesimals (or fragments of planetesimals) left over from the birth of our solar system. Asteroids and meteorites are therefore closely related: Most meteorites are pieces of asteroids that orbited the Sun for billions of years before falling to Earth.

What are asteroids like?

The word *asteroid* means "starlike," but asteroids are starlike only in their appearance through a telescope. Asteroids are virtually undetectable by the naked eye and remained unnoticed for almost two centuries after the invention of the telescope. The first asteroids were discovered about 200 years ago, and it took 50 years to discover the first 10. Today, advanced telescopes can discover far more than that in a single night, and around 600,000 asteroids have been cataloged. Asteroids can be recognized in telescopic images because they move relative to the stars (FIGURE 12.1).

Newly discovered asteroids first get a provisional name based on the discovery year and month and order of discovery; for example, the first asteroid discovered in January 2015 would be called Asteroid 2015 AA. (Once letters run out, numbers are added after the letters.) An asteroid's orbit can be calculated from the law of gravity [**Section 4.4**], even after observation of only a fraction of a complete orbit, but less than half of the asteroids identified in images have been tracked long enough for their orbits to be calculated. In those cases, the discoverer may choose a name for the asteroid, subject to approval by the International Astronomical Union. The earliest discovered asteroids bear the names of mythological figures. More recent discoveries often carry names of scientists, cartoon heroes, pets, rock stars, or textbook authors.

Asteroid Sizes, Numbers, and Shapes Asteroids come in a wide range of sizes. The largest, Ceres, is just under 1000 kilometers in diameter, which is a little over a quarter of the Moon's diameter. About a dozen others are large enough that we would call them medium-size moons if they orbited a planet. Smaller asteroids are far more numerous. There are probably more than a million asteroids with diameters greater than 1 kilometer, and many more even smaller in size. Despite their large numbers, asteroids don't add up to much in total mass. If we could put all the asteroids together and allow gravity to compress them into a sphere, they'd make an object less than 2000 kilometers in diameter—just over half the diameter of our Moon.

FIGURE 12.1 interactive photo Because asteroids orbit the Sun, they move through our sky relative to the stars. In this long-exposure photograph, stars show up as distinct dots, while the motion of an asteroid relative to the stars makes it show up as a short streak.

10 km

Annefrank
(*Stardust*)

Dactyl (*Galileo*)

Ida
(*Galileo*)

Steins (*Rosetta*)

Eros
(*NEAR*)

Braille (*Deep Space 1*)

Gaspra
(*Galileo*)

Itokawa (*Hayabusa*)

Mathilde
(*NEAR*)

Lutetia
(*Rosetta*)

Vesta

Size of the Moon to scale

FIGURE 12.2 Images of all the asteroids visited by spacecraft as of 2013 shown to scale. Some objects were the destinations of dedicated missions; others were imaged on the way to different targets. The size of Earth's Moon is included for comparison.

Asteroid shapes depend on the strength of the asteroid's gravity. If an object is large enough, over time gravity can mold it into a spherical shape, even if the object is solid throughout. Some large bodies may also have had enough heat to have been molten inside at one time, allowing gravity to work faster. Among asteroids, Ceres is large enough for gravity to have compressed it into a roughly spherical shape—allowing it to qualify as a *dwarf planet* (see Special Topic, page 8). The next two largest asteroids are somewhat "squashed" (Pallas, with equatorial diameter 580 kilometers and polar diameter 500 kilometers; and Vesta, with equatorial diameter 570 kilometers and polar diameter 460 kilometers). For smaller asteroids, gravity is too weak to reshape the rocky material. Much like potatoes, these asteroids have a variety of shapes. Some objects that appear to be single asteroids are probably two or more distinct objects held in contact by a weak gravitational attraction, while other small asteroids are little more than weakly bound piles of rubble.

Measuring Sizes and Shapes Given that most asteroids appear even to powerful telescopes as little more than moving dots of light similar to that in Figure 12.1, you may wonder how we can make general statements about their sizes and shapes. In about a dozen cases, we've sent spacecraft to visit asteroids, giving us clear pictures of what they look like (**FIGURE 12.2**). Note the numerous craters, confirming that asteroids, like planets and moons, have been battered by impacts.

For the majority of asteroids, which we can observe only through telescopes, we can learn about sizes through careful measurements of brightness. Asteroids shine with reflected sunlight, so an asteroid's brightness in our sky depends on its size, distance, and reflectivity. For example, if two asteroids at the same distance have the same reflectivity, the one that appears brighter must be larger in size. We can determine an asteroid's distance from its position in its orbit. Determining reflectivity is more difficult, but we can do it by comparing the asteroid's brightness in visible light to its brightness in infrared light. The visible light is reflected sunlight, while the infrared light is thermal radiation emitted by the asteroid itself [**Section 5.4**]; the latter depends on the asteroid's temperature, which in turn depends on how much sunlight it absorbs. Comparing the visible and infrared brightness therefore tells us the proportions of incoming sunlight that an asteroid reflects and absorbs. Once we know these proportions, the asteroid's brightness and distance tell us its size. This technique has been used to make size estimates for more than a thousand asteroids.

THINK ABOUT IT

Suppose you discover two asteroids of similar size that are equally bright in visible light, but infrared observations tell you that Asteroid 1 is more reflective than Asteroid 2. Which one is farther away? Explain.

Determining asteroid shapes without close-up photographs is difficult but not impossible. In some cases, we can determine shape by monitoring brightness variations as an asteroid rotates: A nonspherical asteroid with a uniformly bright surface will reflect more light when it presents its larger side toward the Sun and our telescopes. In other cases, astronomers have determined shapes by bouncing radar signals off asteroids that have passed close to Earth.

Asteroid Compositions Analysis of light can also tell us about asteroid compositions. Recall that spectra of distant objects contain spectral lines that are essentially "fingerprints" left by the objects' chemical constituents [**Section 5.4**]. Thousands of asteroids have been analyzed through spectroscopy. The results are consistent with what we expect from our theory of solar system formation: Asteroids are made mostly of metal and rock, because they condensed within the frost line in the solar nebula. Those near the outskirts of the asteroid belt contain larger proportions of dark, carbon-rich material, because this material was able to condense at the relatively cool temperatures found in this region of the solar nebula but not in the regions closer to the Sun; some even contain small amounts of water, telling us that they formed close to the frost line. A few asteroids appear to be made mostly of metals, such as iron, suggesting that they may be fragments of the metal cores of shattered worlds.

Asteroid Masses and Densities The only direct way to measure a distant object's mass is to observe its gravitational effect on another object. We've been able to observe the gravitational effects of asteroids in only a few cases: those in which a spacecraft has passed by close enough to have its trajectory altered by the asteroid's gravity, and those in which asteroids have even smaller asteroids as tiny, orbiting "moons." For asteroids with moons, such as the asteroid Ida with its tiny moon Dactyl (see Figure 12.2) and the asteroid Eugenia in FIGURE 12.3, we can determine the mass of the central asteroid by applying Newton's version of Kepler's third law to the orbital characteristics of the moon [**Section 4.4**]. Astronomers have found a few dozen asteroid masses by this method.

Once we have measured an asteroid's mass and size, we can calculate its density. The density can offer valuable insights into the asteroid's origin and makeup. For example, the asteroid Eros (see Figure 12.2) has a density of 2.4 g/cm³, which is close to the value expected for solid rock; notice the subtle pattern of surface ridges and troughs that hints at a set of parallel faults and fractures in its interior. In contrast, the asteroid Mathilde has a density of only 1.5 g/cm³, which is so low that it must be a loosely bound "rubble pile," held together by its weak gravity, rather than a solid chunk of rock. Support for this idea comes from the fact that Mathilde has a huge, central crater (see Figure 12.2): The impact that formed this crater would have shattered a solid object, but a "rubble pile" could absorb the shock and remain intact.

Asteroid Orbits The vast majority of the asteroids that have been cataloged are located in the asteroid belt between the orbits of Mars and Jupiter (FIGURE 12.4). All asteroids orbit the Sun in the same direction as the planets, but their orbits tend to be more elliptical and more highly inclined to the ecliptic plane (up to 20°–30°) than those of planets.

Science fiction movies often show the asteroid belt as a crowded and hazardous place, but the asteroid belt is so large that asteroids are quite far apart on average. The average distance between asteroids in the asteroid belt is millions of kilometers—the equivalent of grains of sand separated by kilometers.

Not all asteroids are located in the asteroid belt. Two sets of asteroids, called *Trojan asteroids*, share Jupiter's 12-year orbit around the Sun. One clump of Trojan asteroids always stays 60° ahead of Jupiter in its orbit and the other clump always

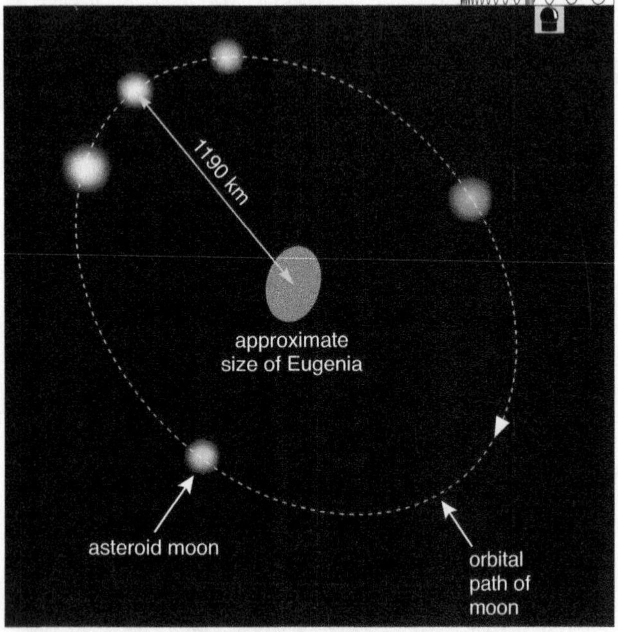

FIGURE 12.3 This set of images, made by a telescope using adaptive optics [**Section 6.3**], shows a small moon observed in five positions in its orbit around the asteroid Eugenia. The moon completes one orbit around the asteroid every 4.7 days. The asteroid itself was blocked out during the observations and is shown as the gray oval in the image.

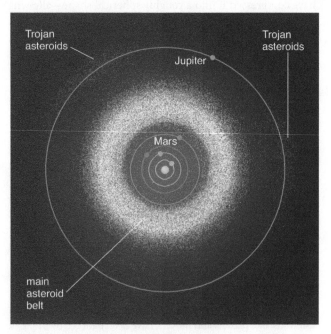

FIGURE 12.4 This figure shows the positions of more than 150,000 asteroids on a single night. To scale, the asteroids themselves would be much smaller than shown. The asteroids that share Jupiter's orbit, found 60° ahead of and behind Jupiter, are called *Trojan asteroids*.

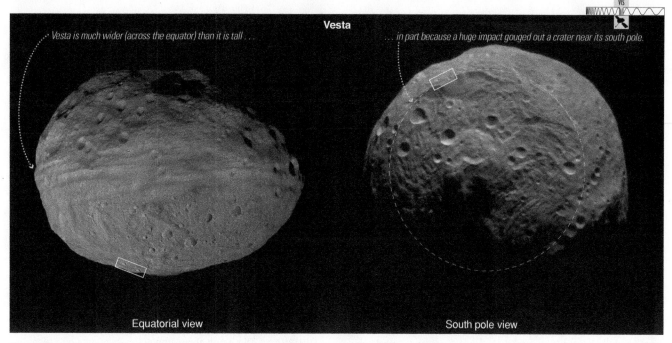

Vesta

Vesta is much wider (across the equator) than it is tall . . .

. . . in part because a huge impact gouged out a crater near its south pole.

Equatorial view

South pole view

FIGURE 12.5 Global images of Vesta taken by the *Dawn* spacecraft. The white boxes show the same pair of craters in the two views, and the dashed circle is the outline of the huge polar crater.

stays 60° behind. The number of Trojan asteroids could be as large as the number in the asteroid belt, but the greater distance to the Trojan asteroids (and their darker surfaces) makes them more difficult to study or even count from Earth.

A relatively small number of asteroids have orbits that pass through the inner solar system—including the *near-Earth asteroids* that pass near Earth's orbit. These asteroids are probably "impacts waiting to happen." Many asteroids with similar orbits must have hit our planet in the past. In Section 12.4, we will discuss both past impacts and the future dangers these asteroids may pose.

The *Dawn* Mission Our most detailed knowledge of asteroids comes from those few that have been visited by spacecraft. The most in-depth studies are under way with the *Dawn* spacecraft, which spent a year orbiting Vesta, the second-most-massive asteroid (Pallas is slightly larger in size but smaller in mass), in 2011/12. *Dawn* is scheduled to enter orbit of the largest asteroid, Ceres, in 2015.

It's long been suspected that Vesta is massive enough to have undergone differentiation, giving it a metallic core, a low-density rocky crust, and a mantle in between. *Dawn* images (FIGURE 12.5) revealed that Vesta is relatively far from being a perfect sphere, as it is nearly 25% wider (equatorial) than it is tall (polar). This irregular shape is probably in large part a result of the impact that gouged out the huge impact crater at Vesta's south pole. Nevertheless, the nonspherical shape makes it debatable whether Vesta should qualify as a dwarf planet, and as of 2012 no official decision had been made.

Vesta's south polar crater is remarkable in many ways. Like many large craters, it has a central mountain formed from the rebound after the impact. But at 23 kilometers tall, this mountain may be the largest in the solar system. The impact that formed this crater excavated so deeply into Vesta's interior that it should have blasted out substantial amounts of rock from the crust and mantle. Measurements from the *Dawn* spacecraft and from the Hubble Space Telescope confirm that the composition of rock near the crater's center is unlike that of surface rocks anywhere else in the solar system, but matches the composition of rock expected deep inside terrestrial worlds. The specific spectral signature of this rock matches that of many small asteroids and of many meteorites that have been found on Earth (including the meteorite shown on the right in Figure 12.9b), suggesting that these asteroids and meteorites are pieces of Vesta that were blasted away by the impact that formed the south polar crater.

Vesta still presents numerous mysteries. For example, the spectral signature of basalt, a volcanic rock, is present on Vesta and in the asteroids and meteorites that appear to have come from it, but *Dawn* scientists have not yet identified any ancient volcanoes or lava flows. Perhaps they've been hidden by billions of years of cratering. In addition, Vesta's equator is ringed with ridges that currently defy explanation.

Why is there an asteroid belt?

The asteroid belt between Mars and Jupiter gets its name from the fact that it is where we find the majority of asteroids. But why are asteroids concentrated in this region, and why didn't a full-fledged planet form here? The answers lie in *orbital resonances* much like those that explain the elliptical orbits of Jupiter's moons Io, Europa, and Ganymede [**Section 11.2**] and the gaps and other structures in Saturn's rings [**Section 11.3**].

Recall that an orbital resonance occurs whenever two objects periodically line up with each other. Because gravity tugs at the objects in the same direction at each alignment, the effects can build up over time. Objects will periodically line up—and hence have an orbital resonance—whenever one object's orbital period is a simple ratio of another object's period, such as $\frac{1}{2}$, $\frac{1}{4}$, or $\frac{2}{5}$.

In the asteroid belt, orbital resonances occur between asteroids and Jupiter, the most massive planet by far. These resonances tend to clear gaps in the asteroid belt, much as resonances clear gaps in Saturn's rings. For example, any asteroid in an orbit in which it takes 6 years to circle the Sun—half of Jupiter's 12-year orbital period—would receive the same gravitational nudge from Jupiter every 12 years and therefore would soon be pushed out of this orbit. The same is true for asteroids with orbital periods of 4 years ($\frac{1}{3}$ of Jupiter's period) and 3 years ($\frac{1}{4}$ of Jupiter's period). Music offers an elegant analogy: When a vocalist sings into an open piano, the strings of notes "in resonance" with the voice—not just the note being sung but also notes with a half or a quarter of the note's frequency—are "nudged" and begin to vibrate.

We can see the results of these orbital resonances on a graph of the numbers of asteroids with various orbital periods (**FIGURE 12.6**). For example, notice the lack of asteroids with periods exactly $\frac{1}{2}$, $\frac{1}{3}$, or $\frac{1}{4}$ of Jupiter's—periods for which the gravitational tugs from Jupiter have cleared gaps in the asteroid belt. (The gaps are often called *Kirkwood gaps,* after their discoverer.)

Orbital resonances with Jupiter likely also explain why no planet ever formed between Mars and Jupiter. When the solar system was forming, this region of the solar nebula probably contained enough rocky material to form another planet as large as Earth or Mars. However, resonances with the young planet Jupiter disrupted the orbits of this region's planetesimals, preventing them from accreting into a full-fledged planet. Over the ensuing 4.5 billion years, ongoing orbital disruptions gradually kicked pieces of this "unformed planet" out of the asteroid belt altogether. Once booted from the asteroid belt, these objects either crashed into a planet or moon or were flung out of the solar system. The asteroid belt thereby lost most of its original mass, which explains why the total mass of all its asteroids is now less than that of any terrestrial planet.

THINK ABOUT IT

Why are the gaps due to orbital resonances so easy to see in Figure 12.6 but so hard to see in Figure 12.4? (*Hint:* The top axis in Figure 12.6 is the *average* orbital distance.)

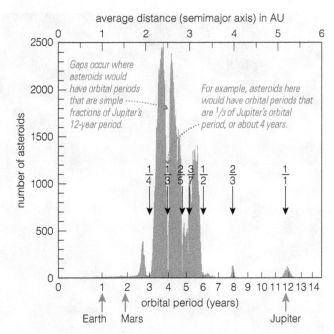

FIGURE 12.6 This graph shows the numbers of asteroids with various orbital periods, which correspond to different average distances from the Sun (labeled along the top). Notice the gaps created by orbital resonances with Jupiter.

The asteroid belt is still undergoing slow change. Jupiter's gravity continues to nudge asteroid orbits, sending asteroids on collision courses with each other and occasionally the planets. A major collision occurs somewhere in the asteroid belt every 100,000 years or so. Over long periods of time, larger asteroids therefore tend to be broken into smaller ones, along with numerous dust-size particles. The asteroid belt has been grinding itself down for more than 4 billion years and will continue to do so for as long as the solar system exists.

Most orbital resonances result in gaps, but some actually gather asteroids. Such is the case for the Trojan asteroids. Their orbits remain stable in the zones 60° ahead of and behind Jupiter, because any asteroid that wanders away from one of these zones is nudged back into the zone by Jupiter's gravity. That explains why we see a grouping of asteroids, rather than a gap, at the $\frac{1}{1}$ resonance (where orbital periods are the same as Jupiter's) in Figure 12.6.

How are meteorites related to asteroids?

Because asteroids are leftovers from the birth of our solar system, studying samples of them should teach us a lot about how Earth and the other planets formed. You might think it would be difficult to obtain such samples, but in fact, we already have tens of thousands of them—the rocks called *meteorites* that fall from the sky.

The Difference Between Meteors and Meteorites

In everyday language, people often use the terms *meteors* and *meteorites* interchangeably. Technically, however, a **meteor** (which means "a thing in the air") is only a flash of light caused by a particle entering our atmosphere at high speed, not the particle itself. Meteors are sometimes called *shooting stars* or *falling stars*, because some people once thought they really were stars falling from the sky.

The vast majority of the particles that make meteors are no larger than peas and burn up completely before reaching the ground. Only in rare cases is a meteor caused by a chunk of rock large enough to survive the plunge through our atmosphere and leave a *meteorite* (which means "associated with meteors") on the ground. Those cases make unusually bright meteors, called *fireballs*. Observers find a few meteorites each year by following the trajectories of fireballs. Meteorites found in this way can be especially valuable to science, because we can trace their trajectories back to learn exactly where they came from and because they can be collected before they have much time to be contaminated by terrestrial material.

Meteorite Falls People didn't always accept that rocks fall from the sky. Stories of such events arose occasionally in human history, and sometimes even affected it. For example, stories of "fallen stars" influenced the philosophy of the ancient Greek scientist Anaxagoras (see Figure 3.12), who concluded that planets and stars were flaming rocks in the sky. Anaxagoras's assumption that meteorites fell from the heavens made him the first person in history known to believe that the heavens and Earth are made of the same materials, even though his guess about the nature of planets and stars was not quite correct. Many later scientists regarded stories of fallen stars more skeptically. Upon hearing of a meteorite fall in Connecticut, Thomas Jefferson (who was a student of science as well as politics) reportedly said, "It is easier to believe that Yankee professors would lie than that stones would fall from heaven."

Today we know that rocks really do fall from the heavens (FIGURE 12.7). Meteorites are often blasted apart in their fiery descent through our atmosphere, scattering fragments over an area several kilometers across. A direct hit on the head by a meteorite would be fatal, but there are no reliable accounts of human deaths from meteorites. Of course, most meteorites fall into the ocean, which covers three-fourths of Earth's surface.

Unless you actually see a meteorite fall, it can be difficult to distinguish a meteorite from an Earth rock. Fortunately, a few clues can help. Meteorites are usually covered with a dark, pitted crust resulting from their fiery passage through the atmosphere (FIGURE 12.8). Some have an unusually high metal content, enough to attract a magnet hanging on a string. The ultimate judge of extraterrestrial origin is laboratory analysis: Meteorites often contain elements such as iridium that are very rare in Earth rocks, and even common elements in meteorites tend to have different ratios among their isotopes [**Section 5.3**] than are found in rocks from Earth. If you suspect that you have found a meteorite, many museums will analyze a small chip free of charge.

Scientists have found and cataloged more than 30,000 meteorites, some found by accident and others by organized meteorite searches. Antarctica is one of the best places to hunt for meteorites, not because more fall there but because the icy surface makes them easier to find. Few terrestrial rocks end up on the ice, so a rock found on the ice has a good chance of being a meteorite. Moreover, the slow movement of Antarctic glaciers tends to carry meteorites along, concentrating them in small areas where the ice floes run into mountains. The majority of meteorites now in museums and laboratories were found in Antarctica.

Types of Meteorites The origin of meteorites was long a mystery, but in recent decades we've been able to determine where in our solar system they come from. The most direct evidence comes from the relatively few meteorites whose trajectories have been observed or filmed as they fell to the ground. In every case so far, these meteorites clearly originated in the asteroid belt.

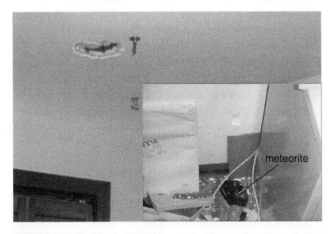

FIGURE 12.7 On March 26, 2003, a meteorite crashed through the roof of this home in Chicago. The main photo shows the hole in the ceiling; the inset shows the meteorite at rest on the floor. No one was hurt.

FIGURE 12.8 This large meteorite, called the Ahnighito Meteorite, is located at the American Museum of Natural History in New York. Its dark, pitted surface is a result of its fiery passage through Earth's atmosphere.

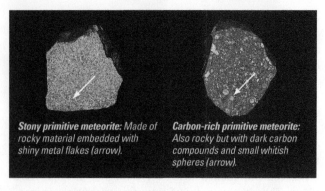

Stony primitive meteorite: *Made of rocky material embedded with shiny metal flakes (arrow).*

Carbon-rich primitive meteorite: *Also rocky but with dark carbon compounds and small whitish spheres (arrow).*

a Primitive meteorites.

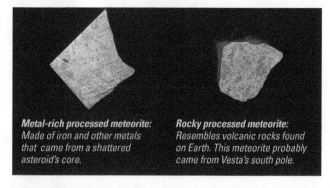

Metal-rich processed meteorite: *Made of iron and other metals that came from a shattered asteroid's core.*

Rocky processed meteorite: *Resembles volcanic rocks found on Earth. This meteorite probably came from Vesta's south pole.*

b Processed meteorites.

FIGURE 12.9 There are two basic types of meteorites: primitive and processed. Each also has two subtypes. They are shown slightly smaller than actual size. (The meteorites have flat faces because they have been sliced with rock saws.)

Detailed analysis of thousands of meteorites shows that they come in two basic types, primitive and processed,* each of which can be further classified into two subtypes:

- **Primitive meteorites** (FIGURE 12.9a) are "primitive" in the sense of being the first (or primary) type of meteorite to have formed. Radiometric dating [**Section 8.3**] shows them to be nearly 4.6 billion years old, making them remnants from the birth of our solar system, essentially unchanged since they first accreted in the solar nebula. Primitive meteorites come in two subtypes:

  - *Stony primitive meteorites* are composed of rocky minerals with a small but noticeable fraction of pure metallic flakes mixed in.

  - *Carbon-rich primitive meteorites* are generally similar to stony primitive meteorites, but they also contain substantial amounts of carbon compounds and, sometimes, a small amount of water.

- **Processed meteorites** (FIGURE 12.9b) apparently once were part of a larger object that "processed" the original material of the solar nebula into another form. Radiometric dating shows that processed meteorites are generally younger than the primitive meteorites by a few hundred million years. The processed meteorites can also be divided into two subtypes:

  - *Metal-rich processed meteorites* are made mostly of high-density iron and nickel mixed with smaller amounts of other metals. That is, they resemble the terrestrial planet cores in composition.

  - *Rocky processed meteorites* have lower densities and are made of rock with compositions resembling that of terrestrial mantles and crusts. A few have compositions remarkably close to that of the basalts [**Section 9.2**] that erupt from terrestrial volcanoes.

The Origin of Primitive Meteorites The vast majority of all meteorites are primitive, and their structures confirm what their radiometric ages tell us: They are pieces of rock

that accreted in the solar nebula and orbited the Sun for billions of years before finally falling to Earth. The individual flakes may represent the tiny particles that first condensed from the gas of the solar nebula. The small, roundish features visible in Figure 12.9a may be solidified droplets splashed out in the accretion process.

Why are some primitive meteorites stony in composition while others are carbon-rich? Both theory and observation indicate that the answer depends on where they formed in the solar nebula. The nebular theory tells us that all meteorites accreted inside the frost line and are therefore made of metal and rock. However, models tell us that, beyond about 3 AU from the Sun, temperatures in the solar nebula were low enough for condensation of carbon compounds. This suggests that carbon-rich primitive meteorites come from the outer regions of the asteroid belt, while stony primitive meteorites come from closer in. Laboratory studies of primitive meteorites confirm these ideas. The composition of carbon-rich meteorites matches the composition of dark, carbon-rich asteroids in the outer part of the asteroid belt. The composition of stony meteorites matches the composition of asteroids in the inner part of the asteroid belt.

Curiously, most of the meteorites collected on Earth are of the stony variety even though most asteroids are of the carbon-rich variety. Evidently, orbital resonances are more effective at pitching material our way from the inner part of the asteroid belt than from more distant regions.

Scientists are taking the study of the asteroid-meteorite connection to the next level with sample return missions. In 2010, the Japanese *Hayabusa* mission, overcoming a host of technical challenges, returned a small dust sample from the asteroid Itokawa (FIGURE 12.10), confirming that this asteroid represents material in the stony primitive category. In 2016, NASA hopes to launch the *Osiris-REX* mission, which will collect a sample from the near-Earth asteroid 1999 RQ36. This asteroid is thought to be a carbon-rich primitive object, perhaps representative of the kind that brought the ingredients for oceans, atmosphere, and life to Earth.

The Origin of Processed Meteorites The processed meteorites tell a more complex story. Their compositions look similar to those of the cores, mantles, or crusts of

---

*Primitive meteorites are also called *chondrites* because of the roundish features visible in them, known as *chondrules*. Processed meteorites lack these features and hence are called *achondrites* (a- means "not").

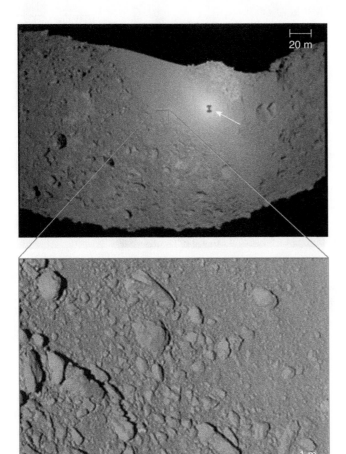

FIGURE 12.10 The top panel shows the central portion of the 500-meter-long asteroid Itokawa. The dark spot near the center is the shadow of the Japanese spacecraft *Hayabusa*, dominated by its two large solar panels. The spacecraft descended to the surface, where it picked up a small sample, at the location of the zoom-in. *Hayabusa*, appropriately, means "hawk."

the terrestrial worlds. We conclude that these meteorites are fragments of larger asteroids that underwent *differentiation* [**Section 9.1**], in which their interiors melted so that metals sank to the center and rocks rose to the surface. This idea explains why we find two types of processed meteorites.

Rocky processed meteorites are often so close in composition to volcanic rocks on Earth that they must have been made by lava flows. We conclude that these meteorites are rocks from the surfaces of large asteroids that once were volcanically active, probably chipped off by collisions with smaller asteroids. Perhaps as many as a dozen large asteroids were geologically active shortly after the formation of the solar system. The fact that the processed meteorites date to only a few tens to hundreds of millions of years after the birth of the solar system tells us that this active period was short-lived; the interiors of the geologically active asteroids must have cooled quickly. As noted earlier, spectroscopy indicates that numerous rocky processed meteorites were chipped from the surface of the asteroid Vesta by the impact that created Vesta's south polar crater.

Metal-rich processed meteorites have core-like compositions, suggesting that they are fragments of larger asteroids that shattered in collisions. These shattered worlds not only lost a chance to grow into planets but also sent many fragments onto collision courses with other asteroids and planets, including Earth. Moreover, these processed meteorites present us with an opportunity to study a "dissected planet," and they represent a form of direct proof that large worlds really do undergo differentiation, confirming what we infer from seismic studies of Earth.

Meteorites from the Moon and Mars In a few cases, the compositions of processed meteorites do not match those of asteroids but instead appear to match either the Moon or Mars. Careful analysis of these meteorites' compositions makes us very confident that we really do have a few meteorites that were once part of the Moon or Mars. Moderately large impacts can blast surface material from terrestrial worlds into interplanetary space. Once they are blasted into space, the rocks orbit the Sun until they come crashing down on another world. Calculations show that it is not surprising that we should have found a few meteorites chipped off the Moon and Mars in this way.

Study of these *lunar meteorites* and *Martian meteorites* is providing new insights into conditions on the Moon and Mars. One Martian meteorite sparked debate over whether it contains evidence of past life on Mars [**Section 24.2**].

12.2 COMETS

Asteroids are one of the two major categories of small bodies in the solar system. The other is comets, to which we now turn our attention. Asteroids and comets have much in common. Both are leftover planetesimals from the birth of our solar system. Both come in a wide range of sizes. The primary difference between them is in composition. Asteroids are rocky because they formed in the inner solar system where only metal and rock condensed. Comets are ice-rich because they formed beyond the frost line, where abundant hydrogen compounds condensed into ice [**Section 8.2**]. Note that we refer to any icy leftover planetesimal orbiting the Sun as a comet, regardless of its size, whether it has a tail, or where it resides or comes from.

What are comets like?

For most of human history, comets were familiar only from their occasional presence in the night sky. Every few years, a comet becomes visible to the naked eye, appearing as a fuzzy ball with a long tail. Indeed, the word *comet* comes from the Greek word for "hair," because comets were recognized by the long, hair-like tails they can display in our sky (**FIGURE 12.11**).

In comet photographs, the tails make it look as if the comets were racing across the sky, but they are not. If you watch a comet for minutes or hours, you'll see it staying nearly stationary relative to the stars around it in the sky. Over many days it will rise and set just like the stars, while gradually moving relative to the constellations. You may be able to see it night after night for several weeks or more, until it finally fades from view.

a Comet Hyakutake.

b Comet Hale-Bopp, photographed over Phoenix.

FIGURE 12.11 **interactive photo** Brilliant comets can appear at almost any time, as demonstrated by the back-to-back appearances of Comet Hyakutake in 1996 and Comet Hale-Bopp in 1997.

Today, we know that the vast majority of comets do not have tails and never venture anywhere close to Earth. Instead, they remain in the outer reaches of our solar system, orbiting the Sun far beyond the orbit of Neptune. The comets that appear in the night sky are the rare ones that have had their orbits changed by the gravitational influences of planets, other comets, or stars passing by in the distance. Their new orbits may carry them much closer to the Sun, eventually bringing them into the inner solar system, where they may grow the tails that allow us to see them in the sky. Most of these comets will not return to the inner solar system for thousands of years, if ever. A few happen to pass near enough to a planet to have their orbits changed further, and some end up on elliptical orbits that periodically bring them close to the Sun.

SEE IT FOR YOURSELF

Bright comets can be quite photogenic. Search the Web for comet images taken from Earth. Which is your favorite? Which has the best combination of beauty and scientifically interesting detail?

Comets in Human History The occasional presence of a bright comet in the night sky was hard to miss before the advent of electric lights. In some cultures, these rare intrusions into the unchanging heavens foretold bad or good luck. The ancient Chinese, for example, believed that the appearance of a comet led to a time of major and tumultuous change.

Few ancient cultures made any attempt to explain comets in astronomical terms. In fact, comets were generally thought to be within Earth's atmosphere until 1577, when Tycho Brahe [**Section 3.3**] used observations made from different locations on Earth to prove that a comet lay far beyond the Moon. A century later, Newton correctly deduced that comets orbit the Sun. Then, in a book published in 1705, English scientist Edmond Halley (1656–1742) used Newton's law of gravitation to calculate the orbit of a comet that had been seen in 1682. He showed that it was the same comet that had been observed on numerous prior occasions, which meant that it orbited the Sun every 76 years. Halley predicted that the comet would return in 1758. Although he had died by that

time, the comet returned as he predicted and was then named in his honor. Halley's Comet last passed through the inner solar system in 1986, and it will return in 2061.

Today, both professional and amateur astronomers routinely scan the skies with telescopes and binoculars in hopes of discovering a new comet. Several comets are discovered every year. The first observers (up to three) to report a comet discovery to the International Astronomical Union have the comet named after them. In that sense, comets now bring a form of good luck to their discoverers. More generally, comets are good luck for astronomers seeking to understand the solar system. These leftover planetesimals teach us about the history of the outer solar system just as asteroids teach us about the history of the inner solar system.

The surprise champion of comet discovery is the *SOHO* spacecraft, an orbiting solar observatory. *SOHO* has detected more than 2100 "Sun-grazing" comets, most on their last pass by the Sun (**FIGURE 12.12**).

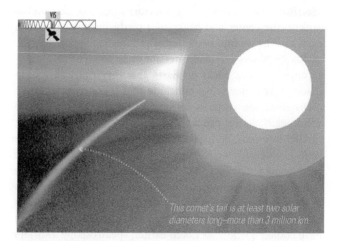

This comet's tail is at least two solar diameters long—more than 3 million km.

FIGURE 12.12 Comet SOHO-6's final blaze of glory. The *SOHO* spacecraft observed this "Sun-grazing" comet a few hours before it passed just 50,000 kilometers above the Sun's surface. The comet did not survive its passage, because of the intense solar heating and tidal forces. In this image, the large, orange disk blocks out the Sun; the Sun's size is indicated by the white circle.

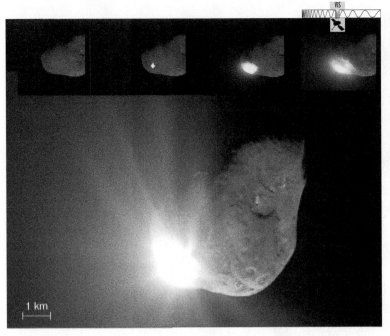

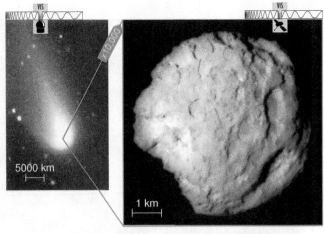

b The first image shows Comet Wild 2 photographed from Earth, and the inset shows its nucleus photographed by the *Stardust* spacecraft. The irregular surface probably shows effects from a combination of impacts and uneven vaporization rates in different regions.

a These photos were taken by the *Deep Impact* spacecraft as its 370-kg impactor crashed into Comet Tempel 1. The entire sequence, which starts just before impact at the upper left, unfolded over just 67 seconds.

FIGURE 12.13 interactive photo Comet nuclei.

Comet Composition We have learned about the composition of comets by studying their spectra. The results are just what we expect for objects that formed in the cold outer solar system: Comets are basically chunks of ice mixed with rocky dust and some more complex chemicals, and hence they are often described as "dirty snowballs."

Spectra of comets confirm their distant origin because they show the presence of compounds that could have condensed only in the cold outer regions of the solar nebula. For example, comet spectra invariably show emission features from hydrogen compounds, including water. They also show emissions from carbon dioxide and carbon monoxide, gases that condensed only in the very coldest and most distant regions of the solar nebula. Comet spectra also show evidence of many more complex molecules, including some organic molecules, leading some scientists to speculate that much of the organic material that made life possible on Earth was brought by comets.

Telescopic spectroscopy tells us about the material comets shed into space, but is this material representative of their internal compositions? NASA's *Deep Impact* mission was designed to answer this and other questions about comets. The main spacecraft carried a 370-kilogram impactor that it released as it approached Comet Tempel 1. Instruments on the spacecraft then observed the results as the impactor slammed into the comet at a speed of 37,000 kilometers per hour on July 4, 2005 (FIGURE 12.13a). The blast created a plume of hot gas composed of material vaporized from deep within the comet. Spectroscopy showed this material to contain many complex organic molecules, as expected. The plume also contained a huge amount of dust, telling us that the surface must have been covered by dust to a depth of tens of meters. However, because images show that Comet Tempel 1 looks quite different from other comets, we cannot conclude that all comets have similar compositions or similar amounts of surface dust.

We've learned even more about comet composition by studying comet material in the laboratory. In 2004, NASA's *Stardust* spacecraft used a material called "aerogel" to capture dust particles from Comet Wild 2 (pronounced "Vilt 2") (FIGURE 12.13b). The aerogel was then sealed in a re-entry capsule, which returned to Earth in 2006. Scientists are looking forward to data from the European Space Agency's *Rosetta* mission, on track to enter orbit of Comet Churyumov-Gerasimenko in May 2014 and to drop a lander to the surface in November 2014.

The Flashy Lives of Comets Comets grow tails only as they enter the inner solar system, where they are heated by the warmth of the Sun. To see what happens, let's look at the comet path shown in FIGURE 12.14a and the comet anatomy in FIGURE 12.14b.

Far from the Sun, the comet is completely frozen—in essence, a "dirty snowball." It begins to shed gas and dust as it approaches the Sun, but it still has its central chunk of ice, which we call the **nucleus**. Our best views of comet nuclei have come during spacecraft flybys: The first was a flyby of Halley's Comet by the European Space Agency's *Giotto* spacecraft in 1986, followed more recently by the *Deep Impact* and *Stardust* missions. Despite their icy compositions, comet nuclei are darker than charcoal, reflecting less than 5% of the light that falls on them. Apparently, it doesn't take much rocky or carbon-rich material to darken a comet. Density measurements show that comet nuclei are not packed very solidly. For example, the density of Halley's nucleus is considerably less than the density of water (1 g/cm^3), suggesting that the nucleus is part ice and part empty space.

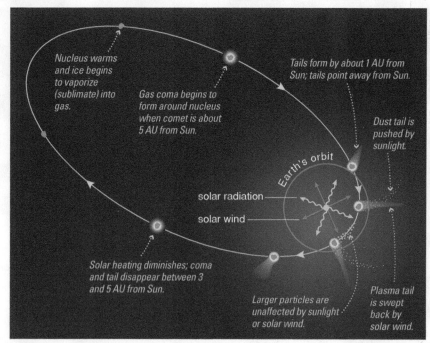

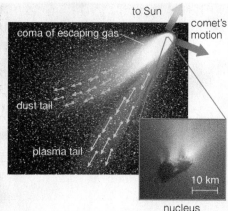

b Anatomy of a comet. The larger image is a ground-based photo of Comet Hale-Bopp. The inset shows the nucleus of Halley's Comet photographed by the *Giotto* spacecraft.

a This diagram (not to scale) shows the changes that occur when a comet's orbit takes it on a passage into the inner solar system.

FIGURE 12.14 A comet grows a coma and tail around its nucleus only if it happens to come close to the Sun. Most comets never do this, instead remaining perpetually frozen in the far outer solar system.

The scale bars in Figures 12.13 and 12.14b show that comet nuclei are typically less than about 20 kilometers across. How can such small objects put on such spectacular shows? As a comet accelerates toward the Sun, its surface temperature increases, and ices begin to vaporize into gas that easily escapes the comet's weak gravity. Some of the escaping gas drags away dust particles from the nucleus, and the gas and dust create a huge, dusty atmosphere called a **coma**. The coma is far larger than the nucleus it surrounds. Spacecraft observations show that the release of gas from the comet's nucleus can be quite violent, with jets of gas and dust shooting out at speeds of hundreds of meters per second from the interior of the nucleus into space.

The coma grows as the comet continues into the inner solar system, and tails form as extensions of the coma. Comet tails can be hundreds of millions of kilometers in length. Because they look much like exhaust trails behind rockets, many people mistakenly guess that tails extend behind comets as they travel through their orbits. In fact, comet tails generally point away from the Sun, regardless of the direction in which the comet is traveling.

Comets have two visible tails, one made of ionized gas, or *plasma,* and the other made of dust. The **plasma tail** consists of gas escaping from the coma. Ultraviolet light from the Sun ionizes the gas, and the solar wind then carries this gas straight outward from the Sun at speeds of hundreds of kilometers per second. That is why the plasma tail extends almost directly away from the Sun at all times. The **dust tail** is made of dust-size particles escaping from the coma. These particles are not affected by the solar wind and instead are

pushed away from the Sun by the much weaker pressure of sunlight itself (*radiation pressure*). The dust tail therefore points generally away from the Sun, but has a slight curve back in the direction the comet came from.

After the comet loops around the Sun and begins to head back outward, vaporization declines, the coma dissipates, and the tails disappear. Nothing happens until the comet again comes sunward—in a century, a millennium, a million years, or perhaps never.

Comets that repeatedly visit the inner solar system, like Halley's Comet, cannot last long on the time scale of our solar system. A comet probably loses about 0.1% of its ice on every pass around the Sun, so it could not make more than a few hundred passages before losing most of its original ice. Changes in composition may end the comet's "life" even faster. In a close pass by the Sun, a comet may shed a layer of material a meter thick. Dust that is too heavy to escape accumulates on the surface. This thick, dusty deposit helps make comets dark and may eventually block the escape of interior gas, preventing the comet from growing a coma or tails on future passes by the Sun. Several possible fates await a comet after its ices can no longer vaporize into gas and escape. In some cases, the remaining dust may disguise the dead comet as an asteroid. In other cases, the comet may come "unglued" and break apart, or even disintegrate along its orbit (**FIGURE 12.15**).

Comets striking Earth do not strew meteorites across the surface as asteroids do. The icy materials of a small comet vaporize on entry, and most of the rocky material takes the form of dust or pebbles that also vaporize as they are heated by friction in Earth's atmosphere.

500 km

FIGURE 12.15 This photo shows a comet fragment (one of dozens that made up Comet Schwassmann-Wachmann 3) disintegrating as it passed Earth in 2006.

TABLE 12.1 Major Annual Meteor Showers

Shower Name	Approximate Date	Associated Comet
Quadrantids	January 3	?
Lyrids	April 22	Thatcher
Eta Aquarids	May 5	Halley
Delta Aquarids	July 28	?
Perseids	August 12	Swift-Tuttle
Orionids	October 22	Halley
Taurids	November 3	Encke
Leonids	November 17	Tempel-Tuttle
Geminids	December 14	Phaeton
Ursids	December 23	Tuttle

Comet Tails and Meteor Showers In addition to the plasma and dust in their two visible tails, the gas escaping from comets also carries away sand- to pebble-size pieces of rocky material. These particles are too big to be affected by either the solar wind or sunlight, so they drift away slowly and spread along the orbital path. These particles essentially form a third, invisible tail that follows the comet around its orbit. They are also the particles responsible for most meteors and meteor showers.

We see a meteor when one of these small particles (or a similar-size particle from an asteroid) burns up in our atmosphere. The sand- to pebble-size particles are much too small to be seen themselves, but they enter the atmosphere at such high speeds—up to about 250,000 kilometers per hour (70 km/s)—that they make the surrounding air glow with heat. It is this glow that we see as the brief but brilliant flash of a meteor. The small particles are vaporized by the heat and never reach the ground. An estimated 25 million particles of comet dust enter the atmosphere worldwide every day, burning up as meteors and adding hundreds of tons of comet dust to Earth daily.

Comet dust is sprinkled throughout the inner solar system, but the "third tails" of ejected particles make the dust much more concentrated along the orbits of comets. This dust rains down on our planet whenever we cross a comet's orbit, producing a **meteor shower**. A meteor shower recurs at about the same time each year, because the orbiting Earth passes through a particular comet's orbit at the same time each year. For example, the meteor shower known as the *Perseids* occurs about August 12 each year, when Earth passes through the orbit of Comet Swift-Tuttle. **TABLE 12.1** lists major annual meteor showers and their parent comet, if known.

You can typically see a few meteors each hour on any clear night, but you may see far more during one of the annual meteor showers. During a "good" shower at a dark site, you may see dozens of meteors per hour. Remember that you are watching the effects of comet dust entering our planet's atmosphere from space. The meteors generally appear to radiate from a particular direction in the sky, for essentially the same reason that snow or heavy rain seems to come from a particular direction in front of a moving car (**FIGURE 12.16**). Because more meteors hit Earth from the front than from behind (just as more snow hits the front windshield of a moving car), meteor showers are best observed in the predawn sky, when part of the sky faces in the direction of Earth's motion.

SEE IT FOR YOURSELF

Try to observe the next meteor shower (see Table 12.1); be prepared with a star chart, a marker pen, and a dim (preferably red) flashlight. Each time you see a meteor, record its path on your star chart. Record at least a dozen meteors, and try to determine the *radiant* of the shower—that is, the constellation from which the meteors appear to radiate. Does the meteor shower live up to its name?

Where do comets come from?

We've already stated that comets come from the outer solar system, but we can be much more specific. By analyzing the orbits of comets that pass close to the Sun, scientists learned that there are two major "reservoirs" of comets in the outer solar system.

Most comets that visit the inner solar system follow orbits that seem almost random. They do not orbit the Sun in the same direction as the planets, and their elliptical orbits can be tilted at any angle relative to the ecliptic plane. Moreover, their orbits show that they come from far beyond the orbits of the planets—sometimes nearly a quarter of the distance to the nearest star. These comets must come plunging sunward from a vast, spherical region of space that scientists call the **Oort cloud** (after astronomer Jan Oort; rhymes with "court"). Be sure to note that the Oort cloud is not a cloud of gas, but rather a collection of many individual comets. Based on the number of Oort cloud comets that enter the inner solar

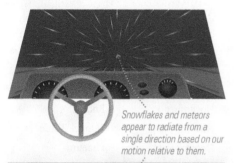

Snowflakes and meteors appear to radiate from a single direction based on our motion relative to them.

a Meteors appear to radiate from a particular point in the sky for the same reason that we see snow or heavy rain come from a single point in front of a moving car.

b This digital composite photo, taken in Australia during the 2001 Leonid meteor shower, shows meteors as streaks of light. The large rock is Uluru, also known as Ayers Rock.

FIGURE 12.16 The geometry of meteor showers.

system each year, we estimate that the Oort cloud must contain about a trillion (10^{12}) comets orbiting the Sun at distances up to about 50,000 AU.

A smaller number of the comets that visit the inner solar system have a pattern to their orbits. They travel around the Sun in the same direction and in nearly the same plane as the planets, and their elliptical orbits carry them no more than about twice as far from the Sun as Neptune. These comets must come from a ring of comets that orbit the Sun beyond the orbit of Neptune. This ring is usually called the **Kuiper belt** (after astronomer Gerald Kuiper; rhymes with "piper"). FIGURE 12.17 contrasts the general features of the Kuiper belt and the Oort cloud.

How did comets end up in these far-flung regions of the solar system? The only answer that makes scientific sense comes from thinking about what happened to the leftover icy planetesimals that roamed the region in which the jovian planets formed.

The leftover planetesimals that cruised the spaces between Jupiter, Saturn, Uranus, and Neptune were doomed to suffer either a collision or a close gravitational encounter with one of the young jovian planets. Recall that when a small object passes near a large planet, the planet is hardly affected but the small object may be flung off at high speed [**Section 4.5**]. The planetesimals that escaped being swallowed up by the jovian planets tended to be flung off in all directions. Some may have been cast away at such high speeds that they completely escaped the solar system and now drift through interstellar space. The rest ended up on orbits with very large average distances from the Sun, becoming the comets of the Oort cloud. The random directions in which they were flung

explain why the Oort cloud is roughly spherical in shape. Oort cloud comets are so far from the Sun that they can be nudged by the gravity of nearby stars (and even by the mass

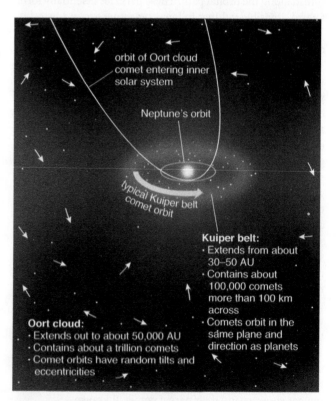

orbit of Oort cloud comet entering inner solar system

Neptune's orbit

typical Kuiper belt comet orbit

Kuiper belt:
· Extends from about 30–50 AU
· Contains about 100,000 comets more than 100 km across
· Comets orbit in the same plane and direction as planets

Oort cloud:
· Extends out to about 50,000 AU
· Contains about a trillion comets
· Comet orbits have random tilts and eccentricities

FIGURE 12.17 The comets we occasionally see in the inner solar system come from two major reservoirs in the outer solar system: the Kuiper belt and the Oort cloud.

of the galaxy as a whole), preventing some of them from ever returning near the planets and sending others plummeting toward the Sun.

Beyond the orbit of Neptune, the icy planetesimals were much less likely to be cast off by gravitational encounters. Instead, they remained in orbits going in the same directions as planetary orbits and concentrated relatively near the ecliptic plane. These are the comets of the donut-shaped Kuiper belt. Kuiper belt comets can be nudged by the gravity of the jovian planets through orbital resonances, sending some on close passes through the inner solar system. The Kuiper belt extends to only about twice Neptune's orbital distance, because at greater distances the density of the solar nebula was apparently too low to allow the accretion of planetesimals.

To summarize, the comets of the Kuiper belt seem to have originated farther from the Sun than the comets of the Oort cloud, even though the Oort cloud comets are now much more distant. The Oort cloud consists of leftover planetesimals that were flung outward after forming between the jovian planets, while the Kuiper belt consists of leftover planetesimals that formed and still remain in the outskirts of the planetary realm, roughly between the orbit of Neptune and twice Neptune's distance from the Sun.

(MA) Formation of the Solar System Tutorial, Lesson 3

12.3 PLUTO: LONE DOG NO MORE

Pluto was considered the "ninth planet" for some 75 years after its discovery in 1930, but it had long seemed a misfit among the planets. Its 248-year orbit is more elliptical and more inclined to the ecliptic plane than that of the first eight planets (FIGURE 12.18). In fact, Pluto sometimes comes closer to the Sun than Neptune, although there is no danger of collision: Neptune orbits the Sun precisely three times for every two Pluto orbits, and this stable orbital resonance means that Neptune is always a safe distance away whenever Pluto

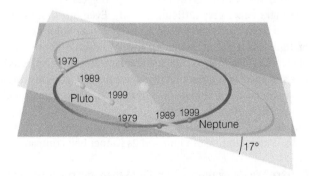

FIGURE 12.18 interactive figure Pluto's orbit is significantly elliptical and tilted relative to the ecliptic. Pluto comes closer to the Sun than Neptune for 20 years in each 248-year orbit, as was the case between 1979 and 1999. There's no danger of a collision, however, thanks to an orbital resonance in which Neptune completes three orbits for every two of Pluto's.

approaches its orbit. Neptune and Pluto will probably continue their dance of avoidance until the end of the solar system.

As we learned more about Pluto, it proved to be a misfit among the planets in size and composition as well: It is far smaller than even the terrestrial planets, and its ice-rich composition fits neither the terrestrial nor the jovian category. These seeming oddities made Pluto seem like a lone dog of the outer solar system. But it is not: We now know that Pluto is part of a huge pack of similar objects—essentially large comets—that orbit in its region of the solar system. In fact, Pluto is not even the largest member of this pack.

How big can a comet be?

We've known since the 1950s that many of the comets that visit the inner solar system come from the reservoir that we call the Kuiper belt. We've also known that Pluto orbits the Sun near the middle of this reservoir. We now realize that Pluto's location is no mere coincidence, but rather evidence of an astonishing fact: Some of the objects that populate the Kuiper belt are far larger than any of the comets that we ever see in the inner solar system. This fact forces us to reconsider just exactly what we mean by a "comet."

All the comets we've observed in the inner solar system are fairly small, with nuclei no larger than about 20 kilometers across. This shouldn't be surprising based on our understanding of comet origins, because only relatively small objects are likely to have their orbits changed enough to send them from the Kuiper belt or Oort cloud into the inner solar system. But given that the comets we see are rare and relatively small visitors from distant reaches of the solar system, could these outer realms hold much larger objects as well?

Large Comets of the Kuiper Belt According to our understanding of solar system formation, the icy planetesimals of the Kuiper belt should have been able to continue their accretion as long as other icy particles were nearby. In principle, one of these planetesimals could have grown large enough to become the seed of a fifth jovian planet, beyond Neptune, but that did not occur—probably because the density of material was too low at this great distance from the Sun. Nevertheless, it's reasonable to think that many of them grew to hundreds or even thousands of kilometers in diameter.

You might think it would be easy to observe icy objects of such sizes, but it requires powerful telescope technology. Trying to see a 1000-kilometer iceball at Pluto's distance from Earth is equivalent to looking for a snowball the size of your fist that is 600 kilometers away (and in dim light, too). Aside from Pluto, the first large objects in the Kuiper belt were discovered in the early 1990s. The discoveries have come at a rapid pace ever since.

As astronomers surveyed more and more of the sky in search of large, icy objects, the record size seemed to rise with each passing year. In 2002, the record was set by an object named Quaoar (pronounced "kwa-o-whar"), which is more than half the diameter of Pluto. Two objects announced in 2004—Orcus and Sedna—are between about two-thirds and

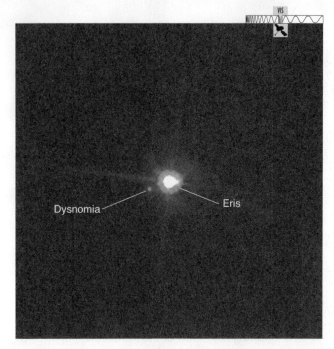

FIGURE 12.19 Eris and its moon, photographed by the Hubble Space Telescope.

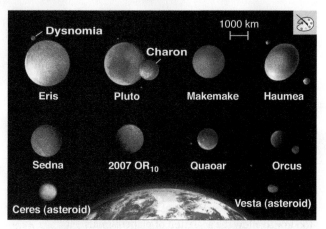

FIGURE 12.20 Artist paintings of the largest known objects of the Kuiper belt (as of 2012), along with their known moons, shown to scale with Earth and the asteroids Ceres and Vesta for comparison. Pluto, Eris, Makemake, and Haumea officially qualify as dwarf planets, and others may yet join the list. The paintings are guesses about appearance, since the Kuiper belt objects have not been photographed with high resolution.

three-quarters of Pluto's size. It seemed only a matter of time until scientists would find an object larger than Pluto, and the time came in 2005, when Caltech astronomer Michael Brown (who had also discovered Quaoar, Orcus, and Sedna) announced the discovery of the object now named Eris (FIGURE 12.19). Eris is named for a Greek goddess who caused strife and arguments among humans (a commentary on the arguments its discovery caused about the definition of "planet"). Eris even has a moon, named Dysnomia, a mythological goddess of lawlessness and daughter of Eris.

Eris currently lies about twice as far as Pluto from the Sun. Its 557-year orbit is inclined to the ecliptic plane more than twice as much as Pluto's, and it is so eccentric that Eris must sometimes come closer to the Sun than Pluto. The latest observations place Pluto and Eris in a virtual tie for largest Kuiper belt object, although Eris is about 27% larger in mass.

Classification of Kuiper Belt Comets What should we call Pluto, Eris, and other big iceballs? The terminology has been a topic of much debate, but the science behind it seems clear. By 2012, more than 1100 icy objects had been directly observed in the Kuiper belt, allowing scientists to infer that the region contains at least 70,000 objects more than 100 kilometers across, and many more that are smaller. The new Pan-STARRS telescopes should discover tens of thousands of them. The smaller ones are easy to refer to as comets, but the larger ones pose a classification challenge, as you can see by comparing object sizes (FIGURE 12.20). Note that the Kuiper belt has numerous objects significantly larger than the largest asteroids, but still far smaller than Earth and the other terrestrial planets.

Under the current classification scheme (see Special Topic, page 8), four objects of the Kuiper belt (Pluto, Eris,

Makemake, and Haumea[*]) qualify as *dwarf planets* because they are big enough to be round but have not cleared their orbital neighborhoods. Dozens of other objects of the Kuiper belt may yet qualify as dwarf planets, though further observations will be needed to establish whether these objects are really round.

Regardless of what we call them, all the objects of the Kuiper belt—from the smallest boulders to the largest dwarf planets—probably share the same basic composition of ice and rock. In other words, they are all essentially comets of different sizes. That is why we often refer to all of them as *comets* of the Kuiper belt. However, some astronomers object to calling objects "comets" if they never venture into the inner solar system and show tails; therefore, you may also hear these objects referred to as *Kuiper belt objects* (*KBOs*) or *trans-Neptunian objects* (*TNOs*).

What are the large objects of the Kuiper belt like?

The small sizes and great distances of objects in the Kuiper belt make them very difficult to study. Even our best photographs from Earth show little more than fuzzy blobs or dots of light. As a result, we generally know little about these objects besides their orbits and the fact that their reflectivities and spectra suggest that they have ice-rich compositions. This should soon change, as scientists hope to learn much more when the *New Horizons* spacecraft flies past Pluto in the summer of 2015. In the meantime, let's look at our preflyby understanding of Pluto and its Kuiper belt companions.

Pluto We know more about Pluto than any other object in the Kuiper belt, largely because it was discovered back in 1930, decades before any of the others. In addition, the fact that

---

[*]Haumea is actually oblong, but it counts as a dwarf planet because it would be round if not for its high rotation rate.

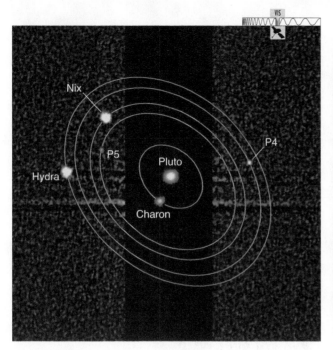

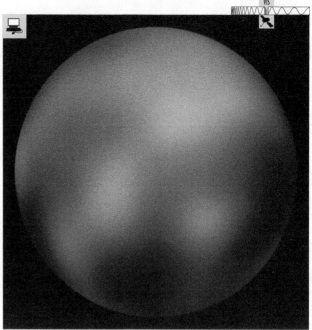

a This Hubble Space Telescope photo shows Pluto and its five known moons, along with orbital paths for the moons. Horizontal stripes are scattered light from Charon and Pluto in the long exposure.

b The surface of Pluto in approximately true color, based on a computer-processed series of Hubble Space Telescope images, each just a few pixels across. Comparison with images taken 8 years earlier reveals changes in surface markings, which may be due to the gradual change in seasons on Pluto.

FIGURE 12.21 Pluto's great distance and small size make it difficult to study.

Pluto has moons (**FIGURE 12.21a**) meant scientists could learn much more. The 1978 discovery of Pluto's largest moon, Charon, was especially important. Recall that we can determine an object's mass using Newton's version of Kepler's third law only if we can observe its gravitational effect on some other object [**Section 4.4**]. As a result, Charon's discovery allowed the first precise determination of Pluto's mass, which was a key step in learning how greatly Pluto differed from either the terrestrial or the jovian planets.

Charon soon provided another opportunity for scientists to learn about Pluto through some good luck in timing: Just a few years after Charon's discovery, Pluto and Charon entered a period of time (lasting from 1985 to 1990) during which they eclipsed each other every few days as seen from Earth—something that happens only about every 120 years. Detailed analysis of brightness variations during these eclipses allowed the calculation of accurate sizes, masses, and densities for both Pluto and Charon. These measurements confirmed that Pluto and Charon are both made of ice mixed with rock, just like comets. The eclipse data even allowed astronomers to construct rough maps of Pluto's surface markings. More recent images show that Pluto's surface is being altered, probably because of seasonal changes, which on Pluto are affected both by axis tilt and by changing distance from the Sun (**FIGURE 12.21b**).

Comparing Pluto and Charon leads to some interesting surprises. Charon is closer in distance and in relative size to its parent planet than our Moon is to Earth; it has more than half the diameter and about $\frac{1}{8}$ the mass of Pluto, and orbits only 20,000 kilometers away. (For comparison, our Moon has a mass $\frac{1}{80}$ of Earth's and orbits 400,000 kilometers away.) Charon is also slightly lower in density than Pluto. Together, these facts have led astronomers to guess that Charon was created by a *giant impact* similar to the one thought to have formed our Moon [**Section 8.2**]. A large comet crashing into Pluto may have blasted away its low-density outer layers, which then formed a ring around Pluto and eventually re-accreted to make Charon and the smaller moons. The impact may also explain why Pluto rotates almost on its side.

Pluto is very cold, with an average temperature of only 40 K, as we would expect at its great distance from the Sun. Nevertheless, Pluto currently has a thin atmosphere of nitrogen and other gases formed by vaporization of surface ices. The atmosphere should gradually refreeze onto the surface as Pluto's 248-year orbit carries it farther from the Sun, although recent results have puzzled astronomers by showing the opposite effect. In fact, it now appears that Pluto has started to eject carbon monoxide gas, perhaps released as Pluto's frigid pole turns slowly toward the Sun.

Despite the cold, the view from Pluto would be stunning. Charon would dominate the sky, appearing almost 10 times as large in angular size as our Moon appears from Earth. The mutual tidal forces acting between Pluto and Charon long ago made them rotate synchronously with each other [**Section 4.5**], so Charon is visible from only one side of Pluto and always shows the same face to Pluto. This synchronous rotation also means that Pluto's "day" is the same length as Charon's "month" (orbital period) of 6.4 Earth days. Viewed from Pluto's surface, Charon neither rises nor sets but instead hangs motionless as it cycles through its phases every 6.4 days. The Sun would appear more than a thousand times fainter than it appears here on Earth and would be no larger in angular size than Jupiter appears in our skies.

Other Kuiper Belt Objects We don't know nearly as much about any other large comets of the Kuiper belt, though scientists hope to send the *New Horizons* spacecraft to at least one or two others after its encounter with Pluto. Nevertheless, because all Kuiper belt comets presumably formed in the same region of the solar system, we expect them to be similar in nature and composition to Pluto. One key piece of evidence of similarities comes from careful study of orbits. Like Pluto, many Kuiper belt comets have stable orbital resonances with Neptune. In fact, hundreds of Kuiper belt comets have the *same* orbital period and average distance from the Sun as Pluto itself (and are nicknamed "Plutinos").

Other evidence comes from the fact that several other Kuiper belt comets (including Eris) are also known to have moons, so in those cases we can calculate masses and densities. These results, along with spectral information, confirm the idea that these objects have comet-like compositions of ice and rock. One remarkable object, Haumea (see Figure 12.20), seems to have suffered a giant impact like the one thought to have created Charon. The impact created two moons and seems to have set Haumea spinning so fast (once every 4 hours) that its shape has become very elongated. Four other known Kuiper belt comets may also be fragments from the same impact, since their orbits resemble that of Haumea and they have similar spectral properties.

Perhaps most intriguingly, if you think back to what we learned in our tour of jovian moons in Chapter 11, you'll realize that Pluto probably will *not* be the first Kuiper belt comet to be photographed close up. Instead, that honor probably belongs to Neptune's moon Triton. Recall that Triton's "backward" orbit indicates that it must be a captured object [**Section 11.2**]. Its location suggests that it was most likely captured from the Kuiper belt, since many Kuiper belt comets have orbits that cross Neptune's orbit. In that case, *Voyager* images of Triton (see Figure 11.31) represent images of a *former* member of the Kuiper belt.

The fact that Triton appears to be quite similar in nature to Pluto lends further support to the idea that it once orbited the Sun within the Kuiper belt. Moreover, Triton is about 15% larger than Pluto (in diameter), which suggests that other objects bigger than Pluto were able to form in the Kuiper belt. Some may still await discovery, and others may have been destroyed in giant impacts. Those that did not gain the stability provided by being in an orbital resonance may have fallen inward in the solar system, eventually being accreted by one of the jovian planets, or may have been thrown outward and ejected from the solar system. All in all, it seems quite likely that the Kuiper belt, like the asteroid belt, once held many more large objects than it does today.

12.4 COSMIC COLLISIONS: SMALL BODIES VERSUS THE PLANETS

The hordes of small bodies orbiting the Sun are slowly shrinking in number through collisions with the planets and ejection from the solar system. Many more must have roamed the solar system in the days of the heavy bombardment, when most impact craters formed [**Section 8.2**]. Plenty of small bodies remain, however, and cosmic collisions still occur on occasion. These collisions have had important effects on Earth and other planets.

Have we ever witnessed a major impact?

We have never witnessed a major impact on a terrestrial world, but have seen one on Jupiter: the 1994 impact of a comet named *Shoemaker-Levy 9*, or *SL9* for short. Rather than having a single nucleus, Comet SL9 consisted of a string of nuclei (**FIGURE 12.22a**). Apparently, tidal forces from Jupiter had ripped apart a single comet nucleus during a previous close pass by the planet. Chains of craters observed on some of Jupiter's moons provide evidence that similar breakups of comets have occurred near Jupiter in the past.

Comet SL9 was discovered more than a year before it collided with Jupiter, and orbital calculations told astronomers precisely when the collision would occur. When the impacts began, they were observed with nearly every major telescope in existence, as well as by spacecraft that were in position to get a view. Each of the individual nuclei crashed into Jupiter with an energy equivalent to that of a million hydrogen bombs (**FIGURE 12.22b** and **c**). Comet nuclei barely a kilometer across left scars large enough to swallow Earth. The scars lasted for months before Jupiter's strong winds finally swept them from view.

The SL9 impacts allowed scientists to study both the impact process and material splashed out from deep inside Jupiter. Scientists felt quite fortunate, because estimates suggested that impacts as large as those of SL9 occur only about once in a thousand years. Astronomers were therefore surprised when another impact occurred on Jupiter in 2009. This impact was first noticed by an amateur astronomer from Australia, who reported a new "dark spot" on Jupiter that was soon recognized as the aftermath of an unseen impact (**FIGURE 12.22d**). Two amateur astronomers independently recorded images of an even smaller impact event in 2010. Astronomers are still not sure if these recent events signify that Jupiter impacts are more common than previously thought, or if improved monitoring of Jupiter can now capture smaller impact events, which occur more frequently than impacts of SL9's magnitude. Either way, we now know

a Jupiter's tidal forces ripped apart the single comet nucleus of SL9 into a chain of smaller nuclei.

b This painting shows how the SL9 impacts might have looked from the surface of Io. The impacts occurred on Jupiter's night side.

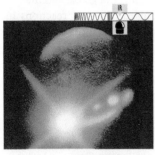

c This infrared photo shows the brilliant glow of a rising fireball from the impact of one SL9 nucleus in 1994. Jupiter is the round disk, with the impact occurring near the lower left.

d The black spot in this Hubble Space Telescope photo is a scar from the impact of an unknown object that struck Jupiter in July 2009.

FIGURE 12.22 The impacts of Comet Shoemaker-Levy 9 on Jupiter allowed astronomers their first direct view of a cosmic collision.

that violent impacts have happened on other planets in our lifetime. Could they also happen on Earth?

Did an impact kill the dinosaurs?

There's no doubt that major impacts have occurred on Earth in the past. Meteor Crater in Arizona (see Figure 9.8a) formed about 50,000 years ago when a metallic asteroid roughly 50 meters across crashed to Earth with the explosive power of a 20-megaton hydrogen bomb. Although the crater is only a bit more than 1 kilometer across, the blast and ejecta probably battered an area covering hundreds of square kilometers. Meteor Crater is relatively small and recent. Despite the fact

that erosion and other geological processes have erased most of Earth's impact craters, geologists have identified more than 150 impact craters on our planet. So before we consider whether an impact might occur in our lifetimes, it's worth examining the potential consequences if it did. Clearly, an impact could cause widespread physical damage. But a growing body of evidence, accumulated over the past three decades, suggests that an impact can do much more—in some cases, large impacts may have altered the entire course of evolution.

In 1978, while analyzing geological samples collected in Italy, a scientific team led by Luis and Walter Alvarez (father and son) made a startling discovery. They found that a thin layer of dark sediments deposited about 65 million years ago—about the time the dinosaurs went extinct—was unusually rich in the element iridium. Iridium is a metal that is rare on Earth's surface (because it sank to Earth's core when our planet underwent differentiation) but common in meteorites. Subsequent studies found the same iridium-rich layer in 65-million-year-old sediments around the world (FIGURE 12.23).* The Alvarez team suggested a stunning hypothesis: The extinction of the dinosaurs was caused by the impact of an asteroid or comet.

In fact, the death of the dinosaurs was only a small part of the biological devastation that seems to have occurred 65 million years ago. The fossil record suggests that up to 99% of all living organisms died around that time and that up to 75% of all existing *species* were driven to extinction. This makes the event a clear example of a **mass extinction**—the rapid extinction of a large fraction of all living species. Could it really have been caused by an impact?

Evidence for the Impact There's still some scientific debate about whether the impact was the sole cause of the mass extinction or just one of many causes, but there's

---

*The layer marks what geologists call the *K-T boundary*, because it separates sediments deposited in the Cretaceous and Tertiary periods (the K comes from the German word for Cretaceous, *Kreide*). The mass extinction that occurred 65 million years ago is therefore called the *K-T event*.

A layer rich in iridium and soot tells us a huge impact occurred at this point in geological (and biological) history.

5 cm

FIGURE 12.23 Around the world, sedimentary rock layers dating to 65 million years ago share the evidence of the impact of a comet or asteroid. Fossils of dinosaurs and many other species appear only in rocks below the iridium-rich layer.

little doubt that a major impact coincided with the death of the dinosaurs. Key evidence comes from further analysis of the sediment layer. Besides being unusually rich in iridium, this layer contains four other unusual features: (1) high abundances of several other metals, including osmium, gold, and platinum; (2) grains of "shocked" quartz, quartz crystals with a distinctive structure that indicates they experienced the high-pressure conditions of an impact; (3) spherical rock droplets of a type known to form when drops of molten rock cool and solidify in the air; and (4) soot (at some sites) that appears to have been produced by widespread forest fires.

All these features point to an impact. The metal abundances look much like what we commonly find in meteorites rather than what we find elsewhere on Earth's surface. Shocked quartz is also found at other impact sites, such as Meteor Crater in Arizona. The rock droplets presumably were made from molten rock splashed into the air by the force and heat of the impact. Some debris would have been blasted so high that it rose above the atmosphere, spreading worldwide before falling back to Earth. On their downward plunge, friction would have heated the debris particles until they became a hot, glowing rain of rock. The soot probably came from vast forest fires ignited by radiation from this impact debris.

In addition to the evidence within the sediments, scientists have identified a large impact crater that appears to match the age of the sediment layer. The crater, called the *Chicxulub crater* after a nearby fishing village, is about 200 kilometers across and is located on the coast of Mexico's Yucatán Peninsula, about half on land and half underwater (FIGURE 12.24). Its size indicates that it was created by the impact of an asteroid or a comet measuring about 10 kilometers across, which is large enough to account for the iridium and other metals found in the sediment layer.

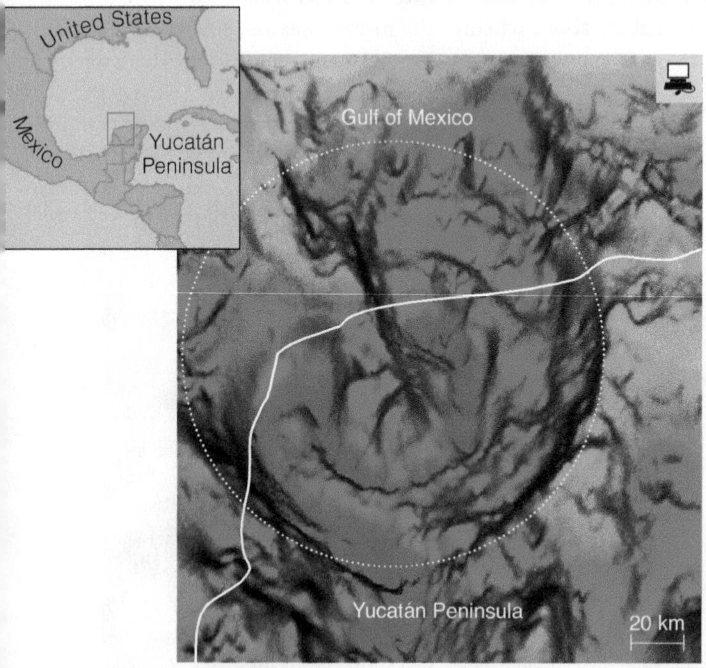

The Mass Extinction If the impact was indeed the cause of the mass extinction, here's how it probably happened: On that fateful day some 65 million years ago, the asteroid or comet slammed into Mexico with the force of a hundred million hydrogen bombs (FIGURE 12.25). It apparently hit at a slight angle, sending a shower of red-hot debris across the continent of North America. A huge tsunami sloshed more than 1000 kilometers inland. Much of North American life may have been wiped out almost immediately. Not long after, the hot debris raining around the rest of the world ignited fires that killed many other living organisms.

The longer-term effects were even more severe. Dust and smoke remained in the atmosphere for weeks or months, blocking sunlight and causing temperatures to fall as if Earth were experiencing a global and extremely harsh winter. The reduced sunlight would have stopped photosynthesis for up to a year, killing large numbers of species throughout the food chain. This period of cold may have been followed by a period of unusual warmth. Some evidence suggests that the impact site was rich in carbonate rocks, so the impact may have released large amounts of carbon dioxide into the atmosphere. The added carbon dioxide would have strengthened the greenhouse effect, and the months of global winter may have been followed by decades or longer of global summer.

The impact probably also caused chemical reactions in the atmosphere that produced large quantities of harmful compounds, such as nitrous oxides. These compounds dissolved in the oceans, where they would have killed vast numbers of marine organisms. Acid rain may have been another by-product, killing vegetation and acidifying lakes around the world.

FIGURE 12.24 This computer-generated image, based on measurements of small local variations in the strength of gravity, shows an impact crater (dashed circle) in the northwest corner of Mexico's Yucatán Peninsula; the inset shows the location on a map. The crater measures about 200 kilometers across, and about half of it lies underwater off the coast.

FIGURE 12.25 This painting shows an asteroid or comet moments before its impact on Earth, some 65 million years ago. The impact probably caused the extinction of the dinosaurs, and if it hadn't occurred the dinosaurs might still rule Earth today.

Perhaps the most astonishing fact is not that 75% of all species died but that 25% survived. Among the survivors were a few small mammals. These mammals may have survived in part because they lived in underground burrows and managed to store enough food to outlast the global winter that immediately followed the impact.

The evolutionary impact of the extinctions was profound. For 180 million years, dinosaurs had diversified into a great many species large and small, while mammals (which had arisen at almost the same time as the dinosaurs) had generally remained small and rodent-like. With the dinosaurs gone, mammals became the new kings of the planet. Over the next 65 million years, the mammals rapidly evolved into an assortment of much larger mammals—ultimately including us.

Controversies and Other Mass Extinctions

There seems little doubt that a major impact coincided with the mass extinction of 65 million years ago, but does it tell the entire story? The jury is still out. The fossil record can be difficult to read when we are trying to understand events that happened over just a few years rather than a few million years. Some scientists suspect that the dinosaurs were already in decline and the impact was only the last straw. Others suggest that major volcanic eruptions also may have played a role.

Was the dinosaur extinction a unique event? Measuring precise extinction rates becomes more difficult as we look to older fossils, but there appear to have been at least four other mass extinctions during the past 500 million years. None of the other mass extinctions is as closely tied to an impact as the dinosaur extinction, but impacts almost certainly played a role. Sediments from the times of other mass extinctions reveal evidence similar to that found in the iridium-rich layer tied to the death of the dinosaurs. In some cases, impact craters have been found that date to about the right times. Much more research is needed, but impacts appear to have played a major role in shaping the history of life on Earth.

Is the impact threat a real danger or media hype?

On June 14, 2002, the 100-meter-wide asteroid 2002 MN passed within 120,000 kilometers of Earth (less than a third of the Earth-Moon distance). There was no advance warning; in fact, the asteroid wasn't discovered until after it had passed by. Since then, more than 30 smaller asteroids have passed even closer. Most recently, the 1-meter-wide asteroid 2011 CQ1 passed less than 6000 kilometers above the Pacific Ocean in 2011. Although asteroids of these sizes would not cause global devastation, one of the larger ones (tens of meters or more across) could kill millions of people in the unlikely event that it struck a large city. How concerned should we be about the possibility of objects like this striking Earth—or, worse yet, even larger objects such as those that may have caused past mass extinctions?

One way to gauge the threat is to look at evidence from past impacts. Geological data show that impacts large enough to cause mass extinctions happen many tens of millions of years apart on average, which means that while another such

FIGURE 12.26 This photo shows forests burned and flattened by the 1908 impact over Tunguska, Siberia.

impact will probably occur in the future, it's highly unlikely to be within the next few thousand years. We're far more likely to do ourselves in than to be done in by a large asteroid or comet.

Smaller impacts can be expected more frequently. While such impacts would not wipe out our civilization, they could kill thousands or millions of people. We know of one close call in modern times. In 1908, a tremendous explosion occurred over Tunguska, Siberia (FIGURE 12.26). Entire forests were flattened and set on fire, and air blasts knocked over people and furniture up to 200 kilometers away. Seismic disturbances were recorded at distances of up to 1000 kilometers, and atmospheric pressure fluctuations were detected almost 4000 kilometers away. The explosion, now estimated to have released energy equivalent to that of several atomic bombs, is thought to have been caused by a small asteroid no more than about 40 meters across. Atmospheric friction caused it to explode completely before it hit the ground, so it left no impact crater. If the asteroid had exploded over a major city instead of over Siberia, it would have been the worst natural disaster in human history.

A less devastating impact occurred in 2007, when eyewitnesses saw a bright fireball streak across the mid-day sky near Carancas, Peru. A stony meteorite about 1–2 meters across slammed into the ground and excavated a crater 15 meters across (FIGURE 12.27). The impact spewed debris more than 300 meters and shattered windows as far as a kilometer away.

Another way to gauge the threat is to look at objects in space that might strike Earth. As of 2012, astronomers had identified nearly 9000 asteroids with orbits that pass near Earth's orbit, including more than 1300 that could potentially hit Earth someday. Orbital calculations show that none of these known objects will collide with Earth in the foreseeable future. However, while astronomers estimate that more than 90% of the "potentially hazardous asteroids" larger than 1 kilometer have been found, the estimates also suggest

FIGURE 12.27 The impact crater made by a stony meteorite 1–2 meters across near Carancas, Peru, in 2007. The crater filled with groundwater soon after the impact.

that more than 15,000 asteroids with diameters between 100 meters and 1 kilometer also pass near Earth's orbit but remain undiscovered. The threat from comets is lower, but we are unlikely to see a comet plunging in from the outer solar system until it is well on its way, giving us no more than a few years to prepare for the impact.

We can use the data from both geology and astronomy to estimate how often, on average, we expect objects of different sizes to hit Earth. The results are shown in FIGURE 12.28. Objects a few meters across probably enter Earth's atmosphere every week or so, each liberating energy equivalent to that of an atomic bomb as it burns up. Larger impacts are obviously more devastating but thankfully more rare. Hundred-meter impacts that forge craters similar to Meteor Crater in Arizona probably strike only every few thousand years or so. Objects of the size that caused the Tunguska event probably strike our planet every few hundred years

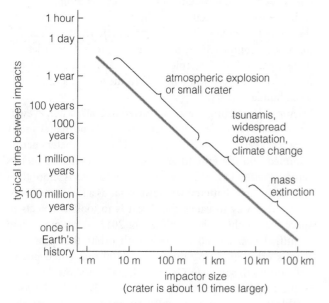

FIGURE 12.28 This graph shows that larger objects (asteroids or comets) hit Earth less frequently than smaller ones. The labels describe the effects of impacts of different sizes.

or so, making them a real threat. Fortunately, these impacts are unlikely to strike densely populated areas, because most of Earth's surface is ocean, and even on land humans are concentrated in relatively small urban areas.

If we were to find an asteroid or a comet on a collision course with Earth, could we do anything about it? Many people have proposed schemes to save Earth by using nuclear weapons or other means to demolish or divert an incoming asteroid, but no one knows whether current technology is really up to the task. We can only hope that the threat doesn't become a reality before we're ready.

THINK ABOUT IT

Based on the potential dangers summarized in Figure 12.28, how much time and money do you think we should be spending to counter the impact threat? Defend your opinion.

While near-Earth asteroids may pose real dangers, they may also offer opportunities. These asteroids bring valuable resources tantalizingly close to Earth. Iron-rich asteroids are particularly enticing, because they probably contain many precious metals that have mostly sunk to the core on Earth. In the future, it may prove technically feasible and financially profitable to mine metals from asteroids and bring these resources to Earth. It may also be possible to gather fuel and water from asteroids for use in missions to the outer solar system.

How do the jovian planets affect impact rates and life on Earth?

Ancient people imagined that the mere movement of planets relative to the visible stars in our sky could somehow have an astrological influence on our lives. Although scientists no longer give credence to this ancient superstition, we now know that planets can have a real effect on life on Earth. By catapulting asteroids and comets in Earth's direction, other planets have caused cosmic collisions that helped shape Earth's destiny.

Jupiter and the other jovian planets have had the greatest effects because of their influence on the small bodies of the solar system. As we saw earlier in this chapter, Jupiter disturbed the orbits of rocky planetesimals outside Mars's orbit, preventing a planet from forming and creating the asteroid belt. The jovian planets ejected icy planetesimals to create the distant Oort cloud, and orbital resonances with Neptune shape the orbits of many comets in the Kuiper belt. Ultimately, every asteroid or comet that has impacted Earth since the end of the heavy bombardment was in some sense sent our way by the influence of Jupiter or one of the other jovian planets. FIGURE 12.29 summarizes the ways the jovian planets have controlled the motions of asteroids and comets.

We thereby find a deep connection between the jovian planets and the survival of life on Earth. If Jupiter did not exist, the threat from asteroids might be much smaller, since the objects that make up the asteroid belt might instead have become part of a planet. On the other hand, the threat from comets might be much greater: Jupiter probably ejected more comets to the Oort cloud than any other jovian planet, and

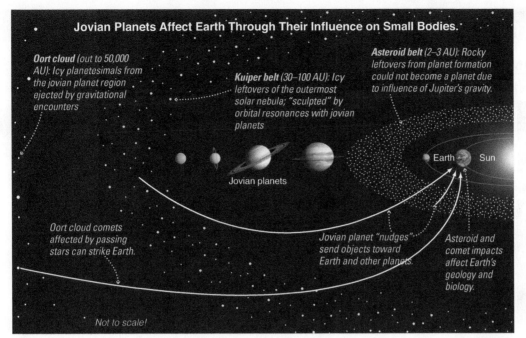

FIGURE 12.29 The connections between the jovian planets, small bodies, and Earth. The gravity of the jovian planets helped shape both the asteroid belt and the Kuiper belt, and the Oort cloud consists of comets ejected from the jovian planet region by gravitational encounters with these large planets. Ongoing gravitational influences sometimes send asteroids or comets toward Earth.

without Jupiter, those comets might have remained dangerously close to Earth. Of course, even if Jupiter has protected us from impacts, it's not clear whether that has been good or bad for life overall. The dinosaurs appear to have suffered from an impact, but the same impact may have paved the way for our existence. So while some scientists argue that more impacts would have damaged life on Earth, others argue that more impacts might have sped up evolution.

The role of Jupiter has led some scientists to wonder whether we could exist if our solar system had been laid out differently. Could it be that civilizations can arise only in solar systems that happen to have a Jupiter-like planet in a Jupiter-like orbit? No one yet knows the answer to this question. What we do know is that Jupiter has had profound effects on life on Earth and will continue to have effects in the future.

The Big Picture

Putting Chapter 12 into Context

In this chapter we concluded the study of our own solar system by focusing on its smallest objects, finding that these objects can have big consequences. Keep in mind the following "big picture" ideas:

- Asteroids, comets, and meteorites may be small compared to planets, but they provide evidence that has helped us understand how the solar system formed.

- The small bodies are subject to the gravitational whims of the largest. The jovian planets shaped the asteroid belt, the Kuiper belt, and the Oort cloud, and they continue to nudge objects onto collision courses with the planets.

- Collisions not only bring meteorites and leave impact craters but also can profoundly affect life on Earth. An impact probably was responsible for wiping out the dinosaurs, and future impacts pose a threat that we cannot ignore.

12.1 ASTEROIDS AND METEORITES

■ **What are asteroids like?** Asteroids are rocky leftovers from 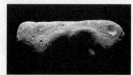 the era of planetary formation. Most are small, and despite their enormous numbers their total mass is less than that of any terrestrial planet.

■ **Why is there an asteroid belt?** Orbital resonances with 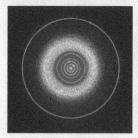 Jupiter disrupted the orbits of planetesimals in the asteroid belt, preventing them from accreting into a planet. Many were ejected but some remained and make up the asteroid belt today. Most asteroids in other regions of the inner solar system accreted into one of the planets.

■ **How are meteorites related to asteroids?** Most meteorites are pieces of asteroids. **Primitive meteorites** are essentially unchanged since the birth of the solar system. **Processed meteorites** are fragments of larger asteroids that underwent differentiation.

12.2 COMETS

■ **What are comets like?** Comets are icy leftovers from the  era of planet formation, and most orbit far from the Sun. If a comet approaches the Sun, its **nucleus** heats up and its ice vaporizes into gas. The escaping gases carry along some dust, forming a **coma** and two tails: a **plasma tail** of ionized gas and a **dust tail**. Larger particles can also escape, becoming the particles that cause **meteor showers** on Earth.

■ **Where do comets come from?** Comets come from two reservoirs: the **Kuiper belt** and the **Oort cloud**. The Kuiper belt  comets still reside in the region beyond Neptune in which they formed. The Oort cloud comets formed between the jovian planets, and were flung out to great distances from the Sun by gravitational encounters with the planets.

12.3 PLUTO: LONE DOG NO MORE

■ **How big can a comet be?** In the Kuiper belt, icy planetesimals were able to grow to hundreds or thousands of kilometers in size. Eris is the largest known of these objects, and Pluto is the second largest.

■ **What are the large objects of the Kuiper belt like?**

Eris   Pluto

Sedna   2007 OR₁₀

Like smaller comets, these objects are ice-rich in composition. They orbit the Sun roughly between the orbit of Neptune and twice that distance from the Sun. Their orbits tend to be more elliptical and more inclined to the ecliptic plane than those of the terrestrial and jovian planets. Many share orbital resonances with Neptune. A few, including Pluto and Eris, have moons.

12.4 COSMIC COLLISIONS: SMALL BODIES VERSUS THE PLANETS

■ **Have we ever witnessed a major impact?** In 1994, we observed the impacts of Comet Shoemaker-Levy 9 on Jupiter. The comet had fragmented into a string of individual nuclei, so there was a string of impacts that left Jupiter's atmosphere scarred for months.

■ **Did an impact kill the dinosaurs?** It may not have been 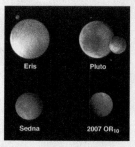 the sole cause, but a major impact clearly coincided with the **mass extinction** in which the dinosaurs died out, about 65 million years ago. Sediments from the time contain iridium and other clear evidence of an impact, and an impact crater of the right age lies near the coast of Mexico.

■ **Is the impact threat a real danger or media hype?** Impacts certainly pose a threat, though the probability of a major impact in our lifetimes is fairly low. Impacts like the Tunguska event may occur every couple of hundred years, and would be catastrophic if they struck populated areas.

■ **How do the jovian planets affect impact rates and life on Earth?** Impacts are always linked in at least some way  to the gravitational influences of Jupiter and the other jovian planets. These influences have shaped the asteroid belt, the Kuiper belt, and the Oort cloud, and continue to determine when an object is flung our way.

Use the following questions to check your understanding of some of the many types of visual information used in astronomy. Answers are provided in Appendix J. For additional practice, try the Chapter 12 Visual Quiz at MasteringAstronomy®.

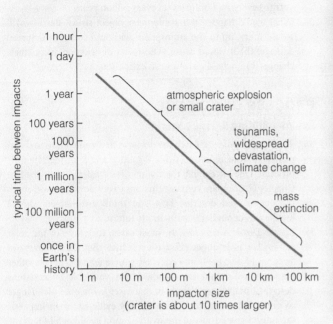

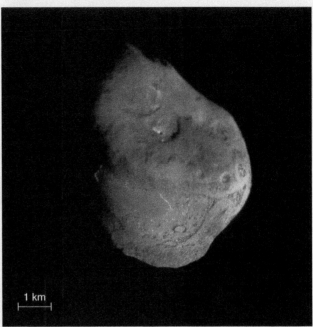

The graph above (Figure 12.28) shows how often impacts occur for objects of different sizes. The photo above shows Comet Tempel 1 moments before the Deep Impact spacecraft crashed into it.

1. Estimate Comet Tempel 1's diameter, using the scale bar in the photo above.
2. According to the graph above, how frequently do objects the size of Comet Tempel 1 strike Earth?
   a. once in Earth's history
   b. about once every hundred million years
   c. about once every million years
   d. about once every thousand years
3. Consider an object twice the size of Comet Tempel 1. What kind of damage would this object cause if it hit our planet?
   a. mass extinction
   b. widespread devastation and climate change
   c. atmospheric explosion or a small crater

4. Meteor Crater in Arizona is about 1.2 kilometers across. According to the graph, about how big was the object that made this crater? (*Note*: Be sure to read the axis labels carefully.)
   a. 1 meter
   b. 10 meters
   c. 100 meters
   d. 1 kilometer
5. How often do objects big enough to create craters like Meteor Crater impact Earth?
   a. once in Earth's history
   b. about once every ten thousand years
   c. about once every few million years
   d. about once every day, but most burn up in the atmosphere or land in the ocean

EXERCISES AND PROBLEMS

For instructor-assigned homework go to MasteringAstronomy®.

MasteringAstronomy®

REVIEW QUESTIONS

Short-Answer Questions Based on the Reading

1. Briefly describe the general characteristics of asteroids—including sizes, masses, densities, and compositions—and how we measure them.
2. How does the largest asteroid compare in size to the planets? How does the total mass of all asteroids compare to the mass of a terrestrial world?
3. Where is the *asteroid belt* located, and why? Briefly explain how orbital resonances with Jupiter have affected the asteroid belt.
4. What is the difference between a *meteor* and a *meteorite*? Distinguish between *primitive meteorites* and *processed meteorites* in terms of both composition and origin.
5. What does a comet look like when it is far from the Sun? Why do only a few comets ever enter the inner solar system?

6. What produces the *coma* and *tails* of a comet? What is the *nucleus*? Why do tails point away from the Sun?

7. How are *meteor showers* linked to comets, and why do they recur at about the same time each year?

8. Describe the *Kuiper belt* and *Oort cloud* in terms of their locations and the orbits of comets within them. How did comets come to exist in these two regions?

9. Briefly describe Pluto and Charon. Why won't Pluto collide with Neptune? How do we think Charon formed?

10. How are other Kuiper belt comets similar to Pluto?

11. Briefly describe the impact of Comet Shoemaker-Levy 9 on Jupiter.

12. Briefly describe the evidence suggesting that an impact caused the *mass extinction* that killed off the dinosaurs. How might the impact have led to the mass extinction?

13. How often should we expect impacts of various sizes on Earth? How serious a threat do we face from these impacts?

14. Summarize the role of the jovian planets in shaping the orbits of small bodies in the solar system. Why do some people think that Jupiter's existence is critical to our own?

TEST YOUR UNDERSTANDING

Surprising Discoveries?

Suppose we found a solar system with the property described. (These are not real discoveries.) In light of what you've learned about the formation of our own solar system, decide whether the discovery should be considered reasonable or surprising. Explain.

15. A small asteroid that orbits within the asteroid belt has an active volcano.

16. Scientists discover a meteorite that, based on radiometric dating, is 7.9 billion years old.

17. An object that resembles a comet in size and composition is discovered orbiting in the inner solar system.

18. Studies of a large object in the Kuiper belt reveal that it is made almost entirely of rocky (as opposed to icy) material.

19. Astronomers discover a previously unknown comet that will be brightly visible in our night sky about 2 years from now.

20. A mission to Eris finds that it has lakes of liquid water on its surface.

21. Geologists discover a crater from a 5-kilometer object that impacted Earth more than 100 million years ago.

22. Archaeologists learn that the fall of ancient Rome was caused in large part by an asteroid impact in Asia.

23. In another solar system, astronomers discover an object the size of Earth orbiting its star at the distance of the Kuiper belt.

24. Astronomers discover an asteroid with an orbit suggesting that it will collide with Earth in the year 2064.

Quick Quiz

Choose the best answer to each of the following. Explain your reasoning with one or more complete sentences.

25. The asteroid belt lies between the orbits of (a) Earth and Mars. (b) Mars and Jupiter. (c) Jupiter and Saturn.

26. Jupiter nudges the asteroids through the influence of (a) tidal forces. (b) orbital resonances. (c) magnetic fields.

27. Can an asteroid be pure metal? (a) No; all asteroids contain rock. (b) Yes; it must have formed where only metal could condense in the solar nebula. (c) Yes; it must have been the core of a shattered asteroid.

28. Did a large terrestrial planet ever form in the region of the asteroid belt? (a) No, because there was never enough mass there. (b) No, because Jupiter prevented one from accreting. (c) Yes, but it was shattered by a giant impact.

29. What does Pluto most resemble? (a) a terrestrial planet (b) a jovian planet (c) a comet

30. How big an object causes a typical shooting star? (a) a grain of sand or a small pebble (b) a boulder (c) an object the size of a car

31. Which have the most elliptical and tilted orbits? (a) asteroids (b) Kuiper belt comets (c) Oort cloud comets

32. Which are thought to have formed farthest from the Sun? (a) asteroids (b) Kuiper belt comets (c) Oort cloud comets

33. About how often does a 1-kilometer object strike Earth? (a) every year (b) every million years (c) every billion years

34. What would happen if a 1-kilometer object struck Earth? (a) It would break up in the atmosphere without causing widespread damage. (b) It would cause widespread devastation and climate change. (c) It would cause a mass extinction.

PROCESS OF SCIENCE

Examining How Science Works

35. *The Pluto Debate.* Research the decision to demote Pluto to dwarf planet. In your opinion, is this a good example of the scientific process? Does it exhibit the hallmarks of science described in Chapter 3? Compare your conclusions to opinions you find about the debate, and describe how you think astronomers should handle this or similar debates in the future.

36. *Life or Death Astronomy.* In most cases, the study of the solar system has little direct effect on our lives. But the discovery of an asteroid or comet on a collision course with Earth is another matter. How should the standards for verifiable observations described in Chapter 3 apply in this case? Is the potential danger so great that any astronomer with any evidence of an impending impact should spread the word as soon as possible? Or is the potential for panic so great that even higher standards of verification ought to be applied? What kind of review process, if any, would you set in place? Who should be informed of an impact threat, and when?

GROUP WORK EXERCISE

37. *Assessing Impact Danger.* Your task in this exercise is to assess the risks we face on Earth from meteorite and comet impacts. Before you begin, assign the following roles to the people in your group: *Scribe* (collects data and takes notes on the group's activities), *Proposer* (proposes hypotheses and explanations of the data), *Skeptic* (points out weaknesses in the hypotheses and explanations), *Moderator* (leads group discussion and makes sure everyone contributes). Each person should write down the answers from each part of the exercise.
a. Estimate the odds that human civilization will be destroyed by an impact during your lifetime. The *Moderator* should lead a discussion about how to go about making such an estimate. As a group, determine the kinds of information you would need, develop a method for making the estimate, and write down your method. **b.** *Scribe* analyzes Figure 12.28, determines whether it contains any of the necessary information, and shares his or her findings with the group. **c.** *Proposer* uses the group's method to estimate the probability that civilization will be destroyed by an impact during your lifetime, which you can assume to be 100 years for the purpose of this exercise. *Skeptic* should check *Proposer's* work. **d.** Estimate the probability that an impact will cause widespread devastation somewhere on Earth during your lifetime. *Moderator* should lead the discussion about how to make this estimate. *Scribe* should gather the information from Figure 12.28. *Proposer* should do the calculation, and *Skeptic* should check *Proposer's* work. **e.** Finding near-Earth asteroids early greatly increases our chances of deflecting them. Given the probabilities

from parts c and d and considering the damage these events would cause, decide as a group how much money per year should be spent on finding near-Earth asteroids and explain your reasoning.

INVESTIGATE FURTHER

In-Depth Questions to Increase Your Understanding

Short-Answer/Essay Questions

38. *The Role of Jupiter.* Suppose that Jupiter had never existed. Describe at least three ways in which our solar system would be different, and clearly explain why.

39. *Life Story of an Iron Atom.* Imagine that you are an iron atom in a processed meteorite made mostly of iron. Tell the story of how you got to Earth, beginning from the time you were part of the gas in the solar nebula 4.6 billion years ago. Include as much detail as possible. Your story should be scientifically accurate but also creative and interesting.

40. *Asteroid Discovery.* You have discovered two new asteroids and named them Albert and Isaac. Both lie at the same distance from Earth and have the same brightness when you look at them through your telescope, but Albert is twice as bright as Isaac at infrared wavelengths. What can you deduce about the relative reflectivities and sizes of the two asteroids? Which would make a better target for a mission to mine metal? Which would make a better target for a mission to obtain a sample of a carbon-rich planetesimal? Explain.

41. *Asteroids vs. Comets.* Contrast the compositions and locations of comets and asteroids, and explain in your own words why they have turned out differently.

42. *Comet Tails.* Describe in your own words why comets have tails. Why do most comets have two distinct visible tails, and why do the tails go in different directions? Why is the third, invisible tail of small pebbles of interest to us on Earth?

43. *Oort Cloud vs. Kuiper Belt.* Explain in your own words how and why there are two different reservoirs of comets. Be sure to discuss where the two groups of comets formed and what kinds of orbits they travel on.

44. *Project: Dirty Snowballs.* If there is snow where you live or study, make a dirty snowball. (The ice chunks that form behind tires work well.) How much dirt does it take to darken snow? Find out by allowing your dirty snowball to melt in a container and measuring the approximate proportions of water and dirt afterward.

Quantitative Problems

Be sure to show all calculations clearly and state your final answers in complete sentences.

45. *Adding Up Asteroids.* It's estimated that there are a million asteroids 1 kilometer across or larger. If a million asteroids 1 kilometer across were all combined into one object, how big would it be? How many 1-kilometer asteroids would it take to make an object as large as the Earth? (*Hint:* You can assume they're spherical. The expression for the volume of a sphere is $\frac{4}{3}\pi r^3$, where r is the radius.)

46. *Impact Energies.* A relatively small impact crater 20 kilometers in diameter could be made by a comet 2 kilometers in diameter traveling at 30 kilometers per second (30,000 m/s).
a. Assume that the comet has a total mass of 4.2×10^{12} kilograms. What is its total kinetic energy? (*Hint:* The kinetic energy is equal to $\frac{1}{2}mv^2$, where m is the comet's mass and v is its speed. If you use mass in kilograms and velocity in m/s, the answer for kinetic energy will have units of joules.) **b.** Convert your answer from part a to an equivalent in megatons of TNT, the unit used for nuclear bombs. Comment on the degree of devastation the

impact of such a comet could cause if it struck a populated region on Earth. (*Hint:* One megaton of TNT releases 4.2×10^{15} joules of energy.)

47. *The "Near Miss" of Toutatis.* The 5-kilometer asteroid Toutatis passed a mere 1.5 million kilometers from Earth in 2004. Suppose Toutatis were destined to pass *somewhere* within 1.5 million kilometers of Earth. Calculate the probability that this "somewhere" would have meant that it slammed into Earth. Based on your result, do you think it is fair to call the 2004 passage a "near miss"? Explain. (*Hint:* You can calculate the probability by considering an imaginary dartboard of radius 1.5 million kilometers in which the bull's-eye has Earth's radius, 6378 kilometers.)

48. *Room to Roam.* It's estimated that there are a trillion comets in the Oort cloud, which extends out to about 50,000 AU. What is the total volume of the Oort cloud, in cubic AU? How much space does each comet have in cubic AU, on average? Take the cube root of the average volume per comet to find the comets' typical spacing in AU. (*Hints:* For the purpose of this calculation, you can assume the Oort cloud fills the whole sphere out to 50,000 AU. The volume of a sphere is given by $\frac{4}{3}\pi r^3$, where r is the radius.)

49. *Comet Temperatures.* Find the "no greenhouse" temperatures for a comet at distances from the Sun of 50,000 AU (in the Oort cloud), 3 AU, and 1 AU (see Mathematical Insight 10.1). Assume that the comet reflects 3% of the incoming sunlight. At which location will the temperature be high enough for water ice to vaporize (about 150 K)? How do your results explain comet anatomy? Explain.

50. *Comet Dust Accumulation.* A few hundred tons of comet dust are added to Earth daily from the millions of meteors that enter our atmosphere. Estimate the time it would take for Earth to get 0.1% heavier at this rate. Is this mass accumulation significant for Earth as a planet? Explain.

Discussion Questions

51. *Rise of the Mammals.* Suppose the impact 65 million years ago had not occurred. How do you think our planet would be different? For example, do you think that mammals still would eventually have come to dominate Earth? Would we be here? Defend your opinions.

52. *How Should Kids Count Planets?* The new definitions that have officially demoted Pluto from planet to dwarf planet have many educational implications. For example, many children learn songs in school that refer to "nine planets" and Pluto. How would you recommend that school teachers deal with the new definitions? Be sure to consider the fact that while these definitions have "official" status today (from the International Astronomical Union), it is possible that they may change again in the future.

Web Projects

53. *Asteroid and Comet Missions.* Learn about a past or present space mission to study asteroids or comets, such as *NEAR*, *Dawn*, or *Rosetta*. What did it (or will it) accomplish? Write a one- to two-page summary of your findings.

54. *The New Horizons Mission to Pluto.* Find out the current status of the *New Horizons* mission. What are its science goals? What has it done so far? Summarize your findings in a few paragraphs.

55. *Impact Hazards.* Many groups are searching for near-Earth asteroids that might impact our planet. They use something called the *Torino Scale* to evaluate the possible danger posed by an asteroid based on how well we know its orbit. What is this scale? What object has reached the highest level on this scale? What were the estimated chances of impact, and when?

b

c

20 AU
0.5"

e

d

This infrared image from the Keck Telescope shows direct detection of a four-planet system (planets marked b, c, d, e) orbiting the star HR 8799. Light from the star itself (center) was mostly blocked out during the exposure.

13 OTHER PLANETARY SYSTEMS
THE NEW SCIENCE OF DISTANT WORLDS

13.1 DETECTING PLANETS AROUND OTHER STARS

- Why is it so challenging to learn about extrasolar planets?
- How can a star's motion reveal the presence of planets?
- How can changes in a star's brightness reveal the presence of planets?

13.2 THE NATURE OF PLANETS AROUND OTHER STARS

- What properties of extrasolar planets can we measure?
- How do extrasolar planets compare with planets in our solar system?

13.3 THE FORMATION OF OTHER SOLAR SYSTEMS

- Can we explain the surprising orbits of many extrasolar planets?
- Do we need to modify our theory of solar system formation?

13.4 THE FUTURE OF EXTRASOLAR PLANETARY SCIENCE

- How will future observations improve our understanding?

How vast those Orbs must be, and how inconsiderable this Earth, the Theatre upon which all our mighty Designs, all our Navigations, and all our Wars are transacted, is when compared to them. A very fit consideration, and matter of Reflection, for those Kings and Princes who sacrifice the Lives of so many People, only to flatter their Ambition in being Masters of some pitiful corner of this small Spot.

—Christiaan Huygens, c. 1690

For more than 450 years after Copernicus recognized Earth as one member of our Sun's planetary system, the study of planetary systems remained limited to our own. Then, about two decades ago, a new scientific revolution began with the first discoveries of planets around other stars. This revolution is now in full bloom, with new discoveries coming at a rapid pace.

The rapidly advancing science of extrasolar planets has dramatic implications for our understanding of our place in the universe. The fact that planets are common in the universe makes it seem more likely that we might someday find life elsewhere, perhaps even intelligent life. Moreover, having many more worlds to compare to our own vastly enhances our ability to learn how planets work, which may help us better understand our home planet, Earth. It also allows us to test the nebular theory of solar system formation in new settings. In this chapter, we'll focus our attention on the exciting new science of other planetary systems.

 Detecting Extrasolar Planets Tutorial, Lessons 1–3

13.1 DETECTING PLANETS AROUND OTHER STARS

The very idea of planets around other stars, or **extrasolar planets** for short, would have shattered the world views of many people throughout history. After all, cultures of the western world long regarded Earth as the center of the universe, and nearly all ancient cultures imagined the heavens to be a realm distinct from Earth.

The Copernican revolution, which taught us that Earth is a planet orbiting the Sun, opened up the possibility that planets might also orbit other stars. Still, until the 1990s, no extrasolar planets were known. Given that the number of known or suspected extrasolar planets is now in the thousands and growing rapidly, you may wonder what took so long.

Why is it so challenging to learn about extrasolar planets?

We've known for centuries that other stars are distant suns (see Special Topic, page 368), making it natural to suspect that they would have their own planetary systems. The nebular theory of solar system formation, well established decades ago, made extrasolar planets seem even more likely.

As we discussed in Chapter 8, the nebular theory explains our planetary system as a natural consequence of processes that accompanied the birth of our Sun. The theory therefore seems to predict that planets should be common around other stars. However, it took many decades for technology to reach the point at which this prediction could be put to the test.

The first technological challenge is one we already discussed in the context of our scale model solar system in Chapter 1. Recall that on a 1-to-10-billion scale, the Sun is the size of a grapefruit, Earth is a pinhead orbiting 15 meters away, and Jupiter is a marble orbiting 80 meters away. On the same scale, the distance to the nearest stars (besides the Sun) is equivalent to the distance across the United States. Therefore, looking for planets orbiting even the nearest stars would be like looking from San Francisco for pinheads and marbles orbiting a grapefruit in Washington, D.C. Most stars are much farther away, making the challenge far greater.

A second challenge comes from the fact that a Sun-like star is a *billion times* brighter than the light reflected from any of its planets. Because even the best telescopes blur the light from stars at least a little, the glare of scattered starlight generally overwhelms any small spots of planetary light, even if those spots are bright enough to be detectable in principle. The problem is somewhat lessened if we observe in infrared light, because planets emit their own infrared light and Sun-like stars are dimmer in the infrared, but it is still significant.

As recently as the early 1990s, these challenges made even some astronomers think that we were still decades away from finding extrasolar planets. But human ingenuity proved greater than the pessimists had guessed. Thanks to technological advances, clever planet-hunting strategies, and some unexpected differences between our solar system and others, we are discovering vast numbers of planets orbiting other stars. Although it is too soon to know for sure, it seems likely that our Milky Way Galaxy is home to billions of planetary systems.

Nevertheless, the combination of the distance scale and the vast differences in brightness between stars and planets still adds up to a tremendous technological challenge as we seek to obtain images or spectra of extrasolar planets. This brings us to a key point about our current ability to study planets around other stars. In general, there are two ways to learn about distant objects: *directly*, which means by obtaining images or spectra of the objects themselves, and *indirectly*, which means by inferring existence or properties without actually seeing the objects under study.

In principle, direct study is always preferable and allows us to learn far more. In the case of extrasolar planets, direct study could mean imaging of visible light reflected by the planets or of infrared light that the planets emit, or it could mean obtaining visible or infrared spectra of the planets. We've achieved some success in direct detection, but we will need significant advances in technology before we are able to obtain images or spectra of many extrasolar planets with even moderate resolution. The best we can do today is exemplified by images such as the one on the chapter opening page (page 366), in which we see dots of infrared light for planets that are much larger and farther from their star than the planets of our own solar system. We'll discuss present and future direct detection efforts in more detail in Section 13.4.

In the meantime, the difficulty of direct study means that nearly everything we know today about extrasolar planets comes from indirect study. There are two major approaches to indirectly finding and studying extrasolar planets:

1. Observing the motion of a star to detect the subtle gravitational effects of orbiting planets.

2. Observing changes to a star's brightness that occur when one of its planets passes in front of the star as viewed from Earth.

The earliest discoveries of extrasolar planets came primarily through the first approach, but the current champion of extrasolar planet discoveries—NASA's *Kepler* mission—uses the second. We can learn even more in cases in which we can combine both indirect approaches, because each can provide different information about a distant planet.

Because these two approaches to indirect study are so important to current understanding of extrasolar planets, we will devote the rest of this section to studying them in somewhat more detail.

How can a star's motion reveal the presence of planets?

The first approach to indirect study relies on observing stars in order to detect motion that we can attribute to gravitational tugs from orbiting planets. This type of detection is indirect because we discover the planets by observing their stars without actually seeing the planets themselves.

Although we usually think of a star as remaining still while planets orbit around it, that is only approximately correct. In reality, all the objects in a star system, including the star itself, orbit the system's "balance point," or *center of mass* [**Section 4.4**]. To understand how this fact allows us to discover extrasolar planets, imagine the viewpoint of extraterrestrial astronomers observing our solar system from afar.

Let's start by considering only the influence of Jupiter, the most massive planet in our solar system. The center of mass between the Sun and Jupiter lies just outside the Sun's visible surface (**FIGURE 13.1**), so what we usually think of as Jupiter's 12-year orbit around the Sun is really a 12-year orbit around the center of mass. Because the Sun and Jupiter are always on opposite sides of the center of mass (otherwise it wouldn't be a "center"), the Sun must orbit this point with the same 12-year period. The Sun's orbit traces out only a small circle (or ellipse) with each 12-year period, because the Sun's average orbital distance is barely larger than its own radius; that is why

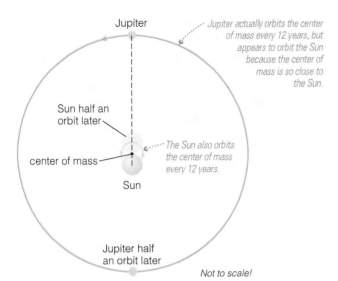

FIGURE 13.1 This diagram shows how both the Sun and Jupiter orbit around their mutual center of mass, which lies very close to the Sun. The diagram is not to scale; the sizes of the Sun and its orbit are exaggerated about 100 times compared to the size shown for Jupiter's orbit, and Jupiter's size is exaggerated even more.

In the diagram:
- Jupiter
- *Jupiter actually orbits the center of mass every 12 years, but appears to orbit the Sun because the center of mass is so close to the Sun.*
- Sun half an orbit later
- center of mass
- *The Sun also orbits the center of mass every 12 years.*
- Sun
- Jupiter half an orbit later
- *Not to scale!*

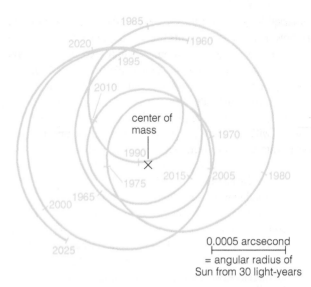

0.0005 arcsecond = angular radius of Sun from 30 light-years

FIGURE 13.2 This diagram shows the orbital path of the Sun around the center of mass of our solar system as it would appear from a distance of 30 light-years away, for the period 1960–2025. Notice that the entire range of motion during this period is only about 0.0015 arcsecond, which is almost 100 times smaller than the angular resolution of the Hubble Space Telescope. Nevertheless, if alien astronomers could measure this motion, they could learn of the existence of planets in our solar system.

we generally don't notice the Sun's motion. Nevertheless, with sufficiently precise measurements, extraterrestrial astronomers could detect this orbital movement of the Sun and thereby deduce the existence of Jupiter, even without having observed Jupiter itself. They could even determine Jupiter's mass from the orbital characteristics of the Sun as it goes around the center of mass. A more massive planet at the same distance would pull the center of mass farther from the Sun's center, giving the Sun a larger orbit and a faster orbital speed around the center of mass.

SEE IT FOR YOURSELF

To see how a small planet can make a big star wobble, find a pencil and tape a heavy object (such as a set of keys) and a lighter object (perhaps a few coins) to opposite ends. Tie a string (or piece of floss) at the balance point—the center of mass—so that the pencil is horizontal. Then tap the lighter object into "orbit" around the heavier object. What does the heavier object do, and why? How does your setup correspond to a planet orbiting a star? You can experiment further with objects of different weights or shorter pencils; try to explain the differences you see.

Now let's add in the effects of Saturn. Saturn takes 29.5 years to orbit the Sun, so by itself it would cause the Sun to orbit their mutual center of mass every 29.5 years. However, because Saturn's influence is secondary to that of Jupiter, this 29.5-year period appears as a small effect added on top of the Sun's 12-year orbit around its center of mass with Jupiter. In other words, every 12 years the Sun would return to *nearly* the same orbital position around its center of mass with Jupiter, but the precise point of return would move around with Saturn's 29.5-year period. By measuring this motion carefully over many years, an extraterrestrial astronomer could deduce the existence and masses of both Jupiter and Saturn.

The other planets also exert gravitational tugs on the Sun, which further affect the Sun's orbital motion around the solar system's center of mass (FIGURE 13.2). These extra effects are smaller still, and so are even more difficult to measure in practice, but extremely precise observations could in principle allow an extraterrestrial astronomer to discover all the planets in our solar system. If we turn this idea around, it means we can search for planets in other star systems by carefully watching for the tiny orbital motion of a star around the center of mass of its star system.

Astronomers use two distinct observation methods to search for this type of orbital motion by stars. The first, called the **astrometric method** (*astrometry* means "measurement of the stars"), uses very precise measurements of stellar positions in the sky to look for the slight motion caused by orbiting planets. The second, called the **Doppler method**, takes advantage of the Doppler effect [**Section 5.4**], which allows us to measure changes in a star's velocity toward or away from us that are caused by orbiting planets.

The Astrometric Method The astrometric method has been used for decades to identify binary star systems, because two orbiting stars move periodically around their center of mass. The technique works especially well for binary systems in which the two stars are not too close together, because the stellar motions tend to be larger in those cases. In the case of planet searches, however, the expected stellar motion is much more difficult to detect.

For example, from a distance of 10 light-years, a Jupiter-size planet in a Jupiter-like orbit (5 AU from a Sun-like star) would cause its star to move slowly over a side-to-side angular distance of only about 0.003 arcsecond—approximately the width of a hair seen from a distance of 5 kilometers.

Remarkably, with careful telescope calibration, astronomers can now measure movements this small. In fact, the European Space Agency's *GAIA* mission, scheduled to operate from 2013 to 2018, has the ambitious goal of performing astrometric observations of a billion stars in our galaxy to an accuracy that in some cases will be better than 10 microarcseconds. (A microarcsecond is one-millionth of an arcsecond.)

Even with such precise measurements, two unavoidable constraints limit the number of planetary systems that can be studied with the astrometric method. The first constraint comes from the fact that the farther away a star is, the smaller its side-to-side movement will appear. For example, while Jupiter causes the Sun to move by about 0.003 arcsecond as seen from 10 light-years away, the observed motion is only half as large when seen from 20 light-years away and one-tenth as large when seen from 100 light-years away. The astrometric method therefore works best for detecting the gravitational effects of massive planets around relatively nearby stars.

The second constraint arises from the fact that, for a planet of any particular mass, a greater orbital distance means a larger astrometric effect on its star, but it also means that the effect takes longer to measure. For example, moving Jupiter farther from the Sun would increase the angular extent of the Sun's side-to-side motion as seen from a distance (because moving Jupiter outward would also move the center of mass outward from the Sun), but Kepler's third law tells us that this move would also increase the period of Jupiter's orbit. For example, if Jupiter moved to Neptune's distance from the Sun, at which the orbital period is 165 years, it might take a century or more of patient observation to be confident that stellar motion was occurring in a 165-year cycle.

As a result of these constraints, the astrometric method has been of only limited use to date. Nevertheless, the *GAIA* mission should vastly increase the number of planets detected with this method (see Section 13.4). If all is successful, *GAIA* will likely discover thousands of new worlds, with more and more discoveries as the mission goes on and is able to observe motions caused by planets in more distant orbits.

The Doppler Method The Doppler method also looks for the gravitational influence of a planet on a star, but instead of looking for side-to-side motion of the star in the sky, we look for back-and-forth motion that can be measured from Doppler shifts in a star's spectrum (FIGURE 13.3). Recall that the Doppler effect causes a blueshift when a star is moving toward us and a redshift when it is moving away from us, so alternating blueshifts and redshifts (relative to a star's average Doppler shift) indicate orbital motion around a center of mass.

The Doppler method has the distinction of having been used for the first discovery of an extrasolar planet around a Sun-like star*: a planet orbiting a star called 51 Pegasi, found in 1995 by Swiss astronomers Michel Mayor and Didier Queloz, and soon confirmed by a team led by American astronomers Geoffrey W. Marcy and R. Paul Butler. The discovery came

---

*The first actual detection of extrasolar planet-size objects occurred in 1992, when precise timing measurements revealed the existence of three objects with Earth-like masses orbiting a type of "dead" star known as a *pulsar* [**Section 18.2**]. Because pulsars are created when stars die in supernova explosions, these "planets" must be either the charred remains of preexisting planets or, more likely, objects that somehow formed from supernova debris. Either way, they are not planets in the same sense as those that form during star birth; in this chapter, we will focus only on planets orbiting ordinary stars like our Sun.

The Names of Extrasolar Planets

The planets in our solar system have familiar names rooted in mythology. Unfortunately, there's not yet a well-accepted scheme for naming extrasolar planets. Astronomers still generally refer to extrasolar planets by the star they orbit, such as "the planet orbiting the star named…." Worse still, the stars themselves often have confusing or even multiple names, reflecting naming schemes used in star catalogs made by different people at different times in history.

A few hundred of the brightest stars in the sky carry names from ancient times. Many of these names are Arabic—such as Betelgeuse, Algol, and Aldebaran—because of the work of the Arab scholars of the Middle Ages [**Section 3.2**]. In the early 1600s, German astronomer Johann Bayer developed a system that gave names to many more stars: Each star gets a name based on its constellation and a Greek letter indicating its ranking in brightness within that constellation. For example, the brightest star in the constellation Andromeda is called Alpha Andromedae, the second brightest is Beta Andromedae, and so on. Bayer's system worked for only the 24 brightest stars in each constellation, because there are only 24 letters in the Greek alphabet. About a century later, English astronomer John Flamsteed published a more extensive star catalog in which he used numbers once the Greek letters were exhausted. For example, 51 Pegasi gets its name from Flamsteed's catalog. (Flamsteed's numbers are based on position within a constellation rather than brightness.)

As more powerful telescopes made it possible to discover more and fainter stars, astronomers developed many new star catalogs. The names we use today usually come from one of these catalogs. For example, the star HD 209458 appears as star number 209458 in a catalog compiled by Henry Draper (HD). You may see star names consisting of numbers preceded by other catalog names, including Gliese, Ross, and Wolf; these catalogs are also named for the astronomers who compiled them. Because the same star is often listed in several catalogs, a single star can have several different names.

Objects orbiting other stars usually carry the star name plus a letter denoting their order of discovery around that star. If the second object is another star, a capital B is added to the star name; a lowercase b is added if it's a planet. For example, HD 209458b is the first planet discovered orbiting star number 209458 in the Henry Draper catalog; Upsilon Andromedae d is the third planet discovered orbiting the twentieth brightest star (because upsilon is the twentieth letter in the Greek alphabet) in the constellation Andromeda. Some recently discovered planets have been named for the observing program that discovered them. For example, Kepler 11g is the sixth planet in the eleventh planetary system announced by the *Kepler* mission. Many astronomers hope soon to devise a better naming system for these wonderful new worlds.

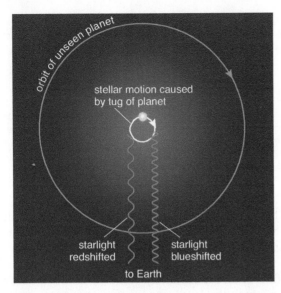

FIGURE 13.3 **interactive figure** The Doppler technique for discovering extrasolar planets: The star's Doppler shift alternates toward the blue and toward the red, allowing us to detect its slight motion—caused by an orbiting planet—around the center of mass.

from careful measurements showing that the spectrum of 51 Pegasi has alternating blueshifts and redshifts with a period of about 4 days (FIGURE 13.4).

The 4-day period of the star's motion must be the orbital period of its planet. We therefore know that the planet lies so close to the star that its "year" lasts only 4 Earth days and its surface temperature is probably over 1000 K. The Doppler data also allow us to determine the planet's approximate mass, because a more massive planet has a greater gravitational effect on the star (for a given orbital distance) and therefore causes the star to move at higher speed around the

system's center of mass. In the case of 51 Pegasi, the data show that the planet has about half the mass of Jupiter. The combination of the planet's high mass with its closeness to its star makes it an example of what we call a **hot Jupiter**, because it has a Jupiter-like mass but a much higher surface temperature.

Current techniques can measure a star's velocity to within about 1 meter per second—walking speed—which corresponds to a Doppler wavelength shift of just 0.0000003%. We can therefore find planets that exert a considerably smaller gravitational tug on their stars than the planet orbiting 51 Pegasi does on its star. More than 700 planets have been detected by the Doppler method as of 2012, many by the same teams of astronomers that made the discovery around 51 Pegasi. In fact, the Doppler data are often good enough to allow us to measure the gravitational tugs of two or more planets on a single star; as of 2012, nearly 100 multiple-planet systems had been identified by the Doppler method.

Despite the success of the Doppler method, it has some limitations. The fact that the Doppler method, like the astrometric method, searches for gravitational tugs from orbiting planets means that it is much better for finding massive planets like Jupiter than small planets like Earth. However, the Doppler method is best suited to identifying massive planets that orbit relatively *close* to their star (in contrast to the astrometric method, which works better for planets farther from their star), because being closer means a stronger gravitational tug and hence a greater velocity for the star as it orbits the center of mass. The fact that the Doppler method, like all indirect methods, requires observing long enough to see a star's orbit around the center of mass—which is equivalent to the orbital period of the planet causing the motion—means that the Doppler method is biased toward finding close-in planets with short orbital periods. That is why many of the earliest

a A periodic Doppler shift in the spectrum of the star 51 Pegasi shows the presence of a large planet with an orbital period of about 4 days. Dots are actual data points; bars through dots represent measurement uncertainty.

b Artist's conception of the planet orbiting 51 Pegasi, which probably has a mass similar to that of Jupiter but orbits its star at only about one-eighth of Mercury's orbital distance from the Sun. It probably has a surface temperature above 1000 K, making it an example of what we call a hot Jupiter.

FIGURE 13.4 The discovery of a planet orbiting 51 Pegasi.

discoveries of extrasolar planets were of hot Jupiters like 51 Pegasi b. Finally, the Doppler method requires a fairly large telescope in order to obtain spectra with high enough resolution to look for very small Doppler shifts, which limits the number of stars that can be studied with this method.

How can changes in a star's brightness reveal the presence of planets?

The second general approach to detecting planets indirectly relies on searching for slight changes in a star's brightness. This approach has its greatest use in what we call the **transit method**, which is the method used by the *Kepler* mission to search for planets around other stars.

Transits If we were to examine a large sample of stars with planets, a small number of them—typically one in several hundred—would by chance be aligned in such a way that one or more of its planets would pass directly between us and the star once each orbit. In such cases, we say that a planet's orbital tilt, or *inclination*, is aligned with the direction to Earth. The result is a **transit**, in which the planet appears to move across the face of the star. We occasionally witness this effect in our own solar system when Mercury or Venus crosses in front of the Sun (see Figure S1.5). Other star systems are so far away that we cannot actually see a planetary dot set against the face of the star as we can see Mercury or Venus against the face of the Sun. Nevertheless, a transiting planet will block a little of its star's light, allowing us to detect its passage as the star appears temporarily dimmer (**FIGURE 13.5**). The larger the planet, the more dimming it will cause. Many transiting planets also offer a measurable **eclipse** as the planet goes behind the star, during which we see a dip in the system's brightness. The reason is that the system's total brightness comes from the star and planet together (perhaps with additional contributions from other planets in the system), so this brightness goes down when the planet is hidden behind the star during the eclipse. Eclipse observations are more easily accomplished in the infrared, because planets contribute a greater proportion of a system's infrared brightness than visible-light brightness.

THINK ABOUT IT

Suppose you were an alien astronomer searching for planets going around our Sun. Where would your star system have to be located in order for you to observe transits across the Sun? Which planets in our solar system would be the easiest to discover through transits? Explain.

Note that, because most stars exhibit intrinsic variations in brightness, we can be confident that we have detected a planet only if we observe the dips in brightness to repeat with a regular period, indicating that the same planet is passing in front of the star repeatedly with each orbit. (Intrinsic stellar brightness variations tend to be more random.) In that case, the period of the repeated dimmings tells us the orbital period of the transiting planet. Scientists generally require at least three repeated transits before concluding that a planet is probably responsible. Using the transit method to discover a planet therefore requires monitoring a star's brightness for at least three full orbits of the planet. For example, we would need at least about three years of monitoring with the transit method to detect a planet in an Earth-like orbit.

Putting these ideas together, we find that the first requirement for success with the transit method is that a system have planet orbits aligned "just right" so that they pass in front of their star as seen from Earth. When that is the case, the transit method will always be able to find close-in planets with short orbital periods before it can find more distant planets, simply because less time is needed to observe repeated transits of the closer-in planets. Adding the fact that larger planets create bigger dips in brightness means that transits are easiest to measure for hot Jupiters, because they are large and close in.

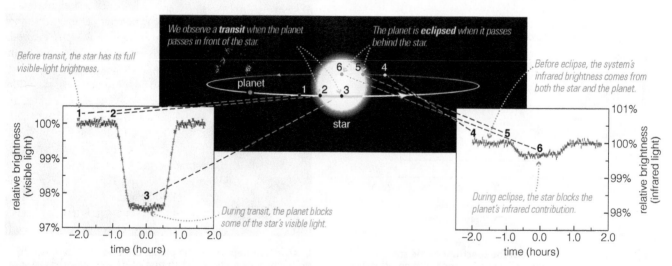

FIGURE 13.5 interactive figure This diagram represents transits and eclipses of the planet orbiting the star HD 189733. The graph shows that each transit lasts about 2 hours, during which the star's visible-light brightness dips by about 2.5%. The eclipses are observable in the infrared, because the star blocks the infrared contribution of the planet. The transits and eclipses each occur once during every 2.2-day orbit of the planet.

The first success of the transit method came in 1999, when a relatively small ground-based telescope detected transit dips from a hot Jupiter known as HD 209458b. This planet had already been detected by the Doppler method, so the transits in this case served as confirmation rather than discovery. Nevertheless, this success spurred scientists to begin searching more deliberately for transits, and many dozens of planets have now been discovered with ground-based searches. The transit method has met even greater success with space-based telescopes, beginning with the European Space Agency's *COROT* mission, launched in 2006. NASA's Spitzer Space Telescope, which observes infrared light, has also successfully observed transits, even though it was not designed for that purpose. But the study of extrasolar planets through transits truly came of age with the launch of the *Kepler* spacecraft in 2009.

The *Kepler* Mission The *Kepler* mission was conceived with the ambitious goal of discovering Earth-size planets in Earth-like orbits. This poses a much greater technical challenge than detecting hot Jupiters. There are three major challenges, each of which was addressed in the mission's design.

The first challenge comes from the statistics of orbital alignments. Remember that only a small fraction of planets will by chance have their orbits oriented in such a way as to pass in front of their star from our vantage point on Earth. The chance declines with a planet's distance from its star. Calculations show that only about 1 in 200 planetary systems should by chance have an orientation that would allow us to see a transit by an Earth-size planet in an Earth-like orbit. To compensate for these low odds, *Kepler* must monitor a large number of stars in order to have reasonable expectation of a small number of successes. *Kepler* monitors about 150,000 stars by keeping its telescope continuously pointed at a relatively wide field of view in the constellation Cygnus.

The second challenge comes from transit timing. For an Earth-like planet in an Earth-like orbit, a transit will last no more than a few hours and occur only once a year. As a result, we may miss transits unless we watch for them both day and night over a period of years. *Kepler* was therefore placed into an orbit around the Sun rather than Earth, so that Earth does not get in the way of its observations at any time. To make sure no transit is missed, *Kepler* measures the brightnesses of all its stars about every 30 minutes. To allow time for observing multiple transits, the mission was designed to last for at least four years.

The final challenge is in the need for extraordinarily precise measurement, because the dips in brightness caused by Earth-size planets are very small. For example, viewed from afar, a transit of Earth across the Sun would dim the Sun's light by only about 0.008%—not quite one part in 10,000. *Kepler*'s cameras are sensitive enough to detect transits of Earth-size planets around Sun-like stars, and transits of planets as small as Mercury around smaller, dimmer stars. As a result, *Kepler* is currently capable of finding much smaller planets than can be found with any other method, especially if the planets are at larger distances from their star.

The early success of *Kepler* has been nothing short of phenomenal. Because it was designed to detect planets as small as Earth on year-long orbits, it's had no trouble finding Jupiter- and Neptune-size planets on shorter orbits. As of mid-2012, *Kepler* mission scientists had sifted through data from only the first 16 months of observations, and had already identified planet "candidates" around nearly 1800 stars. More than 300 of these stars have two or more planet candidates, making a total of more than 2300 planet candidates. The detections are called "candidates" until they're confirmed by follow-up observations (such as detection by the Doppler method), because even when three dips in a star's brightness that look like transits are observed, there's a small possibility that the dips are being caused by something besides an orbiting planet. Statistically, though, it's expected that about 90% of the candidates will eventually be confirmed. Given this early success, it's likely that the *Kepler* mission will have found hundreds or even thousands of additional planets by the time you are reading this book.

> **THINK ABOUT IT**
> Check the current status of the *Kepler* mission online. How many planets has it found? What is the most Earth-like planet discovered by the mission so far?

Advantages and Limitations of the Transit Method The most obvious limitation of the transit method is that it can work only for the small fraction of planetary systems in which planet orbits are oriented edge-on to Earth. This method therefore will never be able to detect more than a very small fraction of the planets that actually exist. Nevertheless, as the *Kepler* mission demonstrates, this limitation can be counterbalanced by observing large numbers of stars, so that even a small fraction can represent large numbers of planets. The transit method shares the bias of the other methods toward finding planets with shorter orbital periods, simply because it takes longer to observe planets with longer periods.

The transit method also has several advantages over the astrometric and Doppler methods. Of greatest significance, the transit method can reveal planets far smaller than can currently be found with the astrometric or Doppler method. There are two reasons for this advantage. First, although small planets cause only a very small dimming of their star, the *Kepler* mission proves that such dimmings are measurable for planets as small as Earth. Second, in a multiplanet system, the astrometric and Doppler methods can detect the existence of small planets only as small effects added to the much larger gravitational effects of larger planets in the system. In contrast, a small planet leaves a distinct signature with the transit method, because planets with different periods will rarely transit in front of a star at the same time.

Perhaps most remarkably, in some cases transits cause enough stellar dimming to be measurable even with small, personal telescopes. A telescope as small as 4 inches in diameter has been used to discover an extrasolar planet, and it's relatively easy to confirm for yourself some of the transits that have already been detected. What was once considered impossible for scientists can now be assigned as homework for students (see Problem 48 at the end of the chapter).

TABLE 13.1   Major Advantages and Limitations of Extrasolar Planet Detection Methods

	Major Advantages	Major Limitations	Major Planetary Properties Measured	Confirmed or Candidate Planets (as of mid-2012)
Direct Detection	▪ Allows direct study of images or spectra	▪ Currently possible only in rare cases	▪ Spectra ▪ Surface details (with future technology)	A few
Astrometric Method	▪ Best for detecting massive planets that orbit far from their stars	▪ Currently possible only in rare cases ▪ Works best for nearby stars; for distant planets, requires space observatory	▪ Planet mass ▪ Orbital period and distance (semimajor axis) ▪ Orbital eccentricity ▪ Orbital inclination	A few
Doppler Method	▪ Best for detecting massive planets with close-in orbits ▪ Detects planets in all orbit orientations except face-on	▪ Less sensitive to planets farther from their stars ▪ Requires large telescopes ▪ Provides only minimum mass when orbital inclination to Earth unknown	▪ Minimum planet mass ▪ Orbital period and distance (semimajor axis) ▪ Orbital eccentricity	About 1000
Transit Method	▪ Allows many stars to be observed at once ▪ Can detect very small planets ▪ Feasible with small telescopes ▪ Can provide some atmospheric information in cases of measurable eclipses	▪ Possible only for planets with edge-on orbits as viewed from Earth ▪ For small planets, requires sensitivity possible only from space observatory	▪ Planet size ▪ Orbital period and distance (semimajor axis) ▪ Orbital inclination (edge-on)	About 2000

Summary TABLE 13.1 summarizes the advantages and limitations of the major methods we have discussed for studying extrasolar planets, and Cosmic Context FIGURE 13.6 (pages 376–377) summarizes how these methods work. Note that while these will almost certainly be the most important methods over the long term, several other strategies have met with some success. More than a dozen planets have been detected by what is sometimes called *microlensing*, which is an example of gravitational lensing [**Sections S3.4, 23.2**] in which the light of a star is temporarily magnified as another star passes in front of it and bends its light. Careful study of the microlensing event can reveal whether the foreground star has planets. The major drawback to this method is that the special alignment necessary for microlensing is a one-time event, which generally means that there is no opportunity for confirmation or follow-up observations. A different strategy takes advantage of the fact that many stars are surrounded by disks of dust. A planet within such a disk can exert small gravitational tugs on dust particles to produce gaps, waves, or ripples that may be detectable. Some astronomers are searching for thermal emission attributable to the heat of large impacts on planets in young planetary systems, and others are searching for the special kinds of emission expected from the magnetospheres of jovian planets. As we learn more about extrasolar planets, new search methods are sure to arise.

13.2 THE NATURE OF PLANETS AROUND OTHER STARS

The mere existence of planets around other stars has changed our perception of our place in the universe, because it shows that our planetary system is not unique. Scientifically, however, we want to know much more than just that these planets exist. In principle, the study of extrasolar planets and planetary systems should provide us with opportunities to vastly expand our general understanding of planets and how they form.

There are two basic scientific goals. First, we'd like to know the general characteristics of planets. For example, the planets of our own solar system come in only two basic types, terrestrial and jovian, and all orbit the Sun on nearly circular orbits in nearly the same plane. The study of extrasolar planets should tell us whether our solar system's planets are typical or whether there is a larger range of planetary types. Second, we'd like to know how extrasolar planets formed, and whether the nebular theory, which we use to explain the origin of our own solar system, can work equally well for explaining other planetary systems.

In this section, we'll discuss the types of data that we can acquire about extrasolar planets with present technology, and what these data tell us about the nature of planets around other stars. We'll then be prepared to turn our attention in the next section to the question of how well the nebular theory works for explaining other planetary systems.

What properties of extrasolar planets can we measure?

Despite the challenge of detecting extrasolar planets, we can actually learn a surprising amount about them. Depending on the method or methods used to study a planet, we can determine characteristics including orbital period and distance, orbital eccentricity, mass, size, density, and even a little bit about a planet's atmospheric composition and temperature. Let's briefly explore how we learn about each of these characteristics.

Orbital Period and Distance All three of the major indirect detection methods tell us a planet's orbital period. The astrometric method allows us to observe the star's motion as the star orbits the center of mass, which means we will

know the star's orbital period; the planet's orbital period must be the same. The orbital period for a planet detected by the Doppler method is simply the time between peaks in the velocity curve (see Figure 13.4a). For the transit method, the orbital period is the time between repeated transits.

Once we know the orbital period, we can determine average orbital distance (semimajor axis) with Newton's version of Kepler's third law [**Section 4.4**]. Recall that for a small object like a planet orbiting a much more massive object like a star, this law expresses a relationship between the star's mass, the planet's orbital period, and the planet's average distance. We generally know the masses of the stars with extrasolar planets (through methods we'll discuss in Chapter 15). Therefore, using the star's mass and the planet's orbital period, we can calculate the planet's average orbital distance (see Mathematical Insight 13.1).

Orbital Eccentricity and Inclination All planetary orbits are ellipses, but recall that ellipses vary in eccentricity, which is a measure of how "stretched out" they are [**Section 3.3**]. The planets in our solar system all have nearly circular orbits (low eccentricity), which means that their actual distances from the Sun are always relatively close to their average distances. Planets with higher eccentricity swing in close to their star on one side of their orbit and go much farther from their star on the other side.

MATHEMATICAL INSIGHT 13.1

Finding Orbital Distances for Extrasolar Planets

Recall that Newton's version of Kepler's third law reads

$$p^2 = \frac{4\pi^2}{G(M_1 + M_2)}a^3$$

In the case of a planet orbiting a star, p is the planet's orbital period, a is its average orbital distance (semimajor axis), and M_1 and M_2 are the masses of the star and planet, respectively. G is the gravitational constant; $G = 6.67 \times 10^{-11}$ m³/(kg × s²). Because a star is so much more massive than a planet, we can approximate $M_{star} + M_{planet} \approx M_{star}$ (see Mathematical Insight 4.3). If we make this approximation, then simple algebra allows us to solve for the average orbital distance a:

$$a \approx \sqrt[3]{\frac{GM_{star}}{4\pi^2}p_{planet}^2}$$

EXAMPLE: Doppler measurements show that the planet orbiting 51 Pegasi has an orbital period of 4.23 days; the star's mass is 1.06 times that of our Sun. What is the planet's average orbital distance?

SOLUTION:

Step 1 Understand: We are given both the planet's orbital period and the star's mass, so we can use Newton's version of Kepler's third law to find the average orbital distance. To make the units consistent, we convert the given stellar mass to kilograms (using the fact that the Sun's mass is 2×10^{30} kg) and the orbital period to seconds:

$$M_{star} = 1.06 \times M_{Sun} = 1.06 \times (2 \times 10^{30} \text{ kg}) = 2.12 \times 10^{30} \text{ kg}$$

$$p = 4.23 \text{ day} \times \frac{24 \text{ hr}}{1 \text{ day}} \times \frac{3600 \text{ s}}{1 \text{ hr}} = 3.65 \times 10^5 \text{ s}$$

Step 2 Solve: We use the above values to find the average distance a:

$$a \approx \sqrt[3]{\frac{GM_{star}}{4\pi^2}p_{planet}^2}$$

$$= \sqrt[3]{\frac{6.67 \times 10^{-11}\frac{\text{m}^3}{\text{kg} \times \text{s}^2} \times 2.12 \times 10^{30} \text{ kg}}{4 \times \pi^2}(3.65 \times 10^5 \text{ s})^2}$$

$$= 7.81 \times 10^9 \text{ m}$$

Step 3 Explain: The planet orbits its star at an average distance of 7.8 billion meters, or 7.8 million kilometers. It's easier to interpret this number if we convert it to astronomical units (1 AU $\approx 1.50 \times 10^{11}$ meters):

$$a = 7.81 \times 10^9 \text{ m} \times \frac{1 \text{ AU}}{1.50 \times 10^{11} \text{ m}} = 0.052 \text{ AU}$$

The planet's average orbital distance is 0.052 AU—small even compared to that of Mercury, which orbits the Sun at 0.39 AU. In fact, comparing the planet's 7.8-million-kilometer distance to the size of the star itself (presumably close to the 700,000-kilometer radius of our Sun), we estimate that the planet orbits its star at a distance only a little more than 10 times the star's radius.

The search for planets around other stars is one of the fastest growing and most exciting areas of astronomy. Although it has been less than two decades since the first discoveries, known extrasolar planets already number well into the thousands. This figure summarizes major techniques that astronomers use to search for and study extrasolar planets.

(1) Gravitational Tugs: We can detect a planet by observing the small orbital motion of its star as both the star and its planet orbit their mutual center of mass. The star's orbital period is the same as that of its planet, and the star's orbital speed depends on the planet's distance and mass. Any additional planets around the star will produce additional features in the star's orbital motion.

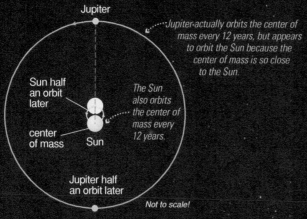

Jupiter

Jupiter actually orbits the center of mass every 12 years, but appears to orbit the Sun because the center of mass is so close to the Sun.

Sun half an orbit later

The Sun also orbits the center of mass every 12 years.

center of mass   Sun

Jupiter half an orbit later

Not to scale!

(1a) The Doppler Method: As a star moves alternately toward and away from us around the center of mass, we can detect its motion by observing alternating Doppler shifts in the star's spectrum: a blueshift as the star approaches and a redshift as it recedes.

(1b) The Astrometric Method: A star's orbit around the center of mass leads to tiny changes in the star's position in the sky. The *GAIA* mission is expected to discover many new planets with this method.

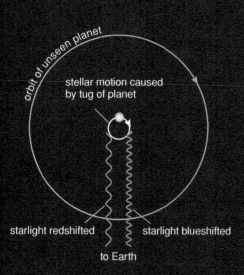

orbit of unseen planet

stellar motion caused by tug of planet

starlight redshifted   starlight blueshifted

to Earth

Current Doppler-shift measurements can detect an orbital velocity as small as 1 meter per second—walking speed.

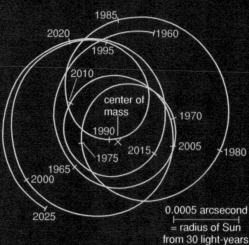

1985
2020   1960
1995
2010
center of mass
1970
1990
1975   2015   2005   1980
1965
2000
2025

0.0005 arcsecond
= radius of Sun
from 30 light-years

The change in the Sun's apparent position, if seen from a distance of 10 light-years, would be similar to the angular width of a human hair at a distance of 5 kilometers.

Artist's conception of another planetary system,
viewed near a ringed jovian planet.

2 **The Transit Method:** If a planet's orbital plane happens to lie along our line of sight, the planet
will transit in front of its star once each orbit, causing a dip in the star's visible-light brightness.
An *eclipse* may occur half an orbit later, during which the system's infrared brightness will
decline because the planet's contribution is blocked by the star.

We observe a **transit** when the
planet passes in front of the star.

When the planet passes behind the
star, we say it is **eclipsed** by the star.

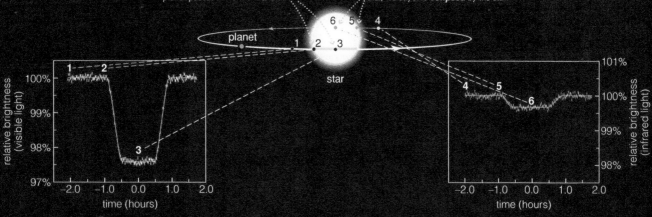

3 **Direct Detection:** In principle, the best way to learn about an extrasolar planet is to observe
directly either the visible starlight it reflects or the infrared light it emits. Current technology is
capable of direct detection in some cases, but only with very low resolution.

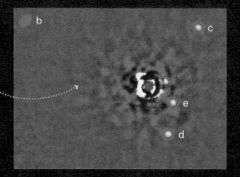

The Keck Telescope imaged the region around
the star HR 8799 in infrared light, discovering
four planets labeled b through e (a refers to
the star itself).

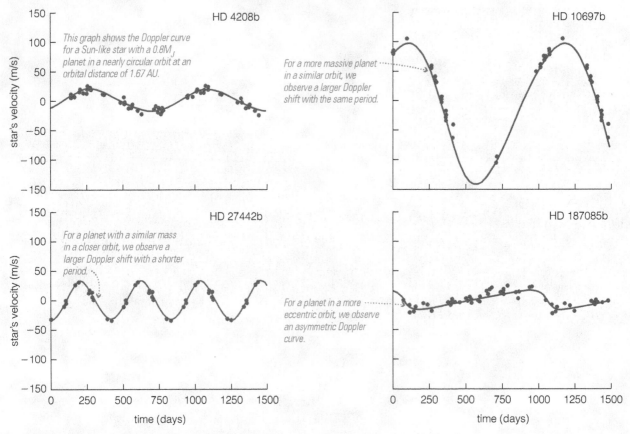

FIGURE 13.7 Sample data showing velocity curves obtained with the Doppler method for four extrasolar planet systems; dots are data and the curves are best-fits to the data. Shapes of the curves tell us about orbital eccentricity, and magnitudes of the velocity changes tell us about mass.

Currently, most of what we know about orbital eccentricities comes from detailed study of Doppler data. (In the future, astrometric data may provide similar information.) A planet with a perfectly circular orbit travels at a constant speed around its star, so its data curve is perfectly symmetric. Any asymmetry in the Doppler curve tells us that the planet is moving with varying speed and therefore must have a more eccentric elliptical orbit. **FIGURE 13.7** shows Doppler curves for four extrasolar planets; notice that the first three are fairly symmetric, implying low eccentricity, but the fourth planet must have a highly eccentric orbit.

Another important question about orbits in other planetary systems is whether the planets all share approximately the same orbital plane, as is the case in our solar system. Unfortunately, the only cases for which we can make strong statements about a shared orbital plane are those of systems with multiplanet transits, since planets observed transiting have very similar orbital planes. In the future, combining transit, astrometric, and Doppler data should in principle allow us to determine precise orbital inclinations for many more planets.

Planetary Mass Both the astrometric and Doppler methods measure motions caused by the gravitational tug of a planet, so both can in principle allow us to estimate planetary masses. However, to date nearly all extrasolar planet masses have come from the Doppler method. The Doppler method tells us about planetary masses because, for a given orbital distance, a more massive planet will cause its star to move at higher velocity around the center of mass; the Doppler velocity curves in Figure 13.7 show the basic idea.

THINK ABOUT IT

Study the four velocity curves in Figure 13.7. How would each be different if the planet were (a) closer to its star? (b) more massive? Explain.

However, there is an important caveat. Recall that Doppler shifts reveal only the part of a star's motion directed toward or away from us (see Figure 5.23). As a result, a planet whose orbit we view face-on (perpendicular to the plane of the orbit) does not cause a Doppler shift in the spectrum of its star, making it impossible to detect such a planet with the Doppler method (**FIGURE 13.8a**). We can observe Doppler shifts in a star's spectrum only if it has a planet orbiting at some angle other than face-on (**FIGURE 13.8b**), and the Doppler shift tells us a star's full orbital velocity only when we view an orbit precisely edge-on.

As a result, planetary masses that we infer from the Doppler method will be accurate only for planets in edge-on orbits, which are the same types of orbits that lead to transits. In other words, the Doppler method generally tells us a planet's precise mass only if we also observe transits of the same planet. In all other cases, the Doppler shift underestimates the true orbital speed of the star and therefore also leads to

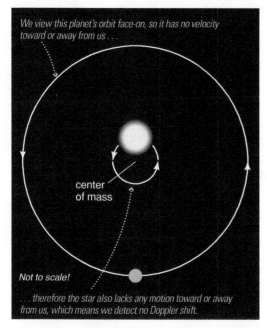

We view this planet's orbit face-on, so it has no velocity toward or away from us . . .

center of mass

Not to scale!

. . . therefore the star also lacks any motion toward or away from us, which means we detect no Doppler shift.

a If we view a planetary orbit face-on, we will not detect any Doppler shift at all.

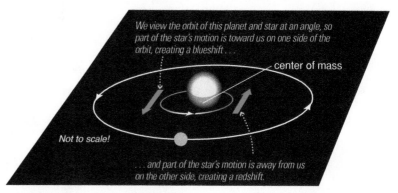

We view the orbit of this planet and star at an angle, so part of the star's motion is toward us on one side of the orbit, creating a blueshift . . .

center of mass

Not to scale!

. . . and part of the star's motion is away from us on the other side, creating a redshift.

b We can detect a Doppler shift only if some part of the orbital velocity is directed toward or away from us. The more an orbit is tilted toward edge-on, the greater the shift we observe.

FIGURE 13.8 The amount of Doppler shift we observe in a star's spectrum depends on the orientation of the planetary orbit that causes the star's motion.

an underestimate of the planet's true mass. Therefore, unless we have some way to determine the planet's precise orbital inclination (such as by combining Doppler data with astrometric data), the mass inferred from the Doppler method alone is the planet's *minimum* possible mass (or a "lower limit" mass). Statistically, however, we expect that the actual planetary mass should be no more than double the minimum mass in at least about 85% of all cases. The minimum masses obtained by the Doppler method are therefore relatively good estimates for most planets.

The transit method cannot by itself tell us masses for single planets, which is one reason scientists often try to follow up transit discoveries with the Doppler method, since the two methods together yield a precise planetary mass. However, the transit method can in some cases reveal planetary masses in multiplanet systems, because the gravitational tug of one planet on another can affect the timing of transits. For example, when another planet is tugging on a transiting planet in the direction in which it is moving, the tug will make the planet move a little faster so that the transit may begin up to tens of minutes earlier than it would otherwise; it may begin tens of minutes late when the planet is tugging from the opposite direction. Precise timing measurements can therefore allow us to measure slight variations in orbital speed and thereby determine the masses of the planets causing these variations. This capability is particularly important for planets with masses too small to be detectable by the Doppler method with current technology.

Planetary Size While knowing its mass gives us some insight into a planet's nature, we can learn much more if we also know a planet's size or radius. Transit observations

are presently the only means by which we can measure sizes. The basic idea is easy to understand: The more of a star's light that a planet blocks during a transit, the larger the planet must be. (See Mathematical Insight 13.3 for details of the calculations.)

The Kepler 11 planetary system offers a great example. **FIGURE 13.9** shows the brightness of the star Kepler 11 over a 110-day period. Each downward dip represents a transit in which a planet blocks a small fraction of the starlight. Careful study shows that there are six different planets (represented by the colored dots) that transit the star with periods ranging from 10 to 120 days; sometimes more than one transits at the same time, causing a larger dip. The panels show a transit of each planet in more detail, along with size of the planet calculated from the depth of the dip; note that more distant planets have wider dips because they orbit more slowly, which means their transits last longer. When we combine these sizes with the orbital distances calculated from the orbital periods (which are the times between transits for each planet), we find that this system's planets have sizes ranging from 2 to 5 times Earth's size and all orbit between 0.1 and 0.5 AU from their star. Transported to our solar system, that would place six planets inside Venus's orbit.

THINK ABOUT IT

New data are coming in so quickly that the records for lowest-mass and smallest-size planets change rapidly. Do a web search to find the current record-holder for extrasolar planet with the lowest confirmed *mass* and for the planet with the smallest measured *size*.

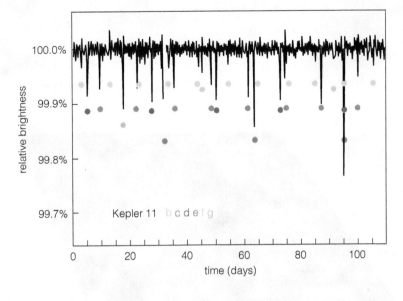

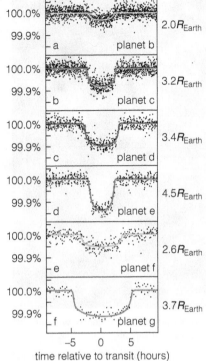

FIGURE 13.9 The Kepler 11 system. The black line shows the brightness of the star Kepler 11 over a 110-day period. Colored dots indicate transits by six different planets. The panels at right show the dips due to each planet separately, and indicate the planet's size in Earth radii.

Planetary Density

No single method measures a planet's average density, but we can calculate it if we know a planet's size from the transit method and its mass from the Doppler method. Note that we can get a precise density value in this case, because transiting planets must have edge-on orbits, so the Doppler method gives an exact (rather than minimum) mass in these cases. The first planet for which scientists obtained both Doppler and transit data was HD 209458b (the planet that we discussed earlier as the first transit success). The planet was first discovered with the Doppler method, which revealed it to have a minimum mass of 0.69 times Jupiter's mass. Once its transits were discovered, we knew that this was an exact mass. The amount of starlight blocked during transits allowed us to calculate its radius, from which we could also find its volume (because $V = 4/3\pi r^3$). We then found its density simply by dividing the mass by the volume; the result is 0.37 g/cm^3. This density is even lower than that of Saturn, which is the lowest-density planet in our solar system.

At the opposite extreme, FIGURE 13.10 shows how the density of Kepler 10b was found to be 8.8 g/cm^3, making it significantly more dense than Earth. With even just these two examples, we see that the variety of densities among extrasolar planets is much greater than that of the planets in our solar system, suggesting that extrasolar planets may come in a wider range of types than just the familiar terrestrial and jovian categories.

Atmospheric Composition and Temperature

For nearly all astronomical objects except extrasolar planets, we learn about their atmospheres and temperatures by studying spectra obtained through direct observations. Because these types of direct observations are not yet technologically feasible for most extrasolar planets, you might guess that we'd be unable to learn anything at all about their atmospheres

and temperatures. However, careful analysis of data collected during transits and eclipses allows us to obtain at least some information.

FIGURE 13.11 shows the basic ideas, using the example of HD 189733b, a hot Jupiter with an orbital period of only 2.2 days, which means it orbits only about 0.04AU from its star. The left graph shows that at most wavelengths, the transits create a 2.5% dip in the star's brightness, which tells us how the planet's radius out to its visible edge compares to its star's radius. However, we know from our own solar system

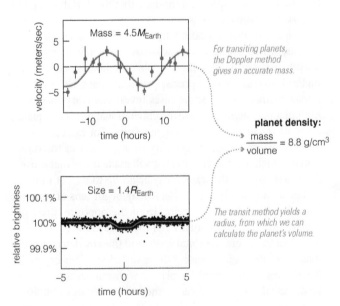

FIGURE 13.10 This diagram summarizes how we can combine data from the Doppler and transit methods to calculate a planet's average density. (The final density calculation requires converting the mass to grams and the volume to units of cubic centimeters.)

that planets can have atmospheric gases that extend above the visible disk, and these gases can absorb light at specific wavelengths. Infrared observations are especially powerful for planetary atmospheres, because many important molecules (such as those of greenhouse gases) have spectral lines in the infrared. By comparing the amount of starlight at these specific wavelengths blocked by the planet's upper atmosphere to the amount blocked by the main disk of the planet, we can identify gases in the planet's atmosphere. For HD 189733b, these types of observations have revealed the presence of water vapor in its atmosphere; in another star (HD 209458b), astronomers used the same technique to identify methane, hydrogen, sodium, and a few other gases.

We can learn more from the eclipses that occur as the planet goes behind the star. Before the eclipse, the light from the star system is the combined light of the star and the planet. During the eclipse, we see the light of the star without the added light of the planet. The difference between these two is the light from the planet by itself. Recall that, because planets emit at infrared wavelengths at which stars are less bright [**Section 5.2**], the dips that occur during eclipses are most easily measured with infrared telescopes. For example, the Spitzer Space Telescope measured the infrared brightness of HD 189733 dropping by about 0.3% during eclipses, telling us that the planet emits 0.3% as much infrared radiation

as the star. By combining this fact with the planet's radius measured during the transits, astronomers calculated the planet's surface (or cloudtop) temperature to be more than 1100 K. Astronomers then used the principles of planetary temperatures (see Mathematical Insight 10.1) to deduce that this planet has a very low reflectivity.

In some cases, changes in the total brightness of a system can even be measured as a planet travels along its orbit. Because planets reflect visible light, we can in principle notice changes in a system's visible-light brightness as the planet presents different phases to Earth: Much as we see phases of Venus from Earth (see Figure 3.22b), we see a planet as "new" during a transit and as nearly "full" just before and after an eclipse. *Kepler* has successfully measured changes in at least one planet's visible reflected light as the planet has gone from new to crescent to gibbous to full and back again. With infrared light, we can observe differences in brightness over a planet's day and night sides as it orbits. Moreover, all planets on close-in orbits are expected to have synchronous rotation so that they show the same face to their star at all times, just as the Moon always shows the same face to Earth [**Section 4.5**]. Therefore, we can in principle use infrared observations to create a crude "weather map" of an extrasolar planet. The first success of this technique came with Spitzer Space Telescope observations of HD 189733 and its planet, which showed that the planet

MATHEMATICAL INSIGHT 13.2

Finding Masses of Extrasolar Planets

The Doppler method allows us to find the mass of an extrasolar planet from the law of conservation of momentum [**Section 4.3**]; recall that momentum = mass × velocity. Consider a star with a single planet, both orbiting their common center of mass with the same orbital period. The system as a whole has no momentum relative to this center of mass (which stays in a fixed place between the star and planet), so the planet's momentum must equal the star's momentum (but in the opposite direction). Using M for mass and v for velocity relative to the center of mass, we write

$$M_{star} v_{star} = M_{planet} v_{planet}$$

Solving this equation for M_{planet}, we find

$$M_{planet} = \frac{M_{star} v_{star}}{v_{planet}}$$

The Doppler method tells us the star's velocity toward or away from us (v_{star}), and as discussed earlier, we generally know the star's mass (M_{star}). We can calculate the planet's orbital velocity (v_{planet}) from its orbital period p (the time between peaks in the Doppler curve) and its average orbital distance a (calculated with the method in Mathematical Insight 13.1). If we assume a circular orbit, the planet travels a distance $2\pi a$ during each orbit that takes time p, so its orbital velocity is $2\pi a_{planet}/p_{planet}$. Substituting this expression for the planet's velocity into the above equation for mass gives

$$M_{planet} = \frac{M_{star} v_{star} p_{planet}}{2\pi a_{planet}}$$

Remember that with velocity data from the Doppler method, this formula gives us the *minimum* mass of the planet.

EXAMPLE: Estimate the mass of the planet orbiting 51 Pegasi.

SOLUTION:

Step 1 Understand: From Mathematical Insight 13.1, we know the planet's orbital period ($p = 3.65 \times 10^5$ s) and orbital distance ($a = 7.81 \times 10^9$ m) and the star's mass ($M_{star} = 2.12 \times 10^{30}$ kg). The graph in Figure 13.4a shows that the star's velocity is about $v_{star} = 57$ m/s. We can therefore use the formula above to calculate the planet's mass.

Step 2 Solve: We enter the values into the mass formula:

$$M_{planet} = \frac{M_{star} v_{star} p_{planet}}{2\pi a_{planet}}$$

$$= \frac{(2.12 \times 10^{30} \text{ kg}) \times \left(57 \frac{m}{s}\right) \times (3.65 \times 10^5 \text{ s})}{2\pi \times (7.81 \times 10^9 \text{ m})}$$

$$\approx 9 \times 10^{26} \text{ kg}$$

Step 3 Explain: The minimum mass of the planet is about 9×10^{26} kilograms. This answer will be more meaningful if we convert it to Jupiter masses. From Appendix E, Jupiter's mass is 1.9×10^{27} kilograms, so the planet's minimum mass is

$$M_{planet} = 9 \times 10^{26} \text{ kg} \times \frac{1 M_{Jupiter}}{1.9 \times 10^{27} \text{ kg}} = 0.47 M_{Jupiter}$$

The planet orbiting 51 Pegasi has a minimum mass of just under half Jupiter's mass. Statistically, most planets will have an actual mass less than double the minimum mass, so the planet probably has a mass similar to or a little less than that of Jupiter.

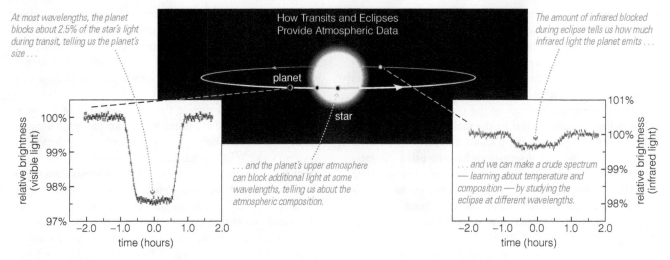

At most wavelengths, the planet blocks about 2.5% of the star's light during transit, telling us the planet's size...

... and the planet's upper atmosphere can block additional light at some wavelengths, telling us about the atmospheric composition.

How Transits and Eclipses Provide Atmospheric Data

The amount of infrared blocked during eclipse tells us how much infrared light the planet emits...

... and we can make a crude spectrum — learning about temperature and composition — by studying the eclipse at different wavelengths.

planet

star

FIGURE 13.11 This diagram summarizes how transit and eclipse observations can give us information about the composition and temperature of an extrasolar planet's atmosphere.

reaches a temperature of nearly 1200 K on its day side and 900 K on its night side (**FIGURE 13.12**). Note that the hottest point does not lie exactly at the center of the Sun-facing side, probably because of winds, which models suggest may blow at an incredible 10,000 km/hr. **TABLE 13.2** summarizes how we measure planetary properties.

How do extrasolar planets compare with planets in our solar system?

The number of known extrasolar planets for which we have measured many key properties is now large enough that we are beginning to gain insight into how these planets compare to the planets of our own solar system. Let's explore the general features of extrasolar planets as we know them today, focusing on orbital properties, masses and sizes, and what we can say about their general nature.

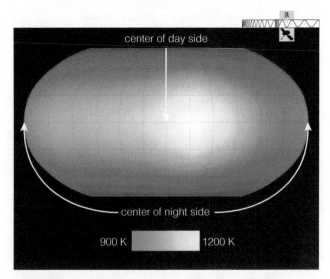

FIGURE 13.12 The first map of an extrasolar planet's temperatures, derived from infrared observations of HD 189733b made by the Spitzer Space Telescope.

Orbital Properties Much as Johannes Kepler first appreciated the true layout of our own solar system [**Section 3.3**], we now have enough data to allow us to step back and see the layout of many other solar systems. The two key orbital properties of extrasolar planets that help us understand planetary system layout are (1) average orbital distance (semimajor axis), which allows us to compare the locations of planets in other solar systems to the locations of planets in our own, and (2) orbital eccentricity, which allows us to determine whether or how much the orbits in other solar systems differ from the nearly circular orbits in our own solar system.

FIGURE 13.13 shows a graph of these two orbital properties for more than 500 extrasolar planets, with average orbital distance on the horizontal axis and orbital eccentricity on the vertical axis. Recall that eccentricity for an elliptical orbit is always between 0 and 1 (see Mathematical Insight 3.1); an eccentricity of 0 is a perfect circle, and higher eccentricity means a more stretched-out ellipse. The sizes of the dots on the graph represent approximate masses of the planets, as shown in the key at the upper left. These planets were detected by the Doppler method, so the indicated masses are actually minimum masses. Be sure to note that the distance scale increases by powers of 10, which makes it easier to plot the large number of planets with relatively close-in orbits.

Look first at the green dots representing the planets in our own solar system. To be sure you are reading the graph correctly, make sure you see how it shows that the four inner planets orbit within about 1.5 AU of the Sun, while the four outer planets are spread out to about 30 AU. Also notice that all but Mercury have very small eccentricities, meaning nearly circular orbits. Now look at the dots representing extrasolar planets. Two differences between many of the extrasolar planets and our solar system's planets should jump out at you:

1. Many of the known extrasolar planets orbit their stars more closely than Mercury orbits the Sun, and none are located as far from their stars as the jovian planets of our solar system.

TABLE 13.2 A Summary of How We Measure Properties of Extrasolar Planets

	Planetary Property	Method(s) Used	Explanation
Orbital Properties	**period**	Doppler, astrometric, or transit	We directly measure orbital period.
	distance	Doppler, astrometric, or transit	We calculate orbital distance from orbital period using Newton's version of Kepler's third law (Mathematical Insight 13.1).
	eccentricity	Doppler or astrometric	Velocity curves and astrometric star positions reveal eccentricity (Figure 13.7).
	inclination	transit or astrometric	Transits identify edge-on orbits; astrometric data measure any inclination angle.
Physical Properties	**mass**	astrometric or Doppler*	For single planets, we can calculate mass based on the amount of stellar motion caused by the planet's gravitational tugs (Mathematical Insight 13.2). The Doppler method gives *minimum* mass unless orbital inclination is known.
	size (radius)	transit	We calculate size based on the amount of dip in a star's brightness during a transit (Mathematical Insight 13.3).
	density	transit and Doppler	We can calculate density by dividing the mass (from Doppler method) by volume (using size from transit method). See Figure 13.10.
	atmospheric composition and temperature	transit or direct detection	Transits and the accompanying eclipses provide data on atmospheric composition and temperature (Figure 13.11); direct spectroscopic observations can in principle give more detailed information.

*Transits in some multiplanet systems allow us to determine masses from the mutual gravitational tugs of the planets.

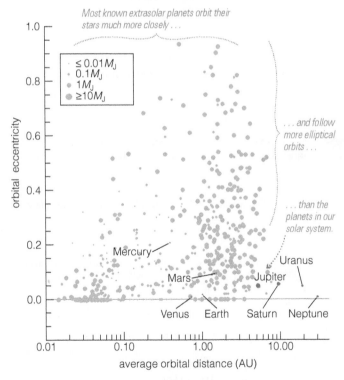

Orbital Properties of Extrasolar Planets

Most known extrasolar planets orbit their stars much more closely . . .

≤ 0.01M_J
0.1M_J
1M_J
≥10M_J

. . . and follow more elliptical orbits . . .

. . . than the planets in our solar system.

Mercury
Mars
Jupiter
Uranus
Venus   Earth   Saturn   Neptune

orbital eccentricity

average orbital distance (AU)

FIGURE 13.13 Orbital properties of the more than 500 extrasolar planets with known masses, distances, and eccentricities as of mid-2012. Dots closer to the left represent planets that orbit closer to their stars, and dots lower down represent planets with more circular orbits. Green dots are planets of our own solar system.

2. Many of these planets also have large orbital eccentricities, telling us that their elliptical orbits have very stretched-out shapes.

Both facts came as a surprise to astronomers when they were first discovered, and in the next section we'll see how they forced scientists to reconsider and ultimately modify the nebular theory.

THINK ABOUT IT

Should we be surprised that we haven't found many planets orbiting as far from their stars as Saturn, Uranus, and Neptune orbit the Sun? Why or why not?

We can learn even more from multiplanet systems, since those allow us to see a more complete layout rather than just a single planet. Several hundred stars have so far been found to have two or more planets (or *Kepler* planet candidates), including the six-planet Kepler 11 system (see Figure 13.9). This fact lends support to the general outline of the nebular theory, because its explanation of planet formation suggests that any star with planets is likely to have multiple planets. We therefore expect to find many more multiple-planet systems as observations improve.

Already, however, we've learned that other planetary systems can sometimes differ from ours in at least two ways. First, many have planets packed much closer to each other than our solar system's planets, often so close that they tug on each other gravitationally in measurable ways (such as the way in which transit timing allows us to measure masses). Second, the *Kepler* mission has identified candidate planets in binary star systems. Scientists had not been sure whether planetary orbits could remain stable in binary star systems, but the data now show that they can, at least in some cases. This has opened the possibility that some worlds might really have two (or more) "suns" in the sky, much like that the fictional planet Tatooine depicted in *Star Wars*.

Masses and Sizes Recall that most of our planetary mass measurements come from the Doppler method, while transits provide our only direct way of measuring sizes. We can therefore look independently at current data on masses and sizes, to see what they tell us about how extrasolar planets compare to the planets of our solar system.

FIGURE 13.14 shows mass data for more than 500 extrasolar planets; these are the same planets shown in Figure 13.13, but the mass data are much easier to study when displayed with a bar graph. The trend shown on the main graph is very clear: Low-mass planets outnumber massive planets, at least down to planets of Jupiter's or possibly Saturn's mass. The inset shows data for even lower-mass planets, and it appears to show a reversal of the trend. However, this reversal is almost certainly a consequence of the fact that it's much more difficult to detect low-mass planets than high-mass planets with the Doppler method. Statistical studies that take this fact into account suggest that Neptune-mass planets are indeed more abundant than Saturn- or Jupiter-mass planets, and Earth-mass planets may be even more common. In other words, the mass evidence is at least consistent with the idea that smaller worlds should outnumber larger worlds, which is what our own solar system should lead us to expect because it has vast numbers of small worlds (including terrestrial planets, moons, asteroids, and comets) and only four large jovian planets.

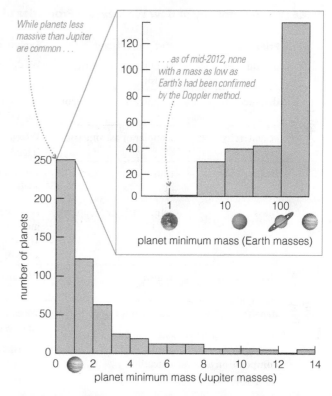

FIGURE 13.14 This bar chart shows the numbers of planets in different mass categories for extrasolar planets with masses measured by the Doppler method as of 2012; it does *not* include *Kepler* planet candidates, some of which are smaller in size and therefore likely to be lower in mass than Earth. Notice that the inset axis uses an exponential scale so that a wide range of masses can fit on the graph, and uses units of Earth masses rather than Jupiter masses.

FIGURE 13.15 shows planetary size data from the *Kepler* mission, with radius compared to Earth radius plotted along

---

Finding Sizes of Extrasolar Planets

We determine planet radii from the fraction of a star's light blocked during a transit. Viewed against the sky, both the star and the planet appear as tiny circular disks. These disks are far too small for our telescopes to resolve, but the fraction of the star's light that is blocked must be equal to the area of the planet's disk (πr^2_{planet}) divided by the area of the star's disk (πr^2_{star}). We generally know the approximate radius of the star (from methods we'll discuss in Chapter 15), so the fractional drop in the star's light during a transit is

$$\frac{\text{fraction of}}{\text{light blocked}} = \frac{\text{area of planet's disk}}{\text{area of star's disk}} = \frac{\pi r^2_{planet}}{\pi r^2_{star}} = \frac{r^2_{planet}}{r^2_{star}}$$

Solving for the planet's radius, we find

$$r_{planet} = r_{star} \times \sqrt{\text{fraction of light blocked}}$$

EXAMPLE: Figure 13.5 shows a transit of the star HD 189733. The star's radius is about 800,000 kilometers ($1.15R_{Sun}$), and the planet

blocks 1.7% of the star's light during a transit. What is the planet's radius?

SOLUTION:

Step 1 Understand: The star's radius (800,000 km) and the fraction of its light blocked during a transit (1.7% = 0.017) are all we need to calculate the planet's radius.

Step 2 Solve: Plugging the numbers into the equation, we find

$$r_{planet} = r_{star} \times \sqrt{\text{fraction of light blocked}}$$
$$= 800,000 \text{ km} \times \sqrt{0.017}$$
$$\approx 100,000 \text{ km}$$

Step 3 Explain: The planet's radius is about 100,000 kilometers, which is about 1.4 times Jupiter's radius of 71,500 kilometers. That is, the planet is about 40% larger than Jupiter in radius.

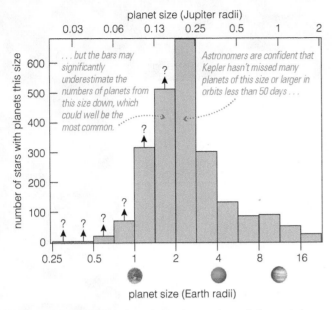

planet size (Jupiter radii)

... but the bars may significantly underestimate the numbers of planets from this size down, which could well be the most common.

Astronomers are confident that Kepler hasn't missed many planets of this size or larger in orbits less than 50 days ...

planet size (Earth radii)

FIGURE 13.15 This bar chart shows the numbers of planets in different size categories for extrasolar planets detected by *Kepler* with orbital periods of less than 50 days. Notice that this plot uses a horizontal axis of Earth radii, so the scale is very different from the one based on Jupiter masses in Figure 13.14.

the horizontal axis. To understand the graph, recall that the *Kepler* mission is monitoring about 150,000 stars, and needs to observe at least three transits of an object before it becomes a planet candidate; at the time the graph was made, full data were available only for transiting planets with periods of less than 50 days. Note that, as we found with the mass data, there is a general trend toward smaller planets being more abundant than larger planets, at least down to a size of two Earth radii. The trend probably continues to smaller worlds, but we cannot be sure from the current data because such worlds are at the limit of *Kepler's* measurement sensitivity; that is, the actual numbers of small worlds are probably significantly higher than shown. Note that *Kepler* has already detected nearly a hundred planet candidates smaller than Earth, though all lie too close to their stars to be habitable. This is about the same number of planets it has found that are larger than Jupiter, even though Jupiter-size planets are more than a hundred times easier to detect than Earth-size planets (for any given orbital period).

Kepler scientists have used the number of planets discovered to make a rough estimate of the fraction of stars harboring planets, at least for those planets with periods short enough to have been detected so far. Current evidence is consistent with as many as a quarter to a third of all stars harboring at least one planet with an orbital period shorter than 50 days. Note that our own solar system would not appear on a list like this, because our closest-in planet (Mercury) has an orbital period of 88 days. Therefore, it seems likely that an estimate based on periods shorter than 50 days significantly underestimates the total fraction of stars with planets. If so, we are led to the remarkable conclusion that most stars harbor planets. Planet searches based on other methods are reaching the same conclusion.

The Nature of Extrasolar Planets We now come to the key question about extrasolar planets: Do they fall into the same terrestrial and jovian categories as the planets in our solar system, or do we find additional types of planets?

We cannot yet know for certain, because we do not yet have direct ways of obtaining spectra with sufficient detail to determine the bulk compositions of extrasolar planets. Nevertheless, because we have measured the abundances of different chemical elements among other stars, we know that all planetary systems must start out from gas clouds generally similar in composition to the solar nebula. That is, all star systems are born from gas clouds containing at least about 98% hydrogen and helium, sprinkled with much smaller amounts of ice, rock, and metal (see Table 8.1). Given this fact, knowing a planet's average density gives us great insight into its likely composition, even without being able to observe the planet directly.

More specifically, we can use our understanding of the behavior of different materials to create *models* that will tell us the expected composition of a planet based on its mass and radius, from which we can also calculate its average density. The results are shown in **FIGURE 13.16** for all planets for which both mass (usually from the Doppler method) and radius (from transits) are known as of mid-2012. Be sure you understand the following key features of the figure:

- The horizontal axis shows planetary mass, in units of Earth masses. (The top of the graph shows the equivalent values in Jupiter masses.) Notice that it uses an exponential scale because the masses vary over such a wide range.

- The vertical axis shows planetary radius in units of Earth radii. (The right side of the graph shows the equivalent values in Jupiter radii.)

- Each dot represents one planet for which both mass and radius have been measured. Planets discussed in this chapter are called out by name. Planets of our solar system are marked in green.

- The paintings around the graph show artist conceptions of what representative worlds might look like.

- Average density is easy to calculate from mass and radius, but the different scales used on the two axes make it difficult to read average density directly from the graph. To help with that, the three curves extending from the lower left to the top show three representative average densities.

- The colored regions indicate models representing the expected compositions of planets with the indicated combinations of mass and radius.

FIGURE 13.16 Masses and sizes of extrasolar planets for which both have been measured, compared to those of [planet]s in our solar system. Each dot represents one planet. Dashed lines are lines of constant density for planets of [differe]nt masses. Colored regions indicate expected planet types based on models of their compositions.

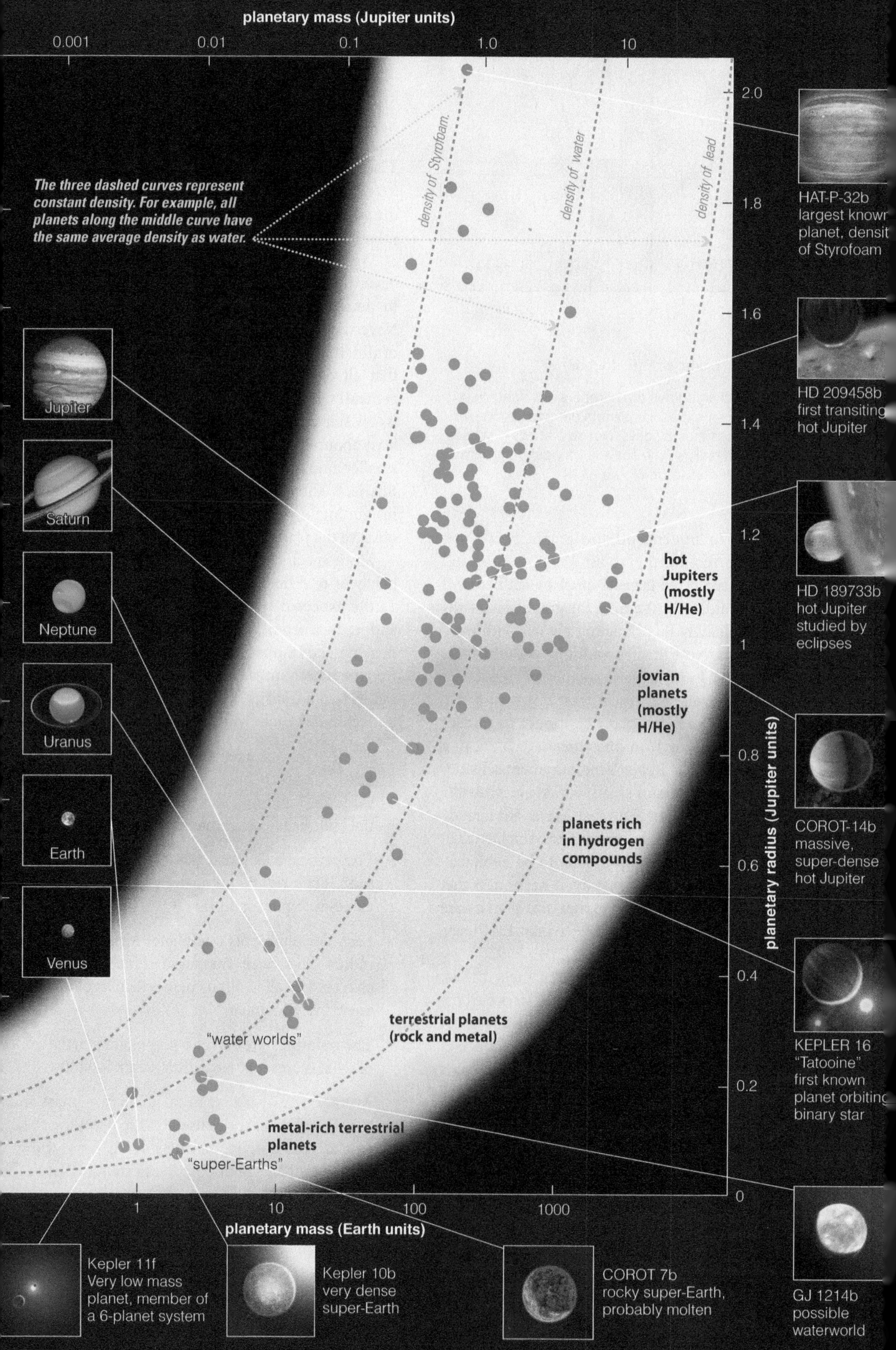

planetary mass (Jupiter units)

0.001   0.01   0.1   1.0   10

The three dashed curves represent constant density. For example, all planets along the middle curve have the same average density as water.

density of Styrofoam

density of water

density of lead

HAT-P-32b largest known planet, density of Styrofoam

HD 209458b first transiting hot Jupiter

HD 189733b hot Jupiter studied by eclipses

Jupiter

Saturn

Neptune

Uranus

Earth

Venus

hot Jupiters (mostly H/He)

jovian planets (mostly H/He)

planets rich in hydrogen compounds

COROT-14b massive, super-dense hot Jupiter

KEPLER 16 "Tatooine" first known planet orbiting binary star

"water worlds"

terrestrial planets (rock and metal)

metal-rich terrestrial planets

"super-Earths"

planetary radius (Jupiter units)

2.0
1.8
1.6
1.4
1.2
1
0.8
0.6
0.4
0.2
0

1   10   100   1000

planetary mass (Earth units)

Kepler 11f Very low mass planet, member of a 6-planet system

Kepler 10b very dense super-Earth

COROT 7b rocky super-Earth, probably molten

GJ 1214b possible waterworld

As you study Figure 13.16, you'll notice that extrasolar planets show much more variety than the planets of our own solar system. For example, HAT-P-32b has more than twice Jupiter's radius despite having the same mass. Therefore it has one of the lowest densities: about 0.14 g/cm^3—similar to the density of Styrofoam. This low average density is probably a result of the fact that this planet orbits only 0.035 AU from its star, putting it more than 10 times closer to its star than Mercury is to the Sun. This close-in orbit gives the planet a very high temperature, which should puff up the planet's atmosphere and may explain why it has such a large size relative to its mass. At the other extreme, the planet COROT-14b is only slightly larger than Jupiter but 8 times as massive, giving it an average density around 7 g/cm^3, greater than the density of lead. Although such a high average density might seem surprising, it is not totally unexpected. Recall that jovian planets more massive than Jupiter are expected to have such strong gravity that they can be compressed to smaller sizes and much higher densities (see Figure 11.2b). Despite the wide spread in their densities, both HAT-P-32b and COROT-14b seem clearly to fall into the jovian planet category, being made largely of hydrogen and helium.

We similarly see many planets that appear to be terrestrial in nature, with compositions of rock and metal. For example, COROT-7b has an average density near 5 g/cm^3, comparable to Earth's density. Because it has a mass about 5 times that of Earth, COROT-7b is an example of what is sometimes called a "super-Earth"; it was the first super-Earth discovered (in 2009). COROT-7b orbits very close to its star, so its surface is probably molten. Kepler 10b is another super-Earth, but with only 4 times Earth's mass. Numerous other super-Earths also are now known; all of them are likely to have a rock/metal composition similar to that of the terrestrial worlds in our solar system.

Perhaps the most surprising planets shown in Figure 13.16 are the ones that are not clearly in either the terrestrial or the jovian category. Several planets cluster in the region of Uranus and Neptune, and perhaps share their composition of hydrogen compounds shrouded in an envelope of hydrogen and helium gas. Others (perhaps GJ 1214b) appear to fit the model for "water worlds," which may be made predominantly of either frozen or liquid water, or perhaps of other hydrogen compounds. Alternatively, some of these worlds might be composed of a dense rocky/metallic core and a thick envelope of low-density hydrogen-helium gas.

Finally, it's worth noting that while we've focused here on composition, orbital distance must also play a role in a planet's nature. In particular, because most of the planets known to date orbit fairly close to their stars, they will be much hotter than similar planets in our own solar system. We've already discussed how this could make hot Jupiters have puffed-up atmospheres and terrestrial worlds have molten surfaces. Hot Jupiters might also have very different clouds than we see on the actual Jupiter, such as clouds of mineral flakes instead of clouds of ammonia snow or water droplets. Worlds that might resemble larger versions of Ganymede or Titan in our solar system would be water worlds at closer orbital distances. Even warmer water worlds might become "steam planets" with vast amounts of water vapor in their atmospheres. Also recall that all close-in planets are expected to be tidally locked in synchronous rotation, forever keeping one face toward their star.

The bottom line is that extrasolar planets are abundant and diverse. Unlike our solar system, with only two clear types of "typical planets," these new solar systems have additional types of planets that defy easy categorization.

Moons, Rings, and Other Remaining Questions

Although we now have a fair amount of information about planets around other stars, there are many questions that we are not yet able to address. For example, based on what we see in our own solar system, we might expect extrasolar jovian planets to be orbited by rings and many moons, but we do not yet know whether this is the case. Answering the question is important not only out of pure curiosity, but also because it might have implications for the search for life. For example, if you look back at Figure 13.14, you'll see that some extrasolar planets are jovian in mass but have Earth-like orbits. As we'll discuss in Chapter 24, such orbits may be conducive to life, though probably not on jovian worlds. However, if the jovian worlds have large moons, these moons might be hospitable to life.

13.3 THE FORMATION OF OTHER SOLAR SYSTEMS

The discovery of extrasolar planets presents us with an opportunity to test our theory of solar system formation. Can our existing theory explain other planetary systems, or do we have to go back to the drawing board?

As we discussed in Chapter 8, the nebular theory holds that our solar system's planets formed as a natural consequence of processes that accompanied the formation of our Sun. If the theory is correct, then the same processes should accompany the births of other stars, so the nebular theory clearly predicts the existence of other planetary systems. In that sense, the discovery of extrasolar planets means the theory has passed a major test, because its most basic prediction has been verified. Some details of the theory also seem supported. For example, the nebular theory says that planet formation begins with condensation of solid particles of rock and ice (see Figure 8.13), which then accrete to larger sizes. We might therefore expect that planets should form more easily in a nebula with a higher proportion of rock and ice, and some evidence supports this idea, at least for jovian planets.

Nevertheless, extrasolar planets have already presented at least two significant challenges to our theory. One concerns the categories of planets; as we saw in Figure 13.16, many extrasolar planets do not fall neatly into either the terrestrial or the jovian category. An even more significant challenge is posed by the orbits of extrasolar planets. According to the nebular theory, jovian planets form as gravity pulls in gas around large, icy planetesimals that accrete in a spinning disk of material around a young star. The theory therefore predicts that jovian planets should form only in the cold outer regions of star systems (because it must be cold for ice to condense), and that these planets should be born with nearly circular orbits (matching the orderly, circular motion of the spinning disk). The many known extrasolar planets that appear jovian in nature but have close-in or highly elliptical orbits present a direct challenge to these ideas.

Can we explain the surprising orbits of many extrasolar planets?

The nature of science demands that we question the validity of a theory whenever it is challenged by any observation or experiment [**Section 3.4**]. If the theory cannot explain the new observations, then we must revise or discard it. The surprising orbits of many known extrasolar planets have indeed caused scientists to reexamine the nebular theory of solar system formation.

Questioning began almost immediately upon the discovery of the first extrasolar planets. The close-in orbits of these massive planets made scientists wonder whether something might be fundamentally wrong with the nebular theory. For example, is it possible for jovian planets to form very close to a star? Astronomers addressed this question by studying many possible models of planet formation and reexamining the entire basis of the nebular theory. Several years of such reexamination did not turn up any good reasons to discard the basic theory. While we can't completely rule out the possibility that a major flaw has gone undetected, it seems much more likely that the basic outline of the nebular theory is correct. Scientists therefore suspect that extrasolar jovian planets were indeed born with circular orbits far from their stars, and that those that now have close-in or eccentric orbits underwent some sort of "planetary migration" or suffered gravitational interactions with other massive objects.

Planetary Migration If hot Jupiters formed in the outer regions of their star systems and then migrated inward, how did these planetary migrations occur? You might think that drag within the solar nebula could cause planets to migrate, much as atmospheric drag can cause satellites in low-Earth orbit to lose orbital energy and eventually spiral into the atmosphere. However, calculations show this drag effect to be negligible. A more likely scenario is that waves propagating through a gaseous disk lead to migration (**FIGURE 13.17**). The gravity of a planet orbiting in a disk can create waves that propagate through the disk, causing material to bunch up as the waves pass by. This "bunched up" matter (in the wave peaks) then exerts a gravitational pull on the planet that reduces its orbital energy, causing the planet to migrate inward toward its star.

Computer models confirm that waves in a nebula can cause young planets to spiral slowly toward their star. In our own solar system, this migration is not thought to have played a significant role because the nebular gas was cleared out before it could have much effect. But planets may form earlier in some other solar systems, allowing time for jovian planets to migrate substantially inward. In a few cases, the planets may form so early that they end up spiraling all the way into their stars. Indeed, astronomers have noted that

The orbiting planet nudges gas and particles in the disk.

...causing material to bunch up. These dense regions in turn tug on the planet, causing it to migrate inward.

FIGURE 13.17 This figure shows a simulation of waves created by a planet embedded in a disk of material surrounding its star.

some stars have an unusual assortment of elements in their outer layers, suggesting that they may have swallowed planets (including migrating jovian planets and possibly terrestrial planets shepherded inward along with the jovian planets). These ideas are not just hypothetical: One recently discovered planet appears to be on a million-year death spiral into its star.

Migration can also occur after the nebula has cleared, as long as small planetesimals are still abundant. Astronomers suspect that this type of migration affected the jovian planets in our own solar system. Recall that the Oort cloud is thought to consist of comets that were ejected outward by gravitational encounters with the jovian planets, especially Jupiter [**Section 12.2**]. In that case, the law of conservation of energy demands that Jupiter must have migrated inward, losing the same amount of orbital energy that the comets gained. It's not known if this kind of migration is common outside our solar system.

Encounters and Resonances Migration may explain close-in orbits, but why do so many extrasolar planets have highly eccentric orbits? Close encounters may be the answer. A close gravitational encounter between two massive planets can send one planet out of the star system entirely while the other is flung inward into a highly elliptical orbit. Repeated encounters can result in significant orbital migration.

Gravitational interactions can also affect orbits through resonances. Recall that Jupiter's moons Io, Europa, and Ganymede share orbital resonances that cause their orbits to be more elliptical than they would be otherwise (see Figure 11.19b). This type of resonance can also occur between planets, and several dozen cases of planetary resonances have been found among known multiplanet systems. Planetary migration may play a role in creating such resonances, forcing two planets into a resonance that they did not have originally. Simulations show that gravitational influences between planets can drive them into orbits that are very eccentric, highly tilted, or even backward. The question is whether resonances are common enough to explain the many planets now known with eccentric or other unusual orbits. On one hand, we have so far observed resonances among planets in only a relatively small number of multiplanet systems. On the other hand, it could be that most of the planets with unusual orbits are in resonance with other planets, but we have not yet detected the other planets.

Do we need to modify our theory of solar system formation?

We began this section by asking whether the nebular theory of solar system formation can hold up in light of our discoveries of planets around other stars. Assuming we are correct about the role of planetary migration in explaining the surprising orbits of hot Jupiters and other extrasolar planets, the basic tenets of the nebular theory still seem to hold. That is, we expect rocky terrestrial worlds to form in the inner regions of solar systems and hydrogen-rich jovian planets to form in the outer regions. Migration may later cause some of the jovian planets to spiral inward, and along the way the jovian planets are likely to alter the orbits of other, smaller planets. The remaining mystery, then, is why other solar systems seem to have planetary types that don't fall neatly into the terrestrial and jovian categories that we identify in our solar system.

Scientists still cannot fully explain the wide range of extrasolar planet properties, but we can envision possible explanations that seem to make sense and that would not fundamentally alter the nebular theory. For example, hydrogen-rich extrasolar planets vary in density by a factor of 100 (see Figure 13.16)—a range far greater than the density range we observe in our own solar system—but it seems reasonable to think that much of this range is attributable to differences in temperature caused by some jovian planets being very close to their stars. As we've discussed, this may puff up their atmospheres to large sizes and low densities, though models cannot yet account for the full density range.

Similarly, the lack of "water world" planets in our solar system may not be as mysterious as it seems. Water worlds may be similar to Uranus and Neptune in our solar system, though in some cases much smaller. These worlds may be much like the ice-rich planetesimals that seeded the formation of jovian planets in our solar system. In that case, perhaps whether water world planets exist depends on when a star clears its nebular gas, halting the epoch of planet formation. In our solar system, this did not occur until the ice-rich planetesimals pulled in vast quantities of hydrogen and helium gas from the solar nebula. Perhaps in other systems, an early solar wind blasted out the hydrogen and helium gas before it could be captured.

Super-Earths pose a different mystery: How did these planets gather so much rocky material, especially so close to their stars, given that rocky material represents such a small proportion of the material from which solar systems are born? The answer is not yet known, though perhaps we should not be too surprised. After all, even though rocky material comprised less than 2% of the solar nebula, this still in principle was enough to build planets much larger than Earth. Perhaps we only need a better understanding of the factors that determine the efficiency with which rocky

material can be incorporated into planets. We may similarly need a better understanding of the conditions under which super-Earths or water worlds may capture hydrogen and helium gas, since that could lead to planets whose true nature is hiding under enormous envelopes of gas. With hundreds of different planets discovered every year, other surprising planetary types are likely to be found in the future.

The bottom line is that discoveries of extrasolar planets have shown us that the nebular theory was incomplete. It explained the formation of planets and the simple layout of a solar system such as ours. However, it needs new features—such as planetary migration and variations in the basic planetary types—to explain the differing layouts of other solar systems. A much wider variety of solar system arrangements now seems possible than we had guessed before the discovery of extrasolar planets.

This leads us to what is perhaps the most profound question still to be addressed in our study of extrasolar planets: Given that we have not yet discovered other solar systems that are quite like ours, does this mean that our solar system is of a rare type, or does it simply mean that we have not yet acquired enough data to see how common solar systems like ours really are? This is a profound question because of its implications for the way we view our place in the universe. If solar systems like ours are common, then it seems reasonable to imagine that Earth-like planets—and perhaps life and civilizations—might also be common. But if our solar system is a rarity or even unique, then Earth might be the lone inhabited planet in our galaxy or even the universe. Only by continuing our search for planets around other stars can we hope to answer this question. As of 2012, we are on the brink of discovering Earth-size planets in Earth-like orbits and Jupiter-size planets in Jupiter-like orbits, so the answer may not be so far off.

13.4 THE FUTURE OF EXTRASOLAR PLANETARY SCIENCE

We have entered a new era in planetary science, one in which our understanding of planetary processes can be based on far more planets than just those of our own solar system. Although our current knowledge of extrasolar planets and their planetary systems is still quite limited, ingenious new observing techniques, dedicated observatories, and ambitious space telescope programs should broaden our understanding dramatically in the coming years and decades. In this section, we'll focus on the more dramatic improvements expected in coming years.

How will future observations improve our understanding?

As noted earlier, the deepest outstanding questions concern how common solar systems like ours may prove to be and, more specifically, whether other Earth-like planets exist. Keep in mind that there is an important distinction between Earth-*size* and Earth-*like*. The *Kepler* mission has already found many planet candidates that are Earth-size, but this does not necessarily mean that they are Earth-like in the sense of having features like continents, oceans, plate tectonics, or life.

Learning whether other planets are Earth-like will probably occur in two steps. First, we'll need to find planets that are Earth-size and have orbits that would in principle allow them to have liquid water on their surfaces. (We'll discuss the range of orbits that fall into this so-called *habitable zone* in Chapter 24.) Second, we'll need some type of direct imaging or spectroscopy to learn whether these planets actually have oceans and atmospheres that might be conducive to life.

Scientists are developing a wide range of techniques for trying to accomplish these observations, including many that rely on ground-based observatories. However, for the remaining years of this decade, it's likely that the greatest advances will come primarily in three ways: with ongoing observations by the *Kepler* mission, with the *GAIA* mission, and with efforts to obtain direct imaging and spectroscopy of extrasolar planets. Let's briefly look at each.

More from *Kepler* The early results from the *Kepler* mission have already exceeded expectations, making scientists optimistic that even greater discoveries are still to come. FIGURE 13.18 shows a graph of planet size versus orbital period, with dots indicating *Kepler's* candidate planets as of early 2012. Notice that any Earth-*like* planets would have to fall into the lower right portion of the graph, for which no data are yet available. The *Kepler* mission is currently scheduled to continue through 2016, which should give it enough time to fill in these regions of the graph (which require observations over a longer time period because of the longer orbital periods between transits).

GAIA We briefly discussed the European Space Agency's *GAIA* mission in Section 13.1. Slated for launch in 2013, *GAIA* is a remarkable space observatory designed primarily to make precise measurements of the positions of more than 1 billion stars in the Milky Way Galaxy. These astrometric measurements should enable scientists to calculate precise distances to these stars, thereby allowing the creation of a three-dimensional map of the galaxy. To make these measurements, *GAIA* actually has two telescopes, each with a collecting area of nearly one square meter, that will work together to give extremely precise measurements of stellar positions (FIGURE 13.19).

Because precise measurements of stellar position also allow scientists to detect changes in those positions, *GAIA* will be capable of discovering planets via the astrometric method, as well as some via the transit method. In fact, mission scientists estimate that they may be able to detect as many as 15,000 extrasolar planets during the life of the mission. Although sorting out the gravitational tug of Earth-size planets from the tugs of larger planets may be difficult, *GAIA* should provide enough data to give us a sense of the layout of thousands of planetary systems. Therefore, even if it does not find Earth-like planets itself, it should give us a much better sense of whether solar systems with layouts like our own are common or rare.

Direct Detection The indirect planet-hunting techniques we have discussed so far have started a revolution in planetary science by demonstrating that our solar system is just one of many planetary systems. But it can be very difficult to learn more than planets' most basic properties from indirect measurements. To learn more about their nature, it would be ideal to observe the planets themselves, obtaining images of their surfaces or spectra of their atmospheres.

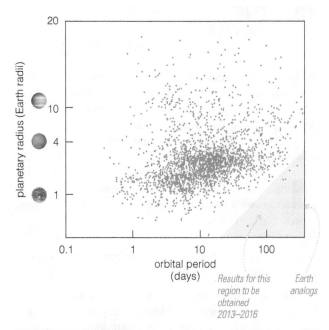

FIGURE 13.18 This figure shows the orbital periods and sizes of all the *Kepler* planet candidates as of early 2012. We do not yet have enough data to learn about the region in the lower right, which would include possible Earth-like planets.

FIGURE 13.19 Artist's conception of the *GAIA* spacecraft.

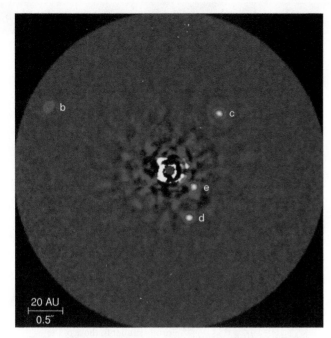

FIGURE 13.20 This infrared image from the Keck Telescope shows direct detection of a four-planet system (planets marked b, c, d, e) orbiting the star HR 8799. We know they are planets because they have moved slightly since their discovery. Light from the star itself (center) was mostly blocked out during the exposure, with its remaining light subtracted as much as possible. These planets are much larger, brighter, and farther from their star than jovian planets in our solar system.

The glare from stars makes direct detection of planets extremely difficult, especially given how close together the stars and planets lie when observed from Earth. To date astronomers have found only a few planets by direct detection. One confirmed direct detection made with infrared light is of a jovian planet orbiting the star Beta Pictoris (see Figure 8.4). This planet's existence was actually first suspected by study of ripples in the dust disk surrounding the star, and then later confirmed through imaging, which has also revealed the planet's orbital motion around its star. **FIGURE 13.20** shows another confirmed detection with infrared light, revealing at least four planets orbiting the star HR 8799. Astronomers are confident the planets are real because subsequent images have shown changes in their positions due to their orbits around the star.

Scientists are rapidly developing new observing capabilities that should allow for more direct observations in the future from large, ground-based observatories. Scientists are also optimistic that the James Webb Space Telescope, a large infrared space telescope with launch currently scheduled for 2018, will be able to make some direct observations.

Nevertheless, the quest to find Earth-like worlds is now in a bittersweet period. Thanks to recent discoveries and rapidly advancing technology, astronomers have begun to design advanced space observatories that should be able to obtain images and spectra of Earth-size planets around other stars, with enough resolution to be able to determine whether they are Earth-like, and perhaps even to detect spectral signatures that would indicate the presence of life. However, while some of these missions could in principle have flown in this decade, budgetary constraints have pushed them at least 10 to 20 years into the future. Answers to age-old questions lie tantalizingly close, but will not be obtained until we find the budget to pay for them.

THINK ABOUT IT

Suppose you were a member of the United States Congress. How much would you be willing to spend to build a space observatory capable of obtaining images and spectra of Earth-like planets around other stars? Defend your opinion.

The Big Picture

Putting Chapter 13 into Perspective

In this chapter, we have explored one of the newest areas of astronomy—the study of solar systems beyond our own. As you continue your studies, please keep in mind the following important ideas:

■ In a period of barely two decades, we have gone from knowing of no other planets around other stars to knowing that many or most stars have one or more planets. As a result, there is no longer any question that planets are common in the universe.

■ The discovery of other planetary systems represents a striking confirmation of a key prediction of the nebular theory of solar system formation. Nevertheless, the precise characteristics of other planets and planetary systems pose challenges to details of the theory that scientists are still investigating.

■ While we have already identified thousands of extrasolar planets or candidate planets, nearly all of these have been found with indirect methods. These methods allow us to determine many properties of the planets, but we will need direct images or spectra to learn about them in much more detail.

■ It is too soon to know if solar systems with layouts like ours are rare or common, but technology now exists that could allow us to answer this question and to learn if Earth-like planets are also common. It is only a matter of time until we know the answer to these fundamental questions.

13.1 DETECTING PLANETS AROUND OTHER STARS

- **Why is it so challenging to learn about extrasolar planets?** The great challenge stems from the great distances to other stars, the small sizes of planets in comparison, and the vast difference in brightness between stars and planets. We can in principle look for planets directly or indirectly. The two major indirect approaches are (1) looking for subtle gravitational effects on stars due to orbiting planets and (2) looking for changes in a star's brightness as one of its planets passes in front of it.

- **How can a star's motion reveal the presence of planets?**

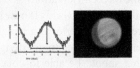 We can look for a planet's gravitational effect on its star through the **astrometric method**, which looks for small shifts in stellar position, or the **Doppler method**, which looks for the back-and-forth motion of stars revealed by Doppler shifts.

- **How can changes in a star's brightness reveal the presence of planets?** A small fraction of all planetary

 systems should by chance be aligned in such a way that their planets can pass in front of their star as seen from Earth. Such a passage, called a **transit**, would occur once each orbit and cause a slight dimming in the measured brightness of the star. The planet may also pass behind the star in an **eclipse** on the other side of the orbit, potentially revealing even more information about the planet. The *Kepler* mission has discovered thousands of candidate planets with the transit method.

13.2 THE NATURE OF PLANETS AROUND OTHER STARS

- **What properties of extrasolar planets can we measure?** All detection methods allow us to determine a planet's orbital period and distance from its star. The astrometric and Doppler methods can provide masses (or minimum masses), while the transit method can provide sizes. In cases where transit and Doppler methods are used together, we can determine average density. In some cases, transits (and eclipses) can provide other data, including limited data about atmospheric composition and temperature.

- **How do extrasolar planets compare with planets in our solar system?** The known extrasolar planets have a

 much wider range of properties than the planets in our solar system. Many orbit much closer to their stars and with more eccentric orbital paths; some jovian planets, called *hot Jupiters*, are also found close to their stars. We also find properties indicating planetary types such as water worlds that do not fall neatly into the traditional terrestrial and jovian categories.

13.3 THE FORMATION OF OTHER SOLAR SYSTEMS

- **Can we explain the surprising orbits of many extrasolar planets?** Jovian planets with close-in and eccentric

 orbits probably were born on orbits similar to those of the jovian planets in our solar system. Several different effects could later have changed their orbits: planetary migration induced by waves in the gaseous disk from which they formed, gravitational encounters with other objects, or orbital resonances with other massive planets.

- **Do we need to modify our theory of solar system formation?** Our basic theory of solar system formation seems to be sound, but we have had to modify it to allow for planetary migration and a wider range of planetary types than we find in our solar system. Many mysteries remain, but they are unlikely to require major change to the nebular theory of solar system formation.

13.4 THE FUTURE OF EXTRASOLAR PLANETARY SCIENCE

- **How will future observations improve our understanding?** In the future, scientists hope to learn whether solar systems with layouts like ours are rare or common, and whether

 Earth-like planets are common. Future observations by the *Kepler* and *GAIA* missions should help answer these questions, but ultimate answers will probably require direct detection with space observatories of the future.

Use the following questions to check your understanding of some of the many types of visual information used in astronomy. Answers are provided in Appendix J. For additional practice, try the Chapter 13 Visual Quiz at MasteringAstronomy®.

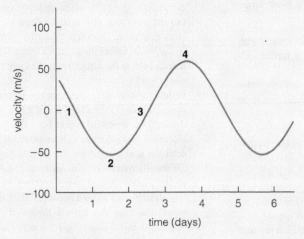

This plot, based on Figure 13.4a, shows the periodic variations in the Doppler shift of a star caused by a planet orbiting around it. Positive velocities mean the star is moving away from Earth, and negative velocities mean the star is moving toward Earth. (You can assume that the orbit appears edge-on from Earth.) Answer the following questions based on the information in the graph.

1. How long does it take the star and planet to complete one orbit around their center of mass?
2. What maximum velocity does the star attain?
3. Match the *star's* position at points 1, 2, 3, and 4 in the plot with the descriptions below.
   a. headed straight toward Earth
   b. headed straight away from Earth
   c. closest to Earth
   d. farthest from Earth

4. Match the *planet's* position at points 1, 2, 3, and 4 in the plot with the descriptions in question 3.
5. How would the plot change if the planet were more massive?
   a. It would not change, because it describes the motion of the star, not the planet.
   b. The peaks and valleys would get larger (greater positive and negative velocities) because of larger gravitational tugs.
   c. The peaks and valleys would get closer together (shorter period) because of larger gravitational tugs.

For instructor-assigned homework go to MasteringAstronomy®.

REVIEW QUESTIONS

Short-Answer Questions Based on the Reading

1. Why are *extrasolar planets* hard to detect directly?
2. What are the two major approaches to detecting extrasolar planets indirectly?
3. How can gravitational tugs from orbiting planets affect the motion of a star? Explain how alien astronomers could deduce the existence of planets in our solar system by observing the Sun's motion.
4. Briefly describe the *astrometric method* and its strengths and limitations.
5. Briefly describe the *Doppler method* and its strengths and limitations.
6. How does the *transit method* work? Could we use this method to find planets around all stars that have them? Why or why not?
7. Briefly describe the *Kepler* mission and how it meets three key challenges posed by the transit method.
8. Briefly summarize the planetary properties we can in principle measure with current detection methods, and state which methods allow us to measure each of these properties.
9. Why does the Doppler method generally allow us to determine only *minimum* planetary masses? In what cases can we be confident that we know precise masses? Explain.

10. Briefly describe what we can learn from careful study of a planet that undergoes transits and eclipses.
11. How do the orbits of known extrasolar planets differ from those of planets in our solar system? Why are these orbits surprising?
12. Summarize the current state of knowledge about extrasolar planet masses and sizes. Based on the evidence, is it likely that smaller planets or larger planets are more common?
13. Summarize the key features shown in Figure 13.16, and briefly describe the nature of planets that would fit each of the model curves shown on the graph.
14. Why do scientists suspect that planetary migration is behind the close-in and eccentric orbits of many extrasolar planets? How might this migration have occurred?
15. How can scientists account for the fact that extrasolar planets seem to come in a wider range of types than the planets of our own solar system?
16. Overall, does the nebular theory seem adequate for describing the origins of other planetary systems? Explain.
17. Briefly describe how *Kepler, GAIA,* and direct observations should improve our understanding of extrasolar planets in coming years.

Decide whether the statement makes sense (or is clearly true) or does not make sense (or is clearly false). Explain clearly; not all these have definitive answers, so your explanation is more important than your chosen answer.

18. An extraterrestrial astronomer surveying our solar system with the Doppler method could discover the existence of Jupiter with just a few days of observation.

19. The fact that we have not yet discovered an Earth-size extrasolar planet in an Earth-like orbit tells us that such planets must be very rare.

20. Within the next few years, astronomers expect to confirm all the planet detections made with the astrometric and Doppler methods by observing transits of these same planets.

21. The infrared brightness of a star system decreases when a planet goes into eclipse.

22. Some extrasolar planets are likely to be made mostly of water.

23. Some extrasolar planets are likely to be made mostly of gold.

24. Current evidence suggests that there could be 100 billion or more planets in the Milky Way Galaxy.

25. It's the year 2018: The *Kepler* mission has announced the discovery of numerous planets with Neptune-like orbits around their stars.

26. It's the year 2020: Astronomers have successfully photographed an Earth-size planet, showing that it has oceans and continents.

27. It's the year 2040: Scientists announce that our first spacecraft to reach an extrasolar planet is now orbiting a planet around a star located near the center of the Milky Way Galaxy.

Quick Quiz

Choose the best answer to each of the following. Explain your reasoning with one or more complete sentences.

28. What method has detected the most extrasolar planets (or candidates) so far? (a) the transit method (b) Hubble images (c) the Doppler method

29. What fraction of extrasolar planets could in principle be detected by the transit method? (a) less than about 1% (b) about 20% (c) 100%

30. The astrometric method is best for finding massive planets that orbit (a) very close to their stars. (b) farther from their stars. (c) around extremely distant stars.

31. Which one of the following can the transit method tell us about a planet? (a) its mass (b) its size (c) the eccentricity of its orbit

32. Which method could detect a planet in an orbit that is face-on to the Earth? (a) Doppler method (b) transit method (c) astrometric method

33. Which detection method can be used with a backyard telescope? (a) Doppler method (b) transit method (c) astrometric method

34. To determine a planet's average density, we can use (a) the transit method alone. (b) the astrometric and Doppler methods together. (c) the transit and Doppler methods together.

35. Based on the model types shown in Figure 13.16, a planet made almost entirely of hydrogen compounds would be considered a (a) terrestrial planet. (b) jovian planet. (c) "water world."

36. What's the best explanation for the location of hot Jupiters? (a) They formed closer to their stars than Jupiter did. (b) They formed farther out like Jupiter but then migrated inward. (c) The strong gravity of their stars pulled them in close.

37. The major obstacle to NASA's building an observatory capable of obtaining moderately high-resolution images and spectra of extrasolar planets is that (a) no one has conceived of a technology that could do it. (b) it would require putting telescopes in space. (c) NASA lacks the necessary budget.

PROCESS OF SCIENCE

Examining How Science Works

38. *When Is a Theory Wrong?* As discussed in this chapter, in its original form the nebular theory of solar system formation does not explain the orbits of many known extrasolar planets, but it can explain them with modifications such as allowing for planetary migration. Does this mean the theory was "wrong" or only "incomplete" before the modifications were made? Explain. Be sure to look back at the discussion in Chapter 3 of the nature of science and scientific theories.

39. *Refuting the Theory.* Consider the following three hypothetical observations: (1) the discovery of a lone planet that is small and dense like a terrestrial planet but has a Jupiter-like orbit; (2) the discovery of a planetary system in which three terrestrial planets orbit the star beyond the orbital distance of two jovian planets; (3) the discovery that a majority of planetary systems have their jovian planets located nearer to their star than 1 AU and their terrestrial planets located beyond 5 AU. Each of these observations would challenge our current theory of solar system formation, but would any of them shake the very foundations of the theory? Explain clearly for each of the three hypothetical observations.

40. *Unanswered Questions.* As discussed in this chapter, we are only just beginning to learn about extrasolar planets. Briefly describe one important but unanswered question related to the study of planets around other stars. Then write 2–3 paragraphs in which you discuss how we might answer this question in the future. Be as specific as possible, focusing on the type of evidence necessary to answer the question and how the evidence could be gathered. What are the benefits of finding answers to this question?

GROUP WORK EXERCISE

41. *Time to Move On.* A common theme in science fiction is "leaving home" to find a new planet for humans to live on. Now that we know about thousands of planets, we can start imagining how to choose. Before you begin, assign the following roles to the people in your group: *Scribe* (takes notes on the group's activities), *Proposer* (proposes explanations to the group), *Skeptic* (points out weaknesses in proposed explanations), and *Moderator* (leads group discussion and makes sure everyone contributes). Then discuss the following questions.
a. Examine the planets in Figure 13.13. Which kinds of planets might make good homes, or poor ones? Are planets missing from the graph that might be better still? Does this graph give enough information? What's missing? **b.** Now examine the planets in Figure 13.16, and again comment on the habitability of planets on different parts of the graph. **c.** Finally, evaluate the planets in Figure 13.18 by the same criteria. **d.** In the end, which graph or combination of graphs would help you make the best decision?

INVESTIGATE FURTHER

In-Depth Questions to Increase Your Understanding

Short-Answer/Essay Questions

42. *Why So Soon?* The detection of extrasolar planets came much sooner than astronomers expected. Was this a result of planets being different than expected or of technology improving faster than expected? Explain.

43. *Explaining the Doppler Technique.* Explain how the Doppler technique works in terms an elementary school child would understand. It may help to use an analogy to explain the difficulty of direct detection and the general phenomenon of the Doppler shift.

44. *Comparing Methods.* What are the strengths and limitations of the Doppler and transit techniques? What kinds of planets are easiest to

detect with each method? Are there certain planets that each method cannot detect, even if the planets are very large? Explain. What advantages are gained if a planet can be detected by both methods?

45. *No Hot Jupiters Here.* How do we think hot jupiters formed? Why didn't one form in our solar system?

46. *Low-Density Planets.* Only one planet in our solar system has a density less than 1 g/cm³, but many extrasolar planets do. Explain why in a few sentences. (*Hint:* Consider the densities of the jovian planets in our solar system, given in Figure 11.1.)

47. *A Year on HD 209458b.* Imagine you were visiting the planet that orbits the star HD 209458, hovering in the upper atmosphere in a suitable spacecraft. What would it be like? What would you see, and how would the view look different from the view you would have while floating in Jupiter's atmosphere? Consider factors like local conditions, clouds, how the Sun would appear, and orbital motion.

48. *Detect an Extrasolar Planet for Yourself.* Most colleges and many amateur astronomers have the equipment necessary to detect known extrasolar planets using the transit method. All that's required is a telescope 10 or more inches in diameter, a CCD camera system, and a computer system for data analysis. The basic method is to take exposures of a few minutes' duration over a period of several hours around the times of predicted transit, and to compare the brightness of the star being transited to that of other stars in the same CCD frame (Figure 13.6). For complete instructions, see the study area of Mastering Astronomy.

Quantitative Problems

Be sure to show all calculations clearly and state your final answers in complete sentences.

49. *Lost in the Glare.* How hard would it be for an alien astronomer to detect the light from planets in our solar system compared to the light from the Sun itself?
    a. Calculate the fraction of the total emitted sunlight that is reflected by Earth. (*Hint:* Imagine a sphere around the Sun the size of the planet's orbit (area = $4\pi a^2$). What fraction of that area does the disk of a planet (area = πr_{planet}^2) take up? Earth's reflectivity is 29%.)
    b. Would detecting Jupiter be easier or harder than detecting Earth? Comment on whether you think Jupiter's larger size or greater distance has a stronger effect on its detectability. You may neglect any difference in reflectivity between Earth and Jupiter.

50. *Transit of TrES-1.* The planet TrES-1, orbiting a distant star, has been detected by both the transit and the Doppler technique, so we can calculate its density and get an idea of what kind of planet it is.
    a. Using the method of Mathematical Insight 13.3, calculate the radius of the transiting planet. The planetary transits block 2% of the star's light. The star TrES-1 has a radius of about 85% of our Sun's radius. **b.** The mass of the planet is approximately 0.75 times the mass of Jupiter, and Jupiter's mass is about 1.9×10^{27} kilograms. Calculate the average density of the planet. Give your answer in grams per cubic centimeter. Compare this density to the average densities of Saturn (0.7 g/cm³) and Earth (5.5 g/cm³). Is the planet terrestrial or jovian in nature? (*Hint:* To find the volume of the planet, use the formula for the volume of a sphere: $V = \frac{4}{3}\pi r^3$. Be careful with unit conversions.)

51. *Planet Around 51 Pegasi.* The star 51 Pegasi has about the same mass as our Sun. A planet discovered orbiting it has an orbital period of 4.23 days. The mass of the planet is estimated to be 0.6 times the mass of Jupiter. Use Kepler's third law to find the planet's average distance (semimajor axis) from its star. (*Hint:* Because the mass of 51 Pegasi is about the same as the mass of our Sun, you can use Kepler's third law in its original form, $p^2 = a^3$ [**Section 3.3**]. Be sure to convert the period into years before using this equation.)

52. *Identical Planets?* Imagine two planets orbiting a star with orbits edge-on to the Earth. The peak Doppler shift for each is 50 m/s, but

one has a period of 3 days and the other has a period of 300 days. Calculate the two minimum masses and say which, if either, is larger. (*Hint:* See Mathematical Insight 13.2.)

53. *Finding Orbit Sizes.* The Doppler method allows us to find a planet's semimajor axis using just the orbital period and the star's mass (Mathematical Insight 13.1).
    a. Imagine that a new planet is discovered orbiting a $2M_{Sun}$ star with a period of 5 days. What is its semimajor axis? **b.** Another planet is discovered orbiting a $0.5M_{Sun}$ star with a period of 100 days. What is its semimajor axis?

54. *One Born Every Minute?* It's possible to make a rough estimate of how often planetary systems form by making some basic assumptions. For example, if you assume that the stars we see have been born at random times over the last 10 billion years, then the rate of star formation is simply the number of stars we see divided by 10 billion years. The fraction of planets with detected extrasolar planets is at least 5%, so this factor can be multiplied in to find the approximate rate of formation of planetary systems.
    a. Using these assumptions, estimate how often a planetary system forms in our galaxy. (Our galaxy contains at least 100 billion stars.)
    b. How often does a planetary system form somewhere in the observable universe, which contains at least 100 billion galaxies?
    c. Write a few sentences describing your reaction to your results. Do you think the calculations are realistic? Are the rates larger or smaller than you expected?

55. *Habitable Planet Around 51 Pegasi?* The star 51 Pegasi is approximately as bright as our Sun and has a planet that orbits at a distance of only 0.052 AU.
    a. Suppose the planet reflects 15% of the incoming sunlight. Using Mathematical Insight 10.1, calculate its "no greenhouse" average temperature. How does this temperature compare to that of Earth? **b.** Repeat part a, but assume that the planet is covered in bright clouds that reflect 80% of the incoming sunlight. **c.** Based on your answers to parts a and b, do you think it is likely that the conditions on this planet are conducive to life? Explain.

Discussion Questions

56. *So What?* What is the significance of the discovery of extrasolar planets, if any? Justify your answer in the context of this book's discussion of the history of astronomy.

57. *Is It Worth It?* The cost of the *Kepler* mission is several hundred million dollars. The cost of a mission that could obtain direct images or spectra of extrasolar planets would likely be several billion dollars. Are these expenses worth it, compared to the results expected? Defend your opinion.

Web Projects

58. *New Planets.* Research the latest extrasolar planet discoveries. Create a "planet journal," complete with illustrations as needed, with a page for each of at least three recently discovered planets. On each page, note the technique that was used to find the planet, give any information we have about the nature of the planet, and discuss how the planet does or does not fit in with our current understanding of planetary systems.

59. *Direct Detections.* In this chapter, we saw only a few examples of direct detection of possible extrasolar planets. Search for new information on these and any other direct detections now known. Have the detections discussed in this chapter been confirmed as planets? Have we made any other direct detections, and if so, how? Summarize your findings in a short written report, including images of the directly detected planets.

60. *Extrasolar Planet Mission.* Learn about a proposed future mission to study extrasolar planets, including its proposed design, capabilities, and goals. Write a short report on your findings.

Comparing the worlds in the solar system has taught us important lessons about Earth and why it is so suitable for life. This illustration summarizes some of the major lessons we've learned by studying other worlds both in our own solar system and beyond it.

① Comparing the terrestrial worlds shows that a planet's size and distance from the Sun are the primary factors that determine how it evolves through time [Chapters 9, 10].

Venus demonstrates the importance of distance from the Sun: If Earth were moved to the orbit of Venus, it would suffer a runaway greenhouse effect and become too hot for life.

The smallest terrestrial worlds, Mercury and the Moon, became geologically dead long ago. They therefore retain ancient impact craters, which provide a record of how impacts must have affected Earth and other worlds.

Mars shows why size is important: A planet smaller than Earth loses interior heat faster, which can lead to a decline in geological activity and loss of atmospheric gas.

② Jovian planets are gas-rich and far more massive than Earth. They and their ice-rich moons have opened our eyes to the diversity of processes that shape worlds [Chapter 11].

Earth and the Moon

Our Moon led us to expect all small objects to be geologically dead . . .

The strong gravity of the jovian planets has shaped the asteroid and Kuiper belts, and flung comets into the distant Oort cloud, ultimately determining how frequently asteroids and comets strike Earth.

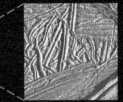

Jupiter and Europa

. . . but Europa—along with Io, Titan, and other moons—proved that tidal heating or icy composition can lead to geological activity, in some cases with subsurface oceans and perhaps even life.

③ Asteroids and comets may be small bodies in the solar system, but they have played major roles in the development of life on Earth [Chapter 12].

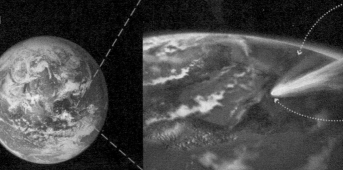

Comets or water-rich asteroids from the outer asteroid belt brought Earth the ingredients of its oceans and atmosphere.

Impacts of comets and asteroids have altered the course of life on Earth and may do so again.

④ The discovery of planets around other stars has shown that our solar system is not unique. Studies of other solar systems are teaching us new lessons about how planets form and about the likelihood of finding other Earth-like worlds [Chapter 13].

Rapid advances in extrasolar planet detection have allowed us to find some planets as small as Earth, and others at the right distances from their stars to be habitable. The discovery of a planet that meets both criteria may have happened by the time you read this book.

S2 SPACE AND TIME

> *Henceforth space by itself, and time by itself,*
> *are doomed to fade away into mere shadows,*
> *and only a kind of union of the two will preserve*
> *an independent reality.*
> —Hermann Minkowski, 1908

The universe consists of matter and energy moving through *space* with the passage of *time*. Up to this point in the book, we have discussed the concepts of space and time as though they are absolute and distinct—just as they seem in everyday life. But what if this appearance is deceiving?

More than a century ago, Albert Einstein discovered that space and time are actually intertwined in a manner that we now understand through Einstein's *theory of relativity*. Contrary to popular myth, this theory is *not* particularly difficult to understand, though it requires us to think in new ways. Moreover, because space and time are such fundamental concepts, understanding relativity is very important to understanding astronomy and the universe. We will therefore devote this chapter and the next to understanding the key ideas of relativity.

S2.1 EINSTEIN'S REVOLUTION

Albert Einstein was born on March 14, 1879, in Ulm, Germany. As a toddler, he was so slow in learning to speak that relatives feared he might have brain damage. Even when he began to show promise, it was in unconventional ways. Young Albert dropped out of high school at the suggestion of a teacher who told him that he would "never amount to anything." Nevertheless, he was admitted to college in Switzerland, in large part because of his proficiency in mathematics.

Einstein hoped to teach after his college graduation, but his Jewish heritage and lack of Swiss citizenship made it difficult for him to find a teaching job. In 1901, he instead took a job with the Swiss patent office, and devoted his free time to the study of unsolved questions in physics.

From the standpoint of history, Einstein burst onto the scene in 1905, when he earned his Ph.D. and published five papers in the *German Yearbook of Physics*. Three of the papers solved three of the greatest mysteries in physics at the time. The first paper dealt with something called the *photoelectric effect,* and essentially presented the first concrete evidence of the wave-particle duality of light that we discussed in Chapter 5. The second paper explained why suspended particles in water jiggle even after the water has been still for a long time (an effect known as *Brownian motion*). Einstein's analysis led to the first direct measurements of molecular motion and molecular and atomic sizes. The third paper introduced the special theory of relativity, which forever changed our understanding of space and time.

Einstein returned to Germany in 1913, where he completed work on his general theory of relativity. After some of its central predictions were confirmed by observation in 1919 [**Section S3.4**], Einstein's fame began to extend beyond the world of science. He received the Nobel Prize in Physics in 1921 and was by this time a household name.

Einstein was a visiting professor at the California Institute of Technology when Hitler came to power in Germany. Recognizing Hitler's evil, Einstein decided to remain in the United States. He played an important role in convincing President Franklin Roosevelt to start the Manhattan Project to build an atomic bomb. Nevertheless, Einstein was a committed pacifist who supported the project only because he feared that Hitler would otherwise develop an atomic bomb first. He expressed great dismay when the bomb was used against Japan, and he spent much of the rest of his life arguing for a worldwide agreement to ban the further manufacture and use of nuclear weapons. He also worked to promote human rights and equality for men and women of all races and nationalities. Einstein died in Princeton, New Jersey, on April 18, 1955. More than a half-century later, he remains the most famous scientist of modern times.

What are the major ideas of special relativity?

We often talk about the *theory of relativity* as though it were a single theory, and in some sense it is. However, Einstein actually developed his theory in two parts that he published separately. The **special theory of relativity**, published in 1905, shows that space and time are intertwined but does not deal with the effects of gravity. The **general theory of relativity**, published in 1915, offers a surprising new view of gravity—a view that we will use to help us understand topics such as the expansion and fate of the universe and the strange objects known as *black holes*. In essence, the special theory is "special" because it deals only with the special case in which we ignore the role of gravity, while the general theory is "general" because it applies with or without gravity. We will focus on the special theory of relativity in this chapter and on the general theory in Chapter S3.

Einstein developed his theories with the aid of "thought experiments"—experiments that could be carried out in principle but that would be very difficult in practice. Thought experiments allow us to think through the consequences of simple ideas or statements. Let's start with a thought experiment designed to show you why the special theory of relativity is so surprising.

Imagine that, with the aid of a long tape measure, you carefully measure the distance you walk from home to work and find it to be 5.0 kilometers. You wouldn't expect any argument about this distance. For example, if a friend drives her car along the same route and measures the distance with her car's odometer, she ought to get the same measurement of 5.0 kilometers (assuming her odometer is accurate). Likewise, you would expect agreement about how much time it takes you to walk this distance. Suppose your friend continues driving and you call her just as you leave your house at 8:00 a.m. and again just as you arrive at work at 8:45 a.m. You'd certainly be surprised if she argued that your walk took an amount of time other than 45 minutes.

Our example illustrates that distances and times appear absolute and distinct in our daily lives. We expect everyone to agree on the distance between two points, such as the locations of home and work, and the time between two events, such as leaving home and arriving at work. However, Einstein showed that these expectations are not strictly correct: With extremely precise measurements, the distance you measure between home and work will be *different* from the distance measured by a friend in a car, and you and your friend will also disagree about the time it takes you to walk to work. At ordinary speeds, the differences will be so small as to be unnoticeable. But if your friend could drive at a speed close to the speed of light, the differences would be substantial.

Disagreements about distances and times only mark the beginning of the astonishing ideas contained in the special theory of relativity. In the rest of this chapter, we will see how this theory leads to each of the following ideas:

- No information can travel faster than the speed of light (in a vacuum), and no material object can even reach the speed of light.

- If you observe anyone or anything moving by you at a speed close to the speed of light, you will conclude that time runs more slowly for that person or moving object. That is, a person moving by you ages more slowly than you, a clock moving by you ticks more slowly than your clock, a computer moving by you runs more slowly than your similar computer, and so on.

- If you observe two events to occur simultaneously, such as flashes of light in two different places at the same time, a person moving by you at a speed close to the speed of light may not agree that the two events were simultaneous.

- If you carefully measure the size of something moving by you at a speed close to the speed of light, you will find that its length (in the direction of its motion) is shorter than it would be if the object were not moving.

- If you could measure the mass of something moving by you at a speed close to the speed of light, you would find its mass to be greater than the mass it would have if it were stationary. As we will see, Einstein's famous equation, $E = mc^2$, follows from this fact.

Although these ideas of special relativity may sound like science fiction or fantasy, a vast body of observational and experimental evidence supports their reality. They also follow logically from a few simple premises. If you keep an open mind and think deeply as you read this chapter, you'll soon understand the basic ideas of relativity.

What is relative about relativity?

Contrary to a common belief, Einstein's theory does *not* in any way tell us that "everything is relative." Rather, the theory takes its name from the idea that *motion* is always relative. You can see why motion must be relative with another simple thought experiment.

Imagine a supersonic airplane that flies at a speed of 1670 km/hr from Nairobi, Kenya, to Quito, Ecuador. How fast is the plane going? At first, this question sounds trivial—we have just said that the plane is going 1670 km/hr.

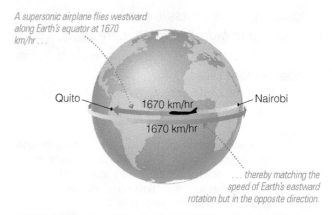

A supersonic airplane flies westward along Earth's equator at 1670 km/hr...

Quito — 1670 km/hr — Nairobi

1670 km/hr

...thereby matching the speed of Earth's eastward rotation but in the opposite direction.

FIGURE S2.1 A plane flying at 1670 km/hr from Nairobi to Quito (westward) travels precisely opposite Earth's eastward rotation. Viewed from the Moon, the plane appears to remain stationary while Earth rotates underneath it.

But wait. Nairobi and Quito are both nearly on Earth's equator, and the equatorial speed of Earth's rotation is the same 1670 km/hr speed at which the plane is flying (see Figure 1.12), but in the opposite direction (**FIGURE S2.1**). Viewed from the Moon, the plane would therefore appear to stay put *while Earth rotated beneath it*. When the flight began, you would see the plane lift off the ground in Nairobi. The plane would then remain stationary while Earth's rotation carried Nairobi away from it and Quito toward it. When Quito finally reached the plane's position, the plane would drop back down to the ground.

We have two alternative viewpoints about the plane's flight. People on Earth say that the plane is traveling westward across the surface of the Earth. Observers on the Moon say that the plane is stationary while Earth rotates eastward beneath it. Both viewpoints are equally valid.

In fact, there are many other equally valid viewpoints about the plane's flight. Observers looking at the solar system as a whole would see the plane moving at a speed of more than 100,000 km/hr, because that is Earth's speed in its orbit around the Sun. Observers living in another galaxy would see the plane moving at about 800,000 km/hr with the rotation of the Milky Way Galaxy. The only thing all these observers would agree on is that the plane is traveling at 1670 km/hr *relative to* the surface of the Earth.

The airplane example shows that questions like "Who is really moving?" and "How fast are you going?" have no absolute answers. Einstein's *theory of relativity* tells us that measurements of motion, as well as measurements of time and space, make sense only when we describe whom or what they are being measured relative to.

THINK ABOUT IT

Suppose you are running on a treadmill and the readout says you are going 8 miles per hour. What is the 8 miles per hour measured relative to? How fast are you going relative to the ground? How fast would an observer on the Moon see you going? Describe a few other possible viewpoints on your speed.

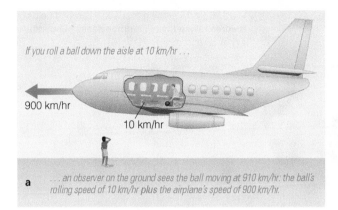

If you roll a ball down the aisle at 10 km/hr . . .

900 km/hr

10 km/hr

a . . . an observer on the ground sees the ball moving at 910 km/hr: the ball's rolling speed of 10 km/hr **plus** the airplane's speed of 900 km/hr.

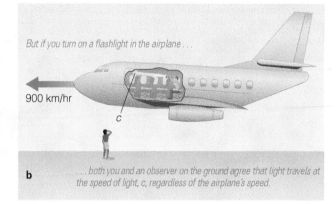

But if you turn on a flashlight in the airplane . . .

900 km/hr

c

b . . . both you and an observer on the ground agree that light travels at the speed of light, c, regardless of the airplane's speed.

FIGURE S2.2 Unlike the speed of material objects, the speed of light is the same in all reference frames.

What is absolute about relativity?

Although the theory of relativity tells us that motion is always relative, the theory's foundations actually rest on the idea that two things in the universe are absolute:

1. The laws of nature are the same for everyone.

2. The speed of light is the same for everyone.

Understanding the Two Absolutes The first of the two absolutes, that the laws of nature are the same for everyone, is probably not surprising. If you're on an airplane with the shades drawn during a very smooth flight, you won't feel any sensation of motion, and you would get the same results from any experiments you performed on the airplane that someone else would get performing those experiments on the ground. These equivalent results demonstrate that the laws of nature are the same in the moving airplane and on the ground. In the language of relativity, the ground and the airplane represent different **reference frames** (or *frames of reference*); we say that two people share the same reference frame if they are *not* moving relative to each other. The idea that the laws of nature are the same for everyone means that these laws do not depend on your reference frame.

The second absolute of relativity, that the speed of light is the same for everyone, is far more surprising. In general, we expect people in different reference frames to give different answers for the speed of the same moving object. For example, suppose you roll a ball down the aisle of an airplane. The ball rolls slowly in your airplane reference frame, but someone on the ground would see the ball moving with the airplane's speed *plus* the speed at which it rolls down the aisle (FIGURE S2.2a). Now, suppose instead that you turn on a flashlight and measure the speed of the emitted light. The idea that the speed of light is the same for everyone means that a person on the ground will measure exactly the same speed for the light beam, even though the light was emitted inside the moving airplane (FIGURE S2.2b). In other words, people in different reference frames can disagree about the speeds of material objects, but everyone always agrees about the speed of light, regardless of where the light comes from.

How do we know that everyone always measures the same speed of light? Observations and experiments are the ultimate judge of any scientific claim, and *the absoluteness of the speed of light is an experimentally verified fact.* We'll discuss some of the experimental evidence later in the chapter. For now, our goal is to understand how the ideas of relativity introduced earlier all follow logically from the two absolutes.

Making Sense of Relativity Before we dive into the details, it's worth taking a moment to prepare yourself for the type of change in thinking that relativity will require. One reason relativity has a reputation for being difficult to grasp, despite its underlying simplicity, is that most of its ideas and consequences are not obvious in everyday life. They become obvious only when we deal with speeds close to the speed of light or, in the case of general relativity, with gravitational fields far stronger than that of Earth. Because we don't commonly experience such extreme conditions, we have no *common* sense about them. Therefore, it's not really accurate to say that relativity violates common sense, because the theory is perfectly consistent with everything we have come to expect in daily life.

Making sense of relativity requires only that you learn to view your everyday experiences from a new, broader perspective. Fortunately, you've done this before. At a young age, you learned "common sense" meanings for *up* and *down*: Up is above your head, *down* is toward your feet, and things tend to fall down. One day, however, you learned that Earth is round. When you looked at a globe with the Northern Hemisphere on the top, you were immediately confronted with a **paradox**—a situation that *seems* to violate common sense or to contradict itself. Your common sense told you that Australians should fall off the Earth (FIGURE S2.3a), but they don't. To resolve this paradox, you were forced to accept that your "common sense" about *up* and *down* was incorrect. You therefore revised your common sense to accept that *up* and *down* are determined relative to the center of Earth (FIGURE S2.3b).

THINK ABOUT IT

Why do you suppose that most maps show the Northern Hemisphere on the top and the Southern Hemisphere on the bottom? If you hung your map upside down and rewrote the words so that they read right side up, would the map be equally valid?

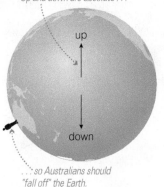

up

down

. . so Australians should "fall off" the Earth.

a

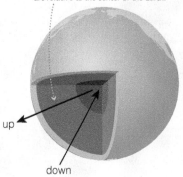

Revised common sense: Up and down are relative to the center of the Earth.

up

down

b

· **FIGURE S2.3** Learning that Earth is round helps children revise their "common sense" understanding of *up* and *down*.

As a teenager, Einstein wondered what the world would look like if he could travel at or beyond the speed of light. He inevitably encountered paradoxes when he thought about this question. Ultimately, he resolved the paradoxes only when he recognized that our common sense ideas about space and time must change if we are to extend them to the realm of very high speeds or very strong gravitational fields. Just as we all once learned a new common sense about up and down, we now must learn a new common sense about space and time.

S2.2 RELATIVE MOTION

We are now ready to explore the theory of relativity by following a series of thought experiments through to their logical conclusions. We will use thought experiments slightly different from the ones Einstein himself used, though the ideas will be essentially the same. Just as Einstein did, we will base all our thought experiments on the assumption that the two absolutes of relativity are true.

What's surprising about the absoluteness of the speed of light?

The idea that everyone always measures the same speed of light may not sound earth-shattering, but Einstein soon realized that it leads to far-ranging consequences—consequences that force us to let go of many of our intuitive beliefs about how the universe works. We will investigate the implications of the absoluteness of the speed of light by constructing a series of thought experiments about relative motion viewed from different reference frames.

Thought Experiments at Ordinary Speeds Because special relativity does not deal with the effects of gravity, we will use thought experiments in which we imagine being in spaceships in deep space, far from any planets or stars and drifting along without engine power. Everything in and around these spaceships is weightless and floats freely, so we call the reference frames of these spaceships **free-float frames** (or *inertial reference frames*). To gain familiarity with the idea, let's begin with thought experiments involving speeds we are familiar with from everyday life.

Thought Experiment 1 Imagine that you are floating freely in a spaceship (**FIGURE S2.4**). Because you feel no sensation of motion, you perceive yourself to be at rest, or traveling at zero speed. As you look out your window, you see your friend Al in his own spaceship, moving away at a constant speed of 90 km/hr. How does the situation appear to Al?

We can answer the question by logically analyzing the experimental situation. Al has no reason to think he is moving. Like you, he is in a free-float frame, floating freely in a spaceship with the engines off. Al will therefore say that *he* is at rest and that *you* are moving away from him at 90 km/hr.

Both points of view—yours and Al's—are equally valid. You both would find the same results for any experiments performed in your own spaceship, and your research would lead you to exactly the same laws of nature. You could argue endlessly about who is really moving, but your argument would be pointless because all motion is relative.

Thought Experiment 2 We begin with the same situation as in Thought Experiment 1, but this time you put on your spacesuit and strap yourself to the outside of your spaceship

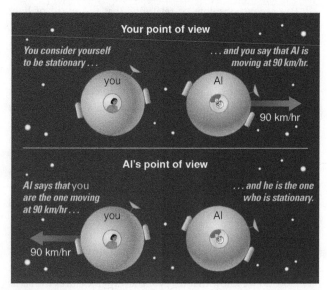

Your point of view

You consider yourself to be stationary . . .

. . . and you say that Al is moving at 90 km/hr.

you

Al

90 km/hr

Al's point of view

Al says that you are the one moving at 90 km/hr . . .

. . . and he is the one who is stationary.

you

Al

90 km/hr

FIGURE S2.4 Thought Experiment 1.

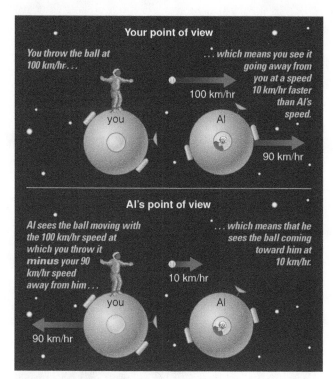

FIGURE S2.5 Thought Experiment 2.

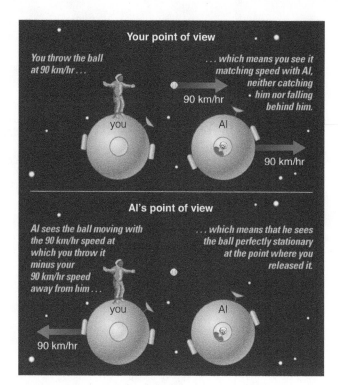

FIGURE S2.6 Thought Experiment 3.

(FIGURE S2.5). You happen to have a baseball, which you throw in Al's direction at a speed of 100 km/hr. How fast is the ball moving relative to Al?

From your point of view, Al and the ball are both going in the same direction. Al is going 90 km/hr and the ball is going 100 km/hr, so the ball is going 10 km/hr faster than he is. The ball will therefore overtake and pass him.

From Al's point of view, *he* is stationary and *you* are moving away from him at 90 km/hr. Therefore, he would say the ball was moving even before you threw it, since it would be going with you at your speed of 90 km/hr. Once you release the ball, he sees it moving toward him at 10 km/hr—the ball's speed of 100 km/hr relative to you *minus* the 90 km/hr at which you are moving relative to him. In other words, although you and Al disagree about the speed of the ball, you both agree that the ball will pass him at a *relative* speed of 10 km/hr.

Thought Experiment 3 This time you throw a baseball in Al's direction at 90 km/hr (FIGURE S2.6). From your point of view, the ball is traveling at exactly the same speed as Al. Therefore, you'll see the ball forever chasing him through space, neither catching up with nor falling behind him.

From Al's point of view, the 90 km/hr at which you threw the ball exactly matches your 90 km/hr speed away from him. Therefore, the ball is *stationary* in his reference frame. Think about this for a moment: Before you throw the baseball, Al sees it moving away from him at 90 km/hr because it is in your hand. At the moment you release the baseball, it suddenly becomes stationary in Al's reference frame, floating in space at a fixed distance from his spaceship. Many hours later, after you have traveled far away, Al will still see the ball floating in the same place. If he wishes, he can put on his spacesuit

and go out to retrieve it, or he can just leave it there. From his point of view, it's not going anywhere, and neither is he.

Thought Experiments at High Speeds The absoluteness of the speed of light did not come into play in our first three thought experiments because the speeds were small compared to the speed of light. For example, 100 km/hr is less than *one ten-millionth* of the speed of light. Now let's raise the speeds much higher and explore the strange consequences of the absoluteness of the speed of light.

Thought Experiment 4 Imagine that Al is moving away from you at 90% of the speed of light, or $0.9c$, where c is the speed of light (FIGURE S2.7*). How does the situation appear to Al?

Other than the much higher speed, this situation is just like that in Thought Experiment 1. Al perceives *himself* to be at rest and sees *you* moving away from him at $0.9c$.

Thought Experiment 5 Now, instead of throwing a baseball, you climb out of your spaceship and point a flashlight in Al's direction (FIGURE S2.8). How fast is the beam of light moving relative to Al?

*For simplicity, this and most other figures in this chapter ignore effects of length contraction, which would make the moving ships shorter in their direction of motion; only Figure S2.13 shows the length contraction effect.

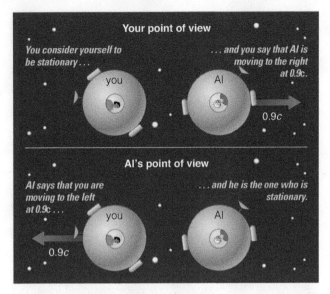

FIGURE S2.7 Thought Experiment 4.

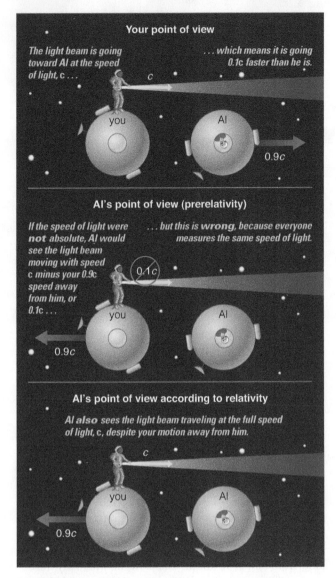

FIGURE S2.8 Thought Experiment 5.

From your point of view, Al is going at 90% of the speed of light, or 0.9c, and the light beam is going in the same direction at the full speed of light, or c. Therefore, you see the light beam going 0.1c faster than Al.* Nothing should be surprising so far.

From Al's point of view, *he* is stationary and *you* are moving away from him at 0.9c. Following the "old common sense" used in our earlier thought experiments, we would expect Al to see the light moving toward him at 0.1c—the light's speed of c minus your speed of 0.9c. *But this answer is wrong!* Relativity tells us that the speed of light is always the same for everyone. Therefore, Al must see the beam of light coming toward him at c, *not* at 0.1c.

In this case, you and Al no longer agree about his speed *relative* to the speed of the light beam: He'll see the light beam pass by him at the speed of light, c, but you'll see it going only 0.1c faster than he is going. By our old common sense, this result sounds preposterous. However, we found it by using simple logic, starting with the assumption that the speed of light is the same for everyone. As long as this assumption is true—and, remember, the absoluteness of the speed of light is an experimentally verified fact—our conclusions follow logically.

THINK ABOUT IT

Suppose Al is moving away from you at a speed of 0.99999c, which is short of the speed of light by only 0.00001 c, or 3 km/s. At what relative rate would you see a light beam catch up with him? How fast will Al see the light going as it passes?

---

*You can't actually see a light beam moving forward. When we say that you "see" the beam moving at the speed of light, we really mean that you would find it to be moving at this speed if you made a careful measurement with instruments at rest in your reference frame.

Why can't we reach the speed of light?

You might be wondering what Al would see if he were moving away from you at the speed of light or faster, which is essentially the question that Einstein asked when he wondered how the world would look if he could travel at or beyond the speed of light. However, once we accept the absoluteness of the speed of light, it follows that neither Al nor you nor any other material object can ever reach the speed of light, let alone exceed it.

Thought Experiment 6 You have just built the most incredible rocket imaginable, and you are taking it on a test ride. Soon you are going faster than anyone had ever imagined possible—and then you put the rocket into second gear! You keep going faster and faster and faster. Here is the key question: Are you ever traveling faster than the speed of light?

Before we answer this question, the fact that all motion is relative forces us to answer another question: In what reference frame is your speed being measured? Let's begin with *your* reference frame. Imagine that you turn on your rocket's headlights. Because the speed of light is the same for everyone, you must see the headlight beams traveling at the speed of light—which means they are racing away from your rocket at a speed you'll measure to be 300,000 km/s. The fact that you'll see your headlight beams racing away is true no matter how long you have been firing your rocket engines. In other words, you cannot possibly keep up with your own headlight beams.

The fact that you cannot outrace your headlight beams, combined with the fact that the speed of light is the same for everyone, means that no observer can ever see you reach or exceed the speed of light. Observers in different reference frames will measure your speed differently, but *all* observers will agree on two key points: (1) Your headlight beams are moving out ahead of you, and (2) these light beams are traveling at $c = 300,000$ km/s. Clearly, if you are being outraced by your headlight beams and if the beams are traveling at the speed of light, you must be traveling *slower* than the speed of light (FIGURE S2.9). It does not matter who is measuring your speed. It can be you, someone on Earth, or anyone else in any other reference frame. No one can ever observe you to be traveling as fast as a light beam.

In case you are still not convinced, let's turn the situation around. Imagine that, as you race by some planet, a person on the planet turns on a light beam. Because the speed of light is absolute, you will see the light beam race past you at $c = 300,000$ km/s. The person on the planet will also see the light traveling at $c = 300,000$ km/s and will see the light outrace you. Again, everyone will agree that you are traveling slower than the speed of light.

The same argument applies to any moving object, and it is true with or without headlights. All light travels at the speed

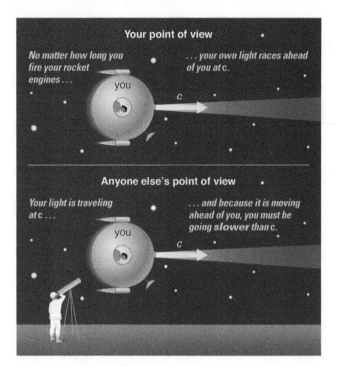

Your point of view

No matter how long you fire your rocket engines . . .

. . . your own light races ahead of you at c.

you

c

Anyone else's point of view

Your light is traveling at c . . .

*. . . and because it is moving ahead of you, you must be going **slower** than c.*

you

c

FIGURE S2.9 Thought Experiment 6.

of light, including the light that reflects off an object (allowing us to see it) and the infrared light that even cool objects emit as thermal radiation [**Section 5.4**]. As long as the speed of light is absolute, no material object can ever keep up with the light it emits or reflects, which means no material object can reach or exceed the speed of light. Building a spaceship to travel at the speed of light is not a mere technological challenge—it simply cannot be done.

SPECIAL TOPIC

What If Light Can't Catch You?

If you're like most students learning about relativity for the first time, you're probably already looking for loopholes in the logic of our thought experiments. For example, confronted with Thought Experiment 6, you might be tempted to ask, "What happens if you're traveling away from some planet faster than light, so the light from the planet can't catch you?" While it's surely true that light couldn't catch you if you were going faster than the speed of light, it also makes the question moot: If you can't see light from the planet, there is no way for you to know that the planet is there, so you couldn't actually make any measurement that would show your speed to be greater than the speed of light.

In fact, what relativity really tells us about the speed of light is that it is a limit on the speed at which *information* can be transmitted. There are numerous circumstances in the universe in which an object may *seem* to be exceeding the speed of light. However, these circumstances do not provide any means of sending information or objects at speeds faster than the speed of light.

As an example, imagine that you held a laser light and swept it across the sky between two stars that are separated by an angular distance of 90° and are each 10 light-years away from Earth. About 10 years from now, you'd see your laser light first make a dot (an extremely dim one!) on the surface of one star and a few

seconds later make a dot on the surface of the second star. That is, your laser dot would seem to have traveled the many light-years from the first star to the second star in just a few seconds—which means at a speed far in excess of the speed of light. However, while the laser dot can carry information from you to each of the individual stars, it clearly cannot be transmitting any information from one star to the other. (After all, you held the laser, not someone at either star.) As a result, there's no violation of relativity.

Other examples of things that *seem* to move faster than the speed of light arise frequently in the world of quantum mechanics (see Chapter S4). According to quantum principles, measuring a particle in one place can (in certain specific circumstances) affect a particle in another place *instantaneously*—even if the particle is many light-years away. In fact, this process has been observed in laboratories over short distances. This instantaneous effect of one particle on another may at first seem to violate relativity, but it does not. The built-in randomness of quantum mechanics prevents this technique from being used to transmit useful information. Moreover, if we wish to confirm that the second particle really was affected, we will have to receive a signal carrying information about the particle—and that signal can travel no faster than the speed of light.

S2.3 THE REALITY OF SPACE AND TIME

In the first section of this chapter, we listed five key ideas of special relativity. Each of these ideas is actually a prediction that arises from the two basic assumptions of the theory—that the laws of nature are the same for everyone and that everyone always measures the same speed of light. So far, we have shown only how relativity predicts that no material object can reach or exceed the speed of light. Let's continue down the path we've started, so that we can see why our old conceptions of time and space must be revised.

How does relativity affect our view of time and space?

The special theory of relativity tells us that measurements of time, length, and mass can all be different in different reference frames. It also tells us that different observers can disagree about whether two events are simultaneous and about the speeds of different objects. Strange as these ideas may sound, we can continue to use simple thought experiments to show why they follow directly from the premises of relativity. We'll begin by considering how relativity affects our view of time, then move on to other effects.

Reference frame inside train

Inside the train, the ball goes straight up and down.

Reference frame outside train

Outside the train, the ball appears to be going faster: It has the same up-and-down speed, plus the forward speed of the train.

The faster the train is moving, the faster the ball appears to be going.

FIGURE S2.10 A ball tossed straight up and down *inside* a moving train appears to an outside observer to follow a slanted path. Thus, the outside observer sees the ball traveling at a faster total speed than does the person inside the train.

Time Differs in Different Reference Frames

In preparation for our next thought experiment, imagine that you are on a moving train tossing a ball straight up so that it bounces straight back down from the ceiling. How do the path and speed of the ball appear to an observer along the tracks outside the train? (We'll ignore the effects of gravity on the ball's speed.)

As shown in **FIGURE S2.10**, the outside observer sees the ball going forward with the train at the same time that it is going up and down, so the ball's path always slants forward. Because the outside observer sees the ball moving with this forward speed *in addition to* its up-and-down speed, while you see the ball going only up and down, he would measure a *faster* overall speed for the ball than you would. If the train is moving slowly, the outside observer sees the ball's path slant forward only slightly and would say that the ball's overall speed was only slightly faster than you would report. If the train is moving rapidly, the ball's path leans much farther forward, and the ball appears to be going considerably faster to the outside observer than to you.

Thought Experiment 7 Inside his spaceship, Al has a laser on his floor that is pointed up to a mirror on his ceiling (**FIGURE S2.11**). He momentarily flashes the laser light and uses a very accurate clock to time how long it takes the light to travel from the floor to the ceiling and back. As Al zips by you at a speed close to the speed of light, you observe his experiment and, using your own very accurate clock, you also time the laser light's trip from Al's floor to his ceiling and back.

Because Al, the laser, and the mirror are all moving from your point of view, the light's path looks slanted as it goes from floor to ceiling and back, just as the ball tossed up and down in the train followed a slanted path to an outside observer.

FIGURE S2.11 Thought Experiment 7.

Therefore, from your point of view, the light travels a *longer* path in going from the floor to the ceiling than it does from Al's point of view, just as the ball in the train took a longer path from the outside observer's point of view.

By our old common sense, this would be no big deal. You and Al would agree on how long it takes the light to go from the floor to the ceiling and back, just as you and an outside observer would agree on how long it takes you to toss a ball up and down on a train. You would explain the light's longer path by saying that the light is moving faster relative to you than it is moving relative to Al, just as the outside observer sees the tossed ball moving faster because of the forward motion of the train. However, because we are dealing with *light,* you and Al must both measure its speed to be the *same*—the speed of light, or 300,000 km/s—even though you see its path slanted forward with the movement of the spaceship. This fact has an astonishing implication.

Remember that, at any given speed, including the speed of light, traveling a longer distance must take a longer time. Because both you and Al see the light traveling at the same speed, but you see it traveling a longer distance, *your clock must record more time* than Al's as the light travels from floor to ceiling and back. And because you can see Al's clock as well as your own, you must see his clock running at a slower rate than yours in order for it to end up reading less elapsed time after the light completes its round trip. In other words, you will see Al's clock running more slowly than your own. Moreover, it doesn't matter what kind of "clock" you and Al use to measure the time for the light trip. *Anything* that can measure time will be going slower in Al's reference frame than in yours, including mechanical clocks, electrical clocks, heartbeats, and biochemical reactions. Our astonishing conclusion: From your point of view, *time itself* is running slower for Al.

How much slower is time running for Al? It depends on his speed relative to you. If he is moving slowly compared to the speed of light, you will scarcely be able to detect the slant of the light path, and your clock and Al's clock will tick at nearly the same rate. The faster he is moving, the more slanted the light path will appear to you and the greater the difference between the rate of his clock and that of yours. Generalizing, we reach the following conclusion:

From your point of view, time runs more slowly in the reference frame of anyone moving relative to you. The faster the other reference frame is moving, the more slowly time passes within it.

This effect is called **time dilation** because it tells us that time is *dilated,* or expanded, in a moving reference frame.

The Relativity of Simultaneity Our old common sense also tells us that everyone must agree on whether two events happen at the same time or one event happens before another. For example, if you see two apples—one red and one green—fall from two different trees and hit the ground at the same time, you expect everyone else to agree that they landed at the same time (assuming you've accounted for any difference in the light travel times from the two trees). If you saw the green apple land before the red apple, you would be very surprised if someone else said that the red apple hit the ground first. Well, prepare yourself to be surprised, because our next thought experiment will show that observers in different reference frames will not necessarily agree about the order or simultaneity of events that occur in different places.

Before we go on, note that observers in different reference frames *must* agree about the order of events that occur in the *same* place. For example, suppose you grab a cookie and eat it. In your reference frame, both events (picking up the cookie and eating it) occur in the same place, so it could not possibly be the case that someone else would see you eat the cookie before you pick it up.

Thought Experiment 8 Al has a brand-new, extra-long space-ship, and he is coming toward you at a speed of 90% of the speed of light, or 0.9*c* (FIGURE S2.12a). He is in the center of his spaceship, which is totally dark except for a flashing green light at its front end and a flashing red light at its back end. Suppose that you see the green and red lights flash at *exactly the same time,* with the flashes occurring at the instant that Al happens to pass you. During the very short time that the light flashes are traveling toward you, Al's forward motion carries him toward the point where you saw the green flash occur. The green flash will therefore reach him before the

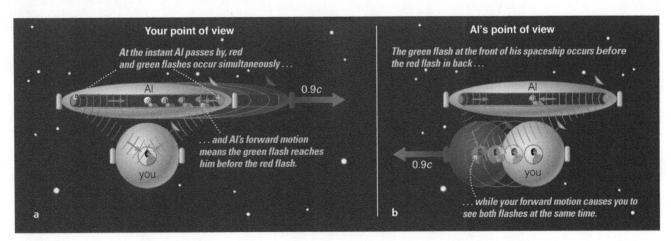

FIGURE S2.12 Thought Experiment 8.

We can find a formula for time dilation by looking at the paths that you and Al see light take from the floor to the ceiling in Figure S2.11. We can use these paths to construct a right triangle as follows (**FIGURE 1**):

- The hypotenuse is the path that *you* see the light take. Let's use *t* to represent the time that *you* measure as the light travels this path. Because *distance = speed × time* and the light travels at the speed of light, the length of this path is $c \times t$.

- The base of the triangle is the distance that Al's spaceship moves forward during the time *t*. If we use *v* for the spaceship's speed relative to you, this distance is $v \times t$.

- The vertical side is the path Al sees the light take. We know that Al measures time differently than you, so we'll use *t′* ("t-prime") to represent the time *he* measures. Therefore, the length of this path is $c \times t'$.

We can now find the time on Al's clock (*t′*) in terms of the time on your clock (*t*) by applying the Pythagorean theorem ($a^2 + b^2 = c^2$, where *a* and *b* are side lengths and *c* is the hypotenuse length) with the side lengths in Figure 1:

$$(ct')^2 + (vt)^2 = (ct)^2$$

Expand the squares:

$$c^2 t'^2 + v^2 t^2 = c^2 t^2$$

Subtract $v^2 t^2$ from both sides:

$$c^2 t'^2 = c^2 t^2 - v^2 t^2 = (c^2 - v^2)t^2$$

Divide both sides by $c^2 t^2$:

$$\frac{t'^2}{t^2} = \frac{c^2 - v^2}{c^2}$$

Simplify:

$$\frac{t'^2}{t^2} = \frac{c^2}{c^2} - \frac{v^2}{c^2} = 1 - \left(\frac{v}{c}\right)^2$$

Take the square root of both sides:

$$\frac{t'}{t} = \sqrt{1 - \left(\frac{v}{c}\right)^2} \quad \text{or} \quad t' = t\sqrt{1 - \left(\frac{v}{c}\right)^2}$$

We have found the *time dilation formula*, which tells us the *ratio* of time in a moving reference frame to time in a reference frame at rest. This ratio is graphed against speed in **FIGURE 2**. Note that $t'/t = 1$ at speeds that are small compared to the speed of light, meaning that clocks in both reference frames tick at about the same rate. As *v* approaches *c*, the amount of time passing in the moving reference frame gets smaller and smaller compared to the time in the reference frame at rest.

EXAMPLE: Suppose Al is moving past you at a speed of 0.9*c*. While 1 hour passes for you, how much time passes for Al?

SOLUTION:

Step 1 Understand: To use the time dilation formula, we must decide whose time is *t* and whose is *t′*. Because Al is moving past you, you expect to see his time running slowly, which means *less* than 1 hour should pass for Al while 1 hour passes for you. Notice that the square root in the time dilation formula always has a value less than 1 (because *v* is always less than *c*), which means that *t′* always ends up less than *t*. Therefore, we want *t′* to represent Al's time and *t* to represent yours.

Step 2 Solve: Al's speed of $v = 0.9c$ means that $v/c = 0.9$, so we use the time dilation formula with this value and your time $t = 1$ hour:

$$t' = t\sqrt{1 - \left(\frac{v}{c}\right)^2}$$
$$= (1 \text{ hr})\sqrt{1 - (0.9)^2}$$
$$= (1 \text{ hr})\sqrt{1 - 0.81}$$
$$= (1 \text{ hr})\sqrt{0.19} \approx 0.44 \text{ hr}$$

Step 3 Explain: We have found that only 0.44 hour, or about 26 minutes, passes for Al while 1 hour passes for you. In other words, you will see his time running less than half as fast as yours.

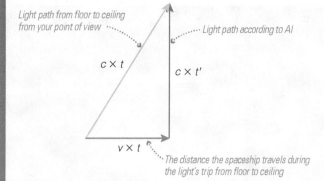

Light path from floor to ceiling from your point of view

Light path according to Al

$c \times t$

$c \times t'$

$v \times t$

The distance the spaceship travels during the light's trip from floor to ceiling

FIGURE 1 The setup for finding the time dilation formula.

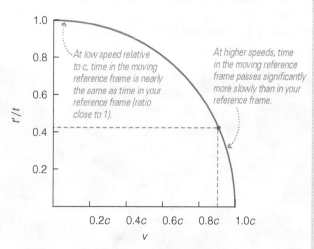

At low speed relative to c, time in the moving reference frame is nearly the same as time in your reference frame (ratio close to 1).

At higher speeds, time in the moving reference frame passes significantly more slowly than in your reference frame.

FIGURE 2 The time dilation factor graphed against speed.

red flash, which means you'll see him illuminated first by green light and then by red light. So far, nothing should be surprising: You see the two flashes simultaneously because you are stationary, but the green flash reaches Al before the red flash because of his forward motion. But let's think about what happens from Al's point of view, in which he is the one who is stationary and you are the one who is moving.

Remember that motion cannot affect the order of events that occur in the same place. Therefore, no one can argue with the fact that you saw the green and red flashes at the same time, and no one can disagree with the fact that the green light reached Al before the red light. However, because Al considers himself to be stationary in the center of his spaceship, the only way that the green light can reach him before the red light is if *the green flash occurred first*. In other words, he'll see the situation as shown in FIGURE S2.12b: He'll say that the green flash occurred before the red flash, and that the reason they both reached you at the same time was because your motion was moving you in the direction of the red flash.

Let's summarize the situation: You both agree on the indisputable reality of what each of you saw—that is, you saw the two flashes at the same time, while Al saw the green flash before the red flash. However, you say this reality occurs because the flashes really did occur at the same time and Al was moving toward the green flash, while Al says it occurs because the green flash really occurred first while you were moving away from it. Who is right?

All motion is relative, so both of you are equally correct. In other words, the flashes that are simultaneous in your reference frame occur at different times in Al's reference frame. That is what we mean when we say that the order or simultaneity of events depends on your frame of reference.

Effects of Motion on Length and Mass

The fact that time is different in different reference frames implies that lengths (or distances) and masses are also affected by motion, although the reasons are a bit subtler. The following two thought experiments use the idea of time dilation to help us understand the effects on length and mass.

Thought Experiment 9 Al is back in his original spaceship, coming toward you at high speed. As usual, both you and he agree on your *relative* speed. You disagree only about who is stationary and who is moving. Now imagine that Al tries to measure the length of your spaceship as he passes by you. He can do this by measuring the time it takes him to pass from one end of your spaceship to the other; recall that *length = speed × time*.

In your reference frame, you say that Al is moving by you and therefore you see Al's time running slowly. Because you agree on his relative speed but his clocks record less time than yours as he passes from one end of your spaceship to the other, he must measure the length of your spaceship to be *shorter* than you measure it to be. Now, remember that your viewpoint and Al's viewpoint are equally valid. The fact that the laws of nature are the same for everyone means that if he measures your spaceship to be shorter than it is at rest in your reference frame, you must also measure his to be shorter than it would be at rest, an effect called **length contraction**.

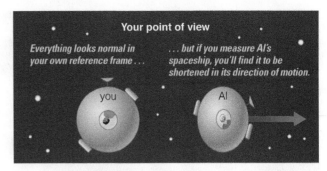

FIGURE S2.13 People and objects moving relative to you are contracted in their direction of motion. The diagram shows only your point of view, but Al's view would be equivalent: He would see himself at "normal" size and you contracted in your direction of motion.

FIGURE S2.13 shows that lengths are affected only in the direction of motion. His spaceship is shorter from your point of view, but its height and depth are unaffected. Generalizing, we reach the following conclusion.

From your point of view, the lengths of objects moving by you (or the distances between objects moving by you) are shorter in their direction of motion than they would be if the objects were at rest. The faster the objects are moving, the shorter the lengths.

Thought Experiment 10 To see how motion affects mass, imagine that Al has an identical twin brother with an identical spaceship, and suppose that his brother is at rest in your reference frame while Al is moving by you at high speed. At the instant Al passes by, you give both Al and his brother identical pushes (FIGURE S2.14). That is, you push them both with the same force for the same amount of time. By our old common sense, we'd expect both of them to accelerate by an identical amount, such as gaining 1 km/s of speed relative to you. But we must instead apply our new common sense, which tells us something different.

Remember that, because Al is moving relative to you and his brother, you'll see Al's time running more slowly than yours and his brother's—which means that he experiences the force of your push for a *shorter* time than does his brother. For example, if you and Al's brother measure the duration of the push to be 1 microsecond, Al's clock will show the duration to be less than 1 microsecond. Moreover, because Al feels the force of your push for a shorter time, the push must have a *smaller* effect on Al's velocity than it has on his brother's velocity. In other words, you'll find that your push has less effect on Al than on his brother, despite the fact that you gave them identical pushes. According to Newton's laws of motion [**Section 4.2**], the same push can have a smaller effect on Al's velocity only if his mass is *greater* than his brother's mass. This effect is sometimes called **mass increase***:

---

*Newton's second law can be stated either as "force = mass × acceleration" or as "force = rate of change in momentum." (Recall that momentum = mass × velocity.) For more advanced work, most physicists prefer the second form, and they therefore prefer to think of the effect in relativity as *momentum increase* rather than mass increase. The two viewpoints are equivalent for the level of discussion in this book.

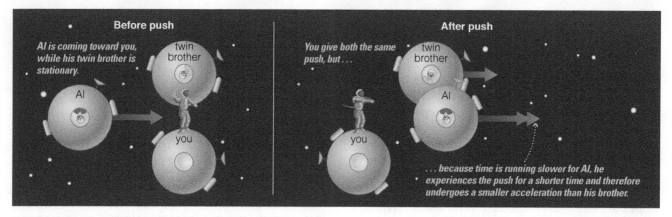

FIGURE S2.14 Thought Experiment 10.

From your point of view, objects moving by you have greater mass than they have at rest. The faster an object is moving, the greater the increase in its mass.

Mass increase provides another way of understanding why no material object can reach the speed of light. The faster an object is moving relative to you, the greater the mass you'll find it to have. Therefore, at higher and higher speeds, the same force will have less and less effect on an object's velocity. As the object's speed approaches the speed of light, you will find its mass to be heading toward infinity. No force can accelerate an infinite mass, so the object can never gain that last little bit of speed needed to push it to the speed of light.

Velocity Addition We have just one more important effect to discuss: As the next thought experiment shows, you and Al will disagree about the speed of a material object moving relative to both of you. The only speed you will agree on is the speed of light.

Thought Experiment 11 Al is moving toward you at $0.9c$ (FIGURE S2.15). Your friend Jackie jumps into her spaceship and starts heading in Al's direction at $0.8c$ (from your point of view). How fast will Al see her approaching him?

By our old common sense, Al should see Jackie coming toward him at $0.9c + 0.8c = 1.7c$. We know this answer is wrong, however, because $1.7c$ is faster than the speed of light. Al must see Jackie coming toward him at a speed less than c, but she will be coming faster than the speed of $0.9c$ at which Al sees you coming. That is, Al will conclude that Jackie's speed is somewhere between $0.9c$ and c. (In this case, the speed turns out to be $0.988c$; see Mathematical Insight S2.2.)

Do the effects predicted by relativity really occur?

The clear logic of our thought experiments has shown that all the major predictions of special relativity follow directly from the absoluteness of the speed of light and from the fact that the laws of nature are the same for everyone. However, logic alone is not good enough in science; our conclusions remain tentative until they pass observational or experimental tests. Does relativity pass the test?

The Absoluteness of the Speed of Light The first thing we might wish to test is the surprising premise of relativity: the absoluteness of the speed of light. In principle, we can test this premise by measuring the speed of light coming from many different objects and going in many different directions and verifying that the speed is always the same.

The speed of light was first measured in the late 17th century, but experimental evidence for the *absoluteness* of the speed of light did not come until 1887, when A. A. Michelson and E. W. Morley performed their now-famous *Michelson-Morley experiment*. This experiment showed that the speed of light is not affected by Earth's motion around the Sun. Countless subsequent experiments have verified and extended the results of the Michelson-Morley experiment. The speed of light coming from opposite sides of the rotating Sun and from

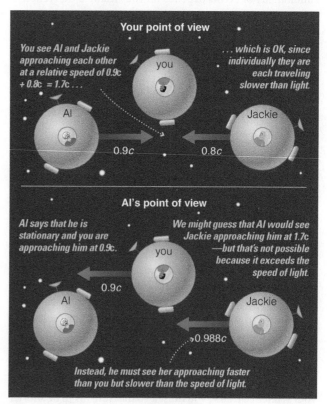

FIGURE S2.15 Thought Experiment 11.

the orbiting stars in binary systems has also been measured, with the same result: The speed of light is always the same.

Experimental Tests of Special Relativity Although *we* cannot yet travel at speeds at which the effects of relativity should be obvious, tiny subatomic particles can reach such speeds, thereby allowing us to test the precise predictions of the formulas of special relativity.

In machines called *particle accelerators,* physicists accelerate subatomic particles to speeds near the speed of light and study what happens when the particles collide. The colliding particles have a great deal of kinetic energy, and the collisions convert some of this kinetic energy into mass-energy that emerges as a shower of newly produced particles. Many of these particles have very short lifetimes, at the end of which they decay (change) into other particles. For example, a particle called the π^+ ("pi plus") meson has a lifetime of about 18 nanoseconds (billionths of a second) when produced at rest. But π^+ mesons produced at speeds close to the speed of light in particle accelerators last much longer than 18 nanoseconds—and the amount longer is always precisely the amount predicted by the time dilation formula.

MATHEMATICAL INSIGHT S2.2
Formulas of Special Relativity

We found a formula for time dilation in Mathematical Insight S2.1. Although we will not go through the derivations, it is possible to find similar formulas for length contraction and mass increase. The three formulas are

$$\text{time}_{\text{(moving frame)}} = \text{time}_{\text{(rest frame)}} \times \sqrt{1 - \left(\frac{v}{c}\right)^2}$$

$$\text{length}_{\text{(moving frame)}} = (\text{rest length}) \times \sqrt{1 - \left(\frac{v}{c}\right)^2}$$

$$\text{moving mass} = \frac{(\text{rest mass})}{\sqrt{1 - \left(\frac{v}{c}\right)^2}}$$

There's also a simple formula for velocity addition. Suppose you see Al moving at speed v_1 and Al sees a second object moving relative to him at speed v_2. By our old common sense, you would see the second object moving at speed $v_1 + v_2$. However, the speed you actually see is

$$\text{speed of second object} = \frac{v_1 + v_2}{1 + \left(\frac{v_1}{c} \times \frac{v_2}{c}\right)}$$

EXAMPLE 1: Al is moving by you at $0.99c$ in a spaceship that is 100 meters long at rest. How long is it as it moves by you?

SOLUTION:

Step 1 Understand: This is a length contraction problem. Because you see Al moving, his spaceship's length should be *shorter* than its rest length of 100 meters.

Step 2 Solve: We use the length contraction formula with Al's speed of $0.99c$, or $v/c = 0.99$, and rest length = 100 m:

$$\text{length}_{\text{(moving frame)}} = (\text{rest length}) \times \sqrt{1 - \left(\frac{v}{c}\right)^2}$$
$$= (100 \text{ m}) \times \sqrt{1 - (0.99)^2} = 14 \text{ m}$$

Step 3 Explain: Al's spaceship is 100 meters long at rest, but only 14 meters long when he is moving by you at 99% of the speed of light.

EXAMPLE 2: A "super fly" has a rest mass of 1 gram but is capable of flying at $0.9999c$. What is its mass at that speed?

SOLUTION:

Step 1 Understand: This time we are asked about mass, so we need the mass increase formula and expect the moving mass to be greater than the rest mass.

Step 2 Solve: We use the mass increase formula with the fly's rest mass = 1 g and $v/c = 0.9999$:

$$\text{moving mass} = \frac{(\text{rest mass})}{\sqrt{1 - \left(\frac{v}{c}\right)^2}}$$
$$= \frac{1 \text{ g}}{\sqrt{1 - (0.9999)^2}} = 70.7 \text{ g}$$

Step 3 Explain: At a speed of $0.9999c$, or 99.99% of the speed of light, the mass of a fly that is 1 gram at rest becomes 70.7 grams, or more than 70 times its rest mass.

EXAMPLE 3: Al is moving toward you at $0.9c$. Your friend Jackie jumps into her spaceship and, from your point of view, goes in Al's direction at $0.8c$ (see Figure S2.15). How fast will Al see Jackie approaching?

SOLUTION:

Step 1 Understand: According to Al, your speed is $v_1 = 0.9c$. Jackie's speed *relative to you* is $v_2 = 0.8c$ in the same direction. We therefore need the velocity addition formula to find Jackie's speed relative to Al.

Step 2 Solve: We substitute the given values $v_1 = 0.9c$ and $v_2 = 0.8c$ into the velocity addition formula:

$$\text{Jackie's speed}_{\text{(relative to Al)}} = \frac{v_1 + v_2}{1 + \left(\frac{v_1}{c} \times \frac{v_2}{c}\right)}$$
$$= \frac{0.9c + 0.8c}{1 + (0.9 \times 0.8)}$$
$$= \frac{1.7c}{1.72} = 0.988c$$

Step 3 Explain: Al sees Jackie moving toward him at $0.988c$, or almost 99% of the speed of light. Notice that, as we expect, Jackie's speed relative to Al is faster than yours but slower than the speed of light.

The same experiments allow the mass increase formula to be checked as well. The amount of energy released when high-speed particles collide depends on the particle masses and speeds. Just as relativity predicts, these masses are greater at high speed than they are at low speed—again by amounts that can be precisely predicted by Einstein's formulas.

Particle accelerators even offer experimental evidence that nothing can reach the speed of light. It is relatively easy to get particles traveling at 99% of the speed of light in particle accelerators. However, no matter how much more energy is put into the accelerators, the particle speeds get only fractionally closer to the speed of light. Some particles have been accelerated to speeds within 0.00001% of the speed of light, but none have ever reached the speed of light.

Although the effects of relativity are obvious only at very high speeds, modern techniques of measuring time are so precise that effects can be measured even at ordinary speeds. For example, experiments conducted in 2010 at the National Institute of Standards and Technology verified the predicted amount of time dilation at speeds of less than 10 meters per second (36 kilometers per hour). All in all, special relativity is one of the best-tested theories in physics, and it has passed every experimental test to date with flying colors.

A Great Conspiracy? Perhaps you're thinking, "I still don't believe it." After all, how can you know that the scientists who report the experimental evidence are telling the truth? Perhaps physicists are making up the whole thing as

part of a great conspiracy designed to confuse everyone else so that they can take over the world!

What you need is evidence that you can see for yourself. So . . . how about nuclear energy? Einstein's famous formula, $E = mc^2$, which explains the energy released in nuclear reactions, is a direct consequence of the special theory of relativity—and one that you can derive for yourself with a bit of algebra (Mathematical Insight S2.3). Every time you see film of an atomic bomb, or use electrical power from a nuclear power plant, or feel the energy of sunlight that the Sun generated through nuclear fusion, you are really experiencing direct experimental evidence of relativity.

Another test you can do yourself is to look through a telescope at a binary star system. If the speed of light were *not* absolute, the speed at which light from each star comes toward Earth would depend on its velocity toward us in the binary orbit (**FIGURE S2.16**). Imagine, for example, that one star is currently moving directly away from us in its orbit. If we added and subtracted speeds according to our old common sense, light from the star at this point would approach us at speed $c - v$. Some time later, when the same star is moving toward us in its orbit, its light would approach us at speed $c + v$. This light would therefore tend to catch up with the light that the star emitted from the other side of its orbit. If the orbital speed and distance were just right, we might see the same star on both sides of the orbit at once! More generally, because the light from each star would come toward us at a different speed from each point in its orbit, we would see each star in multiple positions in its orbit simultaneously, making each star appear as a short line of light rather than as a point—*if* the speed of light were not

---

SPECIAL TOPIC

Measuring the Speed of Light

It is difficult to measure the speed of light, because light travels so fast. If you stand a short distance from a mirror and turn on a light, the reflection seems to appear instantaneously. Such observations led Aristotle (384–322 B.C.) to conclude that light travels at infinite speed, a view that many scientists still held as recently as the late 17th century.

One way to make the measurement easier is to place a mirror at increasingly greater distances. If the speed of light truly were infinite, the reflection would always appear instantaneously. However, if it takes time for the light to travel to and from the mirror, you should eventually find a delay between the time you turn on the light and the time you see the reflection. Galileo tried a version of this experiment using the distance between two tall hills, but he was unable to detect any delay (instead of using a mirror, he stationed an assistant on the distant hill to signal back when he saw the light). He concluded that the speed of light, if not infinite, was too fast to be measured between hills on Earth with the technology of his day.

Galileo's idea was extended to space in 1675 by the Danish astronomer Olaus Roemer. Using the four largest moons of Jupiter as his "mirrors," Roemer successfully measured a delay in the time it took for light from the Sun to be reflected and thereby made the first measurement of the speed of light. His technique worked because, by that time, the orbital periods of Jupiter's large moons were well

known, so it was possible to predict the precise moments at which Jupiter would eclipse each of its moons. Roemer learned that the eclipses occurred earlier than expected when Earth was closer to Jupiter and later than expected when Earth was farther from Jupiter. He realized that the eclipses actually were occurring at the predicted times, but that the light was taking longer to reach us when Earth was farther from Jupiter. His observations proved that the speed of light is finite and allowed him to estimate its precise value. Using estimates of the Sun-Earth and Sun-Jupiter distances that were available in 1675, Roemer calculated the speed of light to be 227,000 km/s. Redoing his calculations using the presently known values of these distances yields the correct value of 300,000 km/s.

As technology advanced, it became possible to measure light travel time between mirrors at much closer distances. In 1849 and 1850, the French physicists Hippolyte Fizeau and Léon Foucault (also famous for the Foucault pendulum) performed a series of experiments using rotating mirrors to measure the speed of light much more precisely. Modern devices for measuring the speed of light take advantage of the wave properties of light, particularly the fact that light waves can interfere with one another. Such devices, called *interferometers*, were refined by A. A. Michelson and used in the Michelson-Morley experiment. Details of how this experiment worked can be found in many physics texts.

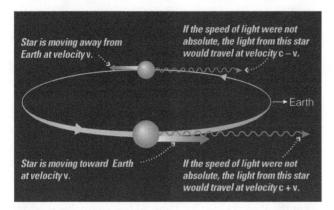

FIGURE S2.16 If the speed of light were *not* absolute, the speed at which light from each star in a binary system comes toward Earth would depend on its velocity toward us in the binary orbit.

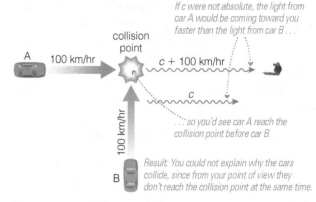

FIGURE S2.17 If the speed of light were *not* absolute, the light from a car coming toward you would approach you faster than the light from a car going across your line of sight.

absolute. Therefore, the fact that we always see distinct stars in binary systems demonstrates that the speed of light *is* absolute.*

Finally, you can explore the paradoxes that would occur if the speed of light were not absolute. For example, imagine

---

*This conclusion would not follow if light waves were carried by a medium in the same way that sound waves are carried by air. Scientists in the 19th century believed that such a medium, which they called the *ether*, permeated all of space. The Michelson-Morley experiment ruled out the existence of such a medium, so we are left with the conclusion that *c* is absolute.

that two cars, both traveling at about 100 km/hr, collide at an intersection (FIGURE S2.17). You witness the collision from far down one street. If the speed of light were *not* absolute, the light from the car that was coming toward you would have a speed of $c + 100$ km/hr, while the light from the other car would approach you at a speed of only c. You therefore would see the car coming toward you reach the intersection slightly *before* the other car and thus would see events unfold differently than the passengers in the car or eyewitnesses in other

---

MATHEMATICAL INSIGHT S2.3

Deriving $E = mc^2$

We can derive the formula $E = mc^2$ from the mass increase formula, which we previously wrote as

$$\text{moving mass} = \frac{(\text{rest mass})}{\sqrt{1 - \left(\dfrac{v}{c}\right)^2}}$$

Let's call the moving mass m and the rest mass m_0, and use the fact that dividing by a square root is the same as raising to the $-\frac{1}{2}$ power:

$$\text{mass increase formula:} \quad m = m_0\left(1 - \frac{v^2}{c^2}\right)^{-\frac{1}{2}}$$

To continue, we need the following mathematical approximation, which you can verify by using a calculator to check that it holds for small values of x (such as $x = 0.05$ or $x = 0.001$):

$$(1 + x)^{-\frac{1}{2}} \approx 1 - \frac{1}{2}x \quad (\text{for } x \text{ small compared to 1})$$

Now, look again at the mass increase formula. The term in parentheses on the right side has the form $(1 + x)^{-\frac{1}{2}}$, as long as we identify x as $-v^2/c^2$. For speeds that are small compared to the speed of light, we can therefore rewrite this term by substituting $x = -v^2/c^2$ into the above approximation:

$$\left(1 + \left[-\frac{v^2}{c^2}\right]\right)^{-\frac{1}{2}} \approx 1 - \frac{1}{2}\left(-\frac{v^2}{c^2}\right)$$

Simplifying, this becomes

$$\left(1 - \frac{v^2}{c^2}\right)^{-\frac{1}{2}} \approx 1 + \frac{1}{2}\frac{v^2}{c^2}$$

We can use this result to rewrite the mass increase formula by replacing the term that appears next to m_0 with the approximation:

$$m \approx m_0\left(1 + \frac{1}{2}\frac{v^2}{c^2}\right)$$

We now expand the right side by multiplying through by m_0:

$$m \approx m_0 + \frac{1}{2}\frac{m_0 v^2}{c^2}$$

Finally, we multiply both sides by c^2, so the formula becomes

$$mc^2 \approx m_0 c^2 + \frac{1}{2}m_0 v^2$$

You may recognize the last term on the right as the *kinetic energy* [**Section 4.3**] of an object with mass m_0. Because the other two terms also have units of mass multiplied by speed squared, they also must represent some kind of energy. Einstein recognized that the term on the left represents the *total* energy of a moving object. He then noticed that, even if the speed is *zero* ($v = 0$) so that there is *no* kinetic energy, the equation states that the total energy is $m_0 c^2$. That is, a nonmoving object still contains energy by virtue of its mass in an amount equal to its rest mass times the speed of light squared. This is the famous formula $E = mc^2$, which we now see as a part of Einstein's theory of relativity.

locations. On Earth, this difference would be scarcely noticeable, because 100 km/hr is only about one-millionth the speed of light. However, imagine that you had a super telescope and watched such a collision on a planet located 1 million light-years from Earth: Because the light from the first car (the one coming toward you) is coming at a speed one-millionth of the speed of light faster than the light from the second car, over a distance of 1 million light-years it would end up reaching you a full *year* ahead of the light from the second car. In other words, you would see the first car reach the intersection a year before the second car. This poses a paradox: From the viewpoint of the passengers in the cars, they have collided, yet you saw one car reach the collision point long before the other car had even started its journey! If we live in a universe in which images show what really does happen, then the only way to avoid the paradox is to assume that we should not have added the car's speed to the speed of light; that is, we must assume that the speed of light is absolute.

THINK ABOUT IT

The preceding paradox presents us with two possibilities. If the speed of light is *not* absolute, different people can witness the same events in very different ways. If the speed of light *is* absolute, measurements of time and space are relative. Einstein preferred the latter. Do you? Explain.

Of course, like any scientific theory, the theory of relativity can never be *proved* beyond all doubt. However, it is supported by a tremendous body of evidence, some of which you can see for yourself. This evidence is real and cannot be made to disappear. If anyone ever comes up with an alternative theory, the new theory will have to explain the many experimental results that seem to support relativity so well.

S2.4 TOWARD A NEW COMMON SENSE

We've used thought experiments to show that our old common sense doesn't work, and we've discussed how actual experiments verify the ideas of our thought experiments. But we haven't yet figured out what new common sense should replace the old. Fortunately, while it may take you many years to become completely comfortable with the ideas of relativity, it's relatively easy to see what you need to do to make yourself comfortable.

How can we make sense of relativity?

Perhaps surprisingly, another thought experiment that may at first make everything seem even more bizarre will help us understand what is really going on, and thereby lead us toward a new common sense.

Thought Experiment 12 Suppose Al is moving by you at a speed close to the speed of light. From our earlier thought experiments, we know that you'll measure his time as running slowly, his length as having contracted, and his mass as having increased. But what would *he* say?

From Al's point of view, he's not going anywhere—*you* are moving by him at high speed. Because the laws of nature are the same for everyone, he must reach exactly the same conclusions from his point of view that you reach from your point of view. That is, he'll say that *your* time is running slowly, *your* length has contracted, and *your* mass has increased!

Now we have what seems to be a serious argument on our hands. Imagine that you are looking into Al's spaceship with a super telescope. You can clearly see that his time is running slowly because everything he does is in slow motion. You send him a radio message saying, "Hi, Al! Why are you doing everything in slow motion?" Because the radio message travels at the absolute speed of light, Al has no trouble receiving your message,* and he responds with his own radio message back to you.

If you listen to his response, you'll hear it in slow motion—"Hheeeelllllloooo tthhheeerrr"—verifying that his time is running slowly. However, if you record the entire message and use your computer to speed up his voice so that it sounds normal, you'll hear Al say, "I'm not moving in slow motion—*you are!*"

You can argue back and forth all you want, but it will get you nowhere. Then you come up with a brilliant idea. You hook up a video camera to your telescope and record a movie showing that Al's clock is moving more slowly than yours. You put your movie into a very fast rocket and shoot it off toward him. You figure that when the movie arrives and he watches it, he'll have visual proof that you are right and that he really is moving in slow motion.

Unfortunately, before you can declare victory in the argument, you learn that Al had the same brilliant idea: A rocket arrives with a movie that he made. As you watch, you see what appears to be clear proof that Al is right—his movie shows that *you* are in slow motion! Apparently, Al really is seeing your time run slowly, just as you are seeing his time run slowly.

How can this be? Think back to our earlier discussion of up and down, and imagine an American child and an Australian child talking by phone. The Australian says, "Isn't the Moon beautiful up in the sky right now?" The American replies, "What are you talking about? The Moon isn't up right now!" According to childhood common sense about up and down, the two children appear to be contradicting each other and could argue endlessly. However, once they realize that up and down are measured *relative* to the center of the Earth, they realize that the argument stems only from incorrect definitions of *up* and *down* (FIGURE S2.18). They are both talking about the same Moon in the same place, and their differing claims arose only from the relative nature of "up" and "down."

In much the same way, the argument between you and Al arises because you are using the old common sense in which we think of space and time as absolutes and expect the speed

---

*Of course, because of the Doppler effect [**Section 5.4**], he'll find that the radio waves are blueshifted from the frequency at which you send them as you come toward him, and redshifted as you move away from him. You'll find the same for his radio broadcasts. But as long as you both tune your radios to the correct Doppler-shifted frequencies, you'll have no problem hearing the broadcast messages.

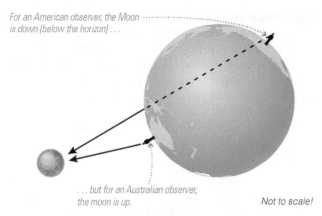

For an American observer, the Moon is down (below the horizon) . . .

. . . but for an Australian observer, the moon is up.

Not to scale!

FIGURE S2.18 The Moon is up for the Australian observer but down for the American observer.

of light to be relative. The theory of relativity tells us that we have it backward. The speed of light is the absolute, and time and space are relative.

By the new common sense, the fact that you and Al disagree about whose time is running slowly is no more surprising than the fact that the two children disagree about whether the Moon is up or down. The disagreement is meaningless because it relies on inadequate definitions of time and space. *Results are what count*, and every experiment that you perform will agree with every experiment that Al performs. You are both experiencing the same laws of nature, albeit in ways different from those our old common sense would have suggested.

How does special relativity offer us a ticket to the stars?

One consequence of accepting the special theory of relativity is the fact that we'll never be able to travel to distant stars at a speed faster than the speed of light. However, while this fact might at first make distant stars seem forever out of reach, time dilation and length contraction actually offer a "ticket to the stars"—if we can ever build spaceships capable of traveling at speeds close to the speed of light.

Suppose you take a trip to the star Vega, about 25 light-years away, in a spaceship that travels at a speed very close to the speed of light—say, at $0.999c$. From the point of view of people on Earth, the trip to Vega must take you just over 25 years, since you are traveling at nearly the speed of light for a distance of 25 light-years. The return trip will take another 25 years. If you leave in the year 2050, you will arrive at Vega in the year 2075 and return to Earth in 2100.

However, from your point of view on the spaceship, you can legitimately claim that you and your spaceship never go anywhere; it is Earth and Vega that make the trip. That is, from your point of view, you remain stationary while Earth rushes away from you and Vega rushes toward you at $0.999c$. You'll therefore find the distance from Earth to Vega contracted from its rest length of 25 light-years; with the length contraction formula, the contracted distance turns out to be just over 1 light-year.* Therefore, because Vega is coming toward you at $0.999c$ and has only 1 light-year to travel to reach you from your point of view, you'll be at Vega in only about 1 year. Your return trip to Earth will also take about 1 year, so the round-trip time is only about 2 years from your point of view (**FIGURE S2.19**). If you leave at age 50, you'll return as a 52-year-old.

Although it sounds like a contradiction by our old common sense, both points of view are correct. If you leave in 2050 at age 50, you'll return to Earth at age 52—but in the year 2100. That is, while you will have aged only 2 years, all your surviving friends and family will be 50 years older than when you left.

You could make even longer trips within your lifetime with a sufficiently fast spaceship. For example, the Andromeda Galaxy is about 2.5 million light-years away, so the round

---

*Given that you see the Earth-Vega distance contracted, shouldn't you also claim that it is *Earth's* time running slowly, rather than yours? This question underlies the so-called *twin paradox*, in which you make the trip while your twin sister stays home on Earth (see Chapter S3). The resolution comes from the fact that, because you must turn around at Vega, you effectively change reference frames relative to Earth at least once during your trip. A careful analysis of the changing reference frames is beyond the scope of this book, but it turns out that you do indeed measure less total time than your stay-at-home twin.

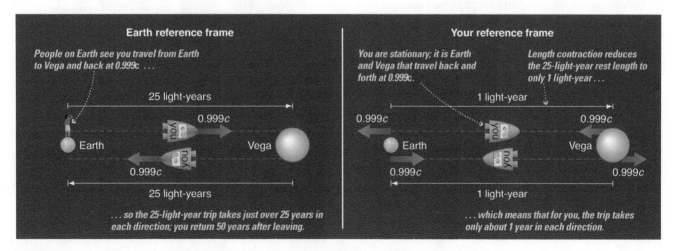

Earth reference frame

People on Earth see you travel from Earth to Vega and back at 0.999c . . .

25 light-years

0.999c

Earth

Vega

0.999c

25 light-years

. . . so the 25-light-year trip takes just over 25 years in each direction; you return 50 years after leaving.

Your reference frame

You are stationary; it is Earth and Vega that travel back and forth at 0.999c.

Length contraction reduces the 25-light-year rest length to only 1 light-year . . .

1 light-year

0.999c

0.999c

Earth

Vega

0.999c

0.999c

1 light-year

. . . which means that for you, the trip takes only about 1 year in each direction.

FIGURE S2.19 A person who travels round-trip at high speed to a distant star will age less than people back home on Earth.

trip to any star in the Andromeda Galaxy would take at least 5 million years from the point of view of observers on Earth. However, if you could travel at a speed within 50 parts in 1 trillion of the speed of light (that is, $c - 5 \times 10^{-11}c$), the trip would take only about 50 years from your point of view. You could leave Earth at age 30 and return at age 80—but you would return to an Earth on which your friends, your family, and everything you knew had been gone for 5 million years.

Thus, in terms of time, relativity offers only a one-way ticket to the stars. You can go a long distance and return to the *place* that you left, but you cannot return to the epoch from which you left.

The Big Picture

Putting Chapter S2 into Context

In this chapter, we have studied Einstein's special theory of relativity, learning that space and time are intertwined in remarkable ways that are quite different from what we might expect from everyday experience. As you look back on our new viewpoint about space and time, keep in mind the following "big picture" ideas:

- The ideas of relativity derive from two simple ideas: The laws of nature are the same for everyone, and the speed of light is absolute. The thought experiments in this chapter showed the consequences of these facts.

- Thought experiments are useful, but the ultimate judge of any theory is observation and experiment. The theory of relativity has been extensively tested and verified.

- Although the ideas of relativity may sound strange at first, you can understand them easily and logically if you allow yourself to develop a "new common sense" that incorporates them.

- Space and time are properties of the universe itself, and the new understanding of them gained through the theory of relativity will enable you to better appreciate how the universe works.

SUMMARY OF KEY CONCEPTS

S2.1 EINSTEIN'S REVOLUTION

- **What are the major ideas of special relativity?** Special relativity tells us that different observers can measure time, distance, and mass differently, even though everyone always agrees on the speed of light. It also tells us that no material object can reach or exceed the speed of light (in a vacuum) and that $E = mc^2$.

- **What is relative about relativity?** The theory of relativity  is based on the idea that all *motion* is relative. That is, there is no correct answer to the question of who or what is really moving in the universe, so motion can be described only for one object relative to another.

- **What is absolute about relativity?** All the predictions of the special theory of relativity follow from two assumptions, both of which have been experimentally verified: (1) The laws of nature are the same for everyone; and (2) the speed of light is the same for everyone.

S2.2 RELATIVE MOTION

- **What's surprising about the absoluteness of the speed of light?** In our everyday lives, we expect velocities to add simply;  for example, an observer on the ground should see a ball in an airplane traveling at the airplane's speed plus the ball's speed. However, this is not true for light, which everyone always measures as traveling at the same speed.

- **Why can't we reach the speed of light?** Light always travels at the same speed, so your own light (the light that you

 emit or reflect) is always moving ahead of you at the speed of light. All other observers will also see your light moving at the speed of light—and because it is moving ahead of you, the observers will always conclude that you are moving slower than the speed of light.

S2.3 THE REALITY OF SPACE AND TIME

- **How does relativity affect our view of time and space?** If you observe an object moving by you at high speed,  you'll find that its time is running more slowly than yours, its length is shorter than its length when at rest, and its mass is greater than its mass when at rest. Moreover, observers in different reference frames may disagree about whether two events are simultaneous and about the speeds of different objects.

- **Do the effects predicted by relativity really occur?** Experiments with light confirm that its speed is always the same. Experiments with subatomic particles in particle accelerators confirm the predictions of time dilation and mass increase at speeds close to the speed of light, and time dilation has also been verified at relatively low speeds. Nuclear power plants and nuclear bombs release energy in accordance with the formula $E = mc^2$, which is also a prediction of special relativity.

S2.4 TOWARD A NEW COMMON SENSE

- **How can we make sense of relativity?** A person moving by you at high speed will see exactly the same effects on you as

you see on her; for example, she'll see your time running slowly while you see her time running slowly. Although this might sound contradictory, it simply tells us that time and space must be relative in much the same way that up and down are relative on Earth.

■ **How does special relativity offer us a ticket to the stars?** Although the theory tells us that journeys to the stars will always take many years from the point of view of Earth, it also tells us that the time for the passengers will be much shorter if they travel at speeds close enough to the speed of light. Thus, the passengers may be able to make very distant journeys within their lifetimes, even though their friends back on Earth will not be there to greet them when they return.

EXERCISES AND PROBLEMS

For instructor-assigned homework go to MasteringAstronomy®.

REVIEW QUESTIONS

Short-Answer Questions Based on the Reading

1. What is the *theory of relativity*? How does *special relativity* differ from *general relativity*?
2. List five major predictions of the special theory of relativity.
3. According to the theory of relativity, what are the two absolutes in the universe? Which one is more surprising, and why?
4. What is a *paradox*? How can a paradox lead us to a deeper understanding of an issue?
5. What do we mean by a *frame of reference*? What is a *free-float frame*?
6. Suppose you see a friend moving by you at some constant speed. Explain why your friend can equally well say that she is stationary and you are moving by her.
7. Construct your own variation on Thought Experiment 6 to prove that no material object can be observed to travel at or above the speed of light.
8. What is *time dilation*? Explain how and why your measurements of time will differ from those of someone moving by you.
9. Explain why observers in different reference frames will not necessarily agree about the order of two events that occur in different places.
10. What is *length contraction*? How will your measurements of the size of a spaceship moving by you differ from your measurements of the same spaceship when it is at rest in your reference frame?
11. What is *mass increase*? How does the mass of an object moving by you compare to its rest mass?
12. Construct your own variation on Thought Experiment 11 to show why velocities must add differently than we would expect according to our "old common sense."
13. Briefly describe experimental tests of special relativity.
14. Why do tests of $E = mc^2$ also test special relativity? Describe several tests of $E = mc^2$ that you can see for yourself.
15. If you watch a friend moving by you at a speed close to that of light, you'll say that her time is running slowly, her length is contracted, and her mass is greater than her rest mass. How will she perceive her own time, length, and mass? Why? How will she perceive *your* time, length, and mass?
16. Suppose you could take a trip to a distant star at a speed very close to the speed of light. How would relativity make it possible for you to make this trip in a reasonably short time? What would you find when you returned home?

TEST YOUR UNDERSTANDING

Does It Make Sense?

Decide whether the statement makes sense (or is clearly true) or does not make sense (or is clearly false). Explain clearly; not all of these have definitive answers, so your explanation is more important than your chosen answer.

17. Einstein proved that everything is relative.
18. An object moving by you at very high speed will appear to have a higher density than it has at rest.
19. You and a friend agree that you each popped a peanut into your mouth at precisely the same instant, but someone moving past you at high speed may observe that you ate your peanut first.
20. You and a friend agree that you each popped a peanut into your mouth at precisely the same instant, but someone moving past you at high speed may observe that you ate cashews rather than peanuts.
21. Relativity is "only a theory," and we have no way to know whether any of its predictions would really occur at speeds close to the speed of light.
22. The detonation of a nuclear bomb is a test of the special theory of relativity.
23. If you could travel away from Earth at a speed close to the speed of light, you would feel uncomfortably heavy because of your increased mass.
24. Future technology should allow us to build rockets capable of accelerating to speeds much faster than the speed of light.
25. If you see someone's time running slowly in a different reference frame, that person must see your time running fast.
26. If you had a sufficiently fast spaceship, you could leave today, make a round trip to a star 500 light-years away, and return home to Earth in the year 2100.

Quick Quiz

Choose the best answer to each of the following. Explain your reasoning with one or more complete sentences.

27. Which of the following is *not* relative in the special theory of relativity? (a) motion (b) time (c) the speed of light
28. Which of the following must be true of a person who shares the same *reference frame* as you? (a) The person must be sitting right next to you. (b) The person must be the same size as you. (c) The person must not be moving relative to you.
29. Which of the following best describes why your rocket could never reach the speed of light? (a) The absoluteness of the speed of light means you could never keep up with the light coming from you and your rocket. (b) Our technology has not advanced enough to make faster-than-light travel possible. (c) A rocket that could reach the speed of light would have to be bigger than the entire Earth.
30. Carla is traveling past you at a speed close to the speed of light. According to *you*, how much time passes for Carla while 1 minute passes for you? (a) 1 minute (b) less than 1 minute (c) more than 1 minute
31. Carla is traveling past you at a speed close to the speed of light. According to *her*, how much time passes for you while 1 minute passes for her? (a) 1 minute (b) less than 1 minute (c) more than 1 minute

32. A subatomic particle that normally decays in 1 microsecond is created in a particle accelerator and is traveling at close to the speed of light. If you measure its lifetime in that case, you'll find that it is (a) less than 1 microsecond. (b) more than 1 microsecond. (c) 1 microsecond.

33. What does the famous formula $E = mc^2$ have to do with special relativity? (a) Nothing; it comes from a different theory. (b) It is one of the two starting assumptions of special relativity. (c) It is a direct consequence of the theory.

34. What provides the strongest evidence that everyone always measures the same speed of light? (a) precise measurements of the speed of light under different circumstances (b) thought experiments showing that we would encounter paradoxes if it were not true (c) the fact that Einstein said so and he was very smart

35. If you observe people moving by you at very high speed, you will say that their time runs slowly, their lengths are contracted in the direction of motion, and their masses are increased from their rest masses. What will they say about you? (a) Your time runs slowly, your length is contracted in the direction of motion, and your mass is increased from your rest mass. (b) Your time runs fast, your length is expanded in the direction of motion, and your mass is decreased from your rest mass. (c) Your time runs fast, but your length and mass are unaffected.

36. Suppose you had a spaceship so fast that you could make a round-trip journey of 1 million light-years (in Earth's reference frame) in just 50 years of ship time. If you left in the year 2030, you would return to Earth (a) in the year 2080. (b) in the year 2130. (c) a million years from now.

PROCESS OF SCIENCE

Examining How Science Works

37. *A Paradigm Shift.* Chapter 3 introduced the idea of a paradigm shift, in which general patterns of scientific thought undergo a major or surprising change. How did the development of relativity theory represent such a shift? Did it mean throwing out old ideas or only modifying them? Defend your opinion.

38. *Thought Experiments.* Science demands that hypotheses be tested by real experiments or observations, yet Einstein developed his theory of relativity largely through the use of thought experiments. How, then, did relativity still come to be accepted as a scientific theory? Explain.

GROUP WORK EXERCISE

39. *Breaking the Light Barrier.* People long said that no one would travel faster than the speed of sound, but that barrier was broken. Is it possible that we'll someday find a way to travel faster than the speed of light? Take a position and argue for or against this possibility. Before you begin, assign the following roles to the people in your group: *Scribe* (takes notes on the group's activities), *Proposer* (proposes explanations to the group), *Skeptic* (points out weaknesses in proposed explanations), and *Moderator* (leads group discussion and makes sure the group works as a team).

INVESTIGATE FURTHER

In-Depth Questions to Increase Your Understanding

Short-Answer/Essay Questions

40. *Stationary Bike.* Suppose you are riding on a stationary bike and the speedometer says you are going 30 km/hr. What does this number mean? What does it tell you about the idea of relative motion?

41. *Walking Trip.* Suppose you go for a walk down the street. In your own reference frame, you are going quite slowly, probably just a few kilometers per hour. About how fast would you appear to be going according to an astronaut on the Moon? Explain.

42. *Relative Motion Practice I.* In all the following, assume that you and your friends are in free-float reference frames.
   a. Bob is coming toward you at a speed of 75 km/hr. You throw a baseball in his direction at 75 km/hr. What does he see the ball doing? **b.** Marie is traveling away from you at a speed of 120 km/hr. She throws a baseball at 100 km/hr (according to her) in your direction. What do you see the ball doing? **c.** José is traveling away from you at 99% of the speed of light when he turns on a flashlight and points it in your direction. How fast will the beam of light be going when it reaches you?

43. *Relative Motion Practice II.* In all the following, assume that you and your friends are in free-float reference frames.
   a. Carol is going away from you at 75 km/hr, and Sam is going away from you in the opposite direction at 90 km/hr. According to Carol, how fast is Sam going? **b.** Consider again the situation in part a. Suppose you throw a baseball in Sam's direction at a speed of 120 km/hr. What does Sam see the ball doing? What does Carol see the ball doing? **c.** Cameron is traveling toward you at 99.9999% of the speed of light when he turns on a flashlight and points it in your direction. How fast will the beam of light be going when it reaches you?

44. *Moving Spaceship.* Suppose you are watching a spaceship go past you at a speed close to the speed of light.
   a. How do clocks on the spaceship run, compared to your own clocks? **b.** If you could measure the length, width, and height of the spaceship as it passed by, how would these measurements compare to your measurements of the size of the spaceship if it were stationary? **c.** If you could measure the mass of the spaceship, how would it compare to its rest mass? **d.** How would a passenger on the spaceship view your time, size, and mass?

45. *Relativity of Simultaneity.* Consider the situation in Thought Experiment 8, about the green and red flashes of light at opposite ends of Al's spaceship. Suppose your friend Jackie is traveling in a spaceship in the opposite direction from Al. Further imagine that she is also precisely aligned with you and Al at the instant the two flashes of light occur (in your reference frame).
   a. According to Jackie, is Al illuminated first by the green flash or the red flash? Explain. **b.** According to you, which flash illuminates Jackie first? Why? **c.** According to Jackie, which flash occurs first? Explain. How does Jackie's view of the order of the flashes compare to your view and to Al's view?

Quantitative Problems

Be sure to show all calculations clearly and state your final answers in complete sentences.

46. *Time Dilation.*
   a. A clever student, after learning about the theory of relativity, decides to apply his knowledge in order to prolong his life. He decides to spend the rest of his life in a car, traveling around the freeways at 55 miles per hour (89 km/hr). Suppose he drives for a period of time during which 70 years pass in his house. How much time will pass in the car? (*Hint:* If you are unable to find a difference, be sure to explain why.) **b.** An even more clever student decides to prolong her life by cruising around the local solar neighborhood at a speed of $0.95c$ (95% of the speed of light). How much time will pass on her spacecraft during a period in which 70 years pass on Earth? Will *she* feel as if her life span has been extended? Explain. **c.** Suppose you stay home on Earth while your twin sister takes a trip to a distant star and back in a

spaceship that travels at 99% of the speed of light. If both of you are 25 years old when she leaves and you are 45 years old when she returns, how old is your sister when she gets back?

47. *Length Contraction.*
   a. Marta flies past you at 75% of the speed of light, traveling in a spaceship that would measure 50 meters from end to end if it were at rest in your reference frame. If you measure the length of her spaceship as it goes by, how long will it be from end to end? **b.** The star Sirius is located 8.6 light-years from Earth (in our Earth-based reference frame). Suppose you travel from Earth to Sirius at 92% of the speed of light. During your trip, how long would you measure the distance from Earth to Sirius to be?

48. *Mass Increase.*
   a. A spaceship has a rest mass of 500,000 tons. If you could measure its mass when it was traveling at half the speed of light, what would it be? **b.** A fly has a mass of 1 gram at rest. How fast would it have to be traveling to have the mass of a large SUV, which is about 3000 kilograms?

49. *Time Dilation with Subatomic Particles.* A π^+ meson produced at rest has a lifetime of 18 nanoseconds (1.8×10^{-8} s). Suppose a π^+ meson is produced in a particle accelerator at a speed of $0.998c$. How long will scientists see the particle last before it decays? Briefly explain how an experiment like this helps verify the special theory of relativity.

50. *Time Dilation on the Space Station.* The Space Station orbits Earth at a speed of about 30,000 km/hr. While 1 hour passes on Earth, how much time passes on the Station? Assume that both the Station and Earth are in free-float frames, although in reality they are not. (*Hint:* Don't forget to convert the Station's speed to km/s before determining its fraction of the speed of light.)

51. *The Betelgeuse Cubs.* Like the fans in Chicago, the fans of interstellar baseball on Betelgeuse (in the constellation Orion) have endured a long championship drought, having not won the Universe Series for more than 100,000 years. In hopes of winning more championships before their star explodes as a supernova, the Cubs management has decided to break some league rules (ideally without getting caught) by recruiting players from Earth. The team persuaded Justin Verlander accept a lucrative offer, though in an interview with the *Intergalactic Press*, Verlander said it was the travel opportunity that lured him to Betelgeuse, rather than the money or extended life span. Verlander was given a ticket to travel to Betelgeuse on an express spaceship at 95% of the speed of light. During the trip, he found that, with the replacement body parts provided by the Cubs management, his fastball was considerably improved: He was now able to throw a pitch at 80% of the speed of light. Assuming that he throws a pitch in the same direction the spacecraft is traveling, use the formula for velocity addition to calculate how fast *we* would see the ball moving if we could watch it from Earth.

52. *Racing a Light Beam I.* A long time ago, in a galaxy far, far away, there was a civilization whose inhabitants hosted an Olympic competition every 4 of their years. Unfortunately, the competition had become tarnished by the use of illegal substances designed to aid performance, and many great athletes were disqualified and stripped of their medals. One famed sprinter, named Jo, finally decided that it was pointless to continue racing humans. Instead, he held a press conference to announce that he would race a beam of light! Sponsors lined up, crowds gathered, and the event was sold to a pay-per-view audience. Everything was set. The starting gun was fired. Jo raced out of the starting block and shattered the old world record, running 100 meters in 8.7 seconds. The light beam, represented by a flashlight turned on at precisely the right moment, of course emerged from its "block" at the speed of light. How long

did it take the light beam to cover the 100-meter distance? What can you say about the outcome of this race?

53. *Racing a Light Beam II.* Following his humiliation in the first race against the light beam (Problem 52), Jo went into hiding for the next 2 years. By that time, most people had forgotten about both him and the money they had wasted on the pay-per-view event. However, Jo was secretly in training during this time. He worked out hard and tested new performance-enhancing substances. One day, he emerged from hiding and called another press conference. "I'm ready for a rematch," he announced. Sponsors were few this time and spectators scarce in the huge Olympic stadium where Jo and the flashlight lined up at the starting line. But those who were there will never forget what they saw, although it all happened very quickly. Jo blasted out of the starting block at 99.9% of the speed of light. The light beam, emitted from the flashlight, took off at the speed of light. The light beam won again—but barely! After the race, TV commentators searched for Jo, but he seemed to be hiding again. Finally, they found him in a corner of the locker room, sulking under a towel. "What's wrong? You did great!" said the commentators. Jo looked back sadly, saying, "Two years of training and experiments, for nothing!" Let's investigate what happened.
   a. As seen by spectators in the grandstand, how much faster than Jo is the light beam? **b.** As seen by Jo, how much faster is the light beam than he is? Explain your answer clearly. **c.** Using your results from parts a and b, explain why Jo can say that he was beaten just as badly as before, while the spectators can think he gave the light beam a good race. **d.** Although Jo was disappointed by his performance against the light beam, he did experience one pleasant surprise: The 100-meter course seemed short to him. In Jo's reference frame during the race, how long was the 100-meter course?

Discussion Questions

54. *Common Sense.* Discuss the meaning of the term *common sense.* How do we develop common sense? Can you think of other examples, besides the example of the meanings of *up* and *down,* of situations in which you've had to change your common sense? Do you think that the theory of relativity contradicts common sense? Why or why not?

55. *Photon Philosophy.* Extend the ideas of time dilation and length contraction to think about how the universe would look if you were a photon traveling at the speed of light. Do you think there's any point to thinking about how a photon "perceives" the universe? If so, discuss any resulting philosophical implications. If not, explain why not.

56. *Ticket to the Stars.* Suppose that we someday acquire the technology to travel among the stars at speeds near the speed of light. Imagine that many people make journeys to many places. Discuss some of the complications that would arise from people aging at different rates depending on their travels.

Web Projects

57. *Relativity Simulations.* Explore some of the simulations of the effects of special relativity available on the Web. Write a short report on what you learn.

58. *Einstein's Life.* Learn more about Einstein's life and work and how he has influenced the modern world. Write a short essay describing some aspect of his life or work.

59. *The Michelson-Morley Experiment.* Find details about the famous Michelson-Morley experiment. Write a one-page description of the experiment and its results, including a diagram of the experimental setup.

S3 SPACETIME AND GRAVITY

LEARNING GOALS

S3.1 EINSTEIN'S SECOND REVOLUTION

- What are the major ideas of general relativity?
- What is the fundamental assumption of general relativity?

S3.2 UNDERSTANDING SPACETIME

- What is spacetime?
- What is curved spacetime?

S3.3 A NEW VIEW OF GRAVITY

- What is gravity?
- What is a black hole?
- How does gravity affect time?

S3.4 TESTING GENERAL RELATIVITY

- How do we test the predictions of the general theory of relativity?
- What are gravitational waves?

S3.5 HYPERSPACE, WORMHOLES, AND WARP DRIVE

- Where does science end and science fiction begin?

S3.6 THE LAST WORD

- How has relativity changed our view of space and time?

The eternal mystery of the world is its comprehensibility. The fact that it is comprehensible is a miracle.

—Albert Einstein

What is gravity? Newton's law of gravity allows us to calculate orbits throughout the universe, but the deeper mystery is how one object can exert a gravitational force on another that may be a great distance away. This mystery was finally solved by Einstein with his general theory of relativity, which explains gravity as a consequence of the structure of space and time.

In this chapter, we will investigate Einstein's revolutionary view of gravity. As we will see, Einstein's theory is crucial to understanding many astronomical phenomena, ranging from the peculiar orbit of Mercury to the bizarre properties of black holes.

S3.1 EINSTEIN'S SECOND REVOLUTION

Imagine that you and everyone around you believe Earth to be flat. As a wealthy patron of the sciences, you decide to sponsor an expedition to the far reaches of the world. You select two fearless explorers and give them careful instructions. Each is to journey along a perfectly straight path, but they are to travel in opposite directions. You provide each with a caravan for land-based travel and boats for water crossings, and you tell each to turn back only after discovering "something extraordinary."

Some time later, the two explorers return. You ask, "Did you discover something extraordinary?" To your surprise, they answer in unison, "Yes, but we both discovered the same thing: We ran into each other, despite having traveled in opposite directions along perfectly straight paths."

Although this outcome would be extraordinarily surprising if you truly believed Earth to be flat, we are not really surprised because we know that Earth is round (FIGURE S3.1a).

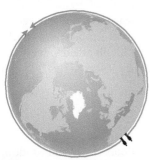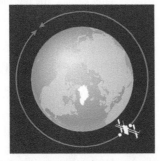

a Travelers going in opposite directions along paths that are as straight as possible will meet as they go around Earth, a fact that we attribute to the curvature of Earth's surface.

b Two space probes launched in opposite directions in Earth orbit will meet as they orbit Earth, a fact that we usually attribute to the mysterious force of gravity.

FIGURE S3.1 Travelers on Earth's surface and orbiting objects follow similar-shaped paths, but we usually explain these paths in very different ways.

In a sense, the explorers followed the *straightest possible paths*, but these "straight" lines follow the curved surface of Earth.

Now let's consider a somewhat more modern scenario. You are floating freely in a spaceship somewhere out in space. Hoping to learn more about space in your vicinity, you launch two small probes along straight paths in opposite directions. Each probe is equipped with a camera that transmits pictures back to your spaceship. Imagine that, to your astonishment, the probes one day transmit pictures of each other! That is, although you launched them in opposite directions and neither has ever fired its engines, the probes have somehow met. This might at first sound surprising, but in fact this situation arises quite naturally with orbiting objects. If you launch two probes in opposite directions from a space station, they will meet as they orbit Earth (FIGURE S3.1b).

Since the time of Newton, we've generally explained curved paths such as those of the two probes as an effect caused by the force of gravity. However, by analogy with the explorers journeying in opposite directions on Earth, might we instead conclude that the probes meet because *space* is somehow curved? Strange as this idea may sound, it lies at the heart of Einstein's second revolution—a revolutionary view of gravity contained in his *general theory of relativity*, published in 1915.

What are the major ideas of general relativity?

Our study of the special theory of relativity has already shown that space and time are inextricably linked. More specifically, we say that the three dimensions of space and the one dimension of time together form a *four*-dimensional combination called **spacetime**. When Einstein extended the special theory to the general case that includes gravity, he discovered that matter shapes the "fabric" of spacetime in a manner somewhat analogous to the way heavy weights distort a taut rubber sheet or trampoline (FIGURE S3.2). The analogy is not perfect—for example, we cannot place weights "upon" spacetime because all matter exists *within* spacetime—but it still useful in discussing the principles of general relativity.

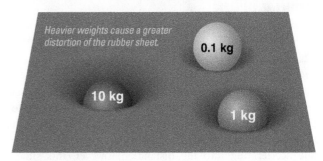

FIGURE S3.2 A rubber sheet analogy to spacetime: Matter distorts the "fabric" of four-dimensional spacetime in a manner analogous to the way heavy weights distort a taut, two-dimensional rubber sheet. The greater the mass, the greater the distortion of spacetime.

It is difficult to overstate the significance of general relativity to our understanding of the universe. In particular, the following ideas all come directly from this theory:

- Gravity arises from distortions of spacetime. The presence of mass causes the distortions, and the resulting distortions determine how other objects move through spacetime.

- Time runs slowly in gravitational fields. The stronger the gravity, the more slowly time runs.

- *Black holes* can exist in spacetime, and falling into a black hole means leaving the observable universe.

- It is possible for the universe to have a finite volume without having a center or boundaries.

- Large masses that undergo rapid changes in motion or structure emit *gravitational waves* that travel at the speed of light.

What is the fundamental assumption of general relativity?

Recall that special relativity begins with two key assumptions—that the laws of nature are the same for everyone and that everyone always measures the same speed of light—from which we can derive all the surprising consequences that we discussed in the last chapter. General relativity also has a starting assumption that leads to all of its astounding predictions. We can understand the origin of this assumption by thinking more deeply about the idea of relative motion.

A Thought Experiment with Acceleration Imagine that you and Al are both floating weightlessly in your spaceships; that is, you are in free-float reference frames. As we saw in Chapter S2, there is no absolute answer to the question "Who is really moving?" because you will both experience the laws of nature in exactly the same way. Now, suppose you decide to fire your rocket engines with enough thrust to give you an acceleration of $1g$ ($= 9.8$ m/s^2), which is the acceleration of gravity on Earth [**Section 4.1**]. Al keeps his engines off and therefore sees you flying off with ever-growing speed, so he sends you a radio message saying, "Good-bye, have a nice trip!"

If *all* motion is relative, you should be free to claim that you are still stationary and that it is Al who is receding into the distance at ever-faster speeds. You might therefore wish to reply, "Thanks, but I'm not going anywhere. You're the one accelerating into the distance." However, this situation has a new element that was not present when we dealt with constant velocities: Because your rocket engines are firing, you feel a force inside your spaceship that means you will no longer be weightless (**FIGURE S3.3**). In fact, with an

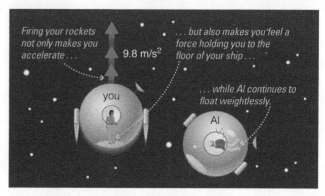

FIGURE S3.3 In deep space with no engines firing, you and Al would both float freely in your spaceships. But when you fire your engines, you feel a force that presses you against the floor of your spaceship, and Al sees you accelerate away. You might wish to claim that *he* is accelerating away from you, but how, then, do you explain the force that you feel and the fact that Al remains weightless?

acceleration of $1g$, you'll be able to walk on your spaceship floor with your normal Earth weight. Al may therefore respond back, "Oh, yeah? If you're not going anywhere, why are you stuck to the floor of your spaceship, and why do you have your engines turned on? And if I'm accelerating as you claim, why am I weightless?"

You must admit that Al is asking good questions. It certainly *looks* as if you really are the one who is accelerating while Al remains stationary. In other words, it seems that motion is no longer relative when we introduce acceleration. This idea did not sit well with Einstein, because he believed that *all* motion should be relative, regardless of whether the motion was at constant velocity or included an acceleration. Einstein therefore needed some way to explain the force you feel due to firing your rocket engines without necessarily assuming that you are accelerating through space. (Einstein did not actually use spaceships in his thought experiments, but the basic ideas are the same.)

The Equivalence Principle In 1907, Einstein hit upon what he later called "the happiest thought of my life." His revelation consisted of the idea that, whenever you feel weight (as opposed to weightlessness), you can attribute it to effects of either acceleration or gravity. This idea is called the **equivalence principle**. Stated more precisely, it says,

The effects of gravity are exactly equivalent to the effects of acceleration.*

To clarify the meaning of the equivalence principle, imagine that you are sitting inside with doors closed and window shades down when your room is magically removed from Earth and sent hurtling through space with an acceleration of $1g$ (**FIGURE S3.4**). According to the equivalence principle, you would have no way of knowing that you'd left Earth.

---

*Technically, this equivalence holds only within small regions of space. Over larger regions, the gravity of a massive object varies in ways that would not occur because of acceleration; for example, such variation gives rise to *tidal forces* that do not arise from acceleration.

The Equivalence Principle

You cannot tell the difference between being in a closed room on Earth . . .

. . . and being in a closed room accelerating through space at 1g.

9.8 m/s²

FIGURE S3.4 The equivalence principle states that the effects of gravity are exactly equivalent to the effects of acceleration. Therefore, you cannot tell the difference between being in a closed room on Earth and being in a closed room accelerating through space at 1*g*.

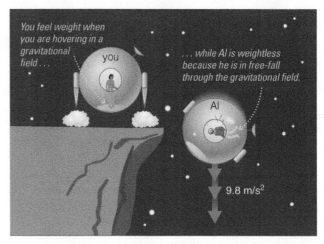

You feel weight when you are hovering in a gravitational field . . .

you

. . . while Al is weightless because he is in free-fall through the gravitational field.

Al

9.8 m/s²

FIGURE S3.5 According to the equivalence principle, you can claim to be stationary in a gravitational field, using your engines to prevent you from falling. You feel weight due to gravity, while Al is weightless because he is in free-fall.

Any experiment you performed, such as dropping balls of different weights, would yield the same results you'd get on Earth.

The equivalence principle gives you a way to answer Al's questions. He asked how you can be stationary when your engines are firing and you feel weight. You can now answer that space is filled with a gravitational field pointing "downward" toward the floor of your spaceship. You are stationary because your rocket engines *prevent* you from falling through this gravitational field, and the gravity also explains your weight. How do you answer Al's second question, about his own weightlessness? Easy: Because he is not using his engines, he and his spaceship are falling through the gravitational field that fills space around you—and anyone in free-fall feels weightless [**Section 4.1**]. In essence, you are

claiming that the situation is much as it would be if you were hovering over a cliff while Al had fallen over the edge (**FIGURE S3.5**). To summarize, you respond, "Sorry, Al, but I still say that you have it backward. I'm using my engines to prevent my spaceship from falling, and I feel weight because of *gravity*. You're weightless because you're in free-fall. I hope you won't be hurt by hitting whatever lies at the bottom of this gravitational field!"

The equivalence principle is the starting point for general relativity. As our thought experiment has shown, it allows us to treat *all* motion as relative, just as Einstein thought should be the case. Moreover, as we'll see in the rest of this chapter, the equivalence principle will also lead us to fundamental changes in the way we think about gravity and the universe.

SPECIAL TOPIC

Einstein's Leap

Given that the similarities in the effects of gravity and of acceleration were well known to scientists as far back as the time of Newton, you may wonder why the equivalence principle came as a surprise. The answer is that, before Einstein, the similarities were generally attributed to coincidence. It was as if scientists imagined that nature was showing them two boxes, one labeled "effects of gravity" and the other labeled "effects of acceleration." They shook, weighed, and kicked the boxes but could never find any obvious differences between them. They concluded, "What a strange coincidence! The boxes seem the same from the outside even though they contain different things." Einstein's revelation was, in essence, to look at the boxes and say that it is not a coincidence at all. The boxes appear the same from the outside because they contain the same thing.

In many ways, Einstein's assertion of the equivalence principle represented a leap of faith, although it was a faith he would willingly test through scientific experiment. He proposed the equivalence principle because he thought the universe would make more sense if it were true, not because of any compelling observational or

experimental evidence for it at the time. This leap of faith sent him on a path far ahead of his scientific colleagues.

From a historical viewpoint, special relativity was a "theory waiting to happen" because it was needed to explain two significant problems left over from the 19th century: the perplexing constancy of the speed of light, demonstrated in the Michelson-Morley experiment [**Section S2.3**], and some seeming peculiarities of the laws of electromagnetism. Indeed, several other scientists were very close to discovering the ideas of special relativity when Einstein published the theory in 1905, and *someone* was bound to come up with special relativity around that time.

General relativity, in contrast, was a *tour de force* by Einstein. He recognized that unsolved problems remained after completing the theory of special relativity, and he alone took the leap of faith required to accept the equivalence principle. Without Einstein, general relativity probably would have remained undiscovered for at least a couple of decades beyond 1915, the year he completed and published the theory.

S3.2 UNDERSTANDING SPACETIME

It's easy to *say* that you can attribute your weight to the effect of gravity or the effect of acceleration, but the two effects tend to *look* very different. A person standing on the surface of Earth appears to be motionless, while an astronaut accelerating through space continually gains speed. How can gravity and acceleration produce such similar effects when they look so different? According to the general theory of relativity, the answer is that they look different only because we're not seeing the whole picture. Instead of looking just at the three dimensions of space, we must learn to "look" at the *four* dimensions of spacetime.

What is spacetime?

The first step in understanding spacetime is understanding what we mean when we say, for example, that something is two-dimensional or three-dimensional. The concept of **dimension** describes the number of independent directions in which movement is possible (FIGURE S3.6). A **point** has zero dimensions. If you were a "geometric prisoner" confined to a point, you'd have no place to go. Sweeping a point back and forth along one direction generates a **line**.

The line is one-dimensional because only one direction of motion is possible (going backward is considered the same as going forward by a negative distance). Sweeping a line back and forth generates a two-dimensional **plane**. The two directions of possible motion are, say, lengthwise and widthwise. Any other direction is just a combination of these two. If we sweep a plane up and down, it fills **three-dimensional space**, with the three independent directions of length, width, and depth.

We live in three-dimensional space and cannot visualize any direction that is distinct from length, width, and depth (and combinations thereof). However, just because we cannot *see* "other" directions doesn't mean they don't exist. If we could sweep space back and forth in some "other" direction, we would generate a **four-dimensional space**.

Although we cannot visualize a four-dimensional space, we are able to describe it mathematically. In algebra, we do one-dimensional problems with the single variable x, two-dimensional problems with the variables x and y, and three-dimensional problems with the variables x, y, and z. A four-dimensional problem simply requires adding a fourth variable, as in x, y, z, and w. We could continue to five dimensions, six dimensions, and so forth. Any space with more than three dimensions is called a **hyperspace**, which means "beyond space."

MATHEMATICAL INSIGHT S3.1

Spacetime Geometry

Spacetime geometry is more complex than the simplest possible four-dimensional geometry, because time enters the equations in a slightly different way than the three spatial dimensions. We can gain insight into the nature of spacetime geometry by thinking about how we define distance in ordinary geometry.

Consider two points in a plane separated by amounts $x = 3$ along the horizontal axis and $y = 4$ along the vertical axis. As shown on the left side of FIGURE 1, the *distance* between the two points is $\sqrt{x^2 + y^2}$, which is 5 in this case. Now, consider what happens if we rotate the coordinate axes so that both points lie along the x-axis (right side of Figure 1). This rotation changes the x and y separations

of the two points, but the distance $\sqrt{x^2 + y^2}$ between the points is still the same. This fact should not be surprising: *Distance* is a real, physical quantity, while the x and y separations depend on the particular coordinate system being used.

The same idea holds if we add a z-axis (perpendicular to the x-y plane) to make a three-dimensional coordinate system. Different observers using different coordinate systems can disagree about the x, y, and z separations, but they will always agree on the distance $\sqrt{x^2 + y^2 + z^2}$.

Spacetime has a fourth axis, which we will call the t-axis, for time. Extending our results from two and three dimensions, we might expect that different observers would always agree on a four-dimensional "distance" that we could write as $\sqrt{x^2 + y^2 + z^2 + t^2}$. However, this is not quite the case. Instead, it turns out that different observers will agree on the value of the quantity $\sqrt{x^2 + y^2 + z^2 - t^2}$, which is called the **interval**. (Technically, the interval formula should use ct rather than t so that all the terms have units of length.) That is, different observers can disagree about the values of x, y, z, and t separating two events, but all will agree on the interval between the two events.

The *minus sign* that goes with the time dimension in the interval formula makes the geometry of spacetime surprisingly complex. For example, the three-dimensional distance between two points can be zero only if the two points are in the same place, but the interval between two events can be zero even if they are in different places in spacetime, as long as $x^2 + y^2 + z^2 = t^2$. For example, the interval is zero between any two events connected by a light path on a spacetime diagram. If you study general relativity further, you will see many more examples of how this strange geometry comes into play.

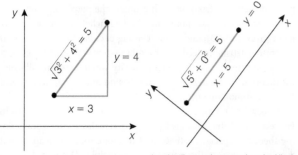

The x- and y-coordinates of two points can be different in different coordinate systems . . .

. . . but the distance between them (red line) is the same either way.

FIGURE 1 The distance between two points in a plane is the same regardless of how we set up a coordinate system.

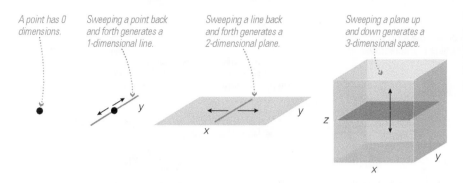

A point has 0 dimensions.

Sweeping a point back and forth generates a 1-dimensional line.

Sweeping a line back and forth generates a 2-dimensional plane.

Sweeping a plane up and down generates a 3-dimensional space.

FIGURE S3.6 An object's number of dimensions is the number of independent directions in which movement is possible within the object. It is zero for a point, one for a line, two for a plane, and three for space.

Spacetime Spacetime is a four-dimensional space in which the four directions of possible motion are length, width, depth, and *time*. Note that time is not "the" fourth dimension; it is simply one of the four. (However, time differs in an important way from the other three dimensions. See Mathematical Insight S3.1.)

We cannot picture all four dimensions of spacetime at once, but we can imagine what things would look like if we could. In addition to occupying the three spatial dimensions of spacetime that we ordinarily see, every object would be stretched out through time. Objects that we see as three-dimensional in our ordinary lives would appear as four-dimensional objects in spacetime. If we could see in four dimensions, we could look through time just as easily as we look to our left or right. If we looked at a person, we could see every event in that person's life. If we wondered what really happened during some historical event, we could simply look to find the answer.

This spacetime view of objects provides a new way of understanding why different observers can disagree about measurements of time and distance. Because we can't visualize four dimensions, we'll use a three-dimensional analogy. Suppose you give the same book to many different people and ask each person to measure the book's dimensions. Everyone will get the same results, agreeing on the three-dimensional structure of the book. Now, suppose instead that you show each person only a two-dimensional picture of the book rather than the book itself. The pictures may look very different, even though they show the same book in all cases (FIGURE S3.7). If the people believed that the two-dimensional pictures reflected reality, they might argue endlessly about what the book really looks like.

In our ordinary lives, we perceive only three dimensions, and we assume that this perception reflects reality. But spacetime is actually four-dimensional. Just as different people can see different two-dimensional pictures of the same three-dimensional book, different observers can see different three-dimensional "pictures" of the same spacetime reality. These

different "pictures" are the differing perceptions of time and space of observers in different reference frames. That is why different observers can get different results when they measure time, length, or mass, even though they are all looking at the same spacetime reality. In the words of a famous textbook on relativity,

> Space is different for different observers.
> Time is different for different observers.
> Spacetime is the same for everyone.*

Spacetime Diagrams Suppose you drive your car along a straight road from home to work as shown in FIGURE S3.8a. At 8:00 a.m., you leave your house and accelerate to 60 km/hr. You maintain this speed until you come to a red light, where you decelerate to a stop. After the light turns green, you accelerate

*From E. F. Taylor and J. A. Wheeler, *Spacetime Physics*, 2nd ed. (Freeman, 1992).

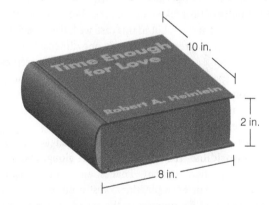

10 in.

2 in.

8 in.

a A book has an unambiguous three-dimensional shape.

b Two-dimensional pictures of the book can look very different.

FIGURE S3.7 Two-dimensional views of a three-dimensional object can appear different, even though the object has only a single real shape. In a similar way, observers in different reference frames may measure space and time differently (because they perceive only three dimensions at once) even though they are all observing the same four-dimensional spacetime reality.

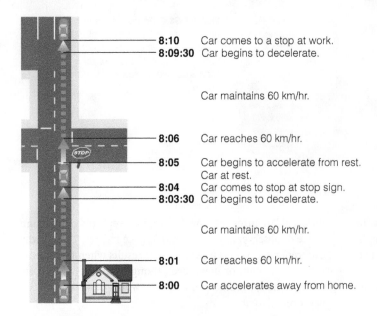

8:10	Car comes to a stop at work.
8:09:30	Car begins to decelerate.
	Car maintains 60 km/hr.
8:06	Car reaches 60 km/hr.
8:05	Car begins to accelerate from rest. Car at rest.
8:04	Car comes to stop at stop sign.
8:03:30	Car begins to decelerate.
	Car maintains 60 km/hr.
8:01	Car reaches 60 km/hr.
8:00	Car accelerates away from home.

a This diagram shows the events that occur during a 10-minute car trip from home to work on a straight road.

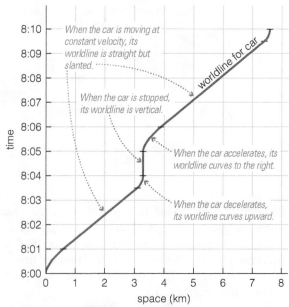

b We make a spacetime diagram for the trip by putting space (in this case, the car's distance from home) on the horizontal axis and time on the vertical axis.

FIGURE S3.8 A spacetime diagram allows us to represent one dimension of space and the dimension of time on a single graph.

again to 60 km/hr, which you maintain until you slow to a stop when you reach work at 8:10. What does your trip look like in spacetime?

If we could see all four dimensions of spacetime, we'd see all three dimensions of your car and your trip stretched out through the 10 minutes of time taken for your trip. We can't visualize all four dimensions at once, but in this case we have a special situation: Your trip progressed along only one dimension of space because you took a straight road. Therefore, we can represent your trip in spacetime by drawing a graph showing your path through one dimension of space on the horizontal axis and your path through time on the vertical axis (**FIGURE S3.8b**). This type of graph is called a **spacetime diagram**.

The car's path through four-dimensional spacetime is called its **worldline**. Any particular point along a worldline represents a particular **event**. That is, an event is a specific place and time. For example, the lowest point on the worldline in Figure S3.8b represents the event of leaving your house, which occurs at a place 0 kilometers from home and a time of 8:00 a.m. As you study Figure S3.8b, you'll notice three important properties of worldlines:

1. The worldline of an object at rest is vertical (that is, parallel to the *time* axis). The object is going nowhere in space, but it still moves through time.

2. The worldline of an object moving at constant velocity is *straight* but slanted. The more slanted the worldline, the faster the object is moving.

3. The worldline of an accelerating object is *curved*. If the object's speed is increasing, its worldline curves toward the horizontal. If its speed is decreasing, its worldline gradually becomes more vertical.

In Figure S3.8b, we use units of minutes for time and kilometers for distance. In relativity, it is usually easier to work with spacetime diagrams in which we use units related to the speed of light, such as *seconds* for time and *light-seconds* for distance, so that light beams make 45° lines (because light travels 1 light-second of distance with each second of time). For example, suppose you are sitting still in your chair, so that your worldline is vertical (**FIGURE S3.9a**). If at some particular time you flash a laser beam pointed to your right, the worldline of the light goes diagonally to the right. If you flash the laser to the left a few seconds later, its worldline goes diagonally to the left. Worldlines for several other objects are shown in **FIGURE S3.9b**.

THINK ABOUT IT

Explain why, in Figure S3.9, the worldlines of all the objects we see in our everyday lives would be nearly vertical.

We can use spacetime diagrams to clarify the relativity of time and space. Suppose you see Al moving past you in a spaceship at 0.9*c*. **FIGURE S3.10a** shows the spacetime diagram from your point of view: You are at rest and therefore have a vertical worldline, while Al is moving and has a slanted worldline. Of course, Al claims that *you* are moving by him and therefore would draw the spacetime diagram shown in **FIGURE S3.10b**, in which his worldline is vertical and yours is slanted. Special relativity tells us that you would see Al's time running slowly, while he would see *your* time running slowly (along with effects on length and mass). We know there is no contradiction here, but simply a problem with our old common sense about space and time.

From a four-dimensional perspective, the problem is that the large angle between your worldline and Al's means that

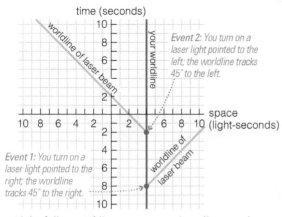

Event 2: You turn on a laser light pointed to the left; the worldline tracks 45° to the left.

Event 1: You turn on a laser light pointed to the right; the worldline tracks 45° to the right.

a Light follows 45° lines on a spacetime diagram that uses units of seconds for time and light-seconds for space.

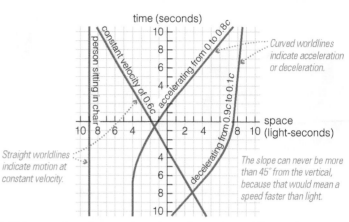

Curved worldlines indicate acceleration or deceleration.

Straight worldlines indicate motion at constant velocity.

The slope can never be more than 45° from the vertical, because that would mean a speed faster than light.

b This spacetime diagram shows several sample worldlines. Objects at rest have vertical worldlines, objects moving at constant velocity have straight but slanted worldlines, and accelerating objects have curved worldlines.

FIGURE S3.9 Spacetime diagrams marked with units of seconds for time and light-seconds for space.

neither of you is looking at the other "straight-on" in spacetime. That is, you and Al are both looking at the same four-dimensional reality but from different three-dimensional perspectives. It's not surprising that, like two people looking at each other cross-eyed, if you see Al's time running slowly, he sees the same thing when he looks at you.

What is curved spacetime?

So far, we've been viewing spacetime diagrams drawn on the flat pages of this book. However, as we discussed in the beginning of this chapter, spacetime can be curved. What do we mean by curved spacetime?

It's easy to visualize the curvature of a *two*-dimensional surface, such as the surface of a bent sheet of paper or the surface of Earth, because we can see it curving *through* the third dimension of space. Note that these surfaces are two-dimensional despite their curvature, because they still allow only two independent directions of travel; for example, two independent directions of travel on Earth's surface are north-south (changes in latitude) and east-west (changes in longitude). Unfortunately, we cannot visualize the curvature of three-dimensional space in a similar way, let alone of four-dimensional spacetime, because we'd need extra dimensions for them to curve through. Nevertheless, we can

determine whether space or spacetime is curved by identifying the rules of geometry that apply. Because we cannot visualize curved space or spacetime, we'll use two-dimensional surfaces in an analogy.

Three Basic Types of Geometry Consider Earth's curved, two-dimensional surface. Because Earth's surface is curved everywhere, there really is no such thing as a "straight" line on Earth. For example, if you take a piece of string and lay it across a globe, it will inevitably curve around the surface. This leads us immediately to one fundamental difference between the rules of geometry on Earth's surface and the more familiar rules of geometry in a flat plane: While the shortest distance between two points in a flat plane is always a straight line, the same cannot be true on Earth's surface, because there is no such thing as a straight line.

What rule gives us the shortest distance on Earth's surface? If you experiment by measuring pieces of string stretched in different ways between two points on a globe, you'll find that the shortest and *straightest possible* path between two points on Earth's surface is a piece of a **great circle**—a circle whose center is at the center of Earth (**FIGURE S3.11a**). For example, the equator is a great circle, and any "line" of longitude is part of a great circle. Note that circles of latitude (besides the equator) are *not* great circles because their centers are *not* at the center of Earth. Therefore, if you are seeking the shortest and straightest route between two cities, you must follow a *great-circle route*. For example, Philadelphia and Beijing are both at about 40°N latitude, but the shortest route between them does *not* follow the circle of 40°N latitude. Instead, it follows a great-circle route that extends far to the north (**FIGURE S3.11b**).

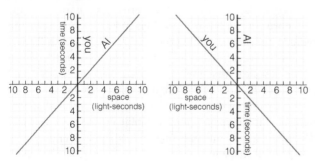

a The spacetime diagram from your point of view.

b The spacetime diagram from Al's point of view.

FIGURE S3.10 Spacetime diagrams for the situation in which Al is moving by you at 0.9*c*.

SEE IT FOR YOURSELF

Find a globe and locate New Orleans and Katmandu (Nepal). Explain why the shortest route between these two cities goes almost directly over the North Pole. Why do you think airplanes try to follow great-circle routes as closely as possible?

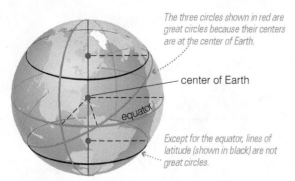

The three circles shown in red are great circles because their centers are at the center of Earth.

center of Earth

equator

Except for the equator, lines of latitude (shown in black) are not great circles.

a A great circle is any circle on the surface of Earth that has its center at the center of Earth.

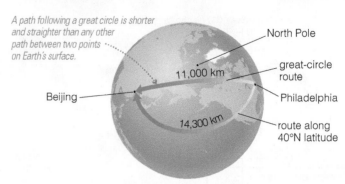

A path following a great circle is shorter and straighter than any other path between two points on Earth's surface.

North Pole

great-circle route

11,000 km

Beijing

Philadelphia

14,300 km

route along 40°N latitude

b The shortest and straightest possible path between two points on Earth is always a piece of a great circle.

FIGURE S3.11 The straightest possible path between any two points on a sphere must be a segment of a great circle.

Other familiar rules of geometry in a flat plane also are different on Earth's curved surface. **FIGURE S3.12a** shows the straight-line rule and several other geometrical rules on a flat surface, and **FIGURE S3.12b** shows how these rules differ for a spherical surface like that of Earth; in the latter case, we must draw "lines" as portions of great circles, because those are the shortest and straightest possible paths. Notice, for example, that lines that are anywhere parallel on a flat plane stay parallel forever, while lines that start out parallel on a sphere eventually converge (just as lines of longitude start out parallel at Earth's equator but all converge at the North and South Poles). Similarly, the sum of the angles in a triangle is always 180° in a flat plane but is greater than 180° on the surface of a sphere, and the circumference of a circle is $2\pi r$ in a flat plane but is *less* than $2\pi r$ on a spherical surface.

Generalizing these ideas to more than two dimensions, we say that space, or spacetime, has a **flat geometry** if the rules of geometry for a flat plane hold. (Flat geometry is also known as *Euclidean geometry,* after the Greek mathematician Euclid [c. 325–270 B.C.].) For example, if the circumference of a circle in space really is $2\pi r$, then space has a flat geometry. However, if the circumference of a circle in space turns out to be less than $2\pi r$, we say that space has a **spherical geometry** because the rules are those that hold on the surface of a sphere.

Flat and spherical geometries are two of three general types of geometry. The third is called **saddle-shaped geometry** (also called *hyperbolic geometry*) because its rules are most easily visualized on a two-dimensional surface shaped like a saddle (**FIGURE S3.12c**). In this case, lines that start out parallel eventually diverge, the sum of the angles in a triangle is *less* than 180°, and the circumference of a circle is *greater* than $2\pi r$.

The Geometry of the Universe The actual geometry of spacetime turns out to be a mixture of all three general types. Earth's surface again provides a good analogy. When we view only small portions of Earth's surface, some regions appear flat while others are curved with hills and valleys. However, when we expand our view to the entire Earth, it's clear that the overall geometry of Earth's surface is like that of the surface of a sphere. In a similar way, but in two more dimensions, the four-dimensional spacetime of our universe obeys different geometrical rules in different regions but presumably has some overall shape. This overall shape must be one of the three general types of geometry shown in Figure S3.12: flat, spherical, or saddle shaped. This fact explains how it is possible for the universe to have no center and no edges, an idea we first discussed in Chapter 1.

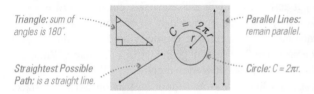

Triangle: sum of angles is 180°.

$C = 2\pi r$

Parallel Lines: remain parallel.

Straightest Possible Path: is a straight line.

Circle: $C = 2\pi r$.

a Rules of flat geometry.

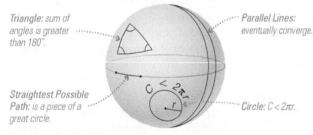

Triangle: sum of angles is greater than 180°.

Parallel Lines: eventually converge.

$C < 2\pi r$

Straightest Possible Path: is a piece of a great circle.

Circle: $C < 2\pi r$.

b Rules of spherical geometry.

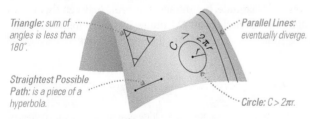

Triangle: sum of angles is less than 180°.

Parallel Lines: eventually diverge.

$C > 2\pi r$

Straightest Possible Path: is a piece of a hyperbola.

Circle: $C > 2\pi r$.

c Rules of saddle-shaped geometry.

FIGURE S3.12 These diagrams contrast three basic types of geometry.

In geometry, a plane is infinite in extent, which means it has no center or edges. An idealized, saddle-shaped (hyperbolic) surface is also infinite in extent. Therefore, if the universe has either a flat or a saddle-shaped geometry overall, then spacetime is infinite and the universe has no center and no edges.

In contrast, if the overall geometry of the universe is spherical, then spacetime is finite, much like the surface of Earth. However, it would still have no center or edges. Just as you can sail or fly around Earth's surface endlessly, you could fly through the universe forever and never encounter an edge. And just as the *surface* of Earth has no center—New York is no more "central" than Beijing or any other place on Earth's surface—there would be no center to the universe. (Of course, the three-dimensional Earth *does* have a center, but this center is not part of the two-dimensional surface of Earth and therefore plays no role in our analogy.)

"Straight" Lines in Curved Spacetime The rules of geometry give us a way to determine the geometry of any localized region of spacetime. In particular, we can learn the geometry of spacetime by observing the paths of objects that are following the *straightest possible* path between two points in spacetime. For example, if the straightest possible path is truly straight, we know that spacetime is flat in that region. If the straightest possible path is curved, then the shape of the curve must be telling us the shape of spacetime. However, given that we can visualize neither the time part of spacetime nor the curvature of spacetime, how can we know whether an object is traveling on the straightest possible path?

Einstein used the equivalence principle to provide the answer. According to the equivalence principle, we can attribute a feeling of weight either to experiencing a force generated by acceleration or to being in a gravitational field. Similarly, any time we feel weightless, we may attribute it either to being in free-fall or to traveling at constant velocity far from any gravitational fields. Because traveling at constant velocity means traveling in a straight line, Einstein reasoned that objects experiencing weightlessness for *any* reason must be traveling in a "straight" line—that is, along a line that is the straightest possible path between two points in spacetime. In other words,

If you are floating freely, then your worldline is following the straightest possible path through spacetime. If you feel weight, then you are not on the straightest possible path.

This fact provides us with a remarkable way to examine the geometry of spacetime. Recall that any orbit is a free-fall trajectory [**Section 4.1**]. The Space Station is always freefalling toward Earth, but its forward velocity always moves it ahead just enough to "miss" hitting the ground. Earth is constantly free-falling toward the Sun, but our planet's orbital speed keeps us going around and around. According to the equivalence principle, all orbits must therefore represent paths of objects that are following the straightest possible path through spacetime. That is, the shapes and speeds of orbits reveal the geometry of spacetime—a fact that leads us to an entirely new view of gravity.

S3.3 A NEW VIEW OF GRAVITY

Newton's law of gravity claims that every mass exerts a gravitational attraction on every other mass, no matter how far away they are from each other. However, on close examination, this idea of "action at a distance" is rather mysterious. For example, how does Earth feel the Sun's attraction and know to orbit it? Newton himself was troubled by this idea. A few years after publishing his law of gravity in 1687, Newton wrote,

That one body may act upon another at a distance through a vacuum, … and force may be conveyed from one to another, is to me so great an absurdity, that I believe no man, who has … a competent faculty in thinking, can ever fall into it.*

Nevertheless, for more than 230 years after Newton published his gravitational law, no one found any better way to explain gravity's mysterious "action at a distance." Einstein changed all that when he realized that the equivalence principle allowed him to explain the action of gravity without requiring any long-distance force.

What is gravity?

Einstein's general theory of relativity removes the idea of "action at a distance" by stating that Earth feels *no* force tugging on it in its orbit, and therefore follows the straightest possible path through spacetime. That is, the fact that Earth goes around the Sun tells us that spacetime itself is curved near the Sun. In other words,

What we perceive as gravity arises from the curvature of spacetime.

Rubber Sheet Analogy We cannot actually picture the curvature of spacetime, but a two-dimensional analogy can help us understand the idea. We represent spacetime by an analogy with a stretched rubber sheet. To make the analogy work, we have to ignore any effects of friction on the rubber sheet, because there is no friction in space.

FIGURE S3.13a shows a flat rubber sheet representing spacetime in a region where it has a flat geometry. Notice that the radial distances between the circles shown on the sheet are the same, and all the circles have circumferences that follow the flat geometry formula of $2\pi r$. If you rolled a marble across this frictionless sheet, it would roll in a straight line at constant speed. This fact essentially illustrates Newton's first law of motion, which says that objects move at constant velocity when they are not affected by gravity or any other forces.

**Letter from Newton, 1692–1693, as quoted in J. A. Wheeler, *A Journey into Gravity and Spacetime* (Scientific American Library, 1990, p. 2).

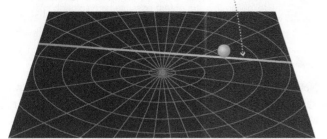

In flat regions of spacetime, freely moving objects move in straight lines.

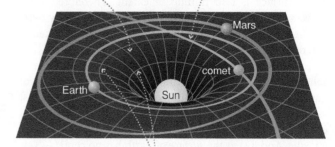

The mass of the Sun causes spacetime to curve . . .

. . . so freely moving objects (such as planets and comets) follow the straightest possible paths allowed by the curvature of spacetime.

Mars

comet

Earth

Sun

Circles that were evenly spaced in flat spacetime become more widely spaced near the central mass.

a On a flat rubber sheet, evenly spaced circles all have circumference $2\pi r$.

b The Sun curves spacetime much like the way a heavy weight curves a rubber sheet.

FIGURE S3.13 interactive figure According to general relativity, planets orbit the Sun for much the same reason that you can make a marble go around in a salad bowl: Each planet is going as straight as it can, but the curvature of spacetime causes its path through space to go round and round.

FIGURE S3.13b shows what happens to spacetime around the Sun. We represent the Sun with a heavy mass on the rubber sheet, which causes the sheet to curve and form a bowl-like depression. The circles that were evenly spaced on the flat sheet now become more widely separated (with circumferences increasingly less than $2\pi r$) near the bottom of the bowl, showing that gravity becomes stronger and the curvature of spacetime becomes greater as we approach the Sun's surface. (Notice that the curvature does *not* continue to increase with depth inside the Sun; in fact, the strength of gravity actually weakens near the Sun's center.) If you rolled marbles on this rubber sheet, they could not go in straight lines, because the sheet itself is curved. Instead, the marbles would follow the *straightest possible* paths given the curvature of the sheet. A particular marble's path would depend on the speed and direction with which you rolled it. You'd find that marbles rolled relatively slowly and close to the center would follow circular or elliptical "orbits" around the center of the bowl, while marbles rolled from farther away or at higher speeds could loop around the center on unbound parabolic or hyperbolic paths.

By analogy, general relativity tells us that, depending on their speed and direction, planets or other objects moving freely in space can follow circular, elliptical, or unbound parabolic or hyperbolic orbits—the same orbital shapes that Newton's universal law of gravitation allows [**Section 4.4**]. However, the explanation for these orbits is now quite different from that in Newton's view of gravity. Rather than orbiting because of a mysterious force exerted on them by the distant Sun, the planets orbit because they follow the *straightest possible paths* allowed by the shape of spacetime around them. The central mass of the Sun is not grabbing them, communicating with them, or doing anything else to influence their motion. Instead, it is simply dictating the shape of spacetime around it. In other words,

A mass like the Sun causes spacetime to curve, and the curvature of spacetime determines the paths of freely moving masses like the planets.

Weightlessness in Space This idea gives us a new way to explain the weightlessness of astronauts in space. Just as the Sun curves spacetime into a "bowl shape" (but in four dimensions) that makes the straightest possible paths of the planets go round and round, Earth curves spacetime in a way that makes orbiting spacecraft go round and round. In other words, spacecraft orbit Earth because, as long as their engines are off and they are unaffected by atmospheric drag, circular or elliptical orbits are the straightest possible paths they can follow through spacetime in Earth's vicinity. That is, instead of having to invoke the idea of free-fall caused by a gravitational attraction to Earth, we can explain the weightlessness of astronauts in the Space Station simply by recognizing that they are following the straightest possible paths through spacetime.

The same idea holds true for any other orbital trajectory. For example, if we launched a human mission to Mars, we would need to give the spaceship escape velocity from Earth. In the rubber sheet analogy, this means launching it with enough speed so that it can escape from the bowl-shaped region around Earth, like a marble shot fast enough to roll out of the bowl and onto the flatter region far away from it. Except when their rockets were firing, the astronauts would still be weightless throughout the trip because they would be following the straightest possible path. Firing the engines, either to accelerate away from Earth or to decelerate near Mars, would make the spaceship deviate from the straightest possible path, so the astronauts would feel weight during those portions of their journey.

Limitations of the Analogy The rubber sheet analogy is useful for understanding how mass affects spacetime, but it also has limitations because it is a two-dimensional representation of a four-dimensional reality. In particular, the analogy has three important limitations that you should keep in mind whenever you use it:

- The rubber sheet is supposed to represent the universe, but it makes no sense to think of placing a mass like the

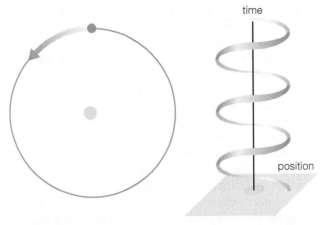

time

position

a If we ignore time, Earth appears to return to the same point with each orbit of the Sun.

b If we include a time axis, we see that Earth never returns to the same point in spacetime because it always moves forward in time.

FIGURE S3.14 Earth's path through spacetime.

Sun "upon" the universe. Instead, we should think of the masses as being *within* the rubber sheet.

- The rubber sheet allows us to picture only two of the three dimensions of space. For example, it allows us to show that different planets orbit at different distances from the Sun and that some have more highly elliptical orbits than others, but it does not allow us to show the fact that the planets do not all orbit the Sun in precisely the same plane.

- The rubber sheet analogy does not show the *time* part of spacetime. Bound orbits on the sheet or in space appear to return to the same point with each circuit of the Sun. However, objects cannot return to the same point in spacetime, because they always move forward through time. For example, with each orbit of the Sun, Earth returns to the same place in space (relative to the Sun) but to a time that is a year later (FIGURE S3.14).

What is a black hole?

Greater curvature of spacetime means stronger gravity, and the rubber sheet analogy suggests two basic ways to increase

the strength of gravity. First, a larger mass causes greater curvature at any particular distance away from it. For example, the Sun curves spacetime more than any planet, and Earth curves spacetime more than the Moon. Note that this idea is consistent with Newton's law of gravity, which says that increasing the mass of an object increases the gravitational attraction at all distances.

The second way to increase the curvature of spacetime around an object is to leave its mass alone but increase its density by making it smaller in size. For example, suppose we could compress the Sun into a type of "dead" star called a *white dwarf* [**Section 18.1**]. Because its total mass would still be the same, there would be no effect on the curvature of spacetime far from the Sun. However, spacetime would be much more curved near the compressed Sun's surface, reflecting the fact that gravity is much stronger on the surface of a compressed white dwarf than on the surface of the Sun. Again, the idea that the surface gravity on an object of a particular mass grows stronger as the object shrinks in radius is consistent with Newton's law of gravity.

Now, imagine that we could continue to compress the Sun to smaller and smaller sizes. Far from the Sun, this compression would have no effect at all, because the same total mass would still be causing the curvature of spacetime. Near the Sun's surface, however, spacetime would become increasingly curved as we shrank the Sun in size. In fact, if we shrank the Sun enough, we could eventually curve spacetime so much that it would in essence become a bottomless pit—a hole in the observable universe. This is what we call a **black hole** (FIGURE S3.15). Note that Newton's view of gravity does not really have any analog to a black hole, because it does not envision the possibility of holes in the universe.

To summarize, a black hole is a place where spacetime is so curved that nothing that falls into it can ever escape. The boundary that marks the "point of no return" is called the **event horizon**, because events that occur within this boundary can have no influence on our observable universe. The idea of black holes is so bizarre that for decades after Einstein published his general theory of relativity, most scientists did not think they could really exist. However, we now have very strong evidence suggesting that black holes are in fact quite common. We'll discuss the nature of black holes in more

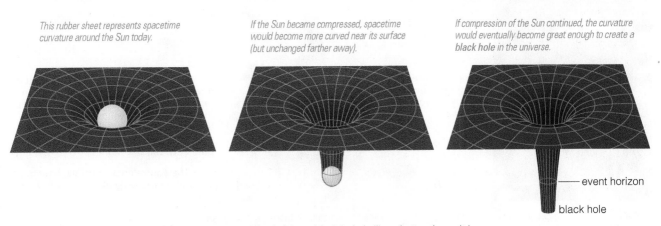

This rubber sheet represents spacetime curvature around the Sun today.

If the Sun became compressed, spacetime would become more curved near its surface (but unchanged farther away).

If compression of the Sun continued, the curvature would eventually become great enough to create a black hole in the universe.

event horizon

black hole

FIGURE S3.15 **interactive figure** According to general relativity, a black hole is like a bottomless pit in spacetime. Once an object crosses the event horizon, it has left our observable universe.

detail in Chapter 18, and will discuss evidence for their existence in both Chapter 18 and Chapter 21.

How does gravity affect time?

Given that gravity arises from the curvature of spacetime, you should not be surprised to learn that gravity affects time as well as space. We can learn about the effects of gravity on time by considering the effects of accelerated motion and then invoking the equivalence principle.

Imagine that you and Al are floating weightlessly at opposite ends of a spaceship. You both have watches that flash brightly each second, which you synchronized beforehand. Because you are both floating freely with no relative motion between you, you are both in the same reference frame. Therefore, you will see each other's watches flashing at the same rate.

Now suppose you fire the spaceship engines so that the spaceship begins to accelerate, with you at the front and Al at the back. When the ship begins accelerating, you and Al will no longer be weightless. The acceleration introduces an even more important change into the situation, which we can understand by imagining the view of someone floating weightlessly outside the spaceship. Remember that observers moving at different relative speeds are in different reference frames. When the spaceship is accelerating, its speed is constantly increasing relative to the outside observer, which means that both you and Al are constantly changing reference frames. Moreover, the flashes from your watches take a bit of time to travel the length of the spaceship. By the time a particular flash from Al's watch reaches you (or a flash from your watch reaches Al), both your reference frames are different from what they were at the time the flash was emitted.

Because you are in the *front* of the accelerating spaceship, your changing reference frames are always carrying you *away* from the point at which each of Al's flashes is emitted. Therefore, the light from each of his flashes will take a little *longer* to reach you than it would if the ship were not accelerating. As a result, instead of seeing Al's flashes 1 second apart, you'll see them coming a little *more* than 1 second apart. That is, you'll see Al's watch flashing more slowly than yours (FIGURE S3.16a). You will therefore conclude that time is running more slowly at the back end of the spaceship.

From Al's point of view at the *back* of the accelerating spaceship, his changing reference frames are always carrying him *toward* the point at which each of your flashes is emitted. Therefore, the light from each of your flashes will take a little *less* time to reach him than it would if the ship were not accelerating, so he'll see them coming a little *less* than 1 second apart. He will see your watch flashing *faster* than his and conclude that time is running *fast* at the front end of the spaceship. Note that you and Al agree: Time is running more slowly at the back end of the spaceship and faster at the front end. The greater the acceleration of the spaceship, the greater the difference in the rate at which time passes at the two ends of the spaceship.

Now we apply the equivalence principle, which tells us that we should get the same results for a spaceship at rest in a gravitational field as we do for a spaceship accelerating through space. This means that if the spaceship were at rest on a planet, time would also have to be running more slowly at the bottom of the spaceship than at the top (FIGURE S3.16b). That is, time must run more slowly at lower altitudes than at higher altitudes in a gravitational field. This effect is known as **gravitational time dilation**.

The stronger the gravity—and hence the greater the curvature of spacetime—the greater the effect of gravitational time dilation. On an object with relatively weak gravity, like Earth, the slowing of time is barely detectable compared to the rate at which time passes in deep space. However, time runs noticeably more slowly on the surface of the Sun than on Earth, and more slowly on the surface of a white dwarf star than on the Sun. Perhaps you've already guessed that the extreme case is a black hole: To anyone watching from a distance, time comes to a stop at the event horizon. If you could observe clocks placed at varying distances from the black hole, you'd see that clocks nearer the event horizon run more slowly and clocks *at* the event horizon show time to be frozen.

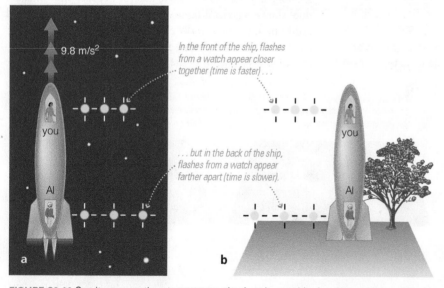

9.8 m/s²

In the front of the ship, flashes from a watch appear closer together (time is faster) . . .

. . . but in the back of the ship, flashes from a watch appear farther apart (time is slower).

you

Al

you

Al

a

b

a In an accelerating spaceship (but not in one at constant velocity), time must run faster at the front end and more slowly at the back end. The yellow dots represent the flashes from the watches, and the spacing between the dots represents the time between the flashes.

b By the equivalence principle, time must also run more slowly at lower altitudes in a gravitational field.

FIGURE S3.16 Gravity causes time to run more slowly at lower altitudes than at higher altitudes, an effect called *gravitational time dilation*. (Note that the effect occurs even in a uniform gravitational field; that is, it does not depend on the additional fact that gravity tends to weaken at higher altitudes.)

S3.4 TESTING GENERAL RELATIVITY

Starting from the principle of equivalence, we've used logic and analogies to develop the ideas of general relativity. However, as always, we should not accept these logical conclusions unless they withstand observational and experimental tests.

How do we test the predictions of the general theory of relativity?

Like the predictions of special relativity, those of general relativity have faced many tests and have passed with flying colors. Let's examine some of the most important tests of general relativity.

Mercury's Peculiar Orbit The first observational test passed by the theory of general relativity concerned the orbit of the planet Mercury. Newton's law of gravity predicts that Mercury's orbit should precess slowly around the Sun because of the gravitational influences of other planets (FIGURE S3.17). Careful observations of Mercury's orbit during the 19th century showed that it does indeed precess, but careful calculations made with Newton's law of gravity could not completely account for the observed precession. Although the discrepancy was small, further observations verified that it was real.

Einstein was aware of this discrepancy and, from the time he first thought of the equivalence principle in 1907, he hoped he would be able to explain it. When he finally succeeded in November 1915, he was so excited that he was unable to work for the next 3 days. He later called the moment of this success the high point of his scientific life.

In essence, Einstein showed that the discrepancy arose because Newton's law of gravity assumes that time is absolute

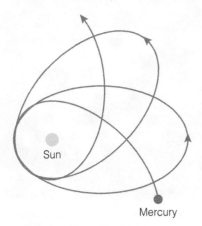

Note: The amount of precession with each orbit is highly exaggerated in this picture.

FIGURE S3.17 Mercury's orbit slowly precesses around the Sun.

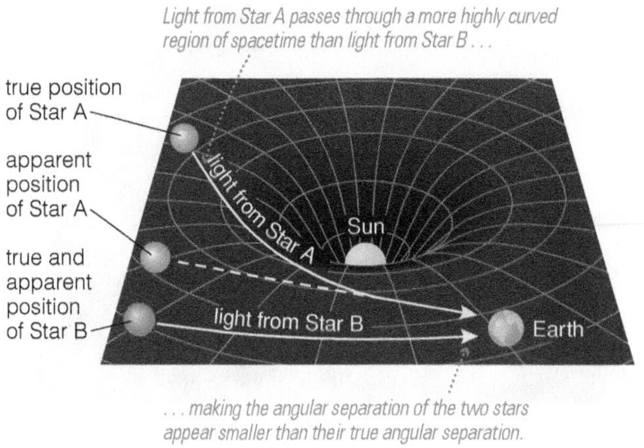

Light from Star A passes through a more highly curved region of spacetime than light from Star B . . .

true position of Star A

apparent position of Star A

true and apparent position of Star B

light from Star A

Sun

light from Star B

Earth

. . . making the angular separation of the two stars appear smaller than their true angular separation.

FIGURE S3.18 When we see starlight that passes near the Sun during a total eclipse, the curvature of spacetime causes a shift in the star's apparent position.

and space is flat. In reality, time runs more slowly and space is more curved on the part of Mercury's orbit that is nearer the Sun. The equations of general relativity take this distortion of spacetime into account, providing a predicted orbit for Mercury that precisely matches its observed orbit.

Gravitational Lensing We can test Einstein's claim that space is curved by observing the trajectories of light rays moving through the universe. Because light always travels at the same speed, which means it never accelerates or decelerates, light must always follow the straightest possible path. If space itself is curved, then light paths will appear curved as well.

Suppose we could carefully measure the angular separation between two stars during the daytime just when the light from one of the stars passed near the Sun. The curvature of space near the Sun should cause the light beam passing closer to the Sun to curve more than the light beam from the other star (FIGURE S3.18). Therefore, the apparent angular separation of the two stars should be smaller than their true angular separation (which we would know from nighttime measurements). This effect was first observed in 1919, when astronomers traveled far and wide to measure stellar positions near the Sun during a total eclipse. The results agreed with Einstein's predictions, and the media attention drawn by the eclipse expeditions brought Einstein worldwide fame.

Even more dramatic effects occur when a distant star or galaxy, as seen from Earth, lies directly behind another object with a strong gravitational field (FIGURE S3.19). The mass of the intervening object curves spacetime in its vicinity, altering the trajectories of light beams passing nearby. Different light paths can curve so much that they end up converging at

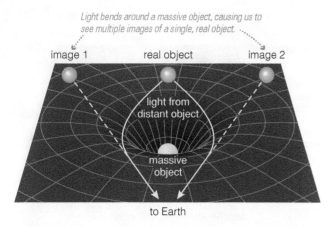

Light bends around a massive object, causing us to see multiple images of a single, real object.

image 1   real object   image 2

light from distant object

massive object

to Earth

FIGURE S3.19 Gravitational lensing can create distorted or multiple images of a distant object whose light passes by a massive object on its way to Earth.

Earth, grossly distorting the appearance of the star or galaxy. Depending on the precise four-dimensional geometry of spacetime between us and the observed star or galaxy, the image we see may be magnified or distorted into arcs, rings, or multiple images of the same object (**FIGURE S3.20**). This type of distortion is called **gravitational lensing**, analogous to the lensing of light when it is bent by a glass lens.

Gravitational lensing can be used to search for objects within the Milky Way that are too small and dim to be seen by their own light, such as dim stars, planets, or even black holes. If such an object happens to drift across our line of sight to a brighter but more distant star, the small object's gravity will focus more of the star's light directly toward Earth. The distant star will therefore appear brighter than usual for days or weeks as the lensing object passes in front of it, in what is often called a *microlensing* event (**FIGURE S3.21**). We cannot see the object that causes the microlensing itself, but the duration of the event reveals its mass. Over the past couple of decades, astronomers have undertaken several large observational programs to search for microlensing events. These studies have helped place constraints on the number of small, dim objects that inhabit our galaxy, and in some cases have even been used to identify extrasolar planets [**Section 13.1**]. We'll see more examples of gravitational lensing in Chapter 23.

Gravitational Time Dilation We can test the prediction of gravitational time dilation by comparing clocks located in places with different gravitational field strengths. Even in Earth's weak gravity, experiments demonstrate that clocks at low altitude tick more slowly than identical clocks at higher altitude; recent experiments at the National Institute of Standards and Technology successfully measured gravitational time dilation over a distance of only 1 meter. Although the effect would add up to only a few billionths of a second over a human lifetime, the differences agree precisely with the predictions of general relativity. In fact, the global positioning system (GPS) takes these effects into account; if it didn't, it would be far less accurate in locating positions on Earth.

Surprisingly, it's even easier to compare the passage of time on Earth with the passage of time on the surface of the Sun and other stars. Because stellar gases emit and absorb *spectral lines* with particular frequencies [**Section 5.4**], they serve as natural atomic clocks. Suppose that, in a laboratory on Earth, we find that a particular type of gas emits a spectral

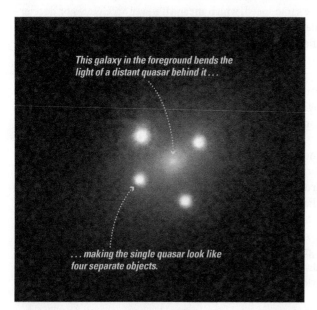

This galaxy in the foreground bends the light of a distant quasar behind it . . .

. . . making the single quasar look like four separate objects.

a This Hubble Space Telescope image shows an *Einstein cross*, in which light from a single distant quasar has been bent so that it reaches us along four different paths, creating four distinct images of the single object.

This massive foreground galaxy distorts the light of a distant galaxy behind it . . .

. . . creating this blue ring of light.

b The blue ring in this Hubble Space Telescope image, called an *Einstein ring*, is an example of the gravitational lensing that occurs when one galaxy lies almost directly behind another.

FIGURE S3.20 Examples of gravitational lensing.

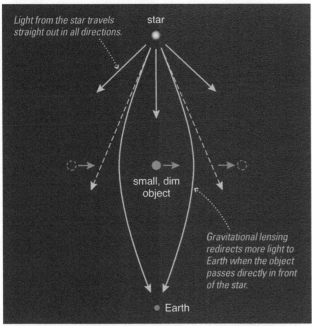

Light from the star travels straight out in all directions.

star

small, dim object

Gravitational lensing redirects more light to Earth when the object passes directly in front of the star.

Earth

Result: Images show the star appearing brighter during the lensing event.

before   during   after

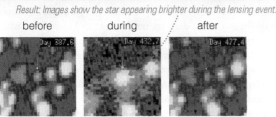

Day 387.6   Day 432.7   Day 477.4

FIGURE S3.21 When a small, dim object (such as a dim star, a planet, or a black hole) passes in front of a brighter, more distant star, gravitational lensing temporarily makes the star appear brighter. Because of the small objects involved, this type of gravitational lensing is often called *microlensing*.

line with a frequency of 500 trillion cycles per second. If this same gas is present on the Sun, it will also emit a spectral line with a frequency of 500 trillion cycles per second.

However, general relativity claims that time should be running slightly more slowly on the Sun than on Earth. That is, 1 second on the Sun lasts *longer* than 1 second on Earth, or, equivalently, a second on Earth is shorter than a second on the Sun. During 1 second on Earth, we therefore see *fewer* than 500 trillion cycles from the gas on the Sun. Because lower frequency means longer, or redder, wavelengths, the spectral lines from the Sun ought to be *redshifted*. This redshift has nothing to do with the Doppler shifts that we see from moving objects [**Section 5.4**]. Instead, it is a **gravitational redshift**, caused by the fact that time runs more slowly in gravitational fields. Gravitational redshifts have been measured for spectral lines from the Sun and from many other stars. The results agree with the predictions of general relativity, confirming that time slows down in stronger gravitational fields.

What are gravitational waves?

According to general relativity, a sudden change in the curvature of space in one place should propagate outward through space like ripples on a pond. For example, the effect of a star suddenly imploding or exploding should be rather like the effect of dropping a rock into a pond, and two massive stars orbiting each other closely and rapidly should generate ripples of curvature in space rather like those of a blade turning in water. Einstein called these ripples **gravitational waves**. Similar in character to light waves but far weaker, gravitational waves are predicted to have no mass and to travel at the speed of light. But do they actually exist?

The distortions of space carried by gravitational waves should compress and expand objects as they pass by. In principle, we could detect gravitational waves by looking for such waves of compression and expansion, but these effects are expected to be extremely weak. So far, no one has succeeded in making an unambiguous detection of gravitational waves, though efforts are under way in several different nations. In the United States, the best known is the *Laser Interferometer Gravitational-Wave Observatory* (LIGO), which currently consists of large detectors in Louisiana and Washington State that search in tandem for telltale signs of gravitational waves.

Despite the lack of direct detection, scientists are quite confident that gravitational waves exist because of a special set of observations carried out since 1974, when astronomers Russell Hulse and Joseph Taylor discovered an unusual binary star system in which both stars are highly compressed *neutron stars* [**Section 18.2**]. The small sizes of these objects allow them to orbit each other extremely closely and rapidly. General relativity predicts that this system should be emitting a substantial amount of energy in gravitational waves. If the system is losing energy to these waves, the orbits of the two stars should steadily decay. Observations show that the rate at which the orbital period is decreasing matches the prediction of general relativity, a strong suggestion that the system really is losing energy by emitting gravitational waves (**FIGURE S3.22**). Indeed, in 1993 Hulse and Taylor received the Nobel Prize for their discovery, indicating that the scientific community believes their work all but

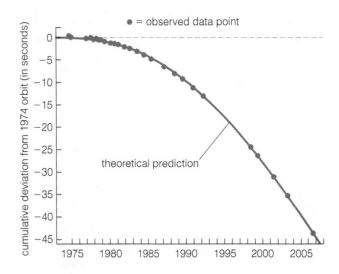

FIGURE S3.22 The decrease in the orbital period of the Hulse-Taylor binary star system matches what we expect if the system is emitting gravitational waves. (Data courtesy of Joel Weisberg and Joseph Taylor.)

settled the case for gravitational waves. In 2003, astronomers announced the discovery of another neutron binary system with orbits decaying as expected due to emission of gravitational waves. The neutron stars in this system are currently orbiting each other every 2.4 hours, and the energy they are losing to gravitational waves will cause them to collide with each other "just" 85 million years from now.

S3.5 HYPERSPACE, WORMHOLES, AND WARP DRIVE

If you're a fan of *Star Trek, Star Wars,* or other science fiction, you're familiar with spaceships bounding about the galaxy with seemingly little regard for Einstein's prohibition

---

The Twin Paradox

Imagine two twin sisters, one of whom stays home on Earth while the other takes a high-speed trip to a distant star and back. In Chapter S2, we said that the twin who takes the trip will age less than the twin who stays home. But shouldn't the traveling twin be allowed to claim that she remained stationary while *Earth* made a trip away from her and back? And in that case, shouldn't she conclude that the twin on Earth would age less? This question underlies the so-called *twin paradox*. It can be analyzed in several different ways, but we will use an approach that offers some insights into the nature of spacetime.

Suppose you and Al are floating weightlessly next to each other with synchronized watches. While you remain weightless, Al uses his engines to accelerate a short distance away from you, decelerate to a stop a bit farther away, and then turn around and return. From your point of view, Al's motion means that you'll see his watch ticking more slowly than yours. Therefore, upon his return, you expect to find that less time has passed for Al than for you. But how does Al view the situation?

The two of you can argue endlessly about who is really moving, but one fact is obvious to both of you: During the trip, you remained weightless while Al felt *weight* holding him to the spaceship floor. Al can account for his weight in either of two ways. First, he can agree with you that he was the one who accelerated, in which case he'll agree that his watch ran more slowly than yours because time runs more slowly in an accelerating spaceship. Alternatively, he can claim that he felt weight because his engines counteracted a gravitational field in which he was stationary while you fell freely. Note, however, that he'll still agree that his watch ran more slowly than yours, because time also runs slowly in gravitational fields. No matter how you or Al look at it, the result is the same: Less time passes for Al.

The left side of **FIGURE 1** shows a spacetime diagram for this experiment. You and Al both moved between the same two events in

spacetime: the start and end points of Al's trip. However, your path between the two events is shorter than Al's. Because we have already concluded that less time passes for Al, we are led to a remarkable insight about the passage of time: *Between any two events in spacetime, more time passes on the shorter (and hence straighter) path.* The maximum amount of time you can record between two events in spacetime occurs if you follow the straightest possible path—that is, the path on which you are weightless.

The subtlety arises if Al chooses to claim that he is at rest and attributes his weight to gravity. In that case, he might be tempted to draw the spacetime diagram on the right in Figure 1, on which *he* appears to have the shorter path through spacetime. The rule that more time passes on shorter paths would then seem to imply that *your* watch should have recorded less time than Al's. But there is a problem with Al's diagram: If he wishes to assert that he felt gravity, he must also acknowledge that this gravity curves spacetime in his vicinity. This curvature means that his spacetime diagram must be distorted when he draws it on a flat piece of paper.

Al's problem is analogous to that of planning a flight from Philadelphia to Beijing with a flat map. As we saw in Figure S3.11b, the shortest and straightest path is a great-circle route that passes near the North Pole; this path is much shorter than a route following constant latitude. The fact that a flat map makes the constant latitude route appear shorter (**FIGURE 2**) does not change this reality. A flat map of Earth distorts the paths because the actual geometry of Earth's surface is spherical.

Just as distortions on a map do not change the actual distances between cities, the way we choose to draw a spacetime diagram does not alter the reality of spacetime. The solution to the twin paradox is that the two twins do not share identical situations. The twin who turns around at the distant star has a more strongly curved worldline than the stay-at-home twin, which is why the traveler does indeed age less during the journey.

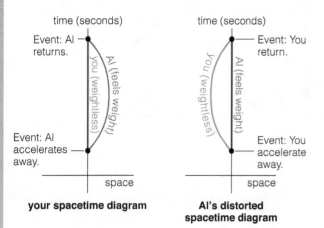

your spacetime diagram   **Al's distorted spacetime diagram**

FIGURE 1 A person floating weightlessly must be following the straightest possible path through spacetime (left). Because this is not the case in Al's diagram (right), his diagram must be distorted.

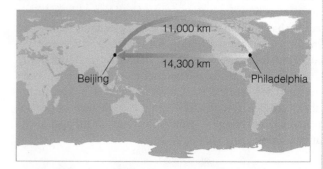

FIGURE 2 This flat map shows the same two paths on Earth shown in Figure S3.11b. However, the distortion involved in making the map flat means that what looks like a straight line is not really as straight or as short as possible.

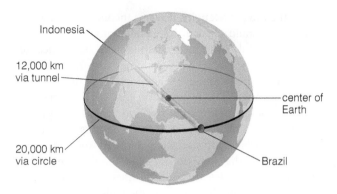

FIGURE S3.23 If you could take a shortcut *through* Earth, the trip from Brazil to Indonesia would be shorter than is possible on Earth's surface.

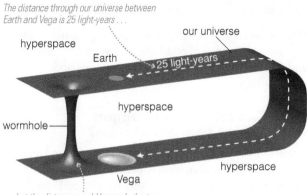

The distance through our universe between Earth and Vega is 25 light-years . . .

. . . but the distance would be much shorter if we could travel through a wormhole.

FIGURE S3.24 The curved sheet represents our universe, in which a trip from Earth to Vega covers a distance of 25 light-years. This trip could be much shorter if a wormhole existed that created a shortcut through hyperspace. (Adapted from a drawing by Caltech physicist Kip Thorne.)

on traveling faster than the speed of light. In fact, these stories do not necessarily have to violate the precepts of relativity as long as they exploit potential "loopholes" in the known laws of nature. General relativity *might* provide the necessary loopholes.

Where does science end and science fiction begin?

Let's begin with an analogy. Suppose you want to take a trip between Brazil and Indonesia, which happen to lie on exact opposite sides of Earth's surface (FIGURE S3.23). Ordinarily, we are restricted to traveling along Earth's surface by car, boat, or plane, and the most direct trip would cover a distance of about 20,000 kilometers. However, suppose you could somehow drill a hole through the center of the Earth and fly through the hole from Brazil to Indonesia. In that case, the trip would be only about 12,000 kilometers. You could thereby fly between Brazil and Indonesia in much less time than we would expect if we thought you could travel only along the surface.

Now consider a trip from Earth to the star Vega, about 25 light-years away. From the point of view of someone who stays home on Earth, this trip must take at least 25 years in each direction. However, suppose space happens to be curved in such a way that Earth and Vega are much closer together as viewed from a multidimensional *hyperspace,* just as Brazil and Indonesia are closer together if we go through Earth than if we must stay on its surface. Further, suppose there is a tunnel through hyperspace, often called a **wormhole**, through which we can travel (FIGURE S3.24). If the tunnel is short—say, just a few kilometers in length— then a spaceship would need to travel only a few kilometers through the wormhole to go from Earth to Vega. The trip might then take only a few minutes in each direction! Relativity is not violated because the spaceship has not exceeded the speed of light. It has simply taken a shortcut through hyperspace.

If no wormhole is available, perhaps we might discover a way to "jump" through hyperspace and return to the universe anywhere we please. Such hyperspace jumps are the fictional devices used for space travel in the *Star Wars* movies.

Alternatively, we might discover a way to warp spacetime to our own specifications, thereby allowing us to make widely separated points in space momentarily touch in hyperspace. This fictional device is the basic premise behind *warp drive* in the *Star Trek* series.

Do wormholes really exist and, if so, could we really travel through them? Is it possible that we might someday discover a way to jump into hyperspace or create a warp drive? Our current understanding of physics is insufficient to answer these questions definitively. For the time being, the known laws of physics do not prohibit any of these exotic forms of travel. These loopholes are therefore ideal for science fiction writers, because they might allow rapid travel among distant parts of the universe without violating the established laws of relativity.

However, many scientists believe we will eventually find that these exotic forms of travel are *not* possible. Their primary objection is that wormholes seem to make time travel possible. If you could jump through hyperspace to another place in our universe, couldn't you also jump back to another *time*? If you used a trip through hyperspace to travel into the past, could you prevent your parents from ever meeting?

The paradoxes we encounter when we think about time travel are severe and seem to have no resolution. Most scientists therefore believe that time travel will prove to be impossible, even though we don't yet know of any laws of physics that prohibit it. In the words of physicist Stephen Hawking, time travel should be prohibited "to keep the world safe for historians."

If time travel is not possible, it is much more difficult to see how shortcuts through hyperspace could be allowed. Nevertheless, neither time travel nor travel through hyperspace can yet be ruled out in the same way that we can rule out the possibility of accelerating to a speed greater than the speed of light. Until we learn otherwise, the world remains safe for science fiction writers who choose their fictional space travel techniques with care, avoiding any conflicts with relativity and other known laws of nature.

S3.6 THE LAST WORD

Having now spent two chapters discussing Einstein's special and general theories of relativity, we are ready to stand back and look at what these theories mean to our understanding of the universe.

How has relativity changed our view of space and time?

In our daily lives, space and time seem separate and distinct, and for most of human history people simply assumed that this appearance must reflect reality. Thanks to Einstein, we now know otherwise: Space and time are intertwined in ways that earlier generations never even began to consider. As Hermann Minkowski said in 1908 (see the opening quote in Chapter S2), "Henceforth space by itself, and time by itself, are doomed to fade away into mere shadows, and only a kind of union of the two will preserve an independent reality."

In the more than 100 years since Einstein first published his special theory of relativity, both the special and the general theory have been subjected to extensive and precise testing. So far, both theories have passed every test. While it remains possible that future tests will force modifications to the theories of relativity, it seems inconceivable that new discoveries could change their underlying message about the intertwined nature of spacetime, with its implications for our understanding of everything from the passage of time to black holes to the overall geometry of the universe.

The astonishing transformation that relativity brings to our view of space and time has also caused philosophers to debate its implications for concepts such as fate and free will. These debates are fascinating and well worth exploring, but remember that they do not affect the data from which the scientific theories are built. In other words, while there are many different viewpoints on the philosophical implications of relativity, only the scientific aspects of the theory are confirmed by data.

With that in mind, let's turn to Einstein himself for our last word on relativity. Here is what he said about a month before his death, on April 18, 1955:

> *"Death signifies nothing. ... the distinction between past, present, and future is only a stubbornly persistent illusion."**

---

*This quotation was found with the aid of Alice Calaprice, author of *The Quotable Einstein* (Princeton University Press, 1996).

The Big Picture

Putting Chapter S3 into Context

Just as the Copernican revolution overthrew the ancient belief in an Earth-centered universe, Einstein's revolution overthrew the common belief that space and time are distinct and absolute. We have explored Einstein's revolution in some detail in the past two chapters. Keep in mind the following "big picture" ideas:

- We live in four-dimensional spacetime. Disagreements among different observers about measurements of time and space occur because the different observers are looking at a single four-dimensional reality from different three-dimensional perspectives.

- Gravity arises from the curvature of spacetime. Once we recognize this fact, the orbits of planets, moons, and all other objects can be understood as natural consequences of the curvature, rather than results of a mysterious "force" acting over great distances.

- Although the predictions of relativity may seem quite bizarre, they have been well verified by many observations and experiments.

- Some questions remain well beyond our current understanding. In particular, we do not yet know whether travel through hyperspace might be possible, in which case some of the imaginative ideas of science fiction might become reality.

SUMMARY OF KEY CONCEPTS

S3.1 EINSTEIN'S SECOND REVOLUTION

- **What are the major ideas of general relativity?** General relativity tells us that gravity arises from the curvature of **spacetime** and that the curvature arises from the presence of masses. This idea leads us to a view of gravity in which time runs more slowly in gravitational fields, black holes can exist in spacetime, and the universe has no center or edges. It also predicts the existence of gravitational waves propagating through space.

- **What is the fundamental assumption of general relativity?** The starting point for general relativity is the **equivalence principle**, which states that the effects of gravity are exactly equivalent to the effects of acceleration.

S3.2 UNDERSTANDING SPACETIME

- **What is spacetime?** Spacetime is the four-dimensional combination of space and time that forms the "fabric" of our universe.

- **What is curved spacetime?** Spacetime can be curved much like a rubber sheet but in more dimensions. We can recognize spacetime curvature from the rules of geometry. The three possible geometries are a **flat geometry**, in which the ordinary laws of flat (Euclidean) geometry apply; a **spherical geometry**, in which lines that start out parallel tend to converge; and a **saddle-shaped geometry**, in which lines that start out parallel tend to diverge.

S3.3 A NEW VIEW OF GRAVITY

- **What is gravity?** Gravity arises from the curvature of spacetime. Mass causes spacetime to curve, and the curvature of spacetime determines the paths of freely moving masses.

- **What is a black hole?** A **black hole** is a place where spacetime is curved so much that it essentially forms a bottomless pit, making it like a hole in spacetime.

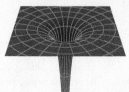

- **How does gravity affect time?** Time runs more slowly in places where gravity is stronger, an effect called **gravitational time dilation**.

S3.4 TESTING GENERAL RELATIVITY

- **How do we test the predictions of the general theory of relativity?** Observations of the precession of Mercury's orbit match the precession predicted by Einstein's theory. Observations of stars during eclipses and photos of **gravitational lensing** provide spectacular confirmation of the idea that light can travel curved paths through space. **Gravitational redshifts** observed in the light of objects with strong gravity confirm the slowing of time predicted by general relativity, a prediction that has also been confirmed with clocks at different altitudes on Earth.

- **What are gravitational waves?** General relativity predicts that accelerating masses produce **gravitational waves** that travel at the speed of light. Observations of binary neutron stars provide strong but indirect evidence that gravitational waves really exist.

S3.5 HYPERSPACE, WORMHOLES, AND WARP DRIVE

- **Where does science end and science fiction begin?** No known physical laws prevent hyperspace, **wormholes**, or warp drive from offering "loopholes" that could allow us to get from one place to another in less time than we could by traveling through ordinary space. However, if any one of them proves to be real, then cause and effect might not be absolute, a proposition troubling to many scientists.

S3.6 THE LAST WORD

- **How has relativity changed our view of space and time?** Prior to Einstein, space and time were viewed as separate and distinct. We now know that they are deeply intertwined as *spacetime* and that understanding spacetime is crucial to understanding many aspects of astronomy, including black holes and the overall geometry of the universe.

EXERCISES AND PROBLEMS

MasteringAstronomy®

For instructor-assigned homework go to MasteringAstronomy®.

REVIEW QUESTIONS

Short-Answer Questions Based on the Reading

1. What do we mean by the *straightest possible path* on Earth's surface?
2. List five major ideas that come directly from the general theory of relativity.
3. What is the *equivalence principle*? Give an example that clarifies its meaning.
4. What do we mean by *dimension*? Describe a *point*, a *line*, a *plane*, a *three-dimensional space*, and a *four-dimensional space*. What does *hyperspace* mean?
5. Explain the meaning of the statement "Space is different for different observers. Time is different for different observers. Spacetime is the same for everyone."
6. What is a *spacetime diagram*? Define *worldline* and *event*. What is the significance of whether a worldline is vertical, slanted, or curved?
7. How do rules of geometry differ depending on whether the geometry is *flat*, *spherical*, or *saddle shaped*?
8. Explain how the idea of spacetime geometry means that the universe has no center and no edges.
9. How can you tell whether you are following the straightest possible path through spacetime?
10. According to general relativity, what is gravity and why does Earth orbit the Sun? Describe both the use and the limitations of the rubber sheet analogy for picturing gravity.
11. What is a *black hole*? What do we mean by the *event horizon* of a black hole?
12. What is *gravitational time dilation*? What determines how much time is slowed in a gravitational field?

13. Briefly describe several observational tests that support general relativity, including Mercury's orbit, examples of *gravitational lensing*, and measurements of *gravitational redshift*.

14. What are *gravitational waves*, and why are we confident they exist?

15. What is the current evidence regarding the possibility of travel through hyperspace, wormholes, or warp drive?

TEST YOUR UNDERSTANDING

Does It Make Sense?

Decide whether the statement makes sense (or is clearly true) or does not make sense (or is clearly false). Explain clearly; not all of these have definitive answers, so your explanation is more important than your chosen answer.

16. The equivalence principle tells us that experiments performed on a spaceship accelerating through space at 1g will give the same results as experiments performed on Earth.

17. The equivalence principle tells us that there's no difference at all between a planet and a human-made spaceship.

18. A person moving by you at high speed will measure time and space differently than you will, but you will both agree that there is just a single reality in spacetime.

19. With a sufficiently powerful telescope, we could search for black holes by looking for funnel-shaped objects in space.

20. Time runs slightly more slowly on the surface of the Sun than it does here on Earth.

21. Telescopes sometimes see multiple images of a single object, just as we would expect from the general theory of relativity.

22. When I walk in circles, I am causing curvature of spacetime.

23. Although special relativity deals only with relativity of motion, general relativity tells us that *everything* is relative.

24. The shortest distance between two points is always a straight line.

25. General relativity tells us that it is impossible to travel through hyperspace or to use anything like *Star Trek*'s "warp drive."

Quick Quiz

Choose the best answer to each of the following. Explain your reasoning with one or more complete sentences.

26. Spacetime is (a) another name for gravity. (b) the combination of time and the three dimensions of space. (c) a curved rubber sheet.

27. The equivalence principle tells us that effects of these two things are indistinguishable: (a) space and time. (b) gravity and acceleration. (c) gravity and curvature of spacetime.

28. The surface of Earth has _____ dimensions. (a) one (b) two (c) three

29. If two lines begin parallel but later diverge, the geometry is (a) flat. (b) spherical. (c) saddle shaped.

30. You know that you are following the straightest possible path through spacetime if (a) you are standing still. (b) you are moving directly from one place to another. (c) you are weightless.

31. According to general relativity, Earth goes around the Sun rather than flying straight off into space because (a) gravity creates an invisible bond holding Earth and the Sun together. (b) Earth is going as straight as possible, but the shape of spacetime makes this path go round and round. (c) in its own reference frame, Earth can consider itself to be stationary.

32. On the surface of which of the following objects would time run most slowly? (a) the Sun (b) an object with the same mass as the Sun but twice the radius (c) an object with the same mass as the Sun but only half the radius

33. Gravitational lensing occurs because (a) gravity causes light to slow down. (b) gravity curves space and light always follows the straightest possible path through space. (c) the effects of gravity are indistinguishable from the effects of glass lenses.

34. Why do we think that gravitational waves really exist? (a) We have observed them with telescopes in space. (b) We have observed orbiting objects that are losing precisely the amount of energy we expect them to be losing to gravitational waves. (c) They are predicted to exist by the general theory of relativity.

35. If wormholes are real, which of the following best describes what one is? (a) a place where it is possible to travel faster than light (b) a shortcut between distant parts of the universe (c) a black hole with a wormlike shape

PROCESS OF SCIENCE

Examining How Science Works

36. *Hallmarks of Science.* Chapter 3 discusses both the idealized scientific method and a set of hallmarks by which you can distinguish science from nonscience. Did Einstein follow the idealized scientific method in his work on general relativity? Does general relativity satisfy the hallmarks of science? Explain.

37. *Why Keep Testing?* General relativity has been extensively tested in many different ways and has passed every test with flying colors. Yet scientists continue to test it with sensitive measurements and attempts to detect gravitational waves. Why do scientists keep testing a theory that works so well? What would happen if it failed some future test? Explain.

GROUP WORK EXERCISE

38. *Einstein's Quote.* Discuss the quote from Einstein at the very end of the chapter, and debate whether the distinction among past, present, and future is real or an illusion. Before you begin, assign the following roles to the people in your group: *Scribe* (takes notes on the group's discussions), *Proposer* (proposes key points on each side of the debate), *Skeptic* (points out weaknesses in proposed arguments), and *Moderator* (leads group discussion and makes sure the group works as a team).

INVESTIGATE FURTHER

In-Depth Questions to Increase Your Understanding

Short-Answer/Essay Questions

39. *Northward Journey.* Suppose two people start out traveling due north from the same latitude, one near Denver and one near San Francisco. Are their paths parallel when they start? Will their paths stay parallel, or will they meet? If they will meet, where will they meet? Summarize your answers with a one- or two-paragraph description of the people's journey, and explain what the results tell us about the geometry of Earth.

40. *Alternative Geometries.* Find an everyday object that obeys the rules of each of the three basic types of geometry—*flat, spherical,* and *saddle shaped.* Describe the object and explain how you know which geometry it has.

41. *Funnels in Space?* Many people have seen rubber sheet diagrams that show black holes looking like funnels, as in Figure S3.15, and therefore they assume that black holes really are funnel shaped. Imagine that you are talking to a person who believes this misconception to be true. Write a one- or two-paragraph explanation in words the person would understand that explains how the misconception arises and what a black hole would really look like if we could see one. (For example, what shape would it be?)

42. *Black Hole Sun.* Suppose the Sun were magically replaced by a black hole of precisely the same mass.
   a. How would the curvature of spacetime change in the region where the Sun used to be located? **b.** How would the curvature of spacetime change in the region of Earth's orbit? **c.** What effect would the change have on Earth's orbit?

43. *Galileo and the Equivalence Principle.* Galileo demonstrated that all objects near Earth's surface should fall with the same acceleration, regardless of their mass. According to general relativity, why shouldn't the mass of a falling object affect its rate of fall? Explain in one or two paragraphs.

44. *Movie Science Fiction.* Choose a popular science fiction movie that depicts interstellar travel and study it closely as you watch it. What aspects of the movie are consistent with relativity and other laws of physics? What aspects of the movie violate the laws of relativity or other laws of physics? Write a two- to three-page summary of your findings.

45. *Research: The Eötvös Experiment.* Galileo's result that all objects fall to Earth with the same acceleration (neglecting air resistance) is very important to general relativity—if it were not true, general relativity would be in serious trouble. Describe the experiments of Baron Roland von Eötvös, who tested Galileo's conclusions in the late 19th century. How did the results of these experiments influence Einstein as he worked on general relativity? Write a one- to two-page summary.

46. *Research: Wormholes.* Some scientists have thought seriously about wormholes and their consequences. Find and read a popular article or book about wormholes. Write a short summary of your reading, and discuss your opinion of the implications of wormholes raised in it.

Quantitative Problems

Be sure to show all calculations clearly and state your final answers in complete sentences.

47. *Worldlines at Low Speed.* Make a spacetime diagram and draw a worldline for each of the following situations. Explain your drawings.
   a. a person sitting still in a chair **b.** a person driving by at a constant velocity of 50 km/hr **c.** a person driving by at a constant velocity of 100 km/hr **d.** a person accelerating from rest to a speed of 50 km/hr **e.** a person decelerating from 50 km/hr to a stop

48. *Worldlines at High Speed.* Make a spacetime diagram on which the time axis is marked in seconds and the space axis is marked in light-seconds. Assume you are floating weightlessly and therefore consider yourself at rest.
   a. Draw your own worldline. **b.** Draw a worldline for Sebastian, who is moving to your right at 0.5c. **c.** Draw a worldline for Michaela, who is moving to your left at 0.7c. **d.** Draw a worldline for Angela, who is traveling away from you at a speed of 100,000 km/s.

49. *Highly Sloped Worldline.* Make a spacetime diagram on which the time axis is marked in seconds and the space axis is marked in light-seconds. Draw a worldline with a slope of 30° (from the horizontal). At what speed would an object have to be traveling to have this worldline? Can any object have this worldline? Explain.

50. *Triangle on Earth.* Draw a simple sketch of Earth (a plain sphere will do), with a triangle on it that connects the following three points: (1) the equator at longitude 0°; (2) the equator at longitude 90°W; (3) the North Pole. What is the sum of the angles in this triangle? Explain how you know the angles, and what the sum tells you about the geometry of Earth's surface.

51. *Long Trips at Constant Acceleration: Earth Time.* Suppose you stay on Earth and watch a spaceship leave on a long trip at a constant acceleration of 1g.
   a. At an acceleration of 1g, approximately how long will it take before you see the spaceship traveling away from Earth at *half* the speed of light? Explain. (Use $g = 9.8$ m/s^2.) **b.** Describe how you will see its speed change as it continues to accelerate. Will it keep gaining speed at a rate of 9.8 m/s each second? Why or why not? **c.** Suppose the ship travels to a star that is 500 light-years away. From your perspective on Earth, *approximately* how long will this trip take? Explain.

52. *Long Trips at Constant Acceleration: Spaceship Time.* Consider again the spaceship from Problem 51 on a long trip with a constant acceleration of 1g. As long as the ship is gone from Earth for many years, the amount of time that passes on the spaceship during the trip turns out to be approximately

$$t_{ship} = \frac{2c}{g}\ln\left(\frac{g \times D}{c^2}\right)$$

where D is the distance to the destination and ln stands for the natural logarithm (which you can calculate with the "ln" key on most scientific calculators). If D is in meters, $g = 9.8$ m/s^2, and $c = 3 \times 10^8$ m/s, the answer will be in units of seconds. Use the formula to determine how much time will pass on the ship during its trip to a star that is 500 light-years away. Compare this to the amount of time that will pass on Earth. (*Hint:* Be sure you convert the distance from light-years to meters and your answer from seconds to years.)

53. *Trip to the Center of the Galaxy.* Use the same scenario as in Problem 52, but this time suppose the ship travels to the center of the Milky Way Galaxy, about 27,000 light-years away. How much time will pass on the ship? Compare this to the amount of time that will pass on Earth.

54. *Trip to Another Galaxy.* The Andromeda Galaxy is about 2.5 million light-years away. Suppose you had a spaceship that could constantly accelerate at 1g. Could you go to the Andromeda Galaxy and come back within your lifetime? Explain. What would you find when you returned to Earth? (*Hint:* You'll need the formula from Problem 52.)

55. *Gravitational Time Dilation on Earth.* For a relatively weak gravitational field, such as that of a planet or an ordinary star, the following formula tells us the fractional amount of gravitational time dilation at a distance r from the center of an object of mass M_{object}:

$$\frac{1}{c^2} \times \frac{GM_{object}}{r}$$

[$G = 6.67 \times 10^{-11}$ m^3/(kg $\times$ s^2); $c = 3 \times 10^8$ m/s.] For example, while 1 hour passes in deep space far from the object, the amount of time that passes at a distance r is 1 hour multiplied by the factor above. (This formula does *not* apply to strong gravitational fields, like those near black holes.) Calculate the amount of time that passes on Earth's surface while 1 hour passes in deep space.

56. *Gravitational Time Dilation on the Sun.* Use the formula given in Problem 55 to calculate the percentage by which time runs slower on the surface of the Sun than in deep space. Based on your answer, approximately how much of a gravitational redshift should you expect for a spectral line with a rest wavelength of 121.6 nm?

57. *Relativity and Fate.* In principle, if we could see all four dimensions of spacetime, we could see future events as well as past events. In his novel *Slaughterhouse Five,* writer Kurt Vonnegut used this idea to argue that our futures are predetermined and that there is no such thing as free will. Do you agree with this argument? Why or why not?

58. *Philosophical Implications of Relativity.* According to our description of spacetime, you exist in spacetime as a "solid" object stretching through time. In that sense, you cannot erase anything you've ever said or done from spacetime. If we could see in four dimensions, we would be able to see your entire past. Do you think these ideas have any important philosophical implications? Discuss.

59. *Wormholes and Causality.* Suppose that travel through wormholes *is* possible and that it is possible to travel into the past. Discuss some of the paradoxes that would occur. In light of these paradoxes, do you believe that travel through wormholes will turn out to be prohibited by as-yet-undiscovered laws of nature? Why or why not?

60. *Person of the Century. Time* magazine chose Einstein as its "Person of the Century" for the 20th century. Find out why, and write a short essay in which you either defend or oppose the choice.

61. *Effects of Earth.* Learn more about two predicted effects of Earth on spacetime, known as *frame dragging* and the *geodetic effect.* Find the current status of efforts to measure these effects, and write a short report explaining how well the measurements agree with predictions of general relativity.

62. *Gravitational Wave Detectors.* Learn more about the Laser Interferometer Gravitational-Wave Observatory (LIGO) or other gravitational wave observatories. Write a short report about how the observatory seeks to detect gravitational waves and its prospects for success.

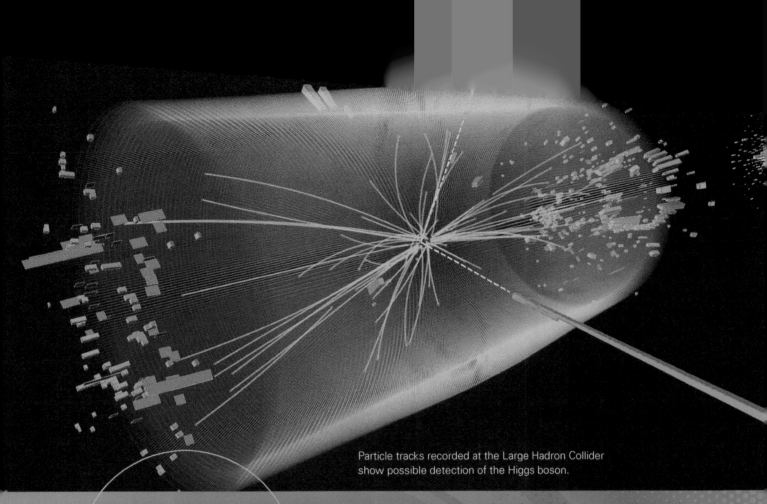

Particle tracks recorded at the Large Hadron Collider show possible detection of the Higgs boson.

S4 BUILDING BLOCKS OF THE UNIVERSE

LEARNING GOALS

S4.1 THE QUANTUM REVOLUTION

- How has the quantum revolution changed our world?

S4.2 FUNDAMENTAL PARTICLES AND FORCES

- What are the basic properties of subatomic particles?
- What are the fundamental building blocks of nature?
- What are the fundamental forces in nature?

S4.3 UNCERTAINTY AND EXCLUSION IN THE QUANTUM REALM

- What is the uncertainty principle?
- What is the exclusion principle?

S4.4 KEY QUANTUM EFFECTS IN ASTRONOMY

- How do the quantum laws affect special types of stars?
- How is quantum tunneling crucial to life on Earth?
- How empty is empty space?
- Do black holes last forever?

There is a theory which states that if ever anyone discovers exactly what the Universe is for and why it is here, it will instantly disappear and be replaced by something even more bizarre and inexplicable.

There is another which states that this has already happened.

—Douglas Adams, from *The Restaurant at the End of the Universe*

The microscopic realm of atoms and subatomic particles seems far removed from the vast realm of planets, stars, and galaxies. Nevertheless, because everything is made from small particles, we cannot fully understand the universe unless we understand the tiny building blocks of the cosmos.

In this chapter, we will look more deeply into the building blocks of nature, investigating current knowledge of the fundamental particles and forces that make up the universe. We will see that the laws of the microscopic world play a crucial role in diverse processes such as nuclear fusion in the Sun and the collapse of a star into a black hole.

S4.1 THE QUANTUM REVOLUTION

Around the same time that Einstein was discovering the principles of relativity, he and others were also investigating the behavior of matter and energy. Their discoveries in this area were no less astonishing. In 1905, the same year he published his special theory of relativity, Einstein showed that light behaves like particles (photons) in addition to behaving like waves [**Section 5.2**]. In 1911, British physicist Ernest Rutherford (1871–1937) discovered that atoms consist mostly of empty space, raising the question of how matter can ever feel solid. In 1913, Danish physicist Niels Bohr (1885–1962) suggested that electrons in atoms can have only particular energies; that is, electron energies are *quantized* [**Section 5.3**]. For this reason, the realm of the very small is called the *quantum realm,* and the science of this realm is called **quantum mechanics**.

How has the quantum revolution changed our world?

Other scientists soon built on the work of Einstein, Rutherford, and Bohr. By the mid-1920s, our ideas about the structure and nature of atoms and subatomic particles were undergoing a total revolution. The repercussions of this *quantum revolution* continue to reverberate today. They have forced us to reexamine our "common sense" about the nature of matter and energy. They have also driven a technological revolution, because the laws of quantum mechanics make modern electronics possible. Most important, at least from an astronomical point of view, the combination of new ideas

and new technology enables us to look ever deeper into the heart of matter and energy—the ultimate building blocks of the universe. In this chapter, we will investigate the following key ideas of the quantum revolution:

- Atoms are built from two categories of particles, called *quarks* and *leptons,* which in turn belong to an even more general category called *fermions.* Photons belong to an entirely distinct category of particles called *bosons.*

- *Antimatter* is real and is readily produced in the laboratory. When a particle and its antiparticle meet, the result is mutual annihilation and the release of energy.

- Four basic forces govern all interactions between particles: gravity, electromagnetism, the strong force, and the weak force. These four forces are themselves manifestations of a smaller number of truly fundamental forces, perhaps even of a single unified force.

- Our everyday experience tells us that particles and waves are different, but the quantum laws show that *all* tiny particles exhibit the same *wave-particle duality* that Einstein demonstrated for photons.

- Quantum laws have astronomical consequences. For example, a quantum effect called *degeneracy pressure* can prevent the core of a dying star from collapsing, *quantum tunneling* helps make nuclear fusion possible in the Sun, and phantom-like *virtual particles* may be important to the ultimate fate of black holes and the universe.

No matter how bizarre the quantum laws may seem, they lead to concrete predictions that can be tested experimentally and observationally. Some of these tests require sophisticated technological equipment found only in advanced physics laboratories. Others require billion-dollar particle accelerators. But some are performed every day, right before your eyes. Every time you see a ray of sunlight, you are seeing the product of nuclear reactions made possible by the quantum laws. Every time you turn on a modern electronic device, the laws of quantum mechanics are being put to work for your benefit. Indeed, almost every aspect of our "information society"—including cell phones, computers, and the Internet—has been made possible by the science of quantum mechanics.

S4.2 FUNDAMENTAL PARTICLES AND FORCES

More than 2400 years ago, Democritus proposed that matter was made from particles that he called *atoms* [**Section 5.3**], which meant "indivisible," because he believed that atoms were **fundamental particles** that could not be divided into smaller units. By this definition, the particles we now call atoms are not truly fundamental. By the 1930s, we knew that atoms are made of protons, neutrons, and electrons. Later, as scientists explored more extreme conditions, they found that protons and neutrons are made from even smaller building blocks, and also discovered a variety of other particles that had previously been unknown.

What are the basic properties of subatomic particles?

Physicists explore the properties of particles under extreme conditions with the aid of *particle accelerators* (sometimes called *atom smashers*). Today, the most powerful accelerator is the Large Hadron Collider on the border between Switzerland and France (FIGURE S4.1). Particle accelerators use large magnets to accelerate familiar particles such as electrons or protons to very high speeds—often extremely close to the speed of light—which leads to a highly concentrated energy release when the particles collide with one another or with a stationary target. Some of this energy spontaneously turns into mass (which is possible because $E = mc^2$ tells us both that matter can be changed into energy and that energy can be changed into matter), producing a shower of particles of many different types.

Careful study of the results from experiments in particle accelerators has led scientists to realize that each distinct particle type has a unique behavior determined by just a few basic properties. The most important properties are mass, electrical charge, and something called *spin*. While mass and electrical charge are familiar from everyday life, spin is evident only in the quantum realm.

Recall that a spinning ice skater or a spinning baseball has rotational angular momentum [**Section 4.3**]. By analogy, subatomic particles have **spin angular momentum**—or **spin**, for short—as they "spin" on their axes. Note, however, that subatomic particles do not really look like tiny spinning balls; rather, *spin* is simply a term used to describe the angular momentum that inherently belongs to a particle. For example, just as all electrons have exactly the same mass and electric charge, all electrons have exactly the same amount of spin. More generally, every particle of a particular type has precisely the same amount of mass, charge, and spin.

Just as electrical charge comes only in distinct amounts—such as +1 for protons, −1 for electrons, and 0 (neutral) for

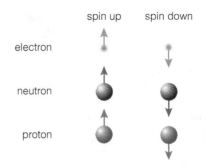

FIGURE S4.2 The two possible states of the spin of an electron, neutron, or proton are spin up and spin down, represented here by arrows.

neutrons—spin also comes in distinct amounts. In the units used in quantum mechanics,[*] values of spin can be either integers (0, 1, 2, …) or half-integers ($\frac{1}{2}$, $\frac{3}{2}$, $\frac{5}{2}$, …). Particles with half-integer spins—which include electrons, protons, and neutrons—can be oriented in two ways, usually called *spin up* and *spin down*. These two orientations, which correspond to the two opposite senses of rotation (clockwise and counterclockwise), are often represented by arrows (FIGURE S4.2). Keep in mind that denoting a particle's spin by an arrow on a small sphere is a representation of convenience and that subatomic particles are *not* tiny spinning balls.

What are the fundamental building blocks of nature?

By the 1960s, scientists had discovered dozens of different particle types, each with a unique set of basic properties. Physicist Murray Gell-Mann made sense of this great variety by proposing a scheme in which all particles could be built from just a few fundamental components, and his proposal soon blossomed into what physicists now call the **standard model**. The standard model has proved so successful that it has been used to predict the existence of new particles that were later discovered in particle accelerators.

In the standard model, the most fundamental distinction between particle types depends on spin. Particles with half-integer spins are known as **fermions**, named for Enrico Fermi (1901–1954); particles with integer spins are known as **bosons**, named for Satyendra Bose (1894–1974). The most familiar fermions are electrons, neutrons, and protons. The most familiar bosons are photons.

THINK ABOUT IT

Another "famous" boson is the *Higgs boson*, which the standard model uses to explain the origin of mass. Detection of the Higgs boson was first announced in 2012. Has this discovery stood up in subsequent research? Is the Higgs boson behaving as expected?

FIGURE S4.1 Aerial photograph of the Large Hadron Collider. The large circle traces the path of the main particle acceleration ring, which lies underground and has a circumference of 27 kilometers.

---

[*]Physicists measure the angular momentum of subatomic particles in units of Planck's constant divided by 2π.

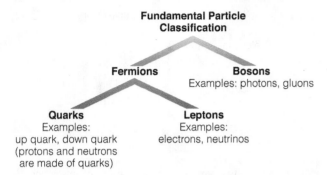

Fundamental Particle Classification

Fermions

Bosons
Examples: photons, gluons

Quarks
Examples:
up quark, down quark
(protons and neutrons
are made of quarks)

Leptons
Examples:
electrons, neutrinos

FIGURE S4.3 Classification of fundamental particles in the standard model.

The fermions are further subdivided into two categories known as **quarks** and **leptons**. Both are thought to be fundamental particles that cannot be divided into smaller pieces, but there are important differences between them. The technical distinction surrounds the way they interact with one another: Quarks interact with one another via the *strong force* (which we'll discuss in more detail shortly) while leptons do not. However, a more practical distinction comes in how the particles are found in nature. Quarks are never seen by themselves, but instead are found in combinations that make larger subatomic particles, including protons and neutrons. In contrast, leptons exist as isolated particles; electrons are the most familiar type of lepton. **FIGURE S4.3** summarizes the basic classification scheme for fundamental particles.

Particles Made from Quarks
Protons and neutrons are the only particles made from quarks that we find in the matter we encounter in everyday life. Protons and neutrons each contain two different types of quarks: the **up quark**, which has an electric charge of $+\frac{2}{3}$, and the **down quark**, which has an electric charge of $-\frac{1}{3}$. (Charge values are in the same units that give +1 for protons and −1 for electrons.) Two up quarks and one down quark form a proton, giving it an overall charge of $+\frac{2}{3} + \frac{2}{3} - \frac{1}{3} = +1$. One up quark and two down quarks form a neutron, making it neutral: $+\frac{2}{3} - \frac{1}{3} - \frac{1}{3} = 0$ (**FIGURE S4.4**).

Although protons and neutrons are the most familiar particles made from quarks, many others have been found through particle accelerator experiments. These other particles are generally short-lived, decaying a fraction of a second after they are produced in collisions. Nevertheless, scientists can observe their behavior during their short lives, usually with detectors placed in or near the particle accelerators.

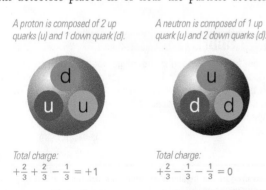

A proton is composed of 2 up quarks (u) and 1 down quark (d).

A neutron is composed of 1 up quark (u) and 2 down quarks (d).

Total charge:
$+\frac{2}{3} + \frac{2}{3} - \frac{1}{3} = +1$

Total charge:
$+\frac{2}{3} - \frac{1}{3} - \frac{1}{3} = 0$

FIGURE S4.4 Protons and neutrons are made from quarks.

TABLE S4.1 Fundamental Fermions

The Quarks	The Leptons
Up	Electron
Down	Electron neutrino
Strange	Muon
Charmed	Mu neutrino
Top	Tauon
Bottom	Tau neutrino

The detectors are designed to record the tracks that the particles leave as they pass through, decay, or undergo other collisions. The photo that opens this chapter shows an example of particle tracks. Careful analysis of such tracks allows scientists to determine a particle's quark composition.

The experiments have revealed several important facts that are now incorporated into the standard model. For example, while scientists have found many particles composed of either two or three quarks, no single quark has ever been detected in isolation. Moreover, despite the fact that individual quarks have charges in units of thirds, the total charge of a particle made from quarks is always −1, 0, or +1. Although we won't make much use of the distinction in this book, particles built from two quarks are known as *mesons* while particles built from three quarks are called *baryons*.*

In addition, experiments show that the up and down quarks that make up protons and neutrons are only two of six different types (or "flavors") of quarks. The other four types of quarks have the rather exotic names *strange, charmed, top,* and *bottom*. The experimental detection of the top quark in 1995—more than 20 years after it was first predicted to exist—was a particularly impressive success of the standard model. The first column of **TABLE S4.1** lists the six types of quarks.

Leptons
The electron is the only type of lepton that we find in the matter of everyday life, but the standard model predicts the existence of six lepton types to match up with the six quark types. Table S4.1 also lists the six leptons. All six predicted lepton types have been identified experimentally.

Note that three of the leptons bear the name *neutrino*, which means "little neutral one." This name reflects the fact that all three types of neutrinos are electrically neutral and extremely lightweight—far less massive than electrons. No one has yet succeeded in measuring the precise masses of neutrinos, but these particles are extremely common, outnumbering protons, neutrons, and electrons combined by a factor of roughly a billion. Nevertheless, neutrinos are so lightweight that they are thought to make up only a small fraction of the total mass of the universe. In later chapters, we will see that neutrinos are very important in several astronomical processes, including nuclear fusion and the explosive deaths of stars as supernovas.

---

*Another term, *hadrons* (which appears in the name of the Large Hadron Collider), is used for any particle built from quarks, which means that mesons and baryons are subsets of the hadrons.

Antimatter Science fiction fans will be familiar with **antimatter**, popularized as fuel for starship engines in the *Star Trek* series. But antimatter itself is not science fiction; it really exists. In fact, every quark and every lepton has a corresponding *antiquark* and *antilepton*. The antiparticle is an exact opposite of its corresponding ordinary particle. For example, an *antielectron* (also called a *positron*) is identical to an ordinary electron except that it has a positive charge (+1) instead of a negative charge (−1). Note that while particles and antiparticles are opposites in most respects, they are *not* opposite in mass; as far as we know, there is no such thing as negative mass, so the mass of an antiparticle is precisely the same as the mass of its corresponding particle.

When a particle and its corresponding antiparticle meet, the result is mutual **annihilation** (FIGURE S4.5a). The combined mass of the particle and the antiparticle turns completely into energy in accord with $E = mc^2$. Because the matter in our universe is predominantly of the ordinary type, antimatter generally does not last very long. Whenever an antiparticle is produced, it quickly meets an ordinary particle, and the two annihilate each other to make energy.

This process also works in reverse. When conditions are right, pure energy can turn into a particle-antiparticle pair. For example, whenever an electron "pops" into existence, an antielectron also pops into existence with it (FIGURE S4.5b). This process of **pair production** conserves charge (and satisfies other conservation laws as well). It happens routinely in particle accelerators here on Earth and on a much grander scale in outer space. In fact, during the first few moments after the Big Bang, the universe's energy fields were so intense

that particle-antiparticle pairs popped rapidly in and out of existence at virtually every point in space.

When we include antiparticles, the total number of types of quarks and leptons really is twice that shown in Table S4.1. That is, there are 12 types of quarks: the six quarks listed and their six corresponding antiquarks (for example, the up quark and the anti-up quark). Similarly, there are 12 types of leptons: the six listed and their six corresponding antileptons. The net total of 24 different fundamental particles seems quite complex.* As we'll see shortly, this complexity leads many scientists to believe that simplifying principles of particle physics still await discovery.

What are the fundamental forces in nature?

Without forces, the universe would be infinitely boring, a uniform sea of fundamental particles drifting aimlessly about. Forces supply the means through which particles interact and exchange momentum, attracting or repelling one another depending on their properties. For example, particles with mass interact with one another via the force of *gravity*, and particles with charge interact with one another via the *electromagnetic* force.

The Four Forces According to present understanding, only four fundamental forces operate under ordinary conditions in the universe today. **Gravity** and **electromagnetism** are the most familiar of the four. The other two known forces are called the **strong force** and the **weak force**.

The strong and weak forces act only on extremely short-distance scales—so short that these forces can be felt only *within* atomic nuclei. You can see why the strong force must exist by remembering that the nuclei of all elements except hydrogen (which has just a single proton) contain more than one proton. Protons are positively charged, so the electromagnetic force pushes them apart. If the electromagnetic force were unopposed, atomic nuclei would fly apart. The strong force, so named because it is strong enough to overcome electromagnetic repulsion, is what holds nuclei together. The weak force, also very important in nuclear reactions, is a bit more subtle. All particles made from quarks respond to the strong force, but neutrinos, for example, feel only the weak force.

According to the standard model, each force is transmitted by an **exchange particle** that transfers momentum between two interacting particles. For example, photons are the exchange particle for the electromagnetic force. To understand the idea, think about how we see a star. Motions of electrons in the star create photons. The photons then cross light-years of space to our eyes, where they generate an electromagnetic disturbance that we see as starlight. In other words, the photons have carried the electromagnetic force from the particles in the star to particles in our eyes.

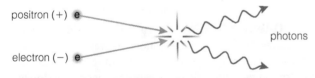

a An electron and a positron (antielectron) collide, resulting in annihilation in which all their energy emerges as a pair of photons.

b The energy of two photons combines to create an electron and a positron.

FIGURE S4.5 Every particle of matter has a corresponding antiparticle. When a particle meets its antiparticle, the result is mutual annihilation. Pair production creates a particle and an antiparticle from energy.

*Moreover, each of the six quarks and six antiquarks is believed to come in three distinct varieties, called *colors*. (The term *color* is not meant to be literal. Rather, it describes a property of quarks that we cannot visualize.) For example, the up quark comes in three colors, often called red, green, and blue.

TABLE S4.2 The Four Forces

Force	Relative Strength Within Nucleus*	Relative Strength Beyond Nucleus	Exchange Particles	Major Role
Strong	100	0	Gluons	Holding nuclei together
Electromagnetic	1	1	Photons	Chemistry and biology
Weak	10^{-5}	0	Weak bosons	Nuclear reactions
Gravity	10^{-43}	10^{-43}	Gravitons	Large-scale structure

*The relative values for the strong and weak forces are rough approximations.

In a similar way, exchange particles called *gravitons* are thought to carry the gravitational force through the universe.* *Gluons,* which get their name because they act like glue to bind nuclei together, carry the strong force. The weak force is carried by particles known as *weak bosons,* which come in three types known as W^+, W^-, and Z. Note that all of the exchange particles are bosons.

Relative Strength of the Four Forces TABLE S4.2
lists the four forces and their exchange particles. It also has two columns that describe the relative strengths of the four forces. One column shows the relative strengths of the forces within an atomic nucleus, and the next shows relative strengths outside nuclei. The values in these columns represent the relative attraction or repulsion that would be felt between two particles affected by the forces. For example, consider the relative strengths indicated for the electromagnetic force and gravity. The numbers in the table mean that if we took two protons and put them a certain distance apart, the electromagnetic force of repulsion between them would be 10^{43} times as strong as the gravitational force of attraction between them. That is why two protons repel each other through their electrical charge rather than attracting each other through gravity.

The relative strengths explain why the different forces tend to be important in different ways. For example, notice that within the nucleus, the strong force is about 100 times as strong as the electromagnetic force. That is why the strong force can hold nuclei together despite the electromagnetic repulsion between protons. The zero relative strength for the strong and weak forces outside the nucleus expresses the fact that these forces vanish beyond very short distances, leaving only gravity and electromagnetism to govern the interactions we notice in our daily lives.

In fact, if you remember that a typical atom (with its electrons) is 100,000 times as large as an atomic nucleus [**Section 5.3**], you'll realize that the strong and weak forces cannot even affect interactions between atoms. Gravity is almost equally ineffective between atoms, because it is so incredibly weak compared to electromagnetism. That leaves electromagnetism as the only force that affects the interactions of atoms—which means it is the one and only force that can group electrons and nuclei into atoms, atoms into molecules, and molecules into living cells. Remarkable as it may seem, the force of electromagnetism governs every aspect of chemistry and biology, and in essence is responsible for the existence of life itself.

Given the extreme weakness of gravity in comparison to the other forces, you might wonder how it can be important at all. The answer is that for very massive objects, gravity essentially wins a game of elimination. As we've already seen, the strong and weak forces cannot operate on large distance scales. The electromagnetic force loses importance for massive objects because it effectively cancels itself out. Like gravity, the electromagnetic force can act on large distance scales; in fact, its strength declines with distance in the same way that the gravitational force declines with distance (according to an inverse square law). However, the electromagnetic force differs from gravity in a very important way: It can be either attractive or repulsive depending on the charges of the particles, while gravity always attracts. Large objects always contain virtually equal numbers of protons and electrons, because if they didn't, the strength of the electromagnetic force would quickly either drive out the excess charge or draw in oppositely charged particles to balance it. The charge balance means that large objects are electrically neutral overall, and therefore unresponsive to the electromagnetic force. Therefore, gravity is the only force left to act between massive enough objects, and it grows stronger as an object's mass grows larger. That is why gravity dominates the structure of the universe on large scales, despite its weakness among individual particles.

The Quest for Simplicity The standard model has four forces that mediate interactions between particles built from six types of quarks and six types of leptons, plus their corresponding antiparticles. It explains many experimental and observational results quite successfully. However, many scientists think that this model is still too complicated. They seek an even more basic theory of matter that reduces the number of forces and fundamental particles.

Theoretical work in the 1970s, verified experimentally in the 1980s, showed that the electromagnetic and weak forces are really just two different aspects of a single force, called the *electroweak force.* Many scientists hope that future discoveries will show three or even all four forces to be different aspects of a single, unified force governing *all* interactions in nature. As we will see in Chapter 22, these *unified theories* might be necessary to understanding what happened during the first fraction of a second after the Big Bang.

---

*General relativity tells us that gravitational waves transmit changes in space-time curvature through the universe, so the correspondence between *gravitons* and gravitational waves is analogous to the correspondence between photons and electromagnetic waves. Gravitons have not yet been detected.

S4.3 UNCERTAINTY AND EXCLUSION IN THE QUANTUM REALM

We often use the word *particles* as if we were talking about objects that you might hold in your hand, but subatomic particles can exhibit behavior that seems very strange to us. In particular, like photons of light, particles of matter can act both as particles and as waves. In other words, all subatomic particles—whether particles of matter like protons and electrons or exchange particles like photons—exhibit what we call **wave-particle duality**.

The fact that matter can sometimes act like tiny baseballs and other times spread out like water waves explains why even professional physicists have difficulty forming a mental picture of the subatomic world. Nevertheless, the science of quantum mechanics allows us to model the properties of matter with great accuracy, which is why we have been able to use it to build computers and other modern electronic devices. In this section, we will discuss two fundamental laws of quantum mechanics: the *uncertainty principle* and the *exclusion principle*.

What is the uncertainty principle?

The **uncertainty principle** was first described by Werner Heisenberg (1901–1976) in 1927. Here is one way of stating it:

FIGURE S4.6 A photograph of a ball taken with a blinking strobe light allows us to determine both where the ball was and where it was going at each moment in time.

The Uncertainty Principle: *The more we know about a particle's location, the less we can know about its momentum, and conversely, the more we know about its momentum, the less we can know about its location.*

We can illuminate the meaning of the uncertainty principle by considering how we might measure the trajectories of a ball and an electron. In the case of a ball, we could photograph it with a blinking strobe light. The resulting photograph would show us both where the ball was and where it was going at each moment in time (**FIGURE S4.6**). In scientific terms, knowing the path of the ball means measuring both

---

SPECIAL TOPIC

What Is String Theory?

During the past 400 years, the history of physics has been marked by discoveries that have revealed nature to be ever simpler. For example, Newton showed that we need only one set of physical laws for both Earth and the heavens, Einstein showed that gravity could be viewed more simply than as a mysterious "action at a distance," and the quantum laws show that forces can be understood through the interactions of exchange particles. Perhaps as a result of this history, most physicists today suspect that nature is even simpler than we now understand it to be in terms of the standard model of fundamental particles and forces discussed in this chapter. Many physicists have devoted their lives to the search for a simpler theory of nature. Even Einstein spent much of the latter part of his life searching for such a "theory of everything."

Many approaches have been tried, but for the past couple of decades many physicists have hoped to discover a simpler model of nature through an approach known as *string theory*. String theory is not really a single theory, but rather a family of theories that share a common idea—that all the particles and forces of the standard model arise from tiny structures called *strings*. The term *string* comes from an analogy to little pieces of string that can be shaped into loops or that can vibrate like strings on a violin. However, the strings of string theory are hypothesized to exist in ten or more dimensions. Aside from the three ordinary dimensions of space and the one dimension of time, the remaining six or more dimensions are thought to be "folded up" in a way that does not allow them to be detected on macroscopic scales. Some variations on string theory include multi-dimensional analogies to membranes, called *branes*, and an idea called *M-theory* unites different versions of string theory.

Despite all the work that has gone into string theory, scientists do not yet know whether the basic tenets of the theory are correct. The problem is that, at least so far, most of the predictions of string theory would be observable only at energies in excess of what current particle accelerators can achieve. Thus, by our usual definitions in science, string theory should really be called "string hypothesis," because it does not meet the high standard of verification required for a scientific theory. (String theory does make some predictions that are consistent with current knowledge of the universe, giving theorists hope that it is on the right track.)

Indeed, in its current form, string theory is really more of a mathematical theory than a scientific one. That is, scientists and mathematicians are developing new theorems as they work out the mathematics of multidimensional strings and branes. Their hope is that as they learn more about the mathematics, they will eventually be able to use it to make testable predictions. Meanwhile, the mathematical results give tantalizing hints of a new view of nature, one that could potentially be as revolutionary as any past revolution in physics.

Nevertheless, it's important to keep in mind that "string theory" has not yet passed the rigorous testing needed to be considered a valid model of the underlying reality of nature. Only through further observations and experiments will we learn whether strings lie at the heart of nature or are simply a dead-end idea that must be abandoned in our ongoing quest to discover an underlying simplicity in nature.

its *location* and its *velocity* at each instant, or, equivalently, its location and its *momentum*. (Recall that momentum is mass times velocity.)

Now, imagine trying to observe an electron in the same way. We will detect the electron only if it manages to scatter some of the photons streaming by it. However, while photons are tiny particles of light when compared to a ball, they are quite large when compared to an electron. The precision with which we can pinpoint the electron's location depends on the wavelengths of the photons. If we use visible light with a wavelength of 500 nanometers, we can measure the electron's location only to within 500 nanometers—which is about *5000 times* the size of a typical atom. That is, if we see a flash of 500-nanometer light from a row of 5000 atoms, we cannot even know which atom contains the electron that caused the flash!

To locate the electron more precisely, we must use shorter-wavelength light, such as ultraviolet light or X rays, but this creates a problem for measuring its momentum. To determine the electron's momentum we must track its path, which means we must observe a series of flashes from the electron's interactions with photons. However, each photon's energy delivers a "kick" that disturbs the electron and thereby changes the momentum we are trying to measure. The shorter the wavelength of the photon—which means the higher its energy—the more it alters the electron's momentum.

It is almost as if nature were playing a perverse trick on us. Locating the electron precisely requires hitting it with a short-wavelength photon, but the high energy of this photon prevents us from determining the electron's momentum. Conversely, measuring the electron's momentum requires hitting it with low-energy photons that will not disturb it much. But because low-energy light has long wavelengths, we'll no longer have a very good idea of where the electron is located.

THINK ABOUT IT

Colloquially, we often express the uncertainty principle by saying that we can't know both where a particle is and where it is going. How does this statement relate to the more precise statement that we can't know both the particle's location and its momentum? In what ways is the colloquial statement accurate, and in what ways is it an oversimplification?

The uncertainty principle applies to *all* particles, not just to electrons. In fact, it even applies to macroscopic objects, meaning objects large enough to be seen without a microscope (*macro* comes from the Greek word for "large"). For example, consider what happens when we observe a baseball with visible light with a 500-nanometer wavelength. Just as with the electron, we can locate any part of the baseball only to within 500 nanometers. However, an uncertainty of 500 nanometers (about 0.00002 inch) is negligible compared with the size of the baseball. Moreover, the energy of visible light is so small compared to the energy of the baseball (including its mass-energy) that it has no noticeable effect on the baseball's momentum. That is why Newton's laws work perfectly well when we deal with the motions of baseballs, cars, and planets; they fail us only in the microscopic quantum realm, where we must deal with the implications of the uncertainty principle.

Wave-Particle Duality Our thought experiment about measuring an electron's position and momentum with photons might at first seem to suggest that the electron somehow "hides" its precise path from us. However, the uncertainty principle runs deeper than this—it implies that the electron *does not even have* a precise path. From this point of view, the concepts of location and momentum do not exist independently for electrons in the way they appear to exist for objects in everyday life. Instead of imagining the electron to be following some complex but hidden path, we need to think of the electron as being "smeared out" over some volume of space [**Section 5.3**]. This "smearing out" of electrons and other particles holds the essence of the idea of wave-particle duality.

If we choose to regard the electron as a particle, we are imagining that we can locate it precisely by hitting it with a short-wavelength photon. In that case, we can measure the electron's precise location at each instant in time but can never predict where it will be at the next instant. In other words, we can see the electron in one place at one moment and in another place at another moment, but we'll have no idea how it passed through the regions in between. If we made many such measurements, we could make a map of an atom in which we used lots of dots to represent electron locations at different times, but we could not draw the electron's actual path between the dots. In fact, a mathematical description of quantum mechanics allows us to calculate the *probability* that we'll find the electron in any particular place at any particular time. **FIGURE S4.7** shows the probability patterns for the electron in several energy levels of hydrogen. The brighter regions in the figure show where the electron has a higher probability of being found at any particular instant.

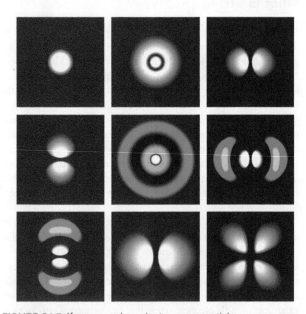

FIGURE S4.7 If we regard an electron as a particle, we can map out its location within the atom at different times. These diagrams show calculated probabilities for finding the electron at various places in a hydrogen atom; brighter regions are those where the probability of finding the electron is higher. The nucleus, which consists of a single proton, is in the center in each case. The nine patterns shown here represent the probability patterns for an electron in nine different energy levels.

FIGURE S4.8 A wave has a well-defined momentum (represented by the arrow) but not a single precise location. If we regard an electron as a wave, we can imagine it as a three-dimensional wave occupying some volume around an atom, but we cannot pinpoint its location.

Alternatively, we can choose to regard the electron as a wave. We can measure the momentum of a wave, such as that of a ripple moving across a pond, but we cannot say that a wave has a single precise location (**FIGURE S4.8**). Instead, the wave is spread out over some region of the water. In the same way, regarding an electron as a wave means that we see it spread out over some region of space; that is, the electron is viewed as a three-dimensional wave surrounding an atom. Note that the wave viewpoint also leads us to conclude that the electron is "smeared out" over some volume of space.

The fact that electrons exhibit both particle and wave properties demonstrates that our common sense about the macroscopic world does not translate well to the quantum world. It also explains what we mean when we say that electrons and other subatomic particles exhibit wave-particle duality. We call them *particles* only for convenience. Like a photon of light, each particle has a wavelength.* When the wavelength of the particle is small, we can locate the particle fairly precisely, but its momentum is highly uncertain.

---

*Electrons usually have very small wavelengths and therefore can be used to locate other particles with high precision. This is the principle behind *electron microscopes,* which use short-wavelength electrons rather than light. Electron microscopes can achieve resolutions of less than 0.1 nanometer, far better than the roughly 500-nanometer resolution of visible-light microscopes.

When the wavelength of the particle is large, its momentum becomes well defined, but its location grows fuzzy.

Quantifying the Uncertainty Principle We can quantify the uncertainty principle with a simple mathematical statement:

$$\frac{\text{uncertainty}}{\text{in location}} \times \frac{\text{uncertainty}}{\text{in momentum}} \approx \text{Planck's constant}$$

Planck's constant is a fundamental constant in nature, rather like the gravitational constant (G) in Newton's law of gravity and the speed of light (c). Its numerical value is 6.626×10^{-34} joule $\times$ s. (We encountered Planck's constant earlier in the formula for the energy of a photon [**Section 5.2**].)

The mathematical statement of the uncertainty principle quantifies what we have already learned: Because the product of the uncertainties is roughly constant, when one uncertainty (either location or momentum) goes down, the other must go up. For example, if we determine the location of an electron with a particular amount of uncertainty (such as within 500 nanometers), we can use the formula to calculate the amount of uncertainty in the electron's momentum. The numerical value of Planck's constant is quite small, which explains why uncertainties are scarcely noticeable for macroscopic objects.

A second way of writing the uncertainty principle is mathematically equivalent but leads to additional insights. Instead of expressing the uncertainty principle in terms of location and momentum, this alternative version expresses it in terms of the amount of *energy* that a particle has and *when* it has this energy. This version reads

$$\frac{\text{uncertainty}}{\text{in energy}} \times \frac{\text{uncertainty}}{\text{in time}} \approx \text{Planck's constant}$$

SPECIAL TOPIC

Does God Play Dice?

Suppose we knew all the laws of nature and, at some particular moment in time, what every single particle in the universe was doing. Could we then predict the future of the universe for all time?

Until the 20th century, most philosophers would have answered "yes." In fact, many philosophers concluded that God was like a watchmaker: God simply started up the universe, and the future was forever after determined. The idea that everything in the universe is predictable from its initial state is called *determinism,* and a universe that runs predictably, like a watch, is called a *deterministic universe.*

The discovery of the uncertainty principle shattered the idea of a deterministic universe because it tells us that, at best, we can make statements only about the *probability* of the precise future location of a subatomic particle. Because everything is made of subatomic particles, the uncertainty principle implies a degree of randomness built into the universe.

The idea that nature is governed by probability rather than certainty unsettled many people, including Einstein. Although he was well aware that the theories of quantum physics had survived many experimental tests, Einstein believed that the theories were incomplete and that scientists would one day discover a deeper level of nature at which uncertainty would be removed. To summarize his philosophical objections to uncertainty, Einstein said, "God does not play dice."

Einstein did more than simply object on philosophical grounds. He also proposed a number of thought experiments in which he showed that the uncertainty principle implies paradoxical results. Claiming that such paradoxes made no sense, he argued that the uncertainty principle must not be correct. In the decades since Einstein's death in 1955, advances in technology have made it possible to perform some of Einstein's quantum thought experiments. The results have proved to be just as strange as Einstein expected them to be, even as they have confirmed the uncertainty principle.

What can we make of an idea, such as the uncertainty principle, that seems to violate common sense at the same time that it survives every experimental test? Under the tenets of science, experiment is the ultimate judge of theory, and we must accept the results despite philosophical objections. In a sense, Einstein's objection that "God does not play dice" reflected his beliefs about how the universe *should* behave. Niels Bohr argued instead that nature need not fit our preconceptions, and he famously replied to Einstein by saying, "Stop telling God what to do."

An amusing way to gain further appreciation for the uncertainty principle in both its forms is to imagine a game of "quantum baseball." Suppose a quantum pitcher is pitching an electron that you must try to hit with your quantum bat. You'll find it extremely difficult. With the first version of the uncertainty principle, the problem is that you'll never know both where the electron is and where it is headed next. You might see it right in front of you, but because you don't know in which direction it's going, you can't know whether to swing straight, up, down, or sideways. With the second version of the uncertainty principle, your problem is that you might know the electron's energy, which tells you how hard you need to swing, but you'll never know *when* to swing. Either way, your likelihood of hitting the electron is completely a matter of random chance, governed by probabilities that can be calculated with the equations of quantum mechanics.

THINK ABOUT IT

Explain why real baseball players don't have the problems that would arise with quantum baseball.

What is the exclusion principle?

The second fundamental law of quantum mechanics, called the **exclusion principle**, was first described by Wolfgang Pauli (1900–1958) in 1925. In its simplest sense, the exclusion principle says that two particles cannot be in the same place at the same time. A more complete understanding of the exclusion principle requires investigating the properties of particles a little more deeply.

The Quantum State of a Particle Scientists use the term *state* to describe the current conditions of an object. For example, if you are relaxing in a chair, a scientist might say that you are in a "state of rest." A more precise description of your state in the chair might be something like "Your current state is a velocity of zero (at rest), a heart rate of 65 beats per minute, a breathing rate of 12 breaths per minute, a body temperature of 37°C, a metabolic rate of 200 Calories per hour," and so on.

THINK ABOUT IT

Suppose you have the following information about the current state of a friend: velocity 5 km/hr, heart rate 160 beats per minute, metabolic rate 1200 Calories per hour. Which of the following is your friend most likely doing: (a) walking slowly as she reads a book; (b) driving in her car; (c) riding a bicycle downhill; or (d) swimming at a hard pace? Explain.

Completely describing a person's state would be quite complicated. Fortunately, it's much easier to describe the state of a subatomic particle, called its **quantum state**. In general, the complete quantum state specifies the particle's location, momentum, orbital angular momentum, and spin to the extent the uncertainty principle allows. Like the energy of an electron in an atom, each property that describes a particle's quantum state is *quantized,* meaning that it can take on only particular values and not other values in between.

Statement and Meaning of the Exclusion Principle Earlier, we described the exclusion principle in simple terms by saying that two particles cannot be in the same place at the same time. Now it is time to state the exclusion

---

MATHEMATICAL INSIGHT S4.1

Electron Waves in Atoms

In the text, we've said that an electron in an atom is "smeared out" over some volume of space. In fact, the physics is much more precise than this vague statement implies. If we choose to view the electron as a wave, an electron in an atom can be regarded as a *standing wave.*

You are probably familiar with standing waves on a string that is anchored in place at its two ends, such as a violin string. Such waves are called standing waves because each point on the string vibrates up and down but the wave does not appear to move along the length of the string. Moreover, because the string is anchored at both ends, only wave patterns with an integer or half-integer number of wavelengths along the string are possible. Other patterns, such as three-fourths of a wavelength along the string, are not possible because they would mean that one end of the string was broken away from its anchor point (**FIGURE 1**).

An electron viewed as a standing wave is anchored by the electromagnetic force holding it in the atom. As is true for waves on a string, only particular wave patterns are possible; however, wave patterns in an atom are more complex because they are three-dimensional. The allowed wave patterns for an electron in an atom can be calculated with the famous *Schrödinger equation*, developed by Erwin Schrödinger in 1926. These wave patterns correspond directly to the allowed energies of the electron in the atom. That is,

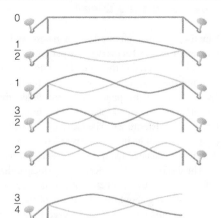

For a string anchored at both ends, waves can have any integer or half-integer number of wavelengths . . .

. . . but no other wave patterns can exist without breaking one end away from its anchor.

FIGURE 1

the Schrödinger equation enables scientists to predict the allowed energies in different atoms. The fact that the Schrödinger equation successfully predicts the energy levels that are measured in the laboratory is one of the great triumphs of quantum mechanics.

principle more precisely. A key point is that the exclusion principle applies only to particles whose spin qualifies them as fermions. For example, the exclusion principle applies to protons, neutrons, and electrons because they are all fermions, but it does not apply to photons because they are bosons. With that in mind, we can state the exclusion principle more precisely as follows:

The Exclusion Principle: *Two fermions of the same type cannot occupy the same quantum state at the same time.*

The exclusion principle has many important implications. One of the most important is in chemistry, where it dictates how electrons occupy the various energy levels in atoms. For example, an electron occupying the lowest energy level in an atom necessarily has a particular amount of orbital angular momentum and a restricted range of locations. The electron's energy level fully determines its quantum state, except for its spin. Because electrons have only two possible spin states, up or down, only two electrons can occupy the lowest energy level. If you tried to put a third electron into the lowest energy level, it would have the same spin—and hence the same quantum state—as one of the two electrons already there. The exclusion principle won't allow that, so the third electron must go into a higher energy level (FIGURE S4.9). If you take a course in chemistry, you'll learn how a similar analysis of higher energy levels explains the chemical properties of all the elements, including their arrangement in the periodic table of the elements (see Appendix D).

The uncertainty principle and the exclusion principle together determine the sizes of atoms and of everything made of atoms, including your own body. The uncertainty principle ensures that electrons cannot be packed into infinitesimally tiny spaces. If you tried to confine an electron in too small a space in an atom, the uncertainty principle tells us that its momentum would become so large that the electromagnetic attraction of the nucleus could no longer retain it. The exclusion principle ensures that each electron has to have its own space. Together, the two fundamental laws of quantum mechanics explain why matter seems solid even though atoms are almost entirely empty space. In the words of physicist Richard Feynman (1918–1988), "It is the fact that electrons cannot all get on top of each other that makes tables and everything else solid."

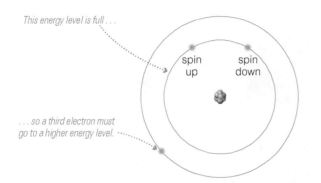

This energy level is full . . .

spin up   spin down

. . . so a third electron must go to a higher energy level.

FIGURE S4.9 The exclusion principle tells us that only two electrons, one with spin up and the other with spin down, can share a single energy level in an atom.

The exclusion and uncertainty principles also govern the behavior of tightly grouped protons, neutrons, and all other kinds of fermions. Just as these principles dictate the sizes of atoms, they also determine the sizes of nuclei, because they limit how closely protons and neutrons can pack together. As we will see shortly, these quantum effects can even influence the lives of stars.

Before we turn to astronomical implications of the quantum laws, it's worth noting that there are also important implications to the fact that photons and other bosons do *not* obey the exclusion principle. For example, laser beams are so intense because many photons *can* be in the same quantum state at the same time. In addition, it is possible under special conditions for two or more fermions to act together like a single boson. Such conditions lead to some amazing behaviors, including *superconductivity,* in which electricity flows without any resistance, and *superfluidity,* in which extremely cold liquids flow with no resistance (viscosity) at all.

S4.4 KEY QUANTUM EFFECTS IN ASTRONOMY

The uncertainty principle and the exclusion principle have clear consequences in the subatomic realm. Amazingly, this microscopic behavior also produces important effects on much larger scales. In fact, we cannot fully understand how stars are born, shine brightly throughout their lives, and die unless we understand the implications of quantum laws. In this section, we investigate four quantum effects of great importance in astronomy: degeneracy pressure, quantum tunneling, virtual particles, and the evaporation of black holes.

How do the quantum laws affect special types of stars?

Under ordinary conditions in gases, pressure and temperature are closely related. For example, suppose we inflate a balloon, filling it with air molecules. The individual molecules zip around inside the balloon, continually bouncing off its walls (FIGURE S4.10). The force of these molecules striking the walls of the balloon creates **thermal pressure**, which keeps the balloon inflated. If we cool the balloon by, say, putting it into a freezer, the molecules slow down. Slowing the molecules reduces the force with which they strike the walls, temporarily reducing the thermal pressure and causing the balloon to shrink.* Heating the balloon speeds up the molecules, temporarily raising the thermal pressure and causing the balloon to expand. Note that thermal pressure gets its name because it depends on temperature.

Thermal pressure is the dominant type of pressure at the low to moderate densities that we experience in everyday life. However, quantum effects produce an entirely different type of pressure under conditions of extremely high density, one that does not depend on temperature at all.

---

*For a balloon, the shrinking (or expanding) occurs only until pressure balance is restored (meaning that the internal pressure is balanced with the combination of the external air pressure and the pressure created by the surface tension in the balloon itself). At that point, the balloon stabilizes in size.

Lowering the temperature reduces the thermal pressure within the balloon, which therefore begins to shrink.

Raising the temperature raises the thermal pressure within the balloon, which therefore begins to expand.

FIGURE S4.10 Thermal pressure is the familiar type of pressure that keeps a balloon inflated. (The dots in this diagram represent molecules, and the lengths of the arrows represent their speeds.)

Consider what happens when we compress a *plasma*, a mixture of positively charged ions and free electrons [**Section 5.3**]. At first, the energy we expend in compressing the plasma makes the electrons and protons move faster and faster, increasing the pressure and the temperature. Now suppose we let the plasma cool off for a while. As the plasma cools, its pressure drops, enabling us to compress it further. Continuing this process of cooling and compression, we can in principle squeeze the plasma down to a very dense state. However, we cannot continue this process indefinitely. According to the exclusion principle, no two electrons in the plasma can have exactly the same position, momentum, and spin. That is, just as in an atom, all the electrons can't get on top of one another at once. The compression must stop at some point, no matter how cold the plasma. This resistance to compression that stems from the exclusion principle is called **degeneracy pressure**.

The following analogy might help you visualize how degeneracy pressure works. Imagine a small number of people moving from chair to chair in an auditorium filled with folding chairs. Each person can move freely about and sit in any empty chair. The chairs represent available quantum states, the people represent electrons darting from place to place, and their motions represent thermal pressure as the electrons move from one quantum state to the next. The exclusion principle corresponds to the rule that two people cannot sit in the same chair at the same time. As long as the chairs greatly outnumber the people, two people will rarely fight over the same chair (**FIGURE S4.11a**).

Suppose ushers begin removing chairs from the front of the auditorium (compression), gradually forcing people to move to the back. Soon, everyone has to crowd toward the back of the auditorium, where the number of remaining chairs is just slightly larger than the number of people. Now when a person moves to a particular chair, there's a good chance that it's already occupied. Ultimately, when the number of people equals the number of chairs, people can still move from place to place, but only if they swap seats with somebody else (**FIGURE S4.11b**). The ushers can't take away any more chairs, and the compression must stop. In other words, all the available states are filled.

The uncertainty principle also influences degeneracy pressure, though in a way that does not perfectly fit this analogy. In a highly compressed plasma, the available space for each electron is very small, which in essence means that each electron's position is precisely defined. According to the uncertainty principle, its momentum must then be extremely uncertain. For the many electrons in the plasma, the great uncertainty in momentum means they must be moving very fast on average. This requirement that highly compressed electrons have to move quickly holds even if the object is very cold.* This quantum-mechanical trade-off between position and momentum is at the root of degeneracy pressure. If you want to compress lots of electrons into a tiny space, you need to exert an enormous force to rein in their momentum.

Degeneracy pressure caused by the crowding of electrons, or **electron degeneracy pressure**, affects the lives of stars in several different ways. In some cases, it can prevent a collapsing cloud of gas from becoming a star in the first place, creating what is called a *brown dwarf* [**Section 16.3**]. In stars like the Sun, it determines how they begin burning helium near

---

*In this sense, an object is *cold* if there's no way to get heat from it. Consider a plasma in which all the available momentum states are filled up to a certain level. To extract heat from the plasma, you'd have to slow down some of its particles. That means moving them to lower-momentum states, which are already taken. The exclusion principle thereby prevents any energy from escaping, so the plasma is cold even though the electrons may be moving at high speeds.

FIGURE S4.11 An auditorium analogy to explain degeneracy pressure. Chairs represent available quantum states, and people who must keep moving from chair to chair represent electrons.

a When there are many more available quantum states (chairs) than electrons (people), an electron is unlikely to try to enter the same state as another electron. The only pressure comes from the temperature-related motion of the electrons, which is thermal pressure.

b When the number of electrons (people) approaches the number of available quantum states (chairs), finding an available state requires that the electrons move faster than they would otherwise. This extra motion creates degeneracy pressure.

the ends of their lives [**Section 17.2**]. When stars die, most leave behind an extremely dense stellar corpse called a *white dwarf*, which is also supported by electron degeneracy pressure [**Section 18.1**].

Not all stars meet this fate, because electron degeneracy pressure cannot grow infinitely strong. Under extreme compression, the average speed of the electrons begins to approach the speed of light. Nothing can go faster than the speed of light, so there is a limit to how much degeneracy pressure the electrons can exert. Once a dying star reaches that limit, electron degeneracy pressure cannot prevent it from shrinking further. The star then collapses until it becomes a ball of neutrons, called a *neutron star* [**Section 18.2**]. Neutron stars support themselves through **neutron degeneracy pressure**, which is just like electron degeneracy pressure except that it is caused by neutrons and occurs at much higher densities. Neutron degeneracy pressure comes into play only at much higher densities because neutrons have much greater mass than electrons. A neutron moving at close to the speed of light possesses over 1800 times as much momentum as an electron moving at the same speed. Therefore, the positions of neutrons can be over 1800 times as precise, enabling them to occupy a much smaller volume of space.

Neutron degeneracy pressure cannot grow infinitely strong either. It begins to fail when the speed of the neutrons approaches the speed of light. At that point, gravity can make an object shrink further, and according to our present understanding, nothing can stop the collapse of an object once its gravity overcomes neutron degeneracy pressure. Such an object collapses indefinitely, becoming a *black hole* [**Section S3.3**].

How is quantum tunneling crucial to life on Earth?

The next quantum effect we'll investigate arises from the uncertainty principle and has important implications not only in astronomy but also for our very existence and for modern technology. Let's start with an analogy.

Imagine that, as the unfortunate result of a case of mistaken identity, you're sitting on a bench in a locked jail cell (**FIGURE S4.12a**). Another bench is on the other side of the cell wall. If you could magically transport yourself from the bench on the inside to the bench on the outside, you'd be free.

Alas, no such magic ever occurs for humans. But what if you were an electron? In that case, the uncertainty principle would prevent us from predicting your precise location. At best, we could state only the probability of your being in various locations. While the probability that you remain in your cell might be very high, there is always some small probability that you will be found outside your cell, despite the existence of the wall. Therefore, you might suddenly find yourself free, thanks to the uncertainty principle (**FIGURE S4.12b**). Although electrons don't get put into jails, an analogous process in which electrons or other subatomic particles "magically" go through wall-like barriers really does happen. We call it **quantum tunneling**.

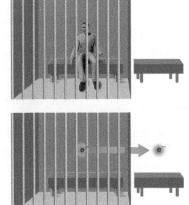

a *A person is confined to the bench inside the jail cell, even though it would take no more energy to sit on the outside bench . . .*

b *. . . but an electron can move to the other side of the wall and become free through the process of quantum tunneling.*

FIGURE S4.12 A jail cell analogy to explain quantum tunneling.

We can gain a deeper understanding of quantum tunneling by thinking in terms of the *energy* needed to cross a barrier. If you are sitting in a jail cell, the barrier is the wall of the cell. The reason you cannot escape the cell is that you don't have enough energy to crash through the wall. Just as the cell wall keeps you imprisoned, a barrier of electromagnetic repulsion can imprison an electron that does not have enough energy to crash through it. However, recall that we can write the uncertainty principle in the following form:

$$\begin{matrix} \text{uncertainty} \\ \text{in energy} \end{matrix} \times \begin{matrix} \text{uncertainty} \\ \text{in time} \end{matrix} \approx \text{Planck's constant}$$

Because of the uncertainty inherent in energy, there is always *some* chance that the electron will have more energy than we think at a particular moment, allowing it to cross the barrier that lies in its way. From this point of view, quantum tunneling comes about because of uncertainty in energy rather than uncertainty in location.

Both points of view on quantum tunneling are equivalent, but the latter viewpoint illustrates a rather remarkable "loophole" in the law of conservation of energy. To cross the barrier, the particle must briefly gain some excess energy. Thanks to the uncertainty principle, this "stolen" energy need not come from anywhere as long as the particle returns it within a time period *shorter* than the uncertainty in time. In that case, we cannot be certain that any energy was ever missing! It's like stealing a dollar and putting it right back before anyone notices, so that no harm is done—except that the particle uses the stolen energy to cross the barrier before returning it.

This tale of phantom quantum energy thefts may at first sound utterly ridiculous, but the process of quantum tunneling is readily observed and extremely important. The microchips used in all modern computers and many other modern electronic devices work because of quantum tunneling by electrons. We can control the rate of quantum tunneling, and hence the electric current, by adjusting the "height" of the energy barrier. The higher the energy barrier, the less likely it is that particles will tunnel through it and the lower the electric current. This control over the electric current is critical to modern electronics.

Even more amazing, our universe would look much different were it not for quantum tunneling. The nuclear fusion reactions that power stars occur when atomic nuclei smash together so hard that they stick. However, nuclei tend to repel each other, because they are positively charged (they contain only positive protons and neutral neutrons) and like charges repel. This repulsion creates an electromagnetic barrier that prevents nuclear fusion under most conditions. Even at the high temperatures found deep in the cores of stars like our Sun, atomic nuclei don't have enough energy to crash through the electromagnetic barrier. Instead, they rely on quantum tunneling to "sneak" through the barrier into the region where the strong force dominates. In other words, quantum tunneling is what makes nuclear fusion possible in stars like our Sun—which means that life on Earth could not exist without it. (Quantum tunneling is not as crucial to fusion in stars that have core temperatures much higher than that of the Sun.)

How empty is empty space?

The same "loophole" in the law of conservation of energy that allows particles to tunnel through otherwise impenetrable barriers also means that space can never be truly empty. According to the uncertainty principle, particles can "pop" into existence from nowhere—their mass made from stolen energy—as long as they "pop" back out of existence before anyone can verify that they ever existed. A somewhat fanciful analogy will help you understand this concept.

Imagine that the law of conservation of energy is enforced by a "great cosmic accountant." (In reality, of course, the law is enforced naturally.) Further, imagine that the cosmic accountant keeps a storehouse of energy in a large bank vault and ensures that any time something borrows some energy, it returns the energy in a precisely equal amount. A particle that pops into existence is like a bank robber who steals some energy from the vault. If the cosmic accountant catches the particle holding its stolen energy, someone will have to pay for the theft. However, the particle won't be caught as long as it pops back out of existence quickly enough, returning the stolen energy before the cosmic accountant notices that anything was ever missing. The length of time the particle has in which to pop back out of existence and return the stolen energy is a time short enough that the uncertainty principle prevents anyone from knowing that energy is missing.

Particles that pop in and out of existence before anyone can possibly detect them are called **virtual particles**. Modern theories of the universe propose that empty space—what we call a *vacuum*—actually "bubbles" with virtual particles that pop rapidly in and out of existence.

You might wonder why a vacuum would seem so empty if it's actually teeming with virtual particles. The reason is that there's usually no way to extract the stolen energy from those virtual particles before they pop back out of existence. Consequently, the real particles that we can detect with our instruments cannot gain any energy by interacting with the virtual particles of the vacuum, making these vacuum particles essentially undetectable. However, the fact that we cannot detect these particles doesn't mean that they are unimportant; theory predicts that virtual particles should exert some measurable effects on real particles, and such effects have indeed been observed in specially designed experiments. For example, theory predicts that placing certain metal surfaces very close together should change the number of virtual photons in the vacuum between them, which should cause a change in the force acting between the metal surfaces. This change in force has been measured, and results agree with the theoretical predictions.

Moreover, the combined energy of the teeming sea of virtual particles in the vacuum, known as the **vacuum energy** (or *zero point energy*), may have a major impact on the universe as a whole. When we apply Einstein's general theory of relativity to the quantum idea of virtual particles, we find that the energy associated with the virtual particles in a vacuum can oppose the gravitational force associated with mass. In essence, the vacuum energy can act as a repulsive force, driving the objects in space farther apart even while the gravity of matter tries to pull them together. That is, the vacuum energy could in principle exert enough repulsion to cause the expansion of the universe to accelerate with time, and strong evidence suggests that the expansion rate is indeed increasing [**Section 23.4**]. However, calculations based on current theories of particle physics predict that if virtual particles were responsible for acceleration, the acceleration would be far greater (by many orders of magnitude) than the acceleration we observe. As a result, the question of whether vacuum energy can explain the acceleration of the expansion remains unanswered.

Do black holes last forever?

Virtual particles are also thought to limit the lifetimes of black holes. We can understand why by extending our cosmic accountant analogy to the case of a virtual electron popping into existence near a black hole. Because electric charge must be conserved (there's no loophole for this conservation law), the virtual electron cannot pop into existence alone. Instead, it must be accompanied by a virtual positron (an antielectron) so that the total electric charge of the two particles is zero. Like all virtual particles, the virtual electron-positron pair essentially comes into existence with stolen energy, so to remain undetected the two particles must return the stolen energy before our imaginary cosmic accountant catches them. They return the energy by quickly annihilating each other (**FIGURE S4.13a**).

However, suppose a virtual electron-positron pair pops into existence very close to, but outside of, the event horizon of a black hole. The electron and positron are supposed to

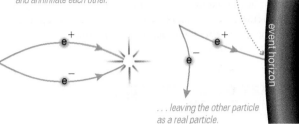

Most of Space	Space Near a Black Hole
Virtual pairs of electrons and positrons continually appear and annihilate each other.	*Near a black hole, one particle may cross the event horizon . . .*
	. . . leaving the other particle as a real particle.

a Pairs of virtual electrons and positrons can pop into existence, as long as they annihilate each other before they can be detected.

b Near the event horizon of a black hole, this same process leads to the creation of real particles, not just virtual ones. The energy to make these particles comes at the expense of the black hole, which loses as much mass as the new particles gain.

FIGURE S4.13 Virtual particles may become real particles near a black hole.

annihilate each other quickly, but a terrible problem arises: One of the particles crosses the event horizon during its brief virtual existence (**FIGURE S4.13b**). From the perspective of our cosmic accountant, this virtual particle was never accounted for in the first place, so there's no problem with the fact that it will never be seen again. But the other particle is suddenly caught like a deer in headlights. Without its virtual mate, it has no way to annihilate itself and is caught red-handed by the cosmic accountant. Because the particle is now holding real rather than virtual energy, the cosmic accountant demands that someone or something pay for the stolen energy. The particle itself cannot pay, because it now has the energy by virtue of its existence and has no way to give it back once its virtual partner is gone. The cosmic accountant

therefore makes the black hole pay for the energy by giving up a little bit of its gravitational potential energy.

If we strip away the fanciful imagery of a cosmic accountant, the end result is the creation of *real* particles, not virtual ones, just outside the event horizon of a black hole. Nothing is escaping from inside the black hole. Rather, these real particles are created from the gravitational potential energy of the black hole. Around the black hole, these *real* electrons and positrons annihilate each other, producing real photons that are radiated into space. To an outside observer, the black hole would therefore appear to be radiating, even though nothing ever escapes from inside it. This effect was first predicted by Stephen Hawking in the 1970s and is therefore called **Hawking radiation**. As we've just seen, the ultimate source of Hawking radiation is the gravitational potential energy, and hence the mass, of the black hole. The continual emission of Hawking radiation must therefore cause the black hole to shrink slowly in mass, or *evaporate*, over very long periods of time.

The idea that black holes can evaporate remains untested, but if it is true, it may have profound implications for both the origin and the fate of the universe. Some scientists speculate that black holes of all sizes might have been created during the Big Bang. If so, some of the smaller ones should be evaporating by now, emitting bursts of gamma rays during their final moments of existence. The fact that we have not yet detected any such evaporation sets limits on the number and size of small black holes that might have formed in the Big Bang.

At the other end of time, if the universe continues to expand forever, black holes may be the last large masses left after all the stars have died. In that case, the slow evaporation caused by Hawking radiation will mean that even black holes cannot last forever, and the universe eventually will contain nothing but a fog of photons and subatomic particles, separated from one another by incredible distances as the universe continues to grow in size.

The Big Picture

Putting Chapter S4 into Context

In this chapter, we have studied the quantum revolution and its astronomical consequences. As you look back, keep in mind the following "big picture" ideas:

■ The quantum revolution can be considered the third great revolution in our understanding of the universe. The first was the Copernican revolution, which demolished the ancient belief in an Earth-centered universe. The second was Einstein's discovery of relativity, which radically revised our ideas about space, time, and gravity. The quantum revolution has changed our ideas about the fundamental nature of matter and energy.

■ Strange as the laws of quantum mechanics may seem, they can be tested and confirmed through observation and experiment. Quantum laws, like relativity, now stand on very solid ground. So far, they have passed every experimental test devised for them.

■ The tiny quantum realm may seem remote from the large scales we are accustomed to in astronomy, but it is exceedingly important. The laws of quantum mechanics are necessary for understanding many astronomical processes, including nuclear fusion in the Sun, the degeneracy pressure that supports stellar corpses, and the possible evaporation of black holes.

S4.1 THE QUANTUM REVOLUTION

- **How has the quantum revolution changed our world?** Quantum mechanics has revolutionized our understanding of particles and forces and made possible the development of modern electronic devices such as computers.

S4.2 FUNDAMENTAL PARTICLES AND FORCES

- **What are the basic properties of subatomic particles?** The three most important properties of a particle are its *mass, charge,* and **spin**.

- **What are the fundamental building blocks of matter?** The **standard model** divides particles into two classes by spin: **fermions**, which include protons, neutrons, and electrons, and **bosons**, which include photons. The fermions are further subdivided into **quarks**, which make up protons and neutrons (as well as many other particles), and **leptons**, which include electrons and neutrinos. There are a total of six different types of quarks and six different types of leptons. Each type of particle of matter also has a corresponding particle of **antimatter**.

- **What are the fundamental forces in nature?** The four fundamental forces are **gravity**, **electromagnetism**, the **weak force**, and the **strong force**. Each force is transmitted through space by one or more **exchange particles**; for example, photons are the exchange particle for electromagnetism. Evidence suggests that the four forces are manifestations of a smaller number of truly fundamental forces.

S4.3 UNCERTAINTY AND EXCLUSION IN THE QUANTUM REALM

- **What is the uncertainty principle?** The **uncertainty principle** tells us that we cannot simultaneously know the precise

 values of an object's position and momentum—or, equivalently, its energy and the precise time during which it has this energy.

- **What is the exclusion principle?** The **exclusion principle** tells us that two fermions of the same type cannot occupy the same quantum state at the same time. This principle does not apply to bosons.

S4.4 KEY QUANTUM EFFECTS IN ASTRONOMY

- **How do the quantum laws affect special types of stars?** **Degeneracy pressure** is a type of pressure that can occur

 even in the absence of heat. It arises from the combination of the exclusion principle and the uncertainty principle. It is the dominant form of pressure in the astronomical objects known as brown dwarfs, white dwarfs, and neutron stars.

- **How is quantum tunneling crucial to life on Earth?** **Quantum tunneling** is a process in which subatomic particles can "tunnel" from one place to another even when they don't actually have enough energy to overcome an energy barrier between the two places. Without this process, fusion in the Sun would not be possible and life on Earth could not exist. It is also important to many other astronomical processes and to modern technology.

- **How empty is empty space?** According to the uncertainty principle, a vacuum cannot be completely empty but must instead be filled with unobservable **virtual particles** that are constantly popping in and out of existence. While virtual particles generally do not affect the particles that we can observe, the **vacuum energy** associated with them may oppose gravity, and in principle could cause the expansion of the universe to accelerate.

- **Do black holes last forever?** No. According to current theory, isolated black holes can gradually evaporate, emitting **Hawking radiation** in the process. Although the theoretical basis of this evaporation seems solid, it has not yet been observed in nature.

MasteringAstronomy®

For instructor-assigned homework go to MasteringAstronomy®.

REVIEW QUESTIONS

Short-Answer Questions Based on the Reading

1. What do we mean by the *quantum* realm? List five major ideas that come from the laws of *quantum mechanics*.
2. What is *spin*? What are the two basic categories of particles based on spin?
3. List the six *quarks* and six *leptons* in the standard model. Describe the quark composition of a proton and of a neutron.
4. What is *antimatter*? What happens when a particle and its antiparticle meet? Why is antimatter always produced along with matter in *pair production*?
5. List the four fundamental forces in nature, and name the *exchange particles* for each.
6. Describe the relative strengths of the four forces. Why does gravity dominate on large scales, even though it is by far the weakest of the four forces?

7. Why do many scientists believe that the standard model will eventually be replaced by an even simpler model of nature?

8. What is the *uncertainty principle*? How is it related to the idea of *wave-particle duality*?

9. Describe two ways of quantifying the uncertainty principle, and give an example showing the meaning of each.

10. What do we mean by the *quantum state* of a particle?

11. What is the *exclusion principle*? What types of particles obey it? Briefly explain how the exclusion principle determines how electrons fill energy levels in atoms.

12. What is *degeneracy pressure*? How does it differ from *thermal pressure*? How is it important in astronomy?

13. What is *quantum tunneling*? How is it important to modern electronics? How is it important to nuclear fusion in the Sun?

14. What do we mean by *virtual particles*? How might they help explain the observed acceleration of the expansion of the universe? How might they lead to gradual evaporation of black holes through *Hawking radiation*?

TEST YOUR UNDERSTANDING

Does It Make Sense?

Decide whether the statement makes sense (or is clearly true) or does not make sense (or is clearly false). Explain clearly; not all of these have definitive answers, so your explanation is more important than your chosen answer.

15. Although there are six known types of quarks, ordinary atoms contain only two of these types.

16. If you put a quark and a lepton close together, they'll annihilate each other.

17. There's no such thing as antimatter, except in science fiction.

18. Some particle accelerators have been known to build up a huge electrical charge because of the electrons produced inside them.

19. According to the uncertainty principle, we can never be certain whether one theory is really better than another.

20. The exclusion principle describes the cases in which the uncertainty principle is excluded from being true.

21. No known astronomical objects exhibit any type of degeneracy pressure.

22. Although we speak of four fundamental forces—gravity, electromagnetic, strong, and weak—it is likely that these forces are different manifestations of a smaller number of truly fundamental forces.

23. Imagine that, somewhere in deep space, you met a person made entirely of antimatter. Shaking that person's hand would be very dangerous.

24. Someday, we may detect radiation coming from an evaporating black hole.

Quick Quiz

Choose the best answer to each of the following. Explain your reasoning with one or more complete sentences.

25. The fundamental particles of matter are (a) atoms and molecules. (b) quarks and leptons. (c) electrons, protons, and neutrons.

26. When an electron is produced from energy in a particle accelerator, the following also always happens: (a) An antielectron (positron) is produced. (b) A quark is produced. (c) The electron disintegrates into a bunch of quarks.

27. Within an atomic nucleus, the strongest of the four forces is (a) gravity. (b) electromagnetism. (c) the strong force.

28. Across a distance of 1 millimeter, the strongest force acting between two protons is (a) gravity. (b) electromagnetism. (c) the strong force.

29. If we measure a subatomic particle's position very precisely, then (a) its momentum will be highly uncertain. (b) its spin will be highly uncertain. (c) we violate the uncertainty principle.

30. In addition to photons, which of the following also behave sometimes as waves and sometimes as particles? (a) fermions (b) bosons (c) all other subatomic particles

31. Which of the following is not allowed by the exclusion principle? (a) knowing both the precise position and the precise momentum of an electron (b) having two electrons in the same quantum state (c) having an electron with a spin that is neither up nor down

32. The strength of degeneracy pressure in an object (such as a white dwarf) depends on (a) its temperature. (b) its density. (c) both its temperature and its density.

33. In which one of the following objects does degeneracy pressure play the most important role? (a) a neutron star (b) the Sun (c) a star 10 times as massive as the Sun

34. According to modern theories based on quantum mechanics, empty space (a vacuum) is (a) truly empty. (b) bubbling with virtual particles. (c) filled with tiny black holes.

PROCESS OF SCIENCE

Examining How Science Works

35. *Hallmarks of Science.* This chapter discussed many ideas that may seem quite bizarre, from the existence of quarks to the uncertainty principle. Choose one of these ideas and evaluate it against the hallmarks of science from Chapter 3. Is the idea science? Defend your opinion.

GROUP WORK EXERCISE

36. *New Particle Discovery.* You are part of a group of scientists doing particle physics research. One of your students runs into your office and says, "I've discovered a new particle!" Make a list of questions that, as responsible scientists, your group should ask and answer before deciding that the discovery is real. Before you begin, assign the following roles to the people in your group: *Scribe* (takes notes on the group's discussions), *Proposer* (proposes key points on each side of the debate), *Skeptic* (points out weaknesses in proposed arguments), and *Moderator* (leads group discussion and makes sure the group works as a team).

INVESTIGATE FURTHER

In-Depth Questions to Increase Your Understanding

Short-Answer/Essay Questions

37. *The Strong Force.* The strong force is the force that holds the protons and neutrons in the nucleus together. Based on the fact that most atomic nuclei are stable, briefly explain how you can conclude that the strong force must be even stronger than the electromagnetic force, at least over very short distances.

38. *Chemistry and Biology.* All chemical and biological reactions involve the creation and breaking of chemical bonds, which are bonds created by interactions between the electrons of one atom and the electrons of others. Given this fact, explain why the electromagnetic force governs all chemical and biological reactions. Also explain why the strong force, the weak force, and gravity play no role in these reactions.

39. *Gravity.* In one or two paragraphs, explain both (1) what we mean when we say that gravity is the weakest of the four forces and (2) why it nevertheless dominates the universe on large scales.

40. *Quantum Tunneling and Life.* In one or two paragraphs, explain the role of quantum tunneling in creating the elements from which we are made. (*Hint:* Recall that we are *star stuff* in the sense

that the elements of our bodies were produced by nuclear fusion inside stars.)

41. *Antimatter Engines.* In the *Star Trek* series, starships are powered by matter-antimatter annihilation. Explain why we should expect matter-antimatter annihilation to be the most efficient possible source of power. What practical problems would we face in developing matter-antimatter engines?

42. *Exchange of Information.* Suppose an electron is moving up and down at some place located far in the distance. How could we learn that the electron is moving? How long after the movement would we know that it had occurred? Does this idea have any practical importance in astronomy? Explain. (*Hint:* Remember that the photon is the exchange particle for the electromagnetic force.)

43. *Nonquantum Baseball.* In your own words, explain why a baseball player does not have to take into account the uncertainty principle when up at bat.

44. *The Electron.* Based on what you have learned in this chapter, how would you explain an electron to a friend? Be sure that you explain why physicists don't think of electrons as tiny, negatively charged, spinning balls. Write your explanation in one or two paragraphs.

Quantitative Problems

Be sure to show all calculations clearly and state your final answers in complete sentences.

45. *Gravity and the EM Force.* In this problem, we compare the strength of gravity to the strength of the electromagnetic (EM) force for two interacting electrons. Because both electrons are negatively charged, they *repel* each other through the EM force. Because electrons have mass, they *attract* each other through gravity. Let's see which effect will dominate. You will need the following information for this problem:

■ The force law for gravitation is

$$F_g = G \times \frac{M_1 M_2}{d^2} \quad \left(G = 6.67 \times 10^{-11} \ \frac{N \times m^2}{kg^2}\right)$$

where M_1 and M_2 are the masses of the two objects, d is the distance between them, and G is the gravitational constant. ("N" is the abbreviation for *newton*, the metric unit of force.)

■ The force law for electromagnetism is

$$F_{EM} = k \frac{q_1 q_2}{d^2} \quad \left(k = 9.0 \times 10^9 \ \frac{N \times m^2}{Coul^2}\right)$$

where q_1 and q_2 are the *charges* of the two objects (in *coulombs*, the standard unit of charge), d is the distance between them, and k is a constant. ("Coul" is an abbreviation for *coulomb*.)

■ The *mass* of an electron is 9.10×10^{-31} kg.

■ The *charge* of an electron is -1.6×10^{-19} Coul.

a. Calculate the gravitational force, in newtons, that attracts the two electrons if a distance of 10^{-10} (about the diameter of an atom) separates them. **b.** Calculate the electromagnetic force, in newtons, that repels the two electrons at the same distance. **c.** How many times stronger is the electromagnetic repulsion than the gravitational attraction for the two electrons?

46. *Large-Scale Gravity.* Suppose Earth and the Sun each had an excess charge equivalent to the charge of just one electron. Using the data from Problem 45, compare the gravitational force between Earth and the Sun to the electromagnetic force between them in that case. What does your answer tell you about why gravity dominates on large scales? (*Hint:* See Appendix E for the data you'll need about Earth and the Sun.)

47. *Evaporation of Black Holes.* The time it takes for a black hole to evaporate through the process of Hawking radiation can be calculated using the following formula, in which M is the mass of the black hole in kilograms and t is the lifetime of the black hole in seconds:

$$t = 10,240\pi^2 \ \frac{G^2 M^3}{hc^4}$$

$$\left(h = 6.63 \times 10^{-34} \ \frac{kg \times m^2}{s}, G = 6.67 \times 10^{-11} \ \frac{m^3}{kg \times s^2}\right)$$

Without doing any calculations, explain how this formula implies that lower-mass black holes have much shorter lifetimes than more massive ones and that the evaporation process accelerates as a black hole loses mass.

48. *Solar Mass Black Holes.* Use the formula from Problem 47 to calculate the lifetime of a black hole with the mass of the Sun ($M_{Sun} = 2.0 \times 10^{30}$ kg). How does your answer compare to the current age of the universe?

49. *Long-Lived Black Holes.* Some scientists speculate that in the far distant future, the universe will consist only of gigantic black holes and scattered subatomic particles. The largest black holes that conceivably might form would have a mass of about a trillion (10^{12}) Suns. Using the formula from Problem 47, calculate the lifetime of such a giant black hole. How does your answer compare to the current age of the universe? (*Hint:* Your calculator may not be able to handle the large numbers involved in this problem, in which case you will need to rearrange the numbers so that you can calculate the powers of 10 without your calculator.)

50. *Mini–Black Holes.* Some scientists speculate that black holes of many different masses might have been formed during the early moments of the Big Bang. Some of these black holes might be mini–black holes, much smaller in mass than those that can be formed by the crush of gravity in today's universe. Use the formula from Problem 47 to calculate the lifetime of a mini–black hole with the mass of Earth (about 6×10^{24} kg). Compare this to the current age of the universe.

51. *Black Holes Evaporating Today.* Starting with the formula from Problem 47, calculate the mass of a mini–black hole that was formed in the Big Bang and would be completing its evaporation today. Compare your answer to the mass of Earth. Assume that the universe is 14 billion years old.

52. *Your Quantum Uncertainty.* Suppose you are running at a speed of about 10 km/hr, but there is an uncertainty of 0.5 km/hr in your precise speed. Given your mass, you can calculate your momentum and the uncertainty of that momentum. What is the corresponding quantum limit to the measurement of your position? Is this significant? Why or why not? (*Hint:* You'll need the first form of the uncertainty principle given on page 451; you can use the value of Planck's constant, h, from Problem 47.)

53. *An Electron's Quantum Uncertainty.* You are conducting an experiment in which you can measure the location of individual electron collisions to within 10^{-10} m. What is the theoretical limit to which you can simultaneously measure the momentum of those collisions? What is the uncertainty in the electron's speed? (The electron has a rest mass of 9.1×10^{-31} kg.)

Discussion Questions

54. *Big Science.* Large particle accelerators cost billions of dollars, more even than large telescopes in space. If you were a member of Congress and the government could afford either a new accelerator or a new large space observatory, which would you choose? Why?

55. *The Meaning of the Uncertainty Principle.* When they first hear about it, many people assume that the uncertainty principle means that we cannot *measure* the position and momentum of a particle precisely. According to current understanding, it really tells us that the particle *does not have* a precise position and momentum in the sense that we would expect from everyday life. How do these two viewpoints differ? Discuss the different philosophical consequences of these two viewpoints.

56. *Common Sense vs. Experiment.* Even the most highly trained physicists find the results of quantum mechanics to be strange and counter to their everyday common sense, yet the predictions of quantum mechanics have passed every experimental test yet posed for them. Does this difficulty in reconciling common sense with experiment or theory pose any problems for science? Defend your opinion.

57. *The Large Hadron Collider.* Visit the website for the Large Hadron Collider. What is its current status? What scientific discoveries has it made, and what hopes do scientists have for it in the future? Write a short report about what you learn.

58. *Quantum Computing.* Learn how computer scientists hope to harness quantum effects to build computers much more powerful than any existing today. Briefly summarize the ideas, and write an essay stating your opinion concerning the benefits and drawbacks of developing this technology.

59. *Beyond the Standard Model.* Research some of the ideas that physicists are considering as possible improvements on the standard model. Choose one such idea, and write a short essay describing its potential effect on physics if it is correct, and how the idea may be tested.

We all have "common sense" ideas about the meaning of space, time, matter, and energy, and in most cases these common-sense ideas serve us quite well. But when we look more closely, we find that our everyday ideas cannot explain all that we observe in nature. The theories of relativity and quantum mechanics have given us a deeper understanding of the nature of space, time, matter, and energy—an understanding that now underlies almost all of our modern understanding of the universe.

(1) **Time Dilation:** Einstein's theory of relativity is based on two simple principles: (1) the laws of nature are the same for everyone, and (2) the speed of light is the same for everyone. One implication of these principles is that the passage of time is relative—time can run at different speeds for different observers. Many observations have confirmed this mind-boggling prediction of relativity, and astronomers must account for it when studying the universe [Chapter S2].

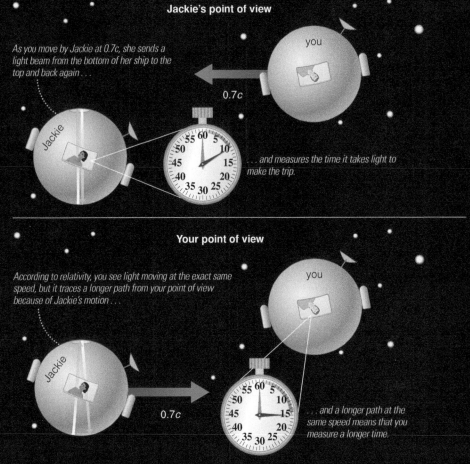

Jackie's point of view

As you move by Jackie at 0.7c, she sends a light beam from the bottom of her ship to the top and back again . . .

you

0.7c

Jackie

. . . and measures the time it takes light to make the trip.

Your point of view

According to relativity, you see light moving at the exact same speed, but it traces a longer path from your point of view because of Jackie's motion . . .

you

Jackie

0.7c

. . . and a longer path at the same speed means that you measure a longer time.

Your conclusion: Time is running slower on Jackie's ship than on yours!

(2) **Matter and Antimatter:** Relativity tells us that mass and energy are equivalent: $E = mc^2$. This formula explains how small amounts of matter can release huge amounts of energy, and how matter-antimatter particle pairs can be produced from pure energy. Pair production has been observed countless times in Earth-based particle accelerators and is crucial to our models of the early universe [Sections S4.2, 22.1].

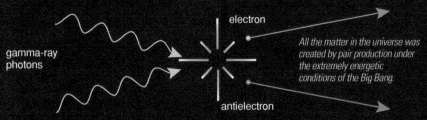

electron

gamma-ray photons

All the matter in the universe was created by pair production under the extremely energetic conditions of the Big Bang.

antielectron

③ Curvature of Spacetime: Special relativity tells us that space and time are inextricably linked as four-dimensional spacetime, and general relativity tells us that gravity arises from curvature of spacetime. Astronomical observations, both in our solar system and beyond, have confirmed Einstein's predictions about the structure of space and time [Chapter S3, Section 23.2].

Curvature of spacetime precisely explains the precession of Mercury's elliptical orbit around the Sun.

Spacetime curvature also explains the bending of light known as gravitational lensing.

The gravity of the galaxy at the center of this image bends the light from a single object behind it

Sun

Mercury

light from distant object

massive object

to Earth

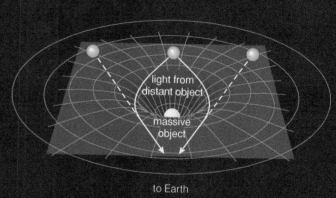

. . . producing four distinct images of the object.

④ Black Holes: Relativity predicts that there can be objects whose gravity is so strong that nothing can escape from inside them— not even light. Observations of these *black holes* help us test the most extreme predictions of relativity [Sections S3.3, 18.3, 19.4].

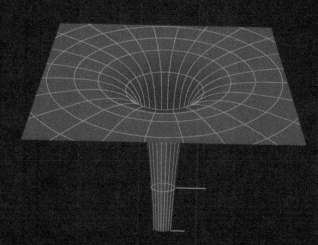

Squeezing a star down to the size of a small city would make the curvature of spacetime (gravity) around it so extreme that the star would turn into a black hole.

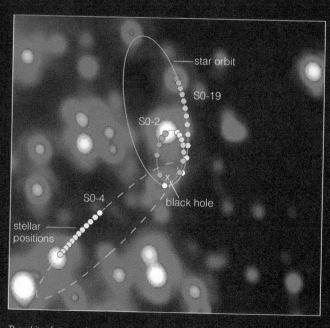

star orbit

S0-19

S0-2

S0-4

black hole

stellar positions

The orbits of stars at the center of the Milky Way Galaxy indicate that it contains a black hole more than 3 million times as massive as our Sun.

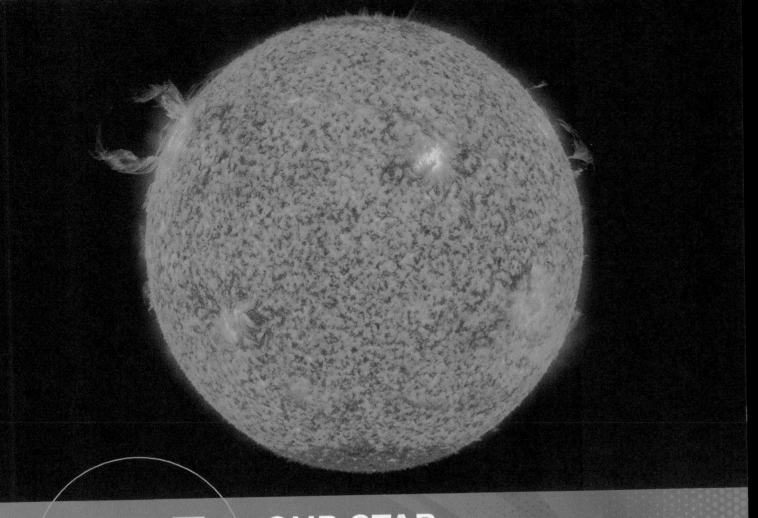

14 OUR STAR

Give me the splendid silent sun with all his beams full-dazzling.
—Walt Whitman (1819–1892), from Leaves of Grass

Astronomy today encompasses the study of the entire universe, but the root of the word *astronomy* comes from the Greek word for "star." Although we have learned a lot about the universe up to this point in the book, only now do we turn our attention to the study of the stars, the namesakes of astronomy.

When we think of stars, we usually think of the beautiful points of light visible on a clear night. But the nearest and most easily studied star is visible only in the daytime—our Sun. In this chapter, we will study the Sun in some detail. We will see how the Sun generates the energy that supports life on Earth. Equally important, we will study our Sun as a star so that it can serve as an introduction to subsequent chapters in which we will study stars throughout the universe.

MA The Sun Tutorial, Lesson 1

14.1 A CLOSER LOOK AT THE SUN

Most people know that the Sun is a star—a giant ball of hot gas that generates light and shines it brightly in all directions. However, scientists realized this fact only quite recently in human history. In this section, we'll consider the age-old question of what makes the Sun shine, and then take an imaginary plunge into the Sun that will get us better acquainted with its general features.

Why does the Sun shine?

The Sun's energy is vital to human existence. Ancient peoples certainly recognized that fact. Some worshipped the Sun as a god. Others created mythologies to explain its daily rise and set. But no one who lived before the 20th century knew the energy source for the Sun's light and heat.

Ancient Ideas Most ancient thinkers imagined the Sun to be some type of fire, perhaps a lump of burning coal or wood. It was a reasonable suggestion for the times, since the idea could not yet be tested. Ancient people did not know the size or distance of the Sun, so they could not imagine how incredible its energy output really is. Nor did they know how long Earth had existed, so they had no way to realize that the Sun has provided light and heat for a very long time.

Modern scientists began to address the question of how the Sun shines around the middle of the 19th century, by which time the Sun's size and distance had been measured with reasonable accuracy. The ancient idea of the Sun being fueled by burning coal or wood was quickly ruled out: Calculations showed that such burning could not possibly account for the Sun's huge output of energy. Other ideas based on chemical processes were likewise ruled out.

Gravitational Contraction In the late 19th century, astronomers came up with an idea that seemed more plausible, at least at first. They suggested that the Sun generates energy by slowly contracting in size, a process called **gravitational contraction** (or *Kelvin-Helmholtz contraction,* after the scientists who proposed the mechanism). Recall that a shrinking gas cloud heats up because the gravitational potential energy of gas particles far from the cloud center is converted into thermal energy as the gas moves inward (see Figure 4.14b). A gradually shrinking Sun would always have some gas moving inward, converting gravitational potential energy into thermal energy. This thermal energy would keep the inside of the Sun hot.

Because of its large mass, the Sun would need to contract only very slightly each year to maintain its temperature—so slightly that the contraction would have been unnoticeable to 19th-century astronomers. Calculations showed that gravitational contraction could have kept the Sun shining steadily for up to about 25 million years. For a while, some astronomers thought that this idea had solved the ancient mystery of how the Sun shines. However, geologists pointed out a fatal flaw: Studies of rocks and fossils had already shown Earth to be far older than 25 million years, which meant that gravitational contraction could not be the mechanism by which the Sun generates its energy.

Einstein's Breakthrough With both chemical processes and gravitational contraction ruled out as possible explanations for why the Sun shines, scientists were at a loss. There was no known way that an object the size of the Sun could generate so much energy for billions of years. A completely new type of explanation was needed, and it came with Einstein's publication of his special theory of relativity in 1905.

Einstein's theory included his famous discovery of $E = mc^2$ [**Sections 4.3, S2.3**]. This equation shows that mass itself contains an enormous amount of potential energy. Calculations immediately showed that the Sun's mass contained more than enough energy to account for billions of years of sunshine, if the Sun could convert the energy of mass into thermal energy. It took a few decades for scientists to work out the details, but by the end of the 1930s we had learned that the Sun converts mass into energy through the process of *nuclear fusion* [**Section 1.2**].

How Fusion Started Nuclear fusion requires extremely high temperatures and densities (for reasons we will discuss in the next section). In the Sun, these conditions are found deep in the core. But how did the Sun become hot enough for fusion to begin in the first place?

The answer invokes the mechanism of gravitational contraction, which astronomers of the late 19th century mistakenly thought might be responsible for the Sun's heat today. Recall that our Sun was born about $4\frac{1}{2}$ billion years ago from a collapsing cloud of interstellar gas [**Section 8.2**]. The contraction of the cloud released gravitational potential energy, raising the interior temperature and pressure. This process continued until the core finally became hot enough to sustain nuclear fusion, because only then did the Sun produce enough energy to give it the stability that it has today.

FIGURE 14.1 An acrobat stack is in gravitational equilibrium: The lowest person supports the most weight and feels the greatest pressure, and the overlying weight and underlying pressure decrease for those higher up.

pressure ⟹
gravity ⟸

The outward push of pressure . . .

. . . precisely balances the inward pull of gravity.

Pressure is greatest deep in the Sun where the overlying weight is greatest.

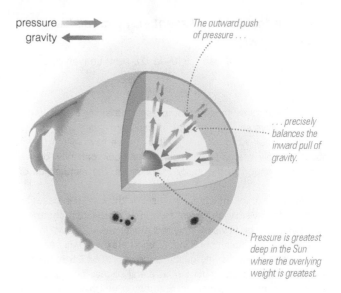

FIGURE 14.2 Gravitational equilibrium in the Sun: At each point inside, the pressure pushing outward balances the weight of the overlying layers.

The second kind of balance is **energy balance** between the rate at which fusion releases energy in the Sun's core and the rate at which the Sun's surface radiates this energy into space (**FIGURE 14.3**). Energy balance is important because without it, the balance between pressure and gravity would

Energy released by fusion in the Sun's core . . .

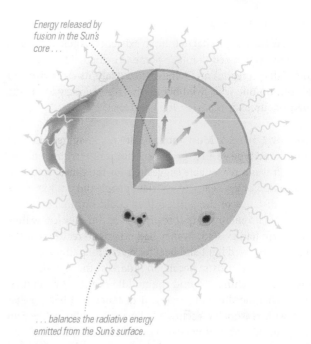

. . . balances the radiative energy emitted from the Sun's surface.

FIGURE 14.3 Energy balance in the Sun: Fusion must supply energy in the core at the same rate the Sun radiates energy from its surface.

The Stable Sun The Sun continues to shine steadily today because it has achieved two kinds of balance that keep its size and energy output stable. The first kind of balance, called **gravitational equilibrium** (or *hydrostatic equilibrium*), is between the outward push of internal gas pressure and the inward pull of gravity. A stack of acrobats provides a simple example of gravitational equilibrium (**FIGURE 14.1**). The bottom person supports the weight of everybody above him, so his arms must push upward with enough pressure to support all this weight. At each higher level, the overlying weight is less, so it's a little easier for each additional person to hold up the rest of the stack.

Gravitational equilibrium works much the same way in the Sun, except the outward push against gravity comes from internal gas pressure rather than an acrobat's arms. The Sun's internal pressure precisely balances gravity at every point within it, thereby keeping the Sun stable in size (**FIGURE 14.2**). Because the weight of overlying layers is greater as we look deeper into the Sun, the pressure must increase with depth. Deep in the Sun's core, the pressure makes the gas hot and dense enough to sustain nuclear fusion. The energy released by fusion, in turn, heats the gas and maintains the pressure that keeps the Sun in balance against the inward pull of gravity.

not remain steady. If fusion in the core did not replace the energy radiated from the surface, thereby keeping the total thermal energy content constant, then gravitational contraction would cause the Sun to shrink and force its core temperature to rise.

In summary, the answer to the question "Why does the Sun shine?" is that about $4\frac{1}{2}$ billion years ago *gravitational contraction* made the Sun hot enough to sustain nuclear fusion in its core. Ever since, energy liberated by fusion has maintained *gravitational equilibrium* and *energy balance* within the Sun, keeping it shining steadily and supplying the light and heat that sustain life on Earth. Calculations show that the Sun was born with enough hydrogen in its core to shine steadily and maintain its gravitational equilibrium for about 10 billion years. The Sun is therefore only about halfway through its 10-billion-year "lifetime." About 5 billion years from now, when the Sun finally exhausts its nuclear fuel, gravitational contraction of the core will begin once again. As we will see in later chapters, some of the most important and spectacular processes in astronomy arise from the changes that occur as the crush of gravity begins to overcome a star's internal sources of pressure.

What is the Sun's structure?

We've already stated that the Sun is a giant ball of hot gas. To be more precise, the Sun is a ball of *plasma*—a gas in which many of the atoms are ionized because of the high temperature [**Section 5.3**]. The differing temperatures and densities of the plasma at different depths give the Sun the layered structure shown in FIGURE 14.4. To make sense of what you see in the figure, let's imagine that you have a spaceship that can somehow withstand the immense heat and pressure of the Sun, and take an imaginary journey from Earth to the center of the Sun. This journey will acquaint you with the basic properties of the Sun, which we'll discuss in greater detail later in this chapter.

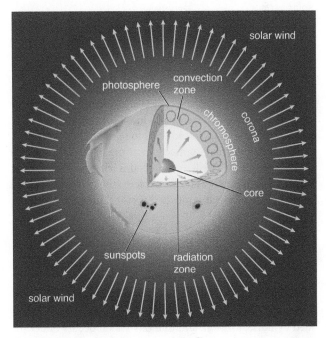

FIGURE 14.4 The basic structure of the Sun.

Basic Properties of the Sun As you begin your journey from Earth, the Sun appears as a whitish ball of glowing gas. Just as astronomers have done in real life, you can use simple observations to determine basic properties of the Sun. Spectroscopy [**Section 5.4**] tells you that the Sun is made almost entirely of hydrogen and helium. From the Sun's angular size and distance, you can determine that its radius is just under 700,000 kilometers, or more than 100 times the radius of Earth. Even **sunspots**, which appear as dark splotches on the Sun's surface, can be larger in diameter than Earth (FIGURE 14.5).

You can measure the Sun's mass using Newton's version of Kepler's third law [**Section 4.4**]. It is about 2×10^{30} kilograms, which is about 300,000 times the mass of Earth and nearly 1000 times the mass of all the planets in our solar system put together. You can observe the Sun's rotation rate by tracking the motion of sunspots or by measuring Doppler shifts on opposite sides of the Sun. Unlike a spinning ball, the entire Sun does *not* rotate at the same rate. Instead, the solar equator completes one rotation in about 25 days, and the rotation period increases with latitude to about 30 days near the solar poles.

The Sun releases an enormous amount of radiative energy into space, which you can measure through the window of your spacecraft. Recall that in science we measure energy in units of joules [**Section 4.3**]. We define **power** as the *rate* at which energy is used or released [**Section 5.1**]. The standard unit of power is the *watt*, defined as 1 joule of energy per second; that is, 1 watt = 1 joule/s. For example, a 100-watt light bulb requires 100 joules of energy for every second it is left turned on. The Sun's total power output, or **luminosity**, is an incredible 3.8×10^{26} watts. If we could somehow capture

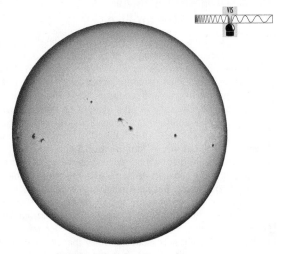

FIGURE 14.5 This photo of the visible surface of the Sun shows several dark sunspots, each large enough to swallow our entire planet.

TABLE 14.1 Basic Properties of the Sun

Radius (R_{Sun})	696,000 km (about 109 times the radius of Earth)
Mass (M_{Sun})	2×10^{30} kg (about 300,000 times the mass of Earth)
Luminosity (L_{Sun})	3.8×10^{26} watts
Composition (by percentage of mass)	70% hydrogen, 28% helium, 2% heavier elements
Rotation rate	25 days (equator) to 30 days (poles)
Surface temperature	5800 K (average); 4000 K (sunspots)
Core temperature	15 million K

and store just 1 second's worth of the Sun's luminosity, it would be enough to meet current human energy demands for roughly the next 500,000 years. TABLE 14.1 summarizes the basic properties of the Sun.

Of course, only a tiny fraction of the Sun's total energy output reaches Earth, with the rest dispersing in all directions into space. Most of this energy is radiated in the form of visible light, but after you've left the protection of Earth's atmosphere, you encounter significant amounts of other types of solar radiation, including dangerous ultraviolet and X rays.

The Sun's Atmosphere Even at great distances from the Sun, you and your spacecraft can feel slight effects from the **solar wind**—the stream of charged particles continually blown outward in all directions from the Sun. The solar wind helps shape the magnetospheres of planets [**Sections 10.1 and 11.1**] and blows back the material that forms the plasma tails of comets [**Section 12.2**].

As you approach the Sun more closely, you begin to encounter the low-density gas that represents what we usually think of as the Sun's atmosphere. The outermost layer of this atmosphere, called the **corona**, extends several million kilometers above the visible surface of the Sun. The temperature of the

COMMON MISCONCEPTIONS

The Sun Is Not on Fire

We often say that the Sun is "burning," a term that conjures up images of a giant bonfire in the sky. However, the Sun does not burn in the same sense as a fire burns on Earth. Fires generate light through chemical changes that consume oxygen and produce a flame. The glow of the Sun has more in common with the glow of embers left over after the flames have burned out. Much like hot embers, the Sun's surface shines because it is hot enough to emit thermal radiation that includes visible light [**Section 5.4**].

Hot embers quickly stop glowing as they cool, but the Sun keeps shining because its surface is kept hot by the energy rising from its core. Because this energy is generated by nuclear fusion, we sometimes say that it is the result of "nuclear burning"—a term intended to suggest nuclear changes in much the same way that "chemical burning" suggests chemical changes. While it is reasonable to say that the Sun undergoes nuclear burning in its core, it is not accurate to speak of any kind of burning on the Sun's surface, where light is produced primarily by thermal radiation.

corona is astonishingly high—about 1 million K—explaining why this region emits most of the Sun's X rays. However, the corona's density is so low that your spaceship absorbs relatively little heat despite the million-degree temperature [**Section 4.3**].

Nearer the surface, the temperature suddenly drops to about 10,000 K in the **chromosphere**, the middle layer of the solar atmosphere and the region that radiates most of the Sun's ultraviolet light. Then you plunge through the lowest layer of the atmosphere, or **photosphere**, which is the visible surface of the Sun. Although the photosphere looks like a well-defined surface from Earth, it consists of gas far less dense than Earth's atmosphere. The temperature of the photosphere averages just under 6000 K, and its surface seethes and churns like a pot of boiling water. The photosphere is also where you'll find sunspots, regions of intense magnetic fields that would cause your compass needle to swing about wildly.

The Sun's Interior Up to this point in your journey, you may have seen Earth and the stars when you looked back. But blazing light engulfs you as you slip beneath the photosphere. You are inside the Sun, and incredible turbulence tosses your spacecraft about. If you can hold steady long enough to see what is going on around you, you'll notice spouts of hot gas rising upward, surrounded by cooler gas cascading down from above. You are in the **convection zone**, where energy generated in the solar core travels upward, transported by the rising of hot gas and falling of cool gas called *convection* [**Section 9.1**]. The photosphere above you is the top of the convection zone, and convection is the cause of the Sun's seething, churning appearance.

About a third of the way down to the center, the turbulence of the convection zone gives way to the calmer plasma of the **radiation zone**, where energy moves outward primarily in the form of photons of light. The temperature rises to almost 10 million K, and your spacecraft is bathed in X rays trillions of times more intense than the visible light at the solar surface.

No real spacecraft could survive, but your imaginary one keeps plunging straight down to the solar **core**. There you finally find the source of the Sun's energy: nuclear fusion transforming hydrogen into helium. At the Sun's center, the temperature is about 15 million K, the density is more than 100 times that of water, and the pressure is 200 billion times that on the surface of Earth. The energy produced in the core today will take a few hundred thousand years to reach the surface.

With your journey complete, it's time to turn around and head back home. We'll continue this chapter by studying fusion in the solar core and then tracing the flow of the energy generated by fusion as it moves outward through the Sun.

 The Sun Tutorial, Lessons 2–3

14.2 NUCLEAR FUSION IN THE SUN

We've seen that the Sun shines because of energy generated by nuclear fusion, and that this fusion occurs under the extreme temperatures and densities found deep in the Sun's

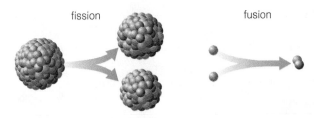

fission   fusion

FIGURE 14.6 Nuclear fission splits a nucleus into smaller nuclei, while nuclear fusion combines smaller nuclei into a larger nucleus.

core. But exactly how does fusion occur and release energy? And how can we claim to know about something taking place out of sight in the Sun's interior?

Before we begin to answer these questions, it's important to realize that the nuclear reactions that generate energy in the Sun are very different from those used to generate energy in human-built nuclear reactors on Earth. Our nuclear power plants generate energy by splitting large nuclei—such as those of uranium or plutonium—into smaller ones. The process of splitting an atomic nucleus is called **nuclear fission.** In contrast, the Sun makes energy by combining, or fusing, two or more small nuclei into a larger one. That is why we call the process **nuclear fusion.** FIGURE 14.6 summarizes the difference between fission and fusion.

How does nuclear fusion occur in the Sun?

Fusion occurs within the Sun because the 15 million K plasma in the solar core is like a "soup" of hot gas, with bare, positively charged atomic nuclei (and negatively charged electrons) whizzing about at extremely high speeds. At any one time, some of these nuclei are on high-speed collision courses with each other. In most cases, electromagnetic forces deflect the nuclei, preventing actual collisions, because positive charges repel one another. If nuclei collide with sufficient energy, however, they can stick together to form a heavier nucleus (FIGURE 14.7).

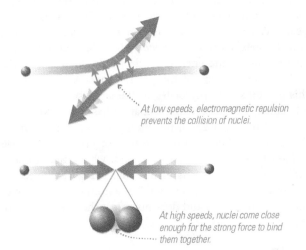

At low speeds, electromagnetic repulsion prevents the collision of nuclei.

At high speeds, nuclei come close enough for the strong force to bind them together.

FIGURE 14.7 Positively charged nuclei can fuse only if a high-speed collision brings them close enough for the strong force to come into play.

Sticking positively charged nuclei together is not easy. The **strong force,** which binds protons and neutrons together in atomic nuclei, is the only force in nature that can overcome the electromagnetic repulsion between two positively charged nuclei [**Section S4.2**]. In contrast to gravitational and electromagnetic forces, which drop off gradually as the distances between particles increase (by an inverse square law [**Section 4.4**]), the strong force is more like glue or Velcro: It overpowers the electromagnetic force over very small distances but is insignificant when the distances between particles exceed the typical sizes of atomic nuclei. The key to nuclear fusion, therefore, is to push the positively charged nuclei close enough together for the strong force to outmuscle electromagnetic repulsion.

The high pressures and temperatures in the solar core are just right for fusion of hydrogen nuclei into helium nuclei. The high temperature is important because the nuclei must collide at very high speeds if they are to come close enough together to fuse. (Quantum tunneling is also important to this process [**Section S4.4**].) The higher the temperature, the harder the collisions, making fusion reactions more likely. The high pressure of the overlying layers is necessary because without it, the hot plasma of the solar core would simply explode into space, shutting off the nuclear reactions.

THINK ABOUT IT

The Sun generates energy by fusing hydrogen into helium, but as we'll see in later chapters, some stars fuse helium or even heavier elements. For the fusion of heavier elements, do temperatures need to be higher or lower than those for the fusion of hydrogen? Why? (*Hint:* How does the positive charge of a nucleus affect the difficulty of fusing it to another nucleus?)

The Proton-Proton Chain Let's investigate the fusion process in the Sun in a little more detail. Recall that hydrogen nuclei are simply individual protons, while the most common form of helium consists of two protons and two neutrons. The overall hydrogen fusion reaction therefore transforms four individual protons into a helium nucleus containing two protons and two neutrons:

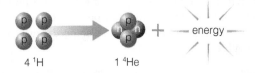

4 ^{1}H   1 ^{4}He

This overall reaction actually proceeds through several steps involving just two nuclei at a time. The sequence of steps that occurs in the Sun is called the **proton-proton chain,** because it begins with collisions between individual protons (hydrogen nuclei). FIGURE 14.8 illustrates the steps in the proton-proton chain:

Step 1: Two protons fuse to form a nucleus consisting of one proton and one neutron, which is the isotope of hydrogen known as *deuterium.* Note that this step

Hydrogen Fusion by the Proton-Proton Chain

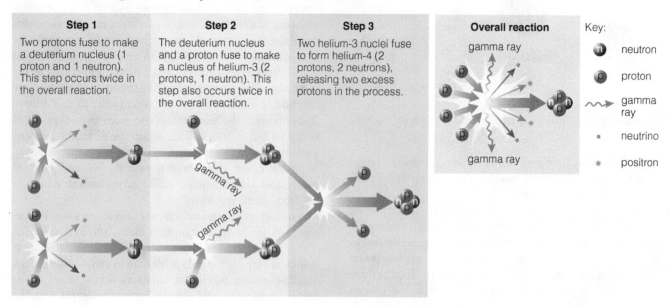

Step 1
Two protons fuse to make a deuterium nucleus (1 proton and 1 neutron). This step occurs twice in the overall reaction.

Step 2
The deuterium nucleus and a proton fuse to make a nucleus of helium-3 (2 protons, 1 neutron). This step also occurs twice in the overall reaction.

Step 3
Two helium-3 nuclei fuse to form helium-4 (2 protons, 2 neutrons), releasing two excess protons in the process.

Overall reaction

gamma ray

gamma ray

Key:

- n neutron
- p proton
- ∿ gamma ray
- · neutrino
- · positron

FIGURE 14.8 interactive figure In the Sun, four hydrogen nuclei (protons) fuse into one helium-4 nucleus by way of the proton-proton chain. Gamma rays and subatomic particles known as neutrinos and positrons carry off the energy released in the reaction.

converts a proton into a neutron, reducing the total nuclear charge from +2 for the two fusing protons to +1 for the resulting deuterium nucleus. The lost positive charge is carried off by a *positron* (antielectron), the antimatter version of an electron with a positive rather than a negative charge [**Section S4.2**]. A **neutrino**—a subatomic particle with a very tiny mass—is also produced in this step.* (The positron won't last long, because it soon meets up with an ordinary electron, resulting in the creation of two gamma-ray photons through matter-antimatter annihilation.) This step must occur twice in the overall reaction, since it requires a total of four protons.

Step 2: A fair number of deuterium nuclei are always present along with the protons and other nuclei in the solar core, since Step 1 occurs so frequently in the Sun (about 10^{38} times per second). Step 2 occurs when one of these deuterium nuclei collides and fuses with a proton. The result is a nucleus of helium-3, a rare form of helium with two protons and one neutron, along with a gamma-ray photon. This step also occurs twice in the overall reaction.

Step 3: The third and final step of the proton-proton chain requires the addition of another neutron to the helium-3, thereby making normal helium-4. This final step can proceed in several different ways, but the most

common is through a collision of two helium-3 nuclei. Each of these helium-3 nuclei resulted from a prior, separate occurrence of Step 2 somewhere in the solar core. The final result is a normal helium-4 nucleus and two protons.

Notice that a total of six protons enter the reaction during Steps 1 and 2, with two coming back out in Step 3. The overall reaction therefore combines four protons to make one helium nucleus. The gamma rays and subatomic particles (neutrinos and positrons) carry off the energy released in the reaction.

Fusion of hydrogen into helium generates energy because a helium nucleus has a mass slightly less (by about 0.7%) than the combined mass of four hydrogen nuclei (see Mathematical Insight 14.1). That is, when four hydrogen nuclei fuse into a helium nucleus, a little bit of mass disappears. The disappearing mass becomes energy in accord with Einstein's formula $E = mc^2$. About 98% of the energy emerges as kinetic energy of the resulting helium nuclei and radiative energy of the gamma rays. As we will see, this energy slowly percolates to the solar surface, eventually emerging as the sunlight that bathes Earth. Neutrinos carry off the other 2% of the energy. Overall, fusion in the Sun converts about 600 million tons of hydrogen into 596 million tons of helium every second, which means that 4 million tons of matter is turned into energy each second. Although this sounds like a lot, it is a minuscule fraction of the Sun's total mass and does not affect the overall mass of the Sun in any measurable way.

The Solar Thermostat Nuclear fusion is the source of all the energy the Sun releases into space. If the fusion rate varied, so would the Sun's energy output, and large variations

---

*Producing a neutrino is necessary because of a law called *conservation of lepton number:* The number of leptons (e.g., electrons or neutrinos [**Chapter S4**]) must be the same before and after the reaction. The lepton number is zero before the reaction because there are no leptons. Among the reaction products, the positron (antielectron) has lepton number −1 because it is antimatter, and the neutrino has lepton number +1. Thus, the total lepton number remains zero.

in the Sun's luminosity would almost surely be lethal to life on Earth. Fortunately, the Sun fuses hydrogen at a steady rate, thanks to a natural feedback process that acts as a thermostat for the Sun's interior. To see how it works, let's examine what would happen if a small change were to occur in the core temperature (FIGURE 14.9).

Suppose the Sun's core temperature rose very slightly. The rate of nuclear fusion is extremely sensitive to temperature, so a slight temperature increase would cause the fusion rate to soar as protons in the core collided more frequently and with more energy. Because energy moves slowly through the Sun's interior, this extra energy would be bottled up in the core, temporarily forcing the Sun out of energy balance and raising the core pressure. The push of this pressure would temporarily exceed the pull of gravity, causing the core to expand and cool. This cooling, in turn, would cause the fusion rate to drop back down until the core returned to its original size and temperature, restoring both gravitational equilibrium and energy balance.

A slight drop in the Sun's core temperature would trigger an opposite chain of events. The reduced core temperature would lead to a decrease in the rate of nuclear fusion, causing a drop in pressure and contraction of the core. As the core shrank, its temperature would rise until the fusion rate returned to normal and restored the core to its original size and temperature.

The Gradually Brightening Sun While the processes involved in gravitational equilibrium prevent erratic changes in the fusion rate, they also ensure that the fusion

---

MATHEMATICAL INSIGHT 14.1

Mass-Energy Conversion in Hydrogen Fusion

Fusion of hydrogen into helium releases energy because the four hydrogen nuclei (protons) that go into the overall reaction have a slightly greater mass than the helium nucleus that comes out. When four protons (each with a mass of 1.6726×10^{-27} kg, for a total mass of 6.690×10^{-27} kg) fuse to make one helium-4 nucleus (mass of 6.643×10^{-27} kg), the amount of mass that "disappears" and becomes energy is

$$(6.690 \times 10^{-27} \text{ kg}) - (6.643 \times 10^{-27} \text{ kg}) = 0.047 \times 10^{-27} \text{ kg}$$

If we divide this lost mass by the original mass of the four protons, we find the fractional loss of mass:

$$\frac{\text{fractional mass loss}}{\text{in hydrogen fusion}} = \frac{0.047 \times 10^{-27} \text{ kg}}{6.69 \times 10^{-27} \text{ kg}} = 0.007$$

That is, a fraction 0.007, or 0.7%, of the original hydrogen mass is converted into energy according to Einstein's equation $E = mc^2$.

EXAMPLE 1: How much hydrogen is converted to helium each second in the Sun?

SOLUTION:

Step 1 Understand: The first step is to realize that we need to know the Sun's total energy output, or luminosity; Table 14.1 shows this to be 3.8×10^{26} watts, which means the Sun produces 3.8×10^{26} joules of energy each second. We can then use Einstein's equation $E = mc^2$ to calculate the total amount of mass converted into energy each second. We then use the fact that 0.7% of the hydrogen mass becomes energy to calculate how much hydrogen fuses each second.

Step 2 Solve: We start by solving Einstein's equation for the mass, m:

$$E = mc^2 \quad \Rightarrow \quad m = \frac{E}{c^2}$$

We plug in 3.8×10^{26} joules for the energy (E) that the Sun produces each second and recall that the speed of light is $c = 3 \times 10^8$ m/s; to make sure we can work with the units properly, we use the fact that 1 joule is equivalent to 1 kg $\times$ m²/s²:

$$m = \frac{E}{c^2} = \frac{3.8 \times 10^{26} \frac{\text{kg} \times \text{m}^2}{\text{s}^2}}{\left(3 \times 10^8 \frac{\text{m}}{\text{s}}\right)^2} = 4.2 \times 10^9 \text{ kg}$$

We've found the amount of mass converted to energy in the Sun each second. Because this mass is 0.7% (= 0.007) of the mass of the hydrogen that fuses, the total mass of the hydrogen that undergoes fusion each second must be

$$\text{mass of hydrogen fused} = \frac{4.2 \times 10^9 \text{ kg}}{0.007} = 6.0 \times 10^{11} \text{ kg}$$

Step 3 Explain: The Sun fuses 600 billion kilograms of hydrogen each second, converting about 4 billion kilograms of this mass into energy; the rest, about 596 billion kilograms, becomes helium.

EXAMPLE 2: How many helium nuclei are created by fusion each second in the Sun?

SOLUTION:

Step 1 Understand: One way to approach this problem is to divide the total amount of mass lost each second in the Sun by the mass loss that occurs with each fusion reaction of four hydrogen nuclei into one helium nucleus. The result will tell us how many times this reaction occurs each second.

Step 2 Solve: From Example 1, the Sun converts 4.2×10^9 kilograms of mass into energy each second, and we learned earlier that each individual fusion reaction converts 0.047×10^{-27} kilogram of mass into energy. We divide to find the number of fusion reactions that occur each second in the Sun:

$$\frac{\text{number of}}{\text{fusion reactions}} = \frac{\text{total mass lost through fusion}}{\text{(per second)}}$$
$$\text{(per second)} \qquad \text{mass lost in each fusion reaction}$$

$$= \frac{4.2 \times 10^9 \text{ kg}}{0.047 \times 10^{-27} \text{ kg}}$$

$$= 8.9 \times 10^{37}$$

Step 3 Explain: Notice that our result, 8.9×10^{37}, is just a little less than 10^{38}. In other words, the overall hydrogen fusion reaction occurs in the Sun nearly 10^{38} times each second.

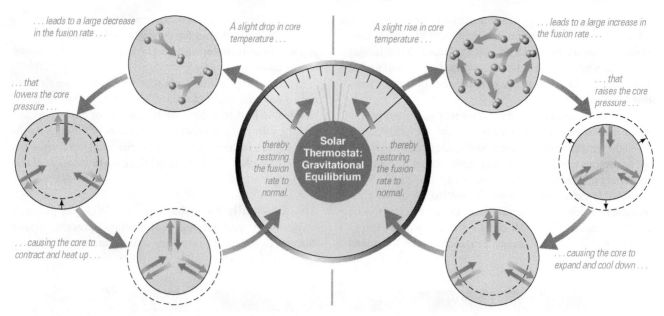

. . . leads to a large decrease in the fusion rate . . .

. . . that lowers the core pressure . . .

A slight drop in core temperature . . .

. . . causing the core to contract and heat up . . .

. . . thereby restoring the fusion rate to normal.

Solar Thermostat: Gravitational Equilibrium

. . . thereby restoring the fusion rate to normal.

A slight rise in core temperature . . .

. . . leads to a large increase in the fusion rate . . .

. . . that raises the core pressure . . .

. . . causing the core to expand and cool down . . .

FIGURE 14.9 interactive figure The solar thermostat. Gravitational equilibrium regulates the Sun's core temperature. Everything is in balance if the amount of energy leaving the core equals the amount of energy produced by fusion. A rise in core temperature triggers a chain of events that causes the core to expand, lowering its temperature to the original value. A decrease in core temperature triggers the opposite chain of events, also restoring the original core temperature.

rate gradually rises over billions of years. This rise in the fusion rate explains a fact we first encountered when we discussed climate change factors in Chapter 10: the gradual brightening of the Sun with time.

Remember that each fusion reaction converts *four* hydrogen nuclei into *one* helium nucleus. The total number of *independent particles* in the solar core therefore gradually decreases with time. This gradual reduction in the number of particles causes the solar core to shrink. The slow shrinkage, in turn, gradually increases the core temperature and fusion rate, keeping the core pressure high enough to counteract the stronger compression of gravity. Theoretical models indicate that the Sun's core temperature should have increased enough to raise its fusion rate and luminosity by about 30% since the Sun was born $4\frac{1}{2}$ billion years ago.

How does the energy from fusion get out of the Sun?

The solar thermostat balances the Sun's fusion rate so that the amount of nuclear energy generated in the core equals the amount of energy radiated from the surface as sunlight. However, the journey of solar energy from the core to the photosphere takes hundreds of thousands of years.

Most of the energy released by fusion starts its journey out of the solar core in the form of photons. Although photons travel at the speed of light, the path they take through the Sun's interior zigzags so much that it takes them a very long time to make any outward progress. Deep in the solar interior, the plasma is so dense that a photon can travel only a fraction of a millimeter in any one direction before it interacts with an electron. Each time a photon "collides" with an electron, the photon gets deflected into a new and random

direction. The photon therefore bounces around the dense interior in a haphazard way (sometimes called a *random walk*) and only very gradually works its way outward from the Sun's center (**FIGURE 14.10**). The technical term for this slow outward migration of photons is **radiative diffusion**; to *diffuse* means to "spread out" and *radiative* refers to the photons of light, or radiation.

Energy released by fusion moves outward through the Sun's radiation zone (see Figure 14.4) primarily by way of these randomly bouncing photons. At the top of the radiation zone,

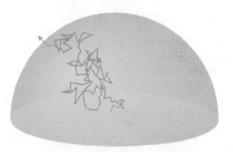

FIGURE 14.10 A photon in the solar interior bounces randomly among electrons, slowly working its way outward.

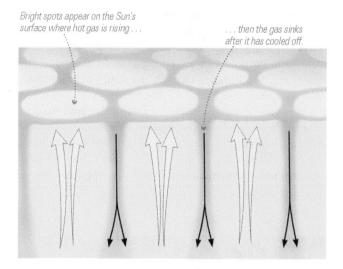

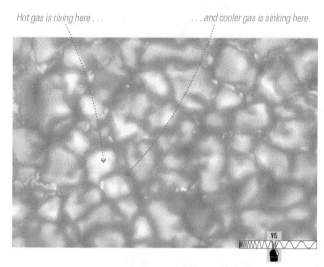

a This diagram shows convection beneath the Sun's surface. Hot gas (light yellow arrows) rises while cooler gas (black arrows) descends around it.

b This photograph shows the mottled appearance of the Sun's photosphere. The bright spots, each about 1000 kilometers across, correspond to the rising plumes of hot gas in part a.

FIGURE 14.11 The Sun's photosphere churns with rising hot gas and falling cool gas as a result of underlying convection.

where the temperature has dropped to about 2 million K, the solar plasma absorbs photons more readily (rather than just bouncing them around). This absorption creates the conditions needed for convection [**Section 9.1**] and hence marks the bottom of the Sun's convection zone.

In the convection zone, convection occurs because hot gas is less dense than cool gas. Like a hot-air balloon, a hot bubble of solar plasma rises upward through the cooler plasma above it. Meanwhile, cooler plasma from above slides around the rising bubble and sinks to lower layers, where it is heated. The rising of hot plasma and sinking of cool plasma form a cycle that transports energy outward from the base of the convection zone to the solar surface, or photosphere (**FIGURE 14.11a**). There, the density of the gas becomes so low that photons can escape to space, which is why we see the photosphere as the "surface" of the Sun.

The convecting gas gives the photosphere the mottled appearance that we see in close-up photographs (**FIGURE 14.11b**): We see bright blobs where hot gas is welling up from inside the Sun and darker borders around those blobs where the cooler gas is sinking.* If we watched a movie of the photosphere, we'd see its surface bubbling rather like a pot of boiling water. Much like the way bubbles in a pot of boiling water burst on the surface and are replaced by new bubbles, each hot blob lasts only a few minutes before being replaced by others bubbling upward. The average temperature of the gas in the photosphere is about 5800 K, but convection causes the precise temperature to vary significantly from place to place.

To summarize, energy produced by fusion in the Sun's core works its way slowly through the radiation zone through random bounces of photons, then gets carried upward by convection in the convection zone. The photosphere lies at the top of the convection zone and marks the place where the density of gas has become low enough that photons can escape to space. The energy produced hundreds of thousands of years earlier in the solar core finally emerges from the Sun as thermal radiation [**Section 5.4**] produced by the 5800 K gas of the photosphere. Once in space, the photons travel straight away at the speed of light, bathing the planets in sunlight.

How do we know what is happening inside the Sun?

We cannot see inside the Sun, so you may wonder how we can claim to know so much about what goes on inside of it. In fact, we can study the Sun's interior in three different ways: through mathematical models of the Sun, observations of solar vibrations, and observations of solar neutrinos.

Mathematical Models Our primary way of learning about the interior of the Sun (and other stars) is by creating *mathematical models* that use the laws of physics to predict internal conditions. A basic model uses the Sun's observed composition and mass as inputs to equations that describe gravitational equilibrium, the solar thermostat, and the rate at which solar energy moves from the core to the photosphere. With the aid of a computer, we can use the model to calculate the Sun's temperature, pressure, and density at any depth. We can then predict the rate of nuclear fusion in the solar core by combining these calculations with knowledge about nuclear fusion gathered in laboratories on Earth.

If a model is a good description of the Sun's interior, it should correctly "predict" the radius, surface temperature,

---

*The blobs are formally called *granules*, and the photosphere's mottled appearance is sometimes referred to as *solar granulation*.

luminosity, age, and many other observable properties of the Sun. Current models do indeed predict these properties quite accurately, giving us confidence that we really do understand what is going on inside the Sun.

Solar Vibrations A second way to learn about the inside of the Sun is to observe vibrations of the Sun's surface that are somewhat similar to the vibrations that earthquakes cause on Earth. These vibrations result from movement of gas within the Sun, which generates waves of pressure that travel through the Sun like sound waves moving through air. We can observe these vibrations on the Sun's surface by looking for Doppler shifts [**Section 5.4**]. Light from portions of the surface that are rising toward us is slightly blueshifted, while light from portions that are falling away from us is slightly redshifted. The vibrations are relatively small but measurable (**FIGURE 14.12**).

In principle, we can deduce a great deal about the solar interior by carefully analyzing these vibrations. (By analogy to seismology on Earth, this type of study of the Sun is called *helioseismology*—*helios* means "sun.") Results to date confirm that our mathematical models of the solar interior

---

MATHEMATICAL INSIGHT 14.2

Pressure in the Sun: The Ideal Gas Law

The pressure that resists gravity inside the Sun comes from the thermal motions of gas particles. Particles in a hot gas move more quickly and collide with more force than those in a cooler gas [**Section 5.3**], and therefore exert more pressure on any surface that tries to contain them. (Recall that pressure is defined as the force per unit area exerted on any surface.) However, pressure also depends on *how many* particles are colliding with each unit area of that surface each second, which means that pressure depends on the *number density* of gas particles—the number of gas particles contained in each cubic centimeter. Mathematically, we express this relationship between temperature, density, and pressure with the **ideal gas law,** which can be written as

$$P = nkT$$

where P represents gas pressure, n represents the number density of particles (in particles per cubic centimeter), T represents gas temperature (on the Kelvin scale), and $k = 1.38 \times 10^{-23}$ joule/K, which is known as *Boltzmann's constant*. This law applies to all gases consisting of simple, freely flying particles, like those in the Sun. In the units used here, the ideal gas law gives pressure in units of joules per cubic centimeter (J/cm^3); these units of energy per unit volume are equivalent to units of force per unit area.

EXAMPLE 1: The Sun's core contains about 10^{26} particles per cubic centimeter at a temperature of 15 million K. How does the gas pressure in the core of the Sun compare to the pressure of Earth's atmosphere at sea level, where there are about 2.4×10^{19} particles per cubic centimeter at a temperature of roughly 300 K?

SOLUTION:

Step 1 Understand: The ideal gas law allows us to calculate pressure from the temperature and the number density of particles in a gas, so we have all the information we need. We can compare the two pressures by dividing the larger (the Sun's core pressure) by the smaller (Earth's atmospheric pressure).

Step 2 Solve: Dividing the Sun's core pressure by Earth's atmospheric pressure, we find that their ratio is

$$\frac{P_{Sun(core)}}{P_{Earth(atmos)}} = \frac{n_{Sun}kT_{Sun}}{n_{Earth}kT_{Earth}} = \frac{10^{26}\ cm^{-3} \times 1.5 \times 10^7\ K}{2.4 \times 10^{19}\ cm^{-3} \times 300\ K}$$

$$= 2 \times 10^{11}$$

Step 3 Explain: The Sun's core pressure is about 200 billion (2×10^{11}) times as great as atmospheric pressure on Earth.

EXAMPLE 2: How would the Sun's core pressure change if the Sun fused all its core hydrogen into helium without shrinking and without its core temperature changing? Use your answer to explain what should happen as fusion occurs in the real Sun, in which the core *can* shrink and heat up. To simplify the problem, assume that the Sun's core begins with pure hydrogen that is fully ionized, so that there are two particles for every hydrogen nucleus (the proton plus one electron that must also be present for charge balance in the core), and ends as pure helium with three particles for each helium nucleus (the nucleus plus two electrons to balance the two protons in helium).

SOLUTION:

Step 1 Understand: The core pressure will change if either the temperature or the number density of particles changes. For this simplified example, we are told that the temperature does not change and that the core does not shrink, so pressure changes are due only to the declining number density that occurs as fusion reduces the total number of particles in the core. We can therefore find the pressure change simply by finding how fusion changes the number of particles in the core.

Step 2 Solve: In this simplified example, the core initially contained two particles for every hydrogen nucleus and finished with three particles for every helium nucleus. Therefore, for each fusion reaction that converts four hydrogen nuclei to one helium nucleus, there are eight particles before the reaction (four electrons and four protons) and three particles after it (one helium nucleus and two electrons); that is, after fusion there are $\frac{3}{8}$ as many particles as there were before it. Because the temperature and volume don't change in this example, the core pressure after all the hydrogen fuses into helium is also $\frac{3}{8}$ of its original value.

Step 3 Explain: If the core volume had stayed constant, the core pressure at the end of the fusion process would have decreased to $\frac{3}{8}$ of its initial value. This decrease in core pressure would tip the balance of gravitational equilibrium in favor of gravity, which is why the core shrinks as fusion progresses in the Sun. This shrinkage decreases the volume of the core, allowing the number density of particles to stay approximately constant. The gradual shrinkage also produces a slight but gradual rise in core temperature and therefore in the fusion rate, which is why the Sun's luminosity gradually increases with time.

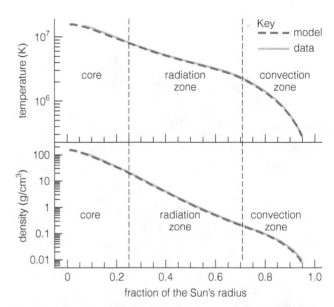

FIGURE 14.13 These graphs show the close agreement between predictions about the Sun's interior structure based on mathematical models and actual data obtained from observations of the Sun's surface vibrations. The agreement gives us confidence that the models are a good representation of the Sun's interior.

-2500 -2000 -1500 -1000 -500 0 500 1000 1500 2000
Velocity (m/s)

FIGURE 14.12 This image shows vibrations on the Sun's surface that have been measured from Doppler shifts. Shades of orange show how quickly each spot on the Sun's surface is moving toward or away from us at a particular moment. Dark shades (negative velocities) represent motion toward us; light shades (positive velocities) represent motion away from us. The large-scale change in color from left to right reflects the Sun's rotation, and the small-scale ripples reflect the surface vibrations.

are on the right track (FIGURE 14.13). At the same time, analyses of the vibrations provide data that help to improve the models further.

Solar Neutrinos A third way to study the Sun's interior is to observe subatomic particles made by fusion reactions in the core. Remember that Step 1 of the proton-proton chain produces neutrinos. These tiny particles rarely interact with other forms of matter and therefore can pass through almost anything. For example, an inch of lead will stop an X ray, but stopping an average neutrino would require a slab of lead more than a light-year thick!

Neutrinos produced in the Sun's core pass outward through the solar interior almost as though it were empty space. Traveling at nearly the speed of light, they reach us in minutes, in principle giving us a way to monitor what is happening in the core of the Sun. In practice, their elusiveness makes neutrinos dauntingly difficult to monitor, because virtually all of them stream right through any detector built to capture and count them. About a thousand trillion solar neutrinos will zip through your body as you read this sentence, but don't panic—they will do no damage at all. In fact, nearly all of them will pass through the entire Earth as well.

Nevertheless, neutrinos *do* occasionally interact with matter, and it is possible to capture a few solar neutrinos with a large enough detector. To distinguish neutrino captures from reactions caused by other particles, scientists usually place neutrino detectors deep underground in mines. The overlying rock blocks most other particles, but the neutrinos have no difficulty passing through.

Early attempts to detect solar neutrinos were only partially successful, capturing only one-third of the number predicted by models of nuclear fusion in the Sun's core. This disagreement between model predictions and actual observations came to be called the *solar neutrino problem*. For more than three decades, the solar neutrino problem was one of the great mysteries in astronomy: Either something was wrong with our understanding of fusion in the Sun or some of the Sun's neutrinos were somehow escaping detection.

We now know that the missing solar neutrinos were going undetected. Neutrinos come in three distinct types, called *electron neutrinos, muon neutrinos,* and *tau neutrinos* [**Section S4.2**]. Fusion reactions in the Sun produce only electron neutrinos, and the early solar neutrino detectors could detect only electron neutrinos. More recent detectors, such as the Sudbury Neutrino Observatory (FIGURE 14.14), can detect all three neutrino types and their results confirm that the total number of solar neutrinos is equal to what we expect from our models of nuclear fusion in the Sun. In other words, some of the electron neutrinos produced by fusion change into neutrinos of the other two types during their trip from the Sun's core to its surface, a fact that has proved very important not only because it confirms our understanding of fusion in the Sun but also because of insights it provides into the fundamental physics of the subatomic world.

14.3 THE SUN-EARTH CONNECTION

Energy liberated by nuclear fusion in the Sun's core eventually reaches the solar surface, where it helps create a wide variety of phenomena that we can observe from Earth. Sunspots are only the most obvious of these phenomena. Because sunspots and other features of the Sun's surface change with time, they constitute what we call *solar weather*, or **solar activity**. The "storms" associated with solar weather are not just of academic interest. Sometimes they are so violent that they affect our day-to-day life on Earth. In this section, we'll explore solar activity and its far-reaching effects.

What causes solar activity?

Most of the Sun's surface churns constantly with rising and falling gas and looks like the close-up photo shown in Figure 14.11b. However, larger features sometimes appear, including sunspots, the huge explosions known as *solar flares*, and gigantic loops of hot gas that extend high into the Sun's corona. All these features are created by magnetic fields, which form and change easily in the convecting plasma in the outer layers of the Sun.

Sunspots and Magnetic Fields Sunspots are the most striking features of the solar surface (FIGURE 14.15a). If you could look directly at a sunspot without damaging your eyes, you would find it blindingly bright. Sunspots appear dark in photographs only because they are less bright than the surrounding photosphere. They are less bright because they are cooler: The temperature of the plasma in sunspots is about 4000 K, significantly cooler than the 5800 K of the plasma that surrounds them.

You may wonder how sunspots can be so much cooler than their surroundings. Gas can usually flow easily, so you might expect the hotter gas from outside a sunspot to mix with the cooler gas within it, quickly warming the sunspot. The fact

FIGURE 14.14 This photograph shows the main tank of the Sudbury Neutrino Observatory in Canada, located at the bottom of a mine shaft, more than 2 kilometers underground. The large sphere, 12 meters in diameter, contains 1000 tons of ultrapure *heavy water*. (Heavy water is water in which one or both hydrogen atoms are replaced by deuterium, making each molecule heavier than a molecule of ordinary water.) Neutrinos of all three types can cause reactions in the heavy water, and detectors surrounding the tank record these reactions when they occur.

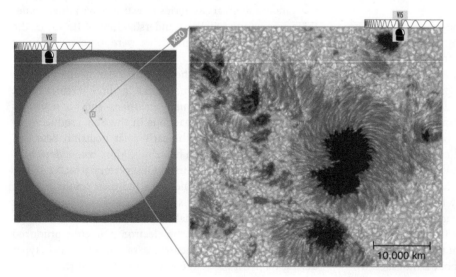

a This close-up view of the Sun's surface shows two large sunspots and several smaller ones. Each of the big sunspots is roughly as large as Earth.

10,000 km

FIGURE 14.15 Sunspots are regions of strong magnetic fields.

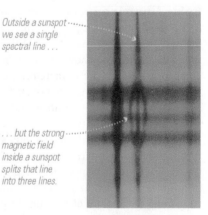

Outside a sunspot we see a single spectral line . . .

. . . but the strong magnetic field inside a sunspot splits that line into three lines.

b Very strong magnetic fields split the absorption lines in spectra of sunspot regions. The dark vertical bands are absorption lines in a spectrum of the Sun. Notice that these lines split where they cross the dark horizontal bands corresponding to sunspots.

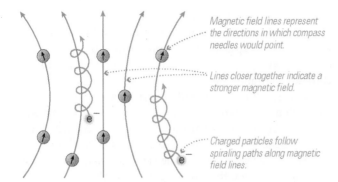

Magnetic field lines represent the directions in which compass needles would point.

Lines closer together indicate a stronger magnetic field.

Charged particles follow spiraling paths along magnetic field lines.

FIGURE 14.16 We draw magnetic field lines (red) to represent invisible magnetic fields. These lines also represent the directions along which charged particles tend to move.

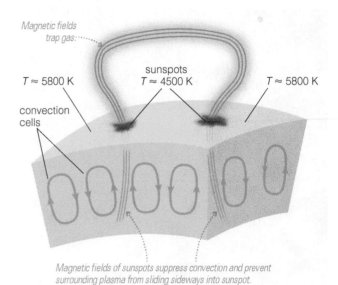

Magnetic fields trap gas.

sunspots
$T \approx 4500$ K

$T \approx 5800$ K $T \approx 5800$ K

convection cells

Magnetic fields of sunspots suppress convection and prevent surrounding plasma from sliding sideways into sunspot.

a Pairs of sunspots are connected by tightly wound magnetic field lines.

X-ray

b This X-ray photo (from NASA's *TRACE* mission) shows hot gas trapped within looped magnetic field lines.

FIGURE 14.17 Strong magnetic fields keep sunspots cooler than the surrounding photosphere, and magnetic loops can arch from the sunspots to great heights above the Sun's surface.

that sunspots stay relatively cool means that something must prevent hot plasma from entering them, and that something turns out to be magnetic fields.

Detailed observations of the Sun's spectral lines reveal sunspots to be regions with strong magnetic fields. These magnetic fields can alter the energy levels in atoms and ions and therefore can alter the spectral lines they produce, causing some spectral lines to split into two or more closely spaced lines (FIGURE 14.15b). Wherever we see this effect (called the *Zeeman effect*), we know that magnetic fields must be present. Scientists can map magnetic fields on the Sun by looking for the splitting of spectral lines in light from different parts of the solar surface.

To understand how sunspots stay cooler than their surroundings, we must investigate the nature of magnetic fields in a little more depth. Magnetic fields are invisible, but we can represent them by drawing **magnetic field lines** (FIGURE 14.16). These lines represent the directions in which compass needles would point if we placed them within the magnetic field. The lines are closer together where the field is stronger and farther apart where the field is weaker. Because these imaginary field lines are so much easier to visualize than the magnetic field itself, we usually discuss magnetic fields by talking about how the field lines would appear. Charged particles, such as the ions and electrons in the solar plasma, cannot easily move perpendicular to the field lines, so they instead follow spiraling paths along them.

Solar magnetic field lines act somewhat like elastic bands, twisted into contortions and knots by turbulent motions in the solar atmosphere. Sunspots occur where tightly wound magnetic fields poke nearly straight out from the solar interior (FIGURE 14.17a). These tight magnetic field lines suppress convection within the sunspot and prevent surrounding plasma from entering the sunspot. With hot plasma unable to enter the region, the sunspot plasma becomes cooler than that of the rest of the photosphere. Individual sunspots typically last up to a few weeks, dissolving when their magnetic fields weaken and allow hotter plasma to flow in.

Sunspots tend to occur in pairs, connected by a loop of magnetic field lines that can arc high above the Sun's surface (FIGURE 14.17b). Gas in the Sun's chromosphere and corona becomes trapped in these loops, making giant **solar prominences**. Some prominences rise to heights of more than 100,000 kilometers above the Sun's surface (FIGURE 14.18).

Individual prominences can last for days or even weeks, disappearing only when the magnetic fields finally weaken and release the trapped gas.

Solar Storms The magnetic fields winding through sunspots and prominences sometimes undergo dramatic and sudden change, producing short-lived but intense storms on the Sun. The most dramatic of these storms are **solar flares**, which send bursts of X rays and fast-moving charged particles shooting into space (FIGURE 14.19).

Flares generally occur in the vicinity of sunspots, which is why we think they are created by changes in magnetic fields. The leading model for solar flares suggests that they occur when the magnetic field lines become so twisted and knotted

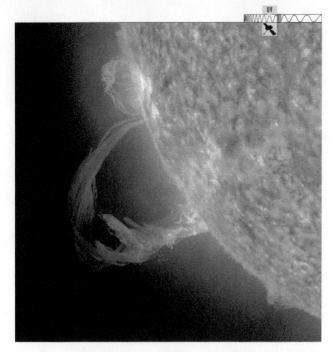

FIGURE 14.18 A gigantic solar prominence erupts from the solar surface in this ultraviolet-light image (from the Solar Dynamics Observatory), taken on December 8, 2011. The height of the prominence is more than 20 times the diameter of Earth.

that they can no longer bear the tension. They are thought to suddenly snap and reorganize themselves into a less twisted configuration. The energy released in the process heats the nearby plasma to 100 million K over the next few minutes or hours, generating X rays and accelerating some of the charged particles to nearly the speed of light.

Heating of the Chromosphere and Corona
As we've seen, many of the most dramatic weather patterns and storms on the Sun involve the very hot gas of the Sun's chromosphere and corona. But why is that gas so hot in the first place?

Remember that temperatures gradually decline as we move outward from the Sun's core to the top of its photosphere. We might expect the decline to continue in the Sun's atmosphere, but instead it reverses, making the chromosphere and corona

much hotter than the Sun's surface. Some aspects of this atmospheric heating remain a mystery today, but we have at least a general explanation: The Sun's strong magnetic fields carry energy upward from the churning solar surface to the chromosphere and corona.

More specifically, the rising and falling of gas in the convection zone probably shakes tightly wound magnetic field lines beneath the solar surface. The magnetic field lines carry this energy upward to the solar atmosphere, where they deposit this energy as heat. The same magnetic fields that keep sunspots cool therefore make the overlying plasma of the chromosphere and corona hot.

Observations confirm the connection between magnetic fields and the structure of the chromosphere and corona. The density of gas in the chromosphere and corona is so low that we cannot see this gas with our eyes except during a total eclipse, when we observe the faint visible light scattered by electrons in the corona (see Figure 2.29). However, we can observe the chromosphere and corona at any time with ultraviolet and X-ray telescopes in space: The roughly 10,000 K plasma of the chromosphere emits strongly in the ultraviolet, and the 1 million K plasma of the corona is the source of virtually all X rays coming from the Sun. FIGURE 14.20 shows an X-ray image of the Sun. The X-ray emission is brightest in regions where hot gas is being trapped and heated in magnetic field loops. Bright spots in the corona tend to be directly above sunspots in the photosphere, confirming that they are created by the same magnetic fields.

Notice that some regions of the corona barely show up in X-ray images; these regions, called **coronal holes**, are nearly devoid of hot coronal gas. More detailed analyses show that the magnetic field lines in coronal holes project out into space like broken rubber bands, allowing particles spiraling along them to escape the Sun altogether. These particles streaming outward from the corona make up the *solar wind*, which blows through the solar system at an average speed of

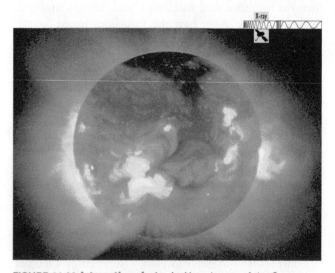

FIGURE 14.20 **interactive photo** An X-ray image of the Sun reveals the million-degree gas of the corona. Brighter regions of this image (yellow) correspond to areas of stronger X-ray emission. The darker regions (such as near the north pole at the top of this photo) are the coronal holes from which the solar wind escapes. (From the Yohkoh Space Observatory.)

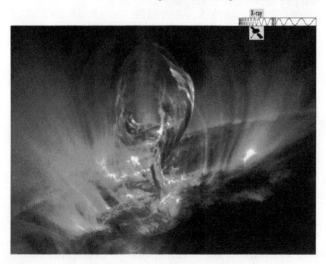

FIGURE 14.19 This X-ray photo (from the *TRACE* spacecraft) shows a solar flare erupting from the Sun's surface.

about 500 kilometers per second and has important effects on planetary surfaces, atmospheres, and magnetospheres.

The solar wind also gives us something tangible to study. In the same way that meteorites provide us with samples of asteroids we've never visited, solar wind particles captured by satellites provide us with a sample of material from the Sun. Analysis of these solar particles has reassuringly verified that the Sun is made mostly of hydrogen, just as we conclude from studying the Sun's spectrum.

How does solar activity affect humans?

Flares and other solar storms sometimes eject large numbers of highly energetic charged particles from the Sun's corona. These particles travel outward from the Sun in huge bubbles called **coronal mass ejections** (FIGURE 14.21). The bubbles have strong magnetic fields and can reach Earth in a couple of days if they happen to be aimed in our direction. Once a coronal mass ejection reaches Earth, it can create a *geomagnetic storm* in Earth's magnetosphere. On the positive side, these storms can lead to unusually strong auroras (see Figure 10.11) that can be visible throughout much of the United States. On the negative side, they can hamper radio communications, disrupt electrical power delivery, and damage the electronic components in orbiting satellites.

During a particularly powerful magnetic storm on the Sun in March 1989, the U.S. Air Force temporarily lost track of more than 2000 satellites, and powerful currents induced in the ground circuits of the Quebec hydroelectric system caused it to collapse for more than 8 hours. The combined cost of the loss of power in the United States and Canada exceeded $100 million. In January 1997, AT&T lost contact with a $200 million communication satellite, probably because of damage

FIGURE 14.21 This X-ray image from the *SOHO* spacecraft shows a coronal mass ejection (the bright arc of gas headed almost straight upward) during the solar storms of 2003. The central red disk blocks the Sun itself, and the white circle represents the size of the Sun in this picture.

caused by particles coming from another powerful solar storm. More recently, a huge coronal mass ejection in early 2012 again threatened Earth's communication and electrical systems, but the systems escaped major damage, in part because of our improved preparedness for solar storms.

Satellites in low Earth orbit are particularly vulnerable during periods of strong solar activity, when the increase in solar X rays and energetic particles heats Earth's upper atmosphere, causing it to expand. The density of the gas surrounding low-flying satellites therefore rises, exerting drag that saps their energy and angular momentum. If this drag proceeds unchecked, the satellites ultimately plummet back to Earth.

THINK ABOUT IT
Solar activity is expected to peak between about 2013 and 2015, with a corresponding increase in the number of solar storms. Search for information on the most recent solar storm. Did it have any effects on satellites or electrical systems?

How does solar activity vary with time?

Solar weather is just as unpredictable as weather on Earth. Individual sunspots can appear or disappear at almost any time, and we have no way to know that a solar storm is coming until we observe it through our telescopes. However, long-term observations have revealed overall patterns in solar activity that make sunspots and solar storms more common at some times than at others.

The Sunspot Cycle The most notable pattern in solar activity is the **sunspot cycle**—a cycle in which the average number of sunspots on the Sun gradually rises and falls (FIGURE 14.22). At the time of *solar maximum*, when sunspots are most numerous, we may see dozens of sunspots on the Sun at one time. In contrast, we may see few if any sunspots at the time of *solar minimum*. The frequency of prominences, flares, and coronal mass ejections also follows the sunspot cycle, with these events being most common at solar maximum and least common at solar minimum.

As you can see in Figure 14.22a, the sunspot cycle varies from one period to the next. Some maximums have much greater numbers of sunspots than others. The length of time between maximums averages 11 years, but we have observed it to be as short as 7 years and as long as 15 years. The locations of sunspots on the Sun also vary with the sunspot cycle (Figure 14.22b). As a cycle begins at solar minimum, sunspots form primarily at mid-latitudes (30° to 40°) on the Sun. The sunspots tend to form at lower latitudes as the cycle progresses, appearing very close to the solar equator as the next solar minimum approaches. Then the sunspots of the next cycle begin to form near mid-latitudes again.

A less obvious feature of the sunspot cycle is that something peculiar happens to the Sun's magnetic field at each solar maximum: The Sun's entire magnetic field starts to flip, turning magnetic north into magnetic south and vice versa. We know this because the magnetic field lines connecting pairs of sunspots (see Figure 14.17) on the same side of the solar

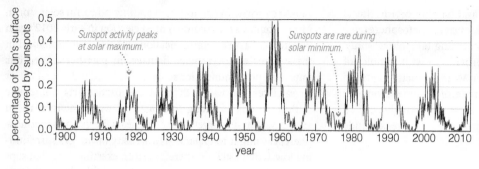

a This graph shows how the number of sunspots on the Sun changes with time. The vertical axis shows the percentage of the Sun's surface covered by sunspots. The cycle has a period of approximately 11 years.

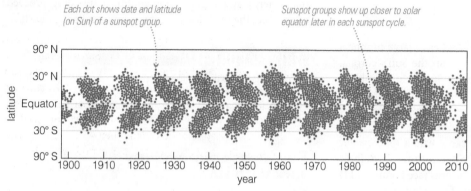

b This graph shows how the latitudes at which sunspot groups appear tend to shift during a single sunspot cycle.

FIGURE 14.22 Sunspot cycle during the past century.

equator all tend to point in the same direction throughout an 11-year cycle. For example, all compass needles might point from the easternmost sunspot to the westernmost sunspot in each sunspot pair north of the solar equator. However, by the time the cycle ends at solar minimum, the magnetic field has reversed: In the subsequent solar cycle, the field lines connecting pairs of sunspots point in the opposite direction. The Sun's *complete* magnetic cycle (sometimes called the *solar cycle*) therefore averages 22 years, since it takes two 11-year sunspot cycles before the magnetic field is back the way it started.

Longer-Term Changes in the Sunspot Cycle

Figure 14.22 shows how the sunspot cycle has varied in length and intensity during the past century, the time during which we've had the most complete records of numbers of sunspots. However, astronomers have observed the Sun telescopically for nearly 400 years, and these longer-term observations suggest that the sunspot cycle can change even more dramatically (**FIGURE 14.23**). For example, astronomers observed virtually no sunspots between the years 1645 and 1715, a period sometimes called the *Maunder minimum* (after E. W. Maunder, who identified it in historical sunspot records).

Is it possible that the Maunder minimum is part of a longer-term cycle of solar activity, one lasting much longer than 11 or 22 years? Some scientists have hypothesized that such cycles might exist, but little evidence has been found to back up these claims. Of course, searching for long-term variations is difficult, because we have very limited observational data predating the invention of the telescope.

The search for long-term cycles therefore relies on less direct evidence. For example, we can make educated guesses about past solar activity from historical descriptions of solar eclipses: When the Sun is more active, the corona tends to have longer and brighter "streamers" visible to the naked eye. We can also gauge solar activity further in the past (a few thousand years) by studying the amount of radioactive carbon-14 in tree rings. This amount varies because carbon-14 is produced in the atmosphere by interactions with high-energy *cosmic rays* [**Section 19.2**] coming from beyond our own solar system. During periods of high solar activity, the solar wind tends to grow stronger, shielding Earth from some of these cosmic rays and reducing the production of carbon-14. Because trees steadily incorporate atmospheric carbon into their rings (through their respiration of carbon dioxide), we can estimate the level of solar activity during each year of a tree's life by measuring the level of carbon-14 in the corresponding ring. These data have not yet turned up any clear evidence of longer-term cycles of solar activity, but the search goes on.

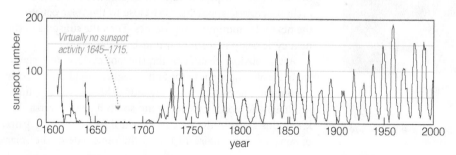

FIGURE 14.23 This graph reconstructs the sunspot cycle over the past 400 years, based on available data from telescopic observations.

The Cause of the Sunspot Cycle The precise reasons for the sunspot cycle are not fully understood, but the leading model ties the sunspot cycle to a combination of convection and the Sun's rotation. Convection is thought to dredge up weak magnetic fields generated in the solar interior, amplifying them as they rise. The Sun's rotation—faster at its equator than near its poles—then stretches and shapes these fields.

Imagine what happens to magnetic field lines that start out running along the Sun's surface from south to north (FIGURE 14.24). At the equator the lines circle the Sun every 25 days, but at higher latitudes they lag behind. As a result, the lines gradually get wound more and more tightly around the Sun. This process, operating at all times over the entire Sun, produces the contorted field lines that generate sunspots and other solar activity.

The detailed behavior of these magnetic fields is quite complex, so scientists attempt to study it with sophisticated computer models. Using these models, scientists have successfully replicated many features of the sunspot cycle, including changes in the number and latitude of sunspots and the magnetic field reversals that occur about every 11 years. However, much still remains mysterious, including why the period of the sunspot cycle varies and why solar activity is different from one cycle to the next.

Over extremely long time periods—hundreds of millions to billions of years—these theoretical models predict a gradual lessening of solar activity. Recall that, according to our theory of solar system formation, the Sun must have rotated much faster when it was young [**Section 8.3**], and a faster rotation rate should have meant much more activity. Observations of other stars that are similar to the Sun but rotate faster confirm that these stars are much more active. We find evidence for many more "starspots" on these stars than sunspots on the Sun, and their relatively bright ultraviolet and X-ray emissions suggest that they have brighter chromospheres and coronas— just as we would expect if they are more active than the Sun.

The Sunspot Cycle and Earth's Climate Despite the changes that occur during the sunspot cycle, the Sun's total output of energy barely changes at all—the largest measured changes have been less than 0.1% of the Sun's average luminosity. However, the ultraviolet and X-ray output of the Sun, which comes from the magnetically heated gas of the chromosphere and corona, can vary much more significantly. Could any of these changes affect the weather or climate on Earth?

Some data suggest connections between solar activity and Earth's climate. For example, the period from 1645 to 1715, when solar activity seems to have virtually ceased (see Figure 14.23), was a time of exceptionally low temperatures in Europe and North America known as the *Little Ice Age*. However, no one really knows whether the low solar activity caused these low temperatures or whether it was just a coincidence. Similarly, some researchers have claimed that certain weather phenomena, such as drought cycles or frequencies of storms, are correlated with the 11- or 22-year cycle of solar activity. A few scientists have even claimed that changes in the Sun may be responsible for Earth's recent global warming, though climate models indicate that the magnitude of the observed warming can be explained only by including human activity (through emissions of greenhouse gases) along with solar changes and other natural factors (see Figure 10.39). Nevertheless, the study of solar activity's possible effects on climate remains an active field of research.

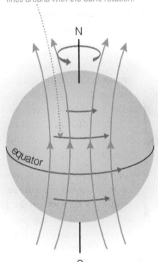
Charged particles tend to push the field lines around with the Sun's rotation.

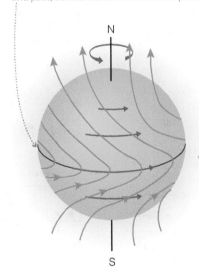
Because the Sun rotates faster near its equator than at its poles, the field lines bend ahead at the equator.

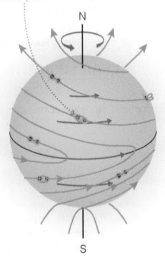
The field lines become more and more twisted with time, and sunspots form when the twisted lines loop above the Sun's surface.

FIGURE 14.24 The Sun rotates more quickly at its equator than it does near its poles. Because gas circles the Sun faster at the equator, it drags the Sun's north-south magnetic field lines into a more twisted configuration. The magnetic field lines linking pairs of sunspots, depicted here as dark blobs, trace out the directions of these stretched and distorted field lines.

Putting Chapter 14 into Context

In this chapter, we examined our Sun, the nearest star. When you look back at this chapter, make sure you understand these "big picture" ideas:

■ The ancient riddle of why the Sun shines has been solved. The Sun shines with energy generated by fusion of hydrogen into helium in the Sun's core. After a journey through the solar interior lasting several hundred thousand years and an 8-minute journey through space, a small fraction of this energy reaches Earth and supplies sunlight and heat.

■ The Sun shines steadily thanks to the balance between pressure and gravity (gravitational equilibrium) and the balance between energy production in the core and energy release at the surface

(energy balance). These two kinds of balance create a natural thermostat that regulates the Sun's fusion rate, keeping the Sun shining steadily and allowing life to flourish on Earth.

■ The Sun's atmosphere displays its own version of weather and climate, governed by solar magnetic fields. Some solar weather, such as coronal mass ejections, clearly affects Earth's magnetosphere. Other claimed connections between solar activity and Earth's climate may or may not be real.

■ The Sun is important not only because it is our source of light and heat, but also because it is the only star near enough for us to study in great detail. In the coming chapters, we will use what we've learned about the Sun to help us understand other stars.

SUMMARY OF KEY CONCEPTS

14.1 A CLOSER LOOK AT THE SUN

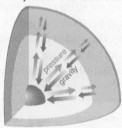

■ **Why does the Sun shine?** The Sun began to shine about $4\frac{1}{2}$ billion years ago when **gravitational contraction** made its core hot enough to sustain nuclear fusion. It has shined steadily ever since because of two types of balance: (1) **gravitational equilibrium**, a balance between the outward push of pressure and the inward pull of gravity, and (2) **energy balance** between the energy released by fusion in the core and the energy radiated into space from the Sun's surface.

■ **What is the Sun's structure?** The Sun's interior layers, from the inside out, are the **core**, the **radiation zone**, and the **convection zone**. Atop the convection zone lies the **photosphere**, the surface layer from which photons can freely escape into space. Above the photosphere are the warmer **chromosphere** and the very hot **corona**.

14.2 NUCLEAR FUSION IN THE SUN

■ **How does nuclear fusion occur in the Sun?** The core's extreme temperature and density are just right for fusion of

hydrogen into helium, which occurs via the **proton-proton chain**. Because the fusion rate is so sensitive to temperature, gravitational equilibrium acts as a thermostat that keeps the fusion rate steady.

■ **How does the energy from fusion get out of the Sun?** Energy moves through the deepest layers of the Sun—the core and the radiation zone—through **radiative diffusion**, in which photons bounce randomly among gas particles. After energy emerges from the radiation zone, convection carries it the rest of the way to the photosphere, where it is radiated into space as sunlight. Energy produced in the core takes hundreds of thousands of years to reach the photosphere.

■ **How do we know what is happening inside the Sun?** We can construct theoretical models of the solar interior using known laws of physics and then check the models against observations of the Sun's size, surface temperature, and energy output. We also use studies of solar vibrations and solar **neutrinos**.

14.3 THE SUN-EARTH CONNECTION

■ **What causes solar activity?** Convection combined with

the rotation pattern of the Sun—faster at the equator than at the poles—causes **solar activity** because these gas motions stretch and twist the Sun's magnetic field. These contortions of the magnetic field are responsible for phenomena such as **sunspots, flares, prominences,** and **coronal mass ejections,** and for heating the gas in the chromosphere and corona.

■ **How does solar activity affect humans?** Bursts of

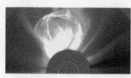

charged particles ejected from the Sun during periods of high solar activity can hamper radio communications, disrupt electrical power generation, and damage orbiting satellites.

■ **How does solar activity vary with time?** The **sunspot**

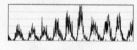

cycle, or the variation in the number of sunspots on the Sun's surface, has an average period of 11 years. The magnetic field flip-flops every 11 years or so, resulting in a 22-year magnetic cycle. Sunspots first appear at mid-latitudes at solar minimum and then become increasingly more common near the Sun's equator as the next minimum approaches. The number of sunspots can vary dramatically from one cycle to the next, and sometimes sunspots seem to be absent altogether.

Use the following questions to check your understanding of some of the many types of visual information used in astronomy. Answers are provided in Appendix J. For additional practice, try the Chapter 14 Visual Quiz at MasteringAstronomy®.

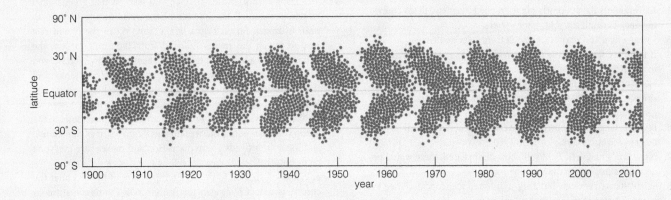

Figure 14.22b, repeated above, shows the latitudes at which sunspots appeared on the surface of the Sun during the last century. Answer the following questions, using the information provided in the figure.

1. Which of the following years had the least sunspot activity?
   a. 1930
   b. 1949
   c. 1961
   d. 1987

2. What is the approximate range in latitude over which sunspots appear?

3. According the figure, how do the positions of sunspots appear to change during one sunspot cycle? Do they get closer to or farther from the equator with time?

MasteringAstronomy®

For instructor-assigned homework go to MasteringAstronomy®.

REVIEW QUESTIONS

Short-Answer Questions Based on the Reading

1. Briefly describe how *gravitational contraction* generates energy. When was it important in the Sun's history? Explain.

2. What two forces are balanced in *gravitational equilibrium*? What does it mean for the Sun to be in *energy balance*?

3. State the Sun's luminosity, mass, radius, and average surface temperature, and put the numbers into a perspective that makes them meaningful.

4. Briefly describe the distinguishing features of each of the layers of the Sun shown in Figure 14.4.

5. What is the difference between nuclear *fission* and nuclear *fusion*? Which one is used in nuclear power plants? Which one does the Sun use?

6. Why does nuclear fusion require high temperatures and pressures?

7. What is the overall nuclear fusion reaction in the Sun? Briefly describe the *proton-proton chain*.

8. Does the Sun's fusion rate remain steady or vary wildly? Describe the feedback process that regulates the fusion rate.

9. Why has the Sun gradually brightened with time?

10. Why does the energy produced by fusion in the solar core take so long to reach the solar surface? Describe the processes by which energy generated by fusion makes its way to the Sun's surface.

11. Explain how mathematical models allow us to predict conditions inside the Sun. How can we be confident that the models are on the right track?

12. What are *neutrinos*? What was the *solar neutrino problem*, and how was it solved?

13. What do we mean by *solar activity*? Describe some of the features of solar activity, including *sunspots, solar prominences, solar flares,* and *coronal mass ejections*.

14. Describe the appearance and temperature of the Sun's photosphere. Why does the surface look mottled? How are sunspots different from the surrounding photosphere?

15. How do magnetic fields keep sunspots cooler than the surrounding plasma? Explain.

16. Why are the chromosphere and corona best viewed with ultraviolet and X-ray telescopes, respectively? Briefly explain how we think the chromosphere and corona are heated.

17. What is the *sunspot cycle*? Why is it sometimes described as an 11-year cycle and sometimes as a 22-year cycle? Are there longer-term changes in solar activity?

18. Describe the leading model for explaining the sunspot cycle. Does the sunspot cycle influence Earth's climate? Explain.

TEST YOUR UNDERSTANDING

Does It Make Sense?

Decide whether the statement makes sense (or is clearly true) or does not make sense (or is clearly false). Explain clearly; not all these have definitive answers, so your explanation is more important than your chosen answer.

19. Before Einstein, gravitational contraction appeared to be a perfectly plausible mechanism for solar energy generation.
20. A sudden temperature rise in the Sun's core is nothing to worry about, because conditions in the core will soon return to normal.
21. If fusion in the solar core ceased today, worldwide panic would break out tomorrow as the Sun began to grow dimmer.
22. Astronomers have recently photographed magnetic fields churning deep beneath the solar photosphere.
23. I wear a lead vest to protect myself from solar neutrinos.
24. If there are few sunspots this year, we should expect many more in about 5 years.
25. News of a major solar flare today caused concern among professionals in the fields of communication and electrical power generation.
26. By observing solar neutrinos, we can learn about nuclear fusion deep in the Sun's core.
27. If the Sun's magnetic field somehow disappeared, there would be no more sunspots on the Sun.
28. Scientists are currently building an infrared telescope designed to observe fusion reactions in the Sun's core.

Quick Quiz

Choose the best answer to each of the following. Explain your reasoning with one or more complete sentences.

29. Which of these groups of particles has the greatest mass? (a) a helium nucleus with two protons and two neutrons (b) four electrons (c) four individual protons
30. Which of these layers of the Sun is coolest? (a) photosphere (b) chromosphere (c) corona
31. Which of these layers of the Sun is coolest? (a) core (b) radiation zone (c) photosphere
32. Scientists estimate the central temperature of the Sun using (a) probes that measure changes in Earth's atmosphere. (b) mathematical models of the Sun. (c) laboratories that create miniature versions of the Sun.
33. Why do sunspots appear darker than their surroundings? (a) They are cooler than their surroundings. (b) They block some of the sunlight from the photosphere. (c) They do not emit any light.
34. At the center of the Sun, fusion converts hydrogen into (a) plasma. (b) radiation and elements like carbon and nitrogen. (c) helium, energy, and neutrinos.
35. Solar energy leaves the core of the Sun in the form of (a) photons. (b) rising hot gas. (c) sound waves.
36. How does the number of neutrinos passing through your body at night compare with the number passing through your body during the day? (a) about the same (b) much smaller (c) much larger
37. What is the most common kind of element in the solar wind? (a) hydrogen (b) carbon (c) helium
38. Which of these things poses the greatest hazard to communication satellites? (a) photons from the Sun (b) solar magnetic fields (c) protons from the Sun

PROCESS OF SCIENCE

Examining How Science Works

39. *Inside the Sun.* Scientists claim to know what is going on inside the Sun, even though they cannot observe the solar interior directly. What is the basis for these claims, and how are they aligned with the hallmarks of science outlined in Section 3.4?
40. *The Solar Neutrino Problem.* Early solar neutrino experiments detected only about a third of the number of neutrinos predicted by the theory of fusion in the Sun. Why didn't scientists simply abandon their models at this point? What features of the Sun did the model get right? What alternatives were there for explaining the mismatch between the predictions and the observations?

GROUP WORK EXERCISE

41. *The Sun's Future.* In this chapter, you learned that gravitational contraction caused the interior of the solar nebula to heat up until hydrogen fusion began in the Sun. When the fusion rate rose to match the energy radiated from the Sun's surface, the Sun came into a long-lasting state of balance. In this exercise, you will discuss what will happen inside the Sun *after* it converts all the hydrogen in the core to helium. Before you begin, assign the following roles to the people in your group: *Scribe* (takes notes on the group's activities), *Proposer* (proposes explanations to the group), *Skeptic* (points out weaknesses in proposed explanations), and *Moderator* (leads group discussion and makes sure everyone contributes). Then discuss the following questions. **a.** What will happen to the core temperature of the Sun after the core runs out of hydrogen for fusion? Will the temperature go up or down? **b.** If you think the temperature will go up, will it rise forever? What could eventually stop the temperature from rising? If you think the temperature will go down, will it decrease forever? What could eventually stop it from falling? **c.** Propose and describe an Earth-based experiment or a set of stellar observations that could test your hypothesis from part b.

INVESTIGATE FURTHER

In-Depth Questions to Increase Your Understanding

Short-Answer/Essay Questions

42. *The End of Fusion I.* Describe what would happen in the Sun if fusion reactions abruptly shut off.
43. *The End of Fusion II.* If fusion reactions were to suddenly shut off in the Sun, how would we be able to tell?
44. *A Really Strong Force.* How would the interior temperature of the Sun be different if the strong force that binds nuclei together were 10 times as strong?
45. *Covered with Sunspots.* Describe what the Sun would look like from Earth if the entire photosphere were the same temperature as a sunspot.
46. *Inside the Sun.* Describe how scientists determine what the interior of the Sun is like. Why haven't we sent a probe into the Sun to measure what is happening there?
47. *Solar Energy Output.* Observations over the past century show that the Sun's visible-light output varies by less than 1%, but the Sun's maximum X-ray output can be as much as 10 times as great as its minimum X-ray output. Explain why changes in X-ray output can be so much more pronounced than those in the output of visible light.
48. *An Angry Sun.* A *Time* magazine cover once suggested that an "angry Sun" was becoming more active as human activity changed Earth's climate through global warming. It's certainly possible for the Sun to become more active at the same time that humans are affecting Earth, but is it possible that the Sun could be responding to human activity? Can humans affect the Sun in any significant way? Explain.

Quantitative Problems

Be sure to show all calculations clearly and state your final answers in complete sentences.

49. *Chemical Burning and the Sun.* Estimate how long the Sun would last if it were merely a huge fire that was releasing chemical energy. Assume that the Sun begins with roughly 10^8 joules per kilogram, a chemical energy content typical of atomic matter.

50. *The Lifetime of the Sun.* The total mass of the Sun is about 2×10^{30} kilograms, of which about 70% was hydrogen when the Sun formed. However, only about 13% of this hydrogen ever becomes available for fusion in the core. The rest remains in layers of the Sun where the temperature is too low for fusion. **a.** Use the given data to calculate the total mass of hydrogen available for fusion over the lifetime of the Sun. **b.** The Sun fuses about 600 billion kilograms of hydrogen each second. Based on your result from part a, calculate how long the Sun's initial supply of hydrogen can last. Give your answer in both seconds and years. **c.** Given that our solar system is now about 4.6 billion years old, when will we need to worry about the Sun running out of hydrogen for fusion?

51. *Solar Power Collectors.* This problem leads you through the calculation and discussion of how much solar power can be collected by solar cells on Earth.
    a. Imagine a giant sphere with a radius of 1 AU surrounding the Sun. What is the surface area of this sphere, in square meters? (*Hint:* The formula for the surface area of a sphere is $4\pi r^2$.) **b.** Because this imaginary giant sphere surrounds the Sun, the Sun's entire luminosity of 3.8×10^{26} watts must pass through it. Calculate the power passing through each square meter of this imaginary sphere in *watts per square meter.* Explain why this number represents the maximum power per square meter that a solar collector in Earth orbit can collect. **c.** List several reasons why the average power per square meter collected by a solar collector on the ground will always be less than what you found in part b. **d.** Suppose you want to put a solar collector on your roof. If you want to optimize the amount of power you can collect, how should you orient the collector? (*Hint:* The optimum orientation depends on both your latitude and the time of year and day.)

52. *Solar Power for the United States.* Total annual U.S. energy consumption is about 2×10^{20} joules.
    a. What is the average power requirement for the United States, in watts? (*Hint:* 1 watt = 1 joule/s.) **b.** With current technologies and solar collectors on the ground, the best we can hope for is that solar cells will generate an average (day and night) power of about 200 watts/m². (You might compare this to the maximum power per square meter you found in Problem 51.) What total area would we need to cover with solar cells to supply all the power needed for the United States? Give your answer in both square meters and square kilometers.

53. *The Color of the Sun.* The Sun's average surface temperature is about 5800 K. Use Wien's law (see Mathematical Insight 5.2) to calculate the wavelength of peak thermal emission from the Sun. What color does this wavelength correspond to in the visible-light spectrum? Why do you think the Sun appears white or yellow to our eyes?

54. *The Color of a Sunspot.* The typical temperature of a sunspot is about 4000 K. Use Wien's law (see Mathematical Insight 5.2) to calculate the wavelength of peak thermal emission from a sunspot. What color does this wavelength correspond to in the visible-light spectrum? How does this color compare with that of the Sun?

55. *Solar Mass Loss.* Estimate how much mass the Sun loses through fusion reactions during its 10-billion-year life. You can simplify the problem by assuming the Sun's energy output remains constant. Compare the amount of mass lost with Earth's mass.

56. *Pressure of the Photosphere.* The gas pressure of the photosphere changes substantially from its upper levels to its lower levels. Near the top of the photosphere, the temperature is about 4500 K and there are about 1.6×10^{16} gas particles per cubic centimeter. In the middle, the temperature is about 5800 K and there are about 1.0×10^{17} gas particles per cubic centimeter. At the bottom of the photosphere, the temperature is about 7000 K and there are about 1.5×10^{17} gas particles per cubic centimeter. Compare the pressures of each of these layers and explain the reason for the trend in pressure that you find. How do these gas pressures compare with Earth's atmospheric pressure at sea level?

57. *Tire Pressure.* Air pressure at sea level is about 15 pounds per square inch. The recommended air pressure in your car tires is about 30 pounds per square inch. How does the density of gas particles inside your tires compare with the density of gas particles in the air outside your tires? What happens to gas pressure in the tire if it springs a leak and loses gas particles? How does your tire respond to this loss of gas particles? How is the tire's response like the response of the Sun's core to the slowly declining number of independent particles within it? How is the tire's response different?

58. *Your Energy Content.* The power needed to operate your body is about 100 watts. Suppose your body could run on fusion power and could convert 0.7% of its mass into energy. How much energy would be available through fusion? For how long could your body then operate on fusion power?

Discussion Questions

59. *The Role of the Sun.* Briefly discuss how the Sun affects us here on Earth. Be sure to consider not only factors such as its light and warmth but also how the study of the Sun has led us to new understandings in science and to technological developments. Overall, how important has solar research been to our lives?

60. *The Sun and Global Warming.* One of the most pressing environmental issues on Earth is the extent to which human emissions of greenhouse gases are warming our planet. Some people claim that part or all of the observed warming over the past century may be due to changes in the Sun, rather than to anything humans have done. Discuss how a better understanding of the Sun might help us comprehend the threat posed by greenhouse gas emissions. Why is it so difficult to develop a clear understanding of how the Sun affects Earth's climate?

Web Projects

61. *Current Solar Weather.* Daily information about solar activity is available at NASA's website spaceweather.com. Where are we in the sunspot cycle right now? When is the next solar maximum or minimum expected? Have there been any major solar storms in the past few months? If so, did they have any significant effects on Earth? Summarize your findings in a one- to two-page report.

62. *Solar Observatories in Space.* Visit NASA's website for the Sun-Earth connection and explore some of the current and planned space missions designed to observe the Sun. Choose one mission to study in greater depth, and write a one- to two-page report on the status and goals of the mission and what it has taught or will teach us about the Sun.

63. *Sudbury Neutrino Observatory.* Visit the website for the Sudbury Neutrino Observatory (SNO) and learn how it has helped to solve the solar neutrino problem. Write a one- to two-page report describing the observatory, any recent results, and what we can expect from it in the future.

64. *Nuclear Power.* There are two basic ways to generate energy from atomic nuclei: through nuclear fission (splitting nuclei) and through nuclear fusion (combining nuclei). All current nuclear reactors are based on fission, but fusion would have many advantages if we could develop the technology. Research some of the advantages of fusion and some of the obstacles to developing fusion power. Do you think fusion power will be a reality in your lifetime? Explain.

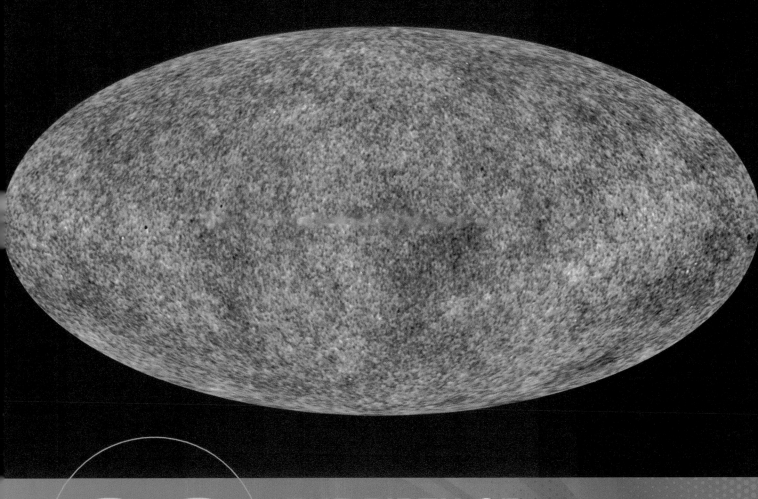

22

THE BIRTH OF THE UNIVERSE

LEARNING GOALS

22.1 THE BIG BANG THEORY
- What were conditions like in the early universe?
- How did the early universe change with time?

22.2 EVIDENCE FOR THE BIG BANG
- How do observations of the cosmic microwave background support the Big Bang theory?
- How do the abundances of elements support the Big Bang theory?

22.3 THE BIG BANG AND INFLATION
- What key features of the universe are explained by inflation?
- Did inflation really occur?

22.4 OBSERVING THE BIG BANG FOR YOURSELF
- Why is the darkness of the night sky evidence for the Big Bang?

Somewhere, something incredible is waiting to be known.

—*Carl Sagan*

Throughout this book, we have studied how the matter produced in the early universe gradually assembled to make galaxies, stars, and planets. However, we have not yet answered one big question: Where did the matter itself come from?

To answer this question, we must go beyond the most distant galaxies and even beyond what we can see near the horizon of the universe. We must go back not just to the origins of matter and energy but all the way back to the beginning of time itself. As we will see, while many questions about the birth of the universe remain unanswered, we now seem to have some understanding of events that must have unfolded as far back as the first fraction of a second after the Big Bang.

 **MA** Hubble's Law Tutorial, Lessons 1–3

22.1 THE BIG BANG THEORY

Is it really possible to study the origin of the entire universe? Not long ago, this topic was considered unfit for scientific study. Scientific attitudes began to change with Hubble's discovery that the universe is expanding, which led to the insight that all things very likely sprang into being at a single moment in time, in an event that we have come to call the *Big Bang.* Today, powerful telescopes allow us to view how galaxies have changed over the past 14 billion years, and at great distances we see young galaxies still in the process of forming [**Section 21.1**]. These observations confirm that the universe is gradually aging, as expected for a universe with an age of 14 billion years.

Unfortunately, we cannot see back to the very beginning of time. Light from the most distant galaxies observed to date shows us what the universe looked like when it was a few hundred million years old. Observing light from earlier times is more difficult because it means looking back to a time before stars existed. Ultimately, however, we face an even more fundamental problem. The universe is filled with a faint glow of radiation that appears to be the remnant heat of the Big Bang. This faint glow is light that has traveled freely through space since the universe was about 380,000 years old, which is when the universe first became transparent to light. Before that time, light could not pass freely through the universe, so there is no possibility of seeing light from earlier times. Just as we must rely on theoretical modeling to determine what the Sun is like on the inside, we must also use modeling to investigate what the universe was like during its earliest moments.

The scientific theory that predicts what the universe was like early in time is called the **Big Bang theory**. It is based on applying known and tested laws of physics to the idea that everything we see today began as an incredibly hot and dense collection of matter and radiation. The Big Bang theory successfully describes how expansion and cooling of this unimaginably intense mixture of particles and photons could have led to the present universe of stars and galaxies, and it explains several aspects of today's universe with impressive accuracy. Our main goal in this chapter is to understand the evidence supporting the Big Bang theory, but first we must explore what the theory tells us about the early universe.

What were conditions like in the early universe?

Observations demonstrate that the universe is cooling with time as it expands, implying that it must have been hotter and denser in the past. Calculating exactly how hot and dense the universe must have been when it was more compressed is much like calculating how the temperature and density of gas in a balloon change when you squeeze it, except that the conditions become much more extreme. FIGURE 22.1 shows how the temperature of the universe has changed with time, according to such calculations.

For most of the universe's history, even back to times just minutes after the Big Bang, conditions were no more extreme than those found in many places in the universe today, such as in the interiors of stars, and therefore can be understood with the same laws of physics that we've applied throughout most of this book. However, at very early times, temperatures were so high that different processes came into play. To understand what the Big Bang theory tells us about events

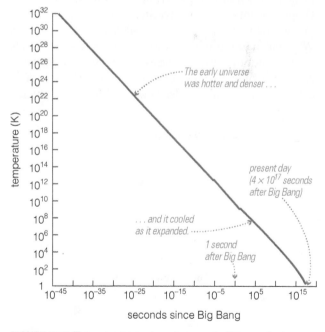

FIGURE 22.1 The universe cools as it expands. This graph shows results of calculations that tell us how the temperature has changed with time. Notice that both axis scales use powers of 10; therefore, even though most of the graph shows temperatures during the first second of the Big Bang, the far right part of the graph actually extends to the present (14 billion years $\approx 4 \times 10^{17}$ s). The kinks correspond to periods of matter-antimatter annihilation.

at those times, we must become more familiar with two aspects of high-energy physics: the creation and annihilation of particles, and the relationships between the fundamental forces that govern matter and energy in the universe.

Particle Creation and Annihilation The universe was so hot during the first few seconds that photons could transform themselves into matter, and vice versa, in accordance with Einstein's formula, $E = mc^2$ [**Section 4.3**]. Reactions that create and destroy matter are now relatively rare in the universe at large, but physicists can reproduce many such reactions in particle accelerators such as the Large Hadron Collider [**Section S4.1**].

One such reaction is the creation or destruction of an *electron–antielectron pair* (FIGURE 22.2). When two photons collide with a total energy greater than twice the mass-energy of an electron (the electron's mass times c^2), they can create two brand-new particles: a negatively charged electron and its positively charged twin, the *antielectron* (also known as a *positron*). The electron is a particle of **matter**, and the antielectron is a particle of **antimatter**. The reaction that creates an electron–antielectron pair also runs in reverse. When an electron and an antielectron meet, they *annihilate* each other totally, transforming all their mass-energy back into photon energy. In order to conserve both energy and momentum, an annihilation reaction must produce two photons instead of just one.

Similar reactions can produce or destroy any particle–antiparticle pair, such as a proton and an antiproton or a neutron and an antineutron. The early universe therefore was filled with an extremely hot and dense blend of photons, matter, and antimatter, converting furiously back and forth. Despite all these vigorous reactions, describing conditions in the early universe is straightforward, at least in principle. We simply need to use the laws of physics to calculate the proportions of the various forms of radiation and matter at each moment in the universe's early history. The only difficulty is our incomplete understanding of the laws of physics.

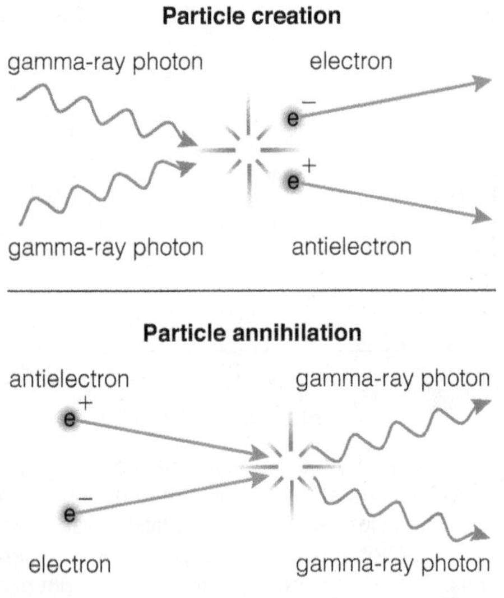

Particle creation

Particle annihilation

FIGURE 22.2 Electron–antielectron creation and annihilation. Reactions like these constantly converted photons to particles, and vice versa, in the early universe.

To date, physicists have investigated the behavior of matter and energy at temperatures as high as those that existed in the universe just *one ten-billionth* (10^{-10}) of a second after the Big Bang, giving us confidence that we actually understand what was happening at that early moment in the history of the universe. Our understanding of physics under the more extreme conditions that prevailed even earlier is less certain, but we do have some ideas about what the universe was like when it was a mere 10^{-38} second old, and perhaps a glimmer of what it was like at the age of just 10^{-43} second. These tiny fractions of a second are so small that, for all practical purposes, we are studying the very moment of creation—the Big Bang itself.

Fundamental Forces To understand the changes that occurred in the early universe, it helps to think in terms of *forces*. Everything that happens in the universe today is governed by four distinct forces: *gravity, electromagnetism,* the *strong force,* and the *weak force* [**Section S4.2**]. We have already encountered examples of each of these forces in action.

Gravity is the most familiar of the four forces, providing the "glue" that holds planets, stars, and galaxies together. The electromagnetic force, which depends on the electrical charge of a particle instead of its mass, is far stronger than gravity. It is therefore the dominant force between particles in atoms and molecules, responsible for all chemical and biological reactions. However, the existence of both positive and negative electrical charges causes the electromagnetic force to lose out to gravity on large scales, even though both forces decline with distance by an inverse square law. Most large astronomical objects (such as planets and stars) are electrically neutral overall, making the electromagnetic force unimportant on that scale. Gravity therefore becomes the dominant force for such objects, because more mass always means more gravity.

The strong and weak forces operate only over extremely short distances, making them important within atomic nuclei but not on larger scales. The strong force binds atomic nuclei together [**Section 14.2**]. The weak force plays a crucial role in nuclear reactions such as fission and fusion, and it is the only force besides gravity that affects weakly interacting particles such as neutrinos.

Although the four forces behave quite differently from one another, current models of fundamental physics predict that they are just different aspects of a smaller number of more fundamental forces, probably only one or two (FIGURE 22.3). These models predict that the four forces would have been merged together at the high temperatures that prevailed in the early universe.

As an analogy, think about ice, liquid water, and water vapor. These three substances are quite different from one another in appearance and behavior, yet they are just different phases of the single substance H_2O. In a similar way, experiments have shown that the electromagnetic and weak forces lose their separate identities under conditions of very high temperature or energy and merge together into a single **electroweak force**. At even higher temperatures and energies, the electroweak force may merge with the strong force and ultimately with gravity. Theories that predict the merger of

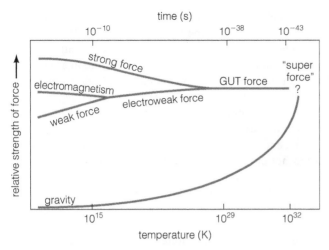

FIGURE 22.3 The four forces are distinct at low temperatures but may merge at very high temperatures, such as those that prevailed during the first fraction of a second after the Big Bang.

the electroweak and strong forces are called **grand unified theories**, or **GUTs** for short. The merger of the strong, weak, and electromagnetic forces is therefore often called the *GUT force*. Many physicists suspect that at even higher energies, the GUT force and gravity merge into a single "super force" that governs the behavior of everything. (You may also hear the names *supersymmetry, superstrings,* and *supergravity* for theories linking all four forces.)

If these ideas are correct, then the universe was governed solely by the super force in the first instant after the Big Bang. As the universe expanded and cooled, the super force split into gravity and the GUT force, which then split further into the strong and electroweak forces. Ultimately, all four forces became distinct. As we'll see shortly, these changes in the fundamental forces probably occurred before the universe was one ten-billionth of a second old.

How did the early universe change with time?

The Big Bang theory uses scientific understanding of particles and forces to reconstruct the history of the universe. Here we will outline this history as a series of *eras,* or time periods. Each era is distinguished from the next by some major change in physical conditions as the universe cools. You'll find it useful to refer to the timeline shown in **FIGURE 22.4** as you read along. Notice that the time scale in Figure 22.4 runs by powers of 10, which means that early eras were very brief, even though they appear spread out on the figure. It will take you longer to read this chapter than it took the universe to progress through the first five eras we will discuss, by which point the chemical composition of the early universe had already been determined.

The Planck Era The first era after the Big Bang is called the **Planck era**, named for physicist Max Planck; it represents times before the universe was 10^{-43} second old. Current theories cannot adequately describe the extreme conditions that must have existed during the Planck era. According to the laws of quantum mechanics, there must have been substantial energy fluctuations from point to point in the very early universe.

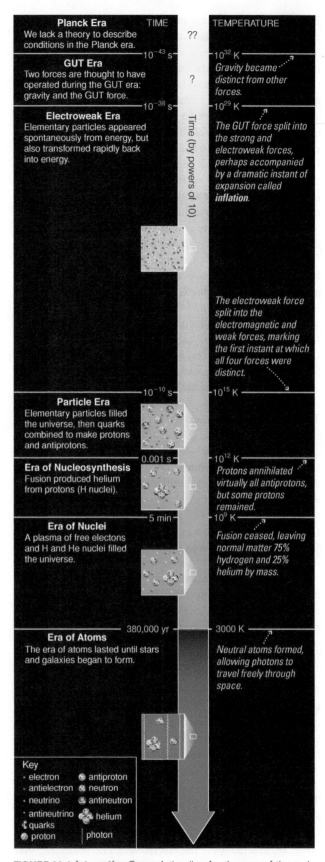

FIGURE 22.4 interactive figure A timeline for the eras of the early universe. The only era not shown is the era of galaxies, which began with the birth of stars and galaxies when the universe was a few hundred million years old.

Because energy and mass are equivalent, Einstein's theory of general relativity tells us that these energy fluctuations must have generated a rapidly changing gravitational field that randomly warped space and time. During the Planck era, these fluctuations were so large that our current theories are inadequate to describe what might have been happening. The problem is that we do not yet have a theory that links quantum mechanics (our successful theory of the very small) and general relativity (our successful theory of the very big). Perhaps someday we will be able to merge these theories of the very small and the very big into a single "theory of everything" (see Special Topic, page 449). Until that happens, science cannot describe the universe during the Planck era.

Nevertheless, we have at least some idea of how the Planck era ended. If you look back at Figure 22.3, you'll see that all four forces are thought to merge into the single, unified super force at temperatures above 10^{32} K—the temperatures that prevailed during the Planck era. In that case, the Planck era would have been a time of ultimate simplicity, when just a single force operated in nature, and it came to an end when the temperature dropped low enough for gravity to become distinct from the other three forces, which were still merged as the GUT force. By analogy to the way ice crystals form as a liquid cools, we say that gravity "froze out" at the end of the Planck era.

The GUT Era

The next era is called the **GUT era**, named for the grand unified theories (GUTs) that predict the merger of the strong, weak, and electromagnetic forces into a single GUT force at temperatures above 10^{29} K (see Figure 22.3). Although different grand unified theories disagree in many details, they all predict that the GUT era was a time during which two forces—gravity and the GUT force—operated in the universe. It came to an end when the GUT force split into the strong and electroweak forces, which happened when the universe was a mere 10^{-38} second old.

Our current understanding of physics allows us to say only slightly more about the GUT era than about the Planck era, and none of our ideas about the GUT era have been sufficiently tested to give us great confidence about what occurred during that time. However, if the grand unified theories are correct, the freezing out of the strong and electroweak forces may have released an enormous amount of energy, causing a sudden and dramatic expansion of the universe that we call **inflation**. In a mere 10^{-36} second, pieces of the universe the size of an atomic nucleus may have grown to the size of our solar system. Inflation sounds bizarre, but as we will discuss later, it explains several important features of today's universe.

The Electroweak Era

The splitting of the GUT force marked the beginning of an era during which three distinct forces operated: gravity, the strong force, and the electroweak force. We call this time the **electroweak era**, indicating that the electromagnetic and weak forces were still merged together. Intense radiation continued to fill all of space, as it had since the Planck era, spontaneously producing matter and antimatter particles that almost immediately annihilated each other and turned back into photons.

The universe continued to expand and cool throughout the electroweak era, dropping to a temperature of 10^{15} K when it reached an age of 10^{-10} second. This temperature is still 100 million times hotter than the temperature in the core of the Sun today, but it was low enough for the electromagnetic and weak forces to freeze out from the electroweak force. After this instant (10^{-10} second), all four forces were forever distinct in the universe.

The end of the electroweak era marks an important transition not only in the physical universe, but also in human understanding of the universe. The theory that unified the weak and electromagnetic forces, which was developed in the 1970s, predicted the emergence of new types of particles (called the W and Z bosons, or *weak bosons*) at temperatures above the 10^{15} K temperature that pervaded the universe when it was 10^{-10} second old. In 1983, particle-accelerator experiments reached energies equivalent to such high temperatures for the first time. The new particles showed up just as predicted, produced from the extremely high energy in accord with $E = mc^2$. We therefore have direct experimental evidence concerning the conditions in the universe at the end of the electroweak era. We do *not* have any direct experimental evidence of conditions before that time. Our theories concerning the earlier parts of the electroweak era and the GUT era consequently are much more speculative than our theories describing the universe from the end of the electroweak era to the present.

The Particle Era

As long as the universe was hot enough for the spontaneous creation and annihilation of particles to continue, the total number of particles was roughly in balance with the total number of photons. Once it became too cool for this spontaneous exchange of matter and energy to continue, photons became the dominant form of energy in the universe. We refer to the time between the end of the electroweak era and the moment when spontaneous particle production ceased as the **particle era**, to emphasize the importance of subatomic particles during this period.

During the early parts of the particle era (and during earlier eras), photons turned into all sorts of exotic particles that we no longer find freely existing in the universe today, including *quarks*—the building blocks of protons and neutrons [**Section S4.2**]. By the end of the particle era, all quarks had combined into protons and neutrons, which shared the universe with other particles such as electrons and neutrinos. The particle era came to an end when the universe reached an age of 1 millisecond (0.001 second) and the temperature had fallen to 10^{12} K. At this point, it was no longer hot enough to produce protons and antiprotons spontaneously from pure energy.

If the universe had contained equal numbers of protons and antiprotons (or neutrons and antineutrons) at the end of the particle era, all of the pairs would have annihilated each other, creating photons and leaving essentially no matter in the universe. From the obvious fact that the universe contains a significant amount of matter, we conclude that protons must have slightly outnumbered antiprotons at the end of the particle era.

We can estimate the ratio of matter to antimatter by comparing the present numbers of protons and photons in the universe. These two numbers should have been similar in the very early universe, but today photons outnumber protons by about a billion to one. This ratio indicates that for every billion antiprotons in the early universe, there must have been about a billion and one protons. That is, for each 1 billion protons and antiprotons that annihilated each other at the end of the particle era, a single proton was left over. This seemingly slight excess of matter over antimatter makes up all the ordinary matter in the present-day universe. Some of those protons (and neutrons) left over from when the universe was 0.001 second old are the very ones that make up our bodies.

The Era of Nucleosynthesis

The eras we have discussed so far all occurred within the first 0.001 second of the universe's existence—less time than it takes you to blink an eye. At this point, the protons and neutrons left over after the annihilation of antimatter began to fuse into heavier nuclei. However, the temperature of the universe remained so high that gamma rays blasted apart most of those nuclei as fast as they formed. This dance of fusion and demolition marked the **era of nucleosynthesis**, which ended when the universe was about 5 minutes old. By this time, the density in the expanding universe had dropped so much that fusion no longer occurred, even though the temperature was still about a billion Kelvin (10^9 K)—much hotter than the temperature of the Sun's core.

When fusion ceased at the end of the era of nucleosynthesis, the chemical content of the universe had become (by mass) about 75% hydrogen and 25% helium, along with trace amounts of deuterium (hydrogen with a neutron) and lithium (the next heaviest element after hydrogen and helium). Except for the small proportion of matter that stars later forged into heavier elements, the chemical composition of the universe remains the same today.

The Era of Nuclei

After fusion ceased, the universe consisted of a very hot plasma of hydrogen nuclei, helium nuclei, and free electrons. This basic picture held for about the next 380,000 years as the universe continued to expand and cool. The fully ionized nuclei moved independently of electrons (rather than being bound with electrons in neutral atoms) during this period, which we call the **era of nuclei**. Throughout this era, photons bounced rapidly from one electron to the next, just as they do deep inside the Sun today [**Section 14.2**], never managing to travel far between collisions. Any time a nucleus managed to capture an electron to form a complete atom, one of the photons quickly ionized it.

The era of nuclei came to an end when the expanding universe was about 380,000 years old. At this point the temperature had fallen to about 3000 K—roughly half the temperature of the Sun's surface today. Hydrogen and helium nuclei finally captured electrons for good, forming stable, neutral atoms for the first time. With electrons now bound into atoms, the universe became transparent, as if a thick fog had suddenly lifted. Photons, formerly trapped among the electrons, began to stream freely across the universe. We still see these photons today as the *cosmic microwave background*, which we will discuss shortly.

The Era of Atoms

We've already discussed the rest of the universe's history in earlier chapters. The end of the era of nuclei marked the beginning of the **era of atoms**, when the universe consisted of a mixture of neutral atoms and plasma (ions and electrons), along with a large number of photons. Because the density of matter in the universe differed slightly from place to place, gravity slowly drew atoms and plasma into the higher-density regions, which assembled into protogalactic clouds [**Section 21.1**]. Stars then formed in these clouds, and the clouds subsequently merged to form galaxies.

The Era of Galaxies

The first full-fledged galaxies had formed by the time the universe was about 1 billion years old, beginning what we call the **era of galaxies,** which continues to this day. Generation after generation of star formation in galaxies steadily builds elements heavier than helium and incorporates them into new star systems. Some of these star systems develop planets, and on at least one of these planets life burst into being a few billion years ago. Now here we are, thinking about it all.

Early Universe Summary FIGURE 22.5 summarizes the major ideas from our brief overview of the history of the universe as it is described by the Big Bang theory. In the rest of this chapter, we will discuss the evidence that supports this theory. Before you read on, be sure to study the visual summary presented in Figure 22.5.

22.2 EVIDENCE FOR THE BIG BANG

What makes us think that a scientific theory can really describe events that occurred nearly 14 billion years ago? Like any scientific theory, the Big Bang theory is a model of nature designed to explain a set of observations. The model was inspired by Edwin Hubble's discovery of the universe's expansion: If the universe has been expanding for billions of years, then simple physical reasoning suggests that conditions ought to have been much denser and hotter in the past. However, the model was not accepted as a valid scientific theory until its major predictions were verified through additional observations and experiments. The Big Bang theory has gained wide scientific acceptance for two key reasons:

- It predicts that the radiation that began to stream across the universe at the end of the era of nuclei should still be present today. Sure enough, we find that the universe is filled with what we call the **cosmic microwave background.** Its characteristics precisely match what we expect according to the Big Bang model.

- It predicts that some of the original hydrogen in the universe should have fused into helium during the era of nucleosynthesis. Observations of the actual helium content of the universe closely match the amount of helium predicted by the Big Bang theory.

The Big Bang theory is a scientific model that explains how the present-day universe developed from an extremely hot and dense beginning. This schematic diagram shows how conditions in the early universe changed as the universe expanded and cooled with time.

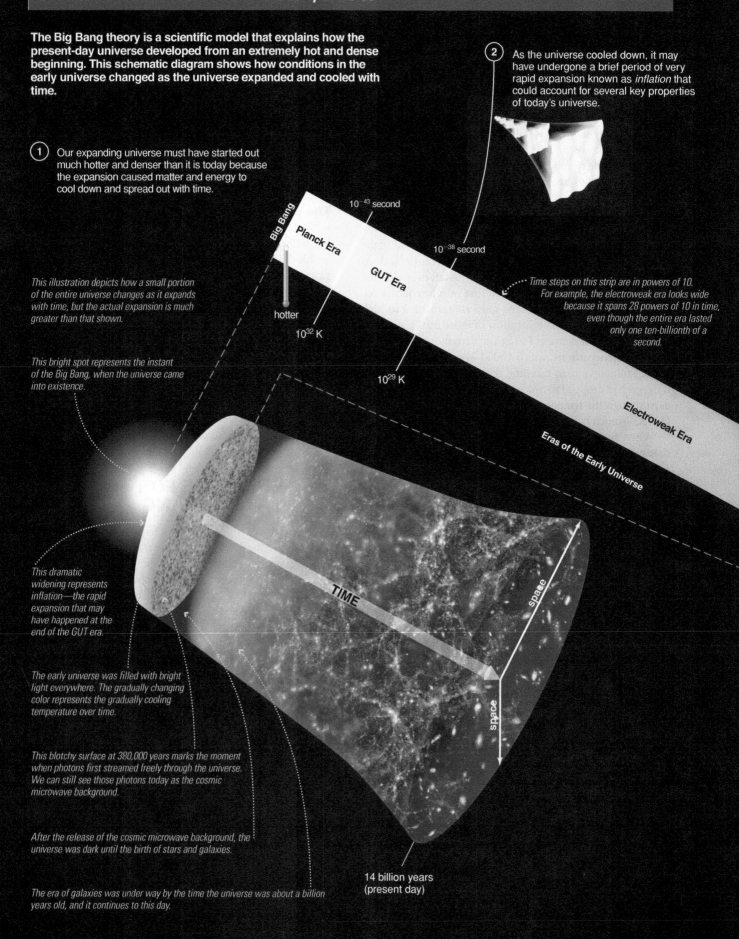

1 Our expanding universe must have started out much hotter and denser than it is today because the expansion caused matter and energy to cool down and spread out with time.

2 As the universe cooled down, it may have undergone a brief period of very rapid expansion known as *inflation* that could account for several key properties of today's universe.

This illustration depicts how a small portion of the entire universe changes as it expands with time, but the actual expansion is much greater than that shown.

This bright spot represents the instant of the Big Bang, when the universe came into existence.

Big Bang

Planck Era

10^{-43} second

10^{-38} second

GUT Era

hotter

10^{32} K

10^{29} K

Time steps on this strip are in powers of 10. For example, the electroweak era looks wide because it spans 28 powers of 10 in time, even though the entire era lasted only one ten-billionth of a second.

Electroweak Era

Eras of the Early Universe

TIME

space

space

This dramatic widening represents inflation—the rapid expansion that may have happened at the end of the GUT era.

The early universe was filled with bright light everywhere. The gradually changing color represents the gradually cooling temperature over time.

This blotchy surface at 380,000 years marks the moment when photons first streamed freely through the universe. We can still see those photons today as the cosmic microwave background.

After the release of the cosmic microwave background, the universe was dark until the birth of stars and galaxies.

The era of galaxies was under way by the time the universe was about a billion years old, and it continues to this day.

14 billion years (present day)

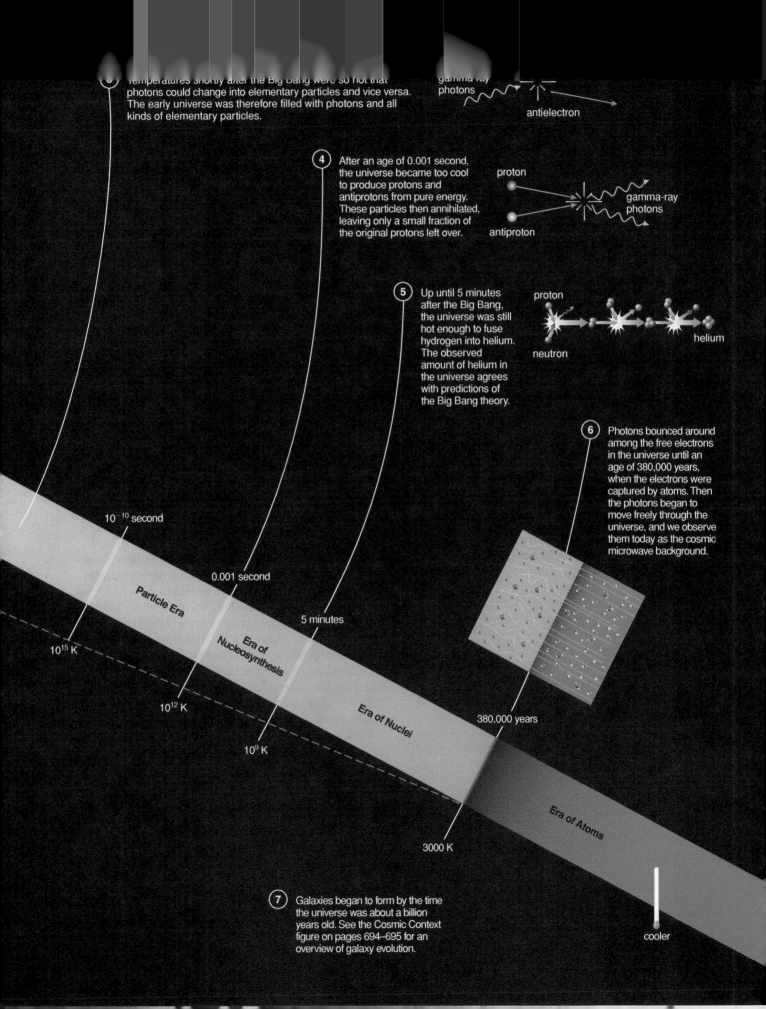

Temperatures shortly after the Big Bang were so hot that photons could change into elementary particles and vice versa. The early universe was therefore filled with photons and all kinds of elementary particles.

gamma-ray photons

antielectron

4 After an age of 0.001 second, the universe became too cool to produce protons and antiprotons from pure energy. These particles then annihilated, leaving only a small fraction of the original protons left over.

proton

gamma-ray photons

antiproton

5 Up until 5 minutes after the Big Bang, the universe was still hot enough to fuse hydrogen into helium. The observed amount of helium in the universe agrees with predictions of the Big Bang theory.

proton

helium

neutron

6 Photons bounced around among the free electrons in the universe until an age of 380,000 years, when the electrons were captured by atoms. Then the photons began to move freely through the universe, and we observe them today as the cosmic microwave background.

10^{-10} second

0.001 second

Particle Era

5 minutes

Era of Nucleosynthesis

10^{15} K

10^{12} K

Era of Nuclei

380,000 years

10^9 K

3000 K

Era of Atoms

7 Galaxies began to form by the time the universe was about a billion years old. See the Cosmic Context figure on pages 694–695 for an overview of galaxy evolution.

cooler

FIGURE 22.6 Arno Penzias and Robert Wilson, discoverers of the cosmic microwave background, with the Bell Labs microwave antenna.

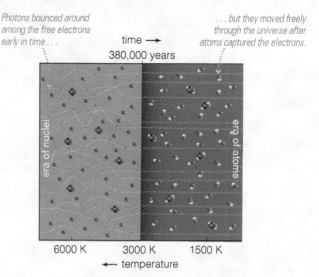

Photons bounced around among the free electrons early in time . . .

time →
380,000 years

. . . but they moved freely through the universe after atoms captured the electrons.

era of nuclei

era of atoms

6000 K   3000 K   1500 K
← temperature

FIGURE 22.7 interactive figure Photons (yellow squiggles) frequently collided with free electrons during the era of nuclei and thus could travel freely only after electrons became bound into atoms. This transition was something like the transition from a dense fog to clear air. The photons released at the end of the era of nuclei, when the universe was about 380,000 years old, make up the cosmic microwave background. Precise measurements of these microwaves tell us what the universe was like at this moment in time.

Let's take a closer look at this evidence, starting with the cosmic microwave background.

How do observations of the cosmic microwave background support the Big Bang theory?

The discovery of the cosmic microwave background was announced in 1965. Arno Penzias and Robert Wilson, two physicists working at Bell Laboratories in New Jersey, were calibrating a sensitive microwave antenna designed for satellite communications (**FIGURE 22.6**). (*Microwaves* fall within the radio portion of the electromagnetic spectrum; see Figure 5.7.) Much to their chagrin, they kept finding unexpected "noise" in every measurement they made. The noise was the same no matter where they pointed the antenna, indicating that it came from all directions in the sky and ruling out any possibility that it came from any particular astronomical object or any place on Earth.

Meanwhile, physicists at nearby Princeton University were busy calculating the expected characteristics of the radiation left over from the heat of the Big Bang.* They concluded that, if the Big Bang had really occurred, this radiation should be permeating the entire universe and should be detectable with a microwave antenna. On a fateful airplane trip home from an astronomical meeting, Penzias sat next to an astronomer who told him of the Princeton calculations. The Princeton group soon met with Penzias and Wilson to compare notes, and both teams realized that the "noise" detected by the Bell Labs antenna was the predicted cosmic microwave background—the first strong evidence that the Big Bang had really happened. Penzias and Wilson received the 1978 Nobel Prize in physics for their discovery.

Origin of the Cosmic Microwave Background

The cosmic microwave background consists of microwave photons that have traveled through space since the end of

the era of nuclei, when most of the electrons in the universe joined with nuclei to make neutral atoms, which interact less strongly with photons. With very few free electrons left to block them, most of the photons from that time have traveled unobstructed through the universe ever since (**FIGURE 22.7**). When we observe the cosmic microwave background, we essentially are seeing back to the end of the era of nuclei, when the universe was only 380,000 years old.

Characteristics of the Cosmic Microwave Background The Big Bang theory predicts that the cosmic microwave background should have an essentially perfect thermal radiation spectrum [**Section 5.4**], because it came from the heat of the universe itself. Moreover, the theory predicts the approximate wavelength at which this thermal radiation spectrum should peak. As we discussed earlier, the theory tells us that the radiation of the cosmic microwave background broke free when the universe had cooled to a temperature of about 3000 K, similar to the surface temperature of a red giant star. The spectrum of the cosmic microwave background therefore should have originally peaked at a wavelength of about 1000 nanometers, just like the thermal radiation from a red star. Because the universe has since expanded by a factor of about 1000, the wavelengths of these photons should by now have stretched to about 1000 times their original wavelengths [**Section 20.3**]. We therefore expect the peak wavelength of the cosmic microwave background now to be about a millimeter, squarely in the microwave portion of the spectrum and corresponding to a temperature of a few degrees above absolute zero.

In the early 1990s, a NASA satellite called the *Cosmic Background Explorer (COBE)* was launched to test these ideas about the cosmic microwave background. The results

---

*The possible existence of microwave radiation left over from the Big Bang was first predicted by George Gamow and his colleagues in the late 1940s, but neither Penzias and Wilson nor the Princeton group were aware of his work.

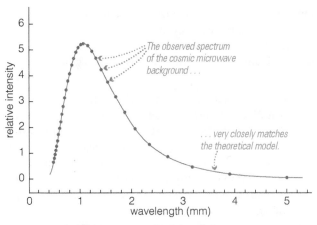

FIGURE 22.8 This graph shows the spectrum of the cosmic microwave background recorded by NASA's *COBE* satellite. A theoretically calculated thermal radiation spectrum (smooth curve) for a temperature of 2.73 K perfectly fits the data (dots). This excellent fit is important evidence in favor of the Big Bang theory.

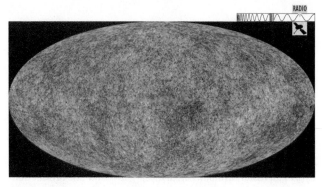

FIGURE 22.9 interactive photo This all-sky map shows temperature differences in the cosmic microwave background measured by *WMAP*. The background temperature is about 2.73 K everywhere, but the brighter regions of this picture are slightly less than 0.0001 K hotter than the darker regions—indicating that the early universe was very slightly lumpy at the end of the era of nuclei. We are essentially seeing what the universe was like at the surface marked "380,000 years" in Figure 22.5. Gravity later drew matter toward the centers of these lumps, forming the structures we see in the universe today.

were a stunning success for the Big Bang theory, and earned the 2006 Nobel Prize in physics for *COBE* team leaders George Smoot and John Mather. As shown in FIGURE 22.8, the cosmic microwave background does indeed have a perfect thermal radiation spectrum, with a peak corresponding to a temperature of 2.73 K.

THINK ABOUT IT

Suppose the cosmic microwave background did not really come from the heat of the universe itself but instead came from many individual stars and galaxies. Explain why, in that case, we would not expect it to have a perfect thermal radiation spectrum. How does the spectrum of the cosmic microwave background lend support to the Big Bang theory?

COBE and its successor missions, the *Wilkinson Microwave Anisotropy Probe (WMAP)* and the European *Planck* satellite, have also mapped the temperature of the cosmic microwave background in all directions (FIGURE 22.9). The temperature turns out to be extraordinarily uniform throughout the universe—just as the Big Bang theory predicts it should be—with variations from one place to another of only a few

parts in 100,000.* Moreover, these slight variations also represent a predictive success of the Big Bang theory. Recall that our theory of galaxy formation depends on the assumption that the early universe was *not quite* perfectly uniform; some regions of the universe must have started out slightly denser than other regions, so that they could serve as seeds for galaxy formation [**Section 21.1**].

In fact, detailed observations of these small temperature variations are very important to studies of galaxy evolution, because all large structures in the universe are thought to have formed around the regions of slightly enhanced density [**Section 23.3**]. Measuring the patterns of variations in the cosmic microwave background therefore tells us both about what must have happened at even earlier times to create the variations and about the starting conditions that we should use in models of galaxy evolution.

---

*Earth's motion (such as our orbit around the Sun and the Sun's orbit around the center of the galaxy) means that we are moving relative to the cosmic microwave background radiation, causing a slight blueshift (about 0.12%) in the direction we're moving and a slight redshift in the opposite direction. Scientists must first subtract these effects before analyzing and making maps of the temperature of the background radiation.

SPECIAL TOPIC

The Steady State Universe

Although the Big Bang theory enjoys wide acceptance among scientists today, alternative ideas have been proposed and considered. One of the cleverest alternatives, developed in the late 1940s, was called the *steady state universe*. This hypothesis accepted the fact that the universe is expanding but rejected the idea of a Big Bang, instead postulating that the universe is infinitely old. The steady state hypothesis may seem paradoxical at first: If the universe has been expanding forever, shouldn't every galaxy be infinitely far away from every other galaxy? Proponents of the steady state universe answered by claiming that new galaxies continually form in the gaps that open up as the universe expands, thereby keeping the same average distance between galaxies at all times. In a sense, the steady

state hypothesis said that the creation of the universe is an ongoing and eternal process rather than one that happened all at once with a Big Bang.

Two key discoveries caused the steady state hypothesis to lose favor. First, the 1965 discovery of the cosmic microwave background matched a prediction of the Big Bang theory but was not adequately explained by the steady state hypothesis. Second, a steady state universe should look about the same at all times, but observations made with increasingly powerful telescopes during the last half-century show that galaxies at great distances look younger than nearby galaxies. As a result of these predictive failures, most astronomers no longer take the steady state hypothesis seriously.

How do the abundances of elements support the Big Bang theory?

The Big Bang theory also solves what had previously been another long-standing astronomical problem: the origin of cosmic helium. Everywhere in the universe, about three-quarters of the mass of ordinary matter (not including dark matter) is hydrogen and about one-quarter is helium. The Milky Way's helium fraction is about 28%, and no galaxy has a helium fraction lower than 25%. Although helium is produced by hydrogen fusion in stars, calculations show that this production can account for only a small proportion of the total observed helium. We therefore conclude that the majority of the helium in the universe must already have been present in the protogalactic clouds that preceded the formation of galaxies.

The Big Bang theory makes a specific prediction about the helium abundance. As we discussed earlier, the theory explains the existence of helium as a consequence of fusion that occurred during the era of nucleosynthesis, when the universe itself was hot enough to fuse hydrogen into helium. Combining the current microwave background temperature of 2.73 K with the number of protons we observe in the universe tells us precisely how hot the universe must have been in the distant past, allowing scientists to calculate exactly how much helium should have been made. The result—25% helium—is another impressive success of the Big Bang theory.

Helium Formation in the Early Universe In order to see why 25% of ordinary matter became helium, we need to understand what protons and neutrons were doing during the 5-minute era of nucleosynthesis. Early in this era, when the universe's temperature was 10^{11} K, nuclear reactions could convert protons into neutrons, and vice versa. As long as the universe remained hotter than 10^{11} K, these reactions kept the numbers of protons and neutrons nearly equal. But as the universe cooled, neutron-proton conversion reactions began to favor protons.

Neutrons are slightly more massive than protons, and therefore reactions that convert protons to neutrons require energy to proceed (in accordance with $E = mc^2$). As the temperature fell below 10^{11} K, the required energy for neutron production was no longer readily available, so the rate of these reactions slowed. In contrast, reactions that convert neutrons

---

MATHEMATICAL INSIGHT 22.1

Temperature and Wavelength of Background Radiation

Figure 22.8 shows that the cosmic microwave background has a nearly perfect thermal radiation spectrum for an object at a temperature of 2.73 K. Wien's law (see Mathematical Insight 5.2) therefore tells us that the wavelength of photons at the peak of the spectrum is

$$\lambda_{max} \approx \frac{2{,}900{,}000}{T \text{ (Kelvin)}} \text{ nm} = \frac{2{,}900{,}000}{2.73} \text{ nm} = 1.1 \times 10^6 \text{ nm}$$

Because 10^6 nm = 1 mm, this peak wavelength is equivalent to 1.1 millimeters. But what was the wavelength of the cosmic microwave photons in the past?

From Mathematical Insight 20.5, the universe has grown in size by a factor of $1 + z$ since the time light left objects that we observe to have a redshift z. Therefore, we find the peak wavelength of cosmic microwave photons at that time by dividing the current peak wavelength by $1 + z$:

$$\lambda_{max} \text{ (at redshift } z) \approx \frac{1.1 \text{ mm}}{1 + z}$$

Combining this result with Wien's law and a little algebra, we find a simple formula for the temperature of the universe at any earlier time at which we see objects with redshift z:

$$T_{universe} \text{ (at redshift } z) \approx 2.73 \text{ K} \times (1 + z)$$

EXAMPLE 1: Photons first moved freely when the universe had cooled to a temperature of about 3000 K. What was the peak wavelength of the photons at that time?

SOLUTION:

Step 1 Understand: We can simply use Wien's law relating peak wavelength to temperature.

Step 2 Solve: We use the temperature of 3000 K in Wien's law:

$$\lambda_{max} \approx \frac{2{,}900{,}000}{T \text{ (Kelvin)}} \text{ nm} = \frac{2{,}900{,}000}{3000} \text{ nm} = 970 \text{ nm}$$

Step 3 Explain: The peak wavelength of the photons when they first began to travel freely was about 970 nanometers, which is in the infrared portion of the electromagnetic spectrum fairly close to the wavelength of red visible light (see Figure 5.7).

EXAMPLE 2: How much has the expansion of the universe stretched the wavelengths of the background radiation since it began to travel freely through the universe?

SOLUTION:

Step 1 Understand: We can use the formula that relates the temperature of the background radiation to the cosmological redshift z. We are given the 3000 K temperature, so we need to find the stretching factor $(1 + z)$.

Step 2 Solve: We divide both sides of the earlier equation by the current temperature of the universe, 2.73 K, to find

$$1 + z = \frac{T_{universe} \text{ (at redshift } z)}{2.73 \text{ K}}$$

In this case, we are looking for the stretching factor corresponding to the time when the universe had a temperature of 3000 K. Plugging this value into the formula, we find

$$1 + z = \frac{3000 \text{ K}}{2.73 \text{ K}} \approx 1100$$

Step 3 Explain: The expansion of the universe has stretched photons by a factor of about 1100 since the time they first began to travel freely across the universe, when the universe was about 380,000 years old. (The answer has no units because it is the *ratio* of the size of the universe now to the size of the universe then.)

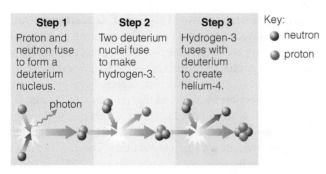

Step 1	Step 2	Step 3	Key:
Proton and neutron fuse to form a deuterium nucleus.	Two deuterium nuclei fuse to make hydrogen-3.	Hydrogen-3 fuses with deuterium to create helium-4.	● neutron ● proton

photon

FIGURE 22.10 During the 5-minute-long era of nucleosynthesis, virtually all the neutrons in the universe fused with protons to form helium-4. This figure illustrates one of several possible reaction pathways.

into protons release energy and therefore are unhindered by cooler temperatures. By the time the temperature of the universe fell to 10^{10} K, protons had begun to outnumber neutrons because the conversion reactions ran only in one direction. Neutrons changed into protons, but the protons didn't change back.

For the next few minutes, the universe was still hot and dense enough for nuclear fusion to take place. Protons and neutrons constantly combined to form *deuterium*—the rare form of hydrogen that contains a neutron in addition to a proton in the nucleus—and deuterium nuclei fused to form helium (**FIGURE 22.10**). However, during the early part of the era of nucleosynthesis, the helium nuclei were almost immediately blasted apart by one of the many gamma rays that filled the universe.

Fusion began to create long-lasting helium nuclei when the universe was about 1 minute old and had cooled to a temperature at which it contained few destructive gamma rays. Calculations show that the proton-to-neutron ratio at this time should have been about 7 to 1. Moreover, almost all the available neutrons should have been incorporated into nuclei of helium-4.

FIGURE 22.11 shows that, based on the 7-to-1 ratio of protons to neutrons, the universe should have had a composition of

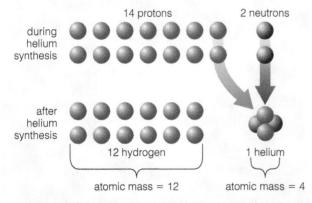

FIGURE 22.11 Calculations show that protons outnumbered neutrons 7 to 1, which is the same as 14 to 2, during the era of nucleosynthesis. The result was 12 hydrogen nuclei (individual protons) for each helium nucleus. Therefore, the predicted hydrogen-to-helium mass ratio is 12 to 4, which is the same as 75% to 25%, in agreement with the observed abundance of helium.

75% hydrogen and 25% helium by mass at the end of the era of nucleosynthesis. This match between the predicted and observed helium ratios provides strong support to the Big Bang theory.

THINK ABOUT IT

Briefly explain why it should not be surprising that some galaxies contain a little more than 25% helium, but why it would be very surprising if some galaxies contained less. (*Hint:* Think about how the relative amounts of hydrogen and helium in the universe are affected by fusion in stars.)

Abundances of Other Light Elements Why didn't the Big Bang produce heavier elements? By the time stable helium nuclei formed, when the universe was about a minute old, the temperature and density of the rapidly expanding universe had already dropped too far for a process like carbon production (three helium nuclei fusing into carbon [**Section 17.2**]) to occur. Reactions between protons, deuterium nuclei, and helium were still possible, but most of these reactions led nowhere. In particular, fusing two helium-4 nuclei results in a nucleus that is unstable and falls apart in a fraction of a second, as does fusing a proton to a helium-4 nucleus.

A few reactions involving hydrogen-3 (also known as *tritium*) or helium-3 can create long-lasting nuclei. For example, fusing helium-4 and hydrogen-3 produces lithium-7. However, the contributions of these reactions to the overall composition of the universe were minor because hydrogen-3 and helium-3 were so rare. Models of element production in the early universe show that, before the cooling of the universe shut off fusion entirely, such reactions generated only trace amounts of lithium, the next heavier element after helium. Aside from hydrogen, helium, and lithium, all other elements were forged much later in the nuclear furnaces of stars. (Beryllium and boron, which are heavier than lithium but lighter than carbon, were created later when high-energy particles broke apart heavier nuclei that formed in stars.)

22.3 THE BIG BANG AND INFLATION

When we discussed the eras of the universe earlier in the chapter, we noted that the universe is thought to have undergone a sudden and dramatic expansion, called *inflation*, which may have occurred at the end of the GUT era, when the universe was 10^{-38} second old.* This idea first emerged in 1981, when physicist Alan Guth was considering the consequences of the separation of the strong force from the GUT force that marked the end of the GUT era. Some theories of high-energy physics predict that this separation of forces

---

*In some models of inflation, the dramatic expansion can happen later, up until the end of the electroweak era.

would have released enormous amounts of energy, and Guth realized that this energy might have caused a short period of inflation. He found that, in a mere 10^{-36} second, inflation could have caused the universe to expand by a factor of 10^{30}. Strange as this idea may sound, it appears to explain several otherwise mysterious features of the present-day universe. Moreover, recent evidence from detailed studies of the cosmic microwave background has provided support for the hypothesis that an early period of inflation really occurred.

What key features of the universe are explained by inflation?

The Big Bang theory has gained wide acceptance because of the strong evidence from the cosmic microwave background and the abundance of helium in the universe. However, without inflation, the theory leaves several major features of our universe unexplained. The three most pressing questions are the following:

- *Where did the density enhancements that led to galaxies come from?* Recall that successful models of galaxy formation start from the assumption that gravity could collect matter together in regions of the early universe that had slightly enhanced density [**Section 21.1**]. We know that such regions of enhanced density were present in the universe at an age of 380,000 years from our observations of variations in the cosmic microwave background, but we have not yet explained how these density variations came to exist.

- *Why is the large-scale universe nearly uniform?* Although the slight variations in the cosmic microwave background show that the universe is not *perfectly* uniform on large scales, the fact that it is smooth to within a few parts in 100,000 is remarkable enough that we would not expect it to have occurred by pure chance.

- *Why is the geometry of the universe flat?* Einstein's general theory of relativity tells us that the overall geometry of the universe can be curved, like the surface of a balloon or a saddle [**Section S3.2**]. However, observational efforts to measure the large-scale geometry of the universe have not yet detected any curvature. As far as we can tell, the large-scale geometry of the universe is flat, which means it is at the precise balance point between being curved like a balloon and curved like a saddle. This precise balance is another fact that is difficult to attribute to chance.

Taking a scientific approach to the early universe demands that we seek answers to these questions that rely on natural processes, and the hypothesis of inflation provides such answers. That is, if we assume inflation occurred, we find that the density enhancements, large-scale uniformity, and flat geometry are all natural and expected consequences. Note that inflation is a *scientific* hypothesis because it is testable with observations we can perform today, and confidence in the hypothesis is growing because it has passed all the tests it has faced so far.

Density Enhancements: Giant Quantum Fluctuations To understand how inflation explains the origin of the density enhancements that led to galaxies, we need to recognize a special feature of energy fields. Laboratory-tested principles of quantum mechanics, especially the uncertainty principle [**Section S4.3**], tell us that on very small scales, the energy fields at any point in space are always fluctuating. The distribution of energy through space is therefore very slightly irregular, even in a complete vacuum. The tiny quantum "ripples" that make up the irregularities can be characterized by a wavelength that corresponds roughly to their size. In principle, quantum ripples in the very early universe could have been the seeds for density enhancements that later grew into galaxies. However, the wavelengths of the original ripples were far too small to explain density enhancements like those we see imprinted on the cosmic microwave background.

Inflation would have dramatically increased the wavelengths of these quantum fluctuations. The rapid growth of the universe during the period of inflation would have stretched tiny ripples from a size smaller than that of an atomic nucleus to the size of our solar system (**FIGURE 22.12**), making them large enough to become the density enhancements from which galaxies and larger structures later formed. If that's the case, then all the structure of today's universe started as tiny quantum fluctuations just before the period of inflation.

Uniformity: Equalizing Temperatures and Densities The remarkable uniformity of the cosmic microwave background might at first seem quite natural, but with further thought it becomes difficult to explain. Imagine observing the cosmic microwave background in a certain part of the sky. You are seeing microwaves that have traveled through the universe since the end of the era of nuclei, just 380,000 years after the Big Bang. You are therefore seeing a region of the universe as it was some 14 billion years ago, when the universe was only

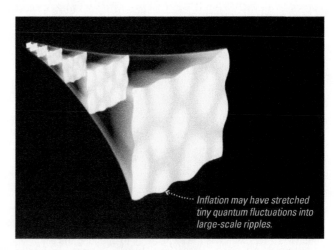

Inflation may have stretched tiny quantum fluctuations into large-scale ripples.

FIGURE 22.12 During inflation, ripples in spacetime would have stretched by a factor of perhaps 10^{30}. The peaks of these ripples then would have become the density enhancements that produced all the structure we see in the universe today.

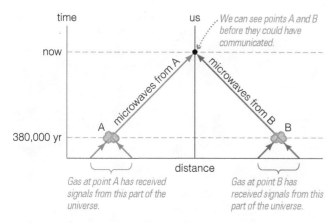

FIGURE 22.13 Without inflation, light would have left the microwave-emitting regions we see on opposite sides of the universe long before they could have communicated with each other and equalized their temperatures, making the fact that their temperatures are virtually identical a puzzle.

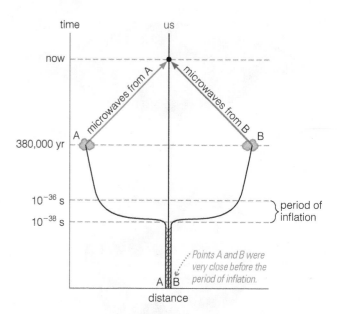

FIGURE 22.14 **interactive figure** With inflation, regions A and B could have been near enough to communicate and equalize their temperatures before inflation pushed them far apart. Today, we can see both A and B, but they are too far apart to see each other.

380,000 years old. Now imagine turning around and looking at the background radiation coming from the opposite direction. You are also seeing this region at an age of 380,000 years, and it looks virtually identical in temperature and density. The surprising part is this: The two regions are so far apart on opposite sides of our observable universe that it seems impossible for them to have exchanged light or any other information, because a signal traveling at the speed of light has not had time to travel from one region to the other (FIGURE 22.13). So how did they come to have the same temperature and density?

The inflation hypothesis answers this question by saying that even though the two regions cannot have had any contact *since* the time of inflation, they were in contact prior to that time. Before the onset of inflation, when the universe was 10^{-38} second old, the two regions were less than 10^{-38} light-second away from each other. Radiation traveling at the speed of light would therefore have had time to bounce between the two regions, and this exchange of energy equalized their temperatures and densities. Inflation then pushed these equalized regions to much greater distances, far out of contact with each other (FIGURE 22.14). Like criminals getting their stories straight before being locked in separate jail cells, the two regions (and all other parts of the observable universe) came to the same temperature and density before inflation spread them far apart.

Because inflation caused different regions of the universe to separate so far in such a short period of time, many people wonder whether it violates Einstein's theories saying that nothing can move faster than the speed of light. It does not, because nothing actually *moves* through space as a result of inflation or the ongoing expansion of the universe. Instead, the expansion of the universe is the expansion of *space itself*. Objects may be separating from one another at a speed faster than the speed of light, but no matter or radiation is able to travel between them during that time. In essence, inflation opens up a huge gap in space between objects that were once close together. The objects get very far apart, but nothing ever travels between them at a speed that exceeds the speed of light.

Density: Balancing the Universe The third question asks why the overall geometry of the universe is "flat." To understand this idea, we must consider the geometry of the universe in a little more detail.

Recall that Einstein's general theory of relativity tells us that the presence of matter can curve the structure of spacetime [**Section S3.3**]. We cannot visualize this curvature in all three dimensions of space (or all four dimensions of spacetime), but we can detect its presence by its effects on how light travels through the universe. Although the curvature of the universe can vary from place to place, the universe as a whole must have some overall shape. Almost any shape is possible, but all the possibilities fall into just three general categories (FIGURE 22.15). Using analogies to objects that we can see in three dimensions, scientists refer to these three categories of shape as *flat* (or critical), *spherical* (or closed), and *saddle shaped* (or open).

According to general relativity, the overall geometry depends on the average density of matter and energy in the universe, and the geometry can be flat only if the combined density of matter plus energy is precisely equal to a value known as the **critical density.** If the universe's average density is less than the critical density, then the overall geometry is saddle-shaped. If its average density is greater than the critical density, then the overall geometry is spherical.

Inflation can explain why the overall geometry is so close to being flat. In terms of Einstein's theory, the effect of inflation on spacetime curvature is similar to the flattening of a balloon's surface when you blow into it (FIGURE 22.16). The flattening of space caused by inflation would have been so enormous that any curvature the universe might have had previously would be noticeable only on size scales much larger than that of the observable universe. Inflation therefore makes the overall geometry of the universe appear flat, which means that the overall density of matter plus energy must be very close to the critical density.

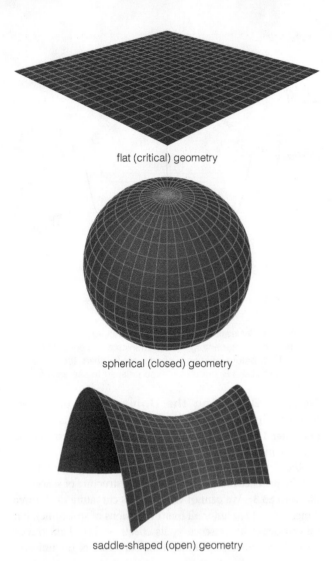

flat (critical) geometry

spherical (closed) geometry

saddle-shaped (open) geometry

FIGURE 22.15 The three possible categories of overall geometry for the universe. Keep in mind that the real universe has these "shapes" in more dimensions than we can see.

Did inflation really occur?

We've seen that inflation offers natural answers to our three key questions about the universe, but did it really happen? We cannot directly observe the universe at the very early time when inflation is thought to have occurred. Nevertheless, we can test the idea of inflation by exploring whether its predictions are consistent with our observations of the universe at later times. Scientists are only beginning to make observations that test inflation, but the findings to date are consistent with the idea that an early inflationary episode made the universe uniform and flat while planting the seeds of structure formation.

The strongest tests of inflation to date come from detailed studies of the cosmic microwave background, and in particular the maps made by the *WMAP* and *Planck* satellites (see Figure 22.9). Remember that these maps show tiny temperature differences corresponding to density variations in the universe at the end of the era of nuclei, when the universe was about 380,000 years old. However, according to models of inflation, these density enhancements were created much

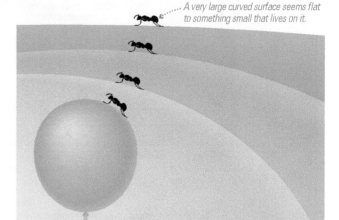

A very large curved surface seems flat to something small that lives on it.

FIGURE 22.16 As a balloon expands, its surface seems increasingly flat to an ant crawling along it. Inflation is thought to have made the universe seem flat in a similar way.

earlier, when inflation caused tiny quantum ripples to expand into seeds of structure. Careful observations of the temperature variations in the microwave background can therefore tell us about the structure of the universe at that very early time.

In particular, detailed calculations based on the Big Bang theory indicate that the largest temperature differences in the cosmic microwave background should typically be between patches of sky separated by about 1° if the overall geometry of the universe is flat. (Similar calculations show that this angular separation would be smaller than 1° if the universe were curved like a saddle, and larger than 1° if the universe were curved like a sphere.) The strongest temperature differences are indeed observed at angular separations of 1°, indicating that the universe is indistinguishable from being geometrically flat, as predicted by inflation.

In addition, the overall pattern of temperature differences agrees with the predictions of models based on inflation, which is why these results support the idea that inflation really occurred. FIGURE 22.17 shows an analysis of the temperature variations observed by *WMAP* in the cosmic microwave background, along with additional data from other microwave telescopes. The graph shows how the typical temperature differences between patches of sky depend on their angular size on the celestial sphere. The dots represent data from the observations, and the red curve shows the inflation-based model that best fits the observations. This model makes specific predictions not only about the data shown in the figure, but also about other characteristics of our universe, such as its overall geometry, composition, and age. In a sense, these new observations of the cosmic microwave background are revealing the characteristics of the seeds from which our universe has grown. To the extent that we have been able to observe these seeds, their nature aligns reassuringly well with the universe we observe at the present time.

This agreement between the seeds inherent in the universe at an age of 380,000 years and our observations of the present-day universe, almost 14 billion years later, is persuasive evidence

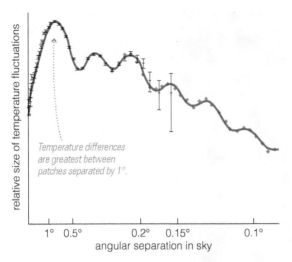

FIGURE 22.17 All-sky maps of the cosmic microwave background like the one in Figure 22.9 allow scientists to measure temperature differences between different patches of the sky. This graph shows how the typical sizes of those temperature differences depend on the angular separation of the patches of sky. The data points (black from WMAP, blue from other microwave telescopes) represent actual measurements of the cosmic microwave background, and the red curve is the prediction of a model that relies on inflation to produce slight variations of temperature and density in the universe. Note the close agreement between the data and the model. (Bars indicate the uncertainty range in the data points.)

Temperature differences are greatest between patches separated by 1°.

relative size of temperature fluctuations

angular separation in sky

in favor of the Big Bang in general and inflation in particular. The bottom line is that, all things considered, inflation does a remarkable job of explaining features of our universe that are otherwise unaccounted for in the Big Bang theory. Many astronomers and physicists therefore suspect that some process akin to inflation did affect the early universe, but the details of the interaction between high-energy particle physics and the evolving universe remain unclear. If these details can be worked out successfully, we face an amazing prospect—a breakthrough in our understanding of the very smallest particles, achieved by studying the universe on the largest observable scales.

22.4 OBSERVING THE BIG BANG FOR YOURSELF

You might occasionally read an article in a newspaper or a magazine questioning whether the Big Bang really happened. We will never be able to prove with absolute certainty that the Big Bang theory is correct. However, no one has come up with any other model of the universe that so successfully explains so much of what we see. As we have discussed, the Big Bang model makes at least two specific predictions that we have observationally verified: the characteristics of the cosmic microwave background and the composition of the universe. It also naturally explains many other features of the universe. So far, at least, we know of nothing that is inconsistent with the Big Bang model.

The Big Bang theory's very success has also made it a target for respected scientists, skeptical nonscientists, and crackpots alike. The nature of scientific work requires that we test established wisdom to make sure it is valid. A sound

scientific disproof of the Big Bang theory would be a discovery of great importance. However, stories touted in the news media as disproofs of the Big Bang usually turn out to be disagreements over details rather than fundamental problems that threaten to bring down the whole theory. Yet scientists must keep refining the theory and tracking down disagreements, because once in a while a small disagreement blossoms into a full-blown scientific revolution.

You don't need to accept all you have read without question. The next time you are musing on the universe's origins, try an experiment for yourself. Go outside on a clear night, look at the sky, and ask yourself why it is dark.

SEE IT FOR YOURSELF

How dark is the night sky where you live? Go outside and observe it on a moonless night. Estimate the total number of stars that are visible to you. How many stars like those do you think it would take to completely cover the entire sky?

Why is the darkness of the night sky evidence for the Big Bang?

If the universe were infinite, unchanging, and everywhere the same, then the entire night sky would blaze as brightly as the Sun. Johannes Kepler [**Section 3.3**] was one of the first people to reach this conclusion, but we now refer to the idea as **Olbers' paradox** after German astronomer Heinrich Olbers (1758–1840).

To understand how Olbers' paradox comes about, imagine that you are in a dense forest on a flat plain. If you look in any direction, you'll likely see a tree. If the forest is small, you might be able to see through some gaps in the trees to the open plains, but larger forests have fewer gaps (FIGURE 22.18). An infinite forest would have no gaps at all—a tree trunk would block your view along any line of sight.

The universe is like a forest of stars in this respect. In an unchanging universe with an infinite number of stars, we would see a star in every direction, making every point in the sky as bright as the Sun's surface. Even the presence of obscuring dust would not change this conclusion. The intense starlight would heat the dust over time until it too glowed like the Sun or evaporated away.

There are only two ways out of this dilemma. Either the universe has a finite number of stars, in which case we would not see a star in every direction, or it changes over time in some way that prevents us from seeing an infinite number of stars. For several centuries after Kepler first recognized the dilemma, astronomers leaned toward the first option. Kepler himself preferred to believe that the universe had a finite number of stars because he thought it had to be finite in space, with some kind of dark wall surrounding everything. Astronomers in the early 20th century preferred to believe that the universe was infinite in space but that we lived inside a finite collection of stars. They thought of the Milky Way as an island floating in a vast black void. However, subsequent observations showed that galaxies fill all of space more or less uniformly. We are therefore left with the second option: The universe changes over time.

FIGURE 22.18 Olbers' paradox can be understood by thinking of the view through a forest.

a In a large forest, a tree will block your view no matter where you look. Similarly, in an unchanging universe with an infinite number of stars, we would expect to see stars in every direction, making the sky bright even at night.

b In a small forest with a smaller number of trees, you can see open spaces beyond the trees. Because the night sky is dark, the universe must similarly have spaces in which we see nothing beyond the stars, which means either that the number of stars is finite or that the universe changes in a way that prevents us from seeing an infinite number of them.

The Big Bang theory resolves Olbers' paradox in a particularly simple way. It tells us that we can see only a finite number of stars because the universe began at a particular moment. While the universe may contain an infinite number of stars, we can see only those that lie within the observable universe, inside our cosmological horizon [**Section 20.3**]. There are other ways in which the universe could change over time and prevent us from seeing an infinite number of stars, so Olbers' paradox does not *prove* that the universe began with a Big Bang. However, we must have some explanation for why the sky is dark at night, and no explanation besides the Big Bang also explains so many other observed properties of the universe so well.

The Big Picture

Putting Chapter 22 into Context

Our "big picture" now extends all the way back to the earliest moments in time. When you think back on this chapter, keep in mind the following ideas:

- Predicting conditions in the early universe is straightforward, as long as we know how matter and energy behave under such extreme conditions.

- Our current understanding of physics allows us to reconstruct the conditions thought to have prevailed in the universe back to the first 10^{-10} second. Our understanding is less certain back to 10^{-38} second. Beyond 10^{-43} second, we run up against the present limits of human knowledge.

- Although it may sound strange to talk about the universe during its first fraction of a second, our ideas about the Big Bang rest on a solid foundation of observational, experimental, and theoretical evidence. We cannot say with absolute certainty that the Big Bang really happened, but no other model has so successfully explained how our universe came to be as it is.

22.1 THE BIG BANG THEORY

■ **What were conditions like in the early universe?** The

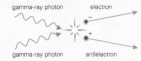

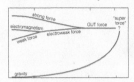

early universe was filled with radiation and elementary particles. It was so hot and dense that the energy of radiation could turn into particles of **matter** and **antimatter**, which then collided and turned back into radiation.

■ **How did the early universe change with time?** The

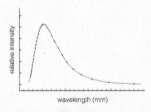

universe has progressed through a series of eras, each marked by unique physical conditions. We know little about the **Planck era**, when the four forces may have all behaved as one. Gravity became distinct at the start of the **GUT era**, and electromagnetism and the weak force became distinct at the end of the **electroweak era**. Matter particles annihilated all the antimatter particles by the end of the **particle era**. Fusion of protons and neutrons into helium ceased at the end of the **era of nucleosynthesis**. Hydrogen nuclei captured all the free electrons, forming hydrogen atoms at the end of the **era of nuclei**. Galaxies began to form at the end of the **era of atoms**. The **era of galaxies** continues to this day.

22.2 EVIDENCE FOR THE BIG BANG

■ **How do observations of the cosmic microwave background support the Big Bang theory?** Telescopes that can detect microwaves allow us to observe the **cosmic micro-**

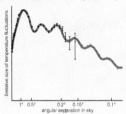

wave background—radiation left over from the Big Bang. Its spectrum matches the characteristics expected of the radiation released at the end of the era of nuclei, spectacularly confirming a key prediction of the Big Bang theory.

■ **How do the abundances of elements support the Big Bang theory?** The Big Bang theory predicts the ratio of protons to neutrons during the era of nucleosynthesis, and

from this predicts that the chemical composition of the universe should be about 75% hydrogen and 25% helium (by mass). The prediction matches observations of the cosmic abundances of elements, another spectacular confirmation of the Big Bang theory.

22.3 THE BIG BANG AND INFLATION

■ **What key features of the universe are explained by**

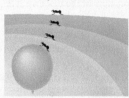

inflation? The hypothesis that the universe underwent a rapid and dramatic period of **inflation** successfully explains three key features of the universe that are otherwise mysterious: (1) the density enhancements that led to galaxy formation, (2) the smoothness of the cosmic microwave background, and (3) the "flat" geometry of the observable universe.

■ **Did inflation really occur?** We can test the idea of inflation because it makes specific predictions about the patterns we

observe in the cosmic microwave background. Observations made with microwave telescopes so far match those predictions, lending credence to the idea that inflation (or something much like it) really occurred.

22.4 OBSERVING THE BIG BANG FOR YOURSELF

■ **Why is the darkness of the night sky evidence for the Big Bang?** **Olbers' paradox** tells us that if the universe were infinite, unchanging, and everywhere the same, the entire night sky would be as bright as the surface of the Sun, and it would not be dark at night. The Big Bang theory solves this paradox by telling us that the night sky is dark because the universe has a finite age, which means we can see only a finite number of stars in the sky.

Use the following questions to check your understanding of some of the many types of visual information used in astronomy. Answers are provided in Appendix J. For additional practice, try the Chapter 22 Visual Quiz at MasteringAstronomy®.

This graph (repeated from Figure 22.1) shows how the temperature of the universe has declined with time; the graph spans many orders of magnitude in both temperature and time. Answer the following questions based on the information provided in the graph.

1. What was the approximate temperature of the universe at an age of 10^{15} s?
   a. about 1 K   b. about 100 K   c. about 10^5 K   d. about 10^{15} K

2. What was the approximate temperature of the universe at an age of 5 minutes?
   a. about 300 K   b. about 10^6 K   c. about 10^9 K   d. about 10^{12} K

3. How much cooler is the universe now (at an age of 4×10^{17} s) than it was at an age of 1 second?
   a. Its current temperature is one hundred-millionth (10^{-8}) the temperature at an age of 1 second.
   b. Its current temperature is one hundred-thousandth (10^{-5}) the temperature at an age of 1 second.
   c. Its current temperature is one-hundredth (10^{-2}) the temperature at an age of 1 second.
   d. Its current temperature is one ten-billionth (10^{-10}) the temperature at an age of 1 second.

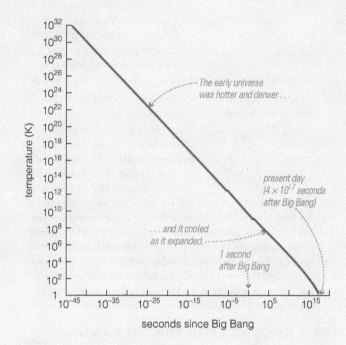

MasteringAstronomy®

For instructor-assigned homework go to MasteringAstronomy®.

REVIEW QUESTIONS

1. Explain what we mean by the *Big Bang theory*.
2. What is *antimatter*? How were particle–antiparticle pairs created and destroyed in the early universe?
3. What are the four forces that operate in the universe today? Why do we think there were fewer forces operating in the early universe?
4. Make a list of the major eras in the history of the universe, summarizing the important events thought to have occurred during each era.
5. Why can't our current theories describe the conditions that existed in the universe during the *Planck era*?
6. What are *grand unified theories*? According to these theories, how many forces operated during the *GUT era*? How are these forces related to the four forces that operate today?
7. What do we mean by *inflation*, and when do we think it occurred?
8. Why do we think there was slightly more matter than antimatter in the early universe? What happened to all the antimatter, and when?

9. How long did the *era of nucleosynthesis* last? Explain why this era was so important in determining the chemical composition of the universe.
10. When we observe the *cosmic microwave background*, at what age are we seeing the universe? How long have the photons in the background been traveling through space? Explain.
11. Briefly describe how the cosmic microwave background was discovered. How do the existence and nature of this radiation support the Big Bang theory?
12. How does the chemical abundance of helium in the universe support the Big Bang theory? Explain.
13. Describe three key questions about the universe that are answered by inflation, and explain how inflation answers each of them.
14. What observational evidence supports the hypothesis of inflation? Be sure to explain how observations of the cosmic microwave background can tell us about the universe at the much earlier time when inflation occurred.
15. What is *Olbers' paradox*, and how is it resolved by the Big Bang theory?

TEST YOUR UNDERSTANDING

Does It Make Sense?

Decide whether the statement makes sense (or is clearly true) or does not make sense (or is clearly false). Explain clearly; not all these have definitive answers, so your explanation is more important than your chosen answer.

16. According to the Big Bang theory, the early universe had nearly equal amounts of matter and antimatter.

17. According to the Big Bang theory, the cosmic microwave background was created when energetic photons ionized the neutral hydrogen atoms that originally filled the universe.

18. Observed characteristics of the cosmic microwave background can be explained by assuming that it comes from individual stars and galaxies.

19. According to the Big Bang theory, most of the helium in the universe was created by nuclear fusion in the cores of stars.

20. According to the hypothesis of inflation, large-scale structure in the universe may have originated as tiny quantum fluctuations.

21. According to the hypothesis of inflation, the "flat" geometry of the universe most likely arose by chance.

22. Inflation is a nice idea, but there are no known ways to test whether it really happened.

23. In the distant past, the cosmic microwave background consisted primarily of infrared light.

24. The main reason the night sky is dark is that stars are so far away.

25. Patterns in the cosmic microwave background tell us about conditions in the early universe that ultimately led to galaxy formation.

Quick Quiz

Choose the best answer to each of the following. Explain your reasoning with one or more complete sentences.

26. The current temperature of the universe as a whole is (a) absolute zero. (b) a few K. (c) a few thousand K.

27. The charge of an antiproton is (a) positive. (b) negative. (c) neutral.

28. When a proton and an antiproton collide, they (a) repel each other. (b) fuse together. (c) convert into two photons.

29. Which of the following does *not* provide strong evidence for the Big Bang theory? (a) observations of the cosmic microwave background (b) observations of the amount of hydrogen in the universe (c) observations of the ratio of helium to hydrogen in the universe

30. When the universe was 380,000 years old, its thermal radiation spectrum consisted mostly of (a) radio and microwave photons. (b) visible and infrared photons. (c) X-ray and ultraviolet photons.

31. Which of the following does inflation help to explain? (a) the uniformity of the cosmic microwave background (b) the amount of helium in the universe (c) the temperature of the cosmic microwave background

32. Which of the following does inflation help to explain? (a) the origin of hydrogen (b) the origin of galaxies (c) the origin of atomic nuclei

33. Which of these pieces of evidence supports the idea that inflation really happened? (a) the enormous size of the observable universe (b) the large amount of dark matter in the universe (c) the apparently "flat" geometry of the universe

34. What is the earliest time from which we observe light in the universe? (a) a few hundred million years after the Big Bang (b) a few hundred thousand years after the Big Bang (c) a few minutes after the Big Bang

35. Which of the following best explains why the night sky is dark? (a) The universe is not infinite in space. (b) The universe has not always looked the way it looks today. (c) The distribution of matter in the universe is not uniform on very large scales.

PROCESS OF SCIENCE

Examining How Science Works

36. *Unanswered Questions.* Briefly describe one important but unanswered question about the events that happened shortly after the Big Bang. If you think it will be possible to answer that question in the future, describe how we might find an answer, being as specific as possible about the evidence necessary to answer the question. If you think the question will never be answered, explain why you think it is impossible to answer.

37. *Darkness at Night.* Suppose you are Kepler, pondering the darkness of the night sky without any knowledge of the Big Bang or the expanding universe. Come up with a hypothesis for the darkness of the night sky that would have been plausible in Kepler's time but does not depend on the Big Bang theory. Propose an experiment that scientists might be able to perform today to test that hypothesis.

GROUP WORK EXERCISE

38. *Testing the Big Bang Theory.* The Big Bang theory is widely accepted because it has successfully predicted many observed characteristics of our universe and because there are no observations that strongly conflict with the theory. In this exercise, you'll consider five hypothetical observations that are not predicted by the Big Bang theory. Before you begin, assign the following roles to the people in your group: *Scribe* (takes notes on the group's activities), *Advocate* (argues in favor of the Big Bang theory), *Skeptic* (points out weaknesses in the Big Bang theory), and *Moderator* (leads group discussion and makes sure everyone contributes). For each observation, discuss whether it (1) could be explained with the Big Bang theory, (2) could be explained with a revision to the Big Bang theory, or (3) would force us to abandon the Big Bang theory. After listening to the *Advocate* and *Skeptic* discuss each discovery, the *Scribe* and *Moderator* should choose option (1), (2), or (3) and write down your team's reasoning for each observation. Here are the hypothetical observations:
a. a star cluster with an age of 15 billion years **b.** a galaxy with an age of 10 million years **c.** a galaxy at a distance of 10 billion light-years whose spectrum is blueshifted **d.** a galaxy containing 90% hydrogen and 10% helium **e.** evidence for an increase of the cosmic microwave background temperature with time

INVESTIGATE FURTHER

In-Depth Questions to Increase Your Understanding

Short-Answer/Essay Questions

39. *Life Story of a Proton.* Tell the life story of a proton from its formation shortly after the Big Bang to its presence in the nucleus of an oxygen atom you have just inhaled. Your story should be creative and imaginative, but it should also demonstrate your scientific understanding of as many stages in the proton's life as possible. You can draw on material from the entire book, and your story should be three to five pages long.

40. *Creative History of the Universe.* The story of creation as envisioned by the Big Bang theory is quite dramatic, but it is usually told in a fairly straightforward, scientific way. Write a more dramatic telling of the story, in the form of a short story, play, or poem. Be as creative as you wish, but be sure to remain accurate according to the science as it is understood today.

41. *Re-creating the Big Bang.* Particle accelerators on Earth can push particles to extremely large speeds. When these particles collide, the amount of energy associated with the colliding particles is much greater than the mass-energy these particles have when at rest. As a result, these collisions can produce many other particles out of pure energy. Explain in your own words how the conditions that occur in these accelerators are similar to the conditions that prevailed shortly after the Big Bang. Also, point out some of the differences between what happens in particle accelerators and what happened in the early universe.

42. *Betting on the Big Bang Theory.* If you had $100, how much money would you wager on the proposition that we have a reasonable scientific understanding of what the universe was like when it was 1 minute old? Explain your bet in terms of the scientific evidence presented in this chapter.

43. *"Observing" the Early Universe.* Explain why we will never be able to observe the era of nucleosynthesis through direct detection of the radiation emitted at that time. How do we learn about this era?

44. *Element Production in the Big Bang.* Nucleosynthesis in the early universe was unable to produce more than trace amounts of elements heavier than helium. Using the information in Figure 17.14, which shows the mass per nuclear particle for many different elements, explain why producing elements like lithium (3 protons), boron (4 protons), and beryllium (5 protons) was so difficult.

45. *Evidence for the Big Bang.* Make a list of at least seven observed features of the universe that are satisfactorily explained by the Big Bang theory (including the idea of inflation).

Quantitative Problems

Be sure to show all calculations clearly and state your final answers in complete sentences.

46. *Energy from Antimatter.* The total annual U.S. power consumption is about 2×10^{20} joules. Suppose you could supply that energy by combining pure matter with pure antimatter. Estimate the total mass of matter–antimatter fuel you would need to supply the United States with energy for 1 year. How does that mass compare with the amount of matter in your car's gas tank? (A gallon of gas has a mass of about 4 kilograms.)

47. *Gravity vs. the Electromagnetic Force.* The amount of electromagnetic force between two charged objects can be computed with an inverse square law similar to Newton's universal law of gravitation; for the electromagnetic force, the law is

$$F = k \times \frac{(\text{charge of object 1}) \times (\text{charge of object 2})}{d^2}$$

In this formula, the charges must be given in units of coulombs (abbreviated C), the distance d between the objects' centers must be in meters, and the constant $k = 9 \times 10^9 \text{ kg} \times \text{m}^3/(\text{C}^2 \times \text{s}^2)$. **a.** Compute the gravitational force between your body and Earth using Newton's universal law of gravitation (see Section 4.4 or Appendix B). **b.** Now suppose all the electrons suddenly disappeared from Earth, making it positively charged, and all the protons in your body suddenly changed into neutrons, making you negatively charged. Compute the strength of the electromagnetic force between the electrons in your body and the protons in Earth. Assume that the charge per unit of mass of both you and Earth is 5×10^7 C/kg. **c.** Compare the electromagnetic force from part b to the gravitational force from part a. Use that result to explain why gravity is considered weaker than the electromagnetic force.

48. *Background Radiation During Galaxy Formation.* What was the peak wavelength of the background radiation at the time light left the most distant galaxies we can currently see? Assume

those galaxies have a cosmological redshift of $z = 7.0$. What is the temperature corresponding to that peak wavelength?

49. *Expansion Since the Era of Nucleosynthesis.* Compare the peak wavelength of the radiation in the universe at the end of the era of nucleosynthesis with its current peak wavelength. Assume the temperature at the end of the era of nucleosynthesis was 10^9 K. How much have the wavelengths of the photons in the universe been stretched since that time?

50. *Temperature of the Universe.* What will the temperature of the cosmic microwave background be when the average distances between galaxies are twice as large as they are today?

51. *Uniformity of the Cosmic Microwave Background.* The temperature of the cosmic microwave background differs by only a few parts in 100,000 across the sky. Compare that level of uniformity to the surface of a table in the following way. Consider a table that is 1 meter in size. How big would the largest bumps on that table be if its surface were smooth to one part in 100,000? Could you see bumps of that size on the table's surface?

52. *Daytime at "Night."* According to Olbers' paradox, the entire sky would be as bright as the surface of a typical star if the universe were infinite in space, unchanging in time, and the same everywhere. However, conditions would not need to be quite that extreme for the "nighttime" sky to be as bright as the daytime sky. **a.** Using the inverse square law for light from Mathematical Insight 15.1, determine the apparent brightness of the Sun in our sky. **b.** Using the inverse square law for light, determine the apparent brightness our Sun would have if it were at a distance of 10 billion light-years. **c.** From your answers to parts a and b, estimate how many stars like the Sun would need to exist at a distance of 10 billion light-years for their total apparent brightness to equal that of our Sun. **d.** Compare your answer to part c with the estimate of the total number of stars in our observable universe from Mathematical Insight 1.3. Use your answer to explain why the night sky is much darker than the daytime sky. How much larger would the total number of stars need to be for "night" to be as bright as day?

Discussion Questions

53. *The Moment of Creation.* You've probably noticed that, in our discussion of the Big Bang theory, we never talk about the first instant. Even our most speculative theories take us back only to within 10^{-43} second of creation. Do you think it will *ever* be possible for science to consider the moment of creation itself? Will science ever be able to answer questions such as *why* the Big Bang happened? Defend your opinions.

54. *The Big Bang.* How convincing do you find the evidence for the Big Bang theory? What are its strengths? What does it fail to explain? Do *you* think the Big Bang really happened? Defend your opinion.

Web Projects

55. *Tests of the Big Bang Theory.* The satellites *COBE* and *WMAP* have provided striking confirmation of several predictions of the Big Bang theory. The more recent *Planck* mission was designed to test the Big Bang theory further. Use the Web to gather pictures and information about *COBE*, *WMAP*, and *Planck*. Write a one- to two-page report about the strength of the evidence compiled by these satellite missions.

56. *New Ideas in Inflation.* The idea of inflation solves many of the puzzles associated with the standard Big Bang theory, but we are still a long way from confirming that inflation really occurred. Find recent articles that discuss some ideas about inflation and how we might test these ideas. Write a two- to three-page summary of your findings.

23 DARK MATTER, DARK ENERGY, AND THE FATE OF THE UNIVERSE

LEARNING GOALS

23.1 UNSEEN INFLUENCES IN THE COSMOS

- What do we mean by dark matter and dark energy?

23.2 EVIDENCE FOR DARK MATTER

- What is the evidence for dark matter in galaxies?
- What is the evidence for dark matter in clusters of galaxies?
- Does dark matter really exist?
- What might dark matter be made of?

23.3 DARK MATTER AND GALAXY FORMATION

- What is the role of dark matter in galaxy formation?
- What are the largest structures in the universe?

23.4 DARK ENERGY AND THE FATE OF THE UNIVERSE

- Why is accelerating expansion evidence for dark energy?
- Why is flat geometry evidence for dark energy?
- What is the fate of the universe?

I soon became convinced, however, that all theorizing would be empty brain exercise and therefore a waste of time unless one first ascertained what the population of the universe really consists of, how its various members interact and how they are distributed through-out cosmic space.

—*Fritz Zwicky, 1971*

Over the past several chapters, we have painted a portrait of the history of the universe that is supported by strong scientific evidence. This evidence indicates that our universe was born about 14 billion years ago in the Big Bang, and that the universe as a whole has been expanding ever since. In regions of the universe that began with slightly enhanced density, gravity was able to take hold and build galaxies, within which some of the hydrogen and helium atoms produced in the Big Bang were assembled into stars. We exist today because galactic recycling has incorporated heavier elements made by early generations of stars into new star systems containing planets like Earth.

Scientists broadly agree with this basic outline of universal history, but at least two major mysteries remain. The first concerns the source of the gravity that forms galaxies and holds them together. The combined mass of all the stars and gas we observe turns out to be insufficient to account for the observed strength of gravity, leading scientists to hypothesize that most of the mass in the universe takes the form of some unseen *dark matter*. The second has emerged from measurements of the universe's expansion rate. Scientists had long expected that gravity would be slowing the expansion rate with time, but observations now indicate the opposite, leading to the idea that a mysterious *dark energy* counteracts the effects of gravity on large scales.

In this chapter, we will explore the evidence for dark matter and dark energy, and the roles they appear to play in shaping our universe. We'll also see why they qualify as two of the greatest mysteries in science, and why the fate of the universe hinges on their properties.

23.1 UNSEEN INFLUENCES IN THE COSMOS

What is the universe made of? Ask an astronomer this seemingly simple question, and you might see a professional scientist blush with embarrassment. Based on all the available evidence today, the answer to this simple question is "We do not know."

It might seem incredible that we still do not know the composition of most of the universe, but you might also wonder why we should be so clueless. After all, astronomers can measure the chemical composition of distant stars and galaxies from their spectra, so we know that stars and gas clouds are made almost entirely of hydrogen and helium, with small amounts of heavier elements mixed in. But notice the key words "chemical composition." When we say these words, we are talking about the composition of material built from atoms of elements such as hydrogen, helium, carbon, and iron.

While it is true that all familiar objects—including people, planets, and stars—are built from atoms, the same may not be true of the universe as a whole. In fact, we now have good reason to think that the universe is *not* composed primarily of atoms. Instead, observations indicate that the universe consists largely of a mysterious form of mass known as *dark matter* and a mysterious form of energy known as *dark energy*.

What do we mean by dark matter and dark energy?

It's easy for scientists to talk about dark matter and dark energy, but what do these terms really mean? They are nothing more than names given to unseen influences in the cosmos. In both cases observational evidence leads us to think that there is something out there, but we do not yet know exactly what the "something" is.

We might naively think that the major source of gravity that holds galaxies together should be the same gas that makes up their stars. However, observations suggest otherwise. By carefully observing gravitational effects on matter that we can see, such as stars or glowing clouds of gas, we've learned that there must be far more matter than meets the eye. Because this matter gives off little or no light, we call it **dark matter**.* In other words, dark matter is simply a name we give to whatever unseen influence is causing the observed gravitational effects. We've already discussed dark matter briefly in Chapters 1 and 19, noting that studies of the Milky Way's rotation suggest that most of our galaxy's mass is distributed throughout its halo while most of the galaxy's light comes from stars and gas clouds in the thin galactic disk (see Figure 1.15).

We infer the existence of the second unseen influence from careful studies of the expansion of the universe. After Edwin Hubble first discovered the expansion, it was generally assumed that gravity must slow the expansion with time. However, evidence collected during the last two decades indicates that the expansion of the universe is actually accelerating, implying that some mysterious force counteracts the effects of gravity on very large scales. **Dark energy** is the name most commonly given to the source of this mysterious force, but it is not the only name; you may occasionally hear the same unseen influence attributed to *quintessence* or to a *cosmological constant*. Note that while dark matter really is "dark" compared to ordinary matter (because it gives off no light), there's nothing unusually "dark" about dark energy—after all, we don't expect to see light from the mere presence of a force or energy field.

Before we continue, it's important to think about dark matter and dark energy in the context of science. Upon first hearing of these ideas, you might be tempted to think that astronomers have "gone medieval," arguing about unseen influences in the same way scholars in medieval times supposedly argued about the number of angels that could dance on the head of a pin. However, strange as the ideas of dark matter and dark energy may seem, they have emerged from careful scientific study conducted in accordance with the hallmarks of science discussed in Chapter 3 (see Figure 3.24). Dark matter

---

*It could just as easily be called *transparent matter*, since light would pass straight through it without interacting.

and dark energy were each proposed to exist because they seemed the simplest ways to explain observed motions in the universe. They've each gained credibility because models of the universe that assume their existence make testable predictions and, at least so far, further observations have borne out some of those predictions. Even if we someday conclude that we were wrong to infer the existence of dark matter or dark energy, we will still need alternative explanations for the observations made to date. One way or the other, what we learn as we explore the mysteries of these unseen influences will forever change our view of the universe.

 Detecting Dark Matter in a Spiral Galaxy Tutorial, Lessons 1–3

23.2 EVIDENCE FOR DARK MATTER

Scientific evidence for dark matter has been building for decades and is now at the point where dark matter seems almost indispensable to explaining the current structure of the universe. For that reason, we will devote most of this chapter to dark matter and its presumed role as the dominant source of gravity in our universe, saving further discussion of dark energy for the final section of the chapter. In this section, we'll begin our discussion of dark matter by examining the evidence for its existence and what the evidence indicates about its nature.

What is the evidence for dark matter in galaxies?

Several distinct lines of evidence point to the existence of dark matter, including observations of our own galaxy, of other galaxies, and of clusters of galaxies. Let's start with individual galaxies and then proceed on to clusters.

Dark Matter in the Milky Way In Chapter 19, we saw how the Sun's motion around the galaxy reveals the total amount of mass within its orbit. Similarly, we can use the orbital motion of any other star to measure the mass of the

Milky Way within that star's orbit. In principle, we could determine the complete distribution of mass in the Milky Way by doing the same thing with the orbits of stars at every different distance from the galactic center.

In practice, interstellar dust obscures our view of disk stars more than a few thousand light-years away from us, making it very difficult to measure stellar velocities. However, radio waves penetrate this dust, and clouds of atomic hydrogen gas emit a spectral line at the radio wavelength of 21 centimeters [**Section 19.2**]. Measuring the Doppler shift of this 21-centimeter line tells us a cloud's velocity toward or away from us. With the help of a little geometry, we can then determine the cloud's orbital speed.

We can summarize the results of these measurements with a diagram that plots the orbital speed of objects in the galaxy against their orbital distances. As a simple example of how we construct such a diagram, sometimes called a *rotation curve*, consider how the rotation speed of a merry-go-round depends on the distance from its center. Every object on a merry-go-round goes around the center in the same amount of time (the rotation period of the merry-go-round). But because objects farther from the center move in larger circles, they must move at faster speeds. The speed is proportional to distance from the center, so the graph illustrating the relationship between speed and distance is a steadily rising straight line (**FIGURE 23.1a**).

In contrast, orbital speeds in our solar system *decrease* with distance from the Sun (**FIGURE 23.1b**). This drop-off in speed with distance occurs because virtually all the mass of the solar system is concentrated in the Sun. The gravitational force holding a planet in its orbit therefore decreases with distance from the Sun, and a smaller force means a lower orbital speed. Orbital speeds must drop similarly with distance in any other astronomical system that has its mass concentrated at its center.

FIGURE 23.1c shows how orbital speed depends on distance in the Milky Way Galaxy. Each individual dot represents the orbital speed and distance from the galactic center of a particular star or gas cloud, and the curve running through the dots represents a "best fit" to the data. Notice that the

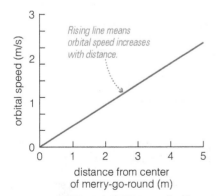

a A rotation curve for a merry-go-round is a rising straight line.

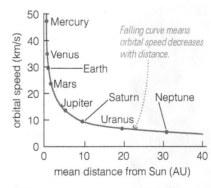

b The rotation curve for the planets in our solar system.

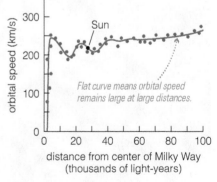

c The rotation curve for the Milky Way Galaxy. Dots represent actual data points for stars or gas clouds.

FIGURE 23.1 **interactive figure** These graphs show how orbital speed depends on distance from the center in three different systems.

orbital speeds remain approximately constant beyond the inner few thousand light-years, so most of the curve is relatively flat. This behavior contrasts sharply with the steeply declining orbital speeds in the solar system, leading us to conclude that most of the Milky Way's mass must *not* be concentrated at its center. Instead, the orbits of progressively more distant gas clouds must encircle more and more mass. The Sun's orbit encompasses about 100 billion solar masses, but a circle twice as large surrounds twice as much mass, and a larger circle surrounds even more mass.

To summarize, orbital speeds in the Milky Way imply that most of our galaxy's mass lies well beyond the orbit of our Sun. A more detailed analysis suggests that most of this mass is distributed throughout the spherical halo that surrounds the disk of our galaxy, extending to distances well beyond those at which we observe globular clusters and other halo stars. Moreover, the total amount of this mass is more than *10 times* the total mass of all the stars in the disk. Because we have detected very little radiation coming from this enormous amount of mass, it qualifies as dark matter. If we are interpreting the evidence correctly, the luminous part of the Milky Way's disk must be rather like the tip of an iceberg, marking only the center of a much larger clump of mass (FIGURE 23.2).

THINK ABOUT IT

Suppose we made a graph of orbital speeds and distances for the moons orbiting Jupiter. Which graph in Figure 23.2 would it most resemble? Why?

Dark Matter in Other Spiral Galaxies Other galaxies also seem to contain vast quantities of dark matter. We can determine the amount of dark matter in a galaxy by comparing the galaxy's mass to its luminosity. (More formally, astronomers calculate the galaxy's *mass-to-light ratio;* see Mathematical Insight 23.1.) The procedure is fairly simple in principle. First, we use the galaxy's luminosity to estimate the amount of mass that the galaxy contains in the form of stars. Next, we determine the galaxy's total mass by applying the law of gravity to observations of the orbital velocities of stars and gas clouds. If this total mass is larger than the mass that we can attribute to stars, then we infer that the excess mass must be dark matter.

We can measure a galaxy's luminosity as long as we can determine its distance with one of the techniques discussed in Chapter 20. We simply point a telescope at the galaxy in question, measure its apparent brightness, and calculate its luminosity from its distance and the inverse square law for light [**Section 15.1**]. Measuring the galaxy's total mass requires measuring orbital speeds of stars or gas clouds as far from the galaxy's center as possible. Atomic hydrogen gas clouds can be found in a spiral galaxy at greater distances from the center than stars, so most of our data come from radio observations of the 21-centimeter line from these clouds. We use Doppler shifts of the 21-centimeter line to determine how fast a cloud is moving toward us or away from us (FIGURE 23.3).

Once we've measured orbital speeds and distances, we can make a graph similar to Figure 23.1c for any spiral galaxy. FIGURE 23.4 shows a few examples illustrating that, like the Milky Way, most other spiral galaxies also have orbital speeds that remain high even at great distances from their centers. Again as in the Milky Way, this behavior implies that a great deal of matter lies far out in the halos of these other spiral galaxies. More detailed analysis tells us that most spiral

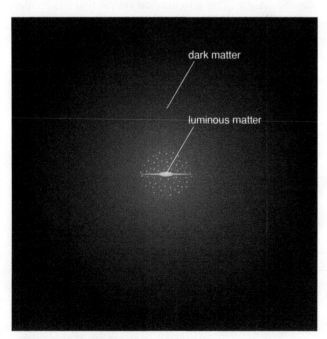

FIGURE 23.2 The dark matter associated with the Milky Way occupies a much larger volume than the galaxy's luminous matter. The radius of this dark-matter halo may be 10 times as large as the galaxy's halo of stars.

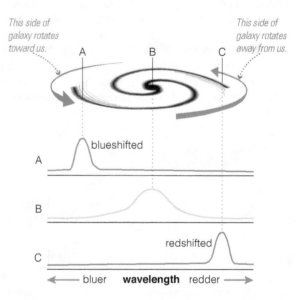

FIGURE 23.3 Measuring the orbital speeds of gas in a spiral galaxy with the 21-centimeter line of atomic hydrogen. Blueshifted lines on the left side of the disk show how fast that side is moving toward us. Redshifted lines on the right side show how fast that side is moving away from us. (This diagram assumes that we first subtract a galaxy's average redshift, so that we can see the shifts that remain due to rotation.)

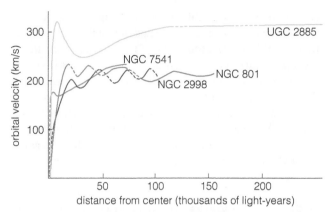

FIGURE 23.4 Graphs of orbital speed versus distance for four spiral galaxies. In each galaxy, the orbital speeds remain nearly constant over a wide range of distances from the center, indicating that dark matter is common in spiral galaxies.

galaxies have at least 10 times as much mass in dark matter as they do in stars. In other words, the composition of typical spiral galaxies is 90% or more dark matter and 10% or less visible matter.

Dark Matter in Elliptical Galaxies We must use a different technique to determine masses of elliptical galaxies, because they do not have large well-organized disks in which we can easily measure how the orbital speeds of stars depend on distance. However, the orbital speeds of their stars still depend on the amount of mass within their orbits, which allows us to measure mass from the width of an elliptical galaxy's spectral lines. If we look at the galaxy as a whole, its spectral lines come from the combination of all its stars. Because each star has its own orbital speed around the center of the galaxy, each produces its own Doppler shift that contributes the overall appearance of the galaxy's spectral lines. Some stars are moving toward the center and others away, so their combined effect is to change any spectral line from a nice narrow line at a particular wavelength to a *broadened* line spanning a range of wavelengths. The greater the broadening of the spectral line, the faster the stars must be moving (**FIGURE 23.5**).

When we compare spectral lines representing regions of elliptical galaxies out to different distances, we find that the speeds of the stars remain fairly constant even quite far from the galaxy's center. Just as in spirals, we conclude that most of

---

MATHEMATICAL INSIGHT 23.1

Mass-to-Light Ratio

An object's mass-to-light ratio (M/L) is its total mass in units of *solar masses* divided by its total *visible* luminosity in units of *solar luminosities*. For example, the mass-to-light ratio of the Sun is

$$\frac{M}{L} \text{ for Sun} = \frac{1 M_{\text{Sun}}}{1 L_{\text{Sun}}} = 1 \frac{M_{\text{Sun}}}{L_{\text{Sun}}}$$

We read this answer with its units as "1 solar mass per solar luminosity." The following examples clarify the idea of the mass-to-light ratio and explain what it can tell us about the existence of dark matter.

EXAMPLE 1: What is the mass-to-light ratio of a $1 M_{\text{Sun}}$ red giant with a luminosity of $100 L_{\text{Sun}}$?

SOLUTION:

Step 1 Understand: Finding a mass-to-light ratio simply requires knowing an object's total mass in solar masses and its total luminosity in solar luminosities. We have been given both.

Step 2 Solve: We divide to find the mass-to-light ratio:

$$\frac{M}{L} = \frac{1 M_{\text{Sun}}}{100 L_{\text{Sun}}} = 0.01 \frac{M_{\text{Sun}}}{L_{\text{Sun}}}$$

Step 3 Explain: The red giant has a mass-to-light ratio of 0.01 solar mass per solar luminosity. Note that the ratio is *less* than 1 because a red giant puts out *more* light per unit mass than the Sun. More generally, stars *more luminous* than the Sun have mass-to-light ratios *less* than 1 and stars *less luminous* than the Sun have mass-to-light ratios *greater* than 1.

EXAMPLE 2: The Milky Way Galaxy contains about 90 billion (9×10^{10}) solar masses of material within the Sun's orbit, and the total luminosity of stars within that same region is about 15 billion (1.5×10^{10}) solar luminosities. What is the mass-to-light ratio of the matter in our galaxy within the Sun's orbit?

SOLUTION:

Step 1 Understand: Again, we simply divide the mass of this region by its luminosity, both in solar units.

Step 2 Solve: The mass-to-light ratio within the Sun's orbit is

$$\frac{M}{L} = \frac{9 \times 10^{10} M_{\text{Sun}}}{1.5 \times 10^{10} L_{\text{Sun}}} = 6 \frac{M_{\text{Sun}}}{L_{\text{Sun}}}$$

Step 3 Explain: The mass-to-light ratio of the matter within the Sun's orbit is about 6 solar masses per solar luminosity. This is *greater* than the Sun's ratio of 1 solar mass per solar luminosity, telling us that most matter in this region is *dimmer* per unit mass than our Sun. This is not surprising, because most stars are smaller and dimmer than our Sun.

EXAMPLE 3: Observations of orbital speeds in a spiral galaxy indicate that its total mass is $5 \times 10^{11} M_{\text{Sun}}$; its luminosity is $1.5 \times 10^{10} L_{\text{Sun}}$. What is its mass-to-light ratio?

SOLUTION:

Step 1 Understand: This problem is essentially the same as the others, but with different implications.

Step 2 Solve: We divide the galaxy's mass by its luminosity:

$$\frac{M}{L} = \frac{5 \times 10^{11} M_{\text{Sun}}}{1.5 \times 10^{10} L_{\text{Sun}}} = 33 \frac{M_{\text{Sun}}}{L_{\text{Sun}}}$$

Step 3 Explain: The galaxy has a mass-to-light ratio of 33 solar masses per solar luminosity, which is more than five times the mass-to-light ratio for the matter in the Milky Way Galaxy within the Sun's orbit. We conclude that, on average, the mass in this galaxy is *much less* luminous than the mass found in the inner regions of the Milky Way, suggesting that the galaxy must contain a lot of mass that emits little or no light.

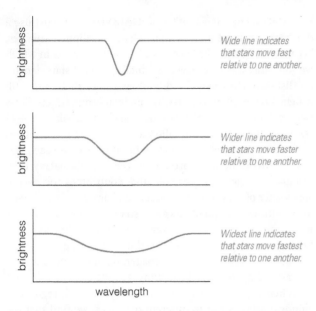

Wide line indicates that stars move fast relative to one another.

Wider line indicates that stars move faster relative to one another.

Widest line indicates that stars move fastest relative to one another.

wavelength

FIGURE 23.5 The broadening of absorption lines in an elliptical galaxy's spectrum tells us how fast its stars move relative to one another.

the matter in elliptical galaxies must lie beyond the distance where the light trails off and hence must be dark matter. The evidence for dark matter is even more convincing for cases in which we can measure the speeds of globular star clusters orbiting at large distances from the center of an elliptical galaxy. These measurements suggest that elliptical galaxies, like spirals, contain 10 times or more as much mass in dark matter as they do in the form of stars.

What is the evidence for dark matter in clusters of galaxies?

The evidence we have discussed so far indicates that stars and gas clouds make up less than 10% of a typical galaxy's mass—the remaining mass consists of dark matter. Observations of galaxy clusters suggest that the total proportion of dark matter is even greater. The mass of dark matter in clusters appears to be as much as 50 times the mass in stars.

The evidence for dark matter in clusters comes from three different ways of measuring cluster masses: measuring the speeds of galaxies orbiting the center of the cluster, studying the X-ray emission from hot gas between the cluster's galaxies, and observing how the clusters bend light as *gravitational lenses*. Let's investigate each of these techniques more closely.

Orbits of Galaxies in Clusters The idea of dark matter is not particularly new. In the 1930s, astronomer Fritz Zwicky was already arguing that clusters of galaxies held enormous amounts of this mysterious stuff (FIGURE 23.6). Few of his colleagues paid attention, but later observations supported Zwicky's claims.

Zwicky was one of the first astronomers to think of galaxy clusters as huge swarms of galaxies bound together by gravity. It seemed natural to him that galaxies clumped closely together in space should all be orbiting one another, just like the stars in a star cluster. He therefore assumed that he could measure cluster masses by observing galaxy motions and applying Newton's laws of motion and gravitation.

Armed with a spectrograph, Zwicky measured the redshifts of the galaxies in a particular cluster and used these redshifts to calculate the speeds at which the individual galaxies are moving away from us. He determined the *recession speed* of the cluster as a whole—that is, the speed at which the expansion of the universe carries it away from us—by averaging the speeds of its individual galaxies.

Once he knew the recession speed for the cluster, Zwicky could subtract this speed from each individual galaxy's speed to determine the speeds of galaxies relative to the cluster center. Of course, this method told him only the average

Pioneers of Science

Scientists always take a risk when they publish what they think are groundbreaking results. If their results turn out to be in error, their reputations may suffer. When it came to dark matter, the pioneers in its discovery risked their entire careers. A case in point is Fritz Zwicky and his proclamations in the 1930s about dark matter in clusters of galaxies. Most of his colleagues considered him an eccentric who leapt to premature conclusions.

Another pioneer in the discovery of dark matter was Vera Rubin, an astronomer at the Carnegie Institution. Working in the 1960s, she became the first woman to observe under her own name at California's Palomar Observatory, then the largest telescope in the world. (Another woman, Margaret Burbidge, was permitted to observe at Palomar earlier but was required to apply for time under the name of her husband, also an astronomer.) Rubin first saw the gravitational signature of dark matter in spectra that she recorded of stars in the Andromeda Galaxy. She noticed that stars in the outskirts of Andromeda moved at surprisingly high speeds, suggesting a stronger gravitational attraction than the mass of the galaxy's stars alone could explain.

Working with a colleague, Kent Ford, Rubin went on to measure orbital speeds of hydrogen gas clouds in many other spiral galaxies (by studying Doppler shifts in the spectra of hydrogen gas) and discovered that the behavior seen in Andromeda is common. Although Rubin and Ford did not immediately recognize the significance of the results, they were soon arguing that the universe must contain substantial quantities of dark matter.

For a while, many other astronomers had trouble believing the results. Some astronomers suspected that the bright galaxies studied by Rubin and Ford were unusual for some reason. So Rubin and Ford went back to work, obtaining orbital measurements for fainter galaxies. By the 1980s, the evidence that Rubin, Ford, and other astronomers measuring rotation curves had compiled was so overwhelming that even the critics came around. Either the theory of gravity was wrong or the astronomers measuring these orbital speeds had discovered dark matter in spiral galaxies. In this case, the risks of the pioneers paid off in a groundbreaking discovery.

FIGURE 23.6 Fritz Zwicky, discoverer of dark matter in clusters of galaxies. Zwicky had an eccentric personality, but some of his ideas that seemed strange in the 1930s proved correct many decades later.

radial component (the speed toward or away from us) of the actual galaxy velocities [**Section 5.4**], but by averaging over enough individual galaxies, Zwicky could get a good average orbital velocity for the cluster's galaxies as a whole. Once he

knew the average orbital velocity of the galaxies, he could use Newton's universal law of gravitation to estimate the cluster's mass (see Mathematical Insight 23.2). Finally, he compared the cluster's mass to its luminosity.

To his surprise, Zwicky found that clusters of galaxies have much greater masses than their luminosities would suggest. That is, when he estimated the total mass of stars necessary to account for the overall luminosity of a cluster, he found that it was far less than the mass he measured by studying galaxy speeds. He concluded that most of the matter within these clusters must not be in the form of stars and instead must be almost entirely dark. Many astronomers disregarded Zwicky's result, believing that he must have done something wrong to arrive at such a strange result. Today, far more sophisticated measurements of galaxy orbits in clusters confirm Zwicky's original finding.

Hot Gas in Clusters A second method for measuring a cluster's mass relies on observing X rays from the hot gas that fills the space between its galaxies (**FIGURE 23.7**). This gas (sometimes called the *intracluster medium*) is so hot that it emits primarily X rays and therefore went undetected until the 1960s, when X-ray telescopes were first launched above Earth's atmosphere. The temperature of this gas is tens of millions of degrees in many clusters and can exceed 100 million degrees in the largest clusters. This hot gas represents a great deal of mass. Large clusters have up to seven times as much mass in the form of X ray–emitting gas as they do in the form of stars.

The hot gas can tell us about dark matter because its temperature depends on the total mass of the cluster. The gas in most clusters is nearly in a state of *gravitational equilibrium*—that is, the outward gas pressure balances gravity's inward pull [**Section 14.1**]. In this state of balance, the average kinetic energies of the gas particles are determined primarily

---

MATHEMATICAL INSIGHT 23.2
Finding Cluster Masses from Galaxy Orbits

Recall that we can use the *orbital velocity law* (see Mathematical Insight 19.1) to calculate the mass, M_r, contained *within* a distance r of a galaxy's center:

$$M_r = \frac{r \times v^2}{G}$$

This law also applies to galaxy clusters if we consider r as the distance from the center of the cluster and assume the galaxies have circular orbits.

EXAMPLE: A galaxy cluster has a radius of 6.2 million light-years, and Doppler shifts show that galaxies orbit the cluster center at an average speed of approximately 1350 km/s. Find the cluster's mass.

SOLUTION:

Step 1 Understand: We can use the orbital velocity law, but to make the units consistent we must convert the radius into meters and the speed into meters per second.

Step 2 Solve: You can confirm for yourself that the radius of 6.2 million light-years is equivalent to 5.9×10^{22} meters; the speed of 1350 km/s becomes 1.35×10^6 m/s. Substituting, we find

$$\begin{aligned}
M_r &= \frac{r \times v^2}{G} \\
&= \frac{(5.9 \times 10^{22}\,\text{m}) \times (1.35 \times 10^6\,\text{m/s})^2}{6.67 \times 10^{-11}\,\text{m}^3/(\text{kg} \times \text{s}^2)} \\
&= 1.6 \times 10^{45}\,\text{kg}
\end{aligned}$$

Step 3 Explain: The result is easier to interpret if we convert from kilograms to solar masses ($1 M_{\text{Sun}} = 2.0 \times 10^{30}$ kg):

$$M_r = 1.6 \times 10^{45}\,\text{kg} \times \frac{1 M_{\text{Sun}}}{2 \times 10^{30}\,\text{kg}} \approx 8.0 \times 10^{14} M_{\text{Sun}}$$

The cluster mass is about 800 trillion solar masses, which is equivalent to about 800 galaxies as large in mass as the Milky Way (including dark matter).

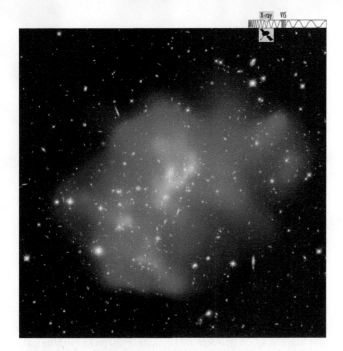

FIGURE 23.7 A distant cluster of galaxies in both visible light and X-ray light. The visible-light photo shows the individual galaxies. The blue-violet overlay shows the X-ray emission from extremely hot gas in the cluster, with blue representing the hottest gas and violet representing cooler gas. Evidence for dark matter comes both from the observed motions of the visible galaxies and from the temperature of the hot gas. (The region shown is about 8 million light-years across.)

by the strength of gravity and hence by the amount of mass within the cluster. Because the temperature of a gas reflects the average kinetic energies of its particles, the gas temperatures we measure with X-ray telescopes tell us the average

speeds of the X ray–emitting particles (see Mathematical Insight 23.3). We can then use these particle speeds to determine the cluster's total mass.

The results obtained with this method agree well with the results found by studying the orbital motions of the cluster's galaxies. Even after we account for the mass of the hot gas, we find that the amount of dark matter in clusters of galaxies is up to 50 times the combined mass of the stars in the cluster's galaxies. In other words, the gravity of dark matter seems to be binding the galaxies of a cluster together in much the same way gravity helps bind individual galaxies together.

THINK ABOUT IT

What would happen to a cluster of galaxies if you instantly removed all the dark matter without changing the velocities of the galaxies?

Gravitational Lensing The methods of measuring galaxy and cluster masses that we've discussed so far all ultimately rely on Newton's laws, including his universal law of gravitation. But can we trust these laws on such large size scales? One way to check is to measure masses in a different way. Today, astronomers can do this with observations of *gravitational lensing.*

Gravitational lensing occurs because masses distort spacetime—the "fabric" of the universe [**Section S3.3**]. Massive objects can therefore act as **gravitational lenses** that bend light beams passing nearby. This prediction of Einstein's general theory of relativity was first verified in 1919 during an eclipse of the Sun [**Section S3.4**]. Because the light-bending angle of a gravitational lens depends on

---

MATHEMATICAL INSIGHT 23.3

Finding Cluster Masses from Gas Temperature

To find a cluster's mass from the temperature of its hot, X ray–emitting gas, we need a formula relating the gas temperature to the speeds of individual particles in the gas, which is mostly hydrogen. Although we will not present a derivation here, the following formula applies:

$$v_{\mathrm{H}} = (140 \text{ m/s}) \times \sqrt{T}$$

where v_{H} is the average orbital speed of the hydrogen nuclei and T is the temperature on the Kelvin scale. Once we find the speeds of the hydrogen nuclei, we can use them in the orbital velocity law to find the cluster mass.

EXAMPLE: The galaxy cluster from Mathematical Insight 23.2, with a radius of 6.2 million light-years, is filled with hot gas at a temperature of 9×10^7 K. Use this temperature to find the cluster's mass.

SOLUTION:

Step 1 Understand: We can use the formula relating speed and temperature to find the average orbital speed of hydrogen nuclei, which we can then use as the velocity (v) in the orbital velocity law. We already know the cluster's radius, which is the only other information we need.

Step 2 Solve: Using the given formula and the temperature of 9×10^7 K, we find that the average orbital speed of the hydrogen nuclei is

$$v_{\mathrm{H}} = (140 \text{ m/s}) \times \sqrt{T}$$
$$= (140 \text{ m/s}) \times \sqrt{9 \times 10^7}$$
$$= 1.3 \times 10^6 \text{ m/s}$$

We now find the cluster's mass from the orbital velocity law, using the above value as v and the cluster's radius ($r = 6.2$ million ly $\approx 5.9 \times 10^{22}$ m):

$$M_r = \frac{r \times v^2}{G}$$
$$= \frac{(5.9 \times 10^{22} \text{ m}) \times (1.3 \times 10^6 \text{ m/s})^2}{6.67 \times 10^{-11} \text{ m}^3/(\text{kg} \times \text{s}^2)}$$
$$\approx 1.5 \times 10^{45} \text{ kg}$$

Step 3 Explain: The cluster's mass is 1.5×10^{45} kilograms, which you can confirm to be about 750 trillion solar masses. This is very close to the 800 trillion solar masses found in Mathematical Insight 23.2 from the galaxy speeds, so the two methods of estimating mass agree well.

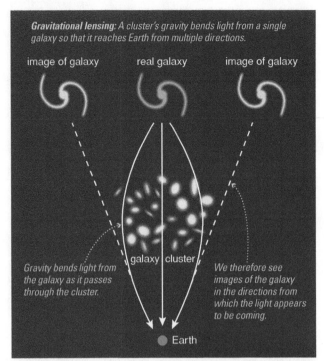

Gravitational lensing: A cluster's gravity bends light from a single galaxy so that it reaches Earth from multiple directions.

image of galaxy   real galaxy   image of galaxy

Gravity bends light from the galaxy as it passes through the cluster.

galaxy cluster

We therefore see images of the galaxy in the directions from which the light appears to be coming.

Earth

Result: Through a telescope on Earth, we see multiple images of what is really a single galaxy.

FIGURE 23.8 **interactive photo** This Hubble Space Telescope photo shows a galaxy cluster acting as a gravitational lens. The yellow elliptical galaxies are cluster members. The small blue ovals (such as those indicated by the arrows) are multiple images of a single galaxy that lies almost directly behind the cluster's center. (The picture shows a region about 1.4 million light-years across.)

FIGURE 23.9 **interactive figure** A cluster's powerful gravity bends light paths from background galaxies to Earth. If light arrives from several different directions, we see multiple images of the same galaxy.

the mass of the object doing the bending, we can measure the masses of objects by observing how strongly they distort light paths.

FIGURE 23.8 shows a striking example of how a cluster of galaxies can act as a gravitational lens. Many of the yellow elliptical galaxies concentrated toward the center of the picture belong to the cluster, but at least one of the galaxies pictured does not. At several positions on various sides of the central clump of yellow galaxies, you will notice multiple images of the same blue galaxy. Each one of these images, whose sizes differ, looks like a distorted oval with an off-center smudge.

The blue galaxy seen in these multiple images lies almost directly behind the center of the cluster, at a much greater distance. We see multiple images of this single galaxy because photons do not follow straight paths as they travel from the galaxy to Earth. Instead, the cluster's gravity bends the photon paths, allowing light from the galaxy to arrive at Earth from a few slightly different directions (FIGURE 23.9). Each alternative path produces a separate, distorted image of the blue galaxy.

Multiple images of a gravitationally lensed galaxy are rare. They occur only when a distant galaxy lies directly behind the lensing cluster. However, single distorted images of gravitationally lensed galaxies are quite common. FIGURE 23.10 shows a typical example. This picture shows numerous normal-looking galaxies and several arc-shaped galaxies. The oddly curved galaxies are not members of the cluster, nor are they really curved. They are normal galaxies lying far beyond the cluster whose images have been distorted by the cluster's gravity.

Careful analyses of the distorted images created by clusters enable us to measure cluster masses without using Newton's laws. Instead, Einstein's general theory of relativity tells us how massive these clusters must be to generate the observed distortions. Cluster masses derived in this way generally agree with those derived from galaxy velocities and X-ray temperatures. It is reassuring that the three different methods all indicate that clusters of galaxies hold substantial amounts of dark matter.

Does dark matter really exist?

Astronomers have made a strong case for the existence of dark matter, but is it possible that there's a completely different explanation for the observations we've discussed? Addressing this question gives us a chance to see how science progresses.

All the evidence for dark matter rests on our understanding of gravity. For individual galaxies, the case for dark matter rests primarily on applying Newton's laws of motion and gravity to observations of the orbital speeds of stars and gas clouds. We've used the same laws to make the case for dark matter in clusters, along with additional evidence based on

FIGURE 23.10 Hubble Space Telescope photo of the cluster Abell 383. The thin, elongated galaxies are images of background galaxies distorted by the cluster's gravity. By measuring these distortions, astronomers can determine the total amount of mass in the cluster. (The region pictured is about 1 million light-years across.)

gravitational lensing predicted by Einstein's general theory of relativity. It therefore seems that one of the following must be true:

1. Dark matter really exists, and we are observing the effects of its gravitational attraction.

2. There is something wrong with our understanding of gravity that is causing us to mistakenly infer the existence of dark matter.

We cannot yet rule out the second possibility, but most astronomers consider it very unlikely. Newton's laws of motion and gravity are among the most trustworthy tools in science. We have used them time and again to measure masses of celestial objects from their orbital properties. We found the masses of Earth and the Sun by applying Newton's

version of Kepler's third law to objects that orbit them [**Section 4.4**]. We used this same law to calculate the masses of stars in binary star systems, revealing the general relationships between the masses of stars and their outward appearances. Newton's laws have also told us the masses of things we can't see directly, such as the masses of orbiting neutron stars in X-ray binaries and of black holes in active galactic nuclei. Einstein's general theory of relativity likewise stands on solid ground, having been repeatedly tested and verified to high precision in many observations and experiments. We therefore have good reason to trust our current understanding of gravity.

Moreover, many scientists have made valiant efforts to come up with alternative theories of gravity that could account for the observations without invoking dark matter. (After all, there's a Nobel Prize waiting for anyone who can substantiate a new theory of gravity.) So far, no one has succeeded in doing so in a way that can also explain the many other observations accounted for by our current theories of gravity. Meanwhile, astronomers keep making observations that are difficult to explain without dark matter. For example, in observations of colliding galaxy clusters, most of the mass detected by gravitational lensing is *not* in the same place as the hot gas, even though the hot gas is several times more massive than the cluster's stars (FIGURE 23.11). This finding is at odds with alternative theories of gravity, which predict that the hot gas should be doing most of the gravitational lensing.

In essence, our high level of confidence in our current understanding of gravity, combined with observations that seem consistent with dark matter but not with alternative hypotheses, gives us high confidence that dark matter really exists. While we should always keep an open mind about the possibility of future changes in our understanding, we will proceed for now under the assumption that dark matter is real.

THINK ABOUT IT

Should the fact that we have three different ways of measuring cluster masses give us greater confidence that we really do understand gravity and that dark matter really does exist? Why or why not?

FIGURE 23.11 **interactive photo**
Observations of the Bullet Cluster show strong evidence for dark matter. The Bullet Cluster actually consists of two galaxy clusters—the smaller one is emerging from a high-speed collision with the larger one. A map of the system's overall mass (blue) made from gravitational lensing observations does *not* line up with X-ray observations (red) showing the location of the system's hot gas. This fact is difficult to explain without dark matter because the gas contains several times as much mass as all the cluster's stars combined. However, it is easy to explain if dark matter exists: The collision has simply stripped the hot gas away from the dark matter on which it was previously centered.

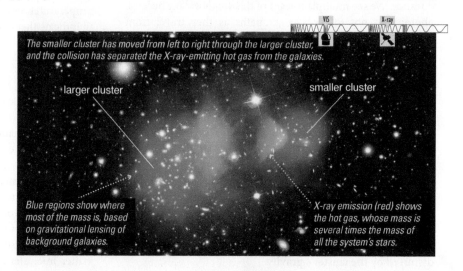

The smaller cluster has moved from left to right through the larger cluster, and the collision has separated the X-ray-emitting hot gas from the galaxies.

larger cluster

smaller cluster

Blue regions show where most of the mass is, based on gravitational lensing of background galaxies.

X-ray emission (red) shows the hot gas, whose mass is several times the mass of all the system's stars.

What might dark matter be made of?

We have seen strong evidence that dark matter really exists and that it contains far more mass than we observe in the stars and gas found in galaxies and clusters of galaxies. But what exactly is all this dark stuff? There are two basic possibilities:

- It could be made of *ordinary matter* (also called *baryonic matter**), meaning the familiar type of matter built from protons, neutrons, and electrons, but in forms too dark for us to detect with current technology.

- It could consist of one or more types of *exotic matter* (also called *nonbaryonic matter*), meaning particles of matter that are different from what we find in ordinary atoms and that do not interact with light at all, in contrast with ordinary matter.

A first step in distinguishing between the two possibilities is to know how much dark matter is out there. When discussing the universe as a whole, astronomers usually focus on density rather than mass. That is, they take the total amount of some type of matter (such as stars, gas, or dark matter) found in a large but typical volume of space and divide by the volume to determine the average density of this type of matter in the universe. These densities are then stated as percentages of the *critical density*—the density of mass-energy needed to make the geometry of the universe flat [**Section 22.3**]. Note that the critical density is quite small: If it were due only to matter (as we'll discuss later, it appears also to have a contribution from dark energy), the critical density would be only 10^{-29} gram per cubic centimeter—roughly equivalent to a few hydrogen atoms in a volume the size of a closet.

The observations we have discussed so far indicate that the total amount of matter in the universe is a significant fraction of the critical density. Only a small proportion of the matter, about 0.5% of the critical density, is in the form of stars. But as we've discussed, observations of galaxy clusters suggest that they contain up to about 50 times as much dark matter as matter in stars. Multiplying the mass in stars by this number leads us to expect the dark matter to amount to about a quarter of the critical density. Clearly, there is a lot of dark matter that needs to be accounted for, and current evidence indicates that most of it must be exotic.

Ordinary Matter: Not Enough Why can't all this dark matter simply be ordinary matter in some hard-to-observe form? After all, matter doesn't necessarily need to be exotic to be dark. Astronomers consider matter to be "dark" as long as it is too dim for us to see at the great distances of the halo of our galaxy or beyond. Your body is dark matter, because our telescopes could not detect you if you were somehow flung into the halo of our galaxy. Similarly, planets, the "failed stars" known as brown dwarfs [**Section 16.3**], and even some faint red main-sequence stars of spectral type M [**Section 15.2**] qualify as dark matter, because they are too dim for current telescopes to see in the halo.

However, calculations made with the Big Bang model allow scientists to place limits on the total amount of ordinary matter in the universe. Recall that, during the era of nucleosynthesis, protons and neutrons first fused into deuterium and the deuterium nuclei then fused into helium [**Section 22.2**]. The fact that some deuterium nuclei still exist in the universe indicates that this process stopped before all the deuterium nuclei were used up. The amount of deuterium in the universe today therefore tells us about the density of protons and neutrons (ordinary matter) during the era of nucleosynthesis: The higher the density, the more efficiently fusion would have proceeded. A higher density in the early universe would have therefore left less deuterium in the universe today, and a lower density would have left more deuterium.

Observations show that about one out of every 40,000 hydrogen atoms in the universe contains a deuterium nucleus—that is, a nucleus with a neutron in addition to its proton. Calculations based on this deuterium abundance indicate that the overall density of ordinary matter in the universe is slightly more than 4% of the critical density (**FIGURE 23.12**), only about one-seventh of the total density of matter. Similar calculations based on the observed abundance of lithium and helium-3 support this conclusion.

Corroborating evidence comes from the temperature patterns in the cosmic microwave background (see Figures 22.9

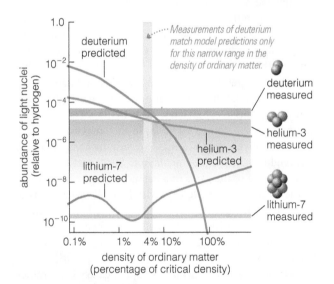

FIGURE 23.12 This graph shows how the measured abundances of deuterium, helium-3, and lithium-7 lead to the conclusion that the density of ordinary matter is about 4% of the critical density. The three horizontal swaths show measured abundances; the thickness of each swath represents the range of uncertainty in the measurements. (The upper edge of the blue swath indicates the upper limit on the helium-3 abundance; a lower limit has not yet been established.) The three curves represent models based on the Big Bang theory; these curves show how the abundance of each type of nucleus is expected to depend on the density of ordinary matter in the universe. Notice that the predictions (curves) match up with the measurements (horizontal swaths) only in the gray vertical strip, which represents a density of about 4% of the critical density.

---

*Ordinary matter is often called *baryonic* matter, because the protons and neutrons that make up most of its mass belong to a category of particles known as *baryons* (which is the technical term for particles made up of three quarks [**Section S4.2**]). As a result, exotic matter is often called *nonbaryonic* matter.

and 22.17). These patterns are produced as the ordinary matter in the universe moves around in response to the gravitational pull of clumps of dark matter. Careful measurement of these patterns therefore reveals the relative proportions of ordinary and exotic matter, and the results confirm that ordinary matter accounts for only about one-seventh of the total amount of matter.

Exotic Matter: The Leading Hypothesis The fact that ordinary matter appears to fall far short of accounting for the total matter density in the universe has forced astronomers to seriously consider the possibility that most of the matter in the universe is made of exotic particles, and probably of a type of exotic particle that has not yet been discovered. Let's begin to explore this possibility by taking another look at a type of exotic particle that we first encountered in connection with nuclear fusion in the Sun: neutrinos [**Section 14.2**]. Neutrinos are dark by nature because they have no electrical charge and cannot emit electromagnetic radiation of any kind. Moreover, they are never bound together with charged particles in the way that neutrons are bound in atomic nuclei, so their presence cannot be revealed by associated light-emitting particles. In fact, neutrinos interact with other forms of matter through only two of the four forces: gravity and the *weak force* [**Sections S4.2, 22.1**]. For this reason, neutrinos are said to be *weakly interacting particles*.

The dark matter in galaxies cannot be made of neutrinos, because these very-low-mass particles travel through the universe at enormous speeds and can easily escape a galaxy's gravitational pull. But what if other weakly interacting particles exist that are similar to neutrinos but considerably heavier? They, too, would evade direct detection, but they would move more slowly, which means that their mutual gravity could hold together a large collection of them. Such hypothetical particles are called **weakly interacting massive particles**, or **WIMPs** for short. Note that they are subatomic particles, so the "massive" in their name is relative—they are massive only in comparison to lightweight particles like neutrinos. Such particles could make up most of the mass of a galaxy or cluster of galaxies, but they would be completely invisible in all wavelengths of light. Most astronomers now consider it likely that WIMPs make up the majority of dark matter, and hence the majority of all matter in the universe.

This hypothesis would also explain why dark matter seems to be distributed throughout spiral galaxy halos rather than concentrated in flattened disks like the visible matter. Recall that galaxies are thought to have formed as gravity pulled together matter in regions of slightly enhanced density in the early universe [**Section 21.1**]. This matter would have consisted mostly of dark matter mixed with some ordinary hydrogen and helium gas. The ordinary gas could collapse to form a rotating disk because individual gas particles could lose orbital energy: Collisions among many gas particles can convert some of their orbital energy into radiative energy that escapes from the galaxy in the form of photons. In contrast, WIMPs cannot produce photons, and they rarely interact and exchange energy with other particles. As the gas collapsed to form a disk, WIMPs would therefore have remained stuck in orbits far out in the galactic halo—just where most dark matter seems to be located.

Searching for Dark Matter Particles The case for the existence of WIMPs seems fairly strong but is still circumstantial. Detecting the particles directly would be much more convincing, and physicists are currently searching for them in two different ways. The first and most direct way is with detectors that can potentially capture WIMPs from space. Because these particles are thought to interact only very weakly, the search requires building large, sensitive detectors deep underground, where they are shielded from other particles from space. As of 2012, these detectors have provided some tantalizing signals, but so far no proof that dark matter particles really exist.

The second way scientists are currently searching for dark matter particles is with particle accelerators. Recall that particle collisions in these huge machines produce a variety of subatomic particles, because much of the energy in each collision is converted into mass according to $E = mc^2$ [**Sections S4.2, 22.1**]. None of the particles found as of 2012 has the characteristics of a WIMP, but scientists are optimistic that the Large Hadron Collider (see Figure S4.1), the most powerful accelerator in the world, will soon reach collision energies great enough to produce the elusive dark matter particles and finally solve this major scientific mystery.

THINK ABOUT IT

What do you think of the idea that much of the universe is made of as-yet-undiscovered particles? Can you think of other instances in the history of science in which the existence of something was predicted before it was discovered?

23.3 DARK MATTER AND GALAXY FORMATION

The nature of dark matter remains enigmatic, but we are rapidly learning more about its role in the universe. Because galaxies and clusters of galaxies seem to contain much more dark matter than luminous matter, dark matter's gravitational pull must be the primary force holding these structures together. Therefore, we strongly suspect that the gravitational attraction of dark matter is what pulled galaxies and clusters together in the first place.

What is the role of dark matter in galaxy formation?

Stars, galaxies, and clusters of galaxies are all *gravitationally bound systems*—their gravity is strong enough to hold them together. In most of the gravitationally bound systems we have discussed so far, gravity has completely overwhelmed the expansion of the universe. That is, while the universe as a whole is expanding, space is *not* expanding within our solar system, our galaxy, or our Local Group of galaxies.

Our best guess at how galaxies formed, outlined in Section 21.2, envisions them growing from slight density enhancements that were present in the very early universe. During the first few million years after the Big Bang, the universe expanded everywhere. Gradually, the stronger gravity in regions of enhanced density pulled in matter until these regions stopped expanding and became protogalactic clouds, even as the universe as a whole continued (and still continues) to expand.

If dark matter is indeed the most common form of mass in galaxies, it must have provided most of the gravitational attraction responsible for creating the protogalactic clouds. The hydrogen and helium gas in the protogalactic clouds collapsed inward and gave birth to stars, while weakly interacting dark matter remained in the outskirts because of its inability to radiate away orbital energy. According to this model, the luminous matter in each galaxy must still be nestled inside the larger cocoon of dark matter that initiated the galaxy's formation (see Figure 23.2), just as observational evidence seems to suggest.

The formation of galaxy clusters probably echoes the formation of galaxies. Early on, all the galaxies that will eventually constitute a cluster are flying apart with the expansion of the universe, but the gravity of the dark matter associated with the cluster eventually reverses the trajectories of these galaxies. The galaxies ultimately fall back inward and start orbiting each other with random orientations, much like the stars in the halo of our galaxy.

Some clusters apparently have not yet finished forming, because their immense gravity is still drawing in new galaxies. For example, the relatively nearby Virgo Cluster of galaxies (about 60 million light-years away) appears to be drawing in the Milky Way and other galaxies of the Local Group. The evidence comes from careful study of galaxy speeds. Plugging the Virgo Cluster's distance into Hubble's law tells us the speed at which the Milky Way and the Virgo Cluster should be drifting apart as a result of universal expansion [**Section 20.3**]. However, the measured speed is about 400 kilometers per second slower than the speed we predict from Hubble's law alone. We conclude that this 400 kilometers per second discrepancy (sometimes called a *peculiar velocity*) arises because the Virgo Cluster's gravity is pulling us back against the flow of universal expansion. In other words, while the Milky Way and other galaxies of our Local Group are still moving away from the Virgo Cluster with the expansion of the universe, the rate at which we are separating from the cluster is slowing with time. Eventually, the cluster's gravity may stop the separation altogether, at which point the cluster will begin pulling in the galaxies of our Local Group, ultimately making them members of the cluster.

Many other large clusters of galaxies also appear to be drawing in new members, judging from the velocities of

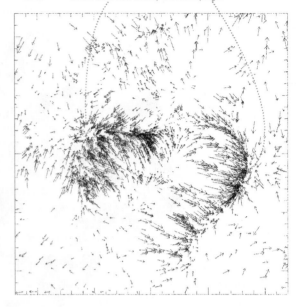

Gravity pulls galaxies into regions of the universe where the matter density is relatively high.

FIGURE 23.13 This diagram represents the motions of galaxies attributable to effects of gravity. Each black arrow represents the amount by which a galaxy's actual velocity (inferred from a combination of observations and modeling) differs from the velocity we'd expect it to have from Hubble's law alone. The Milky Way is at the center of the picture, which shows an area about 600 million light-years across. (Only a representative sample of galaxies is shown.) Notice how the galaxies tend to flow into regions where the density of galaxies is already high. These vast, high-density regions are probably superclusters in the process of formation.

galaxies near the outskirts of those clusters. On even larger scales, clusters themselves seem to be tugging on one another, hinting that they might be parts of even bigger gravitationally bound systems, called **superclusters**, that are still in the early stages of formation (**FIGURE 23.13**). But some structures are even larger than superclusters.

What are the largest structures in the universe?

Beyond about 300 million light-years from Earth, deviations from Hubble's law owing to gravitational tugs are insignificant compared with the universal expansion, so Hubble's law becomes our primary method for measuring galaxy distances [**Section 20.3**]. Using this law, astronomers can make maps of the distribution of galaxies in space. Such maps reveal **large-scale structures** much vaster than clusters of galaxies.

Mapping Large-Scale Structures Making maps of galaxy locations requires an enormous amount of data. A long-exposure photo showing galaxy positions is not enough, because it does not tell us the galaxy distances. We must also measure the redshift of each individual galaxy so that we can estimate its distance by applying Hubble's law. These measurements once required intensive labor, and up until a couple decades ago it took years of effort to map the locations of just a few hundred galaxies. However, astronomers have since developed technology that allows redshift measurements for hundreds of galaxies to be made during a single night

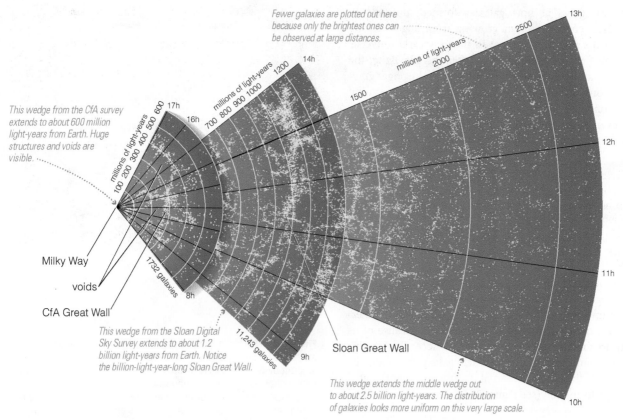

Fewer galaxies are plotted out here because only the brightest ones can be observed at large distances.

This wedge from the CfA survey extends to about 600 million light-years from Earth. Huge structures and voids are visible.

Milky Way

voids

CfA Great Wall

1732 galaxies

This wedge from the Sloan Digital Sky Survey extends to about 1.2 billion light-years from Earth. Notice the billion-light-year-long Sloan Great Wall.

11,243 galaxies

Sloan Great Wall

This wedge extends the middle wedge out to about 2.5 billion light-years. The distribution of galaxies looks more uniform on this very large scale.

millions of light-years
100 200 300 400 500 600
700 800 900 1000 1200
1500 2000 2500

17h 16h 14h 13h 12h 11h 10h 9h 8h

FIGURE 23.14 Each of these three wedges shows a "slice" of the universe extending outward from our own Milky Way Galaxy. The dots represent galaxies, shown at their measured distances from Earth. We see that galaxies trace out long chains and sheets surrounded by huge voids containing very few galaxies. (The wedges are shown flat but actually are a few angular degrees in thickness; the CfA wedge at left does not actually line up with the two Sloan wedges.)

of telescopic observation. As a result, we now have redshift measurements—and hence estimated distances—for millions of distant galaxies.

FIGURE 23.14 shows the distribution of galaxies in three slices of the universe, each extending farther out in distance. Our Milky Way Galaxy is located at the vertex at the far left, and each dot represents an entire galaxy of stars. The slice at the left comes from one of the first surveys of large-scale structures, performed at the Harvard-Smithsonian Center for Astrophysics (CfA) in the 1980s. This map, which required years of effort by many astronomers, dramatically revealed the complex structure of our corner of the universe. It showed that galaxies are not scattered randomly through space but are instead arranged in huge chains and sheets that span many millions of light-years. Clusters of galaxies are located at the intersections of these chains. Between these chains and sheets of galaxies lie giant empty regions called **voids**. The other two slices show data from the more recent Sloan Digital Sky Survey. The Sloan Survey has measured redshifts for more than a million galaxies spread across about one-fourth of the sky.

Some of the structures in these pictures are amazingly large. The so-called Sloan Great Wall, clearly visible in the center slice, extends more than 1 billion light-years from end to end. Immense structures such as these apparently have not yet collapsed into randomly orbiting, gravitationally bound systems.

The universe may still be growing structures on these very large scales. However, there seems to be a limit to the size of the largest structures. If you look closely at the rightmost slice in Figure 23.14, you'll notice that the overall distribution of galaxies appears nearly uniform on scales larger than about a billion light-years. In other words, on very large scales the universe looks much the same everywhere, in agreement with what we expect from the *Cosmological Principle* [**Section 20.3**].

The Origin of Large Structures Why is gravity collecting matter on such enormous scales? Just as we suspect that galaxies formed from regions of slightly enhanced density in the early universe, we suspect that these larger structures were also regions of enhanced density. Galaxies, clusters, superclusters, and the Sloan Great Wall probably all started as mildly high-density regions of different sizes. The voids in the distribution of galaxies probably started as mildly low-density regions.

If this picture of structure formation is correct, then the structures we see in today's universe mirror the original distribution of dark matter very early in time. Supercomputer models of structure formation in the universe can now simulate the growth of galaxies, clusters, and larger structures from tiny density enhancements as the universe evolves (FIGURE 23.15). Models of extremely large regions reveal how dark matter should be distributed throughout the entire observable universe (FIGURE 23.16). The results of these models look remarkably similar to the slices of the universe in Figure 23.14, bolstering

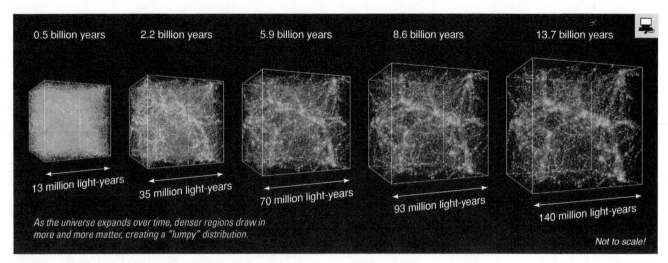

As the universe expands over time, denser regions draw in more and more matter, creating a "lumpy" distribution.

Not to scale!

FIGURE 23.15 interactive figure Frames from a supercomputer simulation of structure formation. The five boxes depict the development of a cubical region that is now 140 million light-years across. The labels above the boxes give the age of the universe, and the labels below give the size of the box as it expands with time. Notice that the distribution of matter is only slightly lumpy when the universe is young (left frame). Structures grow more pronounced with time as the densest lumps draw in more and more matter.

our confidence in this scenario. Moreover, the patterns of mass distribution are consistent with the patterns of density enhancements revealed in maps of the cosmic microwave background (see Figures 22.9 and 22.17). Overall, we now seem to have a basic picture of how galaxies and large-scale structures formed in the universe, perhaps starting from quantum fluctuations that occurred when the universe was a tiny fraction of a second old [**Section 22.3**].

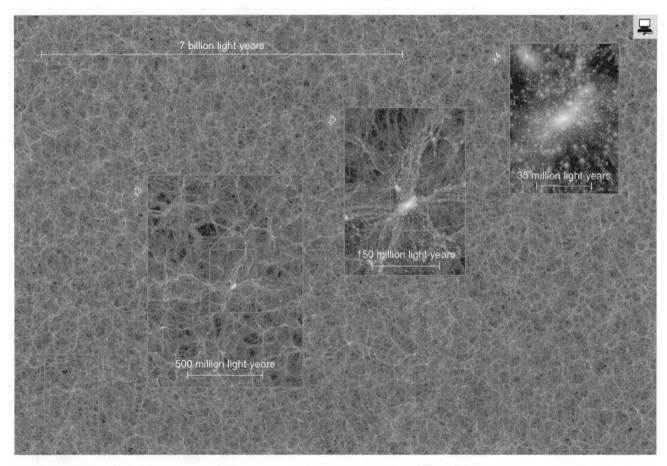

FIGURE 23.16 These images from an extremely large computer simulation illustrate the structure of dark matter in the universe. The main image shows a region similar in size to our observable universe, and the image sequence zooms in on a massive cluster of galaxies. The images show structure as it would appear if we could see dark matter—the brightest clumps in the image represent the highest densities of dark matter. Notice that the large-scale distribution of dark matter has a uniform web-like pattern.

23.4 DARK ENERGY AND THE FATE OF THE UNIVERSE

Some say the world will end in fire,
Some say in ice.
From what I've tasted of desire
I hold with those who favor fire.
But if it had to perish twice,
I think I know enough of hate
To say that for destruction ice
Is also great
And would suffice.
                    —Robert Frost, Fire and Ice

Over the past few chapters, we have seen that the large-scale development of the universe to date has been governed by two competing processes:

1. the ongoing expansion that began in the Big Bang, which tends to drive galaxies apart from one another, and

2. the gravitational attraction of matter in the universe, which assembles galaxies and larger-scale structures around the density enhancements that emerged from the Big Bang.

These ideas naturally lead us to one of the ultimate questions in astronomy: How will the universe end? After Edwin Hubble discovered the expansion of the universe, astronomers generally assumed that the end would be like one of the two fates in Robert Frost's poem. If gravity were strong enough, the expansion would someday halt and reverse; the universe would then begin collapsing and heating back up, eventually ending in a fiery and cataclysmic crunch. Alternatively, if the total strength of gravity were too weak, gravity would never slow the expansion enough for it to halt and reverse, leading to an icy end in which the universe would grow ever colder as its galaxies moved ever farther apart.

Astronomers therefore began trying to determine whether the gravitational attraction of matter was sufficient to stop the expansion. For many years, the question seemed to hinge on the total amount of dark matter in the universe. However, through a series of observations begun about two decades ago, astronomers have come to realize that the gravity of dark matter might not be the most powerful force in the universe. Much to their surprise, these measurements have shown that the expansion of the universe has been accelerating with time, suggesting that the fate of the universe may be determined by something else—the repulsive force produced by a mysterious form of energy we have come to call *dark energy*.

Why is accelerating expansion evidence for dark energy?

In order to determine how the expansion of the universe changes with time, astronomers need to compare the value of Hubble's constant today to its value at earlier times in the universe's history. Recall that the current value of Hubble's constant is approximately 22 kilometers per second per million light-years [**Section 20.2**]. So, for example, we expect a galaxy located at distance of 100 million light-years to be moving away from us with the expansion of the universe at a speed of about 2200 kilometers per second.

Hubble's constant is called a "constant" because its value is the same across all of space at a particular moment in time. It does not necessarily stay constant with time. In fact, if the galaxies in the universe had always moved away from us at their current speeds, then the reciprocal of Hubble's constant at any given moment in time would always have been equal to the age of the universe at that time (see Mathematical Insight 20.4). In that case, the value of Hubble's constant would continually *decrease* with time. However, the recession speeds of galaxies do not remain the same if forces like gravity or a repulsion driven by dark energy are in play.

For example, if gravity had always been slowing the expansion, then the recession speeds of galaxies would have been greater in the past, meaning that it took *less time* for them to reach their current distances. We would then infer an age for the universe that was *younger* than the age derived from the reciprocal of Hubble's constant. Conversely, if a repulsive force had always accelerated the expansion, then the recession speeds of galaxies would have been slower in the past, so it would have taken them *more* time to reach their current distances and we would infer an *older* age for the universe than we obtain from the reciprocal of Hubble's constant. Therefore, measuring how Hubble's constant has changed with time not only tells us what forces have been acting upon the universe, with implications for its eventual fate, but also is necessary for learning the universe's precise age.

Four Expansion Models To see how different kinds of forces affect the expansion rate and the age for the universe that we infer from it, let's consider four general models for how the expansion rate changes with time, each illustrated in **FIGURE 23.17**:

- A **recollapsing universe**. In the case of extremely strong gravitational attraction and no repulsive force, the expansion would continually slow down with time and eventually would stop entirely and then reverse. Galaxies would come crashing back together, and the universe would end in a fiery "Big Crunch." We call this a *recollapsing* universe, because the final state, with all matter collapsed together, would look much like the state in which the universe began in the Big Bang.

- A **critical universe**. In the case of gravitational attraction that was not quite strong enough to reverse the expansion in the absence of a repulsive force, the expansion would decelerate forever, leading to a universe that would never collapse but would expand ever more slowly as time progressed. We call this a *critical* universe, because calculations show that it is what we would expect if the total density of the universe were the critical density and only matter (and not dark energy) contributed to this density.

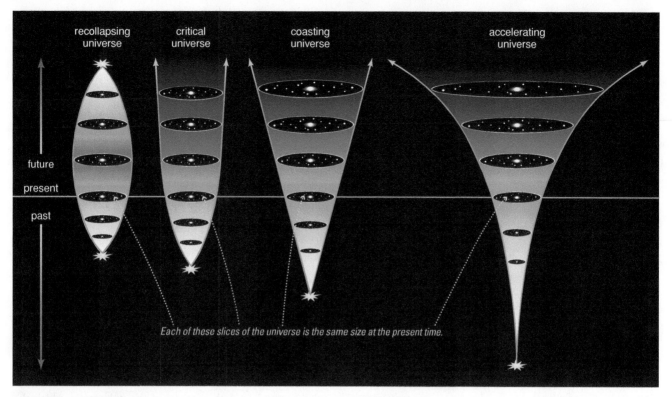

recollapsing universe   **critical universe**   **coasting universe**   **accelerating universe**

future

present

past

Each of these slices of the universe is the same size at the present time.

FIGURE 23.17 Four general models for how the universal expansion rate might change with time. Each diagram shows how the size of a circular slice of the universe changes with time in a particular model. The slices are the same size at the present time, marked by the red line, but the models make different predictions about the sizes of the slices in the past and future.

- A **coasting universe**. In the case of weak gravitational attraction and no repulsive force, galaxies would always move apart at approximately the speeds they have today. We call this a *coasting* universe, because it is what we would find if no forces acted to change the expansion rate, much as a spaceship can coast through space at constant speed if no forces act to slow it down or speed it up.

- An **accelerating universe**. In the case of a repulsive force strong enough to overpower gravity, the expansion would *accelerate* with time, causing galaxies to recede from one another with ever-increasing speed.

Figure 23.17 also shows that each general model leads to a different age for the universe today. In all four models, the size of a particular region of space and the expansion rate of the universe are the same for the present (indicated by the horizontal red line), because those values must agree with our measurements for the average distance between galaxies today and for Hubble's constant today. However, as we expect, the four models each extend different lengths into the past. The coasting model assumes that the expansion rate never changes, and its starting point therefore indicates the age of the universe that we would infer from Hubble's constant alone. The recollapsing and critical models both give younger ages for the universe (they begin less far into the past), while the accelerating model leads to an older age.

Evidence for Acceleration In principle, it is easy to test which of the four models best corresponds to reality. We

simply need to calculate what each one predicts for the universe's expansion rate at different times in the past, and then make observations of how the relationship between redshift and distance changes with time to see which model offers the best match. In practice, measuring how the expansion rate changes through time is quite difficult, because it depends on having reliable standard candles that allow us to determine the distances of extremely distant galaxies. As we discussed in Chapter 20, the most reliable standard candles for great distances are white dwarf supernovae, and in the 1990s two teams of astronomers began large observing programs seeking to detect and measure these stellar explosions.

FIGURE 23.18 shows some of those measurements and compares them with models of how the expansion rate has changed with time. The four solid curves show how the four general models predict that average distance between galaxies should have changed with time; each curve begins at the time at which galaxy distances were zero, which means the time of the Big Bang according to that model. For example, the purple curve for the coasting model shows that if the universe has followed the expansion pattern predicted by this model, then the Big Bang occurred nearly 14 billion years ago; the other curves confirm that the accelerating model would mean a larger age for the universe while the critical and recollapsing models would mean younger ages.

Note that the slopes of the curves represent the predicted expansion rates—the steeper the slope, the faster the expansion— and that only the recollapsing model has a slope that eventually turns downward, indicating a collapsing universe. Also note

FIGURE 23.18 Data from white dwarf supernovae are shown, along with four possible models for the expansion of the universe. Each curve shows how the average distance between galaxies changes with time for a particular model. A rising curve means that the universe is expanding, and a falling curve means that the universe is contracting. Notice that the supernova data fit the accelerating universe better than the other models.

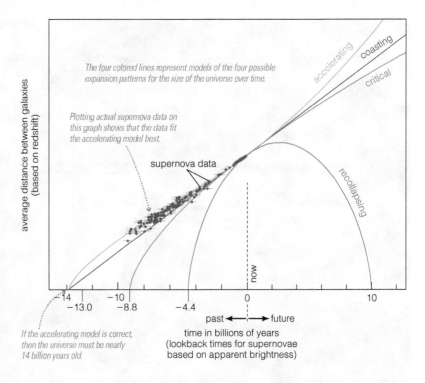

that all the curves pass through the same point and have the same slope at the moment labeled "now," because the current separation between galaxies and the current expansion rate in each case must agree with observations of the present-day universe.

The black dots in Figure 23.18 show actual data from white dwarf supernovae. (The horizontal line through each dot indicates the range of uncertainty in the measured lookback time.) Although there is some scatter in the data points, they clearly fit the curve for the accelerating model better

than any of the other models. In other words, the observations agree best with a model of the universe in which the expansion is accelerating with time.

The discovery of an accelerating expansion, first announced in 1998, came as a great surprise to virtually all astronomers. For several years after the announcement, many astronomers feared that these measurements were being misinterpreted, but additional data have only strengthened the evidence of acceleration. In recognition of the importance of this discovery, three of the leaders of the observing teams were awarded the 2011 Nobel Prize in physics.

The Nature of Dark Energy The acceleration of the expansion clearly implies the existence of some force that acts to push galaxies apart, and the source of this force is what we have dubbed *dark energy*. Keep in mind, however, that we have little idea of what the nature of dark energy might actually be. None of the four known forces in nature could

SPECIAL TOPIC

Einstein's Greatest Blunder

Shortly after Einstein completed his general theory of relativity in 1915, he found that it predicted that the universe could not be standing still: The mutual gravitational attraction of all the matter would make the universe collapse. Because Einstein thought at the time that the universe should be eternal and static, he decided to alter his equations. In essence, he inserted a "fudge factor" called the *cosmological constant* that acted as a repulsive force to counteract the attractive force of gravity.

Had he not been so convinced that the universe should be standing still, Einstein might instead have come up with the correct explanation for why the universe is not collapsing: because it is still expanding from the event of its birth. After Hubble discovered universal expansion, Einstein supposedly called his invention of the cosmological constant "the greatest blunder" of his career.

Now that observations of very distant galaxies (using white dwarf supernovae as standard candles) have shown that the universe's expansion is accelerating, Einstein's idea of a universal repulsive force doesn't seem so far-fetched. In fact, observations to date are consistent with the idea that dark energy has properties virtually identical to those that Einstein originally proposed for the cosmological constant. In particular, the amount of dark energy in each volume of space seems to remain unchanged while the universe expands, as if the vacuum of space itself were constantly rippling with energy—which is just what the cosmological constant does in Einstein's equations. We'll need more measurements to know for sure, but it is beginning to seem that Einstein's greatest blunder may not have been a blunder after all.

provide a force to oppose gravity, and while some theories of fundamental physics suggest ways in which energy could fit the bill, no known type of energy produces the right amount of acceleration.

Continued observations of distant supernovae have the potential to tell us exactly how large an effect dark energy has had throughout cosmic history and whether the strength of this effect has changed with time. Already there are some intriguing hints. For example, it appears that the acceleration of the expansion did not begin immediately after the Big Bang, but rather began a few billion years later, indicating that gravity was strong enough to slow the expansion for the first few billion years until dark energy became dominant. (The curve for the accelerating model in Figure 23.18 shows this scenario.) Interestingly, this type of behavior is consistent with an idea that Einstein once introduced but later disavowed in his general theory of relativity, leading some scientists to suggest that dark energy might successfully be described by a term in Einstein's equations that describe gravity (see Special Topic, page 684). Nevertheless, even if this idea turns out to be correct, we remain a long way from an actual understanding of dark energy's nature.

Why is flat geometry evidence for dark energy?

The evidence for the existence of dark energy provided by observations of an accelerating expansion seems quite strong, but it is important to remember that the evidence we have discussed so far comes entirely from measurements of white dwarf supernovae. While we have good reason to think that these supernovae make reliable standard candles, having just a single source of evidence would be cause for at least some concern. Fortunately, during the past decade or so, an entirely different line of evidence for the existence of dark energy has emerged, and it gives results that are fully consistent with the results indicating an accelerating expansion.

Flatness and Dark Energy Recall that Einstein's general theory of relativity tells us that the overall geometry of the universe can take one of three general forms—spherical, flat, or saddle shaped (see Figure 22.15)—and that we can in principle determine which one corresponds to the real universe with careful observations of the cosmic microwave background [**Section 22.3**]. Moreover, these observations now provide strong evidence that the actual geometry is flat (see Figure 22.17), which implies that the total density of *matter plus energy* in the universe must be exactly equal to the critical density.

However, as we have already seen, the total matter density of the universe is not large enough to make the geometry flat on its own, because the total density of matter amounts to only about one-quarter of the critical density. In that case, the remaining three-quarters of the critical density must be in the form of energy. Tellingly, the amount of dark energy required to explain the observed acceleration of the expansion also is about three-quarters of the critical density. The startling conclusion: About three-quarters of the total mass-energy of the universe takes the form of dark energy.

Inventory of the Universe We began this chapter by noting that astronomers today must admit the embarrassing fact that we do not yet know what most of the universe is made of. It appears to be made of things we call dark matter and dark energy, but we do not yet know the true nature of either one. Nevertheless, the observations we have discussed allow us to make quantitative statements about our ignorance. According to the model that best explains the observed temperature patterns in the cosmic microwave background, the total density of matter plus energy in the universe is equal to the critical density, and it is made up of the following components:

- Ordinary matter (made up of protons, neutrons, electrons) makes up slightly more than 4% of the total mass-energy of the universe. Note that this model prediction agrees with what we find from observations of deuterium in the universe. Some of this matter is in the form of stars (about 0.5% of the universe's mass-energy). The rest is presumed to be in the form of intergalactic gas, such as the hot gas found in galaxy clusters.

- Some form of exotic dark matter—most likely weakly interacting massive particles (WIMPs)—makes up about 22% of the mass-energy of the universe, in close agreement with what we infer from measurements of the masses of clusters of galaxies.

- Dark energy makes up the remaining 74% of the mass-energy of the universe, accounting both for the observed acceleration of the expansion and for the pattern of temperatures in the cosmic microwave background.

FIGURE 23.19 shows this inventory of the universe as a pie chart, and FIGURE 23.20 summarizes the evidence we have discussed for the existence of dark matter and dark energy. We may not yet know what either dark matter or dark energy actually is, but our measurements of how much matter and energy may be out there are becoming quite precise.

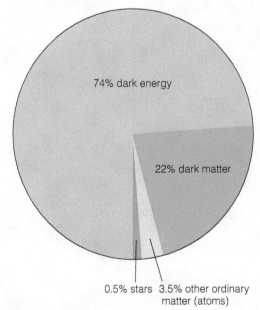

FIGURE 23.19 This pie chart shows the proportion of each of the major components of matter and energy in the universe, based on current evidence.

Scientists suspect that most of the matter in the universe is *dark matter* we cannot see, and that the expansion of the universe is accelerating because of a *dark energy* we cannot directly detect. Both dark matter and dark energy have been proposed to exist because they bring our models of the universe into better agreement with observations, in accordance with the process of science. This figure presents some of the evidence supporting the existence of dark matter and dark energy.

① Dark Matter in Galaxies: Applying Newton's laws of gravity and motion to the orbital speeds of stars and gas clouds suggests that galaxies contain much more matter than we observe in the form of stars and glowing gas.

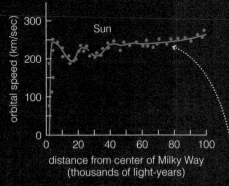

Orbital speeds of stars and gas clouds remain high even quite far from our galaxy's center . . .

. . . indicating that the visible portion of our galaxy lies at the center of a much larger volume of dark matter.

② Dark Matter in Clusters: Further evidence for dark matter comes from studying galaxy clusters. Observations of galaxy motions, hot gas, and gravitational lensing all suggest that galaxy clusters contain far more matter than we can directly observe in the form of stars and gas.

This cluster of galaxies acts as a gravitational lens to bend light from a single galaxy behind it into the multiple blue shapes in this photo. The amount of bending allows astronomers to calculate the total amount of matter in the cluster.

HALLMARK OF SCIENCE A scientific model must seek explanations for observed phenomena that rely solely on natural causes. Orbital motions within galaxies demand a natural explanation, which is why scientists proposed the existence of dark matter.

HALLMARK OF SCIENCE Science progresses through creation and testing of models of nature that explain the observations as simply as possible. Dark matter accounts for our observations of galaxy clusters more simply than alternative hypotheses.

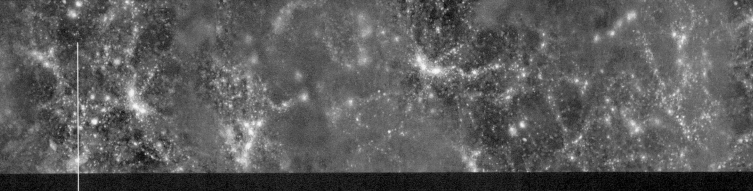

③ **Structure Formation:** If dark matter really is the dominant source of gravity in the universe, then its gravitational force must have been what assembled galaxies and galaxy clusters in the first place. We can test this prediction using supercomputers to model the formation of large-scale structures both with and without dark matter. Models with dark matter provide a better match to what we actually observe in the universe.

④ **Universal Expansion and Dark Energy:** The expansion of a universe consisting primarily of dark matter would slow down over time because of gravity, but observations have shown that the expansion is actually speeding up. Scientists hypothesize that a mysterious *dark energy* is causing the expansion to accelerate. Models that include both dark matter and dark energy agree more closely with observations of distant supernovae and the cosmic microwave background than models containing dark matter alone.

← 140 million light-years →

Supercomputer models in which dark matter is the dominant source of gravity show galaxies organized into strings and sheets similar in size and shape to those we actually observe in the universe.

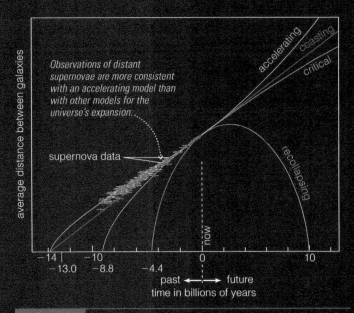

HALLMARK OF SCIENCE **A scientific model makes testable predictions about natural phenomena. If predictions do not agree with observations, the model must be revised or abandoned.** Observations of the universe's expansion have forced us to modify our models of the universe to include dark energy along with dark matter.

The Age of the Universe Models that explain the temperature variations in the cosmic microwave background not only give us an inventory of the universe but also make precise predictions about the age of the universe. According to the model that gives the best agreement to the data (the same model used for the inventory above), the age of the universe is about 13.7 billion years, with an uncertainty of about 0.2 billion years (200 million years). That is why, throughout this book, we have said that the universe is "about 14 billion years old." Note that this age is in good agreement with what we infer from Hubble's constant and observed changes in the expansion, and also agrees well with the fact that the oldest stars in the universe appear to be about 13 billion years old.

What is the fate of the universe?

This is the way the world ends
This is the way the world ends
This is the way the world ends
Not with a bang but a whimper.
　　　　　—T. S. Eliot, from The Hollow Men

We are now ready to return to the question of the fate of the universe. If we think in terms of Robert Frost's poetry at the beginning of this section, the recollapsing universe is the only one of our four possible expansion models that has an end in fire, and the data do not fit that model. Therefore, it seems that the universe is doomed to expand forever, its galaxies receding ever more quickly into an icy, empty future. The end, it would seem, is more likely to be like that in T. S. Eliot's excerpt above.

THINK ABOUT IT
Do you think that one of the possible fates (fire or ice) is preferable to the other? Why or why not?

The Next 10^{100} Years What exactly will happen to the universe as time goes on in an ever-expanding universe? We can use our current understanding of physics to hypothesize about the answer.

First, the answer obviously depends on how much the expansion of the universe accelerates in the future. Some scientists speculate that the repulsive force due to dark energy might strengthen with time. In that case, perhaps in a few tens of billions of years, the growing repulsive force would tear apart our galaxy, our solar system, and even matter itself in a catastrophic event sometimes called the "Big Rip." However, evidence for this type of growing repulsion is very weak, and it seems more likely that the expansion will continue to accelerate more gradually.

If the universe continues to expand in this way, galaxies and galaxy clusters will remain gravitationally bound far into the future. Galaxies will not always look the same, however, because the star–gas–star cycle [**Section 19.2**] cannot continue forever. With each generation of stars, more mass becomes locked up in planets, brown dwarfs, white dwarfs, neutron stars, and black holes. Eventually, about a trillion years from now, even the longest-lived stars will burn out, and the galaxies will fade into darkness.

At this point, the only new action in the universe will occur on the rare occasions when two objects—such as two brown dwarfs or two white dwarfs—collide within a galaxy. The vast distances separating star systems in galaxies make such collisions extremely rare. For example, the probability of our Sun (or the white dwarf that it will become) colliding with another star is so small that it would be expected to happen only once in a quadrillion (10^{15}) years. However, given a long enough period of time, even low-probability events will eventually happen many times. If a star system experiences a collision once in a quadrillion years, it will experience about 100 collisions in 100 quadrillion (10^{17}) years. By the time the universe reaches an age of 10^{20} years, star systems will have suffered an average of 100,000 collisions each, making a time-lapse history of any galaxy look like a cosmic game of billiards.

These multiple collisions will severely disrupt galaxies. As in any gravitational encounter, some objects lose energy in such collisions and some gain energy. Objects that lose energy will eventually fall to the galactic center, forming a supermassive black hole where our galaxy used to be. Objects that gain enough energy will be flung into intergalactic space, to be carried away from their home galaxies with the expansion of the universe. The remains of the universe will consist of widely separated black holes with masses as great as a trillion solar masses, and widely scattered planets, brown dwarfs, and stellar corpses. If Earth somehow survives, it will be a frozen chunk of rock in the darkness of the expanding universe, billions of light-years away from any other solid object.

If grand unified theories [**Section 22.1**] are correct, Earth still cannot last forever. These theories predict that protons will eventually fall apart. The predicted lifetime of protons is extremely long: a half-life of at least 10^{33} years. However, if protons really do decay, then by the time the universe is 10^{40} years old, Earth and all other atomic matter will have disintegrated into radiation and subatomic particles.

The final phase may come through a mechanism proposed by physicist Stephen Hawking. Recall that he predicted that black holes must eventually "evaporate," turning their mass-energy into *Hawking radiation* [**Section S4.4**]. The process is so slow that we do not expect to be able to see it from any existing black holes, but if it really occurs, then black holes in the distant future will disappear in brilliant bursts of radiation. The largest black holes will last the longest, but even trillion-solar-mass black holes will evaporate sometime after the universe reaches an age of 10^{100} years. From then on, the universe will consist only of individual photons and subatomic particles, each separated by enormous distances from the others. Nothing new will ever happen, and no events will ever occur that would allow an omniscient observer to distinguish past from future. In a sense, the universe will finally have reached the end of time.

Forever Is a Long Time Lest any of this sound depressing, keep in mind that we are talking about incredibly long times. Remember that 10^{11} years is already nearly 10 times the current age of the universe (because 14 billion years is the same as 1.4×10^{10} years), 10^{12} years is another 10 times that, and so on. A time of 10^{100} years is so long that we can scarcely describe it, but one way to think about it (thanks to the late Carl Sagan) is to imagine that you wanted to write on a piece of paper a number that consisted of a 1 followed by 10^{100} zeros (that is, the number $10^{10^{100}}$). It sounds easy, but a piece of paper large enough to hold all those zeros *would not fit in the observable universe* today. If that still does not alleviate your concerns, you may be glad to know that a few creative thinkers are already speculating about ways in which the universe might avoid an icy fate or undergo rebirth, even after the end of time.

Perhaps of greater significance, speculating about the future of the universe means speculating about forever, and forever leaves us with a very long time in which to make new discoveries. After all, it is only in the past century that we learned that we live in an expanding universe, and only in the past couple of decades that we were surprised to learn that the expansion is accelerating. The universe may yet hold other surprises that might force us to rethink what might happen between now and the end of time.

The Big Picture

Putting Chapter 23 into Context

We have found that there may be much more to the universe than meets the eye. Dark matter too dim for us to see seems to far outweigh the stars, and a mysterious dark energy may be even more prevalent. Together, dark matter and dark energy have probably been the dominant agents of change in the overall history of the universe. Here are some key "big picture" points to remember about this chapter:

- Dark matter and dark energy sound very similar, but they are each hypothesized to explain different observations. Dark matter is thought to exist because we detect its gravitational influence. Dark energy is a term given to the source of the force that may be accelerating the expansion of the universe.

- Either dark matter exists or we do not understand how gravity operates across galaxy-size distances. There are many reasons to be confident about our understanding of gravity, leading most astronomers to conclude that dark matter is real.

- Dark matter seems to be by far the most abundant form of mass in the universe, and therefore the primary source of the gravity that has formed galaxies and larger-scale structures from tiny density enhancements that existed in the early universe. We still do not know what dark matter is, but we suspect it is largely made up of some type of as-yet-undiscovered subatomic particles.

- The existence of dark energy is supported by evidence from observations both of the expansion rate through time and of temperature variations in the cosmic microwave background. Together, these observations have led to a model of the universe that gives us precise values for the inventory of its contents and its age.

- The fate of the universe seems to depend on whether the expansion of the universe continues forever, and the acceleration of the expansion suggests that it will. Nevertheless, forever is a long time, and only time will tell whether new discoveries will alter our speculations about the distant future.

23.1 UNSEEN INFLUENCES IN THE COSMOS

- **What do we mean by dark matter and dark energy?** Dark matter and dark energy have never been directly observed, but each has been proposed to exist because it seems the simplest way to explain a set of observed motions in the universe. **Dark matter** is the name given to the unseen mass whose gravity governs the observed motions of stars and gas clouds. **Dark energy** is the name given to the form of energy thought to be causing the expansion of the universe to accelerate.

23.2 EVIDENCE FOR DARK MATTER

- **What is the evidence for dark matter in galaxies?** The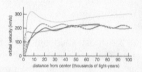
orbital velocities of stars and gas clouds in galaxies do not change much with distance from the center of the galaxy. Applying Newton's laws of gravitation and motion to these orbits leads to the conclusion that the total mass of a galaxy is far larger than the mass of its stars. Because no detectable visible light is coming from this matter, we call it dark matter.

- **What is the evidence for dark matter in clusters of**
galaxies? We have three different ways of measuring the amount of dark matter in clusters of galaxies: from galaxy orbits, from the temperature of the hot gas in clusters, and from the **gravitational lensing** predicted by Einstein. All these methods are in agreement, indicating that the total mass of a galaxy cluster is about 50 times the mass of its stars, implying huge amounts of dark matter.

- **Does dark matter really exist?** We infer that dark matter exists from its gravitational influence on the matter we can see, leaving two possibilities: Either dark matter exists or there is something wrong with our understanding of gravity. We cannot rule out the latter possibility, but we have good reason to be confident about our current understanding of gravity and the idea that dark matter is real.

- **What might dark matter be made of?** Some of the dark matter could be ordinary (baryonic) matter in the form of dim stars or planetlike objects, but the amount of deuterium left over from the Big Bang and the patterns in the cosmic microwave background both indicate that ordinary matter adds up to only about one-seventh of the total amount of matter. The rest of the matter is hypothesized to be exotic (nonbaryonic) dark matter consisting of as-yet-undiscovered particles called **WIMPs**.

23.3 DARK MATTER AND GALAXY FORMATION

- **What is the role of dark matter in galaxy formation?** Because most of a galaxy's mass is in the form of dark matter, the gravity of that dark matter is probably what formed proto-galactic clouds and then galaxies from slight density enhancements in the early universe.

- **What are the largest structures in the universe?**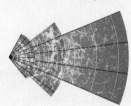
Galaxies appear to be distributed in gigantic chains and sheets that surround great **voids**. These **large-scale structures** trace their origin directly back to regions of slightly enhanced density early in time.

23.4 THE FATE OF THE UNIVERSE

- **Why is accelerating expansion evidence for dark energy?** Observations of distant supernovae show that the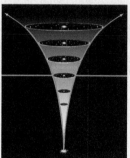
expansion of the universe has been speeding up for the last several billion years. No one knows the nature of the mysterious force that could be causing this acceleration. However, its characteristics are consistent with models in which the force is produced by a form of dark energy that pervades the universe.

- **Why is flat geometry evidence for dark energy?**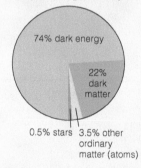
Observations of the cosmic microwave background also support the existence of dark energy because they demonstrate that the overall geometry of the universe is nearly flat. According to Einstein's general theory of relativity, the universe can be flat only if the total amount of mass-energy it contains is equal to the critical density, but measurements of the total amount of matter show that it represents only about one-quarter of the critical density. We therefore infer that about three-quarters of the total mass-energy is in the form of dark energy—the same amount implied by the supernova observations.

- **What is the fate of the universe?** If dark energy is indeed what's driving the acceleration of the universe's expansion, then we expect the expansion to continue accelerating into the future, as long as the effects of dark energy do not change with time and there are no other factors that affect the fate of the universe.

Use the following questions to check your understanding of some of the many types of visual information used in astronomy. Answers are provided in Appendix J. For additional practice, try the Chapter 23 Visual Quiz at MasteringAstronomy®.

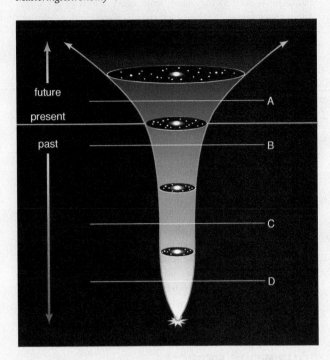

The schematic figure to the left shows a more complicated expansion history than the four idealized models shown in Figure 23.17. Answer the following questions, using the information given in this figure.

1. At time A, is the expansion of the universe accelerating, coasting, or decelerating?
2. At time B, is the expansion of the universe accelerating, coasting, or decelerating?
3. At time C, is the expansion of the universe accelerating, coasting, or decelerating?
4. At time D, is the expansion of the universe accelerating, coasting, or decelerating?

EXERCISES AND PROBLEMS

MasteringAstronomy®

For instructor-assigned homework go to MasteringAstronomy®.

REVIEW QUESTIONS

Short-Answer Questions Based on the Reading

1. Define *dark matter* and *dark energy*, and clearly distinguish between them. What types of observations have led scientists to propose the existence of each of these unseen influences?
2. Describe how orbital speeds in the Milky Way depend on distance from the galactic center. How does this relationship indicate the presence of large amounts of dark matter?
3. How do orbital speeds depend on distance from the galactic center in other spiral galaxies, and what does this tell us about dark matter in spiral galaxies?
4. How do we measure the masses of elliptical galaxies? What do these masses lead us to conclude about dark matter in elliptical galaxies?
5. Briefly describe the three different ways of measuring the mass of a cluster of galaxies. Do the results from the different methods agree? What do they tell us about dark matter in galaxy clusters?
6. What is *gravitational lensing*? Why does it occur? How can we use it to estimate the masses of lensing objects?
7. Briefly explain why the conclusion that dark matter exists rests on assuming that we understand gravity correctly. Is it possible that our understanding of gravity is not correct? Explain.
8. In what sense is dark matter "dark"? Briefly explain why objects like you, planets, and even dim stars qualify as dark matter.
9. What evidence indicates that most of the matter in the universe cannot be ordinary (baryonic) matter?
10. Explain what we mean when we say that a neutrino is a *weakly interacting particle*. Why can't the dark matter in galaxies be made of neutrinos?
11. What do we mean by *WIMPs*? Why does it seem likely that dark matter consists of these particles, even though we do not yet know what they are?
12. Briefly explain why dark matter is thought to have played a major role in the formation of galaxies and larger structures in the universe. What evidence suggests that larger structures are still forming?
13. What do the *large-scale structures* of the universe look like? Explain why we think these structures reflect the density patterns of the early universe.
14. Describe and compare the four general patterns for the expansion of the universe: *recollapsing, critical, coasting,* and *accelerating.* Observationally, how can we decide which of the four general expansion models best describes the present-day universe?
15. How do observations of distant supernovae provide evidence for dark energy?
16. How do observations of the cosmic microwave background provide evidence for dark energy?
17. Based on current evidence, what is the overall inventory of the mass-energy contents of the universe?
18. What implications does the evidence for dark energy have for the fate of the universe?

TEST YOUR UNDERSTANDING

Does It Make Sense?

Decide whether the statement makes sense (or is clearly true) or does not make sense (or is clearly false). Explain clearly; not all these have definitive answers, so your explanation is more important than your chosen answer.

19. Strange as it may sound, most of both the mass and the energy in the universe may take forms that we are unable to detect directly.
20. A cluster of galaxies is held together by the mutual gravitational attraction of all the stars in the cluster's galaxies.
21. We can estimate the total mass of a cluster of galaxies by studying the distorted images of galaxies whose light passes through the cluster.
22. Clusters of galaxies are the largest structures that we have so far detected in the universe.
23. The primary evidence for an accelerating universe comes from observations of young stars in the Milky Way.
24. There is no doubt remaining among astronomers that the fate of the universe is to expand forever.
25. Dark matter is called "dark" because it blocks light from traveling between the stars.
26. Dark energy is the energy associated with the motion of particles of dark matter.
27. Evidence that the expansion of the universe is accelerating comes from observations showing that the average distance between galaxies is increasing faster now than it was 5 billion years ago.
28. If dark matter consists of WIMPs, then we should be able to observe photons produced by collisions between these particles.

Quick Quiz

Choose the best answer to each of the following. Explain your reasoning with one or more complete sentences.

29. Dark matter is inferred to exist because (a) we see lots of dark patches in the sky. (b) it explains how the expansion of the universe can be accelerating. (c) we can observe its gravitational influence on visible matter.
30. Dark energy has been hypothesized to exist in order to explain (a) observations suggesting that the expansion of the universe is accelerating. (b) the high orbital speeds of stars far from the center of our galaxy. (c) explosions that seem to create giant voids between galaxies.
31. Measurements of how orbital speeds depend on distance from the center of our galaxy tell us that stars in the outskirts of the galaxy (a) orbit the galactic center just as fast as stars closer to the center. (b) rotate rapidly on their axes. (c) travel in straight, flat lines rather than elliptical orbits.
32. Strong evidence for the existence of dark matter comes from observations of (a) our solar system. (b) the center of the Milky Way. (c) clusters of galaxies.
33. A photograph of a cluster of galaxies shows distorted images of galaxies that lie behind it at greater distances. This is an example of what astronomers call (a) dark energy. (b) spiral density waves. (c) gravitational lensing.
34. Based on the observational evidence, is it possible that dark matter doesn't really exist? (a) No, the evidence for dark matter is too strong for us to think it could be in error. (b) Yes, but only if there is something wrong with our current understanding of how gravity should work on large scales. (c) Yes, but only if all the observations themselves are in error.
35. Based on current evidence, which of the following is considered a likely candidate for the majority of the dark matter in galaxies? (a) subatomic particles that we have not yet detected in particle physics experiments (b) swarms of relatively dim red stars (c) supermassive black holes

36. Which region of the early universe was most likely to become a galaxy? (a) a region whose matter density was lower than average (b) a region whose matter density was higher than average (c) a region with an unusual concentration of dark energy
37. The major evidence for the idea that the expansion of the universe is accelerating comes from observations of (a) white dwarf supernovae. (b) the orbital speeds of stars within galaxies. (c) the evolution of quasars.
38. Which of the following possible types of universe would *not* expand forever? (a) a critical universe (b) an accelerating universe (c) a recollapsing universe

PROCESS OF SCIENCE

Examining How Science Works

39. *Dark Matter.* Overall, how convincing do you consider the case for the existence of dark matter? Write a short essay in which you explain what we mean by dark matter, describe the evidence for its existence, and discuss your opinion about the strength of the evidence.
40. *Dark Energy.* Overall, how convincing do you consider the case for the existence of dark energy? Write a short essay in which you explain what we mean by dark energy, describe the evidence for its existence, and discuss your opinion about the strength of the evidence.
41. *Alternative Gravity.* Suppose someone proposed a new theory of gravity that claimed to explain observations of motion in galaxies and clusters of galaxies without the need for dark matter. Briefly describe at least one other test that you would expect the new theory to be able to pass if it was, in fact, a better theory of gravity than general relativity, which is currently our best explanation of how gravity works.

GROUP WORK EXERCISE

42. *Dark Matter and Distorted Galaxies.* In this exercise, you will learn about how dark matter in galaxy clusters distorts images of background galaxies through gravitational lensing. Before you begin, assign the following roles to the people in your group: *Scribe* (takes notes on the group's activities), *Proposer* (proposes explanations to the group), *Skeptic* (points out weaknesses in proposed explanations), and *Moderator* (leads group discussion and makes sure everyone contributes).

a. Study the gravitational lensing diagram in Figure 23.9 and notice how gravitational lensing causes the image of a background galaxy to shift to a position *farther* from the center of the cluster. The *Proposer* should explain how this shift affects the lensed image of a galaxy and predict how the lensed image of a spherical galaxy would look. The *Skeptic* should then decide whether she or he agrees with the *Proposer*'s reasoning and, if not, should offer an alternative prediction. b. On a large piece of paper, the *Scribe* should draw a diagram like the one that follows, using a straight edge to make sure the lines are straight. They should all intersect at the same place, and the circle should be close to the point of intersection. (Note that the point at which the lines intersect represents the center of a galaxy cluster, and the circle represents

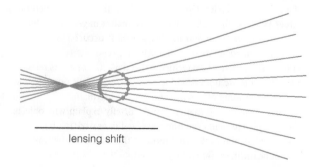

lensing shift

the true position and shape of a spherical galaxy at a much greater distance from Earth.) **c.** The *Moderator* should then determine the effect of the cluster's lensing shift on the galaxy's image as follows. For each dot on the circle, draw another dot farther to the right along the same line, so that the distance between the two dots is equal to the length of the line labeled "lensing shift." Then connect the new dots to see the shape of the lensed image. Does it agree with the *Proposer's* prediction? Was the *Skeptic's* prediction better? How does it compare with the lensed galaxy images in Figure 23.10? Discuss the possible reasons for any discrepancies you find.

INVESTIGATE FURTHER

In-Depth Questions to Increase Your Understanding

Short-Answer/Essay Questions

43. *The Future Universe.* Based on current evidence concerning the growth of structure in the universe, briefly describe what you would expect large-scale structures in the universe to look like about 10 billion years from now.

44. *Dark Matter and Life.* State and explain at least two reasons one might argue that dark matter is (or was) essential for life to exist on Earth.

45. *Orbital Speed vs. Radius.* Draw graphs showing how orbital speed depends on distance from the galactic center for each of the following three hypothetical galaxies. Make sure the horizontal axis has approximate distances labeled.
   a. a galaxy with all its mass concentrated at its center **b.** a galaxy with constant mass density within 20,000 light-years of its center, and zero density beyond that distance **c.** a galaxy with constant mass density within 20,000 light-years of its center, and beyond that an enclosed mass that increases proportionally to the distance from the center

46. *Dark Energy and Supernova Brightness.* When astronomers began measuring the brightnesses and redshifts of distant white dwarf supernovae, they expected to find that the expansion of the universe was slowing down. Instead they found that it was speeding up. Were the distant supernovae brighter or fainter than expected? Explain why. (*Hint:* In Figure 23.18, the position of a supernova point on the vertical axis depends on its redshift. Its position on the horizontal axis depends on its brightness—supernovae seen farther back in time are not as bright as those seen closer in time.)

47. *What Is Dark Matter?* Describe at least three possible constituents of dark matter. Explain how we would expect each to interact with light, and how we might go about detecting its existence.

48. *Alternative Gravity.* How would gravity have to be different in order to explain the rotation curves of galaxies without the need for dark matter? Would gravity need to be stronger or weaker than expected at very large distances? Explain.

Quantitative Problems

Be sure to show all calculations clearly and state your final answers in complete sentences.

49. *White Dwarf M/L.* What is the mass-to-light ratio of a $1M_{Sun}$ white dwarf with a luminosity of $0.001L_{Sun}$?

50. *Supergiant M/L.* What is the mass-to-light ratio of a $30M_{Sun}$ supergiant star with a luminosity of $300,000L_{Sun}$?

51. *Solar System M/L.* What is the mass-to-light ratio of the solar system?

52. *Mass from Orbital Velocities.* Study the graph of orbital speeds for the spiral galaxy NGC 7541, which is shown in Figure 23.4.
   a. Use the orbital velocity law to determine the mass (in solar masses) of NGC 7541 enclosed within a radius of 30,000 light-years from

its center. (*Hint:* 1 light-year = 9.461×10^{15} m.) **b.** Use the orbital velocity law to determine the mass of NGC 7541 enclosed within a radius of 60,000 light-years from its center. **c.** Based on your answers to parts a and b, what can you conclude about the distribution of mass in this galaxy?

53. *Weighing a Cluster.* A cluster of galaxies has a radius of about 5.1 million light-years (4.8×10^{22} m) and an intracluster medium with a temperature of 6×10^7 K. Estimate the mass of the cluster. Give your answer in both kilograms and solar masses. Suppose that the combined luminosity of all the stars in the cluster is $8 \times 10^{12}\, L_{Sun}$. What is the cluster's mass-to-light ratio?

54. *Cluster Mass from Hot Gas.* The gas temperature of the Coma Cluster of galaxies is about 9×10^7 K. What is the mass of this cluster within 15 million light-years of the cluster center?

55. *From Newton to Dark Matter.* Show that the equation $M = r \times v^2/G$ from Mathematical Insight 23.2 is equivalent to Newton's version of Kepler's third law from Mathematical Insight 4.3. Assume that one mass is much larger than the other mass and that the orbit is circular. (*Hint:* What is the mathematical relationship between period *p* and orbital velocity *v* and orbital radius *r* for a circular orbit?)

56. 10^{100} *Years.* Based on current understanding, the final stage in the history of a perpetually expanding universe would come about 10^{100} years from now. Such a large number is easy to write but difficult to understand. This problem investigates some of the incredible properties of very large numbers.
   a. The current age of the universe is around 10^{10} years. How much longer is a trillion years than this current age? How much longer is 10^{15} years? 10^{20} years? **b.** Suppose protons decay with a half-life of 10^{32} years. When will the number of remaining protons be half its current amount? When will it be a quarter of its current amount? How many half-lives will have gone by when the universe reaches an age of 10^{34} years? What fraction of the original protons will remain at this time? Is it reasonable to conclude that *all* protons in today's universe will be gone by the time the universe is 10^{40} years old? Explain. (*Hint:* See Mathematical Insight 8.1.)

Discussion Questions

57. *Dark Matter or Revised Gravity.* One possible explanation for the evidence we find for dark matter is that we are currently using the wrong law of gravity to measure the masses of very large objects. If we really do misunderstand gravity, then many fundamental theories of physics, including Einstein's theory of general relativity, will need to be revised. Which explanation for our observations do you find more appealing: dark matter or revised gravity? Explain why. Why do you suppose most astronomers find dark matter more appealing?

58. *Our Fate.* Scientists, philosophers, and poets alike have speculated about the fate of the universe. How would you prefer the universe as we know it to end: in a "Big Crunch" or through eternal expansion? Explain the reasons behind your preference.

Web Projects

59. *Gravitational Lenses.* Gravitational lensing occurs in numerous astronomical situations. Compile a catalog of examples from the Web with photos of lensed stars, quasars, and galaxies. Give a one-paragraph explanation of what is shown in each photo.

60. *Accelerating Universe.* Search for the most recent information about the acceleration of the expansion of the universe. Write a one- to three-page report on your findings.

61. *The Nature of Dark Matter.* Find and study recent reports on the possible nature of dark matter. Write a one- to three-page report that summarizes the latest ideas about what dark matter is made of.

All galaxies, including our Milky Way, developed as gravity pulled together matter in regions of the universe that started out slightly denser than surrounding regions. The central illustration depicts how galaxies formed over time, starting from the Big Bang in the upper left and proceeding to the present day in the lower right, as space gradually expanded according to Hubble's law.

380,000 years

1 billion years

Big Bang

TIME

① Dramatic inflation early in time is thought to have produced large-scale ripples in the density of the universe. All the structure we see today formed as gravity drew additional matter into the peaks of these ripples [Section 22.3].

Inflation may have stretched tiny quantum fluctuations into large-scale ripples.

② Observations of the cosmic microwave background show us what the regions of enhanced density were like about 380,000 years after the Big Bang [Section 22.2].

RADIO

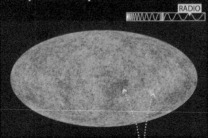

Photo by *WMAP*   *Variations in the cosmic microwave background show that regions of the universe differed in density by only a few parts in 100,000.*

③ Large-scale surveys of the universe show that gravity has gradually shaped early regions of enhanced density into a web-like structure, with galaxies arranged in huge chains and sheets [Section 23.3].

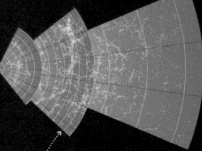

Sloan Digital Sky Survey

The web-like patterns of structure observed in large-scale galaxy surveys agree with those seen in large-scale computer simulations of structure formation.

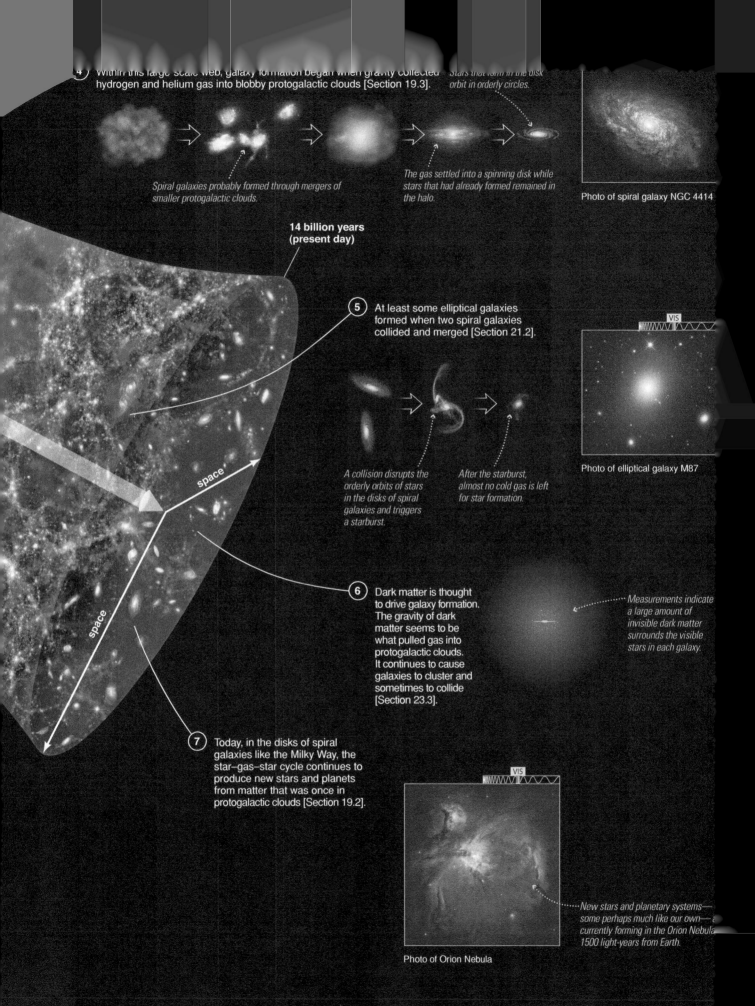

4 Within this large-scale web, galaxy formation began when gravity collected hydrogen and helium gas into blobby protogalactic clouds [Section 19.3].

Stars that form in the disk orbit in orderly circles.

Spiral galaxies probably formed through mergers of smaller protogalactic clouds.

The gas settled into a spinning disk while stars that had already formed remained in the halo.

Photo of spiral galaxy NGC 4414

14 billion years (present day)

space

space

5 At least some elliptical galaxies formed when two spiral galaxies collided and merged [Section 21.2].

VIS

Photo of elliptical galaxy M87

A collision disrupts the orderly orbits of stars in the disks of spiral galaxies and triggers a starburst.

After the starburst, almost no cold gas is left for star formation.

6 Dark matter is thought to drive galaxy formation. The gravity of dark matter seems to be what pulled gas into protogalactic clouds. It continues to cause galaxies to cluster and sometimes to collide [Section 23.3].

Measurements indicate a large amount of invisible dark matter surrounds the visible stars in each galaxy.

7 Today, in the disks of spiral galaxies like the Milky Way, the star–gas–star cycle continues to produce new stars and planets from matter that was once in protogalactic clouds [Section 19.2].

VIS

Photo of Orion Nebula

New stars and planetary systems— some perhaps much like our own— currently forming in the Orion Nebula 1500 light-years from Earth.

24 LIFE IN THE UNIVERSE

We, this people, on a small and lonely planet
Travelling through casual space
Past aloof stars, across the way of indifferent suns
To a destination where all signs tell us
It is possible and imperative that we learn
A brave and startling truth.

— *Maya Angelou, from* A Brave and Startling Truth

We have covered a lot of ground in this book, discussing fundamental questions about the nature and origin of our planet, our star, our galaxy, and our universe. But we have not yet discussed the most profound question of all: Are we alone? The universe contains worlds beyond imagination—more than 100 billion star systems in our galaxy alone, and some 100 billion galaxies in the observable universe—yet we do not know whether any world other than our own has ever been home to life.

In this chapter, we will discuss the possibility of life beyond Earth. We'll begin by considering the history of life on Earth, which will help us understand the prospects of finding life elsewhere. We'll then consider the possibility of finding microbial life elsewhere in our solar system or beyond, and examine efforts to search for extraterrestrial intelligence (SETI). Finally, we'll discuss the astonishing implications that the search for life may hold for our future.

24.1 LIFE ON EARTH

It may seem that aliens are everywhere. Aliens abound in television shows and movies, and it's not hard to find websites claiming alien atrocities or a government conspiracy to hide alien corpses in "Area 51."

Scientists are interested in aliens too, although most scientists remain deeply skeptical about reports of aliens on Earth (see Special Topic, page 712). Scientists are therefore searching for life elsewhere, looking for evidence of life on other worlds in our solar system, trying to learn whether we should expect to find life on planets orbiting other stars, and searching for signals broadcast by other civilizations.

Scientific interest in extraterrestrial life is not new. Belief in life on other worlds was common even among ancient Greek philosophers, and many famous scientists of the past few centuries took it as a given that intelligent beings exist on other planets. For example, Kepler suggested that the Moon was inhabited, and William Herschel (co-discoverer, with his sister Caroline, of Uranus) spoke of life on virtually all the planets in our solar system. Most famously, in the late 19th century, Percival Lowell claimed to see networks of canals on Mars, which he argued were the mark of an advanced civilization [**Section 9.4**] and which formed the basis for H. G. Wells's novel *The War of the Worlds*.

However, until fairly recently, the question of life beyond Earth could be addressed only through guesswork, because there was little actual evidence to go on. The situation has changed dramatically in recent decades, making the search for life beyond Earth a topic of serious scientific study. One major factor has been the discovery of planets around other stars [**Section 13.1**], which confirms that there are plenty of

places to look for life beyond our own solar system. But new discoveries about life on Earth have played an even more important role. In particular, three recent developments in the study of life on Earth have made it seem much more likely that life might exist elsewhere:

1. We have learned that life arose quite early in Earth's history, suggesting that life might also form quickly on other worlds with the right conditions.

2. Laboratory experiments have shown that the chemical constituents thought to have been common on the young Earth combine readily into complex organic molecules. These experiments suggest that life might have arisen through naturally occurring chemistry—in which case the same chemistry could have given rise to life on many other worlds.

3. We have discovered microscopic living organisms that probably could survive in conditions similar to those on at least some other worlds in our solar system, suggesting that the necessities of life may be common in the universe.

Because these three ideas are so important to understanding the modern science of life in the universe, often called *astrobiology*, let's examine each of them in greater detail. Along the way, we'll also discuss the nature and history of life on Earth. We will then be prepared to consider how we might search for life on other worlds.

When did life arise on Earth?

The first of our three major ideas above is that life arose quite early on Earth. But how do we know? We learn about the history of life on Earth through the study of **fossils**, relics of organisms that lived and died long ago. Most fossils form when dead organisms fall to the bottom of a sea (or other body of water) and are gradually buried by layers of sediments. The sediments are produced by erosion on land and carried by rivers to the sea. Over millions of years, sediments pile up on the seafloor, and the weight of the upper layers compresses underlying layers into rock. Erosion or tectonic activity can later expose the fossils (FIGURE 24.1). In some places, such as the Grand Canyon, the sedimentary layers record hundreds of millions of years of Earth's history (FIGURE 24.2). Some fossils are remarkably well preserved (FIGURE 24.3), though the vast majority of dead organisms decay completely and leave no fossils behind.

The Geological Time Scale The key to reconstructing the history of life is to determine the dates at which fossil organisms lived. The *relative* ages of fossils found in different layers are easy to determine: Deeper layers formed earlier and contain more ancient fossils. Radiometric dating [**Section 8.3**] confirms these relative ages and gives us fairly precise absolute ages for fossils. Based on the layering of rocks and fossils, geologists divide Earth's history into a set of distinct intervals that make up what we call the **geological time scale**. FIGURE 24.4 shows the names of the various intervals on a timeline, along with numerous important events in Earth's history.

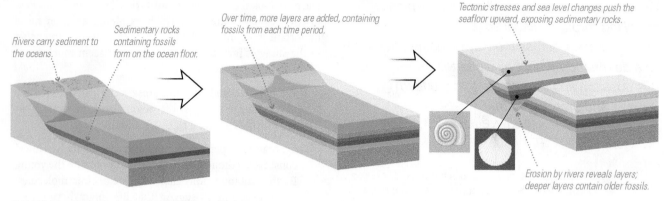

FIGURE 24.1 Formation of sedimentary rock. Each layer represents a particular time and place in Earth's history and is characterized by fossils of organisms that lived in that time and place.

Fossil Evidence for the Early Origin of Life You might wonder why the geological time scale shows so much more detail for the last few hundred million years than it does for earlier times. The answer is that fossils become increasingly difficult to find as we look deeper into Earth's history, for three major reasons. First, older rocks are much rarer than younger rocks, because most of Earth's surface is geologically young. Second, even when we find very old rocks, they often have been subject to transformations (caused by heat and pressure) that would have destroyed any fossil evidence they may have contained. Third, all life prior to a few hundred million years ago was microscopic, and microscopic fossils are much more difficult to identify.

Despite these difficulties, geologists have found a few very old rocks that suggest life was already thriving on Earth 3.5 billion years ago, and possibly for several hundred million years before that. One strong line of evidence comes from rocks called *stromatolites* (**FIGURE 24.5**), which are strikingly similar in size, shape, and interior structure to sections of mats known as "living stromatolites" that are formed today by colonies of microbes. The clear implication is that the stromatolites are fossils of ancient microbes, although there is some controversy about this conclusion because geological processes of sedimentation can mimic the layering found in stromatolites. Moreover, if the microbes that made the stromatolites are like the microbes in the living mats today, then

the implication is that at least some of these ancient microbes produced energy by photosynthesis. Because photosynthesis is a fairly sophisticated metabolic process, we presume that it must have taken at least a moderately long time for this process to evolve in living organisms. In other words, if we are correct in concluding that stromatolites tell us that photosynthetic life already existed some 3.5 billion years ago, then we can infer that more primitive life must have existed even earlier, and that the origin of life itself substantially predates this.

Other evidence for early life comes from recognizable fossils of microbes, known as *microfossils*. Although it is often difficult to distinguish a true microfossil from a microscopic structure formed by mineral processes, scientists are confident that they have found microfossils dating to at least 3.0 billion years ago, and some rocks that contain structures that appear to be microfossils date to 3.5 billion years ago.

More intriguingly, careful study of some of the most ancient rocks on Earth suggests that life was already present

FIGURE 24.2 The rock layers of the Grand Canyon record more than 500 million years of Earth's history.

FIGURE 24.3 Dinosaur fossils preserved in sandstone in Dinosaur National Monument, which straddles Utah and Colorado.

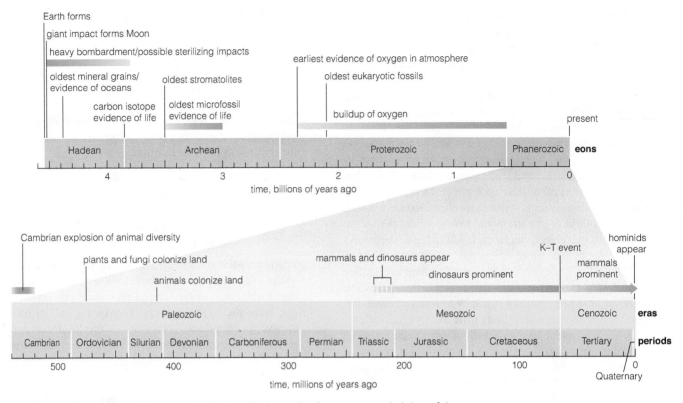

FIGURE 24.4 The geological time scale. Notice that the lower timeline is an expanded view of the last portion of the upper timeline. The eons, eras, and periods are defined by changes observed in the fossil record. The absolute ages come from radiometric dating. (The K-T event is the geological term for the impact linked to the mass extinction of the dinosaurs [**Section 12.4**].)

at least 3.85 billion years ago. These rocks have undergone too much change for them to hold intact fossils, but careful analysis of carbon isotopes within them suggests that they once held living organisms. Carbon has two stable isotopes: carbon-12, with six protons and six neutrons in its nucleus, and carbon-13, which has one extra neutron (see Figure 5.9). Living organisms incorporate carbon-12 slightly more easily than carbon-13. As a result, the fraction of carbon-13 is always a bit lower in fossils than in rock samples that lack fossils. All life and all fossils tested to date show the same characteristic ratio of the

two carbon isotopes, and this ratio has also been found in rocks that are more than 3.85 billion years old, suggesting that they contained life when they formed. (The carbon isotope evidence is found in sedimentary rocks that cannot be dated precisely; however, they must be at least 3.85 billion years old, because that is the age obtained from radiometric dating of volcanic [igneous] rock that cuts through them.)

Could Life Have Arisen Even Earlier? Until recently, many scientists thought that life (or, at least, the life that

a These knee-high mats at Shark Bay, Western Australia, are colonies of microbes known as "living stromatolites."

b The banded structure in this section from one of the Shark Bay stromatolites is formed by layers of sediment attaching to the microbial mats.

c This section of a 3.5-billion-year-old stromatolite (found in the Strelley Pool Formation in Western Australia) shows the same type of structure found in living stromatolites. The black layers are organic deposits that are the remains of ancient microbial mats. (The ruler is marked in centimeters.)

FIGURE 24.5 Rocks called *stromatolites* offer evidence of microbial life existing as early as 3.5 billion years ago.

ultimately evolved into modern organisms) could not have arisen before the end of the heavy bombardment, about 3.9 billion years ago [**Section 8.2**]. Recall that the heavy bombardment was a time during which Earth should have been repeatedly struck by large asteroids or comets, and studies of craters on the Moon suggest that there was an especially strong *late heavy bombardment* toward the end of that time period. Past models suggested that the largest impacts would have completely vaporized the oceans and raised the global surface temperature high enough to melt the upper crust. In that case, these events would have been *sterilizing impacts* that would have killed off any life on Earth at the time. However, more recent models suggest that these effects were overstated, and that while large impacts would have sterilized substantial portions of our planet, microscopic life living underground and in some deep ocean environments could have survived.

If life did arise very early, evidence will be hard to find. The relatively few known rocks that date to earlier than 3.5 billion years ago have been so transformed by heat and pressure that any evidence they contain is likely to be controversial. Indeed, if the carbon isotope evidence really does indicate life some 3.85 billion years ago, the rarity of such old rocks suggests that life must have already been widespread on Earth by that time; otherwise, it would take extraordinary luck to have found the evidence.

To summarize, fossil evidence points to life on Earth thriving 3.5 billion years ago, and carbon isotope evidence may point to widespread life more than 3.85 billion years ago. Life could have arisen even earlier, though evidence would be hard to find. Still, no matter how we look at it, it seems that life on Earth arose within no more than a few hundred million years after Earth's birth about $4\frac{1}{2}$ billion years ago. Geologically speaking, that is a remarkably short time.

How did life arise on Earth?

We have discussed *when* life arose on Earth, but *how* did it arise? To answer this question, we must first consider how life today differs from the earliest life on Earth. Then we can discuss how the first organisms may have originated.

The Theory of Evolution The fossil record clearly shows that life has gone through great changes over time. If we are going to understand how life arose, we must understand what causes these changes, so that we can trace life back to its origin. The unifying theory through which scientists understand the history of life on Earth is the **theory of evolution**, first published by Charles Darwin in 1859.

Evolution simply means "change with time." Even before Darwin, numerous scientists (some going back to ancient times) had recognized evidence for evolution in the fossil record, but no one before Darwin successfully explained how species might undergo change. In essence, the fossil record provides strong evidence that evolution *has* occurred, while Darwin's theory of evolution explains *how* it occurs.

Darwin provided extensive evidence for the occurrence of evolution and, based on this evidence, put forth a simple model to explain how evolution occurs. The underlying logic of Darwin's model is easy to understand. As described

by biologist Stephen Jay Gould (1941–2002), Darwin built his model from "two undeniable facts and an inescapable conclusion":

- *Fact 1: overproduction and competition for survival.* Any localized population of a species has the potential to produce far more offspring than the local environment can support with resources such as food and shelter. This overproduction leads to a competition for survival among the individuals of the population.

- *Fact 2: individual variation.* Individuals in a population of any species vary in many heritable traits (traits passed from parents to offspring). No two individuals are exactly alike, and some individuals possess traits that make them better able to compete for food and other vital resources.

- *The inescapable conclusion: unequal reproductive success.* In the struggle for survival, those individuals whose traits best enable them to survive and reproduce will, on average, leave the largest number of offspring that in turn survive to reproduce. Therefore, in any local environment, heritable traits that enhance survival and successful reproduction will become progressively more common in succeeding generations.

It is this unequal reproductive success that Darwin called **natural selection:** Over time, advantageous genetic traits will naturally win out (be "selected") over less advantageous traits because they are more likely to be passed down through many generations. This process explains how species can change in response to their environment—by favoring traits that improve adaptation—and it is the primary mechanism of evolution. By studying the variety of species in places like the Galápagos Islands, Darwin backed his model with so much evidence that it quickly gained the status of a scientific *theory* [**Section 3.4**].

The Mechanism of Evolution In the more than 150 years since Darwin published his theory, ongoing research has only given it further support. Perhaps the strongest support for the theory has come from study of **DNA** (short for *deoxyribonucleic acid*), the genetic material of all life on Earth, which has allowed scientists to understand the mechanism of evolution on a molecular level.

Living organisms reproduce by copying DNA and passing these copies on to their descendants. A molecule of DNA consists of two long strands—somewhat like the interlocking strands of a zipper—wound together in the spiral shape known as a *double helix* (**FIGURE 24.6**). The instructions for assembling a living organism are written in the precise order of four chemical bases that make up the interlocking portions of the DNA "zipper": adenine (A), thymine (T), guanine (G), and cytosine (C). These bases pair up in a way that ensures that both strands of a DNA molecule contain the same genetic information. By unwinding and allowing new strands (made from chemicals floating around inside a cell) to form alongside the original ones, a single DNA molecule can give rise to two identical copies of itself. That is how genetic material is copied and passed on to future generations.

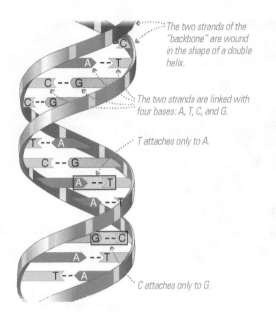

The two strands of the "backbone" are wound in the shape of a double helix.

The two strands are linked with four bases: A, T, C, and G.

T attaches only to A.

C attaches only to G.

FIGURE 24.6 This diagram represents a small piece of a DNA molecule, which looks like a zipper twisted into a spiral. Hereditary information is contained in the "teeth" linking the strands. These "teeth" are the DNA bases. Only four DNA bases are used, and they can link up between the two strands only in specific ways: T attaches only to A, and C attaches only to G. (The color coding is arbitrary and is used only to represent different types of chemical groups; in the backbone, blue and yellow represent sugar and phosphate groups, respectively.)

Evolution occurs because the transfer of genetic information from one generation to the next is not always perfect. An organism's DNA may occasionally be altered by copying errors or by external influences, such as ultraviolet light from the Sun or exposure to toxic or radioactive chemicals. Any change in an organism's DNA is called a **mutation**. Many mutations are lethal, killing the cell in which the mutation occurs. Some, however, may improve a cell's ability to survive and reproduce. The cell then passes on this improvement to its offspring.

Our understanding of the molecular mechanism of natural selection has put the theory of evolution on a stronger foundation than ever. While no theory can ever be proved true beyond all doubt, the theory of evolution is as solid as any theory in science, including the theory of gravity and the theory of atoms. Biologists routinely witness evolution occurring before their eyes among laboratory microorganisms, or over periods of just a few decades among plants and animals subjected to environmental stress. Moreover, the theory of evolution has become the underpinning of virtually all modern biology, medicine, and agriculture. For example, agricultural scientists apply the idea of natural selection to develop pest control strategies that reduce the populations of harmful insects without harming the populations of beneficial ones; medical researchers test new drugs on animals that are genetically similar to humans, because the theory of evolution tells us that genetically similar species should have somewhat similar physiological responses; and biologists study the genetic relationships between organisms by comparing their DNA.

The First Living Organisms The basic chemical nature of DNA is virtually identical among all living organisms. This fact, along with other biochemical similarities shared by all living organisms, tells us that all life on Earth today can trace its origins to a common ancestor that lived long ago.

We are unlikely to find fossils of the earliest organisms, but we can learn about early life through careful studies of the DNA of living organisms. Biologists can determine the evolutionary relationships among living species by comparing the sequences of bases in their DNA. For example, two organisms whose DNA sequences differ in five places for a particular gene are probably more distantly related than two organisms whose gene sequences differ in only one place. Many such DNA comparisons suggest that all living organisms are related in a way depicted schematically by the "tree of life" in FIGURE 24.7. Although details in the structure of this tree remain uncertain (particularly because we now know that different species can swap genes), it indicates that life on Earth is divided into three major groupings, or *domains*, called *bacteria*, *archaea*, and *eukarya*, and that all three domains share a common ancestor. Notice that plants and animals represent only two tiny branches of the domain *eukarya*.

Organisms on branches located closer to the root of the tree of life must contain DNA that is evolutionarily older, suggesting that they more closely resemble the organisms that lived early in Earth's history. Some of the modern-day organisms that appear to be evolutionarily oldest are microbes that live in very hot water around seafloor volcanic vents in the deep oceans (FIGURE 24.8). Unlike most life at Earth's surface, which depends on sunlight, these organisms get energy from chemical reactions in the hot, mineral-rich water around the volcanic vents.

The idea that early organisms might have lived in such "extreme" conditions may at first seem surprising, but it makes sense when we think about it. The deep ocean environment

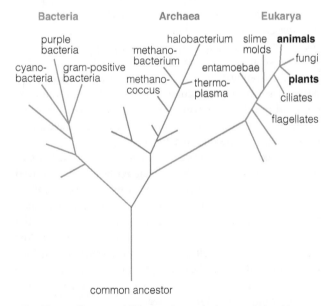

FIGURE 24.7 The tree of life, showing evolutionary relationships determined by comparison of DNA sequences in different organisms. Just two small branches represent *all* plant and animal species. (Only a few of the many relationships are shown and labeled.)

FIGURE 24.8 This photograph shows a volcanic vent on the ocean floor that spews out hot, mineral-rich water. DNA studies indicate that the microbes living near these vents are evolutionarily older than most other living organisms, hinting that early life may have arisen in similar environments.

FIGURE 24.9 Stanley Miller poses with a reproduction of the experimental setup he first used in the 1950s to study pathways to the origin of life. (He worked with Harold Urey, so the experiment is called the Miller-Urey experiment.)

would have been protected from the effects of impacts and from harmful ultraviolet radiation that bathed Earth's surface before our atmosphere had oxygen or an ozone layer. Moreover, the chemical pathways used to extract energy from mineral-rich hot water are simpler than other chemical pathways (such as photosynthesis) used by living organisms to obtain energy. For these reasons, many scientists suspect that life arose near deep-sea vents, or in similar environments that provided chemical energy.

The Transition from Chemistry to Biology The theory of evolution explains how the earliest organisms evolved into the great diversity of life on Earth today. But where did the first organisms come from? We may never know for sure, because we are unlikely to find fossils that would show the transition from nonlife to life. However, over the past several decades, scientists have conducted laboratory experiments designed to mimic the conditions that existed on the young Earth. These experiments suggest that life could have arisen through natural chemical reactions.

Such experiments were first performed in the 1950s (FIGURE 24.9), and they have been refined and improved since that time. In essence, the experiments mix chemicals thought to have been present on the early Earth and then "spark" the chemicals with electricity to simulate lightning or other energy sources. The chemical reactions that follow have produced nearly all the major molecules of life, including amino acids and DNA bases. Many of these molecules are also found in meteorites, suggesting that some organic molecules may have arrived from space.

Laboratory studies of the possible origins of life have advanced greatly in the past few years. Scientists have found that naturally occurring clays, which should have been abundant

in the early oceans, can catalyze the formation of short strands of RNA, a molecule much like a single strand of DNA. Some of these short RNA molecules can in turn catalyze other reactions. Because some RNA molecules (though not those so far produced in the laboratory) are capable of self-replication, many biologists now presume that RNA was the original genetic material of life on Earth, with DNA coming later.

Equally significantly, experiments have also shown that microscopic enclosed membranes can form on the surfaces of the same clay minerals that help assemble RNA molecules, sometimes with RNA inside them (FIGURE 24.10). Self-replicating RNA molecules enclosed in such membranes would have in essence made "pre-cells" in which the RNA might have undergone rapid changes. Pre-cells in which RNA replicated faster and more accurately were more likely to spread, leading to a type of positive feedback that would have encouraged even faster and more accurate replication. Given millions of years of chemical reactions occurring all over Earth, it seems plausible that RNA-based life would have arisen first and then eventually evolved into DNA-based life.

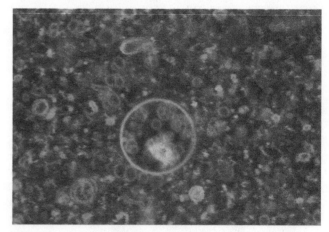

FIGURE 24.10 This microscopic photo (made with the aid of fluorescent dyes) shows short strands of RNA (red) contained within an enclosed membrane (green circle), both of which formed spontaneously with the aid of clay minerals beneath them.

FIGURE 24.11 summarizes the steps by which chemical processes might have led to life on Earth. We may never know whether life really arose in this way, but it seems possible.

Could Life Have Migrated to Earth? Our scenario suggests that life could have arisen naturally here on Earth. However, an alternative possibility is that life arose somewhere else first—perhaps on Venus or Mars—and then migrated to Earth on meteorites. Remember that we have collected meteorites that were blasted by impacts from the surfaces of the Moon and Mars [**Section 12.1**]. Calculations suggest that Venus, Earth, and Mars all should have exchanged many tons of rock, especially in the early days of the solar system when impacts were more common.

The idea that life could travel through space to Earth once seemed outlandish. After all, it's hard to imagine a more forbidding environment than that of space, with no air, no water, and constant bombardment by dangerous radiation from the Sun and stars. However, the presence of organic molecules in meteorites and comets tells us that the building blocks of life can survive in space, and tests have shown that some microbes can survive in space for years.

Evolution and the Schools

You're probably familiar with the public debate about teaching evolution in schools. Much of the controversy comes from misunderstandings on both sides. Scientists sometimes fail to show respect for people's individual religious beliefs, while those opposed to teaching evolution often misunderstand the overwhelming amount of scientific evidence that supports the theory.

The debate centers around the question of what counts as science and what does not, as you can see by considering a common question: Do you believe in creationism or evolution? This question may be philosophically and theologically interesting, but it is poorly phrased from a scientific standpoint: Science is about evidence, not beliefs. Scientific evidence clearly shows that the universe is much older than Earth, that Earth is some $4\frac{1}{2}$ billion years old, that life on Earth has undergone dramatic change since it first arose nearly 4 billion years ago, and that this change has occurred through the mechanism of evolution by natural selection. Nevertheless, all the evidence in the world can never prove a scientific theory to be true beyond all doubt. To take a somewhat extreme case, you could accept the overwhelming evidence for evolution and still believe that God created Earth and the universe a mere 6000 years ago by, for example, assuming that God put all the evidence for evolution in place. Because the evidence would look the same in this case as if evolution actually occurred, science cannot say anything about the validity of such a belief.

We can gain deeper insight by examining the theory of evolution using the hallmarks of science from Chapter 3. The first hallmark says that science seeks explanations for observed phenomena that rely on natural causes, and the theory of evolution does exactly that: It explains the fossil record and observed differences between species in terms of natural selection. Note that this hallmark does *not* preclude the possibility of divine intervention; it just says that if divine intervention has occurred, we cannot study it scientifically. The second and third hallmarks remind us that science progresses through the creation and testing of models designed to explain our observations, and that we must modify or discard models that fail our tests. The theory of evolution exhibits these hallmarks because it is continually subject to testing and verification, and it has indeed been modified as new evidence has come to light. For example, Darwin's original theory has been improved and strengthened by modern molecular understanding of DNA and by observations of evolution in microbes (such as bacteria gaining resistance to antibiotics) and in small, localized populations of plants and animals.

The fact that evolution is such a well-established and important scientific theory makes it a key part of the science curriculum for schools, and few people disagree. However, many people have suggested teaching alternative ideas such as *creationism* or *intelligent design* alongside evolution in school curricula. The scientific response is very simple: Scientists take no position on the general school curriculum, but the *science curriculum* should not include these alternative ideas because they are not science, which we can see by again considering the hallmarks of science.

Let's start with *creationism*, the idea that the world was divinely created. In fact, we can't even define this idea clearly enough to test it against the hallmarks of science. Many religions incorporate stories of creation, and these stories are often quite different from one another. For example, many Native American religious beliefs speak of creation in terms that bear little resemblance to the story in Genesis. Even among Christians who claim a literal belief in the Bible, there are differences of interpretation. Some biblical literalists argue that the creation must have occurred in just 6 days, as the first chapter of Genesis seems to say, but others suggest that the term "day" in Genesis does not necessarily mean 24 hours and that Genesis is therefore compatible with a much older Earth.

The related idea of *intelligent design* holds that the complexity of life is too great to have arisen naturally, and therefore there must have been a "designer." Intelligent design can sound much like science, especially because most of its proponents accept both the idea of an old Earth and the idea that some living things have changed through time as indicated by the fossil record. However, the assumption of an intelligent designer does not yield testable predictions, because it posits that the designer is beyond our scientific comprehension; in essence, the idea of intelligent design means that there is no point in continuing to look for natural causes, because a supernatural process made the universe and life. Whether or not this idea is true, it isn't science. As an analogy, consider the collapse of a bridge. If an engineer declares that the collapse was an act of God, he could well be right—but that belief won't help him learn how to design a better bridge. It is the scientific quest for a natural understanding of life—embodied in the theory of evolution—that has led to the discovery of genetics, DNA, and virtually all modern medicine.

So where does this discussion leave us with regard to the question of teaching evolution in schools? Let's start with what our discussion does *not* tell us. It does not tell us that everyone needs to accept the theory of evolution—whether you choose to do so is up to you. Nor does it tell us whether divine intervention has guided evolution—science does not say anything about the existence or role of God. What it *does* tell us is that the theory of evolution is a clear and crucial part of the study of science, and that without it we cannot fully understand modern science and its impact on our world.

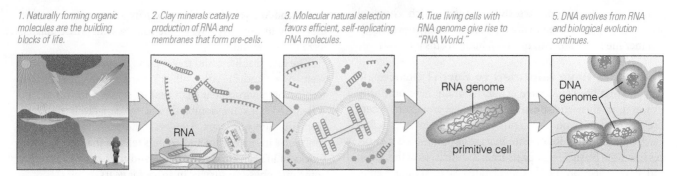

1. Naturally forming organic molecules are the building blocks of life.

2. Clay minerals catalyze production of RNA and membranes that form pre-cells.

3. Molecular natural selection favors efficient, self-replicating RNA molecules.

4. True living cells with RNA genome give rise to "RNA World."

5. DNA evolves from RNA and biological evolution continues.

FIGURE 24.11 A summary of the steps by which chemistry on the early Earth may have led to the origin of life.

In a sense, Earth, Venus, and Mars have been "sneezing" on each other for billions of years. Life could conceivably have originated on any of these three planets and been transported to the others. It's an intriguing thought, but it does not change our basic scenario for the origin of life—it simply moves it from one planet to another.

A Brief History of Life on Earth We are now ready to take a quick look at the history of life on Earth, summarized in Figure 24.4. Earth formed about $4\frac{1}{2}$ billion years ago, and the giant impact thought to have formed the Moon [**Section 8.2**] probably happened soon after. Mineral evidence suggests that Earth had oceans by 4.3 to 4.4 billion years ago, and those early oceans would have been natural laboratories for chemical reactions that could have led to life. Once life started, evolution rapidly diversified it.

Despite the rapid pace of evolution, the most complex organisms remained single-celled for at least a billion years after life first arose. All of these organisms probably lived in the oceans, because the lack of a protective ozone layer made the land inhospitable. Things began to change only when oxygen started building up in Earth's atmosphere.

Nearly all the oxygen in our atmosphere was originally released through photosynthesis by single-celled organisms known as *cyanobacteria* (**FIGURE 24.12**). Fossil evidence indicates that cyanobacteria were producing oxygen via

photosynthesis by at least 2.7 billion years ago, and possibly for hundreds of millions of years before that. However, oxygen did not immediately begin to accumulate in the atmosphere. For hundreds of millions of years, chemical reactions with surface rocks pulled oxygen back out of the atmosphere nearly as fast as the cyanobacteria could produce it. But these tiny organisms were abundant and persistent, and eventually the surface rock was so saturated with oxygen that the rate of oxygen removal slowed down. Oxygen then began to accumulate in the atmosphere, though it may not have reached a level that we could have breathed until just a few hundred million years ago.

Today, we often think of oxygen as a necessity for life. However, oxygen was probably poisonous to most organisms living before about 2 billion years ago (and remains a poison to many microbes still living today). The rise of atmospheric oxygen therefore caused tremendous evolutionary pressure and may have been a major factor in the evolution of complex plants and animals.

There were undoubtedly many crucial changes as primitive microbes gradually evolved into multicellular organisms and early plants and animals, but the fossil record does not allow us to pinpoint the times at which all these changes occurred. However, we see a dramatic change in the fossil record during the *Cambrian period,* beginning about 542 million years ago. During this period, animal life evolved from tiny and primitive organisms into all the basic body types (phyla) that we find on Earth today. This remarkable diversification occurred in such a short time relative to Earth's history that it is often called the *Cambrian explosion.*

Early dinosaurs and mammals arose some 225 to 250 million years ago, but dinosaurs at first proved more successful and dominated for well over 100 million years. Their sudden demise 65 million years ago paved the way for the evolution of large mammals—including humans. The earliest humans appeared on the scene only a few million years ago, or after 99.9% of Earth's history to date had already gone by. Our few centuries of industry and technology have come after 99.99999% of Earth's history.

What are the necessities of life?

If we are going to look for other worlds that might harbor life, the first step is to understand the necessities of life. While it is possible that life on other worlds could be quite different

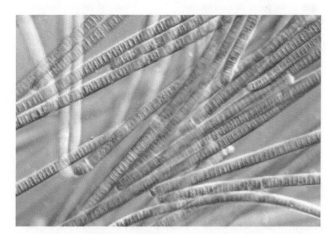

FIGURE 24.12 This photo shows microscopic chains of modern cyanobacteria. The ancestors of these living organisms produced essentially all the oxygen in Earth's atmosphere.

from life on Earth, it's easiest to begin the search for life by looking for conditions in which organisms from Earth could live. So what exactly does Earth life need to survive?

If we think about ourselves, the requirements for life seem fairly stringent: We need abundant oxygen in an atmosphere that is otherwise not poisonous, we need temperatures in a fairly narrow range of conditions, and we need abundant and varied food sources. However, the discovery of life in "extreme" environments—such as in the hot water near undersea volcanic vents—shows that many microbes (often called *extremophiles*) can survive in a much wider range of conditions.

Organisms living in hot water prove that at least some microbes can survive in much higher temperatures than we would have guessed. Other organisms live in other extremes. In the freezing cold but very dry valleys of Antarctica, scientists have found microbes that live *inside* rocks, surviving on tiny droplets of liquid water and energy from sunlight. Microscopic life has also been found deep underground in water that fills pores within subterranean rock. We have found life thriving in environments so acidic, alkaline, or salty that humans would be poisoned almost instantly. We have even found microbes that can survive high doses of radiation, making it possible for them to survive for many years in the radiation-filled environment of space.

If we compare all the different forms of life on Earth, we find that life as a whole has only three basic requirements:

1. A source of nutrients (atoms and molecules) from which to build living cells

2. Energy to fuel the activities of life, whether from sunlight, from chemical reactions, or from the heat of Earth itself

3. Liquid water

These requirements give us a basic road map for the search for life elsewhere. If we want to find life on other worlds, it makes sense to start by searching for worlds that offer these basic necessities.

Interestingly, only the third requirement (liquid water) seems to pose much of a constraint. Organic molecules are present almost everywhere—even on meteorites and comets. Many worlds are large enough to retain internal heat that could provide energy for life, and virtually all worlds have sunlight (or starlight) bathing their surfaces, although the inverse square law for light [**Section 15.1**] means that light provides less energy to worlds farther from their star. Nutrients and energy should therefore be available to some degree on almost every planet and moon. In contrast, liquid water is relatively rare. Therefore, the search for liquid water drives the current search for life in our universe.

You may have noticed that while we've been talking about *life*, we haven't actually defined the term. It's surprisingly difficult to draw a clear boundary between life and nonlife. Life can be so difficult to define that we may be tempted to fall back on the famous words of Supreme Court Justice Potter Stewart, who, in avoiding the difficulty of defining pornography, wrote: "I shall not today attempt further to define [it]. . . . But I know it when I see it." If living organisms on other worlds turn out to be much like those found on Earth, it may prove true that we'll know them when we see them. But if the organisms are fairly different from those on Earth, we'll need clearer guidelines to decide whether they are truly "living."

One approach seeks to identify distinguishing features common to all known life. For example, most or all living organisms on Earth appear to share the following six key properties:

1. *Order:* Living organisms are not random collections of molecules but rather have molecules arranged in orderly patterns that form cell structures.

2. *Reproduction:* Living organisms are capable of reproducing.

3. *Growth and development:* Living organisms grow and develop in patterns determined in part by heredity.

4. *Energy utilization:* Living organisms use energy to fuel their many activities.

5. *Response to the environment:* Living organisms actively respond to changes in their surroundings. For example, organisms may alter their chemistry or movements in the presence of a food source.

6. *Evolutionary adaptation:* Life evolves through natural selection, in which organisms pass on traits that make them better adapted to survival in their local environments.

These six properties are all important, but biologists today regard evolution as the most fundamental and unifying of them. Evolutionary adaptation is the only property that can explain the great diversity of life on Earth. Moreover, understanding how evolution works allows us to understand how all the other properties came to be. A simple definition of life might therefore be "something that can reproduce and evolve through natural selection."

This definition of life can probably suffice for most practical purposes, but some cases may still challenge it. For example, computer scientists can now write programs (that is, lines of computer code) that can reproduce themselves (that is, create additional sets of identical lines of code). By adding instructions that allow random changes to the programs, they can even make "artificial life" that evolves on a computer. Should this "artificial life," which consists of nothing but electronic signals processed by computer chips, be considered alive?

The fact that we have such difficulty distinguishing the living from the nonliving on Earth suggests that we should be very cautious about constraining our search for life elsewhere. No matter what definition of life we choose, there's always the possibility that we'll someday encounter something that challenges it. Nevertheless, the properties of reproduction and evolution seem likely to be shared by most if not all life in the universe and therefore provide a useful starting point as we consider how to explore the possibility of extraterrestrial life.

24.2 LIFE IN THE SOLAR SYSTEM

If we assume that life elsewhere would be at least a little bit like life on Earth, then the search for life begins with a search for **habitable worlds**—worlds that contain the basic necessities for life as we know it, including liquid water. The liquid water requirement rules out most of the worlds in our solar system. Mercury and the Moon are barren and dry, Venus is far too hot to have liquid water on its surface (though its clouds contain droplets of water laced with acid), and most of the small bodies of the outer solar system are too cold. The jovian planets may have droplets of liquid water in some of their clouds, but the strong vertical winds on these planets make them unlikely homes for life. That leaves two major possibilities besides Earth for habitability in our solar system: (1) Mars and (2) a few of the large moons orbiting jovian planets, most notably Europa [**Section 11.2**]. Let's discuss the current evidence about the potential habitability of these worlds.

THINK ABOUT IT

Is it possible for a world to be habitable but not actually have life? Is it possible for a world to have life but not be habitable? Explain.

Could there be life on Mars?

We now have sufficiently detailed images of Mars to be quite confident that no civilizations have ever existed there. The "canals" seen by Percival Lowell were some type of mirage, presumably formed by a combination of real Martian features and his own imagination. Nevertheless, we have good reason to believe that liquid water flowed on Mars in the past [**Section 9.4**], making it seem possible that life could once have found a home there. Moreover, since Mars contains abundant ice today, it's conceivable that life could still survive near sources of volcanic heat, where pockets of liquid water might persist underground.

Missions to Mars Mars is not only the best candidate in our solar system for life beyond Earth but also the only place where we've begun an actual search for life. Our first attempt came with the two *Viking* landers that reached Mars in 1976. Each was equipped with a robotic arm for scooping up soil samples, which were fed into several on-board robotically controlled experiments. Although some of the experiments produced results that seemed suggestive of life, taken as a set the results seem more likely to have been due to nonbiological chemical reactions. Most scientists have therefore concluded that the *Viking* landers did not detect life, though a few scientists take issue with this conclusion.

More recent missions have taught us much more about the possibility of life on Mars, with three rovers providing some of the most important information. The *Spirit* and *Opportunity* rovers landed on Mars in 2004, with *Spirit* operating for about six years and *Opportunity* still collecting data as this book went to press in 2012. Both missions provided an abundance of data about Martian surface conditions and found clear evidence that water was once plentiful in their locations on Mars [**Section 9.4**], giving a boost to the hypothesis that Mars

FIGURE 24.13 This is an artist's conception of *Curiosity*'s ChemCam instrument firing its laser at a rock on Mars, so that it can spectroscopically analyze the composition of the vaporized rock.

was once habitable. Scientists expect to learn far more from the *Curiosity* rover, which landed on Mars in August 2012. *Curiosity* carries sophisticated instruments designed to learn about the habitability of Mars. Its "ChemCam" instrument fires a laser at rocks, vaporizing some of the rocky material so that it can then analyze it spectroscopically (**FIGURE 24.13**). Other instruments can study soil samples scooped up by the rover.

THINK ABOUT IT

Find recent results from the *Curiosity* rover. Has it found anything of significance to the search for life on Mars? Explain.

Methane on Mars Atmospheric studies can also provide clues about potential life, and scientists are intrigued by the claimed detection of methane (CH_4) in the Martian atmosphere. Atmospheric methane is quickly destroyed by ultraviolet light from the Sun, so its presence would mean that it is being continually released from the Martian surface. Moreover, while some scientists think the detection is a measurement error, the amount of methane in the atmosphere appears to vary regionally across Mars, and also seems to vary with the Martian seasons.

If there really is methane in Mars's atmosphere, could it be produced by life, as is the case for most of the methane in Earth's atmosphere? It's possible, but methane can also be produced by nonbiological processes. For example, volcanoes release methane, so low levels of volcanic activity could be responsible for the methane on Mars, and the seasonal variations may be due to escape routes for gas from underground being plugged in the winter and clear in the summer. However, even if the source is volcanic rather than biological, the methane would be significant to the possibility of life. The amount of volcanic heat necessary for methane release would probably also be sufficient to maintain pockets of liquid water underground, which could potentially provide a habitat for life.

Scientists are hoping that the *Curiosity* rover will help to either confirm or disprove the detection of methane. If *Curiosity* does confirm the presence of methane in the Martian atmosphere, it may also be able to investigate the ground source of the methane and help us discover whether the source is volcanic or biological.

The Debate over Martian Meteorites An entirely different approach to the search for life on Mars relies on studies of meteorites whose chemical composition suggests they came from Mars [**Section 12.1**]. One particular meteorite, designated ALH84001, has been the subject of controversial claims that it contains evidence of past life on Mars.

ALH84001 was found on the Antarctic ice in 1984. Careful study of the meteorite shows that it landed in Antarctica about 13,000 years ago, following a 16-million-year journey through space after being blasted from Mars by an impact. The rock itself dates to about 4.1 billion years ago, which means that it resided on Mars during times when the climate may have been warmer and wetter. Analysis of the meteorite reveals several lines of evidence that could indicate the past presence of life on Mars. For example, the rock contains layered carbonate minerals and complex organic molecules (polycyclic aromatic hydrocarbons, or PAHs) that are associated with life when found in Earth rock, as well as microscopic chains of magnetite crystals quite similar to chains made in Earth rocks by living bacteria. However, each of the tantalizing hints of Martian life can also be explained in a nonbiological way. Perhaps more important, terrestrial bacteria have been found living inside the meteorite, indicating that it was contaminated by Earth life during the 13,000 years it resided in Antarctica.

Overall, most scientists now doubt that the Martian meteorite shows true evidence of Martian life. Nevertheless, studies of ALH84001 and other Martian meteorites are continuing, and they may yet turn up surprises. Scientists are particularly excited about study of a meteorite that landed in Morocco in 2011 and appears to be one of the rare meteorites from Mars. Because this meteorite was collected soon after its arrival, it is unlikely to have suffered the same type of contamination as meteorites that have resided longer on Earth's surface.

Could there be life on Europa or other jovian moons?

After Mars, the next most likely candidates for life in our solar system are some of the moons of the jovian planets—especially Jupiter's moons Europa, Ganymede, and Callisto, and Saturn's moons Titan and Enceladus [**Section 11.2**]. Europa is the strongest candidate, because we have good reason to think it contains a deep ocean beneath its icy crust (see Figure 11.21). The ice and rock from which Europa formed undoubtedly included the necessary chemical ingredients for life, and Europa's internal heating (primarily due to tidal heating) is strong enough to power volcanic vents on its seafloor. If life on Earth arose near such undersea volcanic vents, Europa would seem to have everything needed for life to originate.

The possibility of life on Europa is especially interesting because, unlike any potential life on Mars, it would not necessarily have to be microscopic. After all, the several kilometers of surface ice that hide Europa's suspected ocean could also hide large creatures swimming within it. However, the potential energy sources for life on Europa are far more limited than the energy sources for life on Earth, mainly because sunlight could not fuel photosynthesis in the subsurface ocean. As a result, most scientists suspect that any life that might exist on Europa would probably be quite small and primitive.

As we discussed in Chapter 11, some evidence suggests that Jupiter's moons Ganymede and Callisto may also have subsurface oceans. However, these moons would have even less energy for life than Europa. If they have life at all, it is almost certainly small and primitive. Nevertheless, Europa, Ganymede, and Callisto offer the astonishing possibility that Jupiter alone could be orbited by more worlds with life than we find in all the rest of the solar system.

Titan offers another enticing place to look for life. Its surface is far too cold for liquid water, but it has lakes and rivers of liquid methane and ethane [**Section 11.2**]. Although many biologists think it unlikely, it is possible that this liquid could support life as water does on Earth. Titan might also have liquid water or a colder ammonia–water mixture deep underground, so even water-based life is possible.

The discovery of ice fountains on Saturn's moon Enceladus suggests that it, too, could be habitable if these fountains are powered by subsurface liquids. If this proves to be the case, it would open up the possibility that similar liquids—and potentially life—could exist on other solar system bodies, including Neptune's moon Triton and some of the moons of Uranus.

(MA) Detecting Extrasolar Planets Tutorial, Lessons 1–3

24.3 LIFE AROUND OTHER STARS

Studies of extrasolar planets suggest that our galaxy contains billions of planetary systems [**Section 13.2**], which might make prospects for life elsewhere seem quite good. But numbers alone don't tell the whole story. In this section, we'll consider the prospects for life on worlds orbiting other stars.

Before we begin, we must distinguish between *surface* life like that on Earth and *subsurface* life like that we envision as a possibility on Mars or Europa. While large telescopes could in principle allow us to discover surface life on extrasolar planets, no foreseeable technology will allow us to find life that is hidden deep underground in other star systems (unless the subsurface life has a noticeable effect on the planet's atmosphere). We therefore will focus on the search for life on planets with habitable surfaces—surfaces with temperatures and pressures that could allow liquid water to exist.

What kinds of stars might have habitable planets?

The billions of planetary systems likely to exist in our galaxy offer both an opportunity and a challenge. The opportunity is that we have a lot of places to look for planets that are habitable or that have life; the challenge is in narrowing down the search

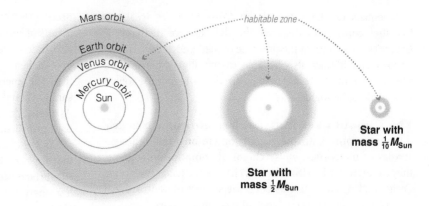

FIGURE 24.14 interactive figure The approximate habitable zones around our Sun, a star with one-half the mass of the Sun (spectral type K), and a star with one-tenth the mass of the Sun (spectral type M), shown to scale. The habitable zone becomes increasingly smaller and close-in for stars of lower mass and luminosity.

to the most promising candidates. Although we'll see that it is difficult to narrow the search down by much, the obvious place to start is in deciding which types of star systems are most likely to have habitable planets. In other words, which stars would make good "suns," providing heat and light to the surfaces of terrestrial planets that happen to orbit them?

Star System Constraints The first key constraint in searching for potential suns concerns stellar lifetimes. Although life on Earth started quite early relative to Earth's history, the actual time was still probably a few hundred million years. If the same idea holds true elsewhere, then we would expect life to be possible only on planets that orbit stars with lifetimes of hundreds of millions of years or more. This would rule out stars with more than a few times the mass of our Sun, because these stars have short lifetimes [**Section 17.3**]. However, because low-mass stars are far more common than high-mass stars, the lifetime constraint rules out only about 1% of all stars.

A second constraint is that the star system must allow planets to have orbits that remain stable for hundreds of millions to billions of years. About half of all stars are in binary or multiple star systems, around which long-term stable planetary orbits are less likely than around single stars. If life were not possible in such systems, then we would rule out about half the stars in our galaxy as potential homes to life. Of course, the other half—which still means 100 billion or more stars—would remain possible homes for life. Moreover, under some circumstances, stable planetary orbits are possible in multiple star systems, and planets in such systems have already been found.

All in all, it seems that the vast majority of stars are at least potentially capable of having life-bearing planets. Even very conservative assumptions suggest enormous numbers of possibilities. For example, limiting the search for habitable planets to stars similar to our Sun (that is, spectral type G) would still mean billions of potential suns in the Milky Way Galaxy.

The Habitable Zone Once we've narrowed the search to star systems with sufficiently long lifetimes and the possibility of stable planetary orbits, the next issue is the size of a star's **habitable zone**—the region in which a terrestrial planet of the right size could have a surface temperature that might allow for liquid water and life. In our own solar system, for example, the habitable zone must be some donut-shaped region around Earth's orbit, because Earth has oceans and life.

Our Sun's habitable zone extends inward to the point where it would become too hot for liquid water to exist. This point must be somewhere between the orbits of Venus and Earth, because moving Earth to the orbit of Venus would cause a runaway greenhouse effect that would boil the oceans away [**Section 10.5**]. On the other end, the habitable zone extends outward to the point at which it would be too cold for liquid water to exist on a planet's surface. This outer bound to the habitable zone is probably somewhere near the orbit of Mars; it may even be beyond Mars, because if Mars had been larger (such as the size of Earth), it might have been able to retain liquid water to this day [**Section 10.4**].

Based on current models, FIGURE 24.14 shows the approximate sizes, to scale, of the habitable zones around our Sun, around a star with about one-half the mass of our Sun (spectral type K), and around a star with about one-tenth the mass of our Sun (spectral type M). Notice that less massive and hence less luminous main-sequence stars have smaller habitable zones. This might make it seem that habitable planets are less likely around lower mass stars, though some models suggest that terrestrial planets might also form more easily around such stars, offsetting the effects of the smaller zones. Moreover, even if an individual low-mass star is less likely to have habitable planets, the fact that low-mass stars are the most common type of star may still make them "suns" to vast numbers of habitable planets.

The *Kepler* mission has already identified dozens of candidate planets that appear to orbit within their stars' habitable zones and to be similar enough in size to Earth that they are likely to be terrestrial planets. The first of these candidates to be confirmed through other methods, Kepler-22b, has a radius a little more than twice that of Earth (making it a "super-Earth") and orbits in the middle of the habitable zone around a star only slightly cooler and less massive than our Sun. As discussed in Chapter 13, it is seeming increasingly likely that terrestrial planets in habitable zones are very common in our galaxy, and may number in the tens of billions.

Confirming Habitability or Life While we are rapidly learning about the number of planets in habitable zones and the sizes of these planets, we can so far at best say that a planet is *potentially* habitable. In order to confirm that it is habitable, we would need to confirm that it actually has surface conditions that allow for liquid water. This will probably require direct images or spectra with at least moderate resolution, so that we might, for example, detect water on the surface. Longer term, images from future telescopes may tell us whether extrasolar planets have continents and oceans like Earth and perhaps even allow us to monitor seasonal changes.

Spectra should prove even more important to the search for life. Moderate-resolution infrared spectra can reveal the presence and abundance of many atmospheric gases, including carbon dioxide, ozone, methane, and water vapor (FIGURE 24.15). Careful analysis of atmospheric makeup might tell us whether a planet has life. On Earth, for example, the large abundance of oxygen (21% of our atmosphere) is a direct result of photosynthetic life. Abundant oxygen in the atmosphere of a distant world might similarly indicate the presence of life, since we know of no nonbiological way to produce an oxygen abundance as high as Earth's. Other evidence might come from the ratio of oxygen to the other detected gases. Scientists are working to improve our understanding of how life influences atmospheric chemistry, in the hope that we will be able to recognize particular gas combinations as signatures of life.

Are Earth-like planets rare or common?

We will not know for certain whether habitable planets exist or how common such planets may be until we are able to study the candidates with much more powerful telescopes. Nevertheless, the fact that we are already finding Earth-size

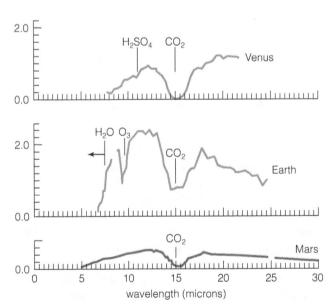

FIGURE 24.15 The infrared spectra of Venus, Earth, and Mars as they might be seen from afar, showing absorption features that point to the presence of carbon dioxide (CO_2), ozone (O_3), and sulfuric acid (H_2SO_4) in their atmospheres. While carbon dioxide is present in all three spectra, only our own planet has appreciable oxygen (and hence ozone)—a product of photosynthesis. If we could make similar spectral analyses of distant planets, we might detect atmospheric gases that would indicate life.

planets within the habitable zones of other stars suggests that *potentially* habitable planets will prove to be very common. But should we expect these planets to have Earth-like conditions in which life is likely to arise and evolve?

Most scientists think so, but a few have raised some interesting questions. In essence, these scientists suggest that Earth's hospitable environment is the result of several rare kinds of planetary luck. According to this idea, sometimes called the "rare Earth hypothesis," the specific circumstances that have allowed life on Earth to survive and evolve into complex forms (such as trees and people) might be so rare that ours could be the only planet in the galaxy that harbors anything but the simplest life. Let's briefly examine some of the key issues in the rare Earth hypothesis.

Galactic Constraints Proponents of the rare Earth hypothesis suggest that Earth-like planets can form in only a relatively small region of the Milky Way Galaxy, making the number of potential homes for life far smaller than we might otherwise expect it to be. In essence, they argue that there is a fairly narrow ring at about our solar system's distance from the center of the Milky Way Galaxy that makes up a *galactic habitable zone* analogous to the habitable zone around an individual star (FIGURE 24.16).

According to the arguments for a galactic habitable zone, outer regions of our galaxy are unlikely to have terrestrial planets because of a low abundance of elements other than hydrogen and helium. Recall that the fraction of heavy elements varies among stars, from less than 0.1% among the old stars in globular clusters to more than 2% among young stars in the galactic disk [**Section 19.3**]. Even within the galactic disk, the abundance tends to decline with distance from the center of the galaxy. Because terrestrial planets are made almost entirely of heavy elements, a lower abundance of these elements might lessen the chance that terrestrial planets

FIGURE 24.16 The highlighted green ring in this painting of the Milky Way Galaxy represents what some scientists suspect to be a galactic habitable zone—the only region of the galaxy in which Earth-like planets are likely to be found. However, other scientists think that Earth-like planets could be far more widespread.

could form. The argument against finding habitable planets in the inner regions of the galaxy concerns supernova rates. Supernovae are more common in the more crowded, inner regions of the galactic disk, making it more likely that a terrestrial planet would be exposed to the intense radiation from a nearby supernova. By assuming that this radiation would be detrimental to life, the proponents of a galactic habitable zone argue against finding habitable planets in the inner regions of the galaxy. Together, the constraints on finding Earth-like planets in the inner and outer regions of the galaxy leave the galactic habitable zone as a relatively narrow ring encompassing no more than about 10% of the stars in the galactic disk.

However, other scientists offer counterarguments to both sets of galactic constraints. Although discoveries of extrasolar planets to date suggest that *large* planets are indeed rarer around stars with very low fractions of heavy elements, we cannot yet say whether terrestrial planets are rare in such systems. Remember that Earth's mass is less than $\frac{1}{100,000}$ of the mass of the Sun, so even a very small heavy-element abundance could be enough to make one or more Earth-like planets. Regarding the radiation danger from supernovae, we do not really know whether such radiation would be detrimental to life. A planet's atmosphere might protect life against the effects of this radiation. It is even possible that the radiation could be beneficial to life by increasing the rate of mutations and thereby accelerating the pace of evolution. If these counterarguments are correct, then habitable planets might be found throughout much or all of the galaxy.

Impact Rates and Jupiter Another issue raised by rare Earth proponents is the impact rate on planets in other star systems. Earth was subjected to numerous large impacts during the heavy bombardment that went on during the first half-billion years or so after our planet's birth, and the evolution of complex life probably could not have occurred if these impacts had continued at such a high rate. In our solar system, the impact rate had lessened dramatically by about 3.9 billion years ago. But could the impact rate remain high much longer in other planetary systems?

The most numerous small objects in our solar system are the trillion or so comets of the distant Oort cloud [**Section 12.2**]. Fortunately for us, nearly all these myriad objects are essentially out of reach, posing no threat to our planet. However, the reason they are out of reach can be traced directly to Jupiter: Recall that the Oort cloud's comets are thought to have formed among the jovian planets, later being "kicked out" to their current orbits by close encounters with these planets, especially Jupiter (see Figure 12.29). If Jupiter did not exist, many of these comets might have remained in regions of the solar system where they could pose an ongoing danger to Earth. In that case, the heavy bombardment might never have ended, and huge impacts would continue to this day. From this viewpoint, our existence on Earth has been possible only because of the "luck" of having Jupiter as a planetary neighbor.

The primary question in this case is just how "lucky" this situation might be. Our discoveries of extrasolar planets suggest that Jupiter-size planets are quite common, although we've also found evidence that many of these planets migrate inward [**Section 13.3**], perhaps disrupting terrestrial planet orbits along the way. Whether most star systems have a Jupiter-like planet in the right place for ejecting comets remains an open question.

Climate Stability Another issue affecting the rarity of Earth-like planets is climate stability. Earth's climate has been stable enough for liquid water to exist throughout the past 4 billion years. This climate stability has almost certainly played a major role in allowing complex life to evolve. If our planet had frozen over like Mars or overheated like Venus, we would not be here today. Advocates of the rare Earth hypothesis point to at least two pieces of "luck" related to Earth's stable climate.

The first piece of "luck" is the existence of plate tectonics. Recall that plate tectonics plays a major role in regulating Earth's climate through the carbon dioxide cycle [**Section 10.6**]. Plate tectonics probably was not necessary to the origin of life, but it seems to have been important in keeping the climate stable enough for the subsequent evolution of plants and animals. But are we really "lucky" to have plate tectonics, or should this geological process be common on similar-size planets elsewhere? We do not yet know. The lack of plate tectonics on Venus [**Section 9.5**], which is quite similar in size to Earth, might seem to argue for plate tectonics being rare. On the other hand, if Venus's lack of plate tectonics is due to its runaway greenhouse effect, as many scientists suspect [**Section 10.5**], then Venus might have had plate tectonics if it had been born a little farther from the Sun. In that case, it's possible that any Earth-size planet within a star's habitable zone would have plate tectonics.

The second piece of "luck" in climate stability is the existence of Earth's relatively large Moon. Models of Earth's rotation and orbit show that if the Moon did not exist, gravitational tugs from other planets would cause large swings in Earth's axis tilt over periods of tens to hundreds of thousands of years. (Such swings in axis tilt are thought to occur on Mars.) Changes in axis tilt would affect the severity of the seasons, which in turn could cause deeper ice ages and more intense periods of warmth. Given that the Moon probably formed as a result of a random giant impact [**Section 8.2**], we might seem to be very lucky to have the Moon and the climate stability it brings.

Again, however, there are other ways to look at the issue. First, the expected changes in axis tilt also depend on rotation rate; if Earth rotated in less than about 12 hours, the axis would be fairly stable even without the Moon. Second, the Moon's presumed formation in a random giant impact does not necessarily mean that large moons are rare, because solar system formation models indicate that at least a few giant impacts should be expected in any planetary system. Finally, even if the axis tilt changes dramatically, this may not have a major impact on potential life. Changes in axis tilt might warm or cool different parts of the planet dramatically, but the changes would probably occur slowly enough for life to adapt or migrate as the climate changed.

The Bottom Line The bottom line is that while the rare Earth hypothesis offers some intriguing arguments, it is too early to say whether any of them will hold up over time. For each potential argument that Earth has been lucky, we've seen counterarguments suggesting otherwise. There's no doubt that our solar system and our world have "personality"—they exhibit properties that might be found only occasionally in other star systems—but we have no clear reason to think that these special properties are essential to the existence of complex or even intelligent life. Indeed, it may be that we have missed out on some helpful phenomena that could have sped evolution on Earth. Until we learn more about other planets in the universe, we cannot know whether Earth-like planets and complex life are common or rare.

24.4 THE SEARCH FOR EXTRATERRESTRIAL INTELLIGENCE

So far, we have focused on search strategies for microbial or other nonintelligent life. However, if intelligent beings and civilizations exist elsewhere, we might be able to find them with a completely different type of strategy. Instead of searching for hard-to-find spectroscopic signs of life, we might simply listen for signals that intelligent beings are sending into interstellar space, either in deliberate attempts to contact other civilizations or as a means of communicating among themselves. The search for signals from other civilizations is generally known as the **search for extraterrestrial intelligence**, or **SETI** for short.

How many civilizations are out there?

SETI efforts have a chance to succeed only if other advanced civilizations are broadcasting signals that we could receive. To judge the chances of SETI success, we'd need to know how many civilizations are broadcasting such signals right now.

Given that we do not even know whether microbial life exists anywhere beyond Earth, we certainly don't know whether other civilizations exist, let alone how many there might be. Nevertheless, for the purposes of planning a search for extraterrestrial intelligence, it is useful to have an organized way of thinking about the number of civilizations that might be out there. To keep our discussion simple, let's consider only the number of potential civilizations in our own galaxy. We can always extend our estimate to the rest of the universe by simply multiplying the result we find for our galaxy by 100 billion, the approximate number of galaxies in the observable universe.

The Drake Equation The first scientific conference on the search for extraterrestrial intelligence was held in 1961 in Green Bank, West Virginia, where a pioneering search for an alien signal had already been conducted. During the meeting, astronomer Frank Drake wrote a simple equation designed to summarize the factors that would determine the number of civilizations we might contact (FIGURE 24.17).

This equation is now known as the **Drake equation**, and in principle it gives us a simple way to calculate the number of civilizations capable of interstellar communication that are currently sharing the Milky Way Galaxy with us. In a form

FIGURE 24.17 Astronomer Frank Drake, with the equation he first wrote in 1961. (With Dr. Drake's approval, we use a slightly modified form of his equation in this book.)

slightly modified from the original, the Drake equation looks like this:

$$\text{Number of civilizations} = N_{\text{HP}} \times f_{\text{life}} \times f_{\text{civ}} \times f_{\text{now}}$$

This equation will make sense once you understand the meaning of each factor:

- N_{HP} is the number of habitable planets in the galaxy—that is, the number of planets that could potentially have life.

- f_{life} is the fraction of habitable planets that actually *have* life. For example, $f_{\text{life}} = 1$ would mean that all habitable planets have life, and $f_{\text{life}} = \frac{1}{1,000,000}$ would mean that only 1 in a million habitable planets has life. Therefore, the product $N_{\text{HP}} \times f_{\text{life}}$ tells us the number of life-bearing planets in the galaxy.

- f_{civ} is the fraction of life-bearing planets on which a civilization capable of interstellar communication *has at some time* arisen. For example, $f_{\text{civ}} = \frac{1}{1000}$ would mean that such a civilization has existed on 1 out of 1000 planets with life, while the other 999 out of 1000 have not had a species that learned to build radio transmitters, high-powered lasers, or other devices for interstellar conversation. When we multiply this factor by the first two factors to form the product $N_{\text{HP}} \times f_{\text{life}} \times f_{\text{civ}}$, we get the total number of planets on which intelligent beings have evolved and developed a communicating civilization at some time in the galaxy's history.

- f_{now} is the fraction of these civilization-bearing planets that happen to have a civilization *now*, as opposed to, say, millions or billions of years in the past. This factor is important because we can hope to contact only civilizations that are broadcasting signals we could receive at present. (In estimating f_{now}, we assume that the light-travel time for signals from other stars has been taken into account.)

Because the product of the first three factors tells us the total number of civilizations that have *ever* arisen in the galaxy, multiplying by f_{now} tells us how many civilizations we could potentially make contact with today. In other words, the result of the Drake equation should in principle tell us the number of civilizations that we might hope to contact. Unfortunately, we don't yet know the value of any of the factors in the Drake equation, so we cannot actually calculate its result. Nevertheless, the equation is a useful way of organizing our thinking, as we can see by considering the potential values for each of its factors.

The Number of Life-Bearing Planets Let's begin with the first two factors in the Drake equation, whose product ($N_{HP} \times f_{life}$) tells us the number of life-bearing planets in our galaxy. We can make a reasonably educated guess only about the first factor, the number of habitable planets (N_{HP}). Current understanding of solar system formation (see Figure 8.13) suggests that terrestrial planets ought to form easily and, as discussed earlier, there ought to be billions of stars in our galaxy with habitable zones large enough to have Earth-like planets. Unless some of the "rare Earth" ideas prove to be correct, it seems reasonable to suppose our galaxy has billions of habitable planets.

The factor f_{life} presents more difficulty. At present, we have no reliable way to estimate the fraction of habitable planets on which life actually arose. The problem is that we cannot generalize when we have only one example to study—our own Earth. Still, the fact that life arose rapidly on Earth suggests that the origin of life was fairly "easy." In that case, we might expect most or all habitable planets to also have life, making the fraction f_{life} close to 1. Of course, until we have solid evidence that life arose anywhere else, such as on Mars, it is also possible that Earth has been very lucky and that f_{life} is so close to zero that life has never arisen on any other planet in our galaxy.

SPECIAL TOPIC

Are Aliens Already Here?

In this chapter, we discuss aliens as a possibility, not a reality. However, opinion polls suggest that up to half the American public believes that aliens are already visiting us. What can science say about this remarkable notion?

The bulk of the claimed evidence for alien visitation consists of sightings of UFOs—unidentified flying objects. Many thousands of UFOs are reported each year, and no one doubts that unidentified objects are being seen. The question is whether they are alien spacecraft.

Aliens have long been a staple of science fiction, but modern interest in UFOs began with a widely reported sighting in 1947. While flying a private plane near Mount Rainier in Washington State, businessman Kenneth Arnold saw nine mysterious objects streaking across the sky. He told a reporter that the objects "flew erratic, like a saucer if you skip it across the water." (One possible explanation is that he saw meteors skipping across the atmosphere.) He did *not* say that the objects were saucer-shaped, but the reporter wrote of "flying saucers." The story was front-page news throughout America, and "flying saucers" soon invaded popular culture, if not our planet.

The flying saucer reports also interested the U.S. Air Force, largely out of concern that the UFOs might represent new types of aircraft developed by the Soviet Union. For two decades, the Air Force hired teams of academics to study UFO reports. In most cases, these experts were able to specify a plausible identification of the UFO. The explanations included bright stars and planets, aircraft rockets, balloons, birds, meteors, atmospheric phenomena, and the occasional hoax. In a few cases, the investigators could not deduce what was seen, but their overall conclusion was that there was no reason to believe the UFOs were either highly advanced Soviet craft or visitors from other worlds.

Believers discounted the Air Force denials, claiming to have other evidence of alien visitation. So far, none of this evidence has withstood scientific scrutiny. Photographs and film clips are nearly always either fuzzy or obviously faked. Crop circles are easily made by pranksters, and claimed pieces of alien spacecraft turn out to have more mundane origins. Champions of alien visitation generally explain away the lack of clear evidence either as a government cover-up or as a failure of the scientific community to take the subject seriously, but neither explanation is compelling.

It's conceivable that a government might *try* to put the lid on evidence of alien visits, though the motivation for doing so is unclear. The usual explanations are that the public couldn't handle the news or that the government is taking secret advantage of the alien materials to design new military hardware (via "reverse engineering"). However, given that half the population already believes in alien visitors, the shock of discovery would seem unlikely to cause panic. As for reverse-engineering extraterrestrial spacecraft, any society that could routinely cross interstellar distances would be far beyond us technologically. Reverse engineering their spaceships is as unlikely as Neandertals constructing personal computers just because a laptop somehow landed in their cave. In addition, while a government might successfully hide evidence for a short time, over decades the lure of talk show fame and riches would surely cause someone to reveal the conspiracy. Moreover, unless the aliens landed only in the United States, the conspiracy would have to include all governments on Earth, which seems highly unlikely given the world's political conditions.

Claims of disinterest on the part of the scientific community also fall apart on scrutiny. Scientists are constantly competing with one another to be the first to make a great discovery, and clear evidence of alien visitors would rank high on the all-time list. The fact that few scientists are engaged in such study reflects not a lack of interest, but a lack of evidence worthy of study.

Of course, absence of evidence is not evidence of absence. Most scientists are open to the possibility that we might someday find evidence of alien visits, and given what we've learned about the prospects of life in the universe, it is at least plausible to imagine that such visits occur. So far, however, we have no hard evidence to support the belief that aliens are already here.

The Question of Intelligence Even if life-bearing planets are very common, civilizations capable of interstellar communication might not be. The fraction of life-bearing planets that at some time have such civilizations, f_{civ}, depends on at least two things. First, a planet would have to have a species evolve with sufficient intelligence to develop interstellar communication. In other words, the planet needs a species at least as smart as we are. Second, that species would have to develop a civilization with technology at least as advanced as ours.

Although we cannot really be sure, most scientists suspect that only the first requirement is difficult to meet. A fundamental assumption in nearly all science today is that we are not "special" in any particular way. We live on a fairly typical planet orbiting an ordinary star in a normal galaxy, and we assume that living creatures elsewhere—whether they prove to be rare or common—would be subjected to evolutionary pressures similar to those that have operated on Earth. Therefore, if species with intelligence similar to ours have arisen elsewhere, we assume that they would have similar sociological drives that would eventually lead them to develop the technology necessary for interstellar communication.

If this assumption is correct, then the fraction f_{civ} depends primarily on the question of whether sufficient intelligence is rare or common among life-bearing planets. As with the question of life of any kind, the short answer is that we just don't know, but we can get at least some insight by considering what happened on Earth.

Look again at Figure 24.4. While life arose quite quickly on Earth, nearly all life remained microbial until just a few hundred million years ago, and it took nearly 4 billion years for us to arrive on the scene. This slow progress toward intelligence might suggest that producing a civilization is very difficult even when life is present. On the other hand, roughly half the stars in the Milky Way are older than our Sun, so if Earth's case is typical, then plenty of planets have existed long enough for intelligence to arise.

Another way to address the question is by considering our level of intelligence in comparison to that of other animals on Earth. We can get a rough measure of intelligence by comparing brain mass to total body mass (a measure sometimes called the *encephalization quotient,* or EQ). FIGURE 24.18 shows the brain weights for a sampling of birds and mammals plotted against their body weight. There is a clear and expected trend in that heavier animals have heavier brains. By drawing a straight line that fits these data, we can define an average value of brain mass for each body mass. Animals whose brain mass falls above the line are smarter than average, while animals whose brain mass falls below the line are less mentally agile. Keep in mind that it is the *vertical* distance above the line that tells us how much smarter a species is than the average, and that the scale goes in powers of 10 on both axes. If you look closely, you'll see that the data point for humans lies significantly farther above the line than the data point for any other species. By this measure of intelligence, we are far smarter than any other species that has ever existed on Earth.

Some people use this fact to argue that even on a planet with complex life, a species as intelligent as we are would be

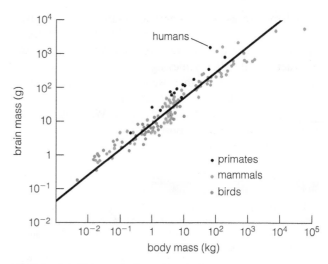

FIGURE 24.18 This graph shows how brain mass compares to body mass for some mammals (including primates) and birds. The straight line represents an average of the ratio of brain mass to body mass, so animals that fall above the line are smarter than average and animals that fall below the line are less smart. Note that the scale uses powers of 10 on both axes. (Data from Harry J. Jerison.)

very rare. They say that even if there is an evolutionary drive toward intelligence in general, it takes extreme luck to reach our level of intelligence. After all, while it's evolutionarily useful to have enough intelligence to capture prey and evade other predators, it's not clear why natural selection would lead to brains big enough to build spacecraft. However, the same data can be used to reach an opposite conclusion. The scatter in the levels of intelligence among different animals tells us that some variation should be expected, and statistical analysis shows that we are not unreasonably far above the average. It might therefore be inevitable that some species would develop our level of intelligence on any planet with complex life.

Technological Lifetimes For the sake of argument, let's assume that life and intelligence are reasonably likely, so thousands or millions of planets in our galaxy have at some time given birth to a civilization. In that case, the final factor in the Drake equation, f_{now}, determines the likelihood of there being someone whom we could contact now. The value of this factor depends on how long civilizations survive.

Consider our own example. In the roughly 12 billion years during which our galaxy has existed, we have been capable of interstellar communication via radio for only about 60 years. Therefore, if we were to destroy ourselves tomorrow, then other civilizations could have received signals from us during only 60 years out of the galaxy's 12-billion-year existence, equivalent to 1 part in 200 million of the galaxy's history. If such a short technological lifetime is typical of civilizations, then f_{now} would be only $\frac{1}{200,000,000}$, and some 200 million civilization-bearing planets would need to have existed at one time or another in the Milky Way in order for us to have a good chance of finding another civilization out there now.

However, we'd expect f_{now} to be so small only if we are on the brink of self-destruction—after all, the fraction will grow larger for as long as our civilization survives. Thus, if civilizations are at all common, survivability is the key factor in whether any are out there now. If most civilizations self-destruct shortly after achieving the technology for interstellar communication, then we are almost certainly alone in the galaxy at present. But if most survive and thrive for thousands or millions of years, the Milky Way may be brimming with civilizations—most of them far more advanced than our own.

THINK ABOUT IT

Describe a few reasons why a civilization capable of interstellar communication would also be capable of self-destruction. Overall, do you believe our civilization can survive for thousands or millions of years? Defend your opinion.

How does SETI work?

If there are indeed other civilizations out there, then in principle we ought to be able to make contact with them. Based on our current understanding of physics, it seems likely that even very advanced civilizations would communicate much as we do—by encoding signals in radio waves or other forms of light. Most SETI researchers use large radio telescopes to search for alien radio signals (FIGURE 24.19). A few researchers are studying other parts of the electromagnetic spectrum. For example, some scientists use visible-light telescopes to search for communications encoded as laser pulses. Of course, advanced civilizations may well have invented communication technologies that we cannot even imagine, let alone detect.

A good way to think about our chances of picking up an alien signal is to imagine what aliens would need to do to pick up signals from us. We have been sending relatively

FIGURE 24.20 In 1974, a short message was broadcast to the globular cluster M13 using the Arecibo radio telescope. The picture shown here was encoded by using two different radio frequencies, one for "on" and one for "off" (the colors used here are arbitrary). To decode the message, the aliens would need to realize that the bits are meant to be arranged in a rectangular grid as shown, but that should not be difficult: The grid has 73 rows and 23 columns, and aliens would presumably know that these are both prime numbers. The picture represents the Arecibo radio dish, our solar system, a human stick figure, and a schematic of DNA and the eight simple molecules used in its construction.

high-power transmissions into space since about the 1950s in the form of television broadcasts. In principle, anyone within about 60 light-years of Earth could watch our old television shows (perhaps a frightening thought). However, in order to detect our broadcasts, they would need far larger and more sensitive radio telescopes than we have today. If their technology were at the same level as ours, they could receive a signal from us only if we deliberately broadcast an unusually high-powered transmission.

To date, humans have made only a few attempts to broadcast our existence in this way. The most famous was a 3-minute transmission made in 1974 with a planetary radar transmitter on the Arecibo radio telescope, in which a simple pictorial message was beamed toward the globular cluster M13 (FIGURE 24.20). This target was chosen in part because it contains a few hundred thousand stars, seemingly offering a good chance that at least one has a civilization around it. However, M13 is about 25,000 light-years from Earth, so it will take some 25,000 years for our signal to get there and another 25,000 years for any response to make its way back to Earth.

Several SETI projects under way or in development would be capable of detecting signals like the one we broadcast from Arecibo if they came from civilizations within a few hundred light-years. These SETI efforts scan millions of radio frequency bands simultaneously. If anyone nearby is deliberately broadcasting on an ongoing basis, we have a good chance of detecting the signals.

FIGURE 24.19 The Allen Telescope Array in Hat Creek, California, is being used to search for radio signals from extraterrestrial civilizations.

THINK ABOUT IT

SETI efforts are often controversial because of their cost and uncertain chance of success, but supporters say the cost is justified because contact with an extraterrestrial intelligence would be such an important discovery. What do *you* think?

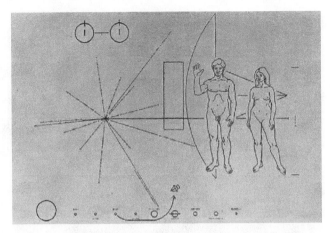

a The *Pioneer* plaque, about the size of an automobile license plate. The human figures are shown in front of a drawing of the spacecraft to give them a sense of scale. The "prickly" graph to their left shows the Sun's position relative to nearby pulsars, and Earth's location around the Sun is shown below. Binary code indicates the pulsar periods; because pulsars slow with time, the periods will allow someone reading the plaque to determine when the spacecraft was launched.

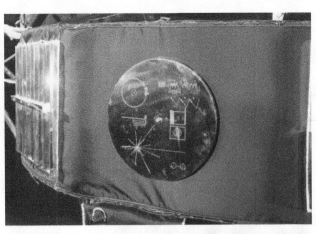

b *Voyagers 1* and *2* carry a phonograph record—a 12-inch gold-plated copper disk containing music, greetings, and images from Earth.

FIGURE 24.21 Messages aboard the *Pioneer* and *Voyager* spacecraft, which are bound for the stars.

24.5 INTERSTELLAR TRAVEL AND ITS IMPLICATIONS FOR CIVILIZATION

So far, we have discussed ways of detecting distant civilizations without ever leaving the comfort of our own planet. Could we ever actually visit other worlds in other star systems? A careful analysis of this question turns out to have profound implications for the future of our civilization. To see why, we first need to consider the prospects for achieving interstellar travel.

How difficult is interstellar travel?

In many science fiction movies, our descendants travel among the stars as routinely as we jet about our planet today in airplanes. They race around the galaxy in starships of all sizes and shapes, circumventing nature's prohibition on faster-than-light travel by entering hyperspace, wormholes, or warp drive. They witness firsthand incredible cosmic phenomena such as stars and planets in all stages of development, accretion disks around white dwarfs and neutron stars, and the distortion of spacetime near black holes. Along the way they encounter numerous alien species, most of which happen to look and act a lot like us.

Unfortunately, Einstein's theory of relativity tells us that real interstellar travel must be at speeds slower than the speed of light [**Section S2.2**], and even to approach that speed we will need to overcome huge technological hurdles. Nevertheless, we have already sent out our first emissaries to the stars, and there's no reason to believe that we won't develop better technologies in the future.

The Challenge of Interstellar Travel To date, we have launched five spacecraft that will leave our solar system and eventually travel among the stars: the planetary probes *Pioneer 10, Pioneer 11, Voyager 1, Voyager 2*, and *New Horizons*

(the spacecraft currently en route to Pluto). These spacecraft are traveling about as fast as anything ever built by humans, but their speeds are still less than $\frac{1}{10,000}$ of the speed of light. It would take each of them some 100,000 years just to reach the next nearest star system (Alpha Centauri), but their trajectories won't take them anywhere near it. Instead, they will simply continue their journey without passing close to any nearby stars, wandering the Milky Way for millions or even billions of years to come. The *Pioneer* and *Voyager* spacecraft carry greetings from Earth, just in case someone comes across one of them someday (**FIGURE 24.21**).

If we want to make interstellar journeys within human lifetimes, we will need starships that can travel at speeds close to the speed of light. We will need entirely new types of engines to reach such high speeds. The energy requirements of interstellar spacecraft may pose an even more daunting challenge. For example, the energy needed to accelerate a single ship the size of *Star Trek*'s *Enterprise* to just half the speed of light would be more than 2000 times the total annual energy use of the world today. Clearly, interstellar travel will require vast new sources of energy. In addition, fast-moving starships will require new types of shielding to protect crew members from instant death. As a starship travels through interstellar gas at near-light speed, ordinary atoms and ions will hit it like a deadly flood of high-energy cosmic rays.

If we succeed in building starships capable of traveling at speeds close to the speed of light, the crews will face significant social challenges. According to the well-tested principles of Einstein's theory of relativity, time will run much more slowly on a spaceship that travels at high speed to the stars than it does here on Earth [**Section S2.4**]. For example, in a ship traveling at an average speed of 99.9% of the speed of light, the 50-light-year round trip to the star Vega would take the travelers only about 2 years—but more than 50 years would pass on Earth while they were gone. The crew would therefore

FIGURE 24.22 Artist's conception of the *Project Orion* starship, showing one of the small hydrogen-bomb detonations that would propel it. Debris from the detonation strikes the "pusher plate" at the back of the spaceship. The central sections (enclosed in a lattice) hold the bombs, and the front sections house the crew.

FIGURE 24.23 Artist's conception of a spaceship powered by an interstellar ramjet. The giant scoop in the front (left) collects interstellar hydrogen for use as fusion fuel.

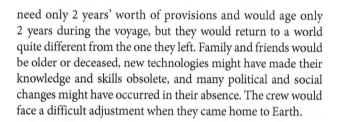

need only 2 years' worth of provisions and would age only 2 years during the voyage, but they would return to a world quite different from the one they left. Family and friends would be older or deceased, new technologies might have made their knowledge and skills obsolete, and many political and social changes might have occurred in their absence. The crew would face a difficult adjustment when they came home to Earth.

Starship Design Despite all the difficulties, some scientists and engineers have already proposed designs that could in principle take us to nearby stars. In the 1960s, a group of scientists proposed *Project Orion,* which envisioned accelerating a spaceship with repeated detonations of relatively small hydrogen bombs. Each explosion would take place a few tens of meters behind the spaceship and would propel the ship forward as the vaporized debris impacted a "pusher plate" on the back of the spacecraft (FIGURE 24.22). Calculations showed that a spaceship accelerated by the rapid-fire detonation of a million H-bombs could reach Alpha Centauri in just over a century. In principle, we could build an *Orion* spacecraft with existing technology, though it would be very expensive and would require an exception to the international treaty banning nuclear detonations in space.

A century to the nearest star isn't bad, but it still wouldn't make interstellar travel easy. Unfortunately, no available technology could go much faster. The problem is mass: Making a rocket faster requires more fuel, but adding fuel adds mass and makes it more difficult for the rocket to accelerate. Calculations show that even in the best case, rockets carrying nuclear fuel could achieve speeds no more than a few percent of the speed of light. Nevertheless, we can envision some possible future technologies that might get around this problem.

One idea suggests powering starships with engines that generate energy through matter–antimatter annihilation. While nuclear fusion converts less than 1% of the mass of

atomic nuclei into energy, matter–antimatter annihilation [**Section 22.1**] converts *all* the annihilated mass into energy. Starships with matter–antimatter engines could probably reach speeds of 90% or more of the speed of light. At these speeds, the slowing of time predicted by relativity becomes noticeable, putting many nearby stars within a few years' journey for the crew members. However, because no natural reservoirs of antimatter exist, we would have to be able to manufacture many tons of antimatter and then store it safely for the trip—capabilities that are far beyond our present means.

An even more speculative and futuristic design, known as an *interstellar ramjet,* would collect interstellar hydrogen with a gigantic scoop, using the collected gas as fuel for its nuclear engines (FIGURE 24.23). By collecting fuel along the way, the ship could avoid carrying the weight of fuel on board. However, because the density of interstellar gas is so low, the scoop would need to be enormous. As astronomer Carl Sagan said, we are talking about "spaceships the size of worlds."

The bottom line is that while we face enormous obstacles to achieving interstellar travel, there's no reason to think it's impossible. If we can avoid self-destruction and if we continue to explore space, our descendants might well journey to the stars.

Where are the aliens?

Imagine that we survive long enough to become interstellar travelers and that we begin to colonize habitable planets around nearby stars. As each colony grows, it may send out explorers to other star systems. Even if our starships traveled at relatively low speeds—say, a few percent of the speed of light—we could have dozens of outposts around nearby stars within a few centuries. In 10,000 years, our descendants would be spread among stars within a few hundred light-years of Earth. In a few million years, we could have outposts throughout the Milky Way Galaxy. We would have become a true galactic civilization.

Now, if we take the idea that *we* could develop a galactic civilization within a few million years and combine it with the reasonable (though unproved) idea that civilizations ought to be common, we are led to an astonishing conclusion: Someone else should already have created a galactic civilization.

To see why, let's take some sample numbers. Suppose the overall odds of a civilization arising around a star are about the same as your odds of winning the lottery, or 1 in a million. Using a low estimate of 100 billion stars in the Milky Way Galaxy, this would mean some 100,000 civilizations in our galaxy alone. Moreover, current evidence suggests that stars and planetary systems like our own could have formed for at least 5 billion years before our solar system was even born, in which case the first of these 100,000 civilizations would have arisen at least 5 billion years ago. Others would have arisen, on average, about every 50,000 years. Under these assumptions, we would expect the youngest civilization besides ours to be some 50,000 years ahead of us technologically, and most would be millions or billions of years ahead of us.

We thereby encounter a strange paradox: Plausible arguments suggest that a galactic civilization should already exist, yet we have so far found no evidence of such a civilization. This paradox is often called *Fermi's paradox,* after the Nobel Prize–winning physicist Enrico Fermi. During a 1950 conversation with other scientists about the possibility of extraterrestrial intelligence, Fermi responded to speculations by asking, "So where is everybody?"

This paradox has many possible solutions, but broadly speaking we can group them into three categories:

1. *We are alone.* There is no galactic civilization because civilizations are extremely rare—so rare that we are the first to have arisen on the galactic scene, perhaps even the first in the universe.

2. *Civilizations are common, but no one has colonized the galaxy.* There are at least three possible reasons why this might be the case. Perhaps interstellar travel is much harder or more expensive than we have guessed, and civilizations are unable to venture far from their home worlds. Perhaps the desire to explore is unusual, and other societies either never leave their home star systems or stop exploring before they've colonized much of the galaxy. Most ominously, perhaps many civilizations have arisen, but they have all destroyed themselves before achieving the ability to colonize the stars.

3. *There IS a galactic civilization,* but it has not yet revealed its existence to us.

We do not know which, if any, of these explanations is the correct solution to the question "Where are the aliens?" However, each category of solution has astonishing implications for our own species.

Consider the first solution—that we are alone. If this is true, then our civilization is a remarkable achievement. It implies that through all of cosmic evolution, among countless star systems, we are the first matter in our galaxy or the universe ever to know that the rest of the universe exists. Through us, the universe has attained self-awareness. Some philosophers and many religions argue that the ultimate purpose of life is to become truly self-aware. If so, and if we are alone, then the destruction of our civilization and the loss of our scientific knowledge would represent an inglorious end to something that took the universe some 14 billion years to achieve. From this point of view, humanity becomes all the more precious, and the collapse of our civilization would be all the more tragic.

The second category of solutions has much more terrifying implications. If thousands of civilizations before us have all failed to achieve interstellar travel on a large scale, what hope do we have? Unless we somehow think differently than all other civilizations, this solution says that we will never go far in space. Because we have always explored when the opportunity arose, this solution almost inevitably leads to the conclusion that failure will come about because we destroy ourselves. We hope that this answer is wrong.

The third solution is perhaps the most intriguing. It says that we are newcomers on the scene of a galactic civilization that has existed for millions or billions of years before us. Perhaps this civilization is deliberately leaving us alone for the time being and will someday decide the time is right to invite us to join it.

No matter what the answer turns out to be, learning it will surely mark a turning point in the brief history of our species. Moreover, this turning point is likely to be reached within the next few decades or centuries. We already have the ability to destroy our civilization. If we do so, then our fate is sealed. But if we survive long enough to develop technology that can take us to the stars, the possibilities seem almost limitless.

The Big Picture

Putting Chapter 24 into Context

Throughout our study of astronomy, we have taken a "big picture" view of understanding how we fit into the universe. Here, at last, we have returned to Earth and examined the role of our own generation in the big picture of human history. Tens of thousands of past human generations have walked this Earth. Ours is the first generation with the technology to study the far reaches of our universe, to search for life elsewhere, and to travel beyond our home planet. It is up to us to decide whether we will use this technology to advance our species or to destroy it.

Imagine for a moment the grand view, a gaze across the centuries and millennia from this moment forward. Picture our descendants living among the stars, having created or joined a great galactic civilization. They will have the privilege of experiencing ideas, worlds, and discoveries far beyond our wildest imagination. Perhaps, in their history lessons, they will learn of our generation—the generation that history placed at the turning point and that managed to steer its way past the dangers of self-destruction and onto the path to the stars.

SUMMARY OF KEY CONCEPTS

24.1 LIFE ON EARTH

- **When did life arise on Earth?** Fossil evidence puts the origin of life at least 3.5 billion years ago, and carbon isotope evidence pushes this date to more than 3.85 billion years ago. Life therefore arose within a few hundred million years after Earth's birth and possibly in a much shorter time.

- **How did life arise on Earth?** Genetic evidence suggests that all life on Earth evolved from a common ancestor, which may have resembled microbes that live today in hot water near undersea volcanic vents. We do not know how this first organism arose, but laboratory experiments suggest that it may have been the result of natural chemical processes on the early Earth. Once life arose, it rapidly diversified and evolved through **natural selection**.

- **What are the necessities of life?** Life on Earth thrives in a wide range of environments, and in general seems to require only three things: a source of nutrients, a source of energy, and liquid water.

24.2 LIFE IN THE SOLAR SYSTEM

- **Could there be life on Mars?** Mars once had conditions that may have been conducive to the origin of life. If life arose, it might still survive in pockets of liquid water underground.

- **Could there be life on Europa or other jovian moons?** Europa probably has a subsurface ocean of liquid water and may have seafloor volcanoes. If so, it has conditions much like those in which early life arose on Earth, making it a good candidate for life. Ganymede and Callisto might have oceans as well. Titan has other liquids on its surface, though it is too cold for liquid water. Perhaps life can survive in these other liquids, or perhaps Titan has liquid water deep underground. Enceladus also shows evidence of subsurface liquids, offering yet another possibility for life.

24.3 LIFE AROUND OTHER STARS

- **What kinds of stars might have habitable planets?**

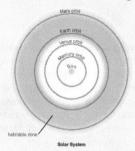

Stars must have sufficiently long lifetimes and the possibility of stable planetary orbits in order to have habitable planets, but these constraints still leave billions of stars with **habitable zones** in which life-bearing planets might exist. Smaller (lower mass and luminosity) stars have smaller habitable zones.

- **Are Earth-like planets rare or common?** We don't know. Arguments can be made on both sides of the question, and at present we lack the data to determine which answer is correct.

24.4 THE SEARCH FOR EXTRATERRESTRIAL INTELLIGENCE

- **How many civilizations are out there?** We don't know, but the **Drake equation** gives us a way to organize our thinking about the question. The equation (in a modified form) says that the number of civilizations in the Milky Way Galaxy with whom we could potentially communicate is $N_{HP} \times f_{life} \times f_{civ} \times f_{now}$, where N_{HP} is the number of habitable planets in the galaxy, f_{life} is the fraction of habitable planets that actually have life on them, f_{civ} is the fraction of life-bearing planets on which a civilization capable of interstellar communication has at some time arisen, and f_{now} is the fraction of all these civilizations that exist now.

- **How does SETI work?** **SETI**, the search for extraterrestrial intelligence, generally involves efforts to detect signals—such as radio or laser communications—coming from civilizations on other worlds.

24.5 INTERSTELLAR TRAVEL AND ITS IMPLICATIONS FOR CIVILIZATION

- **How difficult is interstellar travel?** Convenient interstellar travel remains well beyond our technological capabilities because of the technological requirements for engines, the enormous energy needed to accelerate spacecraft to speeds near the speed of light, and the difficulties of shielding the crew from radiation. Nevertheless, people have proposed ways around all these difficulties, and it seems reasonable to think that we will someday achieve interstellar travel if we survive long enough.

- **Where are the aliens?** A civilization capable of interstellar travel ought to be able to colonize the galaxy in a few million years or less, and the galaxy was around for billions of years before Earth was even born. It therefore seems that some civilization should have colonized the galaxy long ago—yet we have no evidence of other civilizations. Every possible explanation for this surprising fact has astonishing implications for our species and our place in the universe.

Use the following questions to check your understanding of some of the many types of visual information used in astronomy. Answers are provided in Appendix J. For additional practice, try the Chapter 24 Visual Quiz at MasteringAstronomy®.

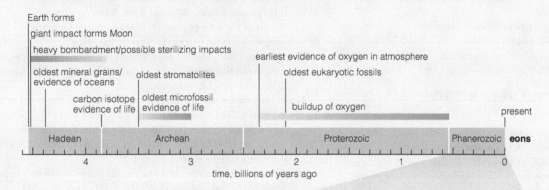

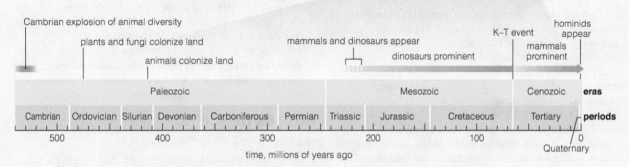

The figure above, which repeats Figure 24.4, shows the geological time scale. Use this figure to answer the following questions.

1. List the following events in the order in which they occurred, from first to last.
   a. earliest humans   b. earliest animals   c. impact causes extinction of dinosaurs   d. earliest mammals   e. earliest plants living on land   f. first time there is significant oxygen in Earth's atmosphere   g. first life on Earth
2. List the following time frames in order of how long they lasted, from longest to shortest.
   a. Hadean eon   b. Proterozoic eon   c. Paleozoic era
   d. Cretaceous period
3. Which time frame(s) do we live in today? (More than one may apply.)

4. a. Quaternary period   b. Tertiary period   c. Cenozoic era
   d. Phanerozoic eon   e. Paleozoic era
4. How long did the Cambrian explosion last?
   a. less than 1 year   b. about a decade   c. about 10,000 years
   d. about 40 million years   e. about 500 million years
5. When did the heavy bombardment end?
   a. about 4.5 billion years ago   b. between about 4.3 and 4.5 billion years ago   c. between about 3.8 and 4.0 billion years ago
   d. exactly 3.85 billion years ago
6. How long have mammals been present on Earth?
   a. about 1 million years   b. about 65 million years
   c. about 225 million years   d. about 510 million years

MasteringAstronomy®

For instructor-assigned homework go to MasteringAstronomy®.

REVIEW QUESTIONS

Short-Answer Questions Based on the Reading

1. Describe three recent developments in the study of life on Earth that make life elsewhere seem more plausible.
2. How do we study the history of life on Earth? Describe the *geological time scale* and a few of the major events along it.
3. Summarize the evidence pointing to an early origin of life on Earth. How far back in Earth's history did life exist?
4. Why is the *theory of evolution* so critical to our understanding of the history of life on Earth? Explain how evolution proceeds by *natural selection*, and what happens to DNA that allows species to evolve.
5. Give a brief overview of the history of life on Earth. What evidence points to a common ancestor for all life? How and when

did oxygen accumulate in Earth's atmosphere? When did larger animals diversify on Earth?
6. How are laboratory experiments helping us study the origin of life on Earth? Explain.
7. Is it possible that life migrated to Earth from elsewhere? Explain.
8. Describe the range of environments in which life thrives on Earth. What three basic requirements apply to life in all these environments?
9. What is a *habitable world*? Which worlds in our solar system seem potentially habitable, and why?
10. Briefly summarize the current status of the search for life on Mars.
11. What do we mean by a star's *habitable zone*? Do we expect many stars to be capable of having habitable planets? Explain.

12. What is the "rare Earth hypothesis"? Summarize the arguments on both sides regarding the validity of this hypothesis.

13. What is *SETI*? Describe the capabilities of current SETI efforts.

14. What is the *Drake equation*? Define each of its factors, and describe the current state of understanding about the potential values of each factor.

15. Why is interstellar travel so difficult? Describe a few technologies that might someday make it possible.

16. What is *Fermi's paradox*? Describe several potential solutions to the paradox and the implications of each to our civilization.

TEST YOUR UNDERSTANDING

Fantasy or Science Fiction?

For each of the following futuristic scenarios, decide whether it is plausible according to our present understanding of science or whether it is unlikely to be possible. Explain clearly; not all these have definitive answers, so your explanation is more important than your chosen answer.

17. The first human explorers on Mars discover the ruins of an ancient civilization, including remnants of tall buildings and temples.

18. The first human explorers on Mars drill a hole into a Martian volcano to collect a sample of soil from several meters underground. Upon analysis of the soil, they discover that it holds living microbes resembling terrestrial bacteria but with a different biochemistry.

19. In 2040, a spacecraft lands on Europa and melts its way through the ice into the Europan ocean. It finds numerous strange, living microbes, along with a few larger organisms that feed on the microbes.

20. It's the year 2075. A giant telescope on the Moon, consisting of hundreds of small telescopes linked together across a distance of 500 kilometers, has just captured a series of images of a planet around a distant star that clearly show seasonal changes in vegetation.

21. A century from now, after completing a careful study of planets around stars within 100 light-years of Earth, astronomers discover that the most diverse life exists on a planet orbiting a young star that formed just 100 million years ago.

22. In 2040, a brilliant teenager working in her garage builds a coal-powered rocket that can travel at half the speed of light.

23. In the year 2750, we receive a signal from a civilization around a nearby star telling us that the *Voyager 2* spacecraft recently crash-landed on its planet.

24. Crew members of the matter–antimatter spacecraft *Star Apollo*, which left Earth in the year 2165, return to Earth in the year 2450, looking only a few years older than when they left.

25. Aliens from a distant star system invade Earth with the intent to destroy us and occupy our planet, but we successfully fight them off when their technology proves no match for ours.

26. A single great galactic civilization exists. It originated on a single planet long ago but is now made up of beings from many different planets, all assimilated into the galactic culture.

Quick Quiz

Choose the best answer to each of the following. Explain your reasoning with one or more complete sentences.

27. Fossil evidence suggests that life on Earth arose (a) almost immediately after Earth formed. (b) very soon after the end of the heavy bombardment. (c) about a billion years before the rise of the dinosaurs.

28. The theory of evolution is (a) a scientific theory backed by extensive evidence. (b) one of several competing scientific models that all seem equally successful in explaining the nature of life on Earth. (c) essentially just a guess about how life changes through time.

29. Plants and animals are (a) the two major forms of life on Earth. (b) the only organisms that have DNA. (c) just two small branches of the diverse "tree of life" on Earth.

30. Which of the following is a reason why early living organisms on Earth could not have survived on the surface? (a) the lack of an ozone layer (b) the lack of oxygen in the atmosphere (c) the fact that these organisms were single-celled

31. According to current understanding, the key requirement for life is (a) photosynthesis. (b) liquid water. (c) an ozone layer.

32. Which of the following worlds is *not* considered a candidate for harboring life? (a) Europa (b) Mars (c) the Moon

33. How does the habitable zone around a star of spectral type G compare to that around a star of spectral type M? (a) It is larger. (b) It is hotter. (c) It is closer to its star.

34. In the Drake equation, suppose that the term f_{life} was equal to $\frac{1}{2}$. What would this mean? (a) Half the stars in the Milky Way Galaxy have a planet with life. (b) Half of all life-forms in the universe are intelligent. (c) Half of the habitable worlds in the galaxy actually have life, while the other half don't.

35. The amount of energy that would be needed to accelerate a large spaceship to half the speed of light is (a) about 100 times the energy needed to launch the Space Shuttle. (b) more than 2000 times the current annual world energy consumption. (c) more than the amount of energy released by a supernova.

36. According to current scientific understanding, the idea that the Milky Way Galaxy might be home to a civilization millions of years more advanced than ours is (a) a virtual certainty. (b) extremely unlikely. (c) one reasonable answer to Fermi's paradox.

PROCESS OF SCIENCE

Examining How Science Works

37. *Extraordinary Claims.* As discussed in the chapter, both the *Viking* results and the study of a Martian meteorite led some scientists to think we had found evidence of life on Mars, even while most scientists disagreed. Those who disagree often point to Carl Sagan's dictum that "extraordinary claims require extraordinary evidence." Briefly discuss one of these cases, and decide whether you think extraordinary evidence should be required before it is accepted. What follow-up evidence might lead scientists to reevaluate their positions?

38. *Unanswered Questions.* In a sense, this entire chapter was about one big unanswered question: Are we alone in the universe? But as we attempt to answer that "big" question, there are many smaller questions that we might wish to answer along the way. Describe one currently unanswered question about life in the universe that we might be able to answer with new missions or experiments over the next couple of decades. What kinds of evidence will we need to answer the question? How will we know when it is answered?

GROUP WORK EXERCISE

39. *Habitable Planets?* In this exercise, you will rank several extrasolar planetary systems in order of the probability that they support life. Before you begin, assign the following roles to the people in your group: *Scribe* (takes notes on the group's activities), *Proposer* (proposes explanations to the group), *Skeptic* (points out weaknesses in proposed explanations), and *Moderator* (leads group discussion and makes sure everyone contributes). List the systems in order of most probable to least probable to support life, and explain the reasons for your ranking in each case.
a. a planet orbiting a star of spectral type B (approximately 10 solar masses) in a circular orbit with an average temperature expected to be 300 K **b.** a planet orbiting a Sun-like star in a circular orbit at a distance twice Earth's orbital distance from the Sun **c.** a planet orbiting a star with a luminosity one-quarter the Sun's luminosity in a circular orbit at a distance one-half Earth's orbital distance from the Sun **d.** a planet orbiting a Sun-like star in an elliptical orbit ranging from Earth's orbital distance to ten times Earth's orbital distance from the Sun

INVESTIGATE FURTHER

In-Depth Questions to Increase Your Understanding

Short-Answer/Essay Questions

40. *Artificial Selection.* Suppose you lived hundreds of years ago (before we knew about genetic engineering) and wanted to breed a herd of cows that would provide more milk than the cows in your current herd. How would you have gone about it? How would this process of "artificial selection" be similar to natural selection? How would it be different?

41. *Statistics of One.* Much of the search for life in the universe is based on what we know about life on Earth. Write a short essay discussing the pros and cons of basing our general understanding of biology on the example of Earth.

42. *Most Likely to Have Life.* Suppose you were asked to vote in a contest to name the world in our solar system (besides Earth) "most likely to have life." Which world would you cast your vote for? Explain and defend your choice in a one-page essay.

43. *Likely Suns.* Study the stellar data for nearby stars given in Appendix F, Table F.1. Which star on the list would you expect to have the largest habitable zone? Which would have the second-largest habitable zone? If we rule out multiple-star systems, which star would you expect to have the highest probability of having a habitable planet? Explain your answers.

44. *Are Earth-Like Planets Common?* Based on what you have learned in this book, do you think Earth-like planets will ultimately prove to be rare, common, or something in between? Write a one- to two-page essay explaining and defending your opinion.

45. *Solution to the Fermi Paradox.* Which of the various possible solutions to the question "Where are the aliens?" do you think is most likely? (If you have no opinion on their likelihood, which do you like best?) Write a one- to two-page essay in which you explain why you favor this solution.

46. *What's Wrong with This Picture?* Many science fiction stories have imagined the galaxy divided into a series of empires, each having arisen from a different civilization on a different world, that hold one another at bay because they all have about the same level of military technology. Is this a realistic scenario? Explain.

47. *Aliens in the Movies.* Choose a science fiction movie (or television show) that involves an alien species. Do you think aliens like this could really exist? Write a one- to two-page critical review of the movie, focusing primarily on the question of whether the movie portrays the aliens in a scientifically reasonable way.

Quantitative Problems

Be sure to show all calculations clearly and state your final answers in complete sentences.

48. *Nearest Civilization.*
   a. Suppose there are 10,000 civilizations in the Milky Way Galaxy. If the civilizations were randomly distributed throughout the disk of the galaxy, about how far (on average) would it be to the nearest civilization? (*Hint:* Start by finding the area of the Milky Way's disk, assuming that it is circular and 100,000 light-years in diameter. Then find the average area per civilization, and use the distance across this area to estimate the distance between civilizations.) **b.** Repeat part a, but this time assume that there are only 100 civilizations in the galaxy.

49. *SETI Search.* Suppose there are 10,000 civilizations broadcasting radio signals in the Milky Way Galaxy right now. On average, how many stars would we have to search before we would expect to hear a signal? Assume there are 500 billion stars in the galaxy. How does the answer change if there are only 100 civilizations instead of 10,000?

50. *SETI Signal.* Consider a civilization broadcasting a signal with a power of 10,000 watts. The Arecibo radio telescope, which is about 300 meters in diameter, could detect this signal if it was coming from as far away as 100 light-years. Suppose instead that the signal is being broadcast from the other side of the Milky Way Galaxy, about 70,000 light-years away. How large a radio telescope would we need to detect this signal? (*Hint:* Use the inverse square law for light.)

51. *Cruise Ship Energy.* Suppose we have a spaceship about the size of a typical ocean cruise ship today, which means it has a mass of about 100 million kilograms, and we want to accelerate the ship to a speed of 10% of the speed of light.
   a. How much energy would be required? (*Hint:* You can find the answer simply by calculating the kinetic energy of the ship when it reaches its cruising speed; because 10% of the speed of light is still small compared to the speed of light, you can use the formula that tells us that kinetic energy $= \frac{1}{2} \times m \times v^2$.) **b.** How does your answer compare to total world energy use at present, which is about 5×10^{22} joules per year? **c.** The typical cost of energy today is roughly 5¢ per 1 million joules. At this price, how much would it cost to generate the energy needed by this spaceship?

52. *Matter–Antimatter Engine.* Consider the spaceship from Problem 51. Suppose you wanted to generate the energy to get it to cruising speed using matter–antimatter annihilation. How much antimatter would you need to produce and take on the ship? (*Hint:* When matter and antimatter meet, they turn all their mass into energy equivalent to mc^2.)

Discussion Questions

53. *Funding the Search for Life.* Imagine that you are a member of Congress and your job includes deciding how much government funding goes to research in different areas of science. How much would you allot to the search for life in the universe compared to the amount allotted to research in other areas of astronomy and planetary science? Why?

54. *Distant Dream or Near Reality?* Considering all the issues surrounding interstellar flight, when (if ever) do you think we are likely to begin traveling among the stars? Why?

55. *The Turning Point.* Discuss the idea that our generation has acquired a greater responsibility for the future than any previous generation. Do you agree with this assessment? If so, how should we deal with this responsibility? Defend your opinions.

Web Projects

56. *Astrobiology News.* Go to NASA's astrobiology site and read some of the recent news about the search for life in the universe. Choose one article and write a one- to two-page summary of the research.

57. *Martian Meteorites.* Research the latest discoveries concerning Martian meteorites. Choose one discovery and write a short summary of how you think it alters the debate about the habitability of Mars.

58. *The Search for Extraterrestrial Intelligence.* Learn more about SETI at the SETI Institute home page, and summarize your findings in one page or less.

59. *Starship Design.* Read about a proposal for starship propulsion or design. How would the starship work? What new technologies would be needed, and what existing technologies could be applied? Write a one- to two-page report on your research.

60. *Advanced Spacecraft Technologies.* NASA supports many efforts to incorporate new technologies into spaceships. Although few of them are suitable for interstellar colonization, most are innovative and fascinating. Learn about one such project, and write a short overview of your findings.

Throughout this book, we have seen that the history of the universe has proceeded in a way that has made our existence on Earth possible. This figure summarizes some of the key ideas, and leads us to ask: If life arose here, shouldn't it also have arisen on many other worlds? We do not yet know the answer, but scientists are actively seeking to learn whether life is rare or common in the universe.

(1) The protons, neutrons, and electrons in the atoms that make up Earth and life were created out of pure energy during the first few moments after the Big Bang, leaving the universe filled with hydrogen and helium gas [Section 22.1].

electron

gamma-ray photons

antielectron

Matter can be created from energy: $E = mc^2$.

(2) Ripples in the density of the early universe were necessary for life to form later on. Without those ripples, matter would never have collected into galaxies, stars, and planets [Section 22.3].

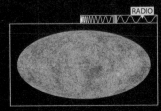

RADIO

We observe the seeds of structure formation in the cosmic microwave background.

(3) The attractive force of gravity pulls together the matter that makes galaxies, stars, and planets [Section 4.4].

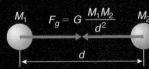

$$F_g = G \frac{M_1 M_2}{d^2}$$

Every piece of matter in the universe pulls on every other piece.

(4) Our planet and all the life on it is made primarily of elements formed by nuclear fusion in high-mass stars and dispersed into space by supernovae [Section 17.3].

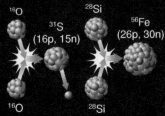

^{16}O ^{31}S (16p, 15n) ^{28}Si ^{56}Fe (26p, 30n)

^{16}O ^{28}Si

High-mass stars have cores hot enough to make elements heavier than carbon.

5 Our galaxy is large enough to retain the elements ejected by supernovae, and it recycles them into new stars and planetary systems [Section 19.2].

New elements mix with the interstellar medium, which then forms new stars and planets.

6 Planets can form in gaseous disks of material around newly formed stars. Earth was built from heavy elements that condensed from the gas as particles of metal and rock, which then gradually accreted to become our planet [Section 8.2].

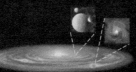

Terrestrial planets formed in warm, inner regions of the solar nebula; jovian planets formed in cooler, outer regions.

7 Life as we know it requires liquid water, so we define the habitable zone around a star to be the zone in which a suitably large planet can have liquid water on its surface [Section 24.3].

The Sun's habitable zone (green) occupies a region from beyond the orbit of Venus to near the orbit of Mars.

8 Early life has had the time needed to evolve into complex forms—including us—because the solar thermostat has kept the Sun shining steadily for billions of years [Section 14.2].

The solar thermostat keeps the Sun's fusion rate stable.

APPENDIXES

A USEFUL NUMBERS

Astronomical Distances

1 AU $\approx 1.496 \times 10^8$ km $= 1.496 \times 10^{11}$ m

1 light-year $\approx 9.46 \times 10^{12}$ km $= 9.46 \times 10^{15}$ m

1 parsec (pc) $\approx 3.09 \times 10^{13}$ km ≈ 3.26 light-years

1 kiloparsec (kpc) $= 1000$ pc $\approx 3.26 \times 10^3$ light-years

1 megaparsec (Mpc) $= 10^6$ pc $\approx 3.26 \times 10^6$ light-years

Universal Constants

Speed of light: $\qquad c = 3.00 \times 10^5$ km/s $= 3 \times 10^8$ m/s

Gravitational constant: $\qquad G = 6.67 \times 10^{-11} \dfrac{m^3}{kg \times s^2}$

Planck's constant: $\qquad h = 6.63 \times 10^{-34}$ joule $\times$ s

Stefan-Boltzmann constant: $\qquad \sigma = 5.67 \times 10^{-8} \dfrac{watt}{m^2 \times K^4}$

Mass of a proton: $\qquad m_p = 1.67 \times 10^{-27}$ kg

Mass of an electron: $\qquad m_e = 9.11 \times 10^{-31}$ kg

Useful Sun and Earth Reference Values

Mass of the Sun: $1M_{Sun} \approx 2 \times 10^{30}$ kg

Radius of the Sun: $1R_{Sun} \approx 696{,}000$ km

Luminosity of the Sun: $1L_{Sun} \approx 3.8 \times 10^{26}$ watts

Mass of Earth: $1M_{Earth} \approx 5.97 \times 10^{24}$ kg

Radius (equatorial) of Earth: $1R_{Earth} \approx 6378$ km

Acceleration of gravity on Earth: $g = 9.8$ m/s^2

Escape velocity from surface of Earth: $v_{escape} = 11.2$ km/s $= 11{,}200$ m/s

Astronomical Times

1 solar day (average) $= 24^h$

1 sidereal day $\approx 23^h56^m4.09^s$

1 synodic month (average) ≈ 29.53 solar days

1 sidereal month (average) ≈ 27.32 solar days

1 tropical year ≈ 365.242 solar days

1 sidereal year ≈ 365.256 solar days

Energy and Power Units

Basic unit of energy: 1 joule $= 1 \dfrac{kg \times m^2}{s^2}$

Basic unit of power: 1 watt $= 1$ joule/s

Electron-volt: 1 eV $= 1.60 \times 10^{-19}$ joule

B USEFUL FORMULAS

■ Universal law of gravitation for the force between objects of mass M_1 and M_2, with distance d between their centers:

$$F = G \frac{M_1 M_2}{d^2}$$

■ Newton's version of Kepler's third law, which applies to any pair of orbiting objects, such as a star and planet, a planet and moon, or two stars in a binary system; p is the orbital period, a is the distance between the centers of the orbiting objects, and M_1 and M_2 are the object masses:

$$p^2 = \frac{4\pi^2}{G(M_1 + M_2)} a^3$$

■ Escape velocity at distance R from center of object of mass M:

$$v_{escape} = \sqrt{\frac{2GM}{R}}$$

■ Relationship between a photon's wavelength (λ), frequency (f), and the speed of light (c):

$$\lambda \times f = c$$

■ Energy of a photon of wavelength λ or frequency f:

$$E = hf = \frac{hc}{\lambda}$$

■ Stefan-Boltzmann law for thermal radiation at temperature T (in Kelvin):

$$\text{emitted power per unit area} = \sigma T^4$$

■ Wien's law for the peak wavelength (λ_{max}) thermal radiation at temperature T (on the Kelvin scale):

$$\lambda_{max} = \frac{2,900,000}{T} \text{ nm}$$

■ Doppler shift (radial velocity is positive if the object is moving away from us and negative if it is moving toward us):

$$\frac{\text{radial velocity}}{\text{speed of light}} = \frac{\text{shifted wavelength} - \text{rest wavelength}}{\text{rest wavelength}}$$

■ Angular separation (α) of two points with an actual separation s, viewed from a distance d (assuming d is much larger than s):

$$\alpha = \frac{s}{2\pi d} \times 360°$$

■ Inverse square law for light (d is the distance to the object):

$$\text{apparent brightness} = \frac{\text{luminosity}}{4\pi d^2}$$

■ Parallax formula (distance d to a star with parallax angle p in arcseconds):

$$d \text{ (in parsecs)} = \frac{1}{p \text{ (in arcseconds)}}$$

$$\text{or } d \text{ (in light-years)} = 3.26 \times \frac{1}{p \text{ (in arcseconds)}}$$

■ The orbital velocity law, to find the mass M_r contained within the circular orbit of radius r for an object moving at speed v:

$$M_r = \frac{r \times v^2}{G}$$

C A FEW MATHEMATICAL SKILLS

This appendix reviews the following mathematical skills: powers of 10, scientific notation, working with units, the metric system, and finding a ratio. You should refer to this appendix as needed while studying the textbook.

C.1 Powers of 10

Powers of 10 indicate how many times to multiply 10 by itself. For example:

$$10^2 = 10 \times 10 = 100$$

$$10^6 = 10 \times 10 \times 10 \times 10 \times 10 \times 10 = 1,000,000$$

Negative powers are the reciprocals of the corresponding positive powers. For example:

$$10^{-2} = \frac{1}{10^2} = \frac{1}{100} = 0.01$$

$$10^{-6} = \frac{1}{10^6} = \frac{1}{1,000,000} = 0.000001$$

TABLE C.1 lists powers of 10 from 10^{-12} to 10^{12}. Note that powers of 10 follow two basic rules:

1. A positive exponent tells how many zeros follow the 1. For example, 10^0 is a 1 followed by no zeros, and 10^8 is a 1 followed by eight zeros.

2. A negative exponent tells how many places are to the right of the decimal point, including the 1. For example, $10^{-1} = 0.1$ has one place to the right of the decimal point; $10^{-6} = 0.000001$ has six places to the right of the decimal point.

Multiplying and Dividing Powers of 10

Multiplying powers of 10 simply requires adding exponents, as the following examples show:

$$10^4 \times 10^7 = \underbrace{10,000}_{10^4} \times \underbrace{10,000,000}_{10^7} = \underbrace{100,000,000,000}_{10^{4+7} = 10^{11}} = 10^{11}$$

$$10^5 \times 10^{-3} = \underbrace{100,000}_{10^5} \times \underbrace{0.001}_{10^{-3}} = \underbrace{100}_{10^{5+(-3)} = 10^2} = 10^2$$

$$10^{-8} \times 10^{-5} = \underbrace{0.00000001}_{10^{-8}} \times \underbrace{0.00001}_{10^{-5}} = \underbrace{0.0000000000001}_{10^{-8+(-5)} = 10^{-13}} = 10^{-13}$$

TABLE C.1 Powers of 10

Zero and Positive Powers			Negative Powers		
Power	Value	Name	Power	Value	Name
10^0	1	One			
10^1	10	Ten	10^{-1}	0.1	Tenth
10^2	100	Hundred	10^{-2}	0.01	Hundredth
10^3	1000	Thousand	10^{-3}	0.001	Thousandth
10^4	10,000	Ten thousand	10^{-4}	0.0001	Ten-thousandth
10^5	100,000	Hundred thousand	10^{-5}	0.00001	Hundred-thousandth
10^6	1,000,000	Million	10^{-6}	0.000001	Millionth
10^7	10,000,000	Ten million	10^{-7}	0.0000001	Ten-millionth
10^8	100,000,000	Hundred million	10^{-8}	0.00000001	Hundred-millionth
10^9	1,000,000,000	Billion	10^{-9}	0.000000001	Billionth
10^{10}	10,000,000,000	Ten billion	10^{-10}	0.0000000001	Ten-billionth
10^{11}	100,000,000,000	Hundred billion	10^{-11}	0.00000000001	Hundred-billionth
10^{12}	1,000,000,000,000	Trillion	10^{-12}	0.000000000001	Trillionth

Dividing powers of 10 requires subtracting exponents, as in the following examples:

$$\frac{10^5}{10^3} = \underbrace{100,000}_{10^5} \div \underbrace{1000}_{10^3} = \underbrace{100}_{10^{5-3}\,=\,10^2} = 10^2$$

$$\frac{10^3}{10^7} = \underbrace{1000}_{10^3} \div \underbrace{10,000,000}_{10^7} = \underbrace{0.0001}_{10^{3-7}\,=\,10^{-4}} = 10^{-4}$$

$$\frac{10^{-4}}{10^{-6}} = \underbrace{0.0001}_{10^{-4}} \div \underbrace{0.000001}_{10^{-6}} = \underbrace{100}_{10^{-4-(-6)}\,=\,10^2} = 10^2$$

Powers of Powers of 10

We can use the multiplication and division rules to raise powers of 10 to other powers or to take roots. For example:

$$(10^4)^3 = 10^4 \times 10^4 \times 10^4 = 10^{4+4+4} = 10^{12}$$

Note that we can get the same end result by simply multiplying the two powers:

$$(10^4)^3 = 10^{4 \times 3} = 10^{12}$$

Because taking a root is the same as raising to a fractional power (e.g., the square root is the same as the $\frac{1}{2}$ power; the cube root is the same as the $\frac{1}{3}$ power, etc.), we can use the same procedure for roots, as in the following example:

$$\sqrt{10^4} = (10^4)^{1/2} = 10^{4 \times (1/2)} = 10^2$$

Adding and Subtracting Powers of 10

Unlike multiplying and dividing powers of 10, there is no shortcut for adding or subtracting powers of 10. The values must be written in longhand notation. For example:

$$10^6 + 10^2 = 1,000,000 + 100 = 1,000,100$$

$$10^8 + 10^{-3} = 100,000,000 + 0.001 = 100,000,000.001$$

$$10^7 - 10^3 = 10,000,000 - 1000 = 9,999,000$$

Summary

We can summarize our findings using n and m to represent any numbers:

- To *multiply* powers of 10, *add* exponents: $10^n \times 10^m = 10^{n+m}$

- To *divide* powers of 10, *subtract* exponents: $\dfrac{10^n}{10^m} = 10^{n-m}$

- To *raise* powers of 10 to other powers, multiply exponents: $(10^n)^m = 10^{n \times m}$

- To add or subtract powers of 10, first write them out longhand.

C.2 Scientific Notation

When we are dealing with large or small numbers, it's generally easier to write them with powers of 10. For example, it's much easier to write the number 6,000,000,000,000 as 6×10^{12}. This format, in which a number *between* 1 and 10 is multiplied by a power of 10, is called **scientific notation**.

Converting a Number to Scientific Notation

We can convert numbers written in ordinary notation to scientific notation with a simple two-step process:

1. Move the decimal point to come after the *first* nonzero digit.

2. The number of places the decimal point moves tells you the power of 10; the power is *positive* if the decimal point moves to the left and *negative* if it moves to the right.

Examples:

$$3042 \xrightarrow[\text{3 places to left}]{\text{decimal needs to move}} 3.042 \times 10^3$$

$$0.00012 \xrightarrow[\text{4 places to right}]{\text{decimal needs to move}} 1.2 \times 10^{-4}$$

$$226 \times 10^2 \xrightarrow[\text{2 places to left}]{\text{decimal needs to move}} (2.26 \times 10^2) \times 10^2 = 2.26 \times 10^4$$

Converting a Number from Scientific Notation

We can convert numbers written in scientific notation to ordinary notation by the reverse process:

1. The power of 10 indicates how many places to move the decimal point; move it to the *right* if the power of 10 is positive and to the *left* if it is negative.

2. If moving the decimal point creates any open places, fill them with zeros.

Examples:

$$4.01 \times 10^2 \xrightarrow[\text{2 places to right}]{\text{move decimal}} 401$$

$$3.6 \times 10^6 \xrightarrow[\text{6 places to right}]{\text{move decimal}} 3,600,000$$

$$5.7 \times 10^{-3} \xrightarrow[\text{3 places to left}]{\text{move decimal}} 0.0057$$

Multiplying or Dividing Numbers in Scientific Notation

Multiplying or dividing numbers in scientific notation simply requires operating on the powers of 10 and the other parts of the number separately.

Examples:

$$(6 \times 10^2) \times (4 \times 10^5) = (6 \times 4) \times (10^2 \times 10^5) = 24 \times 10^7 = (2.4 \times 10^1) \times 10^7 = 2.4 \times 10^8$$

$$\frac{4.2 \times 10^{-2}}{8.4 \times 10^{-5}} = \frac{4.2}{8.4} \times \frac{10^{-2}}{10^{-5}} = 0.5 \times 10^{-2-(-5)} = 0.5 \times 10^3 = (5 \times 10^{-1}) \times 10^3 = 5 \times 10^2$$

Note that, in both these examples, we first found an answer in which the number multiplied by a power of 10 was *not* between 1 and 10. We therefore followed the procedure for converting the final answer to scientific notation.

Addition and Subtraction with Scientific Notation

In general, we must write numbers in ordinary notation before adding or subtracting.

Examples:

$$(3 \times 10^6) + (5 \times 10^2) = 3{,}000{,}000 + 500 = 3{,}000{,}500 = 3.0005 \times 10^6$$

$$(4.6 \times 10^9) - (5 \times 10^8) = 4{,}600{,}000{,}000 - 500{,}000{,}000 = 4{,}100{,}000{,}000 = 4.1 \times 10^9$$

When both numbers have the *same* power of 10, we can factor out the power of 10 first.

Examples:

$$(7 \times 10^{10}) + (4 \times 10^{10}) = (7 + 4) \times 10^{10} = 11 \times 10^{10} = 1.1 \times 10^{11}$$

$$(2.3 \times 10^{-22}) - (1.6 \times 10^{-22}) = (2.3 - 1.6) \times 10^{-22} = 0.7 \times 10^{-22} = 7.0 \times 10^{-23}$$

C.3 Working with Units

Showing the units of a problem as you solve it usually makes the work much easier and also provides a useful way of checking your work. If an answer does not come out with the units you expect, you probably did something wrong. In general, working with units is very similar to working with numbers, as the following guidelines and examples show.

Five Guidelines for Working with Units

Before you begin any problem, think ahead and identify the units you expect for the final answer. Then operate on the units along with the numbers as you solve the problem. The following five guidelines may be helpful when you are working with units:

1. Mathematically, it doesn't matter whether a unit is singular (e.g., meter) or plural (e.g., meters); we can use the same abbreviation (e.g., m) for both.

2. You cannot add or subtract numbers unless they have the *same* units. For example, 5 apples + 3 apples = 8 apples, but the expression 5 apples + 3 oranges cannot be simplified further.

3. You *can* multiply units, divide units, or raise units to powers. Look for key words that tell you what to do.

   - *Per* suggests division. For example, we write a speed of 100 kilometers per hour as

   $$100 \, \frac{\text{km}}{\text{hr}} \quad \text{or} \quad 100 \, \frac{\text{km}}{1 \, \text{hr}}$$

   - *Of* suggests multiplication. For example, if you launch a 50-kg space probe at a launch cost *of* $10,000 per kilogram, the total cost is

   $$50 \, \text{kg} \times \frac{\$10{,}000}{\text{kg}} = \$500{,}000$$

- *Square* suggests raising to the second power. For example, we write an area of 75 square meters as 75 m^2.

- *Cube* suggests raising to the third power. For example, we write a volume of 12 cubic centimeters as 12 cm^3.

4. Often the number you are given is not in the units you wish to work with. For example, you may be given that the speed of light is 300,000 km/s but need it in units of m/s for a particular problem. To convert the units, simply multiply the given number by a *conversion factor*: a fraction in which the numerator (top of the fraction) and denominator (bottom of the fraction) are equal, so that the value of the fraction is 1; the number in the denominator must have the units that you wish to change. In the case of changing the speed of light from units of km/s to m/s, you need a conversion factor for kilometers to meters. Thus, the conversion factor is

$$\frac{1000 \text{ m}}{1 \text{ km}}$$

Note that this conversion factor is equal to 1, since 1000 meters and 1 kilometer are equal, and that the units to be changed (km) appear in the denominator. We can now convert the speed of light from units of km/s to m/s simply by multiplying by this conversion factor:

$$\underbrace{300,000 \ \frac{\text{km}}{\text{s}}}_{\substack{\text{speed of light} \\ \text{in km/s}}} \times \underbrace{\frac{1000 \text{ m}}{1 \text{ km}}}_{\substack{\text{conversion from} \\ \text{km to m}}} = \underbrace{3 \times 10^8 \ \frac{\text{m}}{\text{s}}}_{\substack{\text{speed of light} \\ \text{in m/s}}}$$

Note that the units of km cancel, leaving the answer in units of m/s.

5. It's easier to work with units if you replace division with multiplication by the reciprocal. For example, suppose you want to know how many minutes are represented by 300 seconds. We can find the answer by dividing 300 seconds by 60 seconds per minute:

$$300 \text{ s} \div 60 \ \frac{\text{s}}{\text{min}}$$

However, it is easier to see the unit cancellations if we rewrite this expression by replacing the division with multiplication by the reciprocal (this process is easy to remember as "invert and multiply"):

$$300 \text{ s} \div 60 \ \frac{\text{s}}{\text{min}} = 300 \text{ s} \times \underbrace{\frac{1 \text{ min}}{60 \text{ s}}}_{\text{invert}} = 5 \text{ min}$$

and multiply

We now see that the units of seconds (s) cancel in the numerator of the first term and the denominator of the second term, leaving the answer in units of minutes.

More Examples of Working with Units

Example 1. How many seconds are there in 1 day?

Solution: We can answer the question by setting up a *chain* of unit conversions in which we start with 1 *day* and end up with *seconds*. We use the facts that there are 24 hours per day (24 hr/day), 60 minutes per hour (60 min/hr), and 60 seconds per minute (60 s/min):

$$\underbrace{1 \text{ day}}_{\substack{\text{starting} \\ \text{value}}} \times \underbrace{\frac{24 \text{ hr}}{\text{day}}}_{\substack{\text{conversion} \\ \text{from} \\ \text{day to hr}}} \times \underbrace{\frac{60 \text{ min}}{\text{hr}}}_{\substack{\text{conversion} \\ \text{from} \\ \text{hr to min}}} \times \underbrace{\frac{60 \text{ s}}{\text{min}}}_{\substack{\text{conversion} \\ \text{from} \\ \text{min to s}}} = 86{,}400 \text{ s}$$

Note that all the units cancel except *seconds*, which is what we want for the answer. There are 86,400 seconds in 1 day.

Example 2. Convert a distance of 10^8 cm to km.

Solution: The easiest way to make this conversion is in two steps, since we know that there are 100 centimeters per meter (100 cm/m) and 1000 meters per kilometer (1000 m/km):

$$\underbrace{10^8 \text{ cm}}_{\substack{\text{starting} \\ \text{value}}} \times \underbrace{\frac{1 \text{ m}}{100 \text{ cm}}}_{\substack{\text{conversion} \\ \text{from} \\ \text{cm to m}}} \times \underbrace{\frac{1 \text{ km}}{1000 \text{ m}}}_{\substack{\text{conversion} \\ \text{from} \\ \text{m to km}}} = 10^8 \text{ cm} \times \frac{1 \text{ m}}{10^2 \text{ cm}} \times \frac{1 \text{ km}}{10^3 \text{ m}} = 10^3 \text{ km}$$

Alternatively, if we recognize that the number of kilometers should be smaller than the number of centimeters (because kilometers are larger), we might decide to do this conversion by dividing as follows:

$$10^8 \text{ cm} \div \frac{100 \text{ cm}}{\text{m}} \div \frac{1000 \text{ m}}{\text{km}}$$

In this case, before carrying out the calculation, we replace each division with multiplication by the reciprocal:

$$10^8 \text{ cm} \div \frac{100 \text{ cm}}{\text{m}} \div \frac{1000 \text{ m}}{\text{km}} = 10^8 \text{ cm} \times \frac{1 \text{ m}}{100 \text{ cm}} \times \frac{1 \text{ km}}{1000 \text{ m}}$$

$$= 10^8 \text{ cm} \times \frac{1 \text{ m}}{10^2 \text{ cm}} \times \frac{1 \text{ km}}{10^3 \text{ m}}$$

$$= 10^3 \text{ km}$$

Note that we again get the answer that 10^8 cm is the same as 10^3 km, or 1000 km.

Example 3. Suppose you accelerate at 9.8 m/s² for 4 seconds, starting from rest. How fast will you be going?

Solution: The question asked "how fast?" so we expect to end up with a speed. Therefore, we multiply the acceleration by the amount of time you accelerated:

$$9.8 \frac{\text{m}}{\text{s}^2} \times 4 \text{ s} = (9.8 \times 4) \frac{\text{m} \times \text{s}}{\text{s}^2} = 39.2 \frac{\text{m}}{\text{s}}$$

Note that the units end up as a speed, showing that you will be traveling 39.2 m/s after 4 seconds of acceleration at 9.8 m/s².

Example 4. A reservoir is 2 km long and 3 km wide. Calculate its area, in both square kilometers and square meters.

Solution: We find its area by multiplying its length and width:

$$2 \text{ km} \times 3 \text{ km} = 6 \text{ km}^2$$

Next we need to convert this area of 6 km² to square meters, using the fact that there are 1000 meters per kilometer (1000 m/km). Note that we must square the term 1000 m/km when converting from km² to m²:

$$6 \text{ km}^2 \times \left(1000 \frac{\text{m}}{\text{km}}\right)^2 = 6 \text{ km}^2 \times 1000^2 \frac{\text{m}^2}{\text{km}^2} = 6 \text{ km}^2 \times 1{,}000{,}000 \frac{\text{m}^2}{\text{km}^2}$$

$$= 6{,}000{,}000 \text{ m}^2$$

The reservoir area is 6 km², which is the same as 6 million m².

C.4 The Metric System (SI)

The modern version of the metric system, known as *Système Internationale d'Unites* (French for "International System of Units") or **SI**, was formally established in 1960. Today, it is the primary measurement system in nearly every country in the world with the exception of the United States. Even in the United States, it is the system of choice for science and international commerce. The basic units of length, mass, and time in the SI are

- The **meter** for length, abbreviated m

- The **kilogram** for mass, abbreviated kg

- The **second** for time, abbreviated s

Multiples of metric units are formed by powers of 10, using a prefix to indicate the power. For example, *kilo* means 10^3 (1000), so a kilometer is 1000 meters; a microgram is 0.000001 gram, because *micro* means 10^{-6}, or one millionth. Some of the more common prefixes are listed in **TABLE C.2**.

TABLE C.2 SI (Metric) Prefixes

Prefix	Small Values Abbreviation	Value	Prefix	Large Values Abbreviation	Value
Deci	d	10^{-1}	Deca	da	10^{1}
Centi	c	10^{-2}	Hecto	h	10^{2}
Milli	m	10^{-3}	Kilo	k	10^{3}
Micro	μ	10^{-6}	Mega	M	10^{6}
Nano	n	10^{-9}	Giga	G	10^{9}
Pico	p	10^{-12}	Tera	T	10^{12}

Metric Conversions

TABLE C.3 lists conversions between metric units and units used commonly in the United States. Note that the conversions between kilograms and pounds are valid only on Earth, because they depend on the strength of gravity.

Example 1. International athletic competitions generally use metric distances. Compare the length of a 100-meter race to that of a 100-yard race.

Solution: Table C.3 shows that 1 m = 1.094 yd, so 100 m is 109.4 yd. Note that 100 meters is almost 110 yards; a good "rule of thumb" to remember is that distances in meters are about 10% longer than the corresponding number of yards.

TABLE C.3 Metric Conversions

To Metric	From Metric
1 inch = 2.540 cm	1 cm = 0.3937 inch
1 foot = 0.3048 m	1 m = 3.28 feet
1 yard = 0.9144 m	1 m = 1.094 yards
1 mile = 1.6093 km	1 km = 0.6214 mile
1 pound = 0.4536 kg	1 kg = 2.205 pounds

Example 2. How many square kilometers are in 1 square mile?

Solution: We use the square of the miles-to-kilometers conversion factor:

$$(1 \text{ mi}^2) \times \left(\frac{1.6093 \text{ km}}{1 \text{ mi}}\right)^2 = (1 \text{ mi}^2) \times \left(1.6093^2 \frac{\text{km}^2}{\text{mi}^2}\right) = 2.5898 \text{ km}^2$$

Therefore, 1 square mile is 2.5898 square kilometers.

C.5 Finding a Ratio

Suppose you want to compare two quantities, such as the average density of Earth and the average density of Jupiter. The way we do such a comparison is by dividing, which tells us the *ratio* of the two quantities. In this case, Earth's average density is 5.52 g/cm^3 and Jupiter's average density is 1.33 g/cm^3 (see Figure 11.1), so the ratio is

$$\frac{\text{average density of Earth}}{\text{average density of Jupiter}} = \frac{5.52 \text{ g/cm}^3}{1.33 \text{ g/cm}^3} = 4.15$$

Notice how the units cancel on both the top and bottom of the fraction. We can state our result in two equivalent ways:

- The ratio of Earth's average density to Jupiter's average density is 4.15.

- Earth's average density is 4.15 times Jupiter's average density.

Sometimes, the quantities that you want to compare may each involve an equation. In such cases, you could, of course, find the ratio by first calculating each of the two quantities individually and then dividing. However, it is much easier if you first express the ratio as a fraction, putting the equation for one quantity on top and the other on the bottom. Some of the terms in the equation may then cancel out, making any calculations much easier.

Example 1. Compare the kinetic energy of a car traveling at 100 km/hr to that of the same car traveling at 50 km/hr.

Solution: We do the comparison by finding the ratio of the two kinetic energies, recalling that the formula for kinetic energy is $\frac{1}{2}mv^2$. Since we are not told the mass of the car, you might at first think that we don't have enough information to find the ratio. However, notice what happens when we put the equations for each kinetic energy into the ratio, calling the two speeds v_1 and v_2:

$$\frac{\text{K.E. car at } v_1}{\text{K.E. car at } v_2} = \frac{\frac{1}{2}m_{\text{car}} v_1^2}{\frac{1}{2}m_{\text{car}} v_2^2} = \frac{v_1^2}{v_2^2} = \left(\frac{v_1}{v_2}\right)^2$$

All the terms cancel except those with the two speeds, leaving us with a very simple formula for the ratio. Now we put in 100 km/hr for v_1 and 50 km/hr for v_2:

$$\frac{\text{K.E. car at 100 km/hr}}{\text{K.E. car at 50 km/hr}} = \left(\frac{100 \text{ km/hr}}{50 \text{ km/hr}}\right)^2 = 2^2 = 4$$

The ratio of the car's kinetic energies at 100 km/hr and 50 km/hr is 4. That is, the car has four times as much kinetic energy at 100 km/hr as it has at 50 km/hr.

Example 2. Compare the strength of gravity between Earth and the Sun to the strength of gravity between Earth and the Moon.

Solution: We do the comparison by taking the ratio of the Earth–Sun gravity to the Earth–Moon gravity. In this case, each quantity is found from the equation of Newton's law of gravity. (See Section 4.4.) Thus, the ratio is

$$\frac{\text{Earth–Sun gravity}}{\text{Earth–Moon gravity}} = \frac{G\dfrac{M_{\text{Earth}}M_{\text{Sun}}}{(d_{\text{Earth–Sun}})^2}}{G\dfrac{M_{\text{Earth}}M_{\text{Moon}}}{(d_{\text{Earth–Moon}})^2}} = \frac{M_{\text{Sun}}}{(d_{\text{Earth–Sun}})^2} \times \frac{(d_{\text{Earth–Moon}})^2}{M_{\text{Moon}}}$$

Note how all but four of the terms cancel; the last step comes from replacing the division with multiplication by the reciprocal (the "invert and multiply" rule for division). We can simplify the work further by rearranging the terms so that we have the masses and distances together:

$$\frac{\text{Earth–Sun gravity}}{\text{Earth–Moon gravity}} = \frac{M_{\text{Sun}}}{M_{\text{Moon}}} \times \frac{(d_{\text{Earth–Moon}})^2}{(d_{\text{Earth–Sun}})^2}$$

Now it is just a matter of looking up the numbers (see Appendix E) and calculating:

$$\frac{\text{Earth–Sun gravity}}{\text{Earth–Moon gravity}} = \frac{1.99 \times 10^{30}\ \text{kg}}{7.35 \times 10^{22}\ \text{kg}} \times \frac{(384.4 \times 10^3\ \text{km})^2}{(149.6 \times 10^6\ \text{km})^2} = 179$$

In other words, the Earth–Sun gravity is 179 times stronger than the Earth–Moon gravity.

D   THE PERIODIC TABLE OF THE ELEMENTS

Key

12	— Atomic number
Mg	— Element's symbol
Magnesium	— Element's name
24.305	— Atomic mass*

*Atomic masses are fractions because they represent a weighted average of atomic masses of different isotopes— in proportion to the abundance of each isotope on Earth.

1 **H** Hydrogen 1.00794																	2 **He** Helium 4.003
3 **Li** Lithium 6.941	4 **Be** Beryllium 9.01218											5 **B** Boron 10.81	6 **C** Carbon 12.011	7 **N** Nitrogen 14.007	8 **O** Oxygen 15.999	9 **F** Fluorine 18.988	10 **Ne** Neon 20.179
11 **Na** Sodium 22.990	12 **Mg** Magnesium 24.305											13 **Al** Aluminum 26.98	14 **Si** Silicon 28.086	15 **P** Phosphorus 30.974	16 **S** Sulfur 32.06	17 **Cl** Chlorine 35.453	18 **Ar** Argon 39.948
19 **K** Potassium 39.098	20 **Ca** Calcium 40.08	21 **Sc** Scandium 44.956	22 **Ti** Titanium 47.88	23 **V** Vanadium 50.94	24 **Cr** Chromium 51.996	25 **Mn** Manganese 54.938	26 **Fe** Iron 55.847	27 **Co** Cobalt 58.9332	28 **Ni** Nickel 58.69	29 **Cu** Copper 63.546	30 **Zn** Zinc 65.39	31 **Ga** Gallium 69.72	32 **Ge** Germanium 72.59	33 **As** Arsenic 74.922	34 **Se** Selenium 78.96	35 **Br** Bromine 79.904	36 **Kr** Krypton 83.80
37 **Rb** Rubidium 85.468	38 **Sr** Strontium 87.62	39 **Y** Yttrium 88.9059	40 **Zr** Zirconium 91.224	41 **Nb** Niobium 92.91	42 **Mo** Molybdenum 95.94	43 **Tc** Technetium (98)	44 **Ru** Ruthenium 101.07	45 **Rh** Rhodium 102.906	46 **Pd** Palladium 106.42	47 **Ag** Silver 107.868	48 **Cd** Cadmium 112.41	49 **In** Indium 114.82	50 **Sn** Tin 118.71	51 **Sb** Antimony 121.75	52 **Te** Tellurium 127.60	53 **I** Iodine 126.905	54 **Xe** Xenon 131.29
55 **Cs** Cesium 132.91	56 **Ba** Barium 137.34	72 **Hf** Hafnium 178.49	73 **Ta** Tantalum 180.95	74 **W** Tungsten 183.85	75 **Re** Rhenium 186.207	76 **Os** Osmium 190.2	77 **Ir** Iridium 192.22	78 **Pt** Platinum 195.08	79 **Au** Gold 196.967	80 **Hg** Mercury 200.59	81 **Ti** Thallium 204.383	82 **Pb** Lead 207.2	83 **Bi** Bismuth 208.98	84 **Po** Polonium (209)	85 **At** Astatine (210)	86 **Rn** Radon (222)
87 **Fr** Francium (223)	88 **Ra** Radium 226.0254	104 **Rf** Rutherfordium (263)	105 **Db** Dubnium (262)	106 **Sg** Seaborgium (266)	107 **Bh** Bohrium (267)	108 **Hs** Hassium (277)	109 **Mt** Meitnerium (268)	110 **Ds** Darmstadtium (281)	111 **Rg** Roentgenium (272)	112 **Cn** Copernicium (285)	113 **Uut** Ununtrium (284)	114 **Uuq** Ununquadium (289)	115 **Uup** Ununpentium (288)	116 **Uuh** Ununhexium (292)	117 **Uus** Ununseptium (294)	118 **Uuo** Ununoctium (294)

Lanthanide Series

57 **La** Lanthanum 138.906	58 **Ce** Cerium 140.12	59 **Pr** Praseodymium 140.908	60 **Nd** Neodymium 144.24	61 **Pm** Promethium (145)	62 **Sm** Samarium 150.36	63 **Eu** Europium 151.96	64 **Gd** Gadolinium 157.25	65 **Tb** Terbium 158.925	66 **Dy** Dysprosium 162.50	67 **Ho** Holmium 164.93	68 **Er** Erbium 167.26	69 **Tm** Thulium 168.934	70 **Yb** Ytterbium 173.04	71 **Lu** Lutetium 174.967

Actinide Series

89 **Ac** Actinium 227.028	90 **Th** Thorium 232.038	91 **Pa** Protactinium 231.036	92 **U** Uranium 238.029	93 **Np** Neptunium 237.048	94 **Pu** Plutonium (244)	95 **Am** Americium (243)	96 **Cm** Curium (247)	97 **Bk** Berkelium (247)	98 **Cf** Californium (251)	99 **Es** Einsteinium (252)	100 **Fm** Fermium (257)	101 **Md** Mendelevium (258)	102 **No** Nobelium (259)	103 **Lr** Lawrencium (260)

E PLANETARY DATA

TABLE E.1   Physical Properties of the Sun and Planets

Name	Radius (Eq[a]) (km)	Radius (Eq) (Earth units)	Mass (kg)	Mass (Earth units)	Average Density (g/cm^3)	Surface Gravity (Earth = 1)	Escape Velocity (km/s)
Sun	695,000	109	1.99×10^{30}	333,000	1.41	27.5	—
Mercury	2440	0.382	3.30×10^{23}	0.055	5.43	0.38	4.43
Venus	6051	0.949	4.87×10^{24}	0.815	5.25	0.91	10.4
Earth	6378	1.00	5.97×10^{24}	1.00	5.52	1.00	11.2
Mars	3397	0.533	6.42×10^{23}	0.107	3.93	0.38	5.03
Jupiter	71,492	11.19	1.90×10^{27}	317.9	1.33	2.36	59.5
Saturn	60,268	9.46	5.69×10^{26}	95.18	0.70	0.92	35.5
Uranus	25,559	3.98	8.66×10^{25}	14.54	1.32	0.91	21.3
Neptune	24,764	3.81	1.03×10^{26}	17.13	1.64	1.14	23.6
Pluto[b]	1160	0.181	1.31×10^{22}	0.0022	2.05	0.07	1.25
Eris[b]	1430	0.22	1.66×10^{22}	0.0028	2.30	0.08	1.4

[a]Eq = equatorial.
[b]Under the IAU definitions of August 2006, Pluto and Eris are officially designated "dwarf planets."

TABLE E.2   Orbital Properties of the Sun and Planets

Name	Distance from Sun[a] (AU)	(10⁶ km)	Orbital Period (years)	Orbital Inclination[b] (degrees)	Orbital Eccentricity	Sidereal Rotation Period (Earth days)[c]	Axis Tilt (degrees)
Sun	—	—	—	—	—	25.4	7.25
Mercury	0.387	57.9	0.2409	7.00	0.206	58.6	0.0
Venus	0.723	108.2	0.6152	3.39	0.007	−243.0	177.3
Earth	1.00	149.6	1.0	0.00	0.017	0.9973	23.45
Mars	1.524	227.9	1.881	1.85	0.093	1.026	25.2
Jupiter	5.203	778.3	11.86	1.31	0.048	0.41	3.08
Saturn	9.54	1427	29.5	2.48	0.056	0.44	26.73
Uranus	19.19	2870	84.01	0.77	0.046	−0.72	97.92
Neptune	30.06	4497	164.8	1.77	0.010	0.67	29.6
Pluto	39.48	5906	248.0	17.14	0.248	−6.39	112.5
Eris	67.67	10,120	557	44.19	0.442	15.8	78

[a]Semimajor axis of the orbit.

[b]With respect to the ecliptic.

[c]A negative sign indicates rotation is backward relative to other planets.

TABLE E.3 Satellites of the Solar System (as of 2012)[a]

Planet Satellite	Radius or Dimensions[b] (km)	Distance from Planet (10³ km)	Orbital Period[c] (Earth days)	Mass[d] (kg)	Density[d] (g/cm³)	Notes About the Satellite
Earth						
Moon	1738	384.4	27.322	7.349×10^{22}	3.34	*Moon:* Probably formed in giant impact.
Mars						
Phobos	13 × 11 × 9	9.38	0.319	1.3×10^{16}	1.9	*Phobos, Deimos:* Probable captured asteroids.
Deimos	8 × 6 × 5	23.5	1.263	1.8×10^{15}	2.2	
Jupiter						
Small inner moons (4 moons)	8–83	128–222	0.295–0.674	—	—	*Metis, Adrastea, Amalthea, Thebe:* Small moonlets within and near Jupiter's ring system.
Io	1821	421.6	1.769	8.933×10^{22}	3.57	*Io:* Most volcanically active object in the solar system.
Europa	1565	670.9	3.551	4.797×10^{22}	2.97	*Europa:* Possible oceans under icy crust.
Ganymede	2634	1070.0	7.155	1.482×10^{23}	1.94	*Ganymede:* Largest satellite in solar system; unusual ice geology.
Callisto	2403	1883.0	16.689	1.076×10^{23}	1.86	*Callisto:* Cratered iceball.
Irregular group 1 (7 moons)	4–85	7500–17,000	130–457	—	—	*Themisto, Leda, Himalia, Lysithea, Elara, and others:* Probable captured moons with inclined orbits.
Irregular group 2 (52 moons)	1–30	17,000–29,000	490–980	—	—	*Ananke, Carme, Pasiphae, Sinope, and others:* Probable captured moons in inclined backward orbits.
Saturn						
Small inner moons (12)	3–89	117–212	0.5–1.2	—	—	*Pan, Atlas, Prometheus, Pandora, Epimetheus, Janus, and others:* Small moonlets within and near Saturn's ring system.
Mimas	199	185.52	0.942	3.70×10^{19}	1.17	*Mimas, Enceladus, Tethys:* Small and medium-size iceballs, many with interesting geology.
Enceladus	249	238.02	1.370	1.2×10^{20}	1.24	
Tethys	530	294.66	1.888	6.17×10^{20}	1.26	
Calypso and Telesto	8–12	294.66	1.888	—	—	*Calypso and Telesto:* Small moonlets sharing Tethys's orbit.
Dione	559	377.4	2.737	1.08×10^{21}	1.44	*Dione:* Medium-size iceball, with interesting geology.
Helene and Polydeuces	2–16	377.4	2.737	1.6×10^{16}	—	*Helene and Polydeuces:* Small moonlets sharing Dione's orbit.
Rhea	764	527.04	4.518	2.31×10^{21}	1.33	*Rhea:* Medium-size iceball, with interesting geology.
Titan	2575	1221.85	15.945	1.35×10^{23}	1.88	*Titan:* Dense atmosphere shrouds surface; ongoing geological activity.
Hyperion	180 × 140 × 112	1481.1	21.277	2.8×10^{19}	—	*Hyperion:* Only satellite known not to rotate synchronously.
Iapetus	718	3561.3	79.331	1.59×10^{21}	1.21	*Iapetus:* Bright and dark hemispheres show greatest contrast in the solar system.

Name	Radius (km)	Distance	Period (days)	Mass (kg)	Density	Notes
Phoebe	110	12,952	−550.4	1×10^{19}	—	*Phoebe:* Very dark; material ejected from Phoebe may coat one side of Iapetus.
Irregular groups (37 moons)	2–16	11,300–25,200	450–930 / −550 to −150	—	—	Probable captured moons with highly inclined and/or backward orbits.
Uranus						
Small inner moons (13 moons)	5–81	49–98	0.3–0.9	—	—	*Cordelia, Ophelia, Bianca, Cressida, Desdemona, Juliet, Portia, Rosalind, Cupid, Belinda, Perdita, Puck, Mab:* Small moonlets within and near Uranus's ring system.
Miranda	236	129.8	1.413	6.6×10^{19}	1.26	*Miranda, Ariel, Umbriel, Titania, Oberon:* Small and medium-size iceballs, with some interesting geology.
Ariel	579	191.2	2.520	1.35×10^{21}	1.65	
Umbriel	584.7	266.0	4.144	1.17×10^{21}	1.44	
Titania	788.9	435.8	8.706	3.52×10^{21}	1.59	
Oberon	761.4	582.6	13.463	3.01×10^{21}	1.50	
Irregular group (9 moons)	5–95	4280–21,000	260–2800	—	—	*Francisco, Caliban, Stephano, Trinculo, Sycorax, Margaret, Prospero, Setebos, Ferdinand:* Probable captured moons; several in backward orbits.
Neptune						
Small inner moons (5 moons)	29–96	48–74	0.30–0.55	—	—	*Naiad, Thalassa, Despina, Galatea, Larissa:* Small moonlets within and near Neptune's ring system.
Proteus	218 × 208 × 201	117.6	1.121	6×10^{19}	2.0	
Triton	1352.6	354.59	−5.875	2.14×10^{22}	—	*Triton:* Probable captured Kuiper belt object—largest captured object in solar system.
Nereid	170	5588.6	360.125	3.1×10^{19}	—	*Nereid:* Small, icy moon; very little known.
Irregulars (5 moons)	15–27	16,600–49,300	1880–9750	—	—	*2002 N1, N2, N3, N4, 2003 N1:* Possible captured moons in inclined or backward orbit.
Pluto						
Charon	593	17.5	6.4	1.56×10^{21}	1.6	*Charon:* Unusually large compared to Pluto; may have formed in giant impact.
P5	5	42.0	20.2	—	—	*P5, Nix, P4, Hydra:* Newly discovered moons outside Charon's orbit.
Nix	50	48.7	24.9	—	—	
P4	10	59.0	32.1	—	—	
Hydra	75	64.7	38.2	—	—	
Eris						
Dysnomia	50	37.4	15.8	—	—	*Dysnomia:* Approximate properties determined in June 2007.

[a]*Note:* Authorities differ substantially on many of the values in this table.

[b]$a \times b \times c$ values for the dimensions are the approximate lengths of the axes (center to edge) for irregular moons.

[c]Negative sign indicates backward orbit.

[d]Masses and densities are most accurate for those satellites visited by a spacecraft on a flyby. Masses for the smallest moons have not been measured but can be estimated from the radius and an assumed density.

TABLE F.1 Stars Within 12 Light-Years

Star	Distance (ly)	Spectral Type		RA h	RA m	Dec °	Dec ′	Luminosity (L/L_{Sun})
Sun	0.000016	G2	V	—	—	—	—	1.0
Proxima Centauri	4.2	M5.0	V	14	30	−62	41	0.0006
α Centauri A	4.4	G2	V	14	40	−60	50	1.6
α Centauri B	4.4	K0	V	14	40	−60	50	0.53
Barnard's Star	6.0	M4	V	17	58	+04	42	0.005
Wolf 359	7.8	M5.5	V	10	56	+07	01	0.0008
Lalande 21185	8.3	M2	V	11	03	+35	58	0.03
Sirius A	8.6	A1	V	06	45	−16	42	26.0
Sirius B	8.6	DA2	White dwarf	06	45	−16	42	0.002
BL Ceti	8.7	M5.5	V	01	39	−17	57	0.0009
UV Ceti	8.7	M6	V	01	39	−17	57	0.0006
Ross 154	9.7	M3.5	V	18	50	−23	50	0.004
Ross 248	10.3	M5.5	V	23	42	+44	11	0.001
ε Eridani	10.5	K2	V	03	33	−09	28	0.37
Lacaille 9352	10.7	M1.0	V	23	06	−35	51	0.05
Ross 128	10.9	M4	V	11	48	+00	49	0.003
EZ Aquarii A	11.3	M5	V	22	39	−15	18	0.0006
EZ Aquarii B	11.3	—	—	22	39	−15	18	0.0004
EZ Aquarii C	11.3	—	—	22	39	−15	18	0.0003
61 Cygni A	11.4	K5	V	21	07	+38	42	0.17
61 Cygni B	11.4	K7	V	21	07	+38	42	0.10
Procyon A	11.4	F5	IV–V	07	39	+05	14	8.6
Procyon B	11.4	DA	White dwarf	07	39	+05	14	0.0005
Gliese 725 A	11.5	M3	V	18	43	+59	38	0.02
Gliese 725 B	11.5	M3.5	V	18	43	+59	38	0.01
GX Andromedae	11.6	M1.5	V	00	18	+44	01	0.03
GQ Andromedae	11.6	M3.5	V	00	18	+44	01	0.003
ε Indi A	11.8	K5	V	22	03	−56	45	0.30
ε Indi B	11.8	T1.0	Brown dwarf	22	04	−56	46	—
ε Indi C	11.8	T6.0	Brown dwarf	22	04	−56	46	—
DX Cancri	11.8	M6.0	V	08	30	+26	47	0.0003
τ Ceti	11.9	G8.5	V	01	44	−15	57	0.67
GJ 1061	12.0	M5.0	V	03	36	−44	31	0.001

Note: These data were provided by the RECONS project, courtesy of Dr. Todd Henry (January, 2010). The luminosities are all total (bolometric) luminosities. The DA stellar types are white dwarfs. The coordinates are for the year 2000. The bolometric luminosity of the brown dwarfs is primarily in the infrared and has not been measured accurately yet.

TABLE F.2 Twenty Brightest Stars

Star	Constellation	RA h	RA m	Dec °	Dec ′	Distance (ly)	Spectral Type		Apparent Magnitude	Luminosity (L/L_{Sun})
Sirius	Canis Major	6	45	−16	42	8.6	A1	V	−1.46	26
Canopus	Carina	6	24	−52	41	313	F0	Ib–II	−0.72	13,000
α Centauri	Centaurus	14	40	−60	50	4.4	G2	V	−0.01	1.6
							K0	V	1.3	0.53
Arcturus	Boötes	14	16	+19	11	37	K2	III	−0.06	170
Vega	Lyra	18	37	+38	47	25	A0	V	0.04	60
Capella	Auriga	5	17	+46	00	42	G0	III	0.75	70
							G8	III	0.85	77
Rigel	Orion	5	15	−08	12	772	B8	Ia	0.14	70,000
Procyon	Canis Minor	7	39	+05	14	11.4	F5	IV–V	0.37	7.4
Betelgeuse	Orion	5	55	+07	24	427	M2	Iab	0.41	38,000
Achernar	Eridanus	1	38	−57	15	144	B5	V	0.51	3600
Hadar	Centaurus	14	04	−60	22	525	B1	III	0.63	100,000
Altair	Aquila	19	51	+08	52	17	A7	IV–V	0.77	10.5
Acrux	Crux	12	27	−63	06	321	B1	IV	1.39	22,000
							B3	V	1.9	7500
Aldebaran	Taurus	4	36	+16	30	65	K5	III	0.86	350
Spica	Virgo	13	25	−11	09	260	B1	V	0.91	23,000
Antares	Scorpio	16	29	−26	26	604	M1	Ib	0.92	38,000
Pollux	Gemini	7	45	+28	01	34	K0	III	1.16	45
Fomalhaut	Piscis Austrinus	22	58	−29	37	25	A3	V	1.19	18
Deneb	Cygnus	20	41	+45	16	2500	A2	Ia	1.26	170,000
β Crucis	Crux	12	48	−59	40	352	B0.5	IV	1.28	37,000

Note: Three of the stars on this list, Capella, α Centauri, and Acrux, are binary systems with members of comparable brightness. They are counted as single stars because that is how they appear to the naked eye. All the luminosities given are total (bolometric) luminosities. The coordinates are for the year 2000.

G GALAXY DATA

TABLE G.1 Galaxies of the Local Group

Galaxy Name	Distance (millions of ly)	Type[a]	RA h	RA m	Dec °	Dec ′	Luminosity (millions of L_{Sun})
Milky Way	—	Sbc	—	—	—	—	15,000
WLM	3.0	Irr	00	02	−15	30	50
IC 10	2.7	dIrr	00	20	+59	18	160
Cetus	2.5	dE	00	26	−11	02	0.72
NGC 147	2.4	dE	00	33	+48	30	131
And III	2.5	dE	00	35	+36	30	1.1
NGC 185	2.0	dE	00	39	+48	20	120
NGC 205	2.7	E	00	40	+41	41	370
And VIII	2.7	dE	00	42	+40	37	240
M32	2.6	E	00	43	+40	52	380
M31	2.5	Sb	00	43	+41	16	21,000
And I	2.6	dE	00	46	+38	00	4.7
SMC	0.19	Irr	00	53	−72	50	230
And IX	2.9	dE	00	52	+43	12	—
Sculptor	0.26	dE	01	00	−33	42	2.2
LGS 3	2.6	dIrr	01	04	+21	53	1.3
IC 1613	2.3	Irr	01	05	+02	08	64
And V	2.9	dE	01	10	+47	38	—
And II	1.7	dE	01	16	+33	26	2.4
M33	2.7	Sc	01	34	+30	40	2800
Phoenix	1.5	dIrr	01	51	−44	27	0.9
Fornax	0.45	dE	02	40	−34	27	15.5
EGB0427 + 63	4.3	dIrr	04	32	+63	36	9.1
LMC	0.16	Irr	05	24	−69	45	1300
Carina	0.33	dE	06	42	−50	58	0.4
Canis Major	0.025	dIrr	07	15	−28	00	—
Leo A	2.2	dIrr	09	59	+30	45	3.0
Sextans B	4.4	dIrr	10	00	+05	20	41
NGC 3109	4.1	Irr	10	03	−26	09	160
Antlia	4.0	dIrr	10	04	−27	19	1.7
Leo I	0.82	dE	10	08	+12	18	4.8
Sextans A	4.7	dIrr	10	11	−04	42	56
Sextans	0.28	dE	10	13	−01	37	0.5
Leo II	0.67	dE	11	13	+22	09	0.6
GR 8	5.2	dIrr	12	59	+14	13	3.4
Ursa Minor	0.22	dE	15	09	+67	13	0.3
Draco	2.7	dE	17	20	+57	55	0.3
Sagittarius	0.08	dE	18	55	−30	29	18
SagDIG	3.5	dIrr	19	30	−17	41	6.8
NGC 6822	1.6	Irr	19	45	−14	48	94
DDO 210	2.6	dIrr	20	47	−12	51	0.8
IC 5152	5.2	dIrr	22	03	−51	18	70
Tucana	2.9	dE	22	42	−64	25	0.5
UKS2323-326	4.3	dE	23	26	−32	23	5.2
And VII	2.6	dE	23	38	+50	35	—
Pegasus	3.1	dIrr	23	29	+14	45	12
And VI	2.8	dE	23	52	+24	36	—

[a]Types beginning with S are spiral galaxies classified according to Hubble's system (see Chapter 20). Type E galaxies are elliptical or spheroidal. Type Irr galaxies are irregular. The prefix d denotes a dwarf galaxy. This list is based on a list originally published by M. Mateo in 1998 and augmented by discoveries of Local Group galaxies made between 1998 and 2005.

TABLE G.2 Nearby Galaxies in the Messier Catalog[a, b]

Galaxy Name (M / NGC)[c]	RA h	RA m	Dec °	Dec '	RV_{hel}[d]	RV_{gal}[e]	Type[f]	Nickname
M31 / NGC 224	00	43	+41	16	-300 ± 4	-122	Spiral	Andromeda
M32 / NGC 221	00	43	+40	52	-145 ± 2	32	Elliptical	
M33 / NGC 598	01	34	+30	40	-179 ± 3	-44	Spiral	Triangulum
M49 / NGC 4472	12	30	+08	00	997 ± 7	929	Elliptical/Lenticular/Seyfert	
M51 / NGC 5194	13	30	+47	12	463 ± 3	550	Spiral/Interacting	Whirlpool
M58 / NGC 4579	12	38	+11	49	1519 ± 6	1468	Spiral/Seyfert	
M59 / NGC 4621	12	42	+11	39	410 ± 6	361	Elliptical	
M60 / NGC 4649	12	44	+11	33	1117 ± 6	1068	Elliptical	
M61 / NGC 4303	12	22	+04	28	1566 ± 2	1483	Spiral/Seyfert	
M63 / NGC 5055	13	16	+42	02	504 ± 4	570	Spiral	Sunflower
M64 / NGC 4826	12	57	+21	41	408 ± 4	400	Spiral/Seyfert	Black Eye
M65 / NGC 3623	11	19	+13	06	807 ± 3	723	Spiral	
M66 / NGC 3627	11	20	+12	59	727 ± 3	643	Spiral/Seyfert	
M74 / NGC 628	01	37	+15	47	657 ± 1	754	Spiral	
M77 / NGC 1068	02	43	-00	01	1137 ± 3	1146	Spiral/Seyfert	
M81 / NGC 3031	09	56	+69	04	-34 ± 4	73	Spiral/Seyfert	
M82 / NGC 3034	09	56	+69	41	203 ± 4	312	Irregular/Starburst	
M83 / NGC 5236	13	37	-29	52	516 ± 4	385	Spiral/Starburst	
M84 / NGC 4374	12	25	+12	53	1060 ± 6	1005	Elliptical	
M85 / NGC 4382	12	25	+18	11	729 ± 2	692	Spiral	
M86 / NGC 4406	12	26	+12	57	-244 ± 5	-298	Elliptical/Lenticular	
M87 / NGC 4486	12	30	+12	23	1307 ± 7	1254	Elliptical/Central Dominant/Seyfert	Virgo A
M88 / NGC 4501	12	32	+14	25	2281 ± 3	2235	Spiral/Seyfert	
M89 / NGC 4552	12	36	+12	33	340 ± 4	290	Elliptical	
M90 / NGC 4569	12	37	+13	10	-235 ± 4	-282	Spiral/Seyfert	
M91 / NGC 4548	12	35	+14	30	486 ± 4	442	Spiral/Seyfert	
M94 / NGC 4736	12	51	+41	07	308 ± 1	360	Spiral	
M95 / NGC 3351	10	44	+11	42	778 ± 4	677	Spiral/Starburst	
M96 / NGC 3368	10	47	+11	49	897 ± 4	797	Spiral/Seyfert	
M98 / NGC 4192	12	14	+14	54	-142 ± 4	-195	Spiral/Seyfert	
M99 / NGC 4254	12	19	+14	25	2407 ± 3	2354	Spiral	
M100 / NGC 4321	12	23	+15	49	1571 ± 1	1525	Spiral	
M101 / NGC 5457	14	03	+54	21	241 ± 2	360	Spiral	
M104 / NGC 4594	12	40	-11	37	1024 ± 5	904	Spiral/Seyfert	Sombrero
M105 / NGC 3379	10	48	+12	35	911 ± 2	814	Elliptical	
M106 / NGC 4258	12	19	+47	18	448 ± 3	507	Spiral/Seyfert	
M108 / NGC 3556	11	09	+55	57	695 ± 3	765	Spiral	
M109 / NGC 3992	11	55	+53	39	1048 ± 4	1121	Spiral	
M110 / NGC 205	00	40	+41	41	-241 ± 3	-61	Elliptical	

[a]Galaxies identified in the catalog published by Charles Messier in 1781; these galaxies are relatively easy to observe with small telescopes.

[b]Data obtained from NED: NASA/IPAC Extragalactic Database (http://ned.ipac.caltech.edu). The original Messier list of galaxies was obtained from SED, and the list data were updated to 2001 and M102 was dropped.

[c]The galaxies are identified by their Messier number (M followed by a number) and NGC number, which comes from the *New General Catalog* published in 1888.

[d]Radial velocity in kilometers per second, with respect to the Sun (heliocentric). Positive values mean motion away from the Sun; negative values are toward the Sun.

[e]Radial velocity in kilometers per second, with respect to the Milky Way Galaxy, calculated from the RV_{hel} values with a correction for the Sun's motion around the galactic center.

[f]Galaxies are first listed by their primary type (spiral, elliptical, or irregular) and then by any other special categories that apply (see Chapter 20).

TABLE G.3 Nearby, X-Ray Bright Clusters of Galaxies

Cluster Name	Redshift	Distance[a] (billions of ly)	Temperature of Intracluster Medium (millions of K)	Average Orbital Velocity of Galaxies[b] (km/s)	Cluster Mass[c] ($10^{15} M_{Sun}$)
Abell 2142	0.0907	1.26	101. ± 2	1132 ± 110	1.6
Abell 2029	0.0766	1.07	100. ± 3	1164 ± 98	1.5
Abell 401	0.0737	1.03	95.2 ± 5	1152 ± 86	1.4
Coma	0.0233	0.32	95.1 ± 1	821 ± 49	1.4
Abell 754	0.0539	0.75	93.3 ± 3	662 ± 77	1.4
Abell 2256	0.0589	0.82	87.0 ± 2	1348 ± 86	1.4
Abell 399	0.0718	1.00	81.7 ± 7	1116 ± 89	1.1
Abell 3571	0.0395	0.55	81.1 ± 3	1045 ± 109	1.1
Abell 478	0.0882	1.23	78.9 ± 2	904 ± 281	1.1
Abell 3667	0.0566	0.79	78.5 ± 6	971 ± 62	1.1
Abell 3266	0.0599	0.84	78.2 ± 5	1107 ± 82	1.1
Abell 1651a	0.0846	1.18	73.1 ± 6	685 ± 129	0.96
Abell 85	0.0560	0.78	70.9 ± 2	969 ± 95	0.92
Abell 119	0.0438	0.61	65.6 ± 5	679 ± 106	0.81
Abell 3558	0.0480	0.67	65.3 ± 2	977 ± 39	0.81
Abell 1795	0.0632	0.88	62.9 ± 2	834 ± 85	0.77
Abell 2199	0.0314	0.44	52.7 ± 1	801 ± 92	0.59
Abell 2147	0.0353	0.49	51.1 ± 4	821 ± 68	0.56
Abell 3562	0.0478	0.67	45.7 ± 8	736 ± 49	0.48
Abell 496	0.0325	0.45	45.3 ± 1	687 ± 89	0.47
Centaurus	0.0103	0.14	42.2 ± 1	863 ± 34	0.42
Abell 1367	0.0213	0.30	41.3 ± 2	822 ± 69	0.41
Hydra	0.0126	0.18	38.0 ± 1	610 ± 52	0.36
C0336	0.0349	0.49	37.4 ± 1	650 ± 170	0.35
Virgo	0.0038	0.05	25.7 ± 0.5	632 ± 41	0.20

Note: This table lists the 25 brightest clusters of galaxies in the X-ray sky from a catalog by J. P. Henry (2000).
[a]Cluster distances were computed using a value for Hubble's constant of 21.5 km/s/million light-years.

[b]The average orbital velocities given in this column are the velocity component along our line of sight. This velocity should be multiplied by the square root of 2 to get the average orbital velocity used in Mathematical Insights 23.2 and 23.3.

[c]This column gives each cluster's mass within the largest radius at which the intracluster medium can be in gravitational equilibrium. Because our estimates of that radius depend on Hubble's constant, these masses are inversely proportional to Hubble's constant, which we have assumed to be 21.5 km/s/million light-years.

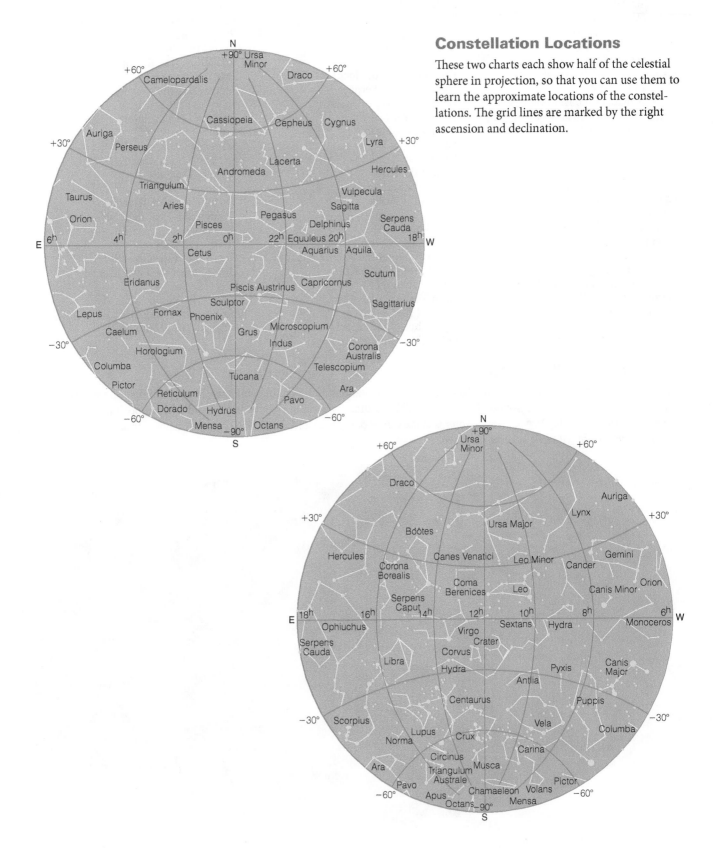

Constellation Locations

These two charts each show half of the celestial sphere in projection, so that you can use them to learn the approximate locations of the constellations. The grid lines are marked by the right ascension and declination.

Constellation Names (English Equivalent in Parentheses)

Andromeda (The Chained Princess)
Antlia (The Air Pump)
Apus (The Bird of Paradise)
Aquarius (The Water Bearer)
Aquila (The Eagle)
Ara (The Altar)
Aries (The Ram)
Auriga (The Charioteer)
Boötes (The Herdsman)
Caelum (The Chisel)
Camelopardalis (The Giraffe)
Cancer (The Crab)
Canes Venatici (The Hunting Dogs)
Canis Major (The Great Dog)
Canis Minor (The Little Dog)
Capricornus (The Sea Goat)
Carina (The Keel)
Cassiopeia (The Queen)
Centaurus (The Centaur)
Cepheus (The King)
Cetus (The Whale)
Chamaeleon (The Chameleon)
Circinus (The Drawing Compass)
Columba (The Dove)
Coma Berenices (Berenice's Hair)
Corona Australis (The Southern Crown)
Corona Borealis (The Northern Crown)
Corvus (The Crow)
Crater (The Cup)
Crux (The Southern Cross)

Cygnus (The Swan)
Delphinus (The Dolphin)
Dorado (The Goldfish)
Draco (The Dragon)
Equuleus (The Little Horse)
Eridanus (The River)
Fornax (The Furnace)
Gemini (The Twins)
Grus (The Crane)
Hercules
Horologium (The Clock)
Hydra (The Sea Serpent)
Hydrus (The Water Snake)
Indus (The Indian)
Lacerta (The Lizard)
Leo (The Lion)
Leo Minor (The Little Lion)
Lepus (The Hare)
Libra (The Scales)
Lupus (The Wolf)
Lynx (The Lynx)
Lyra (The Lyre)
Mensa (The Table)
Microscopium (The Microscope)
Monoceros (The Unicorn)
Musca (The Fly)
Norma (The Level)
Octans (The Octant)
Ophiuchus (The Serpent Bearer)
Orion (The Hunter)

Pavo (The Peacock)
Pegasus (The Winged Horse)
Perseus (The Hero)
Phoenix (The Phoenix)
Pictor (The Painter's Easel)
Pisces (The Fish)
Piscis Austrinus (The Southern Fish)
Puppis (The Stern)
Pyxis (The Compass)
Reticulum (The Reticle)
Sagitta (The Arrow)
Sagittarius (The Archer)
Scorpius (The Scorpion)
Sculptor (The Sculptor)
Scutum (The Shield)
Serpens (The Serpent)
Sextans (The Sextant)
Taurus (The Bull)
Telescopium (The Telescope)
Triangulum (The Triangle)
Triangulum Australe (The Southern Triangle)
Tucana (The Toucan)
Ursa Major (The Great Bear)
Ursa Minor (The Little Bear)
Vela (The Sail)
Virgo (The Virgin)
Volans (The Flying Fish)
Vulpecula (The Fox)

All-Sky Constellation Map

This map of the entire sky shows the locations of all the constellations, in much the same way that a world map shows all of the countries on Earth. It does not use the usual celestial coordinate system of right ascension and declination, but instead is oriented so that the Milky Way Galaxy's center is at the center of the map and the Milky Way's disk (shown in shades of lighter blue) stretches from left to right across the map.

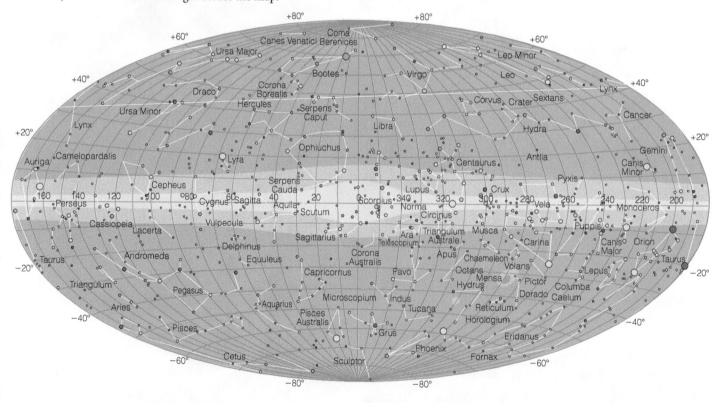

STAR CHARTS

How to use the star charts:

Check the times and dates under each chart to find the best one for you. Take it outdoors within an hour or so of the time listed for your date. Bring a dim flashlight to help you read it.

On each chart, the round outside edge represents the horizon all around you. Compass directions around the horizon are marked in yellow. Turn the chart around so that the edge marked with the direction you're facing (for example, north, southeast) is down. The stars above this horizon now match the stars you are facing. Ignore the rest until you turn to look in a different direction.

The center of the chart represents the sky overhead, so a star plotted on the chart halfway from the edge to the center can be found in the sky halfway from the horizon to straight up.

The charts are drawn for 40°N latitude (for example, Denver, New York, Madrid). If you live far south of there, stars in the southern part of your sky will appear higher than on the chart and stars in the north will be lower. If you live far north of there, the reverse is true.

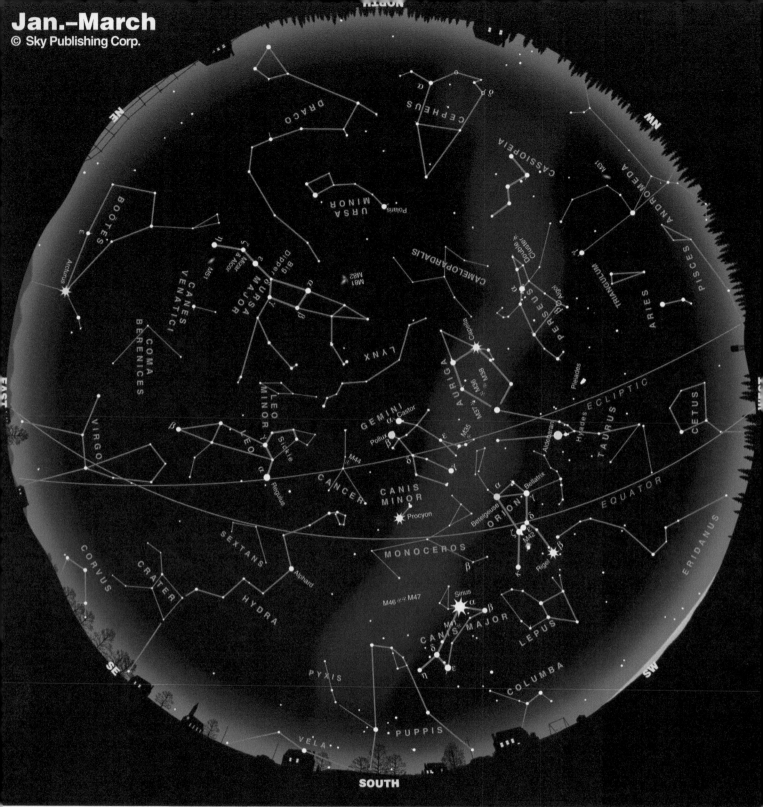

Jan.–March
© Sky Publishing Corp.

© 1999 Sky & Telescope

Use this chart January, February, and March.

Early January—1 A.M. Early February—11 P.M. Early March—9 P.M.
Late January—Midnight Late February—10 P.M. Late March—Dusk

Apr.–June
© Sky Publishing Corp.

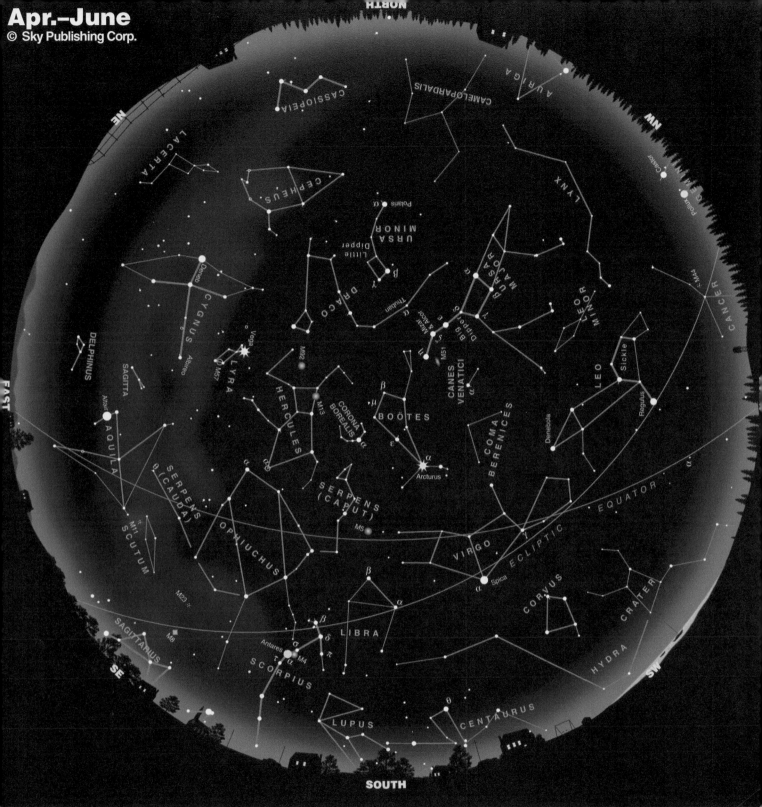

© 1999 Sky & Telescope

Use this chart April, May, and June.

Early April—3 A.M.*   Early May—1 A.M.*   Early June—11 P.M.*
Late April—2 A.M.*   Late May—Midnight*   Late June—Dusk

*Daylight Saving Time

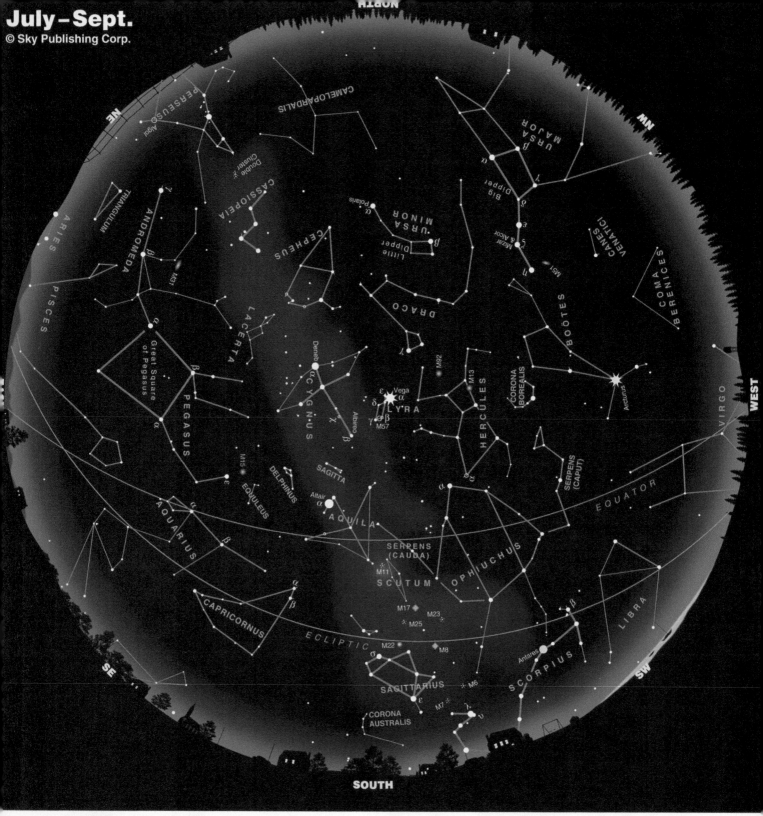

July–Sept.
© Sky Publishing Corp.

© 1999 Sky & Telescope

Use this chart July, August, and September.

Early July—1 A.M.*   Early August—11 P.M.*   Early September—9 P.M.*

Late July—Midnight*   Late August—10 P.M.*   Late September—Dusk

*Daylight Saving Time

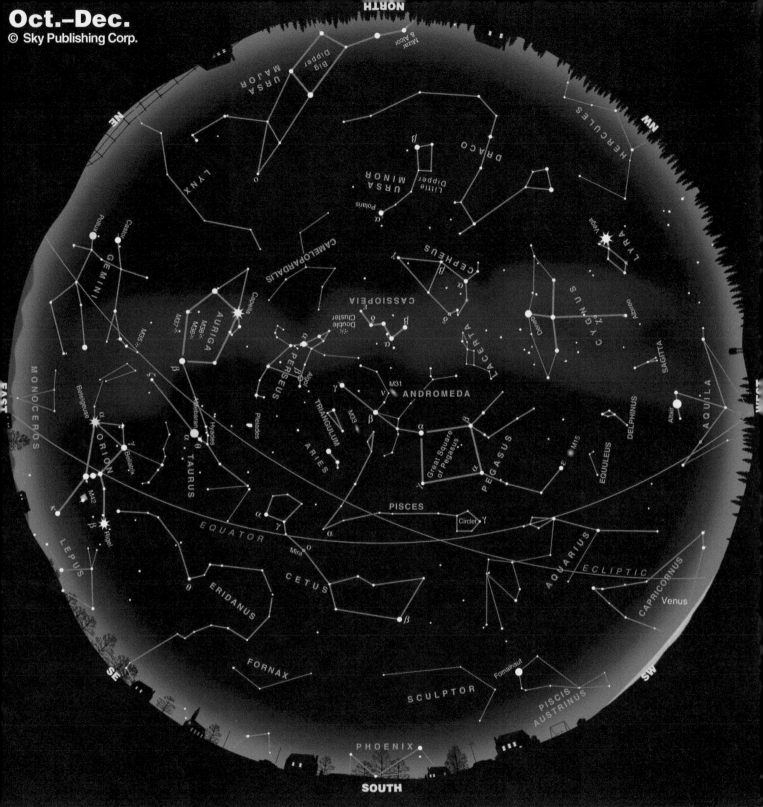

© 1999 Sky & Telescope

Use this chart October, November, and December.

Early October—1 A.M.*   Early November—10 P.M.   Early December—8 P.M.
Late October—Midnight*   Late November—9 P.M.   Late December—7 P.M.

*Daylight Saving Time

Chapter 1

1. b
2. c
3. c
4. No; the nearest stars would not fit on Earth on this scale.

Chapter 2

1. B
2. D
3. C
4. d
5. b
6. d
7. c
8. c

Chapter 3

1. d
2. a
3. d
4. a
5. a
6. a
7. a

Chapter S1

1. a
2. b
3. b, c, f
4. 66.5°S (the Antarctic Circle)
5. d
6. a, b, c
7. Declination is +30°; right ascension cannot be characterized without further information.

Chapter 4

1. b
2. c
3. d
4. d
5. c

Chapter 5

1. 1
2. 5
3. b
4. b
5. c

Chapter 6

1. b
2. a, c, e
3. all
4. a
5. a

Chapter 7

1. From A to H, the planets are Mercury, Mars, Venus, Earth, Neptune, Uranus, Saturn, and Jupiter.
2. The pairs are Mercury and Mars, Venus and Earth, Neptune and Uranus, Saturn and Jupiter.
3. d
4. a. The exponential plot shows information on low-mass planets that can't be seen on the linear plot.
   b. The linear plot
   c. The exponential plot

Chapter 8

1. a
2. d
3. c

Chapter 9

1. a
2. c
3. b
4. b, c, a

Chapter 10

1. d
2. b
3. d
4. c
5. b

Chapter 11

1. c
2. e
3. b
4. b

Chapter 12

1. about 5 km, though its unusual shape could lead to answers between 4 and 8 km
2. b
3. a
4. c
5. b

Chapter 13

1. about 4 days
2. about 50 meters/sec
3. a. 2 b. 4 c. 3 d. 1
4. a. 4 b. 2 c. 1 d. 3
5. b

Chapter 14

1. d
2. Sunspots appear over a range of 40–50°N latitude to 40–50°S latitude.
3. Sunspots get closer to the equator during a sunspot cycle.

Chapter 15

1. b
2. d
3. c
4. luminosity: about $10,000L_{Sun}$; lifetime: slightly longer than 10 million years
5. luminosity: about $100L_{Sun}$; lifetime: slightly shorter than 1 billion years
6. luminosity: about $10L_{Sun}$; lifetime: approximately 1 billion years

Chapter 16

1. 200–300 light-years
2. About 1000 light-years
3. Cool gas is mostly in the centers of the streams.
4. The cold gas heats up when it enters the central cloud.

Chapter 17

1. approximately $10L_{Sun}$
2. approximately 3500 K
3. approximately $10^4 L_{Sun}$
4. approximately $10^{-4} L_{Sun}$

Chapter 18

1. b
2. d
3. b
4. c
5. d

Chapter 19

1. brightest: white; lowest levels of brightness: black/dark blue
2. white
3. Regions with strong radio emission are dark in the visible-light image.
4. Regions with strong radio emission are brighter in the infrared image than they are in the visible-light image.
5. c
6. yes

Chapter 20

1. Cepheids
2. parallax
3. approximately 10 million to 100 million light-years
4. from about 30 million light-years to more than 10 billion light-years
5. Cepheids
6. white dwarf supernovae (distant standards)

Chapter 21

1. white
2. purple
3. approximately 400,000 light-years
4. approximately 20,000 light-years

Chapter 22

1. b
2. c
3. d

Chapter 23

1. accelerating
2. accelerating
3. coasting
4. decelerating

Chapter 24

1. g, f, b, e, d, c, a
2. b, a, c, d
3. a, c, d
4. d
5. c
6. c

GLOSSARY

absolute magnitude A measure of an object's luminosity; defined to be the apparent magnitude the object would have if it were located exactly 10 parsecs away.

absolute zero The coldest possible temperature, which is 0 K.

absorption (of light) The process by which matter absorbs radiative energy.

absorption line spectrum A spectrum that contains absorption lines.

accelerating universe A universe in which a repulsive force (*see* cosmological constant) causes the expansion of the universe to accelerate with time. Its galaxies will recede from one another increasingly faster, and it will become cold and dark more quickly than a coasting universe.

acceleration The rate at which an object's velocity changes. Its standard units are m/s^2.

acceleration of gravity The acceleration of a falling object. On Earth, the acceleration of gravity, designated by g, is 9.8 m/s^2.

accretion The process by which small objects gather together to make larger objects.

accretion disk A rapidly rotating disk of material that gradually falls inward as it orbits a starlike object (e.g., white dwarf, neutron star, or black hole).

active galactic nuclei The unusually luminous centers of some galaxies, thought to be powered by accretion onto supermassive black holes. Quasars are the brightest type of active galactic nuclei; radio galaxies also contain active galactic nuclei.

active galaxy A term sometimes used to describe a galaxy that contains an *active galactic nucleus*.

adaptive optics A technique in which telescope mirrors flex rapidly to compensate for the bending of starlight caused by atmospheric turbulence.

Algol paradox A paradox concerning the binary star Algol, which contains a subgiant star that is less massive than its main-sequence companion.

altitude (above horizon) The angular distance between the horizon and an object in the sky.

amino acids The building blocks of proteins.

analemma The figure-8 path traced by the Sun over the course of a year when viewed at the same place and the same time each day; it represents the discrepancies between apparent and mean solar time.

Andromeda Galaxy (M31; the Great Galaxy in Andromeda) The nearest large spiral galaxy to the Milky Way.

angular momentum Momentum attributable to rotation or revolution. The angular momentum of an object moving in a circle of radius r is the product $m \times v \times r$.

angular resolution (of a telescope) The smallest angular separation that two pointlike objects can have and still be seen as distinct points of light (rather than as a single point of light).

angular size (or **angular distance**) A measure of the angle formed by extending imaginary lines outward from our eyes to span an object (or the space between two objects).

annihilation *See* matter–antimatter annihilation.

annular solar eclipse A solar eclipse during which the Moon is directly in front of the Sun but its angular size is not large enough to fully block the Sun; thus, a ring (or *annulus*) of sunlight is still visible around the Moon's disk.

Antarctic Circle The circle on Earth with latitude 66.5°S.

antielectron The antimatter equivalent of an electron. It is identical to an electron in virtually all respects, except it has a positive rather than a negative electrical charge.

antimatter Any particle with the same mass as a particle of ordinary matter but whose other basic properties, such as electrical charge, are precisely opposite.

aphelion The point at which an object orbiting the Sun is farthest from the Sun.

apogee The point at which an object orbiting Earth is farthest from Earth.

apparent brightness The amount of light reaching us *per unit area* from a luminous object; often measured in units of watts/m^2.

apparent magnitude A measure of the apparent brightness of an object in the sky, based on the ancient system developed by Hipparchus.

apparent retrograde motion The apparent motion of a planet, as viewed from Earth, during the period of a few weeks or months when it moves westward relative to the stars in our sky.

apparent solar time Time measured by the actual position of the Sun in your local sky, defined so that noon is when the Sun is *on* the meridian.

arcminute (or **minute of arc**) 1/60 of 1°.

arcsecond (or **second of arc**) 1/60 of an arcminute, or 1/3600 of 1°.

Arctic Circle The circle on Earth with latitude 66.5°N.

asteroid A relatively small and rocky object that orbits a star; asteroids are officially considered part of a category known as "small solar system bodies."

asteroid belt The region of our solar system between the orbits of Mars and Jupiter in which asteroids are heavily concentrated.

astrobiology The study of life on Earth and beyond; it emphasizes research into questions of the origin of life, the conditions under which life can survive, and the search for life beyond Earth.

astrometric technique The detection of extrasolar planets through the side-to-side motion of a star caused by gravitational tugs from the planet.

astronomical unit (AU) The average distance (semimajor axis) of Earth from the Sun, which is about 150 million km.

atmosphere A layer of gas that surrounds a planet or moon, usually very thin compared to the size of the object.

atmospheric pressure The surface pressure resulting from the overlying weight of an atmosphere.

atmospheric structure The layering of a planetary atmosphere due to variations in temperature with altitude. For example, Earth's atmospheric structure from the ground up consists of the troposphere, stratosphere, thermosphere, and exosphere.

atomic hydrogen gas Gas composed mostly of hydrogen atoms, though in space it is generally mixed with helium and small amounts of other elements as well; it is the most common form of interstellar gas.

atomic mass number The combined number of protons and neutrons in an atom.

atomic number The number of protons in an atom.

atoms Consist of a nucleus made from protons and neutrons, surrounded by a cloud of electrons.

aurora Dancing lights in the sky caused by charged particles entering our atmosphere; called the *aurora borealis* in the Northern Hemisphere and the *aurora australis* in the Southern Hemisphere.

axis tilt (of a planet in our solar system) The amount by which a planet's axis is tilted with respect to a line perpendicular to the ecliptic plane.

azimuth (usually called **direction** in this book) Direction around the horizon from due north, measured clockwise in degrees. For example, the azimuth of due north is 0°, due east is 90°, due south is 180°, and due west is 270°.

bar The standard unit of pressure, approximately equal to Earth's atmospheric pressure at sea level.

barred spiral galaxies Spiral galaxies that have a straight bar of stars cutting across their centers.

baryonic matter Ordinary matter made from atoms (so called because the nuclei of atoms contain protons and neutrons, which are both baryons).

baryons Particles, including protons and neutrons, that are made from three quarks.

basalt A type of dark, high-density volcanic rock that is rich in iron and magnesium-based silicate minerals; it forms a runny (easy flowing) lava when molten.

belts (on a jovian planet) Dark bands of sinking air that encircle a jovian planet at a particular set of latitudes.

Big Bang The name given to the event thought to mark the birth of the universe.

Big Bang theory The scientific theory of the universe's earliest moments, stating that all the matter in our observable universe came into being at a single moment in time as an extremely hot, dense mixture of subatomic particles and radiation.

Big Crunch The name given to the event that would presumably end the universe if gravity ever reverses the universal expansion and the universe someday begins to collapse.

binary star system A star system that contains two stars.

biosphere The "layer" of life on Earth.

blackbody radiation *See* thermal radiation.

black hole A bottomless pit in spacetime. Nothing can escape from within a black hole, and we can never again detect or observe an object that falls into a black hole.

black smokers Structures around seafloor volcanic vents that support a wide variety of life.

BL Lac objects A class of active galactic nuclei that probably represent the centers of radio galaxies whose jets happen to be pointed directly at us.

blowout Ejection of the hot, gaseous contents of a superbubble when it grows so large that it bursts out of the cooler layer of gas filling the galaxy's disk.

blueshift A Doppler shift in which spectral features are shifted to shorter wavelengths, observed when an object is moving toward the observer.

bosons Particles, such as photons, to which the exclusion principle does not apply.

bound orbits Orbits on which an object travels repeatedly around another object; bound orbits are elliptical in shape.

brown dwarf An object too small to become an ordinary star because electron degeneracy pressure halts its gravitational collapse before fusion

becomes self-sustaining; brown dwarfs have mass less than $0.08 M_{Sun}$.

bubble (interstellar) An expanding shell of hot, ionized gas driven by stellar winds or supernovae, with very hot and very low density gas inside.

bulge (of a spiral galaxy) The central portion of a spiral galaxy that is roughly spherical (or football shaped) and bulges above and below the plane of the galactic disk.

Cambrian explosion The dramatic diversification of life on Earth that occurred between about 540 and 500 million years ago.

carbonate rock A carbon-rich rock, such as limestone, that forms underwater from chemical reactions between sediments and carbon dioxide. On Earth, most of the outgassed carbon dioxide currently resides in carbonate rocks.

carbon dioxide cycle (CO_2 cycle) The process that cycles carbon dioxide between Earth's atmosphere and surface rocks.

carbon stars Stars whose atmospheres are especially carbon-rich, thought to be near the ends of their lives; carbon stars are the primary sources of carbon in the universe.

Cassini division A large, dark gap in Saturn's rings, visible through small telescopes on Earth.

CCD (charge coupled device) A type of electronic light detector that has largely replaced photographic film in astronomical research.

celestial coordinates The coordinates of right ascension and declination that fix an object's position on the celestial sphere.

celestial equator (CE) The extension of Earth's equator onto the celestial sphere.

celestial navigation Navigation on the surface of the Earth accomplished by observations of the Sun and stars.

celestial sphere The imaginary sphere on which objects in the sky appear to reside when observed from Earth.

Celsius (temperature scale) The temperature scale commonly used in daily activity internationally, defined so that, on Earth's surface, water freezes at 0°C and boils at 100°C.

center of mass (of orbiting objects) The point at which two or more orbiting objects would balance if they were somehow connected; it is the point around which the orbiting objects actually orbit.

central dominant galaxy A giant elliptical galaxy found at the center of a dense cluster of galaxies, apparently formed by the merger of several individual galaxies.

Cepheid *See* Cepheid variable stars.

Cepheid variable stars A particularly luminous type of pulsating variable star that follows a period–luminosity relation and hence is very useful for measuring cosmic distances.

Chandrasekhar limit *See* white dwarf limit.

charged particle belts Zones in which ions and electrons accumulate and encircle a planet.

chemical enrichment The process by which the abundance of heavy elements (heavier than helium) in the interstellar medium gradually increases over time as these elements are produced by stars and released into space.

chemical potential energy Potential energy that can be released through chemical reactions; for example, food contains chemical potential energy that your body can convert to other forms of energy.

chondrites Another name for primitive meteorites. The name comes from the round chodrules within them. *Achondrites*, meaning "without chondrules," is another name for processed meteorites.

chromosphere The layer of the Sun's atmosphere below the corona; most of the Sun's ultraviolet light is emitted from this region, in which the temperature is about 10,000 K.

circulation cells (or **Hadley cells**) Large-scale cells (similar to convection cells) in a planet's atmosphere that transport heat between the equator and the poles.

circumpolar star A star that always remains above the horizon for a particular latitude.

climate The long-term average of weather.

close binary A binary star system in which the two stars are very close together.

closed universe A universe in which spacetime curves back on itself to the point where its overall shape is analogous to that of the surface of a sphere.

cluster of galaxies A collection of a few dozen or more galaxies bound together by gravity; smaller collections of galaxies are simply called *groups*.

cluster of stars A group of anywhere from several hundred to a million or so stars; star clusters come in two types—open clusters and globular clusters.

CNO cycle The cycle of reactions by which intermediate- and high-mass stars fuse hydrogen into helium.

coasting universe A universe that will keep expanding forever with little change in its rate of expansion; in the absence of a repulsive force (*see* cosmological constant), a coasting universe is one in which the actual mass density is *smaller* than the critical density.

coma (of a comet) The dusty atmosphere of a comet, created by sublimation of ices in the nucleus when the comet is near the Sun.

comet A relatively small, icy object that orbits a star. Like asteroids, comets are officially considered part of a category known as "small solar system bodies."

comparative planetology The study of the solar system by examining and understanding the similarities and differences among worlds.

compound (chemical) A substance made from molecules consisting of two or more atoms with different atomic numbers.

condensates Solid or liquid particles that condense from a cloud of gas.

condensation The formation of solid or liquid particles from a cloud of gas.

conduction (of energy) The process by which thermal energy is transferred by direct contact from warm material to cooler material.

conjunction (of a planet with the Sun) An event in which a planet and the Sun line up in our sky.

conservation of angular momentum (law of) The principle that, in the absence of net torque (twisting force), the total angular momentum of a system remains constant.

conservation of energy (law of) The principle that energy (including mass-energy) can be neither created nor destroyed, but can only change from one form to another.

conservation of momentum (law of) The principle that, in the absence of net force, the total momentum of a system remains constant.

constellation A region of the sky; 88 official constellations cover the celestial sphere.

continental crust The thicker lower-density crust that makes up Earth's continents. It is made when remelting of seafloor crust allows lower-density rock to separate and erupt to the surface. Continental crust ranges in age from very young to as old as about 4 billion years (or more).

continuous spectrum A spectrum (of light) that spans a broad range of wavelengths without interruption by emission or absorption lines.

convection The energy transport process in which warm material expands and rises while cooler material contracts and falls.

convection cell An individual small region of convecting material.

convection zone (of a star) A region in which energy is transported outward by convection.

Copernican revolution The dramatic change, initiated by Copernicus, that occurred when we learned that Earth is a planet orbiting the Sun rather than the center of the universe.

core (of a planet) The dense central region of a planet that has undergone differentiation.

core (of a star) The central region of a star, in which nuclear fusion can occur.

Coriolis effect The effect due to rotation that causes air or objects on a rotating surface or planet to deviate from straight-line trajectories.

corona (solar) The tenuous uppermost layer of the Sun's atmosphere; most of the Sun's X rays are emitted from this region, in which the temperature is about 1 million K.

coronal holes Regions of the corona that barely show up in X-ray images because they are nearly devoid of hot coronal gas.

coronal mass ejections Bursts of charged particles from the Sun's corona that travel outward into space.

cosmic microwave background The remnant radiation from the Big Bang, which we detect using radio telescopes sensitive to microwaves (which are short-wavelength radio waves).

cosmic rays Particles such as electrons, protons, and atomic nuclei that zip through interstellar space at close to the speed of light.

cosmological constant The name given to a term in Einstein's equations of general relativity. If it is not zero, then it represents a repulsive force or a type of energy (sometimes called *dark energy* or *quintessence*) that might cause the expansion of the universe to accelerate with time.

cosmological horizon The boundary of our observable universe, which is where the look-back time is equal to the age of the universe. Beyond this boundary in spacetime, we cannot see anything at all.

Cosmological Principle The idea that matter is distributed uniformly throughout the universe on very large scales, meaning that the universe has neither a center nor an edge.

cosmological redshift The redshift we see from distant galaxies, caused by the fact that expansion of the universe stretches all the photons within it to longer, redder wavelengths.

cosmology The study of the overall structure and evolution of the universe.

cosmos An alternative name for the universe.

crescent (phase) The phase of the Moon (or of a planet) in which just a small portion (less than half) of the visible face is illuminated by sunlight.

critical density The precise average density for the entire universe that marks the dividing line between a recollapsing universe and one that will expand forever.

critical universe A universe that will never collapse, but that expands more and more slowly as time progresses; in the absence of a repulsive force (*see* cosmological constant), a critical universe is one in which the average mass density *equals* the critical density.

crust (of a planet) The low-density surface layer of a planet that has undergone differentiation.

curvature of spacetime A change in the geometry of space that is produced in the vicinity of a massive object and is responsible for the force we call gravity. The overall geometry of the universe may also be curved, depending on its overall mass-energy content.

cycles per second Units of frequency for a wave; describes the number of peaks (or troughs) of a wave that pass by a given point each second. Equivalent to *hertz*.

dark energy Name sometimes given to energy that could be causing the expansion of the universe to accelerate. *See* cosmological constant.

dark matter Matter that we infer to exist from its gravitational effects but from which we have not detected any light; dark matter apparently dominates the total mass of the universe.

daylight saving time Standard time plus 1 hour, so that the Sun appears on the meridian around 1 p.m. rather than around noon.

decay (radioactive) *See* radioactive decay.

declination (dec) Analogous to latitude, but on the celestial sphere; it is the angular north-south distance between the celestial equator and a location on the celestial sphere.

deferent The large circle upon which a planet follows its circle-upon-circle path around Earth in the (Earth-centered) Ptolemaic model of the universe. *See also* epicycle.

degeneracy pressure A type of pressure unrelated to an object's temperature, which arises when electrons (electron degeneracy pressure) or neutrons (neutron degeneracy pressure) are packed so tightly that the exclusion and uncertainty principles come into play.

degenerate object An object, such as a brown dwarf, white dwarf, or neutron star, in which degeneracy pressure is the primary pressure pushing back against gravity.

density (mass) The amount of mass per unit volume of an object. The average density of any object can be found by dividing its mass by its volume. Standard metric units are kilograms per cubic meter, but in astronomy density is more commonly stated in units of grams per cubic centimeter.

deuterium A form of hydrogen in which the nucleus contains a proton and a neutron, rather than only a proton (as is the case for most hydrogen nuclei).

differential rotation Rotation in which the equator of an object rotates at a different rate than the poles.

differentiation The process by which gravity separates materials according to density, with high-density materials sinking and low-density materials rising.

diffraction grating A finely etched surface that can split light into a spectrum.

diffraction limit The angular resolution that a telescope could achieve if it were limited only by the interference of light waves; it is smaller (i.e., better angular resolution) for larger telescopes.

dimension (mathematical) Describes the number of independent directions in which movement is possible; for example, the surface of Earth is two-dimensional because only two independent directions of motion are possible (north-south and east-west).

direction (in local sky) One of the two coordinates (the other is altitude) needed to pinpoint an object in the local sky. It is the direction, such as north, south, east, or west, in which you must face to see the object. *See also* azimuth.

disk (of a galaxy) The portion of a spiral galaxy that looks like a disk and contains an interstellar medium with cool gas and dust; stars of many ages are found in the disk.

disk population The stars that orbit within the disk of a spiral galaxy; sometimes called *Population I*.

DNA (deoxyribonucleic acid) The molecule that represents the genetic material of life on Earth.

Doppler effect (shift) The effect that shifts the wavelengths of spectral features in objects that are moving toward or away from the observer.

Doppler technique The detection of extrasolar planets through the motion of a star toward and away from the observer caused by gravitational tugs from the planet.

double shell–fusing star A star that is fusing helium into carbon in a shell around an inert carbon core and is fusing hydrogen into helium in a shell at the top of the helium layer.

down quark One of the two quark types (the other is the up quark) found in ordinary protons and neutrons. It has a charge of $-\frac{1}{3}$.

Drake equation An equation that lays out the factors that play a role in determining the number of communicating civilizations in our galaxy.

dust (or **dust grains**) Tiny solid flecks of material; in astronomy, we often discuss interplanetary dust (found within a star system) or interstellar dust (found between the stars in a galaxy).

dust tail (of a comet) One of two tails seen when a comet passes near the Sun (the other is the plasma tail). It is composed of small solid particles pushed away from the Sun by the radiation pressure of sunlight.

dwarf elliptical galaxy A small elliptical galaxy with less than about a billion stars.

dwarf galaxies Relatively small galaxies, consisting of less than about 10 billion stars.

dwarf planet An object that orbits the Sun and is massive enough for its gravity to have made it nearly round in shape, but that does not qualify as an official planet because it has not cleared its orbital neighborhood. The dwarf planets of our solar system include the asteroid Ceres and the Kuiper belt objects Pluto, Eris, Haumea, and Makemake.

Earth-orbiters (spacecraft) Spacecraft designed to study Earth or the universe from Earth orbit.

eccentricity A measure of how much an ellipse deviates from a perfect circle; defined as the center-to-focus distance divided by the length of the semimajor axis.

eclipse An event in which one astronomical object casts a shadow on another or crosses our line of sight to the other object.

eclipse seasons Periods during which lunar and solar eclipses can occur because the nodes of the Moon's orbit are aligned with Earth and the Sun.

eclipsing binary A binary star system in which the two stars happen to be orbiting in the plane of our line of sight, so that each star will periodically eclipse the other.

ecliptic The Sun's apparent annual path among the constellations.

ecliptic plane The plane of Earth's orbit around the Sun.

ejecta (from an impact) Debris ejected by the blast of an impact.

electrical charge A fundamental property of matter that is described by its amount and as either positive or negative; more technically, a measure of how a particle responds to the electromagnetic force.

electromagnetic field An abstract concept used to describe how a charged particle would affect other charged particles at a distance.

electromagnetic radiation Another name for light of all types, from radio waves through gamma rays.

electromagnetic spectrum The complete spectrum of light, including radio waves, infrared light, visible light, ultraviolet light, X rays, and gamma rays.

electromagnetic wave A synonym for *light*, which consists of waves of electric and magnetic fields.

electromagnetism (or **electromagnetic force**) One of the four fundamental forces; it is the force that dominates atomic and molecular interactions.

electron degeneracy pressure Degeneracy pressure exerted by electrons, as in brown dwarfs and white dwarfs.

electrons Fundamental particles with negative electric charge; the distribution of electrons in an atom gives the atom its size.

electron-volt (eV) A unit of energy equivalent to 1.60×10^{-19} joule.

electroweak era The era of the universe during which only three forces operated (gravity, strong force, and electroweak force), lasting from 10^{-38} second to 10^{-10} second after the Big Bang.

electroweak force The force that exists at high energies when the electromagnetic force and the weak force exist as a single force.

element (chemical) A substance made from individual atoms of a particular atomic number.

ellipse A type of oval that happens to be the shape of bound orbits. An ellipse can be drawn by moving a pencil along a string whose ends are tied to two tacks; the locations of the tacks are the *foci* (singular: *focus*) of the ellipse.

elliptical galaxies Galaxies that appear rounded in shape, often longer in one direction, like a football. They have no disks and contain very little cool gas and dust compared to spiral galaxies, though they often contain very hot, ionized gas.

elongation (greatest) For Mercury or Venus, the point at which it appears farthest from the Sun in our sky.

emission (of light) The process by which matter emits energy in the form of light.

emission line spectrum A spectrum that contains emission lines.

emission nebula Another name for an ionization nebula. *See* ionization nebula.

energy Broadly speaking, what can make matter move. The three basic types of energy are kinetic, potential, and radiative.

energy balance (in a star) The balance between the rate at which fusion releases energy in the star's core and the rate at which the star's surface radiates this energy into space.

epicycle The small circle upon which a planet moves while simultaneously going around a larger circle (the *deferent*) around Earth in the (Earth-centered) Ptolemaic model of the universe.

equation of time An equation describing the discrepancies between apparent and mean solar time.

equinox *See* fall equinox *and* spring equinox.

equivalence principle The fundamental starting point for general relativity, which states that the effects of gravity are exactly equivalent to the effects of acceleration.

era of atoms The era of the universe lasting from about 500,000 years to about 1 billion years after the Big Bang, during which it was cool enough for neutral atoms to form.

era of galaxies The present era of the universe, which began with the formation of galaxies when the universe was about 1 billion years old.

era of nuclei The era of the universe lasting from about 3 minutes to about 380,000 years after the Big Bang, during which matter in the universe was fully ionized and opaque to light. The cosmic background radiation was released at the end of this era.

era of nucleosynthesis The era of the universe lasting from about 0.001 second to about 3 minutes after the Big Bang, by the end of which virtually all of the neutrons and about one-seventh of the protons in the universe had fused into helium.

erosion The wearing down or building up of geological features by wind, water, ice, and other phenomena of planetary weather.

eruption The process of releasing hot lava on a planet's surface.

escape velocity The speed necessary for an object to completely escape the gravity of a large body such as a moon, planet, or star.

evaporation The process by which atoms or molecules escape into the gas phase from a liquid.

event Any particular point along a worldline; all observers will agree on the reality of an event but may disagree about its time and location.

event horizon The boundary that marks the "point of no return" between a black hole and the outside universe; events that occur within the event horizon can have no influence on our observable universe.

evolution (biological) The gradual change in populations of living organisms responsible for transforming life on Earth from its primitive origins to the great diversity of life today.

exchange particle A type of subatomic particle that transmits one of the four fundamental forces; according to the standard model of physics, these particles are always exchanged whenever two objects interact through a force.

excited state (of an atom) Any arrangement of electrons in an atom that has more energy than the ground state.

exclusion principle The law of quantum mechanics that states that two fermions cannot occupy the same quantum state at the same time.

exosphere The hot, outer layer of an atmosphere, where the atmosphere "fades away" to space.

expansion (of the universe) The idea that the space between galaxies or clusters of galaxies is growing with time.

exposure time The amount of time during which light is collected to make a single image.

extrasolar planet A planet orbiting a star other than our Sun.

extremophiles Living organisms that are adapted to conditions that are "extreme" by human standards, such as very high or low temperature or a high level of salinity or radiation.

Fahrenheit (temperature scale) The temperature scale commonly used in daily activity in the United States; defined so that, on Earth's surface, water freezes at 32°F and boils at 212°F.

fall (September) equinox Refers both to the point in Virgo on the celestial sphere where the ecliptic crosses the celestial equator and to the moment in time when the Sun appears at that point each year (around September 21).

false-color image An image displayed in colors that are *not* the true, visible-light colors of an object.

fault (geological) A place where rocks slip sideways relative to one another.

feedback processes Processes in which a small change in some property (such as temperature) leads to changes in other properties that either amplify or diminish the original small change.

fermions Particles, such as electrons, neutrons, and protons, that obey the exclusion principle.

Fermi's paradox The question posed by Enrico Fermi about extraterrestrial intelligence—"So where is everybody?"—which asks why we have not observed other civilizations even though simple arguments would suggest that some ought to have spread throughout the galaxy by now.

field An abstract concept used to describe how a particle would interact with a force. For example, the idea of a gravitational field describes how a particle would react to the local strength of gravity, and the idea of an electromagnetic field describes how a charged particle would respond to forces from other charged particles.

filter (for light) A material that transmits only particular wavelengths of light.

fireball A particularly bright meteor.

first-quarter (phase) The phase of the Moon that occurs one-quarter of the way through each cycle of phases, in which precisely half of the visible face is illuminated by sunlight.

fission The process by which one atomic nucleus breaks into two smaller nuclei. It releases energy if the two smaller nuclei together are less massive than the original nucleus.

flare star A small, spectral type M star that displays particularly strong flares on its surface.

flat (or Euclidean) geometry The type of geometry in which the rules of geometry for a flat plane hold, such as that the shortest distance between two points is a straight line and that the sum of the angles in a triangle is 180°.

flat universe A universe in which the overall geometry of spacetime is flat (Euclidean), as would be the case if the density of the universe was equal to the critical density.

flybys (spacecraft) Spacecraft that fly past a target object (such as a planet), usually just once, as opposed to entering a bound orbit of the object.

focal plane The place where an image created by a lens or mirror is in focus.

foci Plural of *focus.*

focus (of a lens or mirror) The point at which rays of light that were initially parallel (such as those from a distant star) converge.

focus (of an ellipse) One of two special points within an ellipse that lie along the major axis; these are the points around which we could stretch a pencil and string to draw an ellipse. When one object orbits a second object, the second object lies at one focus of the orbit.

force Anything that can cause a change in momentum.

formation properties (of planets) In this book, for the purpose of understanding geological processes, planets are defined to be born with four formation properties: size (mass and radius), distance from the Sun, composition, and rotation rate.

fossil Any relic of an organism that lived and died long ago.

frame of reference See reference frame.

free-fall The condition in which an object is falling without resistance; objects are weightless when in free-fall.

free-float frame A frame of reference in which all objects are weightless and hence float freely.

frequency The rate at which peaks of a wave pass by a point, measured in units of 1/s, often called *cycles per second* or *hertz.*

frost line The boundary in the solar nebula beyond which ices could condense; only metals and rocks could condense within the frost line.

fundamental forces There are four known fundamental forces in nature: gravity, the electromagnetic force, the strong force, and the weak force.

fundamental particles Subatomic particles that cannot be divided into anything smaller.

fusion The process by which two atomic nuclei fuse together to make a single, more massive nucleus. It releases energy if the final nucleus is less massive than the two nuclei that went into the reaction.

galactic cannibalism The term sometimes used to describe the process by which large galaxies merge with other galaxies in collisions. *Central dominant galaxies* are products of galactic cannibalism.

galactic fountain A model for the cycling of gas in the Milky Way Galaxy in which fountains of hot, ionized gas rise from the disk into the halo and then cool and form clouds as they sink back into the disk.

galactic wind A wind of low-density but extremely hot gas flowing out from a starburst galaxy, created by the combined energy of many supernovae.

galaxy A huge collection of anywhere from a few hundred million to more than a trillion stars, all bound together by gravity.

galaxy cluster *See* cluster of galaxies.

galaxy evolution The formation and development of galaxies.

Galilean moons The four moons of Jupiter that were discovered by Galileo: Io, Europa, Ganymede, and Callisto.

gamma-ray burst A sudden burst of gamma rays from deep space; such bursts apparently come from distant galaxies, but their precise mechanism is unknown.

gamma rays Light with very short wavelengths (and hence high frequencies)—shorter than those of X rays.

gap moons Tiny moons located within a gap in a planet's ring system. The gravity of a gap moon helps clear the gap.

gas phase The phase of matter in which atoms or molecules can move essentially independently of one another.

gas pressure The force (per unit area) pushing on any object due to surrounding gas. *See also* pressure.

general theory of relativity Einstein's generalization of his special theory of relativity so that the theory also applies when we consider effects of gravity or acceleration.

genetic code The "language" that living cells use to read the instructions chemically encoded in DNA.

geocentric model Any of the ancient Greek models that were used to predict planetary positions under the assumption that Earth lay in the center of the universe.

geocentric universe The ancient belief that Earth is the center of the entire universe.

geological activity Processes that change a planet's surface long after formation, such as volcanism, tectonics, and erosion.

geological processes The four basic geological processes are impact cratering, volcanism, tectonics, and erosion.

geological time scale The time scale used by scientists to describe major eras in Earth's past.

geology The study of surface features (on a moon, planet, or asteroid) and the processes that create them.

geostationary satellite A satellite that appears to stay stationary in the sky as viewed from Earth's surface, because it orbits in the same time it takes Earth to rotate and orbits in Earth's equatorial plane.

geosynchronous satellite A satellite that orbits Earth in the same time it takes Earth to rotate (one sidereal day).

giant galaxies Galaxies that are unusually large, typically containing a trillion or more stars. Most giant galaxies are elliptical, and many contain multiple nuclei near their centers.

giant impact A collision between a forming planet and a very large planetesimal, such as is thought to have formed our Moon.

giant molecular cloud A very large cloud of cold, dense interstellar gas, typically containing up to a million solar masses worth of material. *See also* molecular clouds.

giants (luminosity class III) Stars that appear just below the supergiants on the H-R diagram because they are somewhat smaller in radius and lower in luminosity.

gibbous (phase) The phase of the Moon (or of a planet) in which more than half but less than all of the visible face is illuminated by sunlight.

global positioning system (GPS) A system of navigation by satellites orbiting Earth.

global warming An expected increase in Earth's global average temperature caused by human input of carbon dioxide and other greenhouse gases into the atmosphere.

global wind patterns (or **global circulation**) Wind patterns that remain fixed on a global scale, determined by the combination of surface heating and the planet's rotation.

globular cluster A spherically shaped cluster of up to a million or more stars; globular clusters are found primarily in the halos of galaxies and contain only very old stars.

gluons The exchange particles for the strong force.

grand unified theory (GUT) A theory that unifies three of the four fundamental forces—the strong force, the weak force, and the electromagnetic force (but not gravity)—in a single model.

granulation (on the Sun) The bubbling pattern visible in the photosphere, produced by the underlying convection.

gravitation (law of) *See* universal law of gravitation.

gravitational constant The experimentally measured constant G that appears in the law of universal gravitation:

$$G = 6.67 \times 10^{-11} \frac{\text{m}^3}{\text{kg} \times \text{s}^2}$$

gravitational contraction The process in which gravity causes an object to contract, thereby converting gravitational potential energy into thermal energy.

gravitational encounter An encounter in which two (or more) objects pass near enough so that each can feel the effects of the other's gravity and they can therefore exchange energy.

gravitational equilibrium A state of balance in which the force of gravity pulling inward is precisely counteracted by pressure pushing outward.

gravitational lensing The magnification or distortion (into arcs, rings, or multiple images) of an image caused by light bending through a gravitational field, as predicted by Einstein's general theory of relativity.

gravitationally bound system Any system of objects, such as a star system or a galaxy, that is held together by gravity.

gravitational potential energy Energy that an object has by virtue of its position in a gravitational field; an object has more gravitational potential energy when it has a greater distance that it can potentially fall.

gravitational redshift A redshift caused by the fact that time runs slowly in gravitational fields.

gravitational time dilation The slowing of time that occurs in a gravitational field, as predicted by Einstein's general theory of relativity.

gravitational waves Waves, predicted by Einstein's general theory of relativity, that travel at the speed of light and transmit distortions of space through the universe. Although they have not yet been observed directly, we have strong indirect evidence that they exist.

gravitons The exchange particles for the force of gravity.

gravity One of the four fundamental forces; it is the force that dominates on large scales.

grazing incidence (in telescopes) Reflections in which light grazes a mirror surface and is deflected at a small angle; commonly used to focus high-energy ultraviolet light and X rays.

great circle A circle on the surface of a sphere whose center is at the center of the sphere.

greatest elongation *See* elongation (greatest).

Great Red Spot A large, high-pressure storm on Jupiter.

greenhouse effect The process by which greenhouse gases in an atmosphere make a planet's surface temperature warmer than it would be in the absence of an atmosphere.

greenhouse gases Gases, such as carbon dioxide, water vapor, and methane, that are particularly good absorbers of infrared light but are transparent to visible light.

Gregorian calendar Our modern calendar, introduced by Pope Gregory in 1582.

ground state (of an atom) The lowest possible energy state of the electrons in an atom.

group (of galaxies) A few to a few dozen galaxies bound together by gravity. *See also* cluster of galaxies.

GUT era The era of the universe during which only two forces operated (gravity and the grand-unified-theory, or GUT, force), lasting from 10^{-43} second to 10^{-38} second after the Big Bang.

GUT force The proposed force that exists at very high energies when the strong force, the weak force, and the electromagnetic force (but not gravity) all act as one.

H II region Another name for an ionization nebula. *See* ionization nebula.

habitable world A world with environmental conditions under which life could *potentially* arise or survive.

habitable zone The region around a star in which planets could potentially have surface temperatures at which liquid water could exist.

Hadley cells *See* circulation cells.

half-life The time it takes for half of the nuclei in a given quantity of a radioactive substance to decay.

halo (of a galaxy) The spherical region surrounding the disk of a spiral galaxy.

Hawking radiation Radiation predicted to arise from the evaporation of black holes.

heavy bombardment The period in the first few hundred million years after the solar system formed during which the tail end of planetary accretion created most of the craters found on ancient planetary surfaces.

heavy elements In astronomy, generally all elements *except* hydrogen and helium.

helium-capture reactions Fusion reactions that fuse a helium nucleus into some other nucleus; such reactions can fuse carbon into oxygen, oxygen into neon, neon into magnesium, and so on.

helium flash The event that marks the sudden onset of helium fusion in the previously inert helium core of a low-mass star.

helium-fusing star A star that is currently fusing helium into carbon in its core.

helium fusion The fusion of three helium nuclei into one carbon nucleus; also called the *triple-alpha reaction*.

hertz (Hz) The standard unit of frequency for light waves; equivalent to units of 1/s.

Hertzsprung-Russell (H-R) diagram A graph plotting individual stars as points, with stellar luminosity on the vertical axis and spectral type (or surface temperature) on the horizontal axis.

high-mass stars Stars born with masses above about $8M_{Sun}$; these stars will end their lives by exploding as supernovae.

horizon A boundary that divides what we can see from what we cannot see.

horizontal branch The horizontal line of stars that represents helium-fusing stars on an H-R diagram for a cluster of stars.

horoscope A predictive chart made by an astrologer; in scientific studies, horoscopes have never been found to have any validity as predictive tools.

hot Jupiter A class of planet that is Jupiter-like in size but orbits very close to its star, causing it to have a very high surface temperature.

hot spot (geological) A place within a plate of the lithosphere where a localized plume of hot mantle material rises.

hour angle (HA) The angle or time (measured in hours) since an object was last on the meridian in the local sky; defined to be 0 hours for objects that are on the meridian.

Hubble's constant A number that expresses the current rate of expansion of the universe; designated H_0, it is usually stated in units of km/s/Mpc. The reciprocal of Hubble's constant is the age the universe would have *if* the expansion rate had never changed.

Hubble's law Mathematical expression of the idea that more distant galaxies move away from us faster: $v = H_0 \times d$, where v is a galaxy's speed away from us, d is its distance, and H_0 is Hubble's constant.

hydrogen compounds Compounds that contain hydrogen and were common in the solar nebula, such as water (H_2O), ammonia (NH_3), and methane (CH_4).

hydrogen shell fusion Hydrogen fusion that occurs in a shell surrounding a stellar core.

hydrosphere The "layer" of water on Earth consisting of oceans, lakes, rivers, ice caps, and other liquid water and ice.

hydrostatic equilibrium *See* gravitational equilibrium.

hyperbola The precise mathematical shape of one type of unbound orbit (the other is a parabola) allowed under the force of gravity; at great distances from the attracting object, a hyperbolic path looks like a straight line.

hypernova A term sometimes used to describe a supernova (explosion) of a star so massive that it leaves a black hole behind.

hyperspace Any space with more than three dimensions.

hypothesis A tentative model proposed to explain some set of observed facts, but which has not yet been rigorously tested and confirmed.

ice ages Periods of global cooling during which the polar caps, glaciers, and snow cover extend closer to the equator.

ices (in solar system theory) Materials that are solid only at low temperatures, such as the hydrogen compounds water, ammonia, and methane.

ideal gas law The law relating the pressure, temperature, and number density of particles in an ideal gas.

image A picture of an object made by focusing light.

imaging (in astronomical research) The process of obtaining pictures of astronomical objects.

impact The collision of a small body (such as an asteroid or comet) with a larger object (such as a planet or moon).

impact basin A very large impact crater, often filled by a lava flow.

impact crater A bowl-shaped depression left by the impact of an object that strikes a planetary surface (as opposed to burning up in the atmosphere).

impact cratering The excavation of bowl-shaped depressions (*impact craters*) by asteroids or comets striking a planet's surface.

impactor The object responsible for an impact.

inflation (of the universe) A sudden and dramatic expansion of the universe thought to have occurred at the end of the GUT era.

infrared light Light with wavelengths that fall in the portion of the electromagnetic spectrum between radio waves and visible light.

inner solar system Generally considered to encompass the region of our solar system out to about the orbit of Mars.

intensity (of light) A measure of the amount of energy coming from light of specific wavelength in the spectrum of an object.

interferometry A telescopic technique in which two or more telescopes are used in tandem to produce much better angular resolution than the telescopes could achieve individually.

intermediate-mass stars Stars born with masses between about $2M_{Sun}$ and $8M_{Sun}$; these stars end their lives by ejecting a planetary nebula and becoming a white dwarf.

interstellar cloud A cloud of gas and dust between the stars.

interstellar dust grains Tiny solid flecks of carbon and silicon minerals found in cool interstellar clouds; they resemble particles of smoke and form in the winds of red giant stars.

interstellar medium The gas and dust that fills the space between stars in a galaxy.

interstellar ramjet A hypothesized type of spaceship that uses a giant scoop to sweep up interstellar gas for use in a nuclear fusion engine.

interstellar reddening The change in the color of starlight as it passes through dusty gas. The light appears redder because dust grains absorb and scatter blue light more effectively than red light.

intracluster medium Hot, X-ray-emitting gas found between the galaxies within a cluster of galaxies.

inverse square law A law followed by any quantity that decreases with the square of the distance between two objects.

inverse square law for light The law stating that an object's apparent brightness depends on its actual luminosity and the inverse square of its distance from the observer:

$$\text{apparent brightness} = \frac{\text{luminosity}}{4\pi \times (\text{distance})^2}$$

inversion (atmospheric) A local weather condition in which air is colder near the surface than higher up in the troposphere—the opposite of the usual condition, in which the troposphere is warmer at the bottom.

ionization The process of stripping an electron from an atom.

ionization nebula A colorful, wispy cloud of gas that glows because neighboring hot stars irradiate it with ultraviolet photons that can ionize hydrogen atoms.

ionosphere A portion of the thermosphere in which ions are particularly common (because of ionization by X rays from the Sun).

ions Atoms with a positive or negative electrical charge.

Io torus A donut-shaped charged-particle belt around Jupiter that approximately traces Io's orbit.

irregular galaxies Galaxies that look neither spiral nor elliptical.

isotopes Forms of an element that have the same number of protons but different numbers of neutrons.

jets High-speed streams of gas ejected from an object into space.

joule The international unit of energy, equivalent to about 1/4000 of a Calorie.

jovian nebulae The clouds of gas that swirled around the jovian planets, from which the moons formed.

jovian planets Giant gaseous planets similar in overall composition to Jupiter.

Julian calendar The calendar introduced in 46 B.C. by Julius Caesar and used until the Gregorian calendar replaced it.

Kelvin (temperature scale) The most commonly used temperature scale in science, defined such that absolute zero is 0 K and water freezes at 273.15 K.

Kepler's first law Law stating that the orbit of each planet about the Sun is an ellipse with the Sun at one focus.

Kepler's laws of planetary motion Three laws discovered by Kepler that describe the motion of the planets around the Sun.

Kepler's second law The principle that, as a planet moves around its orbit, it sweeps out equal areas in equal times. This tells us that a planet moves faster when it is closer to the Sun (near perihelion) than when it is farther from the Sun (near aphelion) in its orbit.

Kepler's third law The principle that the square of a planet's orbital period is proportional to the cube of its average distance from the Sun (semimajor axis), which tells us that more distant planets move more slowly in their orbits; in its original form, written $p^2 = a^3$. *See also* Newton's version of Kepler's third law.

kinetic energy Energy of motion, given by the formula $\frac{1}{2}mv^2$.

Kirchhoff's laws A set of rules that summarizes the conditions under which objects produce thermal, absorption line, or emission line spectra. In brief: (1) An opaque object produces thermal radiation. (2) An absorption line spectrum occurs when thermal radiation passes through a thin gas that is cooler than the object emitting the thermal radiation. (3) An emission line spectrum occurs when we view a cloud of gas that is warmer than any background source of light.

Kirkwood gaps On a plot of asteroid semimajor axes, regions with few asteroids as a result of orbital resonances with Jupiter.

K–T event (or impact) The collision of an asteroid or comet 65 million years ago that caused the mass extinction best known for wiping out the dinosaurs. *K* and *T* stand for the geological layers above and below the event.

Kuiper belt The comet-rich region of our solar system that spans distances of about 30–100 AU from the Sun. Kuiper belt comets have orbits that lie fairly close to the plane of planetary orbits and travel around the Sun in the same direction as the planets.

Kuiper belt object Any object orbiting the Sun within the region of the Kuiper belt, although the term is most often used for relatively large objects. For example, Pluto and Eris are considered large Kuiper belt objects.

Large Magellanic Cloud One of two small, irregular galaxies (the other is the Small Magellanic Cloud) located about 150,000 light-years away; it probably orbits the Milky Way Galaxy.

large-scale structure (of the universe) Generally refers to the structure of the universe on size scales larger than that of clusters of galaxies.

latitude The angular north-south distance between Earth's equator and a location on Earth's surface.

leap year A calendar year with 366 rather than 365 days. Our current calendar (the Gregorian calendar) incorporates a leap year every 4 years (by adding February 29) except in century years that are not divisible by 400.

length contraction The effect in which you observe lengths to be shortened in reference frames moving relative to you.

lens (gravitational) *See* gravitational lensing.

lenticular galaxies Galaxies that look lens-shaped when seen edge-on, resembling spiral galaxies without arms. They tend to have less cool gas than normal spiral galaxies but more gas than elliptical galaxies.

leptons Fermions *not* made from quarks, such as electrons and neutrinos.

life track A track drawn on an H-R diagram to represent the changes in a star's surface temperature and luminosity during its life; also called an *evolutionary track*.

light-collecting area (of a telescope) The area of the primary mirror or lens that collects light in a telescope.

light curve A graph of an object's intensity against time.

light gases (in solar system theory) Hydrogen and helium, which never condense under solar nebula conditions.

light pollution Human-made light that hinders astronomical observations.

light-year (ly) The distance that light can travel in 1 year, which is 9.46 trillion km.

liquid phase The phase of matter in which atoms or molecules are held together but move relatively freely.

lithosphere The relatively rigid outer layer of a planet; generally encompasses the crust and the uppermost portion of the mantle.

Local Bubble (interstellar) The bubble of hot gas in which our Sun and other nearby stars apparently reside. *See also* bubble (interstellar).

Local Group The group of about 40 galaxies to which the Milky Way Galaxy belongs.

local sidereal time (LST) Sidereal time for a particular location, defined according to the position of the spring equinox in the local sky. More formally, the local sidereal time at any moment is defined to be the hour angle of the spring equinox.

local sky The sky as viewed from a particular location on Earth (or another solid object). Objects in the local sky are pinpointed by the coordinates of *altitude* and *direction* (or azimuth).

local solar neighborhood The portion of the Milky Way Galaxy that is located relatively close (within a few hundred to a couple thousand light-years) to our Sun.

Local Supercluster The supercluster of galaxies to which the Local Group belongs.

longitude The angular east-west distance between the prime meridian (which passes through Greenwich, England) and a location on Earth's surface.

lookback time The amount of time since the light we see from a distant object was emitted. If an object has a lookback time of 400 million years, we are seeing it as it looked 400 million years ago.

low-mass stars Stars born with masses less than about $2M_{Sun}$; these stars end their lives by ejecting a planetary nebula and becoming a white dwarf.

luminosity The total power output of an object, usually measured in watts or in units of solar luminosities ($L_{Sun} = 3.8 \times 10^{26}$ watts).

luminosity class A category describing the region of the H-R diagram in which a star falls. Luminosity class I represents supergiants, III represents giants, and V represents main-sequence stars; luminosity classes II and IV are intermediate to the others.

lunar eclipse An event that occurs when the Moon passes through Earth's shadow, which can occur only at full moon. A lunar eclipse may be total, partial, or penumbral.

lunar maria The regions of the Moon that look smooth from Earth and actually are impact basins.

lunar month *See* synodic month.

lunar phase *See* phase (of the Moon or a planet).

MACHOs One possible form of dark matter in which the dark objects are relatively large, like planets or brown dwarfs; stands for *massive compact halo objects*.

magma Underground molten rock.

magnetic braking The process by which a star's rotation slows as its magnetic field transfers its angular momentum to the surrounding nebula.

magnetic field The region surrounding a magnet in which it can affect other magnets or charged particles.

magnetic field lines Lines that represent how the needles on a series of compasses would point if they were laid out in a magnetic field.

magnetosphere The region surrounding a planet in which charged particles are trapped by the planet's magnetic field.

magnitude system A system for describing stellar brightness by using numbers, called *magnitudes*, based on an ancient Greek way of describing the brightnesses of stars in the sky. This system uses *apparent magnitude* to describe a star's apparent brightness and *absolute magnitude* to describe a star's luminosity.

main sequence The prominent line of points (representing *main-sequence stars*) running from the upper left to the lower right on an H-R diagram.

main-sequence fitting A method for measuring the distance to a cluster of stars by comparing the apparent brightness of the cluster's main sequence with that of the standard main sequence.

main-sequence lifetime The length of time for which a star of a particular mass can shine by fusing hydrogen into helium in its core.

main-sequence stars (luminosity class V) Stars whose temperature and luminosity place them on the main sequence of the H-R diagram. Main-sequence stars are all releasing energy by fusing hydrogen into helium in their cores.

main-sequence turnoff point The point on a cluster's H-R diagram where its stars turn off from the main sequence; the age of the cluster is equal to the main-sequence lifetime of stars at the main-sequence turnoff point.

mantle (of a planet) The rocky layer that lies between a planet's core and crust.

Martian meteorites Meteorites found on Earth that are thought to have originated on Mars.

mass A measure of the amount of matter in an object.

mass-energy The potential energy of mass, which has an amount $E = mc^2$.

mass exchange (in close binary star systems) The process in which tidal forces cause matter to spill from one star to a companion star in a close binary system.

mass extinction An event in which a large fraction of the species living on Earth go extinct, such as the event in which the dinosaurs died out about 65 million years ago.

mass increase (in relativity) The effect in which an object moving past you seems to have a mass greater than its rest mass.

massive star supernova A supernova that occurs when a massive star dies, initiated by the catastrophic collapse of its iron core; often called a *Type II supernova*.

mass-to-light ratio The mass of an object divided by its luminosity, usually stated in units of solar masses per solar luminosity. Objects with high mass-to-light ratios must contain substantial quantities of dark matter.

matter–antimatter annihilation An event that occurs when a particle of matter and a particle of antimatter meet and convert all of their mass-energy to photons.

mean solar time Time measured by the average position of the Sun in your local sky over the course of the year.

meridian A half-circle extending from your horizon (altitude 0°) due south, through your zenith, to your horizon due north.

metallic hydrogen Hydrogen that is so compressed that the hydrogen atoms all share electrons and thereby take on properties of metals, such as conducting electricity. It occurs only under very high-pressure conditions, such as those found deep within Jupiter.

metals (in solar system theory) Elements, such as nickel, iron, and aluminum, that condense at fairly high temperatures.

meteor A flash of light caused when a particle from space burns up in our atmosphere.

meteorite A rock from space that lands on Earth.

meteor shower A period during which many more meteors than usual can be seen.

Metonic cycle The 19-year period, discovered by the Babylonian astronomer Meton, over which the lunar phases occur on the same dates.

microwaves Light with wavelengths in the range of micrometers to millimeters. Microwaves are generally considered to be a subset of the radio wave portion of the electromagnetic spectrum.

mid-ocean ridges Long ridges of undersea volcanoes on Earth, along which mantle material erupts onto the ocean floor and pushes apart the existing seafloor on either side. These ridges are essentially the source of new seafloor crust, which then makes its way along the ocean bottom for millions of years before returning to the mantle at a subduction zone.

Milankovitch cycles The cyclical changes in Earth's axis tilt and orbit that can change the climate and cause ice ages.

Milky Way Used both as the name of our galaxy and to refer to the band of light we see in the sky when we look into the plane of the Milky Way Galaxy.

millisecond pulsars Pulsars with rotation periods of a few thousandths of a second.

minor planets An alternative name for *asteroids*.

model (scientific) A representation of some aspect of nature that can be used to explain and predict real phenomena without invoking myth, magic, or the supernatural.

molecular bands The tightly bunched lines in an object's spectrum that are produced by molecules.

molecular cloud fragments (or **molecular cloud cores**) The densest regions of molecular clouds, which usually go on to form stars.

molecular clouds Cool, dense interstellar clouds in which the low temperatures allow hydrogen atoms to pair up into hydrogen molecules (H_2).

molecular dissociation The process by which a molecule splits into its component atoms.

molecule Technically, the smallest unit of a chemical element or compound; in this text, the term refers only to combinations of two or more atoms held together by chemical bonds.

momentum The product of an object's mass and velocity.

moon An object that orbits a planet.

moonlets Very small moons that orbit within the ring systems of jovian planets.

mutations Errors in the copying process when a living cell replicates itself.

natural selection The process by which mutations that make an organism better able to survive get passed on to future generations.

neap tides The lower-than-average tides on Earth that occur at first- and third-quarter moon, when the tidal forces from the Sun and Moon oppose each other.

nebula A cloud of gas in space, usually one that is glowing.

nebular capture The process by which icy planetesimals capture hydrogen and helium gas to form jovian planets.

nebular theory The detailed theory that describes how our solar system formed from a cloud of interstellar gas and dust.

net force The overall force to which an object responds; the net force is equal to the rate of change in the object's momentum, or equivalently to the object's mass × acceleration.

neutrino A type of fundamental particle that has extremely low mass and responds only to the weak force; neutrinos are leptons and come in three types—electron neutrinos, mu neutrinos, and tau neutrinos.

neutron degeneracy pressure Degeneracy pressure exerted by neutrons, as in neutron stars.

neutrons Particles with no electrical charge found in atomic nuclei, built from three quarks.

neutron star The compact corpse of a high-mass star left over after a supernova; it typically contains a mass comparable to the mass of the Sun in a volume just a few kilometers in radius.

newton The standard unit of force in the metric system:

$$1 \text{ newton} = 1 \frac{\text{kg} \times \text{m}}{s^2}$$

Newton's first law of motion Principle that, in the absence of a net force, an object moves with constant velocity.

Newton's laws of motion Three basic laws that describe how objects respond to forces.

Newton's second law of motion Law stating how a net force affects an object's motion. Specifically, force = rate of change in momentum, or force = mass × acceleration.

Newton's third law of motion Principle that, for any force, there is always an equal and opposite reaction force.

Newton's universal law of gravitation *See* universal law of gravitation.

Newton's version of Kepler's third law A generalization of Kepler's third law used to calculate the masses of orbiting objects from measurements of orbital period and distance; usually written as

$$p^2 = \frac{4\pi^2}{G(M_1 + M_2)}a^3$$

nodes (of Moon's orbit) The two points in the Moon's orbit where it crosses the ecliptic plane.

nonbaryonic matter Matter that is not part of the normal composition of atoms, such as neutrinos or the hypothetical WIMPs. (More technically, particles that are not made from three quarks.)

nonscience As defined in this book, any way of searching for knowledge that makes no claim to follow the scientific method, such as seeking knowledge through intuition, tradition, or faith.

north celestial pole (NCP) The point on the celestial sphere directly above Earth's North Pole.

nova The dramatic brightening of a star that lasts for a few weeks and then subsides; it occurs when a burst of hydrogen fusion ignites in a shell on the surface of an accreting white dwarf in a binary star system.

nuclear fission The process in which a larger nucleus splits into two (or more) smaller particles.

nuclear fusion The process in which two (or more) smaller nuclei slam together and make one larger nucleus.

nucleus (of a comet) The solid portion of a comet—the only portion that exists when the comet is far from the Sun.

nucleus (of an atom) The compact center of an atom made from protons and neutrons.

observable universe The portion of the entire universe that, at least in principle, can be seen from Earth.

Occam's razor A principle often used in science, holding that scientists should prefer the simpler of two models that agree equally well with observations; named after the medieval scholar William of Occam (1285–1349).

Olbers' paradox A paradox pointing out that if the universe were infinite in both age and size (with stars found throughout the universe), then the sky would not be dark at night.

Oort cloud A huge, spherical region centered on the Sun, extending perhaps halfway to the nearest stars, in which trillions of comets orbit the Sun with random inclinations, orbital directions, and eccentricities.

opacity A measure of how much light a material absorbs compared to how much it transmits; materials with higher opacity absorb more light.

opaque Describes a material that absorbs light.

open cluster A cluster of up to several thousand stars; open clusters are found only in the disks of galaxies and often contain young stars.

open universe A universe in which spacetime has an overall shape analogous to the surface of a saddle.

opposition The point at which a planet appears opposite the Sun in our sky.

optical quality The ability of a lens, mirror, or telescope to obtain clear and properly focused images.

orbit The path followed by a celestial body because of gravity; an orbit may be *bound* (elliptical) or *unbound* (parabolic or hyperbolic).

orbital energy The sum of an orbiting object's kinetic and gravitational potential energies.

orbital resonance A situation in which one object's orbital period is a simple ratio of another object's period, such as 1/2, 1/4, or 5/3. In such cases, the two objects periodically line up with each other, and the extra gravitational attractions at these times can affect the objects' orbits.

orbital velocity law A variation on Newton's version of Kepler's third law that allows us to use a star's orbital speed and distance from the galactic center to determine the total mass of the galaxy contained *within* the star's orbit; mathematically,

$$M_r = \frac{r \times v^2}{G}$$

where M_r is the mass contained within the star's orbit, r is the star's distance from the galactic center, v is the star's orbital velocity, and G is the gravitational constant.

orbiters (of other worlds) Spacecraft that go into orbit of another world for long-term study.

outer solar system Generally considered to encompass the region of our solar system beginning at about the orbit of Jupiter.

outgassing The process of releasing gases from a planetary interior, usually through volcanic eruptions.

oxidation Chemical reactions, often with rocks on the surface of a planet, that remove oxygen from the atmosphere.

ozone The molecule O_3, which is a particularly good absorber of ultraviolet light.

ozone depletion The decline in levels of atmospheric ozone found worldwide on Earth, especially in Antarctica, in recent years.

ozone hole A place where the concentration of ozone in the stratosphere is dramatically lower than is the norm.

pair production The process in which a concentration of energy spontaneously turns into a particle and its antiparticle.

parabola The precise mathematical shape of a special type of unbound orbit allowed under the force of gravity. If an object in a parabolic orbit loses only a tiny amount of energy, it will become bound.

paradigm (in science) A general pattern of thought that tends to shape scientific study during a particular time period.

paradox A situation that, at least at first, seems to violate common sense or contradict itself. Resolving paradoxes often leads to deeper understanding.

parallax The apparent shifting of an object against the background, due to viewing it from different positions. *See also* stellar parallax.

parallax angle Half of a star's annual back-and-forth shift due to stellar parallax; related to the star's distance according to the formula

$$\text{distance in parsecs} = \frac{1}{p}$$

where p is the parallax angle in arcseconds.

parsec (pc) The distance to an object with a parallax angle of 1 arcsecond; approximately equal to 3.26 light-years.

partial lunar eclipse A lunar eclipse during which the Moon becomes only partially covered by Earth's umbral shadow.

partial solar eclipse A solar eclipse during which the Sun becomes only partially blocked by the disk of the Moon.

particle accelerator A machine designed to accelerate subatomic particles to high speeds in order to create new particles or to test fundamental theories of physics.

particle era The era of the universe lasting from 10^{-10} second to 0.001 second after the Big Bang, during which subatomic particles were continually created and destroyed, and ending when matter annihilated antimatter.

peculiar velocity (of a galaxy) The component of a galaxy's velocity relative to the Milky Way that deviates from the velocity expected by Hubble's law.

penumbra The lighter, outlying regions of a shadow.

penumbral lunar eclipse A lunar eclipse during which the Moon passes only within Earth's penumbral shadow and does not fall within the umbra.

perigee The point at which an object orbiting Earth is nearest to Earth.

perihelion The point at which an object orbiting the Sun is closest to the Sun.

period–luminosity relation The relation that describes how the luminosity of a Cepheid variable star is related to the period between peaks in its brightness; the longer the period, the more luminous the star.

phase (of matter) The state determined by the way in which atoms or molecules are held together; the common phases are solid, liquid, and gas.

phase (of the Moon or a planet) The state determined by the portion of the visible face of the Moon (or of a planet) that is illuminated by sunlight. For the Moon, the phases cycle through new, waxing crescent, first-quarter, waxing gibbous, full, waning gibbous, third-quarter, waning crescent, and back to new.

photon An individual particle of light, characterized by a wavelength and a frequency.

photosphere The visible surface of the Sun, where the temperature averages just under 6000 K.

pixel An individual "picture element" on a CCD.

Planck era The era of the universe prior to the Planck time.

Planck's constant A universal constant, abbreviated h, with a value of $h = 6.626 \times 10^{-34}$ joule $\times$ s.

Planck time The time when the universe was 10^{-43} second old, before which random energy fluctuations were so large that our current theories are powerless to describe what might have been happening.

planet A moderately large object that orbits a star and shines primarily by reflecting light from its star. More precisely, according to a definition approved in 2006, a planet is an object that (1) orbits a star (but is itself neither a star nor a moon); (2) is massive enough for its own gravity to give it a nearly round shape; and (3) has cleared the neighborhood around its orbit. Objects that meet the first two criteria but not the third, including Ceres, Pluto, and Eris, are designated *dwarf planets.*

planetary geology The extension of the study of Earth's surface and interior to apply to other solid bodies in the solar system, such as terrestrial planets and jovian planet moons.

planetary migration A process through which a planet can move from the orbit on which it is born to a different orbit that is closer to or farther from its star.

planetary nebula The glowing cloud of gas ejected from a low-mass star at the end of its life.

planetesimals The building blocks of planets, formed by accretion in the solar nebula.

plasma A gas consisting of ions and electrons.

plasma tail (of a comet) One of two tails seen when a comet passes near the Sun (the other is the dust tail). It is composed of ionized gas blown away from the Sun by the solar wind.

plates (on a planet) Pieces of a lithosphere that apparently float upon the denser mantle below.

plate tectonics The geological process in which plates are moved around by stresses in a planet's mantle.

polarization (of light) The property of light describing how the electric and magnetic fields of light waves are aligned; light is said to be *polarized* when all of the photons have their electric and magnetic fields aligned in some particular way.

Population I *See* disk population.

Population II *See* spheroidal population.

positron *See* antielectron.

potential energy Energy stored for later conversion into kinetic energy; includes gravitational potential energy, electrical potential energy, and chemical potential energy.

power The rate of energy usage, usually measured in watts (1 watt = 1 joule/s).

precession The gradual wobble of the axis of a rotating object around a vertical line.

precipitation Condensed atmospheric gases that fall to the surface in the form of rain, snow, or hail.

pressure The force (per unit area) pushing on an object. In astronomy, we are generally interested in pressure applied by surrounding gas (or plasma). Ordinarily, such pressure is related to the temperature of the gas (*see* thermal pressure). In objects such as white dwarfs and neutron stars, pressure may arise from a quantum effect (*see* degeneracy pressure). Light can also exert pressure (*see* radiation pressure).

primary mirror The large, light-collecting mirror of a reflecting telescope.

prime focus (of a reflecting telescope) The first point at which light focuses after bouncing off the primary mirror; located in front of the primary mirror.

prime meridian The meridian of longitude that passes through Greenwich, England; defined to be longitude 0°.

primitive meteorites Meteorites that formed at the same time as the solar system itself, about 4.6 billion years ago. Primitive meteorites from the inner asteroid belt are usually stony, and those from the outer belt are usually carbon-rich.

processed meteorites Meteorites that apparently once were part of a larger object that "processed" the original material of the solar nebula into another form. Processed meteorites can be rocky if chipped from the surface or mantle, or metallic if blasted from the core.

proper motion The motion of an object in the plane of the sky, perpendicular to our line of sight.

protogalactic cloud A huge, collapsing cloud of intergalactic gas from which an individual galaxy formed.

proton–proton chain The chain of reactions by which low-mass stars (including the Sun) fuse hydrogen into helium.

protons Particles found in atomic nuclei with positive electrical charge, built from three quarks.

protoplanetary disk A disk of material surrounding a young star (or protostar) that may eventually form planets.

protostar A forming star that has not yet reached the point where sustained fusion can occur in its core.

protostellar disk A disk of material surrounding a protostar; essentially the same as a protoplanetary disk, but may not necessarily lead to planet formation.

protostellar wind The relatively strong wind from a protostar.

protosun The central object in the forming solar system that eventually became the Sun.

pseudoscience Something that purports to be science or may appear to be scientific but that does not adhere to the testing and verification requirements of the scientific method.

Ptolemaic model The geocentric model of the universe developed by Ptolemy in about 150 A.D.

pulsar A neutron star from which we see rapid pulses of radiation as it rotates.

pulsating variable stars Stars that grow alternately brighter and dimmer as their outer layers expand and contract in size.

quantum laws The laws that describe the behavior of particles on a very small scale; *see also* quantum mechanics.

quantum mechanics The branch of physics that deals with the very small, including molecules, atoms, and fundamental particles.

quantum state The complete description of the state of a subatomic particle, including its location, momentum, orbital angular momentum, and spin, to the extent allowed by the uncertainty principle.

quantum tunneling The process in which, thanks to the uncertainty principle, an electron or other subatomic particle appears on the other side of a barrier that it does not have the energy to overcome in a normal way.

quarks The building blocks of protons and neutrons; quarks are one of the two basic types of fermions (leptons are the other).

quasar The brightest type of active galactic nucleus.

radar mapping Imaging of a planet by bouncing radar waves off its surface, especially important for Venus and Titan, where thick clouds mask the surface.

radar ranging A method of measuring distances within the solar system by bouncing radio waves off planets.

radial motion The component of an object's motion directed toward or away from us.

radial velocity The portion of any object's total velocity that is directed toward or away from us. This part of the velocity is the only part that we can measure with the Doppler effect.

radiation pressure Pressure exerted by photons of light.

radiation zone (of a star) A region of the interior in which energy is transported primarily by radiative diffusion.

radiative diffusion The process by which photons gradually migrate from a hot region (such as the solar core) to a cooler region (such as the solar surface).

radiative energy Energy carried by light; the energy of a photon is Planck's constant times its frequency, or $h \times f$.

radioactive decay The spontaneous change of an atom into a different element, in which its nucleus breaks apart or a proton turns into an electron. It releases heat in a planet's interior.

radioactive element (or **radioactive isotope**) A substance whose nucleus tends to fall apart spontaneously.

radio galaxy A galaxy that emits unusually large quantities of radio waves; thought to contain an active galactic nucleus powered by a supermassive black hole.

radio lobes The huge regions of radio emission found on either side of radio galaxies. The lobes apparently contain plasma ejected by powerful jets from the galactic center.

radiometric dating The process of determining the age of a rock (i.e., the time since it solidified) by comparing the present amount of a radioactive substance to the amount of its decay product.

radio waves Light with very long wavelengths (and hence low frequencies)—longer than those of infrared light.

random walk A type of haphazard movement in which a particle or photon moves through a series of bounces, with each bounce sending it in a random direction.

recession velocity (of a galaxy) The speed at which a distant galaxy is moving away from us because of the expansion of the universe.

recollapsing universe A universe in which the collective gravity of all its matter eventually halts and reverses the expansion, causing the galaxies to come crashing back together and the universe to end in a fiery Big Crunch.

red giant A giant star that is red in color.

red-giant winds The relatively dense but slow winds from red giant stars.

redshift (Doppler) A Doppler shift in which spectral features are shifted to longer wavelengths, observed when an object is moving away from the observer.

reference frame (or **frame of reference**) What two people (or objects) share if they are *not* moving relative to one another.

reflecting telescope A telescope that uses mirrors to focus light.

reflection (of light) The process by which matter changes the direction of light.

reflection nebula A nebula that we see as a result of starlight reflected from interstellar dust grains. Reflection nebulae tend to have blue and black tints.

refracting telescope A telescope that uses lenses to focus light.

resonance *See* orbital resonance.

rest wavelength The wavelength of a spectral feature in the absence of any Doppler shift or gravitational redshift.

retrograde motion Motion that is backward compared to the norm. For example, we see Mars in apparent retrograde motion during the periods of time when it moves westward, rather than the more common eastward, relative to the stars.

revolution The orbital motion of one object around another.

right ascension (RA) Analogous to longitude, but on the celestial sphere; the angular east-west distance between the spring equinox and a location on the celestial sphere.

rings (planetary) The collections of numerous small particles orbiting a planet within its Roche tidal zone.

Roche tidal zone The region within two to three planetary radii (of any planet) in which the tidal forces tugging an object apart become comparable to the gravitational forces holding it together; planetary rings are always found within the Roche tidal zone.

rocks (in solar system theory) Materials common on the surface of Earth, such as silicon-based minerals, that are solid at temperatures and pressures found on Earth but typically melt or vaporize at temperatures of 500–1300 K.

rotation The spinning of an object around its axis.

rotation curve A graph that plots rotational (or orbital) velocity against distance from the center for any object or set of objects.

runaway greenhouse effect A positive feedback cycle in which heating caused by the greenhouse effect causes more greenhouse gases to enter the atmosphere, which further enhances the greenhouse effect.

saddle-shaped (or **hyperbolic**) **geometry** The type of geometry in which the rules—such as that two lines that begin parallel eventually diverge—are most easily visualized on a saddle-shaped surface.

Sagittarius Dwarf A small dwarf elliptical galaxy that is currently passing through the disk of the Milky Way Galaxy.

saros cycle The period over which the basic pattern of eclipses repeats, which is about 18 years $11\frac{1}{3}$ days.

satellite Any object orbiting another object.

scattered light Light that is reflected into random directions.

Schwarzschild radius A measure of the size of the event horizon of a black hole.

science The search for knowledge that can be used to explain or predict natural phenomena in a way that can be confirmed by rigorous observations or experiments.

scientific method An organized approach to explaining observed facts through science.

scientific theory A model of some aspect of nature that has been rigorously tested and has passed all tests to date.

seafloor crust On Earth, the thin, dense crust of basalt created by seafloor spreading.

seafloor spreading On Earth, the creation of new seafloor crust at mid-ocean ridges.

search for extraterrestrial intelligence (SETI) The name given to observing projects designed to search for signs of intelligent life beyond Earth.

secondary mirror A small mirror in a reflecting telescope, used to reflect light gathered by the primary mirror toward an eyepiece or instrument.

sedimentary rock A rock that formed from sediments created and deposited by erosional processes.

seismic waves Earthquake-induced vibrations that propagate through a planet.

selection effect (or **selection bias**) A type of bias that arises from the way in which objects of study are selected and that can lead to

incorrect conclusions. For example, when you are counting animals in a jungle it is easiest to see brightly colored animals, which could mislead you into thinking that these animals are the most common.

semimajor axis Half the distance across the long axis of an ellipse; in this text, it is usually referred to as the *average* distance of an orbiting object, abbreviated a in the formula for Kepler's third law.

Seyfert galaxies The name given to a class of galaxies that are found relatively nearby and that have nuclei much like those of quasars, except that they are less luminous.

shepherd moons Tiny moons within a planet's ring system that help force particles into a narrow ring; a variation on *gap moons*.

shield volcano A shallow-sloped volcano made from the flow of low-viscosity basaltic lava.

shock wave A wave of pressure generated by gas moving faster than the speed of sound.

sidereal day The time of 23 hours 56 minutes 4.09 seconds between successive appearances of any particular star on the meridian; essentially, the true rotation period of Earth.

sidereal month The time required for the Moon to orbit Earth once (as measured against the stars); about $27\frac{1}{4}$ days.

sidereal period (of a planet) A planet's actual orbital period around the Sun.

sidereal time Time measured according to the position of stars in the sky rather than the position of the Sun in the sky. *See also* local sidereal time.

sidereal year The time required for Earth to complete exactly one orbit as measured against the stars; about 20 minutes longer than the tropical year on which our calendar is based.

silicate rock A silicon-rich rock.

singularity The place at the center of a black hole where, in principle, gravity crushes all matter to an infinitely tiny and dense point.

Small Magellanic Cloud One of two small, irregular galaxies (the other is the Large Magellanic Cloud) located about 150,000 light-years away; it probably orbits the Milky Way Galaxy.

small solar system body An asteroid, comet, or other object that orbits a star but is too small to qualify as a planet or dwarf planet.

snowball Earth Name given to a hypothesis suggesting that, some 600–700 million years ago, Earth experienced a period in which it became cold enough for glaciers to exist worldwide, even in equatorial regions.

solar activity Short-lived phenomena on the Sun, including the emergence and disappearance of individual sunspots, prominences, and flares; sometimes called *solar weather*.

solar circle The Sun's orbital path around the galaxy, which has a radius of about 28,000 light-years.

solar day 24 hours, which is the average time between appearances of the Sun on the meridian.

solar eclipse An event that occurs when the Moon's shadow falls on Earth, which can occur only at new moon. A solar eclipse may be total, partial, or annular.

solar flares Huge and sudden releases of energy on the solar surface, probably caused when energy stored in magnetic fields is suddenly released.

solar luminosity The luminosity of the Sun, which is approximately 4×10^{26} watts.

solar maximum The time during each sunspot cycle at which the number of sunspots is the greatest.

solar minimum The time during each sunspot cycle at which the number of sunspots is the smallest.

solar nebula The piece of interstellar cloud from which our own solar system formed.

solar neutrino problem The disagreement between the predicted and observed number of neutrinos coming from the Sun.

solar prominences Vaulted loops of hot gas that rise above the Sun's surface and follow magnetic field lines.

solar sail A large, highly reflective (and thin, to minimize mass) piece of material that can "sail" through space using pressure exerted by sunlight.

solar system (or **star system**) A star (sometimes more than one star) and all the objects that orbit it.

solar thermostat *See* stellar thermostat; the solar thermostat is the same idea applied to the Sun.

solar wind A stream of charged particles ejected from the Sun.

solid phase The phase of matter in which atoms or molecules are held rigidly in place.

solstice *See* summer solstice *and* winter solstice.

sound wave A wave of alternately rising and falling pressure.

south celestial pole (SCP) The point on the celestial sphere directly above Earth's South Pole.

spacetime The inseparable, four-dimensional combination of space and time.

spacetime diagram A graph that plots a spatial dimension on one axis and time on another axis.

special theory of relativity Einstein's theory that describes the effects of the fact that all motion is relative and that everyone always measures the same speed of light.

spectral lines Bright or dark lines that appear in an object's spectrum, which we can see when we pass the object's light through a prismlike device that spreads out the light like a rainbow.

spectral resolution The degree of detail that can be seen in a spectrum; the higher the spectral resolution, the more detail we can see.

spectral type A way of classifying a star by the lines that appear in its spectrum; it is related to surface temperature. The basic spectral types are designated by a letter (OBAFGKM, with O for the hottest stars and M for the coolest) and are subdivided with numbers from 0 through 9.

spectrograph An instrument used to record spectra.

spectroscopic binary A binary star system whose binary nature is revealed because we detect the spectral lines of one or both stars alternately becoming blueshifted and redshifted as the stars orbit each other.

spectroscopy (in astronomical research) The process of obtaining spectra from astronomical objects.

spectrum (of light) *See* electromagnetic spectrum.

speed The rate at which an object moves. Its units are distance divided by time, such as m/s or km/hr.

speed of light The speed at which light travels, which is about 300,000 km/s.

spherical geometry The type of geometry in which the rules—such as that lines that begin parallel eventually meet—are those that hold on the surface of a sphere.

spheroidal component (of a galaxy) The portion of any galaxy that is spherical (or football-like) in shape and contains very little cool gas; it generally contains only very old stars. Elliptical galaxies have only a spheroidal component, while spiral galaxies also have a disk component.

spheroidal galaxy Another name for an *elliptical galaxy*.

spheroidal population Stars that orbit within the spheroidal component of a galaxy; sometimes called *Population II*. Elliptical galaxies have only a spheroidal population (they lack a disk population), while spiral galaxies have spheroidal population stars in their bulges and halos.

spin (quantum) *See* spin angular momentum.

spin angular momentum The inherent angular momentum of a fundamental particle; often simply called *spin*.

spiral arms The bright, prominent arms, usually in a spiral pattern, found in most spiral galaxies.

spiral density waves Gravitationally driven waves of enhanced density that move through a spiral galaxy and are responsible for maintaining its spiral arms.

spiral galaxies Galaxies that look like flat white disks with yellowish bulges at their centers. The disks are filled with cool gas and dust, interspersed with hotter ionized gas, and usually display beautiful spiral arms.

spreading centers (geological) Places where hot mantle material rises upward between plates and then spreads sideways, creating new seafloor crust.

spring (March) equinox Refers both to the point in Pisces on the celestial sphere where the ecliptic crosses the celestial equator and to the moment in time when the Sun appears at that point each year (around March 21).

spring tides The higher-than-average tides on Earth that occur at new and full moon, when the tidal forces from the Sun and Moon both act along the same line.

standard candle An object for which we have some means of knowing its true luminosity, so that we can use its apparent brightness to determine its distance with the luminosity–distance formula.

standard model (of physics) The current theoretical model that describes the fundamental particles and forces in nature.

standard time Time measured according to the internationally recognized time zones.

star A large, glowing ball of gas that generates energy through nuclear fusion in its core. The term *star* is sometimes applied to objects that are in the process of becoming true stars (e.g., protostars) and to the remains of stars that have died (e.g., neutron stars).

starburst galaxy A galaxy in which stars are forming at an unusually high rate.

star cluster *See* cluster of stars.

star-gas-star cycle The process of galactic recycling in which stars expel gas into space, where it mixes with the interstellar medium and eventually forms new stars.

star system *See* solar system.

state (quantum) *See* quantum state.

steady state theory A now-discredited theory that held that the universe had no beginning and looks about the same at all times.

Stefan–Boltzmann constant A constant that appears in the laws of thermal radiation, with value

$$\sigma = 5.7 \times 10^{-8} \frac{\text{watt}}{\text{m}^2 \times \text{Kelvin}^4}$$

stellar evolution The formation and development of stars.

stellar parallax The apparent shift in the position of a nearby star (relative to distant objects) that occurs as we view the star from different positions in Earth's orbit of the Sun each year.

stellar thermostat The regulation of a star's core temperature that comes about when a star is in both energy balance (the rate at which fusion releases energy in the star's core is balanced with the rate at which the star's surface radiates energy into space) and gravitational equilibrium.

stellar wind A stream of charged particles ejected from the surface of a star.

stratosphere An intermediate-altitude layer of Earth's atmosphere that is warmed by the absorption of ultraviolet light from the Sun.

stratovolcano A steep-sided volcano made from viscous lavas that can't flow very far before solidifying.

string theory New ideas, not yet well-tested, that attempt to explain all of physics in a much simpler way than current theories.

stromatolites Large bacterial "colonies."

strong force One of the four fundamental forces; it is the force that holds atomic nuclei together.

subduction (of tectonic plates) The process in which one plate slides under another.

subduction zones Places where one plate slides under another.

subgiant A star that is between being a main-sequence star and being a giant; subgiants have inert helium cores and hydrogen-fusing shells.

sublimation The process by which atoms or molecules escape into the gas phase from a solid.

summer (June) solstice Refers both to the point on the celestial sphere where the ecliptic is farthest north of the celestial equator and to the moment in time when the Sun appears at that point each year (around June 21).

sunspot cycle The period of about 11 years over which the number of sunspots on the Sun rises and falls.

sunspots Blotches on the surface of the Sun that appear darker than surrounding regions.

superbubble Essentially a giant interstellar bubble, formed when the shock waves of many individual bubbles merge to form a single giant shock wave.

superclusters The largest known structures in the universe, consisting of many clusters of galaxies, groups of galaxies, and individual galaxies.

supergiants The very large and very bright stars (luminosity class I) that appear at the top of an H-R diagram.

supermassive black holes Giant black holes, with masses millions to billions of times that of our Sun, thought to reside in the centers of many galaxies and to power active galactic nuclei.

supernova The explosion of a star.

Supernova 1987A A supernova witnessed on Earth in 1987; it was the nearest supernova seen in nearly 400 years and helped astronomers refine theories of supernovae.

supernova remnant A glowing, expanding cloud of debris from a supernova explosion.

surface area–to–volume ratio The ratio defined by an object's surface area divided by its volume; this ratio is larger for smaller objects (and vice versa).

synchronous rotation The rotation of an object that always shows the same face to an object that it is orbiting because its rotation period and orbital period are equal.

synchrotron radiation A type of radio emission that occurs when electrons moving at nearly the speed of light spiral around magnetic field lines.

synodic month (or **lunar month**) The time required for a complete cycle of lunar phases, which averages about $29\frac{1}{2}$ days.

synodic period (of a planet) The time between successive alignments of a planet and the Sun in our sky; measured from opposition to opposition for a planet beyond Earth's orbit, or from superior conjunction to superior conjunction for Mercury and Venus.

tangential motion The component of an object's motion directed across our line of sight.

tangential velocity The portion of any object's total velocity that is directed across (perpendicular to) our line of sight. This part of the velocity cannot be measured with the Doppler effect. It can be measured only by observing the object's gradual motion across our sky.

tectonics The disruption of a planet's surface by internal stresses.

temperature A measure of the average kinetic energy of particles in a substance.

terrestrial planets Rocky planets similar in overall composition to Earth.

theories of relativity (special and general) Einstein's theories that describe the nature of space, time, and gravity.

theory (in science) See scientific theory.

theory of evolution The theory, first advanced by Charles Darwin, that explains how evolution occurs through the process of natural selection.

thermal emitter An object that produces a thermal radiation spectrum; sometimes called a *blackbody*.

thermal energy The collective kinetic energy, as measured by temperature, of the many individual particles moving within a substance.

thermal escape The process in which atoms or molecules in a planet's exosphere move fast enough to escape into space.

thermal pressure The ordinary pressure in a gas arising from motions of particles that can be attributed to the object's temperature.

thermal pulses The predicted upward spikes in the rate of helium fusion, occurring every few thousand years, that occur near the end of a low-mass star's life.

thermal radiation The spectrum of radiation produced by an opaque object that depends only on the object's temperature; sometimes called *blackbody radiation*.

thermosphere A high, hot, X-ray-absorbing layer of an atmosphere, just below the exosphere.

third-quarter (phase) The phase of the Moon that occurs three-quarters of the way through each cycle of phases, in which precisely half of the visible face is illuminated by sunlight.

tidal force A force that occurs when the gravity pulling on one side of an object is larger than that on the other side, causing the object to stretch.

tidal friction Friction within an object that is caused by a tidal force.

tidal heating A source of internal heating created by tidal friction. It is particularly important for satellites with eccentric orbits such as Io and Europa.

time dilation The effect in which you observe time running more slowly in reference frames moving relative to you.

timing (in astronomical research) The process of tracking how the light intensity from an astronomical object varies with time.

torque A twisting force that can cause a change in an object's angular momentum.

total apparent brightness See apparent brightness. The word "total" is sometimes added to make clear that we are talking about light across all wavelengths, not just visible light.

totality (eclipse) The portion of a total lunar eclipse during which the Moon is fully within Earth's umbral shadow or a total solar eclipse during which the Sun's disk is fully blocked by the Moon.

total luminosity See luminosity. The word "total" is sometimes added to make clear that we are talking about light across all wavelengths, not just visible light.

total lunar eclipse A lunar eclipse in which the Moon becomes fully covered by Earth's umbral shadow.

total solar eclipse A solar eclipse during which the Sun becomes fully blocked by the disk of the Moon.

transit An event in which a planet passes in front of a star (or the Sun) as seen from Earth. Only Mercury and Venus can be seen in transit of our Sun. The search for transits of extrasolar planets is an important planet detection strategy.

transmission (of light) The process in which light passes through matter without being absorbed.

transparent Describes a material that transmits light.

tree of life (evolutionary) A diagram that shows relationships between different species as inferred from genetic comparisons.

triple-alpha reaction See helium fusion.

Trojan asteroids Asteroids found within two stable zones that share Jupiter's orbit but lie 60° ahead of and behind Jupiter.

tropical year The time from one spring equinox to the next, on which our calendar is based.

Tropic of Cancer The circle on Earth with latitude 23.5°N, which marks the northernmost latitude at which the Sun ever passes directly overhead (which it does at noon on the summer solstice).

Tropic of Capricorn The circle on Earth with latitude 23.5°S, which marks the southernmost latitude at which the Sun ever passes directly overhead (which it does at noon on the winter solstice).

tropics The region on Earth surrounding the equator and extending from the Tropic of Capricorn (latitude 23.5°S) to the Tropic of Cancer (latitude 23.5°N).

troposphere The lowest atmospheric layer, in which convection and weather occur.

Tully–Fisher relation A relationship among spiral galaxies showing that the faster a spiral galaxy's rotation speed, the more luminous it is. It is important because it allows us to determine the distance to a spiral galaxy once we measure its rotation rate and apply the luminosity–distance formula.

turbulence Rapid and random motion.

21-cm line A spectral line from atomic hydrogen with wavelength 21 cm (in the radio portion of the spectrum).

ultraviolet light Light with wavelengths that fall in the portion of the electromagnetic spectrum between visible light and X rays.

umbra The dark central region of a shadow.

unbound orbits Orbits on which an object comes in toward a large body only once, never to return; unbound orbits may be parabolic or hyperbolic in shape.

uncertainty principle The law of quantum mechanics that states that we can never know both a particle's position and its momentum, or both its energy and the time it has the energy, with absolute precision.

universal law of gravitation The law expressing the force of gravity (F_g) between two objects, given by the formula

$$F_g = G \frac{M_1 M_2}{d^2}$$

$$\left(\text{where } G = 6.67 \times 10^{-11} \frac{\text{m}^3}{\text{kg} \times \text{s}^2} \right)$$

universal time (UT) Standard time in Greenwich, England (or anywhere on the prime meridian).

universe The sum total of all matter and energy.

up quark One of the two quark types (the other is the down quark) found in ordinary protons and neutrons; has a charge of $+\frac{2}{3}$.

velocity The combination of speed and direction of motion; it can be stated as a speed in a particular direction, such as 100 km/hr due north.

virtual particles Particles that "pop" in and out of existence so rapidly that, according to the uncertainty principle, they cannot be directly detected.

viscosity The thickness of a liquid described in terms of how rapidly it flows; low-viscosity liquids flow quickly (e.g., water), while high-viscosity liquids flow slowly (e.g., molasses).

visible light The light our eyes can see, ranging in wavelength from about 400 to 700 nm.

visual binary A binary star system in which both stars can be resolved through a telescope.

voids Huge volumes of space between superclusters that appear to contain very little matter.

volatiles Substances, such as water, carbon dioxide, and methane, that are usually found as gases, liquids, or surface ices on the terrestrial worlds.

volcanic plains Vast, relatively smooth areas created by the eruption of very runny lava.

volcanism The eruption of molten rock, or lava, from a planet's interior onto its surface.

waning (phases) The set of phases in which less and less of the visible face of the Moon is illuminated; the phases that come after full moon but before new moon.

watt The standard unit of power in science; defined as 1 watt = 1 joule/s.

wavelength The distance between adjacent peaks (or troughs) of a wave.

waxing (phases) The set of phases in which more and more of the visible face of the Moon is becoming illuminated; the phases that come after new moon but before full moon.

weak bosons The exchange particles for the weak force.

weak force One of the four fundamental forces; it is the force that mediates nuclear reactions, and it is the only force besides gravity felt by weakly interacting particles.

weakly interacting particles Particles, such as neutrinos and WIMPs, that respond only to the weak force and gravity; that is, they do not feel the strong force or the electromagnetic force.

weather The ever-varying combination of winds, clouds, temperature, and pressure in a planet's troposphere.

weight The net force that an object applies to its surroundings; in the case of a stationary body on the surface of Earth, it equals mass × acceleration of gravity.

weightlessness A weight of zero, as occurs during free-fall.

white dwarf limit (or **Chandrasekhar limit**) The maximum possible mass for a white dwarf, which is about $1.4 M_{\text{Sun}}$.

white dwarfs The hot, compact corpses of low-mass stars, typically with a mass similar to that of the Sun compressed to a volume the size of Earth.

white dwarf supernova A supernova that occurs when an accreting white dwarf reaches the white-dwarf limit, ignites runaway carbon fusion, and explodes like a bomb; often called a *Type Ia supernova*.

WIMPs A possible form of dark matter consisting of subatomic particles that are dark because they do not respond to the electromagnetic force; stands for *weakly interacting massive particles*.

winter (December) solstice Refers both to the point on the celestial sphere where the ecliptic is farthest south of the celestial equator and to the moment in time when the Sun appears at that point each year (around December 21).

worldline A line that represents an object on a spacetime diagram.

wormholes The name given to hypothetical tunnels through hyperspace that might connect two distant places in our universe.

X-ray binary A binary star system that emits substantial amounts of X rays, thought to be from an accretion disk around a neutron star or black hole.

X-ray burster An object that emits a burst of X rays every few hours to every few days; each burst lasts a few seconds and is thought to be caused by helium fusion on the surface of an accreting neutron star in a binary system.

X-ray bursts Bursts of X rays coming from sudden ignition of fusion on the surface of an accreting neutron star in an X-ray binary system.

X rays Light with wavelengths that fall in the portion of the electromagnetic spectrum between ultraviolet light and gamma rays.

Zeeman effect The splitting of spectral lines by a magnetic field.

zenith The point directly overhead, which has an altitude of 90°.

zodiac The constellations on the celestial sphere through which the ecliptic passes.

zones (on a jovian planet) Bright bands of rising air that encircle a jovian planet at a particular set of latitudes.

CREDITS

Laboratory; b NASA/Earth Observing System; c NASA/ Jet Propulsion Laboratory 9.10 Paul Chesley/Getty Images 9.11a NASA Earth Observing System; b NASA/Jet Propulsion Laboratory; c zschnepf/shutterstock.com 9.12a U.S. Geological Survey, Denver; b Cornforth Images/Alamy 9.13 (left) NASA Earth Observing System; (right) NASA/Jet Propulsion Laboratory 9.14a Gene Ahrens/Bruce Coleman Inc./Photoshot Holdings, Ltd.; b Joachim Messerschmidt/Bruce Coleman Inc./Photoshot Holdings, Ltd.; c Mytho/Fotolia; d Florian Werner/age fotostock 9.15a and p. 265 NASA; b NASA Earth Observing System 9.17 (left) NASA/Johns Hopkins University Applied Physics Laboratory/Carnegie Institution of Washington; (right) Akira Fujii 9.18 (left) Frank Barrett; (right) malcolm park/Oxford Scientific/gettyimages.com 9.19 Pearson Education 9.20 NASA Earth Observing System 9.21a NASA/Goddard Institute for Space Studies; b NASA/Goddard Space Flight Center 9.22a–c NASA/Johns Hopkins University Applied Physics Laboratory/ Carnegie Institution of Washington 9.23b NASA/Jet Propulsion Laboratory 9.24 (left) NASA Earth Observing System; (right) Lowell Observatory 9.25 NASA/Goddard Institute for Space Studies 9.26 and p. 265 (bottom) NASA/Goddard Institute for Space Studies; (top) NASA/Jet Propulsion Laboratory 9.27 (bottom) NASA/Goddard Institute for Space Studies; (top) NASA 9.28 NASA/Jet Propulsion Laboratory 9.29a EROS Data Center, U.S. Geological Survey; b National Air and Space Museum Smithsonian Institution; c NASA EOS Earth Observing System 9.30 and p. 265 (left) NASA/Jet Propulsion Laboratory; (right) Dr. Marjorie A Chan 9.31 NASA/JPL-Caltech/Cornell/ASU 9.32 NASA/JPL-Caltech/MSSS 9.33 NASA Earth Observing System 9.34 and p. 265 NASA/Jet Propulsion Laboratory 9.35 European Space Agency 9.36 Ted Stryk/NASA 9.37 National Geophysical Data Center 9.41 NASA/Jet Propulsion Laboratory 9.42 NASA/Jet Propulsion Laboratory 9.43 NASA/Jet Propulsion Laboratory 9.44 NASA/Jet Propulsion Laboratory 9.45 (top left) Ronen Zilberman/AP Images; (top center) Nina B/Shutterstock. com; (top right) University of Hawaii/SOEST; (bottom right) Alexander Malahoff p. 266 NASA Earth Observing System

Chapter 10
Opener NASA Earth Observing System 10.1 Mercury: NASA; surface of Venus: from the Voyage scale model solar system, developed by Challenger Center for Space Science Education, the Smithsonian Institution, and NASA, ©2001 David P. Anderson, Southern Methodist University; Earth valley: Dmitry/ Shutterstock; Moon, Mars, Earth: NASA Earth Observing System 10.2 and p. 303 NASA Earth Observing System 10.5 NASA Earth Observing System 10.11b Doug Duncan 10.25 NASA Earth Observing System 10.26 NASA/Jet Propulsion Laboratory 10.27 NASA/Jet Propulsion Laboratory 10.28 NASA Earth Observing System 10.29 NASA/JPL/University of Arizona 10.31 European Space Agency 10.32 NASA 10.33 NASA

Chapter 11
Opener NASA/Jet Propulsion Laboratory 11.1 NASA/Jet Propulsion Laboratory 11.10 NASA/Jet Propulsion Laboratory 11.11a NASA Earth Observing System; b NASA/Jet Propulsion Laboratory; c Lawrence Sromovsky; d NASA/Jet Propulsion Laboratory 11.12 NASA/Jet Propulsion Laboratory 11.14 NASA/Jet Propulsion Laboratory 11.15 Calypso, Janus, Telesto: NASA Earth Observing System; Pandora, Hyperion, Phoebe: NASA/Jet Propulsion Laboratory 11.16 NASA/Jet Propulsion Laboratory 11.17 NASA/Jet Propulsion Laboratory 11.18

NASA/Jet Propulsion Laboratory 11.20 NASA/Jet Propulsion Laboratory 11.21 NASA/Jet Propulsion Laboratory 11.22 NASA/ Jet Propulsion Laboratory 11.23 NASA/Jet Propulsion Laboratory 11.24 (left) NASA/Jet Propulsion Laboratory; (right) NASA Earth Observing System 11.25 NASA/Jet Propulsion Laboratory 11.26 NASA Earth Observing System 11.27 NASA/Jet Propulsion Laboratory 11.28 NASA/Jet Propulsion Laboratory 11.29 NASA/ Jet Propulsion Laboratory 11.30 NASA/Jet Propulsion Laboratory 11.31 NASA/Jet Propulsion Laboratory 11.32 NASA/Jet Propulsion Laboratory 11.33a Lunar and Planetary Laboratory; b NASA/Jet Propulsion Laboratory 11.34 NASA/Jet Propulsion Laboratory 11.35 NASA/Jet Propulsion Laboratory 11.36 Jupiter: Imke de Pater; Saturn, Uranus, Neptune: NASA/Jet Propulsion Laboratory p. 335 NASA/Jet Propulsion Laboratory p. 336 NASA/Jet Propulsion Laboratory

Chapter 12
Opener Photography and Image Processing by Milsolav Druckmuller 12.1 NASA/Jet Propulsion Laboratory 12.2 NASA, ESA, JAXA and Emily Lakdawalla 12.5 NASA/JPL-Caltech/ UCLA/MBS/DLR/IDA 12.7 Ivan and Colby Navarro, NASA 12.8 Jonathan Blair/Corbis 12.9 Robert A. Haag 12.10 (top) ISAS/ JAXA; (bottom) NASA/Jet Propulsion Laboratory 12.11a Peter Ceravolo; b Frank Zullo/Photo Researchers, Inc. 12.12 and p. 362 NASA/Jet Propulsion Laboratory 12.13a NASA/Jet Propulsion Laboratory; b European Space Agency 12.14a BiStar Astronomical Observatory; b European Space Agency 12.15 NASA 12.16 ICSTARS Inc. 12.17 NASA 12.19 ESO 12.21b NASA/Goddard Space Flight Center 12.22a NASA/Jet Propulsion Laboratory; b Joe Bergeron; c MSSO, ANU/Science Library/Photo Researchers, Inc.; d NASA/Goddard Space Flight Center 12.23 Kirk R. Johnson 12.24 Virgil L. Sharpton 12.25 and p. 362 Pearson Education 12.26 Sovfoto/Eastfoto 12.27 La Republica Newspaper/AP Images p. 363 NASA Earth Observing System

Chapter 13
Opener National Research Council Canada, C. Marois & Keck Observatory p. 368 The Print Collector/Alamy 13.6 National Research Council Canada, C. Marois & Keck Observatory 13.12 NASA Earth Observing System 13.20 European Southern Observatory p. 396 Earth's Moon: NASA Earth Observing System; Europa: NASA/Jet Propulsion Laboratory; impact: Pearson Education, Pearson Science

Chapter S2
Opener Bettmann/Corbis

Chapter S3
Opener Andrew Fruchter/NASA S3.20 and p. 439 ESA/ Hubble & NASA

Chapter S4
S4.1 CERN/European Organization for Nuclear Research S4.6 Terry Oakley/Alamy p. 463 NASA/Jet Propulsion Laboratory

Chapter 14
Opener NASA 14.1 Corel Corporation 14.5 NASA/Marshall Space Flight Center 14.11b Institute for Solar Physics 14.12 National Optical Astronomy Observatories (NOAA) 14.14 Lawrence Berkeley National Laboratory 14.15a Institute for Solar Physics; b National Solar Observatory 14.17b NASA/Jet

Propulsion Laboratory 14.18 SDO/GSFC/NASA 14.19 NASA Transition Region and Coronal Explorer 14.20 Lockheed Martin Solar & Astrophysics Laboratory

Chapter 15

Opener Till Credner/AllTheSky.com 15.4 NASA Jet Propulsion Laboratory 15.5 Harvard College Observatory p. 494 (top right) Harvard College Observatory 15.16 and p. 506 Robert Gendler/Photo Researchers 15.17 and p. 506 NASA Jet Propulsion Laboratory

Chapter 16

Opener Far-infrared: ESA/Herschel/PACS/SPIRE/Hill, Motte, HOBYS Key Programme Consortium; X ray: ESA/XMM-Newton/EPIC/XMM-Newton-SOC/Boulanger 16.1 and p. 527 DMI David Malin Images 16.3 NASA Jet Propulsion Laboratory 16.4 Annual Reviews, Inc. 16.5 European Southern Observatory 16.6 (left) ESA; (right) Paul A. Scowen, Research Professional 16.7 NASA Jet Propulsion Laboratory 16.8 Far-infrared: ESA/Herschel/PACS/SPIRE/Hill, Motte, HOBYS Key Programme Consortium; X ray: ESA/XMM-Newton/EPIC/XMM-Newton-SOC/Boulanger 16.10 and p. 527 Matthew Bate, Ph.D. 16.11 NASA/Jet Propulsion Laboratory 16.12 Tom Abel 16.13 NASA Earth Observing System 16.15 NASA Jet Propulsion Laboratory 16.19 European Southern Observatory 16.20 STScI/NASA p. 528 Tom Abel

Chapter 17

Opener NASA Earth Observing System 17.1 NASA/Jet Propulsion Laboratory 17.7 and p. 551 NASA Earth Observing System 17.17 and p. 551 European Southern Observatory 17.18 DMI David Malin Images 17.19 NASA/Jet Propulsion Laboratory

Chapter 18

Opener NASA Earth Observing System 18.1a NASA; b NASA/Jet Propulsion Laboratory 18.3 and p. 571 Pearson Education, Pearson Science 18.4b NASA/Jet Propulsion Laboratory 18.6 NASA/Jet Propulsion Laboratory 18.8 European Southern Observatory p. 567 Chandrasekhar: Bettmann/Corbis; Eddington and Landau: Argelander Institut Fur Astronomie; Oppenheimer: Corbis; Bell: The Regents of the University of California 18.17 NASA/Goddard Space Flight Center 18.18 National Radio Astronomy Observatory

Chapter 19

Opener NASA/Jet Propulsion Laboratory 19.3 NASA/Jet Propulsion Laboratory; NASA; Eagle Nebula: Paul A. Scowen, Research Professional; gas bubble: Robert J. Vanderbei 19.4 NASA, ESA, HEIC, and The Hubble Heritage Team (STScI/AURA) 19.5 Robert J. Vanderbei 19.6 NASA/Jet Propulsion Laboratory 19.7a Stocktrek Images/SuperStock; b NASA 19.8a National Radio Astronomy Observatory; b NASA/CXC/MIT/UMass Amherst/M. D. Stage et al. 19.9b ESO/Manu Mejias 19.10 NASA 19.11 NASA Earth Observing System 19.12a NASA/Jet Propulsion Laboratory; b NASA; c NASA/Jet Propulsion Laboratory; d NASA/Jet Propulsion Laboratory; e Axel Mellinger, A Color All-Sky Panorama Image of the Milky Way, *Publ. Astron. Soc. Pacific 121*, 1180–1187 (2009); f NASA/Jet Propulsion Laboratory; g Fermi-LAT Collaboration/NASA 19.13 NASA 19.14 DMI David Malin Images 19.15 DMI David Malin Images 19.16 and p. 597 NASA/Jet Propulsion Laboratory 19.17 NASA/Jet Propulsion Laboratory 19.20a NASA Headquarters;

b–c National Radio Astronomy Observatory; d European Southern Observatory 19.22 NASA/Jet Propulsion Laboratory p. 598 NASA/Jet Propulsion Laboratory; Axel Mellinger, A Color All-Sky Panorama Image of the Milky Way, *Publ. Astron. Soc. Pacific 121*, 1180–1187 (2009)

Chapter 20

Opener NASA Earth Observing System 20.1 NASA/Jet Propulsion Laboratory 20.2a DMI David Malin Images; b NASA/Jet Propulsion Laboratory; c DMI David Malin Images 20.3 NASA/Jet Propulsion Laboratory 20.4 NASA/Jet Propulsion Laboratory 20.5 NASA/Jet Propulsion Laboratory 20.6a DMI David Malin Images; b NASA/Jet Propulsion Laboratory 20.7b NASA/Jet Propulsion Laboratory; c DMI David Malin Images 20.8 National Optical Astronomy Observatories 20.9 NOAO Gemini Science Center 20.10 NASA/Jet Propulsion Laboratory 20.14 NASA, ESA, A. Riess (STScI and JHU), and S. Rodney (JHU) 20.15 NASA Jet Propulsion Laboratory 20.16 Carnegie Institution of Washington 20.17 Huntington Library/SuperStock p. 620 NASA/Jet Propulsion Laboratory; DMI David Malin Images

Chapter 21

Opener NASA, ESA, and the Hubble Heritage Team (STScI/AURA) 21.2 and p. 641 Volker Springel/Max Planck Institute for Astrophysics 21.4 NASA 21.5 NASA, ESA, and the Hubble Heritage Team (STScI/AURA)-ESA/Hubble Collaboration 21.6 NASA/Jet Propulsion Laboratory 21.7 Space Telescope Science Institute 21.8a DMI David Malin Images; b E. R. Carrasco et al. (2010, ApJ, 816, L160), Gemini Observatory 21.10 NASA/Jet Propulsion Laboratory 21.11a and p. 641 NASA; b Subaru Telescope/National Astronomical Observatory of Japan NAOJ 21.12 NASA, ESA, the Hubble Heritage Team (STScI/AURA), and A. Aloisi (STScI/ESA) 21.13 NASA/Jet Propulsion Laboratory 21.16 National Radio Astronomy Observatory 21.17 National Radio Astronomy Observatory 21.19 NASA/Jet Propulsion Laboratory 21.22 NASA/Jet Propulsion Laboratory

Chapter 22

Opener E. Bunn 22.5 Gas: E. Bunn; galaxy: DMI David Malin Images; Hubble spacecraft: NASA 22.9 E. Bunn 22.18a Photo by Greg Thow/Getty Images; b WDG Photo/Shutterstock.com

Chapter 23

Opener NASA 23.6 California Institute of Technology Archives 23.7 and p. 690 NASA Earth Observing System 23.8 and p. 690 NASA EOS Earth Observing System 23.10 NASA, ESA, J. Richard (Center for Astronomical Research/Observatory of Lyon, France), and J.-P. Kneib (Astrophysical Laboratory of Marseille, France) 23.11 NASA 23.13 Michael Strauss 23.15 and p. 690 Andrey Kravtsov 23.16 NASA Jet Propulsion Laboratory

Chapter 24

Opener Seth Shostak 24.2 Darlene Cutshall/Shutterstock 24.3 James L. Amos/Photo Researchers, Inc. 24.5a Jane Gould/Alamy; b B Christopher/Alamy; c Abigail Allwood/NASA 24.8 and p. 718 Woods Hole Oceanographic Institution 24.9 REUTERS/David McNew 24.10 Martin M. Hanczyc 24.12 M I (Spike) Walker/Alamy 24.13 and p. 718 M. Di Lorenzo, NASA Earth Observing System 24.16 Yeshe Fenner 24.17 Seth Shostak 24.19 and p. 718 Seth Shostak 24.20 National Astronomy and Ionosphere Center 24.21a and b NASA/Jet Propulsion Laboratory 24.22 and p. 718 NASA/Jet Propulsion Laboratory 24.23 NASA/Jet Propulsion Laboratory p. 722 E. Bunn

Scale of Time
Peru terraces: Linda Whitwam/ Dorling Kindersley Media Library; modern skull: Dave King/Dorling Kindersley Media

Library; pyramids: Pius Lee/Shutterstock; homo erectus: Dorling Kindersley Media Library; trilobite: Russell Shively/Shutterstock; Sun and Earth: Paul & Lindamarie Ambrose/Getty Images

TEXT AND ILLUSTRATION CREDITS

Chapter 1
p. 2 Quote from T.S. Eliot, Excerpt from "Little Gidding," Part V, in FOUR QUARTETS, copyright 1942 by T.S. Eliot and renewed 1970 by Esme Valerie Eliot, reprinted by permission of Houghton Mifflin Harcourt Publishing Company. All rights reserved. Reprinted by permission, Faber and Faber, Ltd. (UK). p. 8 Quote by Neil Armstrong, July 21, 1969.

Chapter 2
p. 25 Quote from Mark Twain, *Adventures of Huckleberry Finn*, 1884.

Chapter 3
p. 54 Quote by Maria Mitchell (1818–1889). Figure 3.1 Based on *Ancient Astronomers* by Anthony F. Aveni. p. 64 Quote by Alphonso X (1221–1284). p. 65 Quote by Tycho Brahe, 1601. p. 65 Quote (bottom right) by Johannes Kepler (1571–1630). p. 77 Excerpt from *Tetrabiblios* by Claudius Ptolemy.

Chapter S1
p. 84 Excerpt from *The Republic* by Plato

Chapter 4
p. 111 Isaac Newton in a letter to Robert Hooke, February 1676. Figure 4.4 Based on *Space Station Science: Life in Free Fall* by Marianne Dyson. p. 115 Quote from Douglas Adams, *Hitchhiker's Guide to the Galaxy*. New York: Ballantine Books, 1980. p. 115 Quote by Alexander Pope, 1727.

Chapter 5
p. 138 "Song of the Sky Loom," poem from "Songs of the Tewa" by Herbert Joseph Spinden, appears courtesy of Sunstone Press, Box 2321, Santa Fe, NM 87504.

Chapter 6
p. 166 Quote from Galileo Galilei, *Sidereus Nuncius*, 1610.

Chapter 7
p. 191 Quote from Carl Sagan, *Pale Blue Dot: A Vision of the Human Future in Space*. New York: Random House, ©1994. Courtesy of the Sagan Estate.

Chapter 8
p. 215 Quote from Georges Lemaître, *The Primeval Atom, an Essay on Cosmogony*. New York: Van Nostrand, 1950.

Chapter 9
p. 234 Quote by Ralph Waldo Emerson (1803–1882).

Chapter 10
p. 270 Quote by Ulf Merbold. Figure 10.37 and p. 305 Data from the National Climate Data Center. Figure 10.38 and p. 304 (upper left) Data from *EOS*, Vol. 91, No. 40, October 5, 2010, pages 357–368. (lower left) Data from Jeff Bennett, *Math for Life*. Roberts and Company Publishers, 2011. (right side) Data from Dr. Pieter Tans, NOAA/ESRL (www.esrl.noaa.gov/gmd/ccgg/trends/), and Dr. Ralph Keeling, Scripps Institution of Oceanography (scrippsco2.ucsd.edu/). Figure 10.40 (graph 2) Data from Jeff Bennett, *Math for Life*. Roberts and Company Publishers, 2011. Figure 10.41 Data courtesy of NASA.

Chapter 11
p. 309 Quote by St. Albertus Magnus (1206–1280). Figure 11.6 Data courtesy of NASA. Figure 11.7 Data courtesy of NASA.

Chapter 12
p. 340 Quote by Freeman Dyson, reprinted from *Disturbing the Universe* by Freeman Dyson. Available from Basic Books, an imprint of the Perseus Book Group, copyright ©1979.

Chapter 13
p. 367 Quote from Christiaan Huygens, *New Conjectures Concerning the Planetary Worlds, Their Inhabitants and Productions,* c. 1690. p. 368 Quote from Carl Sagan, *Cosmos*. Random House, 1980. Courtesy of the Sagan Estate.

Chapter S2
p. 399 Quote from Hermann Minkowski, *The Principle of Relativity*. Calcutta: University Press, 1920.

Chapter S3
p. 421 Quote by Albert Einstein (1879–1955). Figure S3.24 Adapted from artwork in *BLACK HOLES AND TIME WARPS: Einstein's Outrageous Legacy* by Kip S. Thorne. Copyright ©1994 by Kip S. Thorne. Used by permission of W.W. Norton & Company, Inc. p. 438 Quote by Albert Einstein. This quotation was found with the aid of Alice Calaprice, author of *The Quotable Einstein* (Princeton University Press, 1996). p. 439 "Space is different …" quote from E. F. Taylor and J. A. Wheeler, *Spacetime Physics*. Freeman, 1992.

Chapter S4
p. 444 Quote from Douglas Adams, *The Restaurant at the End of the Universe*. Harmony Press. Copyright 1980.

Chapter 14
p. 465 Quote from Walt Whitman, *Leaves of Grass*, 1855. Figure 14.22 and pp. 482–483 Data courtesy of NASA.

Chapter 15

p. 487 Excerpt from THE LITTLE PRINCE by Antoine de Saint-Exupéry, copyright 1943 by Harcourt, Inc. and renewed 1971 by Consuelo de Saint-Exupéry, English translation copyright ©2000 by Richard Howard, reproduced by permission of Houghton Mifflin Harcourt Publishing Company. All rights reserved; copyright 1943 by Harcourt, Inc. and renewed 1971 by Consuelo de Saint-Exupéry. Editions Gallimard.

Chapter 16

p. 512 Quote from *Secrets from the Center of the World* by Joy Harjo and Steven Strom. ©1989 the Arizona Board of Regents. Reprinted by permission of the University of Arizona Press.

Chapter 17

p. 533 Quote from Harlow Shapley, *The Universe of Stars* (based on Radio talks from the Harvard College Observatory).

Chapter 18

p. 556 Quote from J. B. S. Haldane, *Possible Worlds*. Transaction Publishers, 1927.

Chapter 19

p. 579 Quote by Immanuel Kant (1724–1804). Figure 19.21 UCLA Galactic Center.

Chapter 20

p. 602 Quote from Edwin Hubble, *Realm of the Nebulae*. Yale University Press, 1936, p. 201.

Chapter 21

p. 625 Quote by Jules Verne (1828–1905).

Chapter 22

p. 647 Quote by Carl Sagan, courtesy of the Sagan Estate.

Chapter 23

p. 668 Quote from Fritz Zwicky, *Catalogue of Selected Compact Galaxies and of Post-eruptive Galaxies*. Guemligen, Switzerland, 1971.

Chapter 24

p. 697 Quote from Maya Angelou, *A Brave and Startling Truth*. New York: Random House, ©1995.

INDEX